STANDARD METHODS
OF
CHEMICAL ANALYSIS

*A Manual of Analytical Methods and General
Reference for the Analytical Chemist
and for the Advanced Student*

EDITED BY

WILFRED W. SCOTT, Sc.D.

*Professor of Chemistry, University of Southern California. Author of "Qualitative
Chemical Analysis," "Technical Methods of Metallurgical Analysis,"
"Inorganic Quantitative Chemical Analysis."*

IN COLLABORATION WITH EMINENT SPECIALISTS

In Two Volumes, Illustrated

VOLUME TWO—SPECIAL SUBJECTS

FOURTH EDITION REVISED
FOURTH PRINTING
Total Issue, Sixteen Thousand

NEW YORK
D. VAN NOSTRAND COMPANY, Inc.
250 FOURTH AVENUE

LANCASTER PRESS, INC
LANCASTER, PA.

THIS BOOK IS AFFECTIONATELY DEDICATED

TO MY FATHER,

𝔑𝔢𝔳. 𝔗𝔥𝔬𝔪𝔞𝔰 𝔍𝔢𝔣𝔣𝔢𝔯𝔰𝔬𝔫 𝔖𝔠𝔬𝔱𝔱, 𝔇.𝔇.

CONTRIBUTORS TO VOLUME TWO

Herbert Abraham, B.S. in Chemistry. President, The Ruberoid Company, New York City. Contribution—Chapter on Determination of Bituminous Substances, Including Asphalts, Tars and Pitches.

J. Bryte Barnitt, Ch.E. Chief of Development Division, Aluminum Company of America, Pittsburgh, Pa. Contribution—Chapter on Standard Methods of Sampling, Solids, Liquids and Gases.

L. E. Barton. Chemical Director, Titanium Pigment Company, Inc., Niagara Falls, N. Y. Author of a number of technical papers. Contribution— Chapter on Titanium, Determination of Nitrogen in Steel.

Robert C. Beckstrom, A.B., A.M. Professor of Petroleum Engineering, Colorado School of Mines. Contribution on Petroleum.

George A. Burrell, Ch.E., D.Sc. Chemical Engineer, Pittsburgh, Pa. Author of papers on oil, gas, gasoline. Contribution on Gas Analysis.

John S. Coye, B.S. Research Chemist, General Chemical Company, Laurel Hill, New York. Contribution—Electrometric Titrations.

Archibald Campbell, Ph.M. Vice-President, Globe Soap Company. Chairman of Committee on Soap. Advisory Editor. Contribution—Chapter on Analysis of Commercial Soap and Soap Products.

S. Collier, B.S. in Chemistry. Chemist in Charge of Rubber Laboratory, Waukegan Plant, Johns-Manville, Inc. Formerly Chemist, U. S. Bureau of Standards. Contribution—Chapter on Rubber.

D. K. French, B.S. Chemical Director, Dearborn Chemical Co., Chicago. Contribution—Chapter on Water.

Henry A. Gardner, B.S. Director, Institute of Paint and Varnish Research, Washington, D. C. Author of technical papers on paint. Contribution —Chapter on Analysis of Paints and Paint Pigments.

Augustus H. Gill, S.B., Ph.D., Sc.D. Professor of Technical Chemical Analysis, Massachusetts Institute of Technology. Author—Gas and Fuel Analysis for Engineers; A Short Handbook of Oil Analysis; Engine Room Chemistry; Automobile Gasoline. Contribution—Chapter on Analysis of Fixed Oils, Fats and Waxes; Gas Analysis.

Frank E. Hale, A.B., Ph.D. Director of Laboratories, Department of Water Supply, Gas and Electricity, New York City. Author of research papers on analysis of coal, water and sewage; on sewage disposal; water sanitation, etc. Contribution—Chapters on Sanitary Analysis of Water. Methods for Analysis of Coal.

George L. Kelley, B.S., Ph.D. Research Chemist, Edward Budd Manufacturing Company, Philadelphia. Author of a number of technical papers dealing with electrometric titrations, steel analysis, transition temperatures of sodium chromate hydrates, steel metallography, etc. Contribution— Chapter on Electrometric Methods of Analysis.

Arthur R. Mass, Ph.D. Professor of Pharmacy and Toxicology, University of Southern California. Author of technical papers on chemistry. Contribution—Chapter on Poisons.

Richard K. Meade, M.S. Consulting Chemical Engineer, Baltimore, Md. Author—Portland Cement; Chemists' Pocket Manual, and a number of papers on methods of volumetric analysis, on cement, potash, lime, barium compounds, etc. Contribution—Chapter on Analysis of Cement.

Roy M. Meiklejohn. Chief Chemist, General Chemical Company, Laurel Hill Laboratory, New York. Contribution—Useful Data of the More Important Inorganic Compounds, Conversion Factors, Chapter on Apparatus.

J. M. Morehead, B.S., E.E. Consulting Engineer of the Union Carbide and Carbon Corporation. Contribution—Chapter on Gas Analysis.

John C. Olsen, Ph.D. Professor of Chemical Engineering, Polytechnic Institute of Brooklyn, New York. Secretary of the American Institute of Chemical Engineers. Author of D. Van Nostrand Chemical Annual, Analytical Methods, and papers on manganese, vapor tension of crystals, pure standard salts, case hardening of steel with gases, etc. Advisory Editor. Contribution—Chapter on Alloys.

S. W. Parr, .MS. Professor of Chemistry, University of Illinois. Author of a number of technical papers on calorimetry of fuels, weathering and combustion of coal, alloys, boiler waters, potash shales, etc. Contribution—Analysis of fuels in chapter on Coal.

William B. Price, Ph.B. Chief Chemist and Metallurgist, Scovill Manufacturing Company, Waterbury, Conn. Author of Technical Analysis of Brass and Non-Ferrous Alloys. Contribution—Chapter on Alloys.

L. E. Salas, M.A., B.Sc. Analytical Research Chemist, London, England. Contribution—Chapter on Analysis of Rubber.

John A. Schaeffer, A.M., Ph.D. Vice-President and Chief Chemist, The Eagle-Picher Lead Company. Contribution—Chapter on Analysis of Paints and Paint Pigments.

Wilfred W. Scott, A.B., A.M., Sc.D. Professor of Analytical Chemistry, University of Southern California. Editor in Chief. Author of a number of technical papers on chemical research and chemical methods of analysis (see also title page). Contribution of a number of chapters throughout the book.

Atherton Seidell, Ph.D. Chemist, Hygienic Laboratory, U. S. Public Health Service, Washington, D. C. Author of "Solubilities of Inorganic and Organic Compounds," Chemistry of Vitamins, of Thyroid, Solubilities and Physical Constants of Pharmacopoeial Compounds, etc. Contribution—Chapter on Methods for the Determination of Solubility.

C. G. Storm, Ph.D. Chief Explosives Section, Ammunition Division, Ordnance Department, Washington, D. C. Author of a number of publications of the Bureau of Mines, and the Journals. Contribution—Chapter on Analysis of Explosives.

Joseph Winlock, A.B. Research Metallurgist, Edward G. Budd Manufacturing Company. Contribution—Chapter on Metallography.

CONTENTS

VOLUME II

SPECIAL SUBJECTS

STANDARD METHODS OF SAMPLING SOLIDS, LIQUIDS, GASES

METHODS FOR SAMPLING SOLIDS.—General outline. Introduction. Sampling unit; collection of the gross sample; carload lots, wheelbarrow lots, bags, barrels, etc.; crane bucket lots, carts, shoots, etc.; shiploads, storage piles, 1003–1005. Sampling of powdered material; sampling wet material; sampling deliquescent materials; kilns, roasters, dryers, furnaces, non-ferrous metals and alloys, etc., 1005–1008. Procedure for reducing the gross sample. Reduction of the gross sample, long pile and alternate shovel method. Cone and quartering, 1008–1011. Apparatus for reduction and preparation of the sample—crushers, grinders, 1012–1015. Mixing and dividing sample; the use of standard sieves, 1016–1018. Containers for shipment to laboratory; drying ovens for moisture determination; references, 1018–1020.

SAMPLING LIQUIDS.—General outline for sampling liquids, 1021. Sampling liquids in quiescent state, 1022. Sampling liquids in motion. Sampling special liquids, 1025. Liquids containing insoluble matter in suspension; liquids composed of immiscible layers; liquids containing crystals due to supersaturation; volatile liquids, 1025–1026. References, 1026.

SAMPLING GASES.—General outline for sampling gases, 1027. General considerations and apparatus—sampling tubes for drawing samples from gases flowing through pipes, collecting a representative sample, the design of apparatus, 1028. Taking a "grab" sample; taking a continuous sample, apparatus and methods of sampling, 1029–1031. References, 1031.

DECOMPOSITION OF THE SAMPLE

Decomposition of the material, 1032. Reagents used—I, Water; II, Acids; III, Fusions, 1033–1034. Properties and special uses of reagents, 1034–1035a. Amount of sample, 1035b.

ANALYSIS OF NON-FERROUS ALLOYS

Difficulty of complete separation of elements, limit of accuracy in analysis, 1036. Tables—Fusible metals—white metals, solders, babbits, antifriction metals, bronzes—piain and special, plain brasses, leaded brasses, tin brass and special brass, cupro nickel and nickel silvers, 1037–1039. Solution of alloys, 1040. Methods of Analysis—alloys of lead, tin, antimony and copper—A. S. T. M. methods, 1041. Determination of lead, copper, arsenic, antimony and tin, 1041–1043. Rapid methods for control work—determination of lead, copper, arsenic, antimony, tin, 1044–1045. White metals—determination of bismuth, iron, copper, zinc and lead, 1046–1047. Analysis of manganese bronze—determination of copper, lead, tin, iron, manganese, and zinc, 1047–1057. Analysis of gun metal—determination of copper, tin, lead, iron, and zinc, 1058–

1063. Determination of phosphorus, 1063–1066. Standard methods of chemical analysis of brass ingots and sand castings, A. S. T. M.—electrolytic method for copper and lead, determination of lead as sulphate, copper and lead simultaneously by electrolytic method, determination of tin, determination of iron, determination of antimony volumetrically, determination of sulphur, 1067–1075. Standard methods of chemical analysis of bronze bearing metal—A. S. T. M.—determination of copper electrolytically, determination of tin in absence and in presence of phosphorus, qualitative test for phosphorus, electrolytic method for lead, lead as sulphate, determination of iron, determination of nickel as glyoxime, determination of zinc, determination of phosphorus by alkalimetric method, determination of antimony volumetrically, determination of sulphur, determination of arsenic, determination of cadmium in brass, 1076–1089. Determination of aluminum in non-ferrous alloys, 1090–1091. Method for the chemical analysis of nickel silver and cupro nickel—determination of tin, copper and lead, determination of iron, determination of manganese, determination of nickel and zinc, 1092–1094. A. S. T. M. methods of analysis of aluminum and light aluminum alloys —analysis of aluminum, non-graphitic silicon, graphitic silicon, total silicon, determination of titanium, determination of iron, determination of copper by electrolytic method, by iodide method, determination of manganese by persulphate method, bismuthate method, determination of carbon, 1095–1102. Analysis of light aluminum alloys, determination of silicon, determination of titanium in absence and in presence of nickel, determination of iron, determination of antimony, tin, lead and copper, nickel, magnesium, manganese, zinc, carbon, sodium, nitrogen, aluminum and aluminum oxide, 1103–1106. Analysis of Monel metal—determination of carbon, copper, nickel, iron, manganese, sulphur, 1106–1107.

FIXED OILS, FATS AND WAXES

Introductory. Examination of the unknown oil, 1108. Petroleum products—(a) burning oils, flash test, fire test, specific gravity, distillation test, method for kerosene. Engler apparatus, condenser, shield, supports, heaters, thermometer, graduate, procedure, accuracy, corrections, 1109–1112e. Determination of sulphur, apparatus, solutions, procedure; detection of acidity, sulphuric acid test, mineral salts, determination of water, color, 1112e–1115. (b) Lubricating oils—viscosity, Engler apparatus, Saybolt viscosimeter, apparatus, temperature of testing, procedure; MacMichael's viscosimeter, absolute viscosity; specific gravity; evaporation test; cold test; cloud and pour points—A. S. T. M., apparatus, procedure for cloud point, procedure for pour point; flash point, apparatus, procedure, heating plate for Cleveland open test, 1115–1120. Detection of soap, caoutchouc, fatty oils, gumming test; carbon residue test—Conradson's method, apparatus, method; gasoline test, microscopical test, heat test, Herschel's demusibility test, friction test, color, 1121–1125. Liquid fuels—gasolene, doctor test (sodium plumbite), corrosion test, copper dish, A. S. T. M. method, method for distillation of gasolene; flash point by means of the Penski-Martins closed tester, apparatus and equipment, procedure, specifications—A. S. T. M., 1125–1130. Sulphur by A. S. T. M. method, apparatus, procedure; water, apparatus, sample, procedure; sediment, apparatus, procedure; water and sediment by centrifuge method, apparatus, procedure, accuracy; water by centrifuge, apparatus, procedure, 1130–1133. Animal and vegetable oils—specific gravity, refractive index, Valenta test, Elaidin test, Maumené test, references, 1133–1136. Iodine number, Hanus's method, standardization of thiosulphate; Hubl's method, iodine solution and requirements of method; oxidized oils, iodine number, bromine number; saponification value, method, apparatus, blank, procedure, specifications, 1136–1140b. Detection of unsaponifiable oils—saponification number, gravity methods, identification of unsaponifiable matter, paraffin, ceresene, higher alcohols, cholesterol, lactones; tests for animal or vegetable oils, table of melting points; tests for antifluorescents, acetyl value, 1140b–1141. Special tests for certain oils, Bechi's test for cotton seed oil, Halpen's test for cotton seed oil; hexabromide test for linseed oil, table of comparison; Bellier's qualitative test for peanut oil, Renard-Tolman qualitative test; Bach's test for rapeseed oil; Liebermann-Storch test for rosin oil; Baudouin's or Camoin's test for sesame oil, Villavecchia test, free acid test, spontaneous combustion test—Mackey's apparatus; drying test upon glass, titer test, references, 1141–1146. Edible fats—examination of fat; hardened oils; waxes; miscellaneous oils and lubricants, properties of some of the mineral oils—table, references, 1146–1149. United States Government specifications for petroleum products—gasoline, burning oils, fuel oils, greases, lubricating oils; characteristics of the fatty acids from some oils—tables; viscosimeter chart; factor tables; reagents used in oil analysis, 1150–1157b.

INTERPRETATION OF ANALYSIS OF PETROLEUM PRODUCTS

Introductory, importance of tests, 1158. Tests on crude oils, interpretation of various tests; tests on gasoline and interpretation; tests on kerosene, mineral seal and gas oil and interpretation; tests on lubricants and interpretation; tests on waxes and interpretation; tests on heavy oils and asphalts and interpretation; tests on shale oils and interpretation of tests, 1158–1160.

ANALYSIS OF PAINTS

Introductory, 1161. Analysis of paint vehicles—composition of liquid part; percentage of liquid by ignition method; percentage of liquid by extraction methods; separation of vehicle components, water, direct distillation of volatiles; detection of resinates; detection of various oils, 1162–1164. Analysis of paint oils—iodine number; analysis of linseed oil, foots, specific gravity, acid number, saponification number, unsaponifiable matter, refractive index, iodine number, time of drying on glass, reagents, tables, 1165–1168. Examination of Tung oil—properties and tests, heating test, quality test, constants of various oils, comparative tables; examination of turpentine—color, specific gravity, refractive index, distillation, polymerization; standards for turpentine, A. S. T. M., 1164–1173. Analysis of varnish—flash point, acid number, ash, solvent, fixed oils and resins, separations of polymerized oils and resins, 1173–1174. Other materials, 1175. The analysis of paint pigments; classification of pigments, 1176. Analysis of white pigments—sublimed white lead, volumetric determination of lead, volumetric determination of zinc, total sulphate; super sublimed white lead, corroded white lead, total lead (gravimetric), total lead (volumetric), carbon dioxide, acetic acid, metallic lead; zinc lead and leaded zinc—moisture, lead, zinc, total soluble sulphates (in absence of $BaSO_4$), total soluble sulphates (in presence of $BaSO_4$), soluble zinc sulphate, sulphur dioxide, calculations; zinc oxide—moisture, carbon dioxide, insoluble matter, sulphuric anhydride, total S as SO_3; lead oxide, gravimetric method, electrolytic method, chlorine, ferric oxide, manganese oxide, arsenous oxide, SO_2 equivalent, zinc oxide; lithopone, albalith, ponolith, Beckton white, Carlton white, etc.—moisture, barium sulphate, total zinc, zinc sulphide, soluble salts; silica or silex—china clay asbestine—moisture, loss on ignition, insoluble matter, carbon dioxide; whiting—Paris white—moisture, loss on ignition, calcium, magnesium, carbon dioxide, sulphates; barytes and blanc fixe—moisture, loss on ignition, barium sulphate, soluble sulphates, carbon dioxide; analysis of a composite white paint—insoluble residue, total lead, alumina and iron oxide, zinc, calcium and magnesium, sulphate, sulphide, carbon dioxide, calculations, 1178–1190. Titanium pigments, titanox, barium sulphate, titanium, reagents, reductor, Bureau of Standards method, moisture, titanium oxide, $BaSO_4$. Paints containing TiO_2. Antimony oxide, 1191–1193. Red and brown pigments—red lead and orange mineral—moisture, organic color, total lead and insoluble residue, lead peroxide (PbO_2) and true red lead (Pb_3O_4), calculation; vermilion—characteristics of; iron oxides, 1193–1196. Blue pigments—ultramarine blue—moisture, silica, aluminum oxide, sodium oxide, total sulphur, sulphur present as sulphate; Prussian blue—moisture, nitrogen, iron and aluminum oxides, sulphuric acid, commercial analysis; sublimed blue lead—total lead, total sulphur, lead sulphate, lead sulphite, lead sulphide, lead carbonate, lead oxide, zinc oxide, carbon and volatile matter, 1196–1198. Yellow and orange pigments—chrome yellow, moisture, insoluble residue, lead, chromium, zinc, calcium and magnesium, sulphuric acid, calculations, 1198. Green pigments, chrome green—moisture, insoluble residue, lead, iron, alumina and chromium, calcium and magnesium, sulphuric acid, nitrogen, calculation, 1198. Black pigments—moisture, oil, carbon, ash, analysis of ash, 1199. Complex compounds—hydroferrocyanic and hydroferricyanic acids, 1199.

CEMENT

Analysis and testing of cements—introductory, 1202. Specifications—definition, chemical limits, physical properties, packages and marking, sampling, specific gravity, fineness, mixing cement pastes and mortars, normal consistency, setting time, table, tension test, apparatus, etc., 1202–1215. Standard method for chemical analysis of Portland cement—solution, silica, alumina and iron, lime, magnesia, alkalies, anhydrous sulphuric acid, total sulphur, loss on ignition, insoluble residue, 1216–1222. Rapid method for chemical analysis of Portland cement, 1220. Rapid method for checking the percentage of calcium carbonate in cement mixture, standard alkali, standard acid, standard sample, standardizing the acid, determination, 1222–1224. Analysis of limestone, cement rock, lime, Rosendale cement, etc., table of composition, 1226.

ANALYSIS OF INDUSTRIAL GASES

Determination of calorific value and operating conditions from analysis of industrial gases, 1227. Properties of carbonic acid gas, (CO_2), illuminants or heavy hydrocarbons, oxygen, carbonic oxide, (CO), hydrogen, methane or marsh gas, nitrogen, air, acetylene, 1227–1227g. Method of analysis—Morehead apparatus, 1228–1228d. Interpretation, industrial producer gas, water gas, 1230–1230c.

GAS ANALYSIS

Sampling—tubes, pumps, containers for samples, 1231–1233. Measurement of gas in large quantities—wet and dry meters, Pitot tube or Davis anemometer, rotameter or Thorpe gauge, capometer, Thomas electric meter, orifice meter, anemometer, 1233–1236. Measurement of gas in small quantities—gas burettes, Hempel Orsat and Elliot burette, separatory funnel and graduate, 1236. Absorption apparatus, tubes and pipettes, 1237. Examination of the gases—detection and determination of the various gases, tables, 1238–1241. Analysis of gaseous mixtures—analysis by means of the Orsat apparatus, determination of carbon dioxide, oxygen, carbon monoxide, hydrocarbons, notes on manipulation; Elliot apparatus, determination of carbon dioxide,

oxygen, carbon monoxide, notes; Hempel apparatus, determination of oxygen in air—
(1) by phosphorus, (2) by pyrogallate of potassium, (3) by explosion with hydrogen;
analysis of illuminating gas—carbon dioxide, illuminants, oxygen, carbonic oxide,
methane and hydrogen, (a) Hinman's method, (b) Hempel's method; nitrogen, notes,
1241–1251. Applications of gas analysis and interpretation of results—I. Chimney
and flue gases—carbonic acid indicators, determination of temperature, composition
of the coal, tables, smoke, 1252–1255. II. Producer and fuel gases, blast-furnace gas—
analysis, dust in, 1255–1256. III. Illuminating gas, candle-power, calorific power,
sulphur, H_2S, ammonia, naphthalene, carbon dioxide, specific gravity, tar, 1256–1264.
IV. Sulphuric acid gases—(a) burner gases—sulphur dioxide in inlet and exit gases,
Reich method for SO_2, absorption of SO_2 in chromic acid solution; (b) nitrogen oxides,
1264–1270. V. Mine gases, 1270. VI. Electrolytic gases, 1271. VII. Acetylene,
1271. VIII. Atmospheric air moisture, carbon dioxide, ozone, carbon monoxide,
bacteria, 1272–1274. IX. Natural gas—sampling, apparatus, procedure of analysis,
1274a–1274c. Qualitative test for carbon monoxide and olefin hydrocarbons in natural
gas, calculations, 1274d. Specific gravities of certain gases, molecular volume—CO_2,
C_2H_4; application of the use of corrected equations to the analysis of natural gas and
other gas mixtures, typical analysis and calculation, 1274e–1274g. Helium—analysis,
1274g–1274i. Determination of moisture in gases, 1275. Determination of nitrogen
by the nitrometer, 1276. Reagents and tables, 1278–1282. Determination of traces
of sulphur dioxide in air, 1283–1286. Vapor in air with charts, 1287–1288. Gas
analysis by the Burrell apparatus, 1288g–1288k.

DETERMINATION OF BITUMINOUS SUBSTANCES. INCLUDING ASPHALTS, TARS AND PITCHES

PART I.   Classification of bituminous substances, 1289.   Chemical composition of,
1289. Table I, 1290. General remarks, 1292. Examination of Crude, Refined and
Blended Bituminous Substances, 1294. Table, 1294. Physical characteristics, 1305–
1307. Fracture; streak on porcelain; specific gravity—hydrometer method, Westphal
balance method, pycnometer method, 1295–1296. Viscosity Engler method, float test,
1296. Hardness or constancy; needle penetrometer; consistometer; susceptibility
factor, 1298–1302. Ductility, 1302. Dow test, 1302. Abraham's test, 1304. Heat
tests, fusing point, 1305. Kramer-Sarnow method, substances fusing below 194° F.,
substances fusing above 194° F., 1305–1307. Ball ring method, substances fusing
below 194° F., substances fusing above 194° F., 1308. Cube method, 1309. Pitches
fusing below and above 170° F., 1309–1311. Volatile matter, 1312. Flash point, 1314.
Pensky-Martens closed tester, 1314. New York State or Elliot tester, 1315. Fixed
carbon, distillation test, flask method of distillation; retort method of distillation, 1315–
1316. Solubility in carbon disulphide, 1317. Carbenes, 1318. Solubility in 88° petroleum ether, 1319. Chemical tests—water, 1320. Substances distilling at high temperatures, 1321. Oxygen in non-mineral matter, 1321. Free carbon in tars, 1322. Solid
paraffines, 1322. Sulphonation residue, unsaponifiable and saponifiable matters, 1323–
1324. Diazo reaction, 1324. Anthraquinone reaction, 1325. Synoptical table of the
most important distinguishing characteristics of bituminous substances, 1326–1327.
PART II.   Examination of Bituminized Mineral Aggregates, 1328. Physical tests
of finished product, 1328. Tensile strength, compressive strength, impact test, distortion under heat, 1328–1330. Separation of the bituminous matter and mineral aggregate, 1330. Forrest's hot extraction method, centrifugal method, recovery of extracted
bituminous matter, recovery of mineral aggregate, 1330–1332. Examination of sepa-

rated bituminous matter, 1332. Examination of separated mineral matter—granular-metric analysis—for sand or other fine highway material, for broken stone or broken slag, for sand with stone, 1333. Elutriation test for sand or fine filler, 1334. Specific gravity—for aggregates whose particles are less than one-fourth inch, and more than one-fourth inch, 1334. Chemical analysis—mineral constituents—white pigments, yellow, red or brown pigments, 1335.

PART III. Examination of Bituminized Fabrics, 1336. Table, 1336. Physical tests—weight, pliability, thickness, strength, resistance to heat, resistance to dampness, resistance to water, resistance to electrical current, 1337–1338. Special tests for ad-hesive insulating tape, 1339. Resistance to weather, 1339. Separation of finished product into its component parts, 1339. Separation of bituminous matter, mineral matter and fibrous matter, 1339. Single-layered fabrics, 1339. Saturated only or coated only, saturated and coated, 1339. Also laminated fabrics, 1339–1341. Weight per 100 sq. ft., detached mineral matter, dry felt, and burlap, total mineral and bitumi-nous matter, bituminous saturation in the felt, weight of bituminous matter in coatings, fine mineral matter in coatings, nature of bituminous matter of coatings, 1342–1343. Examination of separated fabric weight; thickness; strength methods; ash, fibres present, 1344. Examination of separated bituminous coatings and mineral surfacing, 1345.

PART IV. Examination of bituminous solvent compositions—cements, paints, varnishes, etc., 1346. Physical tests of finished product, specific gravity, viscosity, spreading capacity, drying properties, covering power, exposure test, 1346. Separation of finished product into its component parts—solvent—rapid method for determining percentage of, method for recovery and identification of solvent, 1347. Pigment filler, 1347. Base, 1347. Method for analysis of base, 1348. Tables, 1348–1349.

PART V. Examination of bituminous emulsions, 1349.

Valuation of shale for shale oil, method of the Colorado School of Mines.

CHEMICAL ANALYSIS OF PLAIN CARBON STEEL

Introduction, 1351. Determination of carbon by combustion, apparatus, factors influencing rapid combustion, determination of carbon by gravimetric method, 1352–1356. Determination of carbon by the barium hydroxide volumetric method, reagents, apparatus, 1356–1359. Carbon in alloys. Colorimetric method, 1359. Manganese determination by the bismuthate method (absence of cobalt), persulphate method, routine in presence of cobalt; manganese by modified bismuthate method, 1360–1362. Determination of phosphorus by the molybdate-magnesia method, by the alkalimetric method (routine); phosphorus in alloy steels, 1363–1366. Determination of sulphur by the oxidation method, and by the evolution method; sulphur in alloy steels, 1366–1368a. Determination of silicon by the nitro-sulphuric method, by the sulphuric acid method, 1368a–1368b. Determination of copper in steel, 1368c–1368d. Determination of nickel in iron and steel, gravimetric and volumetric glyoxime methods, 1368d–1368e. Determination of chromium in steel, volumetric and colorimetric methods, 1368f. Determination of hydrogen in steel, method of testing apparatus for leaks, 1368g–1368h. Determination of oxygen in steel, 1368i. Determination of aluminum, silicon, titanium, zirconium in steel, 1369–1371. Specifications for steel, 1371–1371d.

EXPLOSIVES

Introduction. Black powder—sampling, moisture, nitrates, sulphur, charcoal, ash, calculation of results, 1372–1373. Nitroglycerin Dynamites "straight" dynamite—sam-pling, qualitative examination, moisture, extraction with ether, reflux condenser method, suction method, evaporation of ether extract, nitroglycerin, sulphur, resins, oils, etc., extraction with water and determination of nitrates, extraction with acid, determination of starch, insoluble residue and ash, 1374–1379. Ammonia dynamite, gelatin dynamite, analysis nitrocellulose, 1379–1381. Low freezing dynamite, moisture, nitrotoluenes, modified Kjeldahl method for nitrogen, separation of nitro-compounds from nitroglycerin, nitrosugars, nitrochlorhydrines, nitropolyglycerin, 1381–1383. Permissible explosives, 1384. Some compounds of low-flame explosives, qualitative analysis, test for nitrostarch, test for chlorides, chlorates, perchlorates. Mechanical separation of solid ingredients—by screening, by specific gravity separations. Moisture, extraction with ether, extraction with water, nitrates, chlorates, perchlorates, Gum Arabic, sugar, extraction with acid, extraction with acetone, nitrocellulose and nitrostarch, insoluble residue and ash, 1384–1389. Nitrostarch explosives—general nature, moisture, extraction with petroleum ether—oils, sulphur, etc., extraction with water—nitrates, gums, etc., insoluble residue—nitrostarch, charcoal, cereal products, etc., starch, nitrostarch, charcoal, 1389–1391. Trinitrotoluene (T.N.T.)—solidification point, ash, moisture, insoluble, acidity, nitrogen, 1391. Picric acid—solidification point, moisture, sulphuric acid, ash, insoluble in water, soluble lead, nitric acid, 1392–1393. Ammonium picrate—moisture, sulphuric acid, nitrates, ash, nitrophenols, 1393–1394. Tetryl melting point, moisture, acidity, insoluble in acetone, ash, sodium salts, 1394–1395. Mercury fulminates—preparation of the sample, mercury fulminate content, acidity insoluble matter, free mercury, chlorides, 1395–1396. Blasting caps and electric detonators—preparation of the sample, moisture, analysis of composition containing mercury fulminate and potassium chlorate, analysis of compositions containing nitrocompounds, 1396–1397. Primers—variations in composition, types of primer compositions—table, preparation of the sample, qualitative examination, quantitative examination, 1398–1399. Nitrocellulose, general, preparation of the sample, nitrogen, solubility in ether-alcohol, (a) guncotton, (b) pyrocellulose; solubility in acetone; ash; stability test—heat test with potassium iodide starch paper, stability test at 135° C.; preparation of methyl violet test paper, 1399–1403. Smokeless powder, 1404. Nitrocellulose powders, moisture and volatiles, diphenylamine, ash, solubility in ether-alcohol, solubility in acetone, solubility test at 135° C., stability test at 115° C., "surveillance" test at 65.5° C., nitrogen, 1404–1406. Nitroglycerin smokeless powders, 1407.

WATER ANALYSIS

General considerations, 1409. Sanitary analysis—organic nitrogen; chloride; oxygen consumed; physical test—turbidity, color, odor—hot or cold; taste, 1410–1411. Chemical tests—free ammonia, albuminoid ammonia, organic nitrogen; nitrogen as nitrite; nitrogen as nitrate by aluminum reduction; oxygen consumed; chlorine as chlorides; total solid residue, 1412–1418. Interpretation of results, 1419. Mineral analysis—general considerations, outline of procedure, silica, manganese and phosphoric acid; iron and alumina gravimetric; iron colorimetric, ferrous iron colorimetric; phosphates, calcium, magnesium, manganese—Knorre's persulphate method, sodium bismuthate method for manganese; sulphates—benzidine method; sodium potassium and lithium; alkalinity, acidity, hydrogen ion concentration, free carbonic acid; chlorine; nitrates; ammonia and its compounds; total mineral residue; hydrogen sulphide; oil; dissolved oxygen by Winkler's method, 1421–1436. Methods for determining small amounts of lead, zinc, copper and tin, 1437. Hardness, preparation of solutions, magnesium chloride, calcium sulphate; lime and soda value, 1438–1441a. Methods of reporting and interpretation, 1441a. Water softening, foaming and priming, corrosion,

scale, irrigating waters, hypothetical combinations, 1441b–1441d. Field assay of
water, 1441d.

SANITARY ANALYSIS OF WATER

Introductory, 1442–1444. Sampling, 1444. Sedgwick-rafter method of examination, 1445. Tabular outline identification of forms, list of organisms, 1448–1451.
Control of microscopic organisms, 1451–1453. References, 1453.

BACTERIOLOGICAL EXAMINATION OF WATER

Introductory—Sampling, 1454. Apparatus and materials required, 1455. Preparation of culture media; titration with Brom Thymol Blue, sterilization, nutrient broth,
sugar broths, nutrient gelatine, nutrient agar, litmus or azolitmin solution, eosin
methylene blue agar, Endo's medium, brilliant-green lactose peptone bile, Hesse agar,
Russell media, 1456–1460. Examination of water for total bacteria, 1461. Examination for B. coli, 1462. Subclassification of B. coli, 1463. Summary of steps in examination, 1464. Routine procedure for examination of samples of water, 1465. Examination for B. Typhi, Widal test, Russell media, 1467–1468. References, 1468.

METHODS FOR THE DETERMINATION OF SOLUBILITY

Introduction, 1469. Apparatus for the determination of the solubility of solids by the
analytical method, 1470–1479. Separation of saturated solution from undissolved solid,
1480. Analysis of the saturated solution, identification of the solid phase, transition
temperatures, synthetic method, freezing point method, volume change method,
titration method, distribution coefficients, electrolytic conductivity method, 1479–1487.
The solubility of gases in liquids, 1487–1490.

ACIDIMETRY AND ALKALIMETRY

Indicators—classification and special uses of, 1491–1492. Ultimate standards—
preparation of pure sodium carbonate, 1491. Preparation of standard acids—sulphuric
acid, hydrochloric acid, benzoic acid, standard caustic solution, 1494–1496. Standard
burettes, 1497. Titration of acids and alkalies, 1497 Methods of weighing acids—
dilute acids non-volatile under ordinary conditions; weighing of strong acids, fuming
or volatile under ordinary conditions; Lunge-Ray pipette, Dely weighing tube, snake
weighing tube, Blay-Burkhard graduated weighing burette, 1498–1500. Analysis
of muriatic acid—total acidity and hydrochloric acid. Impurities in commercial
hydrochloric acid—free chlorine, nitric acid or nitrates; sulphuric acids and sulphates,
arsenic, barium chloride, silica and total solids, 1501–1502. Determination of Specific
Gravity, 1502. Specific Gravity Table for HCl, 1504–1506. Analysis of hydrofluoric
acid—total acidity, hydrofluosilicic acid, sulphuric acid, sulphurous acid, calculation
of results, 1507–1508. Complete analysis of nitric acid—total acidity, sulphuric acid,
hydrochloric acid, lower oxides, nitric acid, iodine, free chlorine, total non-volatile
solids, 1509–1511. Ferrous sulphate method for the direct determination of nitric acid—
standardization of the reagents; general procedure for nitric in sulphuric acid; evaluation of nitric acid or nitrates; determination of nitric acid in oleum or mixed acids;
determination of nitric acid in arsenic and in phosphoric acids, 1512–1516. Determination of nitrous acid or nitrité by the permanganate method, 1516. HNO_3 Specific
Gravity Table, 1517–1520. Volumetric Determination of Phosphoric Acid and Its
Salts, 1521–1522. H_3PO_4 Specific Gravity Table, 1523. Complete Analysis of Sulphuric Acid—Procedure for titration with NaOH, 1524–1525. Determination of

CONTENTS

Impurities in Sulphuric Acid—residue lead in, iron, arsenic, selenium, sulphur dioxide, hydrochloric acid, nitric acid, fluorine, 1525–1528. The analysis of oleum or fuming sulphuric acid and of mixed acid—total acids, lower oxides, sulphuric acid and free sulphuric anhydride, nitric acid, calculating of results, 1529–1533. Table of Specific Gravity, 1534–1539. Table of Specific Gravity Fuming Sulphuric Acid, 1537. Analysis of Chlor-Sulphonic Acid, 1540. Volumetric estimation of free acid in presence of iron salts, 1541. Organic Acids, Acetic Anhydride, 1542. Analysis of acetic acid—impurities in acetic acid, formic acid, furfurol, acetone, sulphuric acid, sulphurous acid, hydrochloric acid, metals in acetic acid, 1545–1548. Acetates, Acetic Acid Specific Gravity Table, 1548. Carbonic Acid—Free, combined as bicarbonate, as carbonate, 1549. Citric Acid, 1549. Oxalic Acid, 1549. Carbolic Acid or Phenol, 1549. Tartaric Acid, Oulman and Goldenberg methods for determination of, 1550. Impurities in tartaric acid, 1551. Alkalies, 1552–1560. Analysis of Sodium Hydroxide and determination of impurities, Na_2CO_3, NaCl, Na_2SO_4, Na_2SiO_3, $Na_2Al_2O_4$, Hydrometer test, Potassium Hydroxide, 1551. Analysis of Sodium Carbonate and determination of impurities, $NaHCO_3$, NaCl, Fe, Al, Ca, Mg, Na_2SO_4, Na_2SO_3, Na_2SiO_3, Na_2S, 1552–1553. Estimation of carbonates and hydrates of potassium and sodium when together in solution, 1552–1558. Tables, NaOH and NH_4OH, 1558–1559. Analysis of aqua ammonia, 1560.

RUBBER

Introductory—function, essential constituent, formula for, rubber a colloid, 1563–1573. Examination of Raw Rubber—technical analysis; laboratory samples; tackiness; commercial evaluation, 1564–1565. Analysis of Crude Rubber—moisture; resin; ash; resin containing rubber; insoluble; protein, 1565–1566. Rubber Proper—(a) Spence's method; (b) Precipitation method; (c) As tetrabromide, Budde's method; (d) Nitrocite method (Alexander). General remarks, 1567–1568. Fillers, organic—vulcanization; the organic; factice, 1569. Analysis of factice—moisture, acetone extract, total sulphur, sulphur in the fatty acids, saponifiable matter, acidity, ash, 1568–1570. Rubber waste and reclaim, 1570. Bitumen and Pitch. Asphaltum. Analysis—asphaltene, softening point, carbon in coal tar pitch, ceresine, 1570. Rubber waste and reclaim, 1570. Compounding materials, fillers (inorganic)—introductory, red lead, magnesia, barytes, ultramarine, whiting, silica, talc, asbestos, zinc oxide, antimony in rubber goods, zinc sulphide, determination of, antimony sulphides, rouge, vermilion, lamp black, bone black, magnesium, lime, zinc compounds, flowers of sulphur, sulphur chloride, etc., 1571–1573. Examination of solvents, 1574. Vulcanized Rubber—properties of manufactured rubber, specific gravity, chief methods of vulcanization, coefficient of vulcanization, 1575. Analysis of Vulcanized Rubber—preparation of sample, acetone extraction, outline table of separations, free sulphur, thiocyanate method, oxidation method; the residue from acetone, chloroform extraction, alcoholic KOH extraction, the coefficient of vulcanization, total combined sulphur, Henrique's method, the isolation of the solid compounding materials, mineral matter, solvent method, total sulphur, Stephen's method, chlorine, 1576–1580. Examination of the rubber (Hübner's method), 1580. Analysis of rubber solutions—ebonite, determination of antimony and mercury in rubber goods, 1581. Analysis of Mechanical Goods—acetone extract, free sulphur, total sulphur, Rosenstein's method, ash, sulphur of ash, sulphide sulphur. Alternate scheme for rubber analysis—table, 1582–1583. Guttapercha and Balita—sampling; analysis—moisture, resin, Gutta; rapid method, dirt, Pontio's method, the residue, 1584. Standard methods for the analysis of rubber goods, A. C. S., 1585. Reasons for the analysis, acetone extract, chloroform extract, alcoholic alkali extract, free sulphur, total sulphur, ash, sulphur in ash, special determinations, rubber, preparation of sample, reagents, 1585–1587. Methods of analysis, specific gravity, chloroform and alcoholic alkali extracts, free and total sulphur, alternative method, ash, sulphur in ash, barium sulphate, total antimony, antimony in ash, free carbon, 1587–1593. Detection of glue, nitrogen calculated as glue, unsaponifiable matter, hydrocarbons A and B, rubber hydrocarbons, cellulose, barium carbonate, calculations, rubber as compounded, rubber by volume, statement of results, 1593–1597. Special methods, 1597a.

STANDARD METHODS FOR THE SAMPLING AND ANALYSIS OF COMMERCIAL SOAPS AND SOAP PRODUCTS

Applicability of the methods, 1598. Sampling-cake soaps, flake and powdered soap products when packed in cans and cartons, flake and powdered soap products when in bulk, liquid soap, paste soap products, 1598–1600. Preparation of the samples —cake soap, powdered and chip soaps, liquid soap, paste soap products, 1600. Methods of analysis—matter volatile at 105° C., total matter insoluble in alcohol, free acid or free alkali, combined alkali, total anhydrous soap, chloride, unsaponified and unsaponifiable matter, rosin, titer test, acid number of fatty acids, borax determination, determination of silica present as alkaline silicates, determination of carbon dioxide (carbonates), determination of phosphates, determination of sulphates, determination of glycerol, sugar, starch, volatile hydrocarbons, 1600–1608.

SLAG ANALYSIS

Introduction, composition of slags, 1609. Decomposition of the sample and analysis, general reverberatory slag, chilled blast furnace slag, determination of silica, lime, iron, 1610–1611. Determination of other constituents of slags—alumina, manganese, zinc, magnesia, copper, 1612–1614. Electrolytic and iodide methods for copper, lead and other constituents, 1615.

METHODS FOR ANALYSIS OF COAL

Sampling, preparation of sample for analysis, ball mill for pulverizing, Fig. 204, 1616–1618. Methods of analysis—moisture, volatile combustible matter, V. M. C. apparatus, Fig. 205, volatile sulphur, turbidimetric table for use with Jackson's candle turbidimeter, 1618–1623. Hot precipitation method for sulphur, fixed carbon, calorific value, Emerson calorimeter, apparatus for charging oxygen, calculations of B.t.u. example of run, standardization of calorimeter, 1623–1629. Determination of fusibility of coal ash, apparatus for determination of fusing point, conversion of percentages of constituents in a substance from one moisture basis to another or to dry basis, etc. References, 1630–1633.

METHODS FOR ANALYSIS OF FUELS

Sodium peroxide method, directions for using the Parr Standard calorimeter, new form, general arrangement, sodium peroxide reagent, potassium chlorate accelerator, preparation of the sample, making up the charge, ignition, temperature readings, correction factors, calculations, example of calculation, 1634–1640. Dismantling apparatus, analysis of fuels—anthracite, coke, petroleum oils, gasoline. Standardization, component factors, notes, 1640–1645. Reuniting the mercury of a thermometer. Determination of sulphur and total carbon—making up the charge, igniting the charge, treatment of the fused material, total carbon, formulae in the ultimate analysis of coal, moisture free, 1645–1650. The oxygen bomb method, definitions, correction for radiation, correction for acids, correction for fuse wire, 1651–1654. Procedure for determining heat values by the oxygen bomb calorimeter, ignition, corrections, standardization, dismantling. Example of computations gross and net values, heat determinations with petroleum oils, table for calculating carbon from CO_2, 1655–1662.

ELECTROMETRIC METHODS

The electrometric determination of the hydrogen ion concentration; electrometric method of titration in oxidation and reduction reactions, 1663–1668. The Kelley electrometric titration apparatus, general description, description of components, 1669–1670. Discussion of oxidation potential, 1671. Directions for assembling, illustrations of apparatus, circuit diagrams, 1671–1676. Methods of analysis, determination of chromium in steel, rapid method, notes and precautions; determination of vanadium in steel, notes and precautions; determination of manganese in steel, notes and precautions; determination of vanadium and chromium in ferro-vanadium, notes and precautions, 1677–1682.

STANDARD LABORATORY APPARATUS

Volumetric apparatus—introductory, preparation of apparatus, stopcock grease, measurement of capacity, direct measurement, volumetric measuring apparatus illustrated, calculation from weight of water, flasks, Morse-Blalock apparatus in position for calibrating flasks (illustration), pipettes, volumetric calibrating apparatus (illustration), burettes, table of buoyancy constants, table of density of water at temperatures from 0° to 102° C., table of apparent weight of water in air, note on use of ml. and cc., 1685–1694.

Standardization of weights—introductory, standardization, first method, second method, adjustment of weights, third method, table, effect of buoyancy, precision and tolerances of weights, table, 1695–1699.

METALLOGRAPHY

Introductory, the microscope, photographic materials, preparation of the material for microscopical examination, 1701–1704. Etching sample for examination, reagents used in etching, 1705. Equilibrium diagrams, microphotograph of pure iron, eutectic definition, 1706–1709. Copper-zinc alloys, microphotograph of brass, 1710. Iron-carbon alloys, microphotographs of carbon steel showing characteristics, 1711–1716. Influence of mechanical work—microphotographs showing characteristics, slip bands, Neumann lines, critical or exaggerated grain growth, 1716–1719. Heat treatment of steel, 1719. Case hardening, 1720. Influence of some elements on iron and steel with microphotographs, 1721–1722.

POISONS, THEIR DETECTION AND ESTIMATION. WITH SPECIAL REFERENCE TO ORGANIC POISONS

Introductory, classification of poisons, general procedure, groupings of poisons, 1723–1724. Group I—yellow phosphorus; hydrocyanic acid, procedures for detection and estimation; chloroform, qualitative and quantitative determinations; ethyl alcohol and methyl alcohol, detection methods for each; carbolic acid, detection and estimation; chloral hydrate, detection, decomposition, 1725–1731. Group II—alkaloids, glucosides and other organic compounds—methods of analysis, list of organic poisons, 1731–1732. Acetanilid, tests; veronal, tests, extractions from bladder contents: nicotine, distribution, detection; strychnine, distribution, detection; brucine, detection; atropine, detection; cocaine, detection; codeine, detection; narcotine, detection; morphine, detection; opium, detection; ptomaines, detection, 1732–1739. Group III—preparation of the solution, detection of arsenic and estimation; determination of carbon monoxide in air, blood solution, determination in blood, special reagents, 1739–1742.

MISCELLANEOUS

Alcohol, detection and estimation, tests, distillation and evaporation, quantitative methods, analysis of grain alcohol (ethyl alcohol, spirits of wine, cologne spirits), aldehydes, qualitative and quantitative methods; determination of furfural; determination of esters expressed as ethyl acetate; determination of fusel oil; detection of nitrates and sulphur compounds, 1743–1747. Determination of methyl alcohol (wood spirit, wood naphtha, wood alcohol, methanal), specific gravity table of alcohol with percentage of alcohol by volume and weight, 1747–1753. Formaldehyde, detection and estimation, 1754. Glycerole, detection and estimation, 1756. Acetone, analysis of, 1759. Tannic acid, analysis of, 1760. Determination of peroxides, methods of estimation, analysis of sodium sulphide, 1761. Beam tests for determining the presence of suspended matter in gases, method and illustrations of apparatus; determination of solid and liquid impurities in a gas, 1763–1766. Preparation of a Gooch crucible, 1767. Determination of moisture and water of crystallization in solids and in gas, 1768–1770. Determination of light oil in coke oven gas, 1771–1772. Methods for testing paper-making materials—aluminum sulphate, sampling, insoluble matter, alumina and iron oxide, iron, sulphuric acid, potassium fluoride, 1773–1775. Rosin, sampling, grade, dirt and foreign matter, saponification number, acid number, ester number, unsaponifiable matter, ash, practical sizing tests of rosin; rosin size, sampling, solubility, free rosin, moisture, total alkali, combined rosin, free alkali, insoluble matter; rapid methods for rosin and moisture in size, total rosin, moisture, free rosin, 1775–1778. Bleaching powder—sampling available chlorine, chlorates, total chlorides, determination of bases and silica, free lime, quality of powder for producing bleach liquor, wood and coarse impurities, sand and grit, 1779–1780. Starch and starch products, sampling, preliminary examination, moisture, ash, acidity, alkalinity, test for presence of starch or alkali, viscosity; converted starches, sampling, moisture and ash, acidity, viscosity, added materials, sizing strength, 1781–1782. Soda ash, sampling, moisture, alkalinity; sulphuric acid, sampling, specific gravity, sediment, acidity, iron; caustic soda, sampling, alkalinity; lime, sampling, moisture, CO_2, impurities, lime, magnesia, causticizing test; rapid methods for calcium, lime containing less than 1% magnesia, free lime, calcium carbonate, moisture, 1783–1785. Analysis of clay—chemical analysis, alkalies, titanium, state of silica, 1786–1788. Analysis of glass—density, preparation of the sample and determination of silica, determination of PbO, Fe_2O_3 and Al_2O_3 (R_2O_3), CaO, MgO, alkalies, B_2O_3, MnO_2, S, BaO, separation of Ba from Ca, 1789–1793. Analysis of the most important glass-making materials—moisture, chlorides, sulphates; feldspar, kaolin and china clay; barium carbonate, separation of iron and alumina, barium from calcium and strontium, strontium and calcium, determination of calcium, magnesium; lime, 1794–1798. Analysis of printing inks—separation of oil and pigment; analysis of the oil; analysis of the pigment: (a) black inks, (b) blue inks, (c) red inks, (d) green inks. Practical tests. Zinc chloride method for CaO in presence of $CaCO_3$, 1799–1805.

LIST OF ILLUSTRATIONS

FIG.   PAGE

75. Apparatus for Sampling Solids... 1006
76. Method of Sampling Ore.. 1010
77. Jaw and Toggle Crusher for Coarse and Medium Fine Grinding........... 1011
77a. Crusher and Grinder in Cross Section................................. 1012
77b. Roll Grinder for Brittle Material..................................... 1013
77c. Roll Grinder with Case Lifted to Show Interior....................... 1013
77d. Disc Grinder Ready to Run.. 1014
77e. Disc Grinder Open for Cleaning....................................... 1014
77f. Crusher Open for Cleaning.. 1015
77g. Combination Crusher and Sampler..................................... 1015
78. Riffle Sampler... 1016
78a. Apron of Cylinder of Riffle Sampler................................. 1016
79. Dryer for Coarse Samples.. 1018
79a and 79b. Drying Oven... 1019
79c. High Temperature Ovens, for operation from room temperature to 260° C. 1019
79d. Vacuum Oven... 1020
80. Sampling Liquids Apparatus... 1021
81. Sampling Liquids Apparatus 1022
82. Apparatus for Sampling Liquids in Motion............................. 1023
82a. Apparatus for Sampling Liquids...................................... 1024
82b. Apparatus for Sampling Liquids in Motion............................ 1024
82c. Apparatus for Sampling Liquids...................................... 1026
83. Apparatus for Sampling Gas... 1027
84, 84a, 84b, 84c, 85. Apparatus for Sampling Gas.............1028, 1029, 1030
86. New York Tester.. 1109
87. Westphal Balance... 1111
87a. Standard 100-cc. Engler Flask for Making Distillation Tests of Gasoline
    and Kerosene.. 1112
87b. Distillation Outfit (A. S. T. M.) Arranged for Use of Gas Burner........1112a
87c. Apparatus for Determination of Sulphur in Oils (A. S. T. M.)........... 1113
88. Engler Viscosimeter... 1116
89. Saybolt Viscosimeter.. 1116
89a. Sectional View of Standard Oil Tube.................................1116b
89b. Receiving Flask...1116b
89c. Apparatus for Cloud and Pour Test..................................1118a
89d. Cleveland Open Cup (A. S. T. M.)...................................1118d
90. Heating Plate for Use with Cleveland Open Cup........................ 1120
90a. Apparatus for Determining Carbon Residue........................... 1123
90b. Pensky-Martens Closed Tester (A. S. T. M.)..........................1128a
90c. Cover for Pensky-Martens Tester (A. S. T. M.).......................1128b
91. Apparatus for Determination of Water................................ 1132
91a. Extraction Apparatus for Determination of Sediment.................1132c
91b. Centrifuge Tubes (A. S. T. M.)...................................... 1133

FIG.   PAGE
92. Refractometer... 1134
92a. Mackey's Apparatus...1144c
92b. Viscosimeter Conversion Chart................................. 1156
92c. Junkers Calorimeter for Liquid Fuels 1157c
93. Le Chatelier Apparatus... 1205
94. Vicat Apparatus.. 1207
95–100. Apparatus for Making Soundness Test of Cement.............. 1208
101. Pat for Determining Setting Time and Soundness................ 1209
102. Appearance of Pats Made from Sound and Unsound Cement after Steaming 1209
103. Gillmore Needles.. 1211
104. Details for Briquette... 1211
105. Gang Mold.. 1212
106. Fairbanks Cement-testing Machine............................. 1214
107. Riehlé Automatic Cement-testing Machine...................... 1215
107a. Apparatus for Determining Calcium Carbonate with Acid and Alkali..... 1224
107b. The Morehead Gas Burette in Use.............................1227a
107c. Gas Analyzing Apparatus.....................................1227h
107d. Gas Analyzing Apparatus.....................................1228e
107e. Gas Analyzing Apparatus.....................................1229a
108. Water-cooled Sampling Tubes.................................. 1231
109, 110. Richards Jet Pump....................................... 1232
111. Bunsen Pump... 1232
112. Containers for Gas Sample.................................... 1233
113. Pitot Tube... 1234
114. Rotameter... 1235
115. Capometer... 1235
115a. Gas Flow Meter.. 1236
116. Friedrichs Spiral Gas Washing Bottle......................... 1237
117. Varentrapp and Will Bulbs.................................... 1237
118. The Wolff Absorption Tube.................................... 1237
119. Winkler's Spiral... 1237
120. Orsat Apparatus.. 1241
121. Elliott's Apparatus... 1244
122. Hempels' Apparatus... 1245
123. Hempels' Combustion Apparatus............................... 1245
124, 125, 126. Junker's Calorimeter.........................1257, 1258
127. Apparatus for Determining Sulphur in Gas.................... 1260
128. Rudorff's Apparatus for CO_2 in Gas....................... 1263
129. Specific Gravity Apparatus for Gas........................... 1263
130. Reich Apparatus for SO_2 in Contact Gas................... 1265
131. Briggs-Scott Modified Orsat Apparatus for SO_2 in Contact Gas.......... 1267
132. Hesse's Apparatus for CO_2 in Air.......................... 1272
133. Absorption Spectrum Chart, CO_2 Determination............. 1274
133a. Laboratory Apparatus for Natural Gas Analysis.............1274c
134. Phosphorus Pentoxide Bulb for Water Vapor in Gas 1275
135. Apparatus for Determining Gasoline Vapor in Gas............. 1275
136. Nitrometer.. 1276
     Bunte's Chart... 1282
137. Apparatus for Testing SO_2 in Air.......................... 1285
     Chart Air Saturation with Water.............................1288a

FIG.   PAGE
Chart Air Saturation with Water.....................................1288b
137a. Burrell Precision Gas Analysis Apparatus............................1288e
138. Float Tester...1297
139. Penetrometer...1299
140. Miniature Penetrometer...1299
141. Consistometer..1301
142. Dow Ductility Mould..1302
143. Smith Ductility Machine..1303
144. Abraham's Ductility Mould..1304
145. Cross-section Abraham's Mould..1304
146. Method of Filling K. & S. Fusing-point Tubes.........................1305
147. Resistance Cell for Fusing-point Determination.......................1306
148. K. & S. Tester for High Fusing-point Substances......................1307
149. Ball and Ring Apparatus..1308
150. Cube-in-Water Method for Low Fusing-point Substances.................1310
151. Cube-in-Air Method for High Fusing-point Substances..................1311
152. Shelf for Volatility Oven..1313
153. Volatility Oven..1314
154. Pensky-Martens Closed Flash-point Tester.............................1314
155. Flask Method of Distillation...1315
156. Asbestos Shield for Retort...1316
157. Retort Method of Distillation..1316
158. Still for Determining Water..1320
159. Cary-Curr Extraction Apparatus.......................................1322
160. Mould for Ascertaining the Tensile Strength of Bituminized Aggregates....1328
161. Apparatus for Recording Distortion of Bituminized Aggregates under Heat. 1330
162. Forrests' Hot-Extraction Apparatus 1331
163. Centrifugal Extractor..1332
164. Goldbeck's Specific Gravity Apparatus................................1335
165. Mandrels for Testing the Pliability..................................1337
166. Tensile Strength Specimen..1338
167. Instrument for Testing the Strength of Bituminized Fabrics...........1338
168. Types of Prepared Roofings...1340
169. Method of Stripping the Coatings from the Saturated Felt 1342
169a. Apparatus for Proximate Valuation of Oil Shale......................1350
169b. Apparatus for the Determination of Carbon by the Direct-Combustion
        Method..1355
169c. Apparatus for Filtration in Determination of Carbon by the Direct-Com-
        bustion Method 1358
169d. Apparatus for Determination of Sulphur by the Evolution Method.......1367
169e. Apparatus for Determining Hydrogen in Steel.........................1368g
169f. Apparatus for Determining Leaks in Combustion Train.................1368h
170. Apparatus for Determining Oxygen in Steel...........................1368i
170a. A "Chessel" Stopcock Remover..1407
171. Ammonia Distillation Apparatus.......................................1412
172. Collection Apparatus for Bacteriological Samples.....................1447
        Plates—Microscopical Water Organisms facing 1448, 1449
173. Microscopical Apparatus, Catskill Laboratory, Ashokan, N. Y..........1453
174. Sampling Apparatus for Deep Samples..................................1454

FIG.   PAGE

175. Bacteriological Apparatus, Fermentation Tubes, Petri Dishes, Pipettes, Culture Media, etc. 1456
176. Microscope for Bacteriological Examination 1462
177. Ocular Micrometer 1462
178. Determination of Solubility of Solids 1470
179. Noyes Apparatus for Determining Solubility of Solids 1471
180, 181, 182. Berkeley's Apparatus for Determining Solubility of Solids ...1472, 1473
183. Victor Meyer Type of Apparatus for Solubility Determination 1474
184. Walton and Judd Apparatus for Solubilities 1474
185. Donnan and White Apparatus for Determining Solubilities 1475
186. Cohen and Quonye Apparatus for Solubilities 1476
187. Bahrs' Apparatus for Determining Solubilities 1476
188. Solubility Apparatus 1478
189. Tyrer's Apparatus for Solubilities 1479
190, 191. McDaniel's Apparatus for Determining Gas Solubilities 1488
192. Arrangement for Heating Sodium Bicarbonate 1493
193. Standard Burette 1497
194. Lunge-Ray Pipette 1498
195. Dely Weighing Tube in Operation 1499
196. Snake Tube 1499
197. Blay-Burkhard Graduated Weighing Burette 1500
198. Hydrometer 1502
199, 200, 201. Charts Showing Specific Gravity and Boiling-points of Sulphuric Acid of Varying Concentrations 1524
202. Method for Rapid Evaporation of Liquids 1529
203. Rubber Analysis Extraction Apparatus 1566
203a. Analytical Balance 1574
203b. Chart, Showing Percentage of Sulphur 1589
204. Quartering Coal, Ball Mill for Pulverizing, and Suction Ventilator 1617
205. N. C. M. Apparatus 1619
206. Methods for Analysis of Coal 1623
207. Calorimeter 1624
208. Bomb 1624
209. Apparatus for C Determination as CO_2 1624
210. Emerson Calorimeter and Accessories 1625
211. Oxygen Cylinders for Calorimeter 1626
212. Hoskins' Electric Furnace, Optical Pyrometric Outfit 1630
213, 213a. Parr Calorimeter 1634
214. Parr Calorimeter, Sectional View. 1635
215. Glass Jar with Lever Fastener 1636
216. Peroxide Bomb 1637
217. Bulbs for Testing Gasolene 1641
218. Apparatus for Obtaining Fusions of Carbon 1647
219. Apparatus for Determining Amount of Carbon Present in CO_2 1648
220. Oxygen Bomb 1651
220a. Charging the Bomb with Oxygen 1656
221. Chart, Electrometric Titration 1665
222. Apparatus for Electrometric Titrations 1666
223, 224. Charts Illustrating Oxidation Potential 1671

FIG.   PAGE

225. Apparatus for Electrometric Titration, Front View...................... 1673

226. Apparatus for Electrometric Titration, Rear View...................... 1674

227. Diagram Showing the Circuits for the Motor and Lamp Circuits.......... 1675

228. Diagram Showing the Galvanometer Circuit............................ 1675

229. Volumetric Measuring Apparatus..................................... 1686

230. Morse-Blalock Apparatus in Position for Calibrating Flasks.............. 1689

231. Volumetric Calibrating Apparatus.................................... 1691

232. Methods of Illumination... 1701

233. Microscope with Paired Oculars...................................... 1704

234. Curves Showing Equilibrium... 1706

235. Microphotograph of Almost Pure Iron................................. 1707

236. Equilibrium Diagram of Alloys Partly Soluble in Solid Steel 1707

237, 238, 239. Photomicrograph of Alloy at Different Angles.................. 1708

240. Equilibrium Diagram of Alloys Forming Definite Compound............. 1708

241. Equilibrium Diagram of the Brasses.................................. 1709

242. Microphotograph of Brass, Cold Rolled and Annealed................... 1710

243. Equilibrium Diagram of the Iron-Carbon Alloys 1711

244. Transformation after Metal has Solidified 1712

245. Microphotograph of .40% Carbon Steel (Cast)......................... 1713

246. Microphotograph of .85% Carbon Steel (Cast)......................... 1713

247. Microphotograph of .85% Carbon Steel................................ 1714

248. Microphotograph of 1.25% Carbon Steel (Cast)........................ 1714

249, 250, 251, 252. Microphotograph of Cast Iron.......................... 1715

253. Influence of Hot Work on Structure of Steel........................... 1716

254. Microphotograph Showing Structure of Hot Worked .30% Carbon Steel ... 1717

255. Microphotograph Showing Structure of Hot Worked Eutectoid Steel 1717

256. Microphotograph Showing the Structure of Hot Worked 1.25% Carbon Steel 1717

257. Microphotograph Showing the Structure Produced by Cold Work in a Steel

     Containing about .20% Carbon 1717

258. Microphotograph Showing Small Strip of Steel Slightly Bent after Polishing

     and Etching... 1718

259. Microphotograph Showing Low Carbon Steel in Normal Condition........ 1718

260. Microphotograph Showing Low Carbon Steel after Grain Growth has

     Taken Place... 1718

261. Microphotograph of 1.25% Carbon Steel Quenched in Water............. 1719

262. Microphotograph of .75% Carbon Steel Quenched in Oil................. 1719

263. Microphotograph Showing the Edge of a Case-hardened Sample of Steel ... 1720

264. Microphotograph Showing Appearance of Manganese Sulphide in Low

     Carbon Cast Steel... 1721

265. Microphotograph Showing Appearance of Manganese Sulphide in Forged

     Low Carbon Steel... 1722

266. Microphotograph Showing Structure of Cast Manganese Steel Austenitic... 1722

267. Microphotograph Showing Structure of Cast High Speed Steel........... 1722

268. Atropine 1 : 500, with Wagner's Reagent.............................1732a

269. Cocaine 1 : 1000, with Gold Chloride.................................1732a

270. Codeine 1 : 200, with Maime's Reagent...............................1732a

271. Narcotine 1 : 1000, with Sodium Carbonate..........................1732a

272. Nicotine 1 : 1000, with Gold Chloride................................1732a

273. Strychnine 1 : 500, with Ammonium Thiocyanate......................1732a

274. ....1732b

LIST OF ILLUSTRATIONS

FIG.   PAGE

275. ....1732b
276. ....1732b
277. ....1732b
278, 279. Pycnometer...1743, 1753
280. Beam Test for Suspended Matters in Gases...........................1764
281. Apparatus for Ascertaining the Pressure of Suspended Material in a Gas by
       Means of a Beam of Light..1764
282. Apparatus for Determining Solids and Liquids Mist in Wet Gases.........1765
283. Filter for Gases..1765
284. Apparatus for Determining Solid or Liquid Impurities in Gases...........1766
285. Filtration with Gooch Crucible.....................................1767
286. Apparatus for Determination of Water...............................1769

VOLUME II

STANDARD METHODS OF SAMPLING

GENERAL OUTLINE FOR SAMPLING SOLIDS

Introduction

An accurate and uniform sampling procedure, applicable to all solid materials from the viewpoint of both producer and consumer, would necessitate the standardization of an infinite number of details, and probably result in a very cumbersome and impractical manipulation. It, therefore, appears advisable to first consider the various steps of the process of sampling, attempting their standardization and then applying this standardization to each particular product or group of related products.

The process of sampling is divided into three major operations:

1. The collection of the "gross" sample.
2. The reduction of the "gross" sample to a proper and convenient size for transportation to the laboratory.
3. The preparation of the sample for analysis.

These essential points and the accuracy with which they are performed determines the value of the subsequent analytical results. Experimental data and general mathematical deductions make it possible to standardize these operations with a fair degree of accuracy.

Sampling Unit

The sampling unit may be defined as that portion of the material which is chosen in such a manner that there is a high probability that it will contain the different sized particles of the material in the proportion in which they occur in the entire bulk of the material. Providing there are no great uncontrollable irregularities in the material, the sampling unit, if taken under carefully prescribed conditions for each different class, should be properly representative of the material. However in order to obviate the necessity of specifying in great detail, and to guard against unforeseen sectional variations in the material, it is more expedient to select a number of sampling units, these depending upon the size of the shipment to be sampled, and combine these sampling units into one large sample called the "Gross Sample."

The character of the material, size of the various particles, uniformity of composition and the prominence of any one or more constituents are factors governing the determination of the amount to be taken as the sampling unit. Without considering a mathematical discussion of the modulus of precision of a condition which would be impossible of duplication and in view of the experimental data compiled on the sampling of coal, it is safe to adopt, as the general sampling unit, an amount of material equal to approximately 500 times the weight of the largest particle. If this is impractical, due to the presence of very large particles, and the material cannot be reduced by passing it through a crusher, it will be necessary to reduce, by hand, the large particles at the various sampling points so that the correct proportion of large particles can be included in the sampling unit. In some cases, however, a different bulk of sampling unit will be found necessary.

Chapter by J. B. Barnitt.

Collection of the Gross Sample

The amount of material to be included in the gross sample depends more upon the size of the individual particles than upon the size of the shipment since it is simply a multiple of the sampling unit. When the shipment is large and frequent sectional variations do not prevail, and, it is being transferred by containers with a capacity approximately equal to the sampling unit, it is advisable to take the entire contents of a definite percentage of the containers as increments of the gross sample.

When the accumulated gross sample is too large to handle conveniently as a unit, it is permissible to reduce the gross sample in small sections by the standard procedure and subsequently combine the reduced portions in the correct ratio.

1. From Carload Lots

(a) **When the Material is to be Unloaded from Flat-bottomed Cars.**—Divide the top surface of the car into eight equal areas and, from each of these sections, take approximately the equivalent of one sampling unit in the following manner: From a stable bank of the material, beginning from the bottom, take with a shovel, at regular and equal intervals from the bottom to the top of the bank, ten equal portions of the material as specified. Combine these sampling units for the gross sample.

The stable bank may be obtained:

1. By digging down to the bottom of the car at the center of each section.
2. As the center of each section of the car is reached during the ordinary process of unloading by shoveling or otherwise.

(b) **When the Material is Being Transferred from or to the Car by Means of Wheelbarrows, Tram-cars, Wagons, Etc.**—Take the specified increment according to the material in question from a specified number of conveying containers. Combine these increments for the gross sample. When at any point a particle is encountered which is larger than the specified increment it should be broken down and a portion of it included in the sample.

(c) **When the Material is Dumped from a Hopper Car into a Hopper, Bin or Pile.**—Under these conditions, the sample is taken from the resulting cone-shaped pile by beginning at the bottom outer edge of the pile and taking the specified increment, according to the character of the material, every two feet on a straight line to the apex of the cone. This operation is repeated on each quadrant of the pile. The entire procedure is repeated after each car has been dumped and all increments combined for the gross sample.

2. From Wheelbarrows, Barrels, Bags, Tram Cars, Carts, Trays, Etc.

(a) From a specified number of containers, take the specified increment and combine them for the gross sample.

(b) Take the entire contents of every nth container and combine them for the gross sample.

(c) If the material is fairly uniform and composed of small particles, sample the container by taking ten equal specified increments uniformly distributed on two right angle diagonals across the surface of the container. Sample the specified number of containers in this way and combine the several portions for the gross sample.

3. From Crane Buckets, Cars, Carts and Similar Containers, Chutes, Etc.

(a) If one container amounts to less than one sampling unit, take every 10th load and combine these for the gross sample.

(b) If one container amounts to approximately 1–3 sampling units, take every 20th load and combine these for the gross sample.

(c) If one container amounts to more than three sampling units, take every 50th load and combine these for the gross sample. Note: When very large shipments are being sampled by the above procedures very large gross samples will result which would be difficult or inconvenient to reduce to the laboratory sample. In this case the gross sample may be reduced periodically as follows. At regular intervals, representing a definite number of tons, the gross sample is quartered, one quarter reserved and three quarters returned to the main bulk. The total combined quarters thus reserved are mixed by shoveling into a cone shaped pile and then further reduced by the Standard Procedure to the laboratory sample.

(d) When the material is composed of particles one inch or less in size, take a specified increment from every nth container.

(e) When the material is being dumped into a crusher from which it flows or is flowing, from a drying kiln or other process kiln, the material may be sampled by taking specified increments from the outflowing stream at stated regular intervals.

4. From Shipholds, Scows, Hoppers, Hopper-cars, Bins, Storage Piles, Etc.

In this case the material may be sampled in any of several ways.

(a) According to the previous section 3, while loading or unloading.

(b) According to the section 1, for carloads while unloading or loading.

(c) While using material from a storage pile, daily or periodic samples may be taken as follows: On ten vertical lines from the bottom to the top of the face of the pile distributed at uniform distances across the face, take ten equal specified increments at equal distances from bottom to top. Combine these increments for the gross sample over any desired period.

5. For Powdered Material

When the material is a fine powder or is composed chiefly of material under 2 mm. and contains a small amount of unsegregated particles up to 10 mm. in the largest dimension, the sampling unit is taken by means of a specially designed thief (Fig. 75-1) or by means of a suitable shovel, dipper, etc.

(a) From large shipments, as shipholds, scows, barges, cars, etc. On a line through the center of the holder lengthwise, take portions with the thief every five feet. Repeat this operation on each of two lines parallel with and half way between the first line and each side of the holder. Combine all the portions for the gross sample. If the shipment is composed of more than one holder, combine the portions from each holder into a composite gross sample.

3

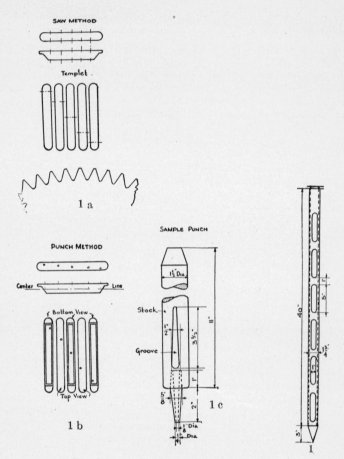

FIG. 75. Apparatus for Sampling Solids.

Sect. 1. Thief for sampling solids ¼″ diameter or smaller. Openings to correspond. Both tubes hollow and to be made from $\frac{1}{16}$″ sheet brass (hard). Inside tube to fit snugly into outside tube. Point to be steel or iron.

Sect. 1a. Saw Method of Sampling Pigs. The bars are sampled in sets of five, according to Template as shown. Saw is sharpened on Emery Wheel to size and shape here shown.

Sect. 1b. Punch Method of Sampling Pigs. The bars selected as samples are placed in a line, with every other bar, bottom side up. The sampling is done according to template in sets of five bars each, as indicated above. The punch must be driven through the bar. If a large sample is desired, the bars are turned over and sampled on the other diagonal.

Sect. 1c. Sample Punch.

(*b*) From tram cars, carts, buggies, etc.

Take a specified portion from each holder with the thief or shovel and combine all portions for the gross sample.

(*c*) From barrels, bags, wheelbarrows, etc.

Take a portion from every *n*th container and combine the portions for the gross sample.

(*d*) From small piles (not more than six feet in height).

With the thief, take one portion vertically at the peak of the pile and one vertically at each of ten points uniformly distributed along a line around the pile half-way between the peak and the edge of the pile. Combine these portions for the gross sample.

(*e*) From a well-mixed bulk of material (from mixers, packing machines, etc.).

After allowing a specified quantity, according to the condition of the material and type of apparatus, to flow past the sampling point, take the specified quantity for a sample. Periodic samples may be taken in the same manner, as often as desired.

6. From Wet Material

Wet materials arrange themselves in several classes:

When the material is thoroughly wet but not dripping, take the sample by any of the foregoing suitable procedures, keeping the collected portions in moisture tight containers.

(*b*) When water is dripping from the material, take the sample as prescribed for the particular material by one of the foregoing procedures and allow the total gross sample to drain, the drainage and remainder of the sample being weighed and recorded. If further elimination of water is necessary either by air drying, artificial drying or pressing, before the gross sample is reduced to the laboratory sample, the total water eliminated must be calculated and taken into account in the final evaluation of the material to the original wet condition. In case this water carries some of the material in solution, it will be necessary to ascertain the amount of this by analysis and include the results in the final evaluation.

(*c*) When fine solid material is non-uniformly suspended in a liquid several vertical sections of the material may be taken by means of a specially designed thief and combined for the gross sample. (See general outline for sampling liquids.)

7. From Hygroscopic or Deliquescent Materials

(*a*) When such material is contained in airtight containers which may be readily opened and closed, take a sample by means of a thief (Sect. 1), when the material does not contain resistant particles, larger than $\frac{1}{2}$ inch in cross section or, otherwise, by means of a small scoop or shovel. These increments should be placed and retained in an air-tight receiver until ready for the analysis.

(*b*) When such material can be sampled while being transferred to the final container for shipment, small and equal increments at uniform and regular intervals, are taken directly from the stream by means of a suitable dipper and combined for the gross sample.

8. From Kilns, Roasters, Dryers, Furnaces, Etc.

This class of material constitutes a special case, and, consequently the size of sampling unit and manner by which it may be taken will be specified according to the size of particles and character and condition of the material.

9. Sampling Non-ferrous Metals and Alloys

(*a*) **In the Form of Pigs, Billets, Ingots, Sheets, Slabs, Etc.**—One pig, etc., should be taken to represent each ton of metal in the lot and each of these should be sampled by one of the following methods after thoroughly cleaning the surface to be sampled.

1. By sawing completely through the specimen as illustrated by Sect. 1*a*, Fig. 75.   The sawdust from all the specimens is then thoroughly mixed and quartered down on a clean surface and the required amount of sample drawn.

2. By punching or drilling completely through if the equipment permits, or halfway through from two opposite sides as illustrated by Sect. 1c, 1b, Fig. 75. In this case the holes shall be spaced along a diagonal line from one corner of the specimen to the other.   Sampling in this manner may be so arranged that one or more holes are made in each of several specimens of a group in such positions that they represent consecutive positions on the diagonal of a single specimen. (See illustration in Sect. 1c.)   These punchings or drillings are carefully melted in a clean graphite crucible, and either granulated by carefully pouring into distilled water and thoroughly drying, or by casting into thin slabs which may be sawed completely through in several places and the sawdust treated as described above.   Drillings may be chipped and mixed if convenient.

(*b*) **In the Form of Sheets.**—In sampling brass discs, and sheets, when they can be crated so that the edges are flush, recourse can be made to a portable milling machine operated by a ¼ H.P. electric motor run transversely across the edges, so adjusted that only a very thin milling is taken from each disc or sheet.   These are coned and quartered for the sample.   By this method the serviceability of the disc or sheet is not destroyed, and the completeness of the sampling depends only on the accuracy of adjusting the edges in the crate.

Procedure for Reducing the Gross Sample

By combining the several sampling units, the gross sample is obtained which should now be so large that large single chance particles of material could be entirely foreign matter or entirely pure substance and affect only slightly if at all the final sample.   Increasing the size of the gross sample increases its accuracy, but cost and convenience of collection and reduction of sample, limit the degree to which this can be carried to advantage.   The reduction of the gross sample to the laboratory sample is an operation which must be performed with accuracy and precision.   Automatic machinery and labor and time saving devices may be used for this operation adhering closely to the following general scheme with the exception that some materials of uniform comparison need not be finally reduced as small as 6 mm.—4 mesh— while it may be necessary to finally reduce other material to .14 mm.—100 mesh—or finer.

In sampling large shipments, the gross sample may become excessively large and unwieldy. This may be obviated by periodically reducing the gross sample by the Standard Long Pile and Alternate Shovel Procedure, and subsequently compositing these reduced portions for the final gross sample.

Reduction of the Gross Sample

(Approx. 1000 lbs.) crushed to about 22.6 mm.—1 mesh; thoroughly mixed and halved by the Long Pile and Alternate Shovel procedure.

Discard   One-half crushed to about 16 mm.—1.5 mesh; mixed and halved by
½   the Long Pile and Alternate Shovel procedure.
½   One-half crushed to about 11.3 mm.—2 mesh; mixed and halved by
           the Long Pile and Alternate Shovel procedure.
½   One-half crushed to about 4 mm.—5 mesh; mixed by rolling on canvas; halved by Cone and Quartering procedure.
½   One-half ground to about 2 mm.—10 mesh; mixed by rolling on canvas; halved by riffling (or sampling machine) or by the quartering procedure.
½   One-half mixed and riffled down to about 8 lbs.

The entire eight pounds is then further reduced and the required sample taken according to the character of the particular material.

A portion for the determination of moisture may be taken at some point during the reduction according to the character of the sample and manner in which the moisture test is made. When a moisture sample is wanted it is necessary that the sampling units be collected and stored under conditions whereby moisture would not be lost or absorbed. The mixing, crushing and halving operations, preceding the taking of the sample for moisture should be accomplished as rapidly as possible.

In case the gross sample contains an excessive amount of water which would be lost in the subsequent operations necessary to reduce it to the laboratory sample, it should be kept in a tight container during the collection of the various increments, after which it is weighed and allowed to air-dry, or it may be dried artificially, and reweighed. It is then in a condition to be reduced to the laboratory sample according to the above scheme, taking into account, of course, the moisture thus driven off from the original gross sample in the final calculation for the evaluation of the material.

Reduction of Gross Sample (Long Pile and Alternate Shovel)

This procedure is based upon the method recommended and used by the U. S. Bureau of Mines.

1. Thoroughly mix the entire gross sample, after crushing in a suitable manner until all pieces are approximately one inch or less in any dimension, by shoveling it into a cone-shaped pile, depositing each shovelful on the apex of the pile. (Fig. 76, A and B.)

2. Shovel all of the material into a pile about the width of the shovel and approximately 10 feet long according to the total amount of material, spreading each shovelful uniformly over the whole length of the pile, beginning alternately from opposite ends.   (Fig. 76, C.)

3. Divide the long pile into two equal portions by beginning on one side of the pile, at either end, and take successive shovelfuls, advancing each time by the width of the shovel around the pile, combining the first and every alternate shovelful into a neat cone-shaped pile as in No. 1 and discarding the second and every alternate shovelful (Fig. 76, D and E).

Fig. 76. Method of Sampling Ore.

4. Repeat the above operation on the reserved portion until a portion of about 500 lbs. is obtained.

5. Crush the material until no piece is greater than approximately three-fourths inch in any dimension, and then repeat the above operation (No. 3).

6. Crush the material until no piece is larger than approximately one-half inch in any dimension and then repeat the above operation (No. 3).

7. A portion of about 125 lbs. is now obtained which is further reduced by the "Cone and Quartering Procedure."

Reduction of Gross Sample (Cone and Quartering)

1. Mix the material amounting to about 125 lbs. by crushing to pass a 4 mm.—5 mesh—sieve and shoveling into a neat cone (Fig. 76, F and G).

2. Flatten the cone by pressing the apex vertically down with the shovel or board so that, when quartered, each quarter will contain the material originally contained therein.

3. Divide the flattened pile into equal quarters by passing a straight edge board vertically twice through center of the pile at right angles, each time drawing half of the pile a few inches to one side (Fig. 76, H and I).

4. Discard two opposite quarters and brush away all fine particles from the exposed surface (Fig. 76, J).

5. Crush the remaining quarters to pass a 2 mm.—10 mesh—sieve. Mix thoroughly by shoveling into a neat cone.

6. Repeat operations No. 3 and 4 or riffle to about 20 pounds.

7. Grind the retained sample to pass a .85 mm.—20 mesh—sieve. Mix the material thoroughly on a clean canvas by raising alternate opposite corners of the canvas, thus rolling the material from side to side one hundred times (Fig. 76, K and L).

8. Treat the sample further as required by the particular material being sampled.

Fig. 77. * Jaw and Toggle Crusher for Coarse and Medium Fine Grinding.

It is, of course, impossible to reduce hygroscopic or deliquescent gross samples to the laboratory sample according to the above scheme unless they can be dried or otherwise transformed into a stable condition. When it is necessary to reduce such material it should be done rapidly and by hand, under the most favorable atmospheric conditions in regard to humidity, etc. When a large sample is taken for analysis the extent of the reduction of the sample will depend upon the size of the sample taken for analysis.

* Courtesy of Sturtevant Mill Co.

Apparatus for Reduction and Preparation of the Sample

Any sampling system which does not properly control the ratio of the size of largest particle to the size of sample can not be depended upon to produce a representative sample. The proper ratio for almost all material will be obtained by following the procedure outlined under the heading "Procedure for Reducing the Gross Sample." This reduction process is greatly facilitated by the use of suitable crushers, grinders, riffle samplers and mixing devices. The following examples of such apparatus are therefore given as an aid to the designing and equipping of the sampling room, the size and capacity of which will be determined by the number, character, and size of the gross samples to be handled.

Fig. 77a.*   Crusher and Grinder in Cross Section.

Crushers.—A jaw and toggle crusher is shown in Fig. 77f. This is a satisfactory crusher for coarse, medium and fine crushing and permits a considerable range of adaptability to suit varying conditions and requirements. Simple adjustments allow the capacity to be varied from about 200 pounds per hour for the production of fine material to 700 pounds per hour for coarser material when considering only one of the several sizes of this type of crusher. The parts are readily accessible for cleaning and repairing. By means of this type of crusher it is possible to reduce the material to about 4 mesh.

Grinders.—*Grinders* are necessary for reducing the material finer than 4 mesh and may be of the roll, disc or coffee mill type, according to the character of the material.

Roll grinders are especially adapted for brittle material. Figures 77b and 77c illustrate a type of roll grinder which may be readily cleaned and has a capacity of 100 to 1,000 lbs. per hour when producing a reduction to a fineness of 60 mesh and 2 mesh respectively. Disc grinders have a somewhat greater range of adaptability than the roll grinder and will reduce brittle or tough material to a high degree of fineness. The grinding is accomplished between a stationary and a revolving steel or iron disc, the output being small and fine or large and coarse according to the adjustment. Figures 77d and 77e illustrate a satisfactory type of disc grinder.

* By courtesy of Sturtevant Mill Co.

The coffee mill type of grinder is adaptable to soft or tough materials which have a tendency to stick to the rolls of the roll grinders or to clog the discs of some types of disc grinders.   Many kinds of coffee mill type grinders have been developed from which selection can be made according to the character of material under consideration.   Figs. 77b and 77d illustrate very good coffee mill types.   When reducing material to extreme fineness the ball mill, special small laboratory grinders, the bucking board and mortar and pestle are always applicable for small samples.

FIG. 77b.*   Roll Grinder for Brittle Material.

FIG. 77c.   Roll Grinder with Case Lifted to Show Interior.

Another type of crusher and grinder which has been developed particularly for sampling coal is shown by Fig. 77a.   This crusher will reduce the material and deliver an accurate ten per cent sample in one operation.   By repeating the operation on the aliquot the sample may be further reduced.

For many materials this crusher would serve to entirely reduce the gross sample to the laboratory sample with a very small amount of labor.

* By courtesy of Sturtevant Mill Co.

FIG. 77d.*   Disc Grinder Ready to Run.

FIG. 77e.*   Disc Grinder Open for Cleaning.

* By courtesy of Sturtevant Mill Co.

FIG. 77f. * Crusher Open for Cleaning.

FIG. 77g. Combination Crusher and Sampler.

* By courtesy of Sturtevant Mill Co.

Mixing and Dividing Samples

Large samples (500 lbs. or more) are usually mixed and divided by the "Long Pile and Alternate Shovel" procedure or (500–100 lbs.) by the "Cone and "Quartering" procedure.

Small samples (less than 100 lbs.) are usually mixed by rolling on a clean canvas, whereby the particles are given a rolling motion in alternately opposite directions, the dividing being done by quartering or, more accurately and rapidly, by passing it through some form of a riffle. A convenient and serviceable type of riffle is illustrated by Fig. 78. Another and more simple type is shown by Fig. 78a.

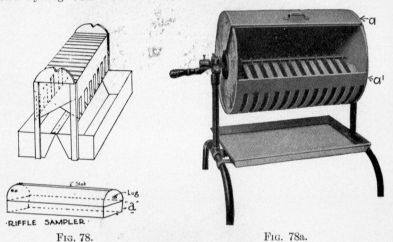

Fig. 78.   Fig. 78a.

FIG. 78. Riffle Sampler. "a," cover to fit tightly over one of the boxes with slot in rounded tops—also fitted with two lugs which fit in ends of riffle and help to rock evenly.

FIG. 78a. The cut shows the apron of the cylinder of this machine open for receiving the sample. After the sample is poured in, the apron's position is shifted, a being moved to a'. The cylinder is then revolved counterclockwise. The closed sides of the riffles plow through and thoroughly mix the sample, and no sample can be discharged through the riffle while the cylinder is revolving in this direction if the level of the sample is below the axis of the cylinder. After the sample has been mixed the cylinder is rotated one turn clockwise; the sample in the cylinder is then cut by the planes of the riffle and half of it is discharged into the receiving tray. The sample remaining is again mixed by revolving the cylinder counterclockwise. By alternately changing the direction, the sample is alternately mixed and halved until twice the size of sample required remains in the cylinder. The tray is then emptied of the discarded material, and the sample remaining, mixed and halved, and the sample caught in the tray is bottled and becomes the official sample, while the sample remaining in the cylinder is bottled and held as the reserve sample. The interior of the machine is easy of access and should be brushed clean after each sampling operation.

The Use of Standard Sieves

This section is based upon the specifications issued by the U. S. Bureau of Standards (1912) and adopted by the Amer. Inst. of Mining Engineers (1917).

The essential quantity in the definition of a sieve of a particular size is, primarily, the size of the openings through which the particles to be sifted are to pass.

A series of sieves of different sizes should have the openings vary uniformly, according to the size of the particles desired to separate. Inasmuch as most of the grinding of substances to fine particles is chiefly with the object of increasing the surface upon which some chemical action is to take place, the opening of such a series of sieves should vary in such a way that the square or fourth powers of the width of the openings shall form a geometrical series.

Designation of Sieve, Metric System	Customary Usage	Opening		Number of Mesh per Linear		Diameter of Wire	
		Mm.	Inch	Centimeter	Inch	Mm.	Inch
128 mm.		128.0	5.04			9.5	0.375
90.5 "		90.5	3.56			9.5	0.375
64 "		64.0	2.52			6.4	0.25
45.3 "		45.3	1.78			5.26	0.207
32.0 "		32.0	1.26			4.85	0.192
22.6 "	1 mesh	22.6	0.891			4.11	0.162
16.0 "		16.0	0.630			3.05	0.120
11.3 "	2 "	11.3	0.445			2.67	0.105
8.0 "		8.0	0.315	1.0	2.54	2.00	0.079
5.66 "		5.66	0.223	1.4	3.56	1.48	0.058
4.00 "	5 "	4.00	0.157	2.0	5.10	1.00	0.039
2.83 "		2.83	0.111	2.75	7.00	0.81	0.032
2.00 "	10 "	2.00	0.079	3.9	9.9	0.56	0.022
1.41 "		1.41	0.0555	5.0	12.7	0.59	0.0232
1.00 "		1.00	0.0394	7.0	17.8	0.43	0.0169
.85 "	20 "	0.85	0.0335	8.0	20.3	0.40	0.0157
.71 "		0.71	0.0280	9.0	22.9	0.40	0.0157
.59 "		0.59	0.0232	10.0	25.4	0.41	0.0161
.5 "	30 "	0.50	0.0197	12.0	30.5	0.33	0.0130
.42 "		0.42	0.0165	14.0	35.6	0.29	0.0114
.36 "	40 "	0.36	0.0142	16.0	40.6	0.26	0.0102
.29 "	50 "	0.29	0.0114	20.0	50.8	0.21	0.0083
.25 "	60 "	0.25	0.0098	23.0	58.4	0.185	0.0073
.21 "	70 "	0.21	0.0083	27.0	68.6	0.16	0.0063
.17 "	80 "	0.17	0.0067	31.0	78.7	0.15	0.0059
.14 "	100 "	0.14	0.0055	39.0	99.1	0.116	0.0046
.125 "	120 "	0.125	0.0049	47.0	119.4	0.089	0.0035
.105 "	150 "	0.105	0.0041	59.0	149.9	0.064	0.0025
.088 "	170 "	0.088	0.0035	67.0	170.2	0.061	0.0024
.074 "	200 "	0.074	0.0029	79.0	200.7	0.053	0.0021
.062 "	250 "	0.062	0.0024	98.0	248.9	0.040	0.0016
.052 "	280 "	0.052	0.0021	110.0	279.4	0.039	0.0015
.044 "	325 "	0.044	0.0017	127.0	323.0	0.035	0.0014

While the sampling process does not require extremely accurate sieves it is advisable to use those which conform approximately to a standard specification. Consequently whenever reference is made to a sieve it will be understood to comply with the following specifications, which have been adopted by a conference of representatives of various scientific and technical societies, government bureaus, and private firms, held at the U. S. Bureau of Standards.

This sieve scale is essentially metric. The sieve having an opening of 1 mm. is the basic one and the sieves above and below this in the series are related to it by using in general the square root of 2 (1.4142), or the fourth root of 2 (1.1892), as the ratio of the width of one opening to the next smaller opening. The first ratio is used for openings between 1 mm. and 128 mm. while the fourth root of 2 is used as the ratio for openings below 1 mm. to give more sieves in that part of the scale.

Containers for Shipment to Laboratory

Samples in which the moisture content is important should always be collected and shipped in moisture-tight containers. A galvanized iron or tin can with a screw top which is sealed with a rubber gasket and adhesive tape is best adapted to this purpose. Glass fruit-jars sealed with rubber gaskets may be used, but require very careful packing to avoid breakage in transit. Samples in which the moisture content is of no importance need no special protection from loss of moisture.

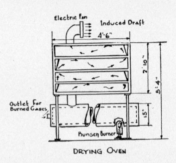

Fig. 79. Dryer for Coarse Samples. The outlet for air at the top may be connected with a chimney or any other device which will furnish a suitable draft. The sample is spread on tared pans, weighed, and dried at 10° to 15° C. above room temperature, and weighed again. The drying should be continued until the loss in weight is not more than 0.1 per cent per hour.

Drying Ovens for Moisture Determination

Samples may be dried by means of a forced draft of air at a slightly elevated temperature, or by heating at 100–110° C. in a well-ventilated oven until a constant weight is obtained. The former procedure is particularly adapted to material which has a tendency to undergo undesirable chemical or physical changes upon prolonged heating at elevated temperatures or for rapidly removing extraneous moisture preparatory to grinding. The latter procedure is usually employed for quantitative determinations on small finely ground samples. In either case a good system of ventilation and a definite uniform temperature are the chief considerations.

Figure 79 illustrates an oven for drying large samples by means of a current of heated air. Figs. 79a and 79b show a type of oven with a good ventilating system. Fig. 79c shows another type of oven, while 79d illustrates a vacuum drying oven which may be necessary for special work.

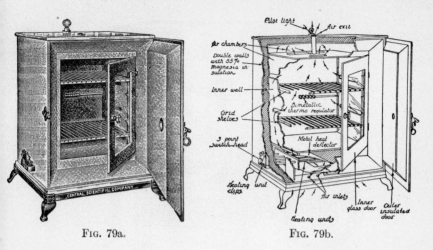

FIG. 79a.   FIG. 79b.

FIGS. 79a and 79b. Drying oven, triple walled, with a layer of air entirely surrounding the inner chamber, the temperature of this layer being practically the same as that of the air in the chamber. This approaches an adiabatic construction which has been approved by the Bureau of Standards as the best type of design for calorimeters and other constant temperature devices. By this construction together with a heavy outer insulation, heat exchanges between the inner chamber and the room outside are practically entirely prevented, and as a result a uniformity of temperature is secured in the heated space. The drying chamber should be entirely shielded from direct radiation from the heating units, and into every part of which heat should be carried by convection currents.

FIG. 79c.*

High Temperature Ovens, for operation from room temperature to 260° C.

* By courtesy of Arthur Thomas Co.

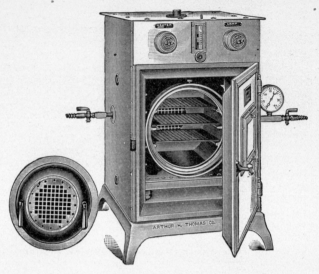

Fig. 79d.*   Vacuum oven. Supplied with a vacuum chamber which may be easily removed, permitting the oven proper to be used as a regular drying oven when the vacuum feature is not desired.   Moisture test of flour can be made in five hours at 75 C., while in an ordinary oven at 100 C. from ten to twelve hours are required.   The same condition apply for organic tests in general, i.e., for fertilizers where the tests must be made at the lowest possible temperature to avoid driving off nitrogen compounds; for powder where there is great danger of igniting the sample; for milk where there is great danger of charring; for operations involving essential oils, etc.

When tests are to be conducted in an atmosphere of hydrogen, nitrogen, carbon dioxide or other gas, it is only necessary to pass a current of the desired gas through the vacuum chamber.

REFERENCES

"Method of Least Squares Applied to Estimating Errors in Coal Analysis."   Technical Paper 171, U. S. Dept. of the Interior.
Bailey, E. G., "Accuracy in Sampling Coal."   J. Ind. and Eng. Chem., 1, 161.
Weld, F. C., "Accuracy in Sampling."   J. Ind. and Eng. Chem., 2, 426.
Camp, J. M., "The Methods of the U. S. Steel Corporation for the Commercial Sampling and Analysis of Iron Ores."   J. Ind. and Eng. Chem., 1, 107.   Professional Paper No. 48, U. S. Geol. Survey.
Pope, Geo. S., "Sampling Coal Deliveries."   Bull. No. 63 and Technical Paper No. 133, U. S. Bur. of Mines.   "The Sampling of Coal," Amer. Soc. for Testing Materials, Standards (1918) 673, 679.
Wolf A. G., "Sampling of Mine Floors."   Eng. and Min. J., 106, p. 537 and 671.
Daman, "An Automatic Ore Sampler."   Eng. and Min. J., 103, p. 188.
Maxwell, "Mill Check on Mine Sampling."   Eng. and Min. J., 104, p. 884.
Herr, "Observations on Sampling."   Eng. and Min. J., 102, p. 1015.
Pearce, "Ore Sampling of a Custom Mill."   Eng. and Min. J., 104, p. 66.   "Preparation of Laboratory Samples."   J. Ind. and Eng. Chem., 9, p. 100.
'Circular No. 39, U. S. Bur. of Standards.
"Standard Screen Scale for Testing Sieves."   Bull. Amer. Inst. of Mining Eng., June, 1917.
Kerr, C. H., "Standard Testing Sieves."   Trans. Am. Ceram. Soc., 15, p. 375–80.
Hoover, T. J., "Standard Series of Screens for Laboratory Testing."   Eng. Min. J., 90, p. 27.
Fairlie, A. M., "Standard Sieves and Screens."   Metal Ind., 12, p. 113.
'Mechanical Preparations of Solids for Chemical Treatment."   Chem. Eng., 9, p. 171.

* By courtesy of Central Scientific Co.

GENERAL OUTLINE FOR SAMPLING LIQUIDS

In general, a uniform and representative sample of liquid material is a feasible possibility because of the usual absence of segregated constituents, the ease with which the separate components may be intimately mixed, and the degree of comminution to which a liquid may be subjected without producing a separation of the individual components.

When the liquid is thin, non-viscous, and does not contain immiscible constituents, a homogeneous condition usually exists, and a sample from any part of the bulk is sufficiently representative of the whole. When viscous or immiscible materials are present, a heterogeneous condition usually exists and extreme care must be exercised to obtain a thoroughly representative sample. The proper selection of a representative sample of a liquid therefore, involves a consideration of the physical laws of liquids, their chemical activity, the miscibility of all components, and the interference of any insoluble materials carried by the liquid.

The sampling of liquids is divided into the three following classes; sampling liquids in quiescent state, sampling liquids in motion, sampling special liquors, *e. g.*, immiscible liquids, volatile liquids, liquids carrying sediment, etc.

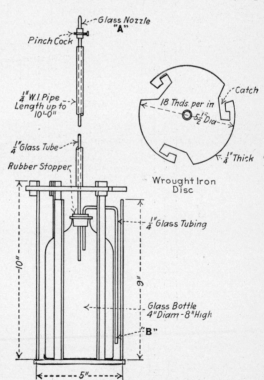

FIG. 80.   Sampling liquids apparatus.

Sampling Liquids in Quiescent State

All liquids not in motion may be sampled by obtaining portions at specified points from the top to the bottom of the liquid by means of a suitable sampling apparatus.

1. **From Storage Tanks, Tank Cars, Boats, Evaporating Kettles, Vats, Crystallizers, Mixers, Settlers, Etc.**

(*a*). If the liquid has been thoroughly agitated or is known to be reasonably uniform in composition, transfer several portions to a container by means of a suitable dipper, the several dippings being taken promiscuously throughout the mass of liquor.

4

(b). If the character and condition of the liquid is such as to permit the formation of zones of different composition, obtain samples by means of a suitable apparatus as shown by Fig. 80, whereby proper proportions of the liquid are taken at every point from the top to the bottom. Combine these samples for the gross sample and, after thoroughly mixing, bottle the required samples (Fig. 80). By slowly lowering the sampling bottle into the liquid with the outlet (A) open, a portion of the liquid from every point passes through (B) into the bottle, whereas if outlet (A) is kept closed until the desired depth is reached, the entire sample may be taken at any desired point.

Lead, wood, or any other material which is resistant to the liquid may be substituted for the iron parts of this device, according to the character of the liquid being sampled. Under some conditions it will be necessary to substitute a ground glass stopper for the rubber one. Openings of different sizes can be attached at (A) to govern the rate at which the sample will flow into the bottle.

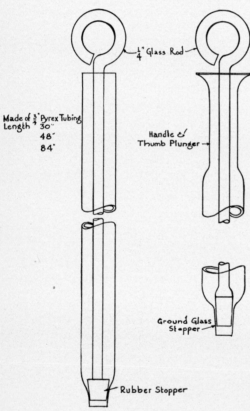

(c). Take a sample from the upper, middle, and lower levels of the liquid by means of a sampling device similar to that shown by Fig. 80, by keeping the outlet tube A closed until the container has been lowered to the desired depth.

2. From Drums, Carboys, Barrels, Etc.

(a) By means of a thief (Fig. 81) take proportional fractions from each container Combine and mix these increments for the composite gross sample. Bottle the amount required for the sample. If the contents of the container are such as to preclude thorough mixing or if the material has a tendency to form strata of varying compositions, the open thief should be lowered into the liquid at such a rate as to keep the levels of liquid inside and outside of the thief very nearly equal, in order to include portions at all points from the top to the bottom of the liquid.

Fig. 81.   Sampling liquids apparatus.

Sampling Liquids in Motion

3. From a Pipe or Conduit Carrying a Continuous Full Flow under a Constant or Varying Head

(*a*) A continuous or intermittent sample may be taken by inserting a small pipe into the line on the discharge side of the pump or propelling force of the flow. This sampling tube should extend one-half of the distance to the center of the flow, with the inner open end turned at an angle of 90° and facing the flow of the liquid. The sampling tube may be supplied with a stopcock in order to regulate the flow into a receiver. The amount drawn during the period of taking a continuous sample constitutes the gross sample. In this instance the stopcock should be adjusted at the beginning of the sampling period, to give the desired flow and no readjustment made during the sampling period. Intermittent samples may be taken by opening the stopcock for a definite period of time at definite intervals. The combined intermittent samples then constitute the gross sample.

4. From a Pipe or Conduit Carrying a Varying Fraction of Flow

(*a*) By means of a sampling weir similar to the apparatus shown by figure 82a, a definite fraction of varying flow can be collected over a required period

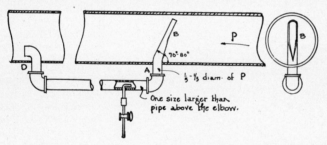

FIG. 82.   Apparatus for Sampling Liquids in Motion.

of time. This gross sample may be mixed and a portion taken for the final sample or by connecting two or more of the above devices in series; a small representative sample may be collected automatically, *e.g.*, if one million gallons of liquid per day are passing through a pipe or conduit line at an irregular rate, it could be sampled by conducting the stream to a series of four sampling weirs, each of which separates 5% or 1/20 of the flow. A final six gallon sample would then represent the entire million gallons. The size of each weir should be such as to give a suitable overflow and the apron over which the flow passes for division should be fixed in a horizontal position.

(*b*) By means of the arrangement illustrated by Fig. 82, an approximate sample ratio can be continuously diverted from a non-uniform flow. This device consists of a pipe *A*, inserted into the flowing stream at an angle of 70–80° provided with an opening *B* facing the flow and extending to the top of pipe *P*. This opening *B* is constructed as shown in the cut (Fig. 82), the width above the center of pipe *P* being equal to the diameter of pipe *A*, then tapering from the center to the bottom of the pipe P.   As the flow passes pipe A, an approximately constant sample ratio is diverted through pipe A and is sampled by a small pipe C, the opening of which faces the flow at a point

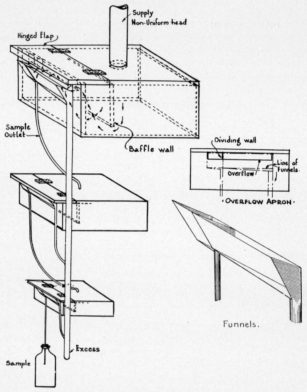

FIG. 82a.   Apparatus for Sampling Liquids.

halfway between the center and bottom of pipe A.   Pipe C is fitted with a stopcock whereby the amount of the sample flow through C may be regulated. Pipe A reënters pipe P at some point which will give sufficient positive flow-head through A.   While this arrangement will not necessarily produce an

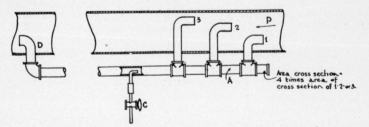

FIG. 82b.   Apparatus for Sampling Liquids in Motion.

accurate sample ratio, an increased flow through P will increase the flow-head through A and consequently increase the amount of sample withdrawn at C and an approximately relative sample ratio will be maintained with one regulation of stopcock C.

(c) With large pipes and large flows, the above arrangement may be modified as shown by Fig. 82b. Three pipes, 1, 2, and 3, bent at 90° angles with openings facing the flow at different levels are inserted in pipe P and connected to a common pipe A. The flow through A is then sampled by a pipe C as described above. An approximately relative sample ratio is thus maintained with one regulation of stopcock C.

Sampling Special Liquids

5. Liquids Containing Insoluble Matter in Suspension

(a) When the sediment remains in reasonably uniform suspension during the period required for taking the sample, the liquid is thoroughly mixed and the sample obtained by one of the foregoing procedures.

(b) When the sediment settles rapidly or is impossible of uniform distribution it is necessary to take special precautions to secure the components of the sample in the proper proportion. This can be accomplished with a fair degree of accuracy by mixing the liquid thoroughly and then rapidly taking a complete column of the liquid by means of the special thief or device shown by Fig. 80 or 81. By repeating this operation a number of times, a fairly representative sample will be obtained. Another procedure of possible application under certain conditions would be to take several portions at as many uniformly distributed points from the top to the bottom by means of the thief Fig. 80 or 81. These portions are then combined and mixed for the gross sample.

(c) To accurately sample a liquid containing insoluble matter, it is necessary to filter the entire liquid, weigh the insoluble material and filtrate separately and then take separate samples of the sediment and liquid, recording the ratio of sediment to liquid for use in the final evaluation of the original material. This, however, is impracticable except in such instances wherein the size of sample allows of economical handling in the manner described.

6. Liquids Composed of Immiscible Layers

The most practical and accurate procedure in this case is to effect a separation of the layers and combine portions of each layer in the proper ratios. If this is impossible, the material may be transferred to a container of uniform cross section, the depth of each layer measured, and then the proper portion taken from each layer, for a composite sample, by means of a sampling thief similar to those shown in Fig. 80 and 81.

7. Liquids Containing Crystals Due to Supersaturation

Frequently conditions are such that a portion of the liquid or certain constituents thereof have crystallized in the container. Oleum and acetic acid are common examples of this class. When practical the material should be warmed sufficiently to dissolve completely or melt the crystals before sampling by one of the foregoing procedures. Otherwise, if the crystals are small and remain in suspension the mass should be sampled as a liquid containing insoluble matter in suspension.

8. Volatile Liquids

(a) Volatile liquids are best sampled from a continuous flow while the liquid is being discharged or by means of a siphon from containers. If the liquid is uniform in composition or can be made so by agitation in some manner, a portion may be run to the bottom of the sampling bottle until the bottle overflows through another tube from the top into another bottle or to the waste pipe, to such an extent as to leave a liquid in the first bottle containing the maximum amount of the volatile constituent (see Fig. 82c). The sample bottle should then be quickly stoppered and sealed for transportation to the laboratory.

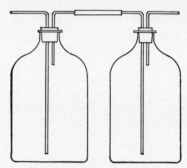

FIG. 82c.   Apparatus for Sampling Liquids.

REFERENCES

"Sampling Creosote Oil."   Amer. Soc. Testing Materials (1918), p. 721.
"Liquid Sampling Specifications."   Am. Gas. Light J., 103, 391.
"Standard Methods for the Sampling and Analysis of Commercial Fats and Oils."   J. Ind. and Eng. Chem., 11, p. 116.

GENERAL OUTLINE FOR SAMPLING GASES

The proper sampling of gases often presents greater difficulties than the analysis. This is particularly true when it is desirable to obtain a representative sample of a gas during a considerable period of time as it passes through a pipe or flue from the source of production. Gases travel through straight pipes and conduits in an irregular succession of waves with a spiral motion, the maximum velocity being at the center of the pipe and the minimum near the walls. The motion of these waves and point of maximum velocity is altered in a varying degree by every bend and obstruction throughout the line of travel. Where gases are encountered which are subject to temperature changes either above or below normal, this factor will also considerably interfere with proper sampling. The temperature of gases will vary throughout the cross-section of the pipe, usually being hottest at points of maximum velocity and coldest next to the walls and in dead pockets. Theoretically if it were possible to discharge the total gas to be sampled into a large holder and provide time for it to thoroughly diffuse, it would then be in the most advantageous condition whereby a true and representative sample could be obtained by simply withdrawing a portion. Unfortunately this is not often the condition under which gases are to be sampled, being usually sampled from a flow possessing varying velocity, temperature, and composition. Under such conditions it is practically impossible to determine a point of approximate average velocity, temperature or composition from which a representative instantaneous sample can be drawn.

Consequently it becomes necessary to collect a sample over an extended period whereby the number of series of gas waves sampled is such that there is a high probability that a true and representative sample will be obtained. Under some conditions, useful and more definite data regarding composition and gas-flow is obtained by taking

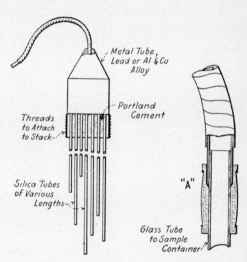

FIG. 83.   Apparatus for Sampling Gas.

frequent "grab" samples. It is, therefore, quite evident that the subject of gas sampling naturally divides itself into two phases for consideration that of continuous sampling and "grab," or instantaneous, sampling.

1. General Considerations and Apparatus

(a) **Sampling-tube for Drawing Samples from Gases Flowing through Pipes.**—Without discussing the merits of the various forms of sampling tubes such as the single-opening tube, and the various types of perforated tubes all of which are more or less useful under certain conditions, the multiple type originated by A. H. White—"Gas and Fuel Analysis"—is apparently best adapted for securing uniform samples (see Fig. 83). This tube should be inserted so that the longest tube reaches the center of the flowing gas.

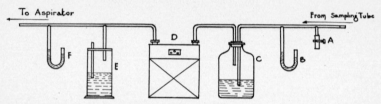

FIG. 84.   Apparatus for Sampling Gas.

(b) **Collecting a Representative Continuous Sample.**—In order that the sample should be truly representative of the total gas flowing during a definite period, it is necessary to constantly draw a definite proportion of the gas. Great elaboration of apparatus and equipment would be necessary if the rate of drawing the sample were adjusted to vary directly with the velocity of the gas, in which case the sample would accurately represent the gas. The most practical approach to this ideal condition would be to take the continuous sample under a constant pressure, whereby the rate of sampling will vary directly with the pressure of the gas being sampled.

Figure 84 illustrates a common form of apparatus whereby a stream of gas at constant pressure is drawn from a gas line. This apparatus consists of a pressure-gage B to indicate any obstruction of the sampling tubes, a bubbling-bottle C to give a visual control of the rate of the stream, a gas-meter D which may be omitted if not needed, a pressure control, E and a pressure gage F on the line to the aspirator. When aspiration is necessary the pressure at the sampling-tube as shown by gage B should be only a few tenths-of-an-inch of water. This may be regulated by the depth to which the tube is immersed in the water of the regulator E. When the gas is under pressure, the aspirator and E and F become unnecessary.

(c) **The Design of Apparatus.**—The design of apparatus—and the sampling procedures—must take into account the solubility and chemical activity of the gas. Saturated magnesium chloride solution, glycerine and water mixtures, and various oils have been used with varying success in overcoming the solubility of gases in the solutions over which they are collected. Further investigations along these lines for specific gases will probably make possible the use of other liquids than mercury for gases having high solubility factors. The corrosive character of the individual gases will determine the type of containers, etc., which may be used.

2. Taking a " Grab " Sample

(a) For a "grab," or instantaneous, sample the ordinary two-bottle aspirator may be used (see Fig. 84a) using care not to draw the sample so fast as to produce a reduced pressure at gage B (Fig. 84).

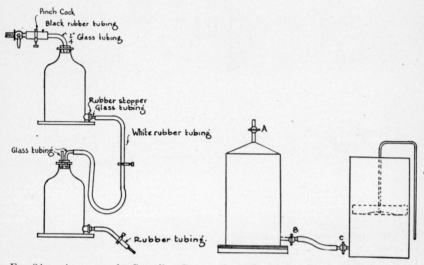

FIG. 84a.   Apparatus for Sampling Gas.   FIG. 84b.   Apparatus for Sampling Gas.

3. Taking a Continuous Sample

(a) For continuous sampling the apparatus illustrated by Fig. 84b will be found convenient.

This apparatus consists of two large galvanized metal tanks, one in the form of an aspirating-bottle in which the sample is taken, and the other, slightly larger, which acts as a reservoir.   A sample of gas taken under constant pressure and at a uniform rate over any specified period of time, which may be varied at will, is obtained by filling the tanks with water, oil or other liquids according to the character of the gas, until the level reaches the top of the aspirating-tank.   A syphon acts as the outlet and a uniform rate, if the pressure of the gas in constant, is obtained by attaching it to a wooden float.   The speed of outflow may be regulated by the length of the syphon and the opening or size of the outlet-nozzle.

By arresting the downward movement of the float and syphon by means of a shoulder or suitable device, a small amount of water remains in the aspirator; this acts as a seal and automatically discontinues the intake of gas. By closing the stopcocks A and B the operation is completed.

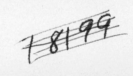

These tanks may be constructed to crate, in compact form for transportation, a 20-liter glass aspirating-bottle, as shown in Fig. 84c.

This bottle is to be used when the gas to be sampled would attack the metal aspirating-tank. If a layer of some non-absorbing oil is placed on the surface of the water the original composition of the gas is unaffected.

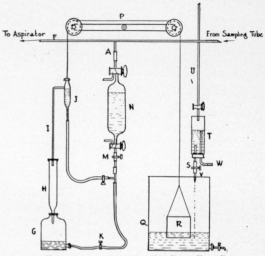

FIG. 85.   Apparatus for Sampling Gas.

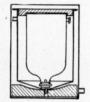

FIG. 84c. Apparatus for
   Sampling Gas.

(b) When mercury must be used because of the solubility of the gas in water, an apparatus similar to that illustrated by Fig. 85, originated by Thomas Gray, J. Soc. Chem. Ind., 32, 1092, will be found convenient.

"It consists essentially of an ordinary gas-sampling tube N, attached to a reservoir J, which is counterpoised by a vessel R floating in a tank Q, the float being connected with J by means of a cord which passes over the pulleys P.

"The float R may be a tinned-iron vessel or glass bottle containing the necessary quantity of water or lead shot to establish the balance. The height of the tank Q must be greater than the length of the sampling-tube N, the overflow-tube I should be slightly longer than N, and the length of the wider tube H, which merely serves to prevent loss of mercury by splashing, should slightly exceed that of I.

"The jet V, under pressure which may be regulated by adjustment of the overflow W, through which the excess of water from U escapes to the waste, delivers sufficient water during the specified period to raise the level in the tank to a height equal to the length of the sampling-tube.

"As the water-level rises, the reservoir J is steadily lowered, drawing the gas uniformly into the sampling tube, and the mercury, thus displaced, escapes through the overflow-tube I to the bottle G. By means of an aspirator a rapid current of gas is drawn along the tube F which is connected to the flue or gas-main by means of the sampling tube (Fig. 83), a suitable filter being interposed, if necessary, to retain any solid particles. The connection A, between the sampling tube and the tube F, is preferably made of capillary tubing 3 to 4 inches long, to prevent the diffusion of the gas backwards from N to F. If desired, a small non-return mercury valve may be inserted at this point.

"To start the apparatus, the tube F is connected with the gas supply and a rapid current of gas is drawn through F by means of the aspirator.

"The rubber tube connecting the jet V with the water-supply is then closed by the clip S, and the water is allowed to run into T and to overflow freely through W the height of which has previously been adjusted to the desired level. Water is now run from the tank Q until the top of the overflow-tube I is at the level of the shoulder of the gas tube N, and J and N are now filled with mercury by means of a small funnel in J. The capillary A is finally filled with mercury by raising the reservoir J, the lower stopcock of the sampling-tube is closed, and J is then lowered to its former position and filled to the overflow-tube with mercury; the operation of sampling may now be commenced by opening the lower stopcock of the gas tube N and starting the flow of water from the jet. The aspirator and the water-supply to T remain in operation during the whole period of the test and the apparatus requires no further attention.

"The period of sampling may be varied in a number of different ways:

(1) "Jets may be constructed to deliver the requisite quantity of water in specified times; these are easily drawn from glass tubing in a blowpipe-flame, the final adjustment being effected by altering the head of water in T.

(2) "Tanks of various diameters may be employed.

(3) "The height of the sampling tube N may be varied."

REFERENCES

Sinnatt, F. S., "A Convenient Apparatus for Obtaining an Average Sample of Gas and for Regulating the Flow of a Gas into an Evacuated Vessel." Analyst, 37, p. 250,
Gray, Thomas, "An Automatic Gas Sampling Apparatus." J. Soc. Chem. Ind., 32. p. 1092.
White, "Gas and Fuel Analysis." International Chemical Series.

The author desires to acknowledge his indebtedness to J. S. Coye for his assistance in preparation of this chapter.

DECOMPOSITION OF THE SAMPLE

Decomposition of the Material. In the instructions for the solution of the material special procedures are often given owing to the predominance of some particular compound or compounds present. Directions are given for example for oxides, others for sulphides, and again others for silicates, etc. The chemist is frequently at loss to know what procedure to select as the mere inspection of the material frequently will furnish him no information as to its predominating trait.

Owing to the variables in ores and alloys it is not possible to have any set procedure applicable to all conditions. It is often necessary to combine two or more methods to effect solution of certain refractory ores. Acid-extractions are frequently followed by fusion methods for the solution of the acid insoluble material, likewise fusions require subsequent water extraction followed by acids. In general, ores should be finely ground, before treatment by wet or fusion method. The following general rules, however, will be of value.

General Procedure. It is advisable to test the solubility of a small amount of the material in a test tube, using water if the material is a salt or hydrochloric acid if an ore, and dilute nitric acid if an alloy or metallic product. In examining an ore the sample should be finely powdered. About 0.5 to 1.0 gram is taken and treated with 10 to 20 cc. of strong hydrochloric acid. A pear-shaped flask, of pyrex glass, is convenient for this decomposition. The solution is heated gently until no further action is evident. If the ore contains sulphur as sulphide, the addition of nitric acid and bromine are recommended, nitric acid in most cases follows the addition of hydrochloric acid, but in case of sulphur determination, nitric acid and bromine are added first to avoid loss of sulphur as H_2S. For alloys dilute nitric acid precedes HCl. Additional HCl and HNO_3 may be necessary to complete the possible action of these acids. Dilute sulphuric acid is now added and the solution evaporated to near dryness. This generally effects complete decomposition. If a residue remains upon adding HCl and water and heating, it is advisable to filter off the solution and fuse the residue by one of the fluxes given under " Fusions," page 1033. It is often advisable to start with a fusion of the original ore—sodium and potassium carbonate for high silicon ores, sulphates of barium, strontium and calcium; potassium acid sulphate fusions made preferably in a pyrex glass flask for oxides of metals. In case of refractory oxides decomposition is assisted by adding a small piece of filter paper to the molten mass.

By Wilfred W. Scott.

1032

Reagent to *Materials*
Effect Solution

I. **Water** will dissolve the alkali salts, ammonium, lithium, potassium and sodium acetates, bromides, chlorates, chlorides, iodides, nitrates, nitrites, sulphates. Also arsenates, arsenites, borates, carbonates, oxalates, phosphates, and tartrates. The halides of silver, mercury, and lead are insoluble in water. The arsenates, arsenites, borates, carbonates, oxalates, phosphates and tartrates of the heavy metals require acid treatment to effect solution. Sulphates of Ba, Sr, Ca, Hg″, Pb are insoluble in water.

II. **Acids**

1. *Hydrochloric acid* decomposes carbonate and oxide ores of B, Ca, Fe, Mn, Mg, P, Sn (reducing agt.), Ti, U, Zn ($SnCl_2$ assists Fe sol.).
2. *Hydrochloric acid* together with or followed by an *oxidizing reagent*, i.e. HNO_3, $KClO_3$, etc. Alloys of Al, Sb, Bi, Cu; Cr, Co and Ni steels, ferro silicon, Ti and V steels, sulphide ores of Cu, Ce, Pb, Mo, U, Zn.
3. *Nitric acid*, dilute or concentrated. Alloys of Bi, Cd, Co, Cu, Pb, Mn, silico manganese, ferro manganese, P and Ti steels, ores of Cd, Cu, Mo, Co and Ni.
4. *Aqua Regia.* The metals and alloys of Au, Ir, Hg, V, Pt. Ores of Cd, Hg, Rh, W.
5. *Sulphuric acid.* Ores of Al, Gl, Mn, Pb, Th, Ti, U.
6. *Sulphuric acid* with HF, silicates, Cu ores and alloys.
7. *Hydrofluoric acid,* usually in conjunction with H_2SO_4, HCl or HNO_3 useful for dissolving ores containing silicates where SiO_2 is not to be determined.
8. *KBr*, *Br*, *HNO_3*, *HCl* combinations to dissolve pyrites of Pb, Ni, Fe, As, etc. Reactions 1–8 (excepting 7) may be made in glass; 7 in platinum.

III. **Fusions**

1. The insoluble residue remaining from an acid treatment of a substance may be brought into solution, generally, by fusion with an appropriate flux. The fusions are made in crucibles (20 cc. capacity) of silica, iron, nickel, silver, " palau " (gold-palladium 80 : 20) or platinum. Potassium bisulphate fusions may be made in silica or glass as well as in platinum; sodium carbonate fusions may be made in iron, nickel, " palau," and platinum; hydroxide or peroxide fusions may be made in iron, nickel or silver crucibles; sodium carbonate potassium nitrate fusions may be made in platinum, but hydrochloric acid should not be used in dissolving the fusion as the chlorine liberated will attack the platinum.

2. In making fusions the sample is well mixed with six to twenty times its weight of the fusion mixture and placed over a thin layer of the flux in the crucible and then covered by a lid of the same material as that of the crucible. Heat is applied cautiously until the mixture melts, the heat being raised during the action. When the melt has reached a quiet fusion and the resulting molten mass has become clear and homogeneous, the action is complete.

(*a*) A stiff platinum rod is placed in the molten mass and held in place until this has cooled sufficiently to solidify around the wire. By reheating the crucible the mass of fusion may be lifted out, cooled and together with the crucible placed in the beaker in which the subsequent treatment is made.

(*b*) The molten mass may be poured into a crucible lid of sufficient capacity and when cooled placed in the beaker together with the crucible.

(*c*) The molten mass is cooled by rotating the crucible or flask in such a way that it solidifies in a layer on the sides.

3. Water is now added to the material and the mixture heated until the mass disintegrates. The beaker is covered by a clock glass and the additional solvent now added. This may be hydrochloric or sulphuric acids, ammonium carbonate or any other appropriate solvent.

The following fluxes are commonly used—

1. *Sodium carbonate.* Decomposes silicates of Al, Ca, Ce, Cr, etc.; halides of Ag; sulphates of Ba, Pb.
2. *Sodium and potassium carbonates.* Silicates of Al, F, Fe, Ni, Se, Te, etc. The mixture fuses at a lower temperature than carbonate alone.
3. *Sodium carbonate with oxidizing agent,* i.e., $KClO_3$, KNO_3, Na_2O_2, ZnO, MgO. Ores of Sb, As, Cr, Fe, Mo, V, Zr, sulphides, pyrites, etc.
4. *Sodium peroxide.* Ores of Sb, As, Cr, Mo, Ni, V, U, Sn. Certain alloys and steel for chromium, etc.
5. *Potassium acid sulphate* (with H_2SO_4). Ores of Al, Sb, Cu, Cr, Co, Fe, Mn, Ni, Rh, Ta, Ti, W. Steel with Cr, Mo, V and W, Th, phosphates, slags, oxides of metals of basic character. Silica remains insoluble. In a bisulphate fusion in a 250 cc. flask, 25–50 cc. of water and 10 cc. HCl are added and the mixture boiled until the cake dissolves. If any dark residue remains, the solution is decanted off and the residue again fused with additional flux. As stated in page 1032, certain refractory oxides require the addition of a reducing agent, such as carbon from a filter paper, to assist the acid sulphate flux. It is better to make two or more fusions on resulting residues remaining from an acid extraction of the melt, rather than to increase the amount of flux in the first charge.
6. *NaOH, KOH,* basic flux (with or without KF). Oxidized Sb ore, ores of Cr, Sn, Zn, Zr. Sulphides and sulphates in sulphur determinations.
7. Other reagents. NH_4Cl and $CaCO_3$—alkali silicates, KCN—tin oxide ore, CaO, Na_2O_2. Organic compounds for halide determination.

Reactions 1, 2, 3 may be carried out in iron, nickel or platinum crucibles, 5 in silica (*porcelain*) or platinum, 4, 6, and 7 in iron, nickel and silver.

Reagents.[1]   *Ammonium acetate*, $NH_4C_2H_3O_2$, is a very effective solvent of lead salts, especially the sulphate. It is prepared by adding strong acetic acid to strong ammonium hydroxide until the solution is just acid.

Ammonium hydroxide, NH_4OH, is a powerful solvent of chloride and bromide of silver.

Ammonium sulphide, $(NH_4)_2S$, readily dissolves the sulphides of arsenic, antimony, and tin. This reagent decomposes slowly, losing NH_3 and forming $(NH_4)_2S_2$. It should be kept in a dark cool place. To prepare the solution pass a rapid current of pure hydrogen sulphide through a solution of ammonia in a reagent bottle.

Hydrochloric acid, HCl, is a powerful solvent and when mixed with HNO_3 in the proportion ($2-HCl : 1-HNO_3$) it will dissolve gold and platinum due to the chlorine which is thus liberated in the nascent state.

Hydrofluoric acid, HFl, is used to decompose silicates, the silica being volatilized.

Nitric acid, HNO_3, is a powerful solvent and oxidizing agent. The fuming variety is a more active oxidizer and desulphurizer.

Sulphuric acid, H_2SO_4, is a powerful solvent and is generally used in a dilute form made by mixing concentrated acid (1.84 sp. gr.) with water in the proportion $1-H_2SO_4 : 5H_2O$.

Argol, $KHC_4H_4O_6$, potassium acid tartrate commercial grade, is a powerful reducing agent and also a basic flux.

Borax, cryst., $Na_2B_4O_7.10H_2O$, is an acid flux sometimes used as a cover in place of NaCl. To dehydrate, fuse it in an iron or chalk lined clay crucible, pour the fused mass on a clean surface and pulverize when cold. Melting point, borax glass, 742° C.

Charcoal is a reducing agent and desulphurizer.

Iron, metallic, a basic flux, and desulphurizer. Nails or wire about $\frac{1}{8}$ inch dia. generally used. Melting point above 1500° C.

Lead, metallic, a basic flux. It is also used as a collector of the precious metals in the assay of gold and silver ores. Granulated lead is used in scorification assays and sheet lead in bullion assays. Its silver content should be determined. Melting point, 327° C.

Lead flux: 16 parts sodium bicarbonate, 16 parts potassium carbonate, 8 parts flour and 4 parts borax glass. This mixture serves as a flux, reducing agent, and desulphurizing agent.

Litharge, PbO, is a basic flux and an oxidizing and desulphurizing agent. Its silver content should be determined. Melting point, 884° C.

Silica, SiO_2, is an acid flux. Powdered lime-glass can be used as a substitute. Melting point, SiO_2, 1775° C.

Potassium bisulphate, $KHSO_4$, is a decomposing agent and an acid flux. Silica is not made soluble by this reagent. Melting point, 200° C., K_2SO_4, 1072° C.

Potassium carbonate, K_2CO_3, acts same as Na_2CO_3 and is frequently mixed with it. A mixture in proportion to the molecular weights of the two substances is an excellent flux for decomposing certain silicates, clays, etc., which are difficult to handle by either carbonate alone. Melting point, K_2CO_3, 909° C.

[1] W. J. Crook, Chemical. Lefax, Philadelphia, November, 1918.

Potassium cyanide, KCN, is a powerful reducing and desulphurizing flux and is frequently used in the fire assay of Pb, Sn, Bi and Sb. Its solution is a solvent of gold and silver. Fuses at red heat.

Potassium hydroxide, KOH, acts same as NaOH and is used for the same purposes. Melting point, 360° C.

Potassium nitrate, KNO_3, is a basic flux and also a powerful oxidizing agent. Melting point, 339° C.

Sodium bicarbonate, $NaHCO_3$, is a desulphurizing agent, a basic flux and sometimes an oxidizing agent. The corresponding potassium salt may also be used.

Sodium carbonate, Na_2CO_3, is used alone or in conjunction with other reagents for the decomposition of silicates, etc. Melting point, 849° C.

Sodium chloride, NaCl, a neutral flux, used as a cover in assay. Melting point, 804° C.

Sodium hydrate, NaOH, is used principally for the decomposition of sulphides and sulphates in sulphur determinations. Sometimes used to decompose certain silicates, oxides and certain organic compounds. It is a basic flux. Melting point of NaOH, 318° C.

Sodium nitrate, $NaNO_3$, is a decomposing and also an oxidizing agent. KNO_3 is also used for same purpose. Melting point, 316° C.

Sodium thiosulphate solution, $Na_2S_2O_3$, is a solvent for AgCl.

Oxidizing Agents. Those in most general use are oxygen, chlorine, bromine, potassium permanganate, potassium bichromate, nitric acid, potassium chlorate, sodium nitrate, hydrogen peroxide and ammonium nitrate.

Reducing Agents. Hydrogen, H, is used in the form of a gas which should be dry and free from impurities. Hydrogen sulphide, H_2S, is prepared by adding dilute H_2SO_4 to pure iron sulphide. If pure iron sulphide is not at hand, it can be prepared by fusing iron nails with sulphur in the proportion of about 1 part iron to 2 parts sulphur, by weight. Sodium sulphite, Na_2SO_3, is used for the reduction of ferric solutions. It separates arsenious sulphide, which is soluble in it, from the sulphides of antimony and tin, which are insoluble in it. Stannous chloride, $SnCl_2$, is frequently used for reducing iron solutions. Solutions of sugar, tartaric acid and many other organic compounds will serve as reducing agents.

Amount of Sample. The quantity of the sample required depends largely upon the substance and the amount of constituent sought in the sample. In case of ores, where the principal constituent is desired, for example, lead in galena, iron in magnetite, alumina in bauxite or sulphur in pyrite, a comparatively small sample is sufficient, namely, 0.5 to 1 gram of the ore. On the other hand, if the constituent sought is present in small percentage down to mere traces, 5, 10 or as much as 100 grams of the sample may be taken. Fortunately colorimetric processes enable us to determine many of the substances in extremely minute amounts so that one-gram samples are generally sufficient for most analyses. In the volumetric determination of constituents in steel, 1–5 grams are generally taken. 0.5 to 1 gram of alloys is generally taken for their analysis.

ANALYSIS OF NON-FERROUS ALLOYS

Difficulty of Complete Separation of Elements. As the great majority of the substances with which the chemist is called upon to deal are complex rather than simple, a careful study of the separation of the elements is of the greatest importance. Only by the closest attention to details can success be attained in the analysis of complex substances. The importance of testing precipitates for impurities and the solution for unprecipitated portions of an element cannot be too strongly urged. Only in this manner can the accuracy of an analysis be assured.

Limit of Accuracy in Analysis. If a complete analysis is made, the sum of all the constituents must be very close to 100%. A summation which is within .5% can generally be obtained if the analysis is conducted with care and reliable methods are used. In general the analysis of an unknown substance should be conducted in duplicate. If the duplicate results do not agree within .2 or at most .3%, a third analysis should be made. As the error of most determinations is at least .1%, it is unnecessary to calculate results to more than hundredths of per cent. As the error in each determination of the analysis of a given substance may be either plus or minus, the practice of dividing the difference between the summation and 100% among the various determinations is not justifiable.

It is in some cases possible to analyze a substance in such a manner that the results are accurate to the hundredth of a per cent. Such results may be computed to the .001 of a per cent. This practice is common in the analysis of metals. Large quantities of the metal are taken, so that considerable quantities of the impurities which are present in small amounts are obtained for determination. The results may then be accurate to the hundredth of a per cent. This does not imply a higher degree of accuracy in the determination of a given element than .1 of a per cent. For example, if iron were present in copper to the extent of .5%, a determination of the iron which is accurate to .01% of the impure copper would represent an error of 1/50 of the amount of iron present in the copper. In giving the results of such analyses the percentage of the main constituent is obtained by difference, so that the summation is exactly 100%.

Chapter by William B. Price with introduction by John C. Olsen.

The principal non-ferrous alloys come under the following classifications
FUSIBLE METALS
WHITE METALS, SOLDERS, BABBITS, ANTIFRICTION

Alloy	Composition					
	Lead	Tin	Antimony	Copper	Zinc	Other Constituents
Ordinary Bearings		96		4		
Kayserzium		92.98	5.44	1.58		
Brittania Metal		90.1	6.3	3.1	0.5	
Babbit Metal		88.9	7.4	3.7		
Berlin Railroads		83	11	6		
Ashberry		79	15	3.0	2.0	Ni, 1.0
Minorfer		66	20	4.0	9.0	Fe, 1.0
Stereotype Metal	20.0	30.0				Bi, 50.0
Pewter		20	80			
Railroad Bearings	60.0	20	20			
Type Metal	70.0	10	18	2.0		
Magnolia Metal	80.0	4.75	15.0	Trace		Bi, .25
Tempered Lead	98.5	.08	.11			Na, 1.31
White Metal	82.0		12.0	6.0		
Solder	75.0	25.0				
Solder	50.0	50.0				
Steam Boiler Plug	48.4				38.8	Bi, 12.8
Sir Isaac Newton's Alloy	30.0	20.0				Bi, 50.0
Rose's Alloy	28.1	21.9				Bi, 50.0
Wood's Alloy	25.0	12.5				Bi, 50.0 Cd, 12.5
Expanding Alloy	66.7		25.0			Bi, 8.3

BRONZES—PLAIN AND SPECIAL

Alloy	Composition				Remarks
	Copper	Tin	Zinc	Other Constituents	
Phono Electric Metal	98.55	1.40		Si, .05	Telephone Wire
Phono Electric Metal	95	.5			
Silicon Bronze	97.00	1.45	1.50	Si, .05	
Bronze	92	8			
Phos. Bronze	90	9.8		P, .20	
U. S. Gun Metal (1875)	90	10			Medals, Whistles
Gun Metal	90	8	2		
Statuary Bronze	90	6	3	Pb, 1.0	
Arsenic Bronze	89	10		As, 1.0	Antifriction
Admiralty Bronze	88	10	2		
British Navy Bronze	87	8	5		
	87	7	3	Pb, 3.0	Carbureters
Locomotive Bearings	86	14			
Large Bells	85	15			
Needle Metal	84.96	7.96	5.31	Pb, 1.77	
Gun Metal	84	14	2		Valves, Screw
Japanese Bronze	83.0	5.0	2.0	Pb, 10.0	
Gun Metal	82	16	2		Bearings
Bell Metal	80	18	2		
Small Bells	80	20			
Ajax	77	11.5		Pb, 11.5	Bearings
Speculum Metal	70.00	30.00	Trace	Fe, Trace Ni, Trace	
Ajax Plastic	65	5.0		Pb, 30.0	Bearings
Retz Alloy	74.3	11.4		Pb, 8.9 Sb, 5.4	
Acid Resisting Metal	82.00	8.0	2.00	Pb, 7.95 P, .05	

PLAIN BRASSES

Alloy	Composition		Remarks
	Copper	Zinc	
Tombac..........................	99.15	.85	Tombac
Tombac..........................	97.8	2.2	
Ctge. Gilding....................	95	5	Ctge. Gilding
Tombac..........................	91.0	9	
French Oreide (Gilding).........	90	10	
Dutch Gold......................	84.5	15.5	Imitation Gold
Bronze Powder...................	84	16	
Pinchbeck.......................	83.3	16.7	
Mannheim Gold...................	80	20	4 and 1 Low Brass
3 and 1 Ctge. Brass.............	75	25	
Ctge. Brass.....................	70	30	
2 and 1 Ctge. Brass.............	67	33	
Common Brass Wire...............	66.6	33.4	
Masonic Gold....................	65	35	
Common High.....................	64.5	35.5	
Muntz Metal.....................	60.0	40	
Bath Metal......................	55	45	
Brazing Solder..................	50	50	
Strong Brass Solder.............	33.34	66.66	

LEADED BRASS

Alloy	Composition		
	Copper	Lead	Zinc
Leaded Oreide Wire..............................	88	1.0	11
Watch Brass....................................	74	1.25	24.75
Swivel Connection Wire..........................	69.5	1.00	29.5
Sign Brass.....................................	66	.5	33.5
Drill Rod......................................	63.5	3	33.5
Engravers Brass................................	63.5	2	34.5
Common Leaded Wire.............................	63	2	35
Clock Brass....................................	61.5	1	37.5

Tin Brass and Special Brass

Alloy	Composition			Other Constituents
	Copper	Tin	Zinc	
Name Plates	86	3.0	9	Pb, 2.0
Trolley Fittings	85	3.0	9	Pb, 3.0
Condenser Brass	70	1	29	
Tobin Bronze	61.00	1.00	37.50	Fe, .15
				Pb, .35
Naval Brass Rod	61.00	1.00	38.00	
Manganese Bronze	57.20	1.18	40.15	Fe, 1.33
				Mn, .02
				Al, .10
				Pb, .02
Rich's Metal	60.0		38.2	Fe, 1.8
Delta Metal	55.94		41.61	Pb, .72
				Fe, .87
				Mn, .84
				P, .02

Cupro Nickel and Nickel Silvers

Alloy	Copper	Nickel	Zinc	Lead	Iron	Other Constituents
5% Nickel Silver	63.0	5.0	32.0			
10% Nickel Silver	60	10.0	30			
10% Cupro Nickel	90	10.0				
Swiss Watch Nickel	58.0	14	25.25	1.50	1.25	
15% Nickel Silver	63	15	22			
15% Watch Nickel	56	15	27.75	1.25		
15% Cupro Nickel	85	15				
Hardware Metal	50	15	34.90			Al, .10
Victor Metal	49.94	15.40	34.27		.28	Al, .11
Sterline	69.00	18.00	13.00			
Special Spoon Stock	61.5	18	20.5			
20% Nickel Silver	61.5	20	18.5			
20% Cupro Nickel	80	20				
U. S. Nickel Coins	75	25				
Argentan	52.0	26.0	22.0			

Solution of Alloys and Outline of Separation

Among the solvents used may be mentioned nitric acid, aqua regia, sulphuric acid, fusion with acid fluxes.

Nitric Acid Method

Treat one or more grams of the alloy filings or drillings with concentrated HNO_3 or HNO_3 1 : 1 until the metal is completely decomposed or in solution, adding water if necessary to assist solution.

(a) *If the metal dissolves*, antimony and tin are absent; omit their tests.

(b) *If the metal forms a turbid solution*, antimony and tin may be present. To a portion, add several volumes of water and boil. (a) If a clear solution is formed treat the entire solution in the same way, and omit tests for Sn and Sb.

(c) If the residue is insoluble, Sb and Sn are indicated, evaporate the entire solution to dryness, gently ignite to expel water, add HNO_3, heat, dilute and filter. If the filtrate is turbid, repeat the filtration until clear.

| Precipitate.—SnO_2; $Sn_3(PO_4)_4$; Sb_2O_4, all white and traces of the copper group metals.
a. Digest from 10 to 20 minutes with strong K_2S, Na_2S or $(NH_4)_2S$ solution and filter.
b. Melt with Na_2CO_3 and sulphur, cool, digest with water, and filter. | Filtrate.—Contains the H_2S group (without tin and antimony) and $(NH_4)_2S$ group.
Add from 1 to 3 cc. of concentrated H_2SO_4 and evaporate to fumes, cool, dilute and filter. |

| Precipitate.—Traces of copper group. If sufficient in quantity, dissolve in HNO_3; add to filtrate containing $(NH_4)_2S$ group. | Filtrate.—Contains Sn, Sb in solution. Just acidify with dilute HCl and filter.
a. Analyze the precipitated sulphides.
b. Test the filtrate for phosphates. | Precipitate.—Pb-SO_4, white. Treat with $NH_4C_2H_3O_2$ solution, filter, and add K_2CrO_4. A yellow precipitate insoluble in KOH proves lead present. | Filtrate.— Contains the H_2S group (without Sn, Sb, and Pb and free from HNO_3) and the $(NH_4)_2S$ group.
Into a portion of the solution pass in H_2S. A precipitate shows the presence of the H_2S group metals. |

a. *If the H_2S group is not present*, as shown by a test on a portion of the solution, make a test for the $(NH_4)_2S$ group.

b. *If the H_2S group is present*, precipitate the metals with H_2S, filter and wash.

| Precipitate.—Contains the H_2S group, sulphides (without lead, tin and antimony).
If mercury is present use $(NH_4)_2S$ to separate the sub-groups.
If mercury is absent digest the precipitate with 20 per cent KOH (2 to 3 grams dissolved in 10 cc. of water), filter and wash. | Filtrate.—Contains the $(NH_4)_2S$ group
a. *Test for Phosphates.* If found present consult notes on this group in Part II.
b. Make a test for the group, by making a small portion ammoniacal, and passing in H_2S, if not present. A precipitate other than sulphur indicates the presence of the metals of this group. Analyze the precipitate by the first procedure on the metals of the $(NH_4)_2S$ group.
c. If a test is made for magnesium, analyze the filtrate by procedures for the alkalies. |
| Precipitate.— Copper group.
Analyze by procedure outlined for the insoluble H_2S subgroup. | Filtrate.—Arsenic group in solution. Acidify, filter and analyze precipitate by the procedure for the soluble H_2S subgroup. | |

STANDARD METHODS OF CHEMICAL ANALYSIS OF ALLOYS OF LEAD, TIN, ANTIMONY AND COPPER, A. S. T. M. METHODS

These methods apply particularly to white metal-bearing alloys (known commercially as " Babbitt Metal ") and to similar lead and tin base alloys. Two sets of methods are here given. The first method is somewhat slow but is recommended as giving the more accurate results where the analysis of these alloys is of comparatively infrequent occurrence. The second method is rapid and is suitable for control work, giving good results after the analyst has become familiar with it.

I. General Methods [1]

A. Determination of Lead, Copper, Antimony and Tin

Determination of Lead

SOLUTIONS REQUIRED

Mixed Acid. Dissolve 20 g. of KCl in 500 cc. of water, add 400 cc. of HCl (sp.gr. 1.20), mix and add 100 cc. of HNO_3 (sp.gr. 1.42).

Alcohol-Hydrochloric Acid Mixture. Mix 400 cc. of 95% ethyl alcohol and 100 cc. of HCl (sp.gr. 1.20).

Acid Ammonium Acetate. To 500 cc. of NH_4OH (sp.gr. 0.90) add 500 cc. of water and then acetic acid (80%), until slightly acid to litmus.

METHOD

Dissolve 1 g. of the finely divided alloy by boiling in 70 to 100 cc. of " mixed acid " solution in a covered beaker. Add more " mixed acid " if a complete solution of the alloy is difficult to obtain, and continue boiling until evaporated to about 50 cc. Add 5 cc. of HCl (sp.gr. 1.20), cool in ice water until the bulk of $PbCl_2$ has crystallized out, then add slowly, with constant stirring, 50 cc. of alcohol (95%), continue stirring for a few minutes and cool in ice water for 10 minutes. Add 50 cc. more alcohol from a pipette, allow to stand in ice water for 20 minutes and filter through 9 cm. paper into an 800-cc. beaker. Wash by decantation three times with alcohol-hydrochloric acid mixture and finally wash the paper twice with the same mixture. Wash the $PbCl_2$ from the paper back into the beaker; wash paper several times with hot water, catching washings in beaker with the bulk of the chloride. Finally wash paper with hot acid ammonium acetate solution. Heat until all $PbCl_2$ is dissolved. Add 15 cc. of saturated solution of $K_2Cr_2O_7$; heat until precipitate is of good orange color; filter on weighed Gooch crucible; wash with water, alcohol and ether; dry at 100° C. and weigh. Calculate percentage of lead by the empirical factor 63.75.

NOTES. 1. With proper manipulation, the $PbCl_2$ precipitate should contain consistently all but 0.003 g. of lead.

2. During the heating of the acid ammonium acetate to dissolve the $PbCl_2$, the solution should remain perfectly clear, any turbidity indicating the presence of tin or antimony, as even 1 mg. of tin or antimony will cause a slight but distinct turbidity.

[1] G. W. Thompson's method. See Journal Soc. Chem. Ind., Vol. 15, p. 179.

Determination of Copper and Antimony

SOLUTIONS REQUIRED

Potassium Hydroxide. Dissolve 100 g. of KOH in 500 cc. of water. **Potassium Cyanide.** Dissolve 3.5 g. of KCN in 1800 cc. of water and standardize against copper of known purity. **Sodium Thiosulphate.** Dissolve 24.8 g. of $Na_2S_2O_3.5H_2O$ in 1000 cc. of water, and allow to stand for 24 hours. Standardize against Antimony Metal c.p., using same quantity of reagents and same procedure as under (c) Determination of Antimony.

METHOD

See " Determination of Lead."

Evaporate the filtrate from $PbCl_2$ filtration by boiling in the loosely covered 800-cc. beaker, and finally take to dryness on a water-bath. Add 10 cc. of KOH solution and after a few minutes add 20 cc. of 3% H_2O_2. Add more KOH, if solution is acid, until an alkaline reaction is shown by litmus paper. Heat on the water-bath for 20 minutes, add 10 g. of ammonium oxalate, 10 g. of oxalic acid, and 200 cc. of water and heat to boiling. Pass in H_2S for 45 minutes with solution near boiling; filter at once; and wash precipitate with hot dilute solution of oxalic acid saturated with H_2S, catching washings with filtrate.

Wash the precipitate of copper and antimony sulphides from the filter paper back into the beaker with the least amount of water possible; treat with 10 cc. of KOH solution; heat on water-bath until the undissolved matter is distinctly black, filter through same paper into a 300-cc. Erlenmeyer flask. Wash the precipitate with hot water containing a small amount of K_2S.

(a) Determination of Copper by Potassium Cyanide Titration

Dry and ignite the precipitate with paper in a small casserole, dissolve in nitric acid (sp.gr. 1.42), boil to expel nitrous fumes, neutralize with Na_2CO_3, add a few drops of NH_4OH and titrate with standard KCN solution.

(b) Determination of Copper by Electrolytic Method

See " Determination of Copper by Potassium Cyanide Titration."

Dry and ignite the sulphide precipitate in a small casserole, dissolve in 10 cc. of HNO_3 (sp.gr. 1.42), boil until oxides of nitrogen are expelled and add 50 cc. of distilled water. Transfer to a tall 200-cc. beaker, wash out casserole, add 5 cc. of H_2SO_4 (sp.gr. 1.84) and determine copper by electrolysis. See the determination of copper by the electrolytic method in the Standard Methods of Chemical Analysis of Manganese Bronze.

NOTES. 1. On filter after heating with KOH solution, the copper remains as sulphide with a small amount of lead sulphide which failed to be precipitated as chloride. If it is desired to determine this lead, it can be done by separation from the copper by ordinary methods.

2. If the amount of antimony and copper is small (less than 10 mg.), the lead which failed to be precipitated as chloride may also fail to come down as sulphide on passing H_2S through the oxalic solution. It will remain in the filtrate from the sulphides and be deposited electrolytically with the tin on the cathode. This can be prevented by adding an oxalic acid solution of a pure antimony salt containing about 100 mg.

of antimony just before passing H_2S. In this case antimony must be determined on a separate portion.

3. If the amount of copper present is from 8 to 10 mg. or more, it should be determined by the electrolytic method. In this case, the small amount of lead precipitated as sulphide with the copper is deposited on the anode as PbO_2 and may be weighed, calculated to lead by factor 86.43 and added to that obtained under "Determinations of Lead."

(c) Determination of Antimony

See " Determination of Copper by Potassium Cyanide Titration."

Add 50 cc. of HCl (sp.gr. 1.20) to the KOH solution of antimony sulphide, and boil down to small volume until all arsenic has been expelled as arsenious chloride.

Add 25 cc. of HCl (sp.gr. 1.20) and 1 g. of $KClO_3$ and boil until colorless. Filter into a 300-cc. Erlenmeyer flask, through glass wool if sulphur has separated, wash out original flask with HCl (sp.gr. 1.20), cool, add 1 g. of KI, 1 cc. of CS_2, and titrate with standard thiosulphate solution.

Determination of Tin

Apparatus for Electrolysis

Electrodes. Cylindrical cathodes of platinum wire gauze—2 by $1\frac{3}{8}$ in. diameter.

Platinum wire spiral anodes.

Method

See " Determination of Copper and Antimony."

Concentrate the filtrate and washings from the precipitated sulphides, if necessary, to a volume of 200 cc. and add 5 g. more of oxalic acid in case the amount of tin is over 0.5 g. Electrolyze until the solution reacts alkaline, using a current of about 0.5 ampere. Remove the cylinder; wash twice with distilled water and once with 95% ethyl alcohol; dry at 110° C. and weigh.

Note. If the electrolysis is carried out over night, it will usually be found by morning that the solution has become alkaline and it may be taken for granted that the tin has all been precipitated on the cathode. The best results are obtained by regulating the current, or the time, so as to render the solution alkaline only a very short time before the cathode is to be removed. The cathode should be placed close to the bottom of the beaker to insure proper agitation of the electrolyte.

B. Determination of Arsenic

Solutions Required

Ferric Chloride. Solution of specific gravity 1.43.
Ammonium Carbonate. Dissolve 75 g. in 500 cc. of water.

Method

Weigh 1 g. of sample into a 250-cc. distillation flask and add 10 cc. of $FeCl_3$ solution, 60 cc. of HCl (sp.gr. 1.20), 20 cc. of water and 5 g. of KCl. Connect the flask with a condenser, heat slowly until solution is complete and boil down to as small a volume as possible, catching distillate in a tall 400-cc. beaker. Cool flask, add 50 cc. HCl (sp.gr. 1.20) and redistill as before, catching distillate in same beaker. Cool distillate and pass H_2S through for one hour, allow to settle and filter the arsenious sulphide on a Gooch crucible. Wash twice with HCl (1 : 4), four times with cold water, three times with alcohol and four times with CS_2. Dry at 110° C. for 10 minutes, and weigh after cooling. Dissolve the arsenious sulphide with $(NH_4)_2CO_3$ solution, wash thoroughly with water, dry for 30 minutes at 110° C. and reweigh after cooling. The difference in weights multiplied by 0.60911 gives the percentage of arsenic.

II. Rapid Methods for Control Work [1]

A. Determination of Lead and Copper

SOLUTIONS REQUIRED

" **Lead Acid.**" Mix 300 cc. of H_2SO_4 (sp.gr. 1.84) and 1800 cc. of distilled water. Dissolve 1 g. of lead acetate c.p. in 300 cc. of distilled water and add this to the hot solution, stirring meanwhile. Let stand at least 24 hours and siphon through a thick asbestos filter.

Dilute Alcohol for Washing. Mix equal parts of denatured alcohol and distilled water.

METHOD

(a) Determination of Lead

In a covered 300-cc. Erlenmeyer flask dissolve 1 g. of the alloy in 20 cc. of H_2SO_4 (sp.gr. 1.84); heat the solution nearly to boiling until the metal is completely decomposed and the $PbSO_4$ is white (this may take 30 minutes or more) and finally boil for several minutes. Allow to cool, but not below 60° C., and then add slowly 50 cc. of water while the solution is agitated. Heat to boiling for several minutes in order to insure complete solution of antimony sulphate. Allow the $PbSO_4$ to settle out until the solution is clear, not letting the temperature fall below 60° C. If the liquid does not clear quickly, it must be heated longer. When clear, pour the solution through a weighed porcelain Gooch crucible with asbestos mat, decanting the solution as completely as possible without allowing more than a very small amount of $PbSO_4$ to go over into the crucible. Now add 10 cc. more of H_2SO_4 (sp.gr. 1.84) to the $PbSO_4$ in the original flask, and boil for several minutes. Cool, add slowly 30 cc. of water, and again heat to boiling for a few minutes; allow the solution to cool to about 60° C. and completely transfer the $PbSO_4$ to the Gooch crucible. Wash with lead acid, retaining the filtrate and these washings for the copper determinations. Remove the beaker containing these solutions and wash out the lead acid with dilute alcohol; set the Gooch crucible inside a porcelain crucible; dry and ignite for five minutes at the full heat of a Tirrill burner; cool and weigh as $PbSO_4$, which contains 68.29% lead.

(b) Determination of Copper

To the filtrate from the $PbSO_4$, which contains the copper and which has been transferred to an Erlenmeyer flask, add NH_4OH (sp.gr. 0.90) until the

---

[1] See "The Analysis of Alloys for Lead, Tin, Antimony and Copper," by D. J. Demorest, Journal Ind. and Eng. Chem., Vol. V, p. 842; "Rapid Analysis of Alloys for Tin, Antimony, and Arsenic," by F. A. Stief, Journal Ind. and Eng. Chem., Vol. VII, p. 211; and "Technical Analysis of Brass," 1917. Price and Meade, p. 182.

solution is slightly alkaline; then add 2 cc. of H_2SO_4 (sp.gr. 1.84); heat nearly to boiling; add 2 g. of Na_2SO_3 and when this is entirely dissolved add 1 g. of KCNS dissolved in 10 cc. of water. Shake well and allow the precipitated CuCNS to settle for one hour while the solution is kept hot. Filter on a close filter paper, wash with cold water and ignite paper and precipitate in a porcelain crucible. Proceed by one of the two following methods:

(1) Dissolve in HNO_3 (sp.gr. 1.42), add 5 cc. H_2SO_4 (sp.gr. 1.84); evaporate until fumes of H_2SO_4 are evolved. Dilute to about 100 cc. with distilled water. Add 1.5 cc. of HNO_3 (sp.gr. 1.42) and determine copper by electrolysis. See the " Determination of Copper by the Electrolytic Method," Standard Methods of Chemical Analysis of Manganese Bronze of the American Society for Testing Materials.

(2) Dissolving the ignited precipitate in HNO_3 (sp.gr. 1.42), as in (1); boil to expel nitrous fumes, neutralize with Na_2CO_3 and determine volumetrically with cyanide as in A of " General Method."

Note. If the amount of copper is very small it may escape detection by this method, in which case it should be determined as in A of "General Method."

B. Determination of Arsenic, Antimony and Tin

APPARATUS

Arsenic Still. A condenser is made from glass tubing in the form of a letter S, about 18 in. long and $\frac{1}{2}$ in. in inside diameter, tapering to about $\frac{1}{4}$ in. at the upper end and to about $\frac{1}{8}$ in. at the lower end. One curve is nearly filled with water, and is submerged in cold water in a 500-cc. beaker. The lower end dips into about 75 cc. of water in a 300-cc. beaker and the upper end is connected by a delivery tube with a 300-cc. Florence flask, closed with a rubber stopper which is fitted with a delivery tube and with a thermometer reaching to about 1 in. above the surface of the liquid in the flask.

SOLUTIONS REQUIRED

Iodine. Dissolve 10.7 g. of iodine in 50 cc. of distilled water which contains 20 g. of KI in solution and dilute to 1000 cc. with distilled water. Standardize against pure tin having exactly the same conditions for titration as are specified for the analysis of the alloy. Each cubic centimeter is equivalent to approximately 0.00500 g. of tin or 0.00315 g. of arsenic.

Potassium Permanganate. Dissolve 2.7 g. of $KMnO_4$ in distilled water, filter through asbestos, and dilute to 1000 cc. with distilled water. Standardize against pure antimony having exactly the same conditions for titration as are specified for the analysis of the alloy. Each cubic centimeter is equivalent to approximately 0.00500 g. of antimony or 0.00465 g. of iron.

Ferrous Ammonium Sulphate. Dissolve 12.4 g. of ferrous ammonium sulphate crystals in 950 cc. of distilled water and add 50 cc. of H_2SO_4 (sp.gr. 1.84).

Starch. To 1000 cc. of boiling water add a cold suspension of 6 g. of starch in 100 cc. of distilled water; cool, add a few drops of chloroform and mix thoroughly.

METHOD

(a) Determination of Arsenic

In a 300-cc. Florence flask, dissolve 0.5 g. of the alloy in exactly 8 cc. of H_2SO_4 (sp.gr. 1.84). The metal must be finely divided, preferably in the form of thin foil-like shavings, although sawings or very fine drillings may be used. Heat the solution to boiling; cool, add about 5 cc. of water and a bulk of about 0.5 cc. of clean granulated pumice stone and boil the covered solution very gently for about five minutes, or until the strong odor of SO_2 can no longer be detected. Finally, being careful to have 5 cc. of water present, cool the solution to about 18° C. and cautiously add 20 cc. of HCl (sp.gr. 1.20). Insert in the flask a rubber stopper fitted with a thermometer and deliver tube and connect the delivery tube with the " S " condenser. Heat the solution to gentle boiling for from 10 to 15 minutes, keeping the vapor temperature at 107° C. for at least 5 minutes. Wash out the condenser into a 300-cc. beaker and add an excess of about 2 g. of $NaHCO_3$. Bring the volume of the solution to about 200 cc.; warm to about 27° C. and titrate with standard iodine solution and starch to the appearance of a deep blue color.

NOTE. A blank determination should be made on corresponding amounts of reagents treated as above, and the results should be corrected accordingly.

(b) Determination of Antimony

Cool the solution which remains in the flask after the arsenic distillation; add about 130 cc. of cold, recently-boiled distilled water to which has been added about 3 cc. of HCl (sp.gr. 1.20) and titrate with standard $KMnO_4$ solution to the appearance of a decided permanent pink color. From a burette add an excess of standard ferrous ammonium sulphate solution until the pink color is discharged and then titrate with standard $KMnO_4$ solution to the reappearance of a pink color.

(c) Determination of Tin

If the sample does not contain 14% (or 0.07 g.) of antimony, add enough dissolved $SbCl_3$ to the solution to bring the contents of antimony up to about 0.07 g. for the purpose of insuring perfect reduction of the tin and uniform conditions for the titration. Then add exactly 6 cc. of H_2SO_4 (sp.gr. 1.84) and 60 cc. of HCl (sp.gr. 1.20) and add about 6 in. of clean, soft No. 14 pure iron wire cut into 2 in. lengths and cleaned with dilute HCl just before using. Boil gently for 30 minutes, add about 6 in. more wire and boil 30 minutes longer. Remove from heat, close flask loosely with a rubber stopper and allow about two minutes for all air to be expelled by hydrogen and acid vapors. Close flask tightly and quickly place it in cold water, cooling the solution to about 20° C. Transfer the solution quickly to a 500-cc. beaker (leaving the iron wires in the flask) and rinse flask and contents with 150 cc. of cold, recently-boiled distilled water. Add rinsings to main solution in the beaker, bring final volume to about 300 to 350 cc. and titrate quickly with standard iodine solution and starch to the appearance of a strong blue color.

NOTES. A blank determination should be made on corresponding amounts of reagents treated as above, and the results should be corrected accordingly.

If the copper content of the alloy is as high as about 3% or over, it prevents a good end-point in the tin titration when the tin percentage is low. Under such conditions, just before titrating, add about 1 g. of KI crystals, stir until nearly dissolved and titrate immediately. If allowed to stand too long at this point, trouble may be encountered due to the precipitation of some of the other constituents.

Other forms of pure iron may be employed, but the wire as above specified has been found convenient.

For accurate work it is desirable to reduce and titrate the solution of tin in an atmosphere of CO_2.

DETERMINATION OF BISMUTH, IRON, COPPER, ZINC AND LEAD IN WHITE METALS

SOLUTIONS REQUIRED

Potassium Hydroxide. Dissolve 200 g. of C.P. Potassium Hydroxide in 1000 cc. distilled water.

Potassium Sulphide Solution for Washing. Dissolve 25 g. of Potassium Hydroxide in 1000 cc. of distilled water. Saturate 500 cc. of this solution with Hydrogen Sulphide and then mix with the remaining 500 cc. of solution.

Dilute NH_4OH (1–2). Mix 300 cc. of NH_4OH (sp.gr. 0.90) with 600 cc. of water.

Dilute HCl (1–3). Mix 200 cc. of HCl (sp.gr. 1.19) with 600 cc. of water.

Acidified Hydrogen Sulphide Wash Water. Dilute 10 cc. of HCl (sp.gr. 1.19) with 1000 cc. of distilled water and saturate with H_2S gas.

Alcohol for Washing. Mix 500 cc. of 95% grain alcohol with 500 cc. of distilled water.

METHOD

Dissolve 10 g. of the sample in 40 cc. of hydrochloric acid (sp.gr. 1.19) and 20 cc. of nitric acid (sp.gr. 1.42) in a 600-cc. beaker. Boil the solution to expel oxides of nitrogen and dilute to 100 cc. with distilled water.

Add 20% potassium hydroxide solution until solution is just alkaline and then add 100 cc. in excess. Dilute to 500 cc. with distilled water and treat with a rapid stream of hydrogen sulphide gas for 15 minutes, digest on the steam-bath for 2–3 hours and finally allow to stand at room temperature over night.

Filter on a No. 40 Whatman filter paper and wash with $\frac{1}{2}$% potassium sulphide solution. Discard the filtrate. Dissolve sulphides on the filter paper in aqua regia, reprecipitate as above, filter and wash as before. Discard the filtrate as before. Dissolve the sulphides of iron, bismuth, copper and lead in 1–1 nitric acid. If the separation has been correctly made, the nitric acid solution should be perfectly clear, except for a slight amount of sulphur. Boil solution a few minutes to remove last traces of H_2S and then filter into a 400-cc. beaker and wash with hot water.

Evaporate solution nearly to dryness, add 25 cc. of HCl (sp.gr. 1.19) and evaporate again to a pasty mass. Repeat this treatment with HCl two or three times or until nitric acid has been removed. Finally add 10 cc. of HCl (sp.gr. 1.19) warm to dissolve all separated salts, and dilute to 200 cc. with distilled water. Treat with H_2S gas to the complete precipitation of copper, lead and bismuth. Filter and wash with hydrogen sulphide water. Save the filtrate for iron and zinc determinations. Dissolve the precipitates of bismuth, copper and lead in 1–1 nitric acid, boil to remove traces of H_2S and filter if solution is not clear into a 600-cc. beaker. Wash with hot water. The volume of solution at this point should be 75–100 cc. Carefully neutralize the greater part of free acid with ammonium hydroxide (1–2). As the neutral point is reached, a faint opalescence appears in the solution; stop the addition of ammonia when this point is reached or before an appreciable precipitate is formed. Now add 1–3 cc. of HCl (1 : 3) and dilute solution to 400 cc. with distilled water.

Allow the precipitate of bismuth oxychloride to settle for an hour on the steam bath and then filter on a weighed Gooch crucible, wash twice with hot water, dry at 105° C. for one hour and weigh. Calculate BiOCl to Bi.

Determination of Copper and Lead

The filtrate from the bismuth oxychloride precipitate contains the copper and lead in the sample. Add 10 cc. of conc. H_2SO_4 and evaporate to strong fumes of H_2S_4. Cool. Dilute to 100 cc. with distilled water, heat to boiling and allow the precipitate of lead sulphate to settle for one hour. Filter on a weighed Gooch crucible, wash with 10% H_2SO_4 solution and finally, after removing filtrate which contains all the copper, with alcohol (1–1). Ignite gradually but finally with the full heat of a Bunsen flame for five minutes. It is best to place crucible on a platinum crucible cover while igniting. Weigh as $PbSO_4$. Calculate Pb.

Determine copper in the filtrate from the lead sulphate filtration as follows:

Neutralize the greater part of the free acid of sample with ammonium hydroxide (sp.gr. .90), then add 5 cc. of nitric acid (sp.gr. 1.42) and electrolyze for copper. See Determination of Manganese Bronze.

Determination of Iron and Zinc

The filtrate from the hydrogen sulphide precipitation of Cu, Bi and Pb contains all the iron and zinc of sample. To determine iron, boil solution for five minutes to expel all hydrogen sulphide, add a few drops of HNO_3 and boil for a few minutes to effect a complete oxidation of iron. Cool somewhat, add 3 to 4 g. of ammonium chloride and make slightly ammoniacal. Heat to boiling, allow precipitate of ferric hydroxide to settle and filter. Wash with hot dilute ammonium hydroxide and hot water. It is best to redissolve this precipitate of iron in hot 1–1 HCl and reprecipitate as before and filter. Combine the two filtrates.

Iron may be determined either by igniting the precipitate of ferric hydroxide and weighing as oxide (Fe_2O_3) or by redissolving the precipitate and titrating with standard potassium permanganate solution after reducing the iron with $SnCl_2$.

The combined filtrates from the double precipitation of the iron contain all the zinc of the sample. Make the solution acid with nitric acid. Zinc may be determined in this solution as described under Analysis of Bronze Bearing Metal.

NOTES. The size of sample weighed out for analysis should be governed by the amount or percentage of element to be determined.

Instead of determining the bismuth as oxychloride, the oxychloride precipitate may be dissolved in nitric acid, bismuth precipitated as basic carbonate, filtered, dissolved in nitric acid, the nitric acid solution evaporated to dryness in a weighed platinum dish and finally ignited. Weigh Bi_2O_3.

ANALYSIS OF MANGANESE BRONZE

Standard Method, A. S. T. M.

General Considerations. Methods are given for the determination of lead, using a large sample when lead is present up to about 0.2 per cent. A method is also given for the electrolytic determination of lead and copper in the same small sample when lead is present in amounts over 0.2 per cent. In this alloy zinc is taken by difference.

Alloy of Copper, Lead, Tin, Iron, Manganese and Zinc
Determination of Copper by the Electrolytic Method

Apparatus for Electrolysis. *Electrodes:* The electrodes recommended are of the stationary and not of the rotating type, as the stationary require less operator's time and there is less chance for erroneous results to be obtained than with the other kind. Rapid and accurate results are obtained with stationary electrodes made from platinum gauze.

Cathodes: Platinum cathodes may be formed either from plain or perforated sheets, or from wire gauze, and may be either open or closed cylinders. They should give a depositing surface, counting both sides, of approximately 100 sq. cm. Gauze cathodes are recommended, and are best made from gauze containing approximately 400 meshes per sq. cm. (45 meshes per linear inch). The cathode should be stiffened by doubling the gauze for about 3 mm. at the top and at the bottom of the cylinder. The cylinder should be approximately 30 mm. in diameter and 30 mm. in height. The stem should be made from 1.14 mm. or 1.29 mm. wire, flattened and welded the entire width of the gauze; the height over all should be approximately 135 mm., and the gauze should be sand blasted.

Anodes: Platinum anodes may be of the spiral type when used in the determination of copper by electrolysis, or in the electrolytic determination of lead when it is present in amounts not over 0.2 per cent. When used in electrolytic determination of copper and lead together in samples containing 0.2 per cent lead or over, the anodes should be of wire gauze. Spiral anodes should be made from 1.02 mm. or 1.14 mm. wire formed into a spiral of 7 turns having a height of approximately 51 mm. and a diameter of 16 mm., the length over all being approximately 145 mm. Platinum gauze used in making anodes should contain approximately 400 meshes per sq. cm. (45 meshes per linear inch). The gauze should be formed into closed cylinders approximately 12 mm. in diameter and 30 mm. in height. The cylinders should be stiffened by doubling the gauze for about 3 mm. at the top and at the bottom. The stem should be made from 1.02 mm. or 1.29 mm. wire, flattened and welded the entire width of the gauze; the height over all should be approximately 135 mm., and the gauze should be sand blasted.

Method. In a 150 cc. beaker dissolve 1 g. of bronze in 10 cc. of HNO_3, sp. gr. 1.42. When the action has ceased, evaporate the solution to dryness, and bake thoroughly on the edge of a hot plate. Moisten thoroughly with HNO_3, sp. gr. 1.42, and after digesting for a short time dilute to 50 cc. with distilled water, heat to boiling, and allow to stand and settle for about one hour, keeping the temperature just below the boiling point. Filter on double 7 cm. papers, keeping the solution hot, and receive the filtrate in a 200 cc. electrolysis beaker. Wash with boiling hot water. Add to the filtrate 5 cc. of H_2SO_4, sp. gr. 1.84, and evaporate until copious fumes of H_2SO_4 are evolved. Dilute to about 100 cc. with distilled water, add 1.5 cc. of HNO_3 sp. gr. 1.42 insert electrodes, cover with a pair of split watch-glasses and electrolyze. For each solution use a current over night of 0.5 ampere at approximately 10 volts, or else use a current of 4 amperes at approximately 10 volts continued for about $2\frac{1}{2}$ hours. The latter case requires the use of gauze cathodes. When the solution is colorless, wash down cover glasses, electrodes, and sides of beaker, raising the level of the liquid slightly and continue the electrolysis about 15 minutes, noting whether or not copper is deposited on the newly exposed surface of the platinum. If no copper appears, transfer about 1 cc. of the colorless solution to the cavity of a porcelain test plate, and add a few drops of fresh H_2S water. If the slightest discoloration occurs continue the electrolysis, repeating the test. Remove the cathode quickly, rinse it in distilled water and then dip it in two successive baths of alcohol. Shake off the excess alcohol and ignite the remainder by bringing it to the flame of an alcohol lamp. Keep the cathode moving continually as the alcohol burns. Weigh as metallic copper.

Accuracy: Duplicate determinations should check within 0.10 per cent of copper.

NOTES. In alloys of the type of manganese bronze, which carry considerable iron, it is impossible to remove the tin quantitatively as metastannic acid (H_2SnO_3), notwithstanding the preliminary baking. Upon testing (by the addition of H_2S water), the liquid in the pits of the test plate may be colored yellow, due to the tin present, but there should be no darkening due to the presence of copper. If the cathode appears dark, as though tin had been deposited on it, dissolve the coating in 10 cc. of HNO_3 sp. gr. 1.42, filter off the tin as before, add to the filtrate 5 cc. of H_2SO_4 sp. gr. 1.84, and redeposit copper by electrolysis. It is rarely necessary thus to purify the deposited copper.

If zinc is to be determined in the alloy be careful to keep the solution quantitative when the electrodes are removed, catching all washings in the beaker containing the electrolyte.

Determination of Lead by the Electrolytic Method

(For Samples Containing up to 0.2 Per Cent of Lead)

Method. In a 250 cc. beaker dissolve 5 g. of bronze in 25 cc. of HNO_3, sp.gr. 1.42. Allow the solution to bake dry on the edge of a hot plate or by standing over night on the steam bath. Add 17 cc. of HNO_3, sp.gr. 1.42, and after digesting for a short time, add 85 cc. of hot water and heat to boiling for a few minutes. Allow the solution to stand for several hours at a temperature just below the boiling point. Filter off the precipitated H_2SnO_3 on double closely woven filter papers, being careful to keep the solution hot throughout the process of filtration. Wash with boiling hot water. Receive the combined filtrate and washings in a 250 cc. beaker. Dilute to about 150 cc. with distilled water and insert electrodes. In the positive terminal use a sand-blasted platinum gauze electrode such as is used for the cathode in the determination of copper; in the negative terminal insert an electrode such as is used for the anode in the determination of copper. Cover with a pair of split watch glasses and electrolyze. For each solution use a current of 1.25 to 1.5 amperes at 10 volts continued for about one hour. Wash down the cover glasses, electrodes and sides of beaker, raising the level of the liquid slightly, and continue the electrolysis for 15 minutes. If no darkening of the newly exposed surface of the platinum can be detected the lead has been entirely deposited. Continue the electrolysis until no darkening of the platinum can be detected when the current has been passed for 15 minutes after the level of the liquid has been raised.

Interrupt the current once or twice for a few seconds during the course of the electrolysis in order to dissolve any metallic lead which may have been deposited on the negative terminal. When the lead has been entirely deposited, remove the anode quickly, rinse it in distilled water and then in alcohol, and dry it at 210° C. for one-half hour. Weigh as PbO_2, using the factor for lead 0.8643 instead of the theoretical value.

Accuracy: Duplicate determinations should check within 0.01 per cent of lead. Results obtained by this method are likely to be about 0.01 per cent too high. For exceptionally accurate or investigation work redissolve the coating from the electrode and determine the lead as sulphate. See the "Determination of Lead as Sulphate."

NOTES. It is impossible to remove the tin quantitatively as H_2SnO_3 in the case of alloys containing over 0.25 per cent of iron, and traces of tin are sometimes found in the PbO_2 deposit. Small amounts of manganese also are occasionally deposited with the PbO_2. Tin and manganese are rarely present in the PbO_2 in amounts which necessitate a purification of the deposit.

Determination of Lead as Sulphate

(For Samples Containing up to 0.2 Per Cent of Lead) (Optional)

Solutions Required. *Lead Acid:* Mix 300 cc. of H_2SO_4, sp.gr. 1.84, and 1800 cc. of distilled water. Dissolve 1 g. of lead acetate, c.p., in 300 cc. of distilled water and add this to the hot solution, stirring meanwhile. Let stand at least 24 hours and syphon through a thick asbestos filter.

Dilute Alcohol for Washing: Mix equal parts of denatured alcohol and distilled water.

Method. In a 250 cc. beaker dissolve 5 g. of bronze in 25 cc. of HNO_3, sp.gr. 1.42. Allow the solution to bake dry on the edge of a hot plate, or by standing over night on the steam bath. Add 17 cc. of HNO_3, sp.gr. 1.42, and after digesting for a short time, add 85 cc. of hot water and heat to boiling for a few minutes. Allow the solution to stand for several hours at a temperature just below the boiling point. Filter off the precipitated H_2SnO_3 on double closely woven filter papers, being careful to keep the solution hot throughout the process of filtration. Wash with boiling hot water. To the combined filtrate and washings add 120 cc. of lead acid, and evaporate until copious fumes of H_2SO_4 are evolved. Cool, add 105 cc. of distilled water to dissolve the salts and to make the acid concentration the same as in lead acid, heat to boiling and allow to cool and settle for 5 hours, or over night if convenient. Filter on a weighed porcelain gooch crucible and wash with lead acid. Wash out the lead acid with dilute alcohol, set the gooch crucible inside a porcelain crucible, dry and ignite for 5 minutes at the full heat of a Tirrell burner, cool and weigh as $PbSO_4$, which contains 68.29 per cent lead.

Accuracy: Duplicate determinations should check within 0.01 per cent of lead. Results obtained by this method are likely to be about 0.01 per cent too low.

NOTE. It is impossible to remove the tin quantitatively as H_2SnO_3 in the case of alloys containing over 0.25 per cent of iron, but by the preliminary baking and long standing, most of the H_2SnO_3 is precipitated.

Determination of Copper and Lead Simultaneously by the Electrolytic Method
(For Samples Containing over 0.2 Per Cent of Lead)

Method. In a 150 cc. beaker dissolve 1 g. of bronze in 10 cc. of HNO_3, sp.gr. 1.42. When the action has ceased, evaporate the solution to dryness, and bake thoroughly on the edge of a hot plate. Add 10 cc. of HNO_3, sp.gr. 1.42, and after digesting for a short time add 50 cc. of distilled water, heat to boiling, and allow to stand and settle for about one hour, keeping the temperature just below the boiling point. Filter on double 7 cm. filter papers, keeping the solution hot, and receive the filtrate in a 200 cc. electrolysis beaker. Wash with boiling hot water, dilute to about 100 cc. and insert electrodes. In the positive terminal insert one of the platinum gauze anodes previously described, and in the negative terminal insert a platinum gauze cathode. Cover with a pair of split watch glasses and electrolyze, using a current of from 3 to 5 amperes at approximately 10 volts for each solution. After about 45 minutes the lead will have been entirely deposited on the anode as PbO_2; without interrupting the current add to the electrolyte 3 to 4 cc. of H_2SO_4, sp.gr. 1.84, and continue the electrolysis. When the solution is colorless, wash down cover glasses, electrodes and sides of beaker, raising the level of the liquid slightly, and continue the passage of the current about 15 minutes, noting whether or not copper is deposited on the newly exposed surface of the platinum. If no copper appears, transfer about 1 cc. of the colorless solution to the cavity of a porcelain test plate, and add a few drops of fresh H_2S water. If the slightest discoloration occurs continue the electrolysis until there is no discoloration whatever upon repeating the test. Remove the solution from the electrodes quickly without interrupting the current. Rinse the electrodes in distilled water and then dip them in two successive baths of alcohol. Dry the anode at 210° C. for one-half hour. Weigh as PbO_2, using the factor for lead 0.8643 instead of the theoretical value. Shake off the excess alcohol from the cathode and ignite the remainder by bringing it to the flame of an alcohol lamp. Keep the cathode moving continually while the alcohol burns. Weigh as metallic copper.

Accuracy: Duplicate copper determinations should check within 0.10 per cent of copper. Duplicate lead determinations should check within 0.02 per cent of lead. Lead results obtained by this method are likely to be about 0.01 per cent too high.

Determination of Tin

Solutions Required. *Dilute Hydrochloric Acid:* Mix 500 cc. of HCl, sp.gr. 1.20, and 500 cc. of distilled water.

Dilute Sulphuric Acid: Mix 300 cc. of H_2SO_4, sp.gr. 1.84, and 600 cc. of distilled water.

Dilute Ammonia: Mix 100 cc. of NH_4OH, sp.gr. 0.90, and 900 cc. of distilled water.

Ammonium Acetate Solution for Washing: Dissolve 10 g. of ammonium acetate in 300 cc. of distilled water. Make slightly acid with acetic acid and saturate with H_2S gas.

Method. In a 150 cc. beaker dissolve 2 g. of bronze in a mixture of 10 cc. of HCl, sp.gr. 1.20, and 5 cc. of HNO_3, sp.gr. 1.42. Dilute to about 75 cc. with distilled water. Add NH_4OH, sp.gr. 0.90, until the basic salts of copper have dissolved and the solution has become a deep blue. Boil and allow to settle, and filter on a closely woven filter paper. Wash with dilute ammonia and with hot water. Dissolve the precipitate on the filter with hot dilute HCl. Dilute the solution to about 1C0 cc. Add NH_4OH, sp.gr. 0.90, until a permanent precipitate forms. Heat the solution to boiling, allow to settle, filter and wash as before. Dissolve the precipitate on the filter with boiling hot dilute H_2SO_4, washing the paper very thoroughly with this acid. Add NH_4OH, sp.gr. 0.90, cautiously until the precipitate which forms at first dissolves rather slowly. Allow the solution to stand for some hours and if any lead sulphate forms filter it off. Dilute the solution to about 200 cc. and saturate it with H_2S gas. Filter the precipitated tin sulphide off on double papers and wash with ammonium acetate solution, retaining the filtrate and washings from the iron determination. Dry the precipitate and place it with the papers in a porcelain crucible which projects part way through a hole in a piece of asbestos board. Heat slowly until any free sulphur has been driven off, but without allowing the sulphur to burn. When the sulphur has been expelled, place the crucible on a triangle and ignite slowly at first and finally at the full heat of the burner. If the precipitate weighs more than 20 mg. heat to constant weight, using a blast lamp. Weigh as SnO_2, which contains 78.81 per cent of tin.

Accuracy: Duplicate determinations should check within 0.06 per cent of tin.

NOTES. If, during ignition, the sulphur is allowed to burn, some tin sulphate may be formed, causing high results. On the other hand, low results may be caused by too high heat, which causes spattering and volatilizes some tin sulphide.

Tin and iron are best determined on the same sample, retaining the filtrate from the tin sulphide precipitate to use for the iron determination.

Determination of Iron

Solutions Required. See "Determination of Tin," and the following:

Dilute Sulphuric Acid for Reductor: Mix 500 cc. of H_2SO_4, sp.gr. 1.84, and 500 cc. of distilled water.

Potassium Permanganate: Dissolve 0.2 g. of $KMnO_4$ in water, filter through asbestos, and dilute to 1000 cc. with distilled water. Standardize against 0.020 g. portions of pure sodium oxalate: or, standardize against 0.020 g. portions of purest iron wire. Each cubic centimeter is equivalent to approximately 0.00033 g. of iron.

Method. Proceed exactly as in the "Determination of Tin" through the filtration and washing of the precipitated tin sulphide. Combine the filtrate and washings from the tin sulphide precipitate and boil until all H_2S is expelled. Add HNO_3 sp.gr. 1.42, until the iron is oxidized, which is shown by the solution becoming clear and of a yellowish color. Add about 5 g. of NH_4Cl, then NH_4OH, sp.gr. 0.90 until a permanent precipitate forms. Boil, allow to settle, filter on a loosely woven filter paper and wash with dilute ammonia and with hot water. Dissolve the precipitate on the paper with hot dilute HCl and add NH_4OH, sp.gr. 0.90 to the solution again until a permanent precipitate forms. Boil, allow to settle, filter on a loosely woven filter paper, and wash with dilute ammonia and with hot water as before. Dissolve the precipitate on the filter with dilute H_2SO_4, transfer the solution to a Jones reductor, and add 40 cc. of the dilute H_2SO_4 used for the reductor. Pass the solution through the reductor, wash first with 150 cc. of distilled water and then with an additional 100 cc. of distilled water, and titrate with the standard $KMnO_4$.

Accuracy: Duplicate determinations should check within 0.03 per cent of iron.

NOTES. A blank determination should be made on corresponding amounts of acid and water passed through the reductor and the results should be corrected accordingly. About 0.5 cc. of the permanganate will be required to give a permanent coloration to the solution.

A small quantity of liquid should always be left in the reductor funnel, and air should never be allowed to enter the body of the reductor.

A description and further details of use of reductor see Vol. I, pages 319, 320.

Determination of Manganese by the Persulphate Method

Solutions Required. *Solution for Dissolving:* Mix 500 cc. of H_2SO_4, sp.gr. 1.84, 200 cc. of HNO_3 sp.gr. 1.42, and 1700 cc. of distilled water.

Silver Nitrate: Dissolve 1.33 g. of $AgNO_3$ in 1000 cc. of distilled water.

Stock Sodium Arsenite: To 15 g. of arsenious oxide (As_2O_3) in a 300 cc. Erlenmeyer flask, add 45 g. of Na_2CO_3 and 150 cc. of distilled water. Heat the flask and contents on the steam bath until the As_2O_3 is dissolved. Cool the solution, filter and make up to 1000 cc. with distilled water.

Standard Sodium Arsenite: Mix 200 cc. of stock sodium arsenite solution with 2500 cc. of distilled water, and standardize against a steel or iron of known manganese content as determined by the Bismuthate Method, or standardize against one of the Bureau of Standards' standard irons or steels. One cc. of this solution should be equivalent to approximately 0.00050 g. of manganese.

Ammonium Persulphate: Dissolve 60 g. of ammonium persulphate in 1000 cc. of distilled water.

Method. In a 250 cc. Erlenmeyer flask dissolve 1 g. of bronze in 24 cc. of the "solution for dissolving." Allow to stand on a steam bath or hot plate until entirely dissolved, and until the oxides of nitrogen are expelled. Add 15 cc. of $AgNO_3$ solution and 20 cc. of ammonium persulphate and leave on the steam bath until the solution has developed a full permanganate color and no bubbles can be seen to come off when the flask is given a whirling motion. Cool to below 25° C. in running water, and add 50 cc. of cold water. Titrate with standard sodium-arsenite solution to the disappearance of the pink color.

Accuracy: Duplicate determinations should check within 0.02 per cent of manganese.

NOTES. Large amounts of permanganic acid are unstable; on that account samples which contain large amounts of manganese should have correspondingly small samples weighed out. For instance, with metal containing 1.5 per cent of manganese use a 0.10 g. sample, while if metal contains 0.75 per cent manganese use a 0.20 g. sample.

The solution must be cold when it is titrated, for high temperatures cause low results to be obtained.

Determination of Manganese by the Bismuthate Method
(Optional)

Solutions Required. *Nitric Acid* (1 : 3): Mix 250 cc. of HNO_3 sp.gr. 1.42, and 750 cc. of distilled water.

Nitric Acid for Washing: Mix 30 cc. of HNO_3 sp.gr. 1.42 and 970 cc. of distilled water.

Ferrous Ammonium Sulphate: Dissolve 12.4 g. of ferrous ammonium sulphate crystals in 950 cc. of distilled water, and add 50 cc. of H_2SO_4 sp.gr. 1.84.

Potassium Permanganate: Dissolve 1 g. of $KMnO_4$ in 1000 cc. of distilled water. Allow it to stand for about one week and then filter it through asbestos. Standardize against 0.10 g. portions of pure sodium oxalate.

Method. In a 250 cc. Erlenmeyer flask dissolve 1 g. of bronze in 50 cc. of HNO_3 (1 : 3). Without filtering off the H_2SnO_3, cool and add 0.5 g. of sodium bismuthate. Heat for a few minutes until the purple color has disappeared, with or without the precipitation of manganese dioxide. Add a little ferrous-ammonium sulphate solution until the solution becomes clear, and boil until the oxides of nitrogen are expelled. Cool, add an excess of sodium bismuthate and agitate for a few minutes. Add 50 cc. of HNO_3 for washing and filter through an alundum crucible or an asbestos pad. Wash with 50 cc. of the HNO_3 for washing. Add from a pipette or a burette 10 cc. of ferrous-ammonium sulphate solution and titrate with $KMnO_4$. Owing to the presence of considerable copper, the end point is somewhat different from the normal pink color.

In exactly the same manner carry through a blank determination, using the same amounts of HNO_3 and sodium bismuthate as was done with the regular sample. Finally add exactly 10 cc. of ferrous-ammonium sulphate solution and titrate with $KMnO_4$. The difference between the two titrations is due to the manganese. Since one manganese as permanganate oxidized five irons, the iron value of the permanganate multiplied by the factor (Mn/5Fe) (or 0.1967) gives the value in terms of manganese.

Accuracy: Duplicate determinations should check within 0.02 per cent of manganese.

NOTES. Instead of employing the method of reducing the permanganic acid by means of standardized ferrous ammonium sulphate solution and titrating the excess of this reagent, it is possible to reduce the permanganic acid by standard sodium arsenite solution. See "Determination of Manganese by the Persulphate Method."

The filtrate from the bismuthate must be perfectly clear, as the least particle of bismuthate carried into the filtrate will vitiate the results.

ANALYSIS OF GUN METAL

Standard Method, A. S. T. M.

General Considerations.   Phosphorus should not be present in this alloy except in very small amounts.   A rapid qualitative test for it is given whereby it is easily seen whether or not it is necessary to make a correction for its presence in the determination of tin.

A special method is also given for the determination of tin in alloys such as phosphor-bronze which contain considerable phosphorus.

Alloy of Copper, Tin, Lead, Iron and Zinc
Determination of Copper by the Electrolytic Method

Apparatus for Electrolysis.   *Electrodes:*   The electrodes recommended are of the stationary and not of the rotating type, as the stationary require less operator's time and there is less chance for erroneous results to be obtained than with the other kind.   Rapid and accurate results are obtained with stationary electrodes made from platinum gauze.

Cathodes: Platinum cathodes may be formed either from plain or perforated sheets, or from wire gauze, and may be either open or closed cylinders.   They should give a depositing surface, counting both sides, of approximately 100 sq. cm.   Gauze cathodes are recommended, and are best made from gauze containing approximately 400 meshes per sq. cm. (45 meshes per linear inch).   The cathode should be stiffened by doubling the gauze for about 3 mm. at the top and at the bottom of the cylinder.   The cylinder should be approximately 30 mm. in diameter and 30 mm. in height.   The stem should be made from 1.14 mm. or 1.29 mm. wire, flattened and welded the entire width of the gauze; the height over all should be approximately 130 mm., and the gauze should be sand blasted.

Anodes: Platinum anodes may be of the spiral type when used in the determination of copper by electrolysis, or in the electrolytic determination of lead when it is present in amounts not over 0.2 per cent.   When used in electrolytic determination of copper and lead together in samples containing 0.2 per cent lead or over, the anodes should be of wire gauze.   Spiral anodes should be made from 1.02 mm. or 1.14 mm. wire formed into a spiral of 7 turns having a height of approximately 51 mm. and a diameter of 16 mm., the length over all being approximately 145 mm.   Platinum gauze used in making anodes should contain approximately 400 meshes per sq. cm. (45 meshes per linear inch).   The gauze should be formed into closed cylinders approximately 12 mm. in diameter and 30 mm. in height.   The cylinders should be stiffened by doubling the gauze for about 3 mm. at the top and at the bottom.   The stem should be made from 1.02 mm. or 1.29 mm. wire, flattened and welded the entire width of the gauze; the height over all should be approximately 137 mm., and the gauze should be sand blasted.

Method.   In a 150 cc. beaker dissolve 1 g. of gun metal in 10 cc. of HNO_3, sp.gr. 1.42.   When the action has ceased, boil until the oxides of nitrogen are expelled, add 50 cc. of distilled water, and allow to stand and settle for about one hour, keeping the temperature just below the boiling point.   Filter on double 7 cm. ashless papers, being careful to keep the solution hot throughout the process of filtration, and receiving the filtrate in a 200 cc. beaker of the tall type used in electrolysis. Wash with boiling hot water. Retain the papers containing the precipitate for subsequent use in the tin determination.

Add to the filtrate 5 cc. of H_2SO_4, sp.gr. 1.84, and determine copper by electrolysis, retaining the electrolyte, after the removal of the copper, for the subsequent determination of zinc. See the "Determination of Copper by the Electrolytic Method," Chemical Analysis of Manganese Bronze.

Accuracy: Duplicate determinations should check within 0.10 per cent of copper.

NOTES. Copper, zinc, and tin are conveniently determined on the same sample, tin being first removed, and any zinc tested for after copper has been deposited by electrolysis.

If the solution becomes cool during the first filtration some of the metastannic acid (H_2SnO_3) may dissolve.

Determination of Tin (For Samples Free from Phosphorus)

Method. See the "Determination of Copper by the Electrolytic Method."

Use the papers containing the H_2SnO_3 which was filtered off in the Determination of Copper by the Electrolytic Method. Ignite the papers with the precipitate, while moist, in a porcelain or platinum crucible, slowly at first, and finally at the full heat of the burner. If the precipitate weighs more than 20 mg. heat to constant weight, using a blast lamp. Weigh as SnO_2, which contains 78.81 per cent of tin.

Accuracy: Duplicate determinations should check within 0.04 per cent of tin.

This method is not accurate for alloys which contain arsenic, antimony or phosphorus, or which contain over 0.25 per cent of iron. The SnO_2 may be contaminated with a slight amount of copper and purification is required in very accurate work, but is generally neglected in routine analysis.

The ignited tin oxide contains the phosphorus which may be present in the alloy. The following test is here made use of to detect phosphorus and to estimate its amount, if any is found.

Qualitative Test for Phosphorus

Solutions Required. *Ferric Chloride:* Dissolve 25 g. of ferric chloride in 100 cc. of distilled water, and add 25 cc. of HCl, sp.gr. 1.20.

Method. Dip a small piece of the alloy into a few cubic centimeters of ferric chloride for about 10 seconds, and then rinse it in running water. Alloys containing phosphorus are darkened noticeably where they have been dipped; alloys containing over 0.25 per cent of phosphorus are rendered almost black by this test. Arsenic and antimony act in a manner similar to phosphorus, but should not be present in this alloy.

Correction for Phosphorus. In alloys containing up to 0.20 per cent of phosphorus a correction for its presence in the ignited tin oxide may be made according to the following empirical method. From the phosphorus content of the alloy, which must be determined on a separate sample, compute the weight of P_2O_5 and subtract two-thirds of this weight from the weight of the ignited tin oxide containing phosphorus. The remainder is considered as pure SnO_2, which contains 78.81 per cent of tin. The factor for converting phosphorus to $\frac{2}{3} \times P_2O_5$ is 152.6 per cent or approximately one and one-half times the phosphorus content of the sample.

If the alloy contains over 0.20 per cent of phosphorus a special method for the determination of tin should be used.

Arsenic and antimony should not be present in weighable amounts in the tin oxide resulting from a sample of gun metal.

Iron may be present in the H_2SnO_3 in very small amounts, but its weight is negligible in this determination.

Determination of Tin (For Samples Containing Phosphorus)

Solutions Required. *Yellow Ammonium Sulphide:* Saturate 200 cc. of NH_4OH, sp.gr. 0.90 with H_2S gas. Dissolve in this solution 3 or 4 g. of sulphur flour and about 1 g. of NH_4Cl. Make up this solution freshly and filter immediately before using.

Dilute Yellow Ammonium Sulphide for Washing: Mix 20 cc. of yellow ammonium sulphide, prepared as above, and 400 cc. of distilled water.

Ammonium Acetate for Washing: Dissolve 10 g. of ammonium acetate in 300 cc. of distilled water, make slightly acid with acetic acid and saturate with H_2S gas.

Method. See the "Determination of Copper by the Electrolytic Method."

Use the papers containing the freshly filtered H_2SnO_3 which was filtered off in the Determination of Copper by the Electrolytic Method. Transfer the papers with the precipitate to a 150 cc. beaker, and cover them with 40 to 50 cc. of yellow ammonium sulphide. Warm for about 15 minutes, or until the H_2SnO_3 has dissolved. Filter and wash thoroughly with dilute yellow ammonium sulphide. Acidify the combined filtrate and washings cautiously with 50 per cent acetic acid. Warm, and allow the precipitated tin sulphide and sulphur to settle. Filter on double papers and wash with ammonium acetate solution. Dry the precipitate, and place it with the papers in a porcelain crucible which projects part way through a hole in a piece of asbestos board. Heat slowly until the free sulphur has been driven off, but without allowing the sulphur to burn. When the sulphur has been expelled, place the crucible on a triangle and ignite slowly at first, and finally at the full heat of the burner. If the precipitate weighs more than 20 mg. heat to constant weight, using a blast lamp. Weigh as SnO_2, which contains 78.81 per cent tin.

Accuracy: Duplicate determinations should check within 0.06 per cent of tin.

NOTES. If during the first filtration the solution becomes cool, some of the H_2SnO_3 may dissolve.

During ignition, if the sulphur is allowed to burn, some tin sulphate may be formed, causing high results. On the other hand, low results may be caused by too high heat, which causes spattering, and volatilizes some tin sulphide.

Determination of Lead by the Electrolytic Method
(For Samples Containing up to 0.2 Per Cent of Lead)

Method. In a 250 cc. beaker dissolve 5 g. of gun metal in 25 cc. of HNO_3, sp.gr. 1.42. Allow the solution to bake dry on the edge of a hot plate or by standing over night on the steam bath. Add 17 cc. of HNO_3 sp.gr. 1.42, and after digesting for a short time, add 85 cc. of hot water and heat to boiling for a few minutes. Allow the solution to stand for several hours at a temperature just below the boiling point. Filter off the precipitated H_2SnO_3 on double closely woven filter papers, being careful to keep the solution hot throughout the process of filtration. Wash with boiling hot water. Receive the combined filtrate and washings in a 250 cc. beaker. Dilute to about 150 cc. with distilled water and insert electrodes. In the positive terminal use a sand-blasted platinum gauze electrode such as is used for the cathode in the determination of copper; in the negative terminal insert an electrode such as is used for the anode in the determination of copper. Cover with a pair of split watch glasses and electrolyze. For each solution use a current of 1.25 to 1.5 amperes at 10 volts continued for about one hour. Wash down the cover glasses, electrodes and sides of beaker, raising the level of the liquid slightly, and continue the electrolysis for 15 minutes. If no darkening of the newly exposed surface of the platinum can be detected the lead has been entirely deposited. Continue the electrolysis until no darkening of the platinum can be detected when the current has been passed for 15 minutes after the level of the liquid has been raised.

Interrupt the current once or twice for a few seconds during the course of the electrolysis in order to dissolve any metallic lead which may have been deposited on the negative terminal. When the lead has been entirely deposited, remove the anode quickly, rinse it in distilled water and then in alcohol, and dry it at 210° C. for one-half hour. Weigh as PbO_2, using the factor for lead 0.8643 instead of the theoretical value.

Accuracy: Duplicate determinations should check within 0.01 per cent of lead. Results obtained by this method are likely to be about 0.01 per cent too high. For exceptionally accurate or investigation work redissolve the coating from the electrode and determine the lead as sulphate. See the "Determination of Lead as Sulphate."

NOTES. It is impossible to remove the tin quantitatively as H_2SnO_3 in the case of alloys containing over 0.25 per cent of iron, and traces of tin are sometimes found in the PbO_2 deposit. Small amounts of manganese also are occasionally deposited with the PbO_2. Tin and manganese are rarely present in the PbO_2 in amounts which necessitate a purification of the deposit.

Determination of Lead as Sulphate

(For Samples Containing up to 0.2 Per Cent of Lead) (Optional)

Solutions Required. *Lead Acid:* Mix 300 cc. of H_2SO_4, sp.gr. 1.84, and 1800 cc. of distilled water. Dissolve 1 g. of lead acetate, c.p., in 300 cc. of distilled water and add this to the hot solution, stirring meanwhile. Let stand at least 24 hours and syphon through a thick asbestos filter.

Dilute Alcohol for Washing: Mix equal parts of denatured alcohol and distilled water.

Method. In a 250 cc. beaker dissolve 5 g. of gun metal in 25 cc. of HNO_3 sp.gr. 1.42. Allow the solution to bake dry on the edge of a hot plate, or by standing over night on the steam bath. Add 17 cc. of HNO_3 sp.gr. 1.42, and after digesting for a short time, add 85 cc. of hot water and heat to boiling for a few minutes. Allow the solution to stand for several hours at a temperature just below the boiling point. Filter off the precipitated H_2SnO_3 on double closely woven filter papers, being careful to keep the solution hot throughout the process of filtration. Wash with boiling hot water. To the combined filtrate and washings add 120 cc. of lead acid, and evaporate until copious fumes of H_2SO_4 are evolved. Cool, add 105 cc. of distilled water to dissolve the salts and to make the acid concentration the same as in lead acid, heat to boiling, and allow to cool and settle for 5 hours, or over night if convenient. Filter on a weighed porcelain gooch crucible and wash with lead acid. Wash out the lead acid with dilute alcohol, set the gooch crucible inside a porcelain crucible, dry and ignite for 5 minutes at the full heat of a Tirrill burner, cool and weigh as $PbSO_4$, which contains 68.29 per cent lead.

Accuracy: Duplicate determinations should check within 0.01 per cent of lead. Results obtained by this method are likely to be about 0.01 per cent too low.

NOTE. It is impossible to remove the tin quantitatively as H_2SnO_3 in the case of alloys containing over 0.25 per cent of iron, but by the preliminary baking and long standing, most of the H_2SnO_3 is precipitated.

Determination of Zinc

Solutions Required. *Dilute Hydrochloric Acid:* Mix 500 cc. of HCl, sp.gr. 1.20 and 500 cc. of distilled water.

Method. See the "Determination of Copper by the Electrolytic Method." After the copper has been completely deposited by electrolysis, quickly remove the cathode and wash it thoroughly in distilled water, catching the washings in the beaker containing the electrolyte. Heat the solution and saturate with H_2S gas. Filter off any precipitate, and boil the solution to expel H_2S. Make the solution barely alkaline with NH_4OH, and add 25 cc. of 85 per cent formic acid. Dilute the solution with distilled water to 300 cc. heat to boiling, and saturate with H_2S gas. Filter and wash with hot water. Dissolve the precipitate with hot dilute HCl, and transfer the solution to a weighed platinum or porcelain dish or crucible. Add a few drops of H_2SO_4, sp.gr. 1.84, and evaporate the solution until copious fumes escape. If the solution is not clear and colorless, cool, add a few cubic centimeters of HNO_3, sp.gr. 1.42 and again evaporate the solution until fumes of H_2SO_4 come off freely. Repeat the treatment with HNO_3 if necessary, until the organic matter is destroyed, and the solution is colorless. Remove the excess of H_2SO_4 by heating the dish cautiously, and finally heat to dull redness. Weigh as zinc sulphate, which contains 40.49 per cent of zinc.

Accuracy: Duplicate determinations should check within 0.05 per cent of zinc.

Determination of Phosphorus by the Alkalimetric Method

Solutions Required. *Nitric Acid for Dissolving:* Mix 1000 cc. of HNO_3, sp.gr. 1.42 and 1200 cc. of distilled water.

Nitric Acid for Washing: Mix 20 cc. of HNO_3, sp.gr. 1.42, and 1000 cc. of distilled water.

Ammonium Molybdate: Solution No. 1. Place in a beaker 100 g. of 85 per cent molybdic acid, mix it thoroughly with 240 cc. of distilled water, add 140 cc. of NH_4OH, sp.gr. 0.90, filter and add 60 cc. of HNO_3, sp.gr. 1.42.

Solution No. 2. Mix 400 cc. of HNO_3, sp.gr. 1.42 and 960 cc. of distilled water.

When the solutions are cold, add solution No. 1 to solution No. 2, stirring constantly; then add 0.1 g. of ammonium phosphate dissolved in 10 cc. of distilled water and let stand at least 24 hours before using.

Potassium Nitrate, 1 *per cent:* Dissolve 10 g. of KNO_3 in 1000 cc. of distilled water.

Phenolphthalein Indicator: Dissolve 0.2 g. of phenolphthalein in 50 cc. of 95 per cent ethyl alcohol and 50 cc. of distilled water.

Standard Sodium Hydroxide: Dissolve 6.5 g. of purified NaOH in 1000 cc. of distilled water, add a slight excess of 1 per cent solution of barium hydroxide, let stand for 24 hours, decant the liquid, and standardize it against a steel of known phosphorus content as determined by the molybdate-magnesia method, so that 1 cc. will be equivalent to 0.01 per cent of phosphorus on the basis of a 2 g. sample (see notes).

Protect the solution from carbon dioxide with a soda-lime tube.

Ferric Chloride: Dissolve 100 g. of ferric chloride (phosphorus free) in 100 cc. of distilled water.

Standard Nitric Acid: Mix 10 cc. of HNO_3, sp.gr. 1.42, and 1000 cc. of distilled water. Titrate the solution against standardized NaOH, using phenolphthalein as indicator, and make it equivalent to the NaOH by adding distilled water.

Method. In a 400 cc. casserole dissolve 1 g. of gun metal in 10 cc. of HNO_3 sp.gr. 1.42. Add 20 cc. of HCl, sp.gr. 1.20, and evaporate to dryness. Moisten with HCl, evaporate to dryness again, and bake to dull redness. Moisten with HCl again, add 3 cc. of ferric chloride solution, and dilute to about 200 cc. with distilled water. Add NH_4OH, sp.gr. 0.90, until the basic salts of copper have dissolved and the solution has become a deep blue. Boil, allow to settle, and filter on a loosely woven filter paper. Wash with dilute ammonia and with hot water. Dissolve the precipitate on the filter with hot dilute HCl, dilute the solution to about 200 cc., add NH_4OH, sp.gr. 0.90, until the precipitate which forms at first dissolves rather slowly, and saturate with H_2S gas. Filter off and reject the precipitate. Boil the filtrate to expel H_2S, and add HNO_3, sp.gr. 1.42, until the iron is oxidized. Add NH_4OH, sp.gr. 0.90, until the solution is alkaline. Boil and filter on a loosely woven filter paper. Wash with dilute ammonia and with hot water. Dissolve the precipitate on the filter with HNO_3 (sp. gr. 1.42) receiving the solution in a 350 cc. Erlenmeyer flask. Add NH_4OH, sp.gr. 0.90, until the iron is entirely precipitated, and then add HNO_3, sp.gr. 1.42, cautiously until the solution just becomes clear. Bring the solution to a temperature of about 80° C., and add 40 cc. of ammonium molybdate at room temperature. Allow to stand for one minute, shake or agitate for 3 minutes, and filter on a 9 cm. paper. Wash the precipitate three times with the 2 per cent HNO_3 solution to free it from iron, and continue the washing with the 1 per cent KNO_3 solution until the precipitate and flask are free from acid.

Transfer the paper and precipitate to a solution flask, add 20 cc. of distilled water, 5 drops of phenolphthalein solution as indicator, and an excess of standard NaOH solution. Insert a rubber stopper and shake vigorously until solution of the precipitate is complete. Wash off the stopper with distilled water and determine the excess of NaOH solution by titrating with standard HNO_3 solution. Each cubic centimeter of standard NaOH solution represents 0.01 per cent of phosphorus.

Accuracy: Duplicate determinations should check within 0.01 per cent of phosphorus.

NOTES. The ammonium-molybdate solution should be kept in a cool place and should always be filtered before using.

All distilled water used in titrations should be freed from carbon dioxide by boiling or otherwise.

Bureau of Standards Standard Steel No. 19 (*a*) is recommended as a suitable steel or standardization of the NaOH solution.

Determination of Phosphorus by the Ferric-Alum Method
(Optional)

Solutions Required. *Ferric Chloride:* Dissolve 100 g. of ferric chloride (phosphorus free) in 100 cc. of distilled water.

Dilute Ammonia: Mix 100 cc. of NH_4OH, sp.gr. 0.90, and 900 cc. of distilled water.

Dilute Hydrochloric Acid: Mix 500 cc. of HCl, sp.gr. 1.20, and 500 cc. of distilled water.

Dilute Sulphuric Acid for Dissolving: Mix 200 cc. of H_2SO_4, sp.gr. 1.84, and 800 cc. of distilled water.

Dilute Sulphuric Acid for Reductor: Mix 500 cc. of H_2SO_4, sp.gr. 1.84, and 500 cc. of distilled water.

Ammonium Molybdate: Solution No. 1. Place in a beaker 100 g. of 85 per cent molybdic acid, mix it thoroughly with 240 cc. of distilled water, add 140 cc. of NH_4OH, sp.gr. 0.90, filter and add 60 cc. of HNO_3, sp.gr. 1.42.

Solution No. 2. Mix 400 cc. of HNO_3, sp.gr. 1.42, and 960 cc. of distilled water.

When the solutions are cold, add solution No. 1 to solution No. 2, stirring constantly, then add 0.1 g. of ammonium phosphate dissolved in 10 cc. of distilled water, and let stand at least 24 hours before using.

Acid Ammonium Sulphate: Mix 25 cc. of H_2SO_4, sp.gr. 1.84, and 1000 cc. of distilled water, and then add 15 cc. of NH_4OH, sp.gr. 0.90.

Ferric Alum: Dissolve 200 g. of ferric ammonium sulphate crystals in 1950 cc. of distilled water. Add 50 cc. of H_2SO_4, sp.gr. 1.84, and 80 cc. of phosphoric acid, 85 per cent.

Potassium Permanganate: Dissolve from 3.0 to 3.2 g. of $KMnO_4$ in 1000 cc. of distilled water. Allow the solution to stand for about one week, and then filter it through an asbestos filter. Standardize by using about 0.200 g. portions of pure sodium oxalate.

Method. In a 400 cc. casserole dissolve 1 g. of gun metal in 10 cc. of HNO₃, sp.gr. 1.42. Add 20 cc. of HCl, sp.gr. 1.20, and evaporate to dryness. Moisten with HCl, evaporate to dryness again, and bake to dull redness. Moisten with HCl again, add 3 cc. of ferric chloride solution, and dilute to about 200 cc. with distilled water. Add NH₄OH, sp.gr. 0.90, until the basic salts of copper have dissolved and the solution has become a deep blue. Boil, allow to settle, and filter on a loosely woven filter paper. Wash with dilute ammonia and with hot water. Dissolve the precipitate on the filter with hot dilute HCl, dilute the solution to about 200 cc., add NH₄OH, sp.gr. 0.90, until the precipitate which forms at first dissolves rather slowly, and saturate with H₂S gas. Filter off and reject the precipitate. Boil the filtrate to expel H₂S, and add HNO₃, sp.gr. 1.42, until the iron is oxidized. Add NH₄OH, sp.gr. 0.90, until the solution is alkaline. Boil and filter on a loosely woven filter paper. Wash with dilute ammonia and with hot water. Dissolve the precipitate on the filter with hot dilute H₂SO₄, receiving the solution in a 350 cc. Erlenmeyer flask. Add NH₄OH, sp.gr. 0.90, until the iron is entirely precipitated, and then add HNO₃, sp.gr. 1.42, cautiously until the solution just becomes clear. Bring the solution to a temperature of about 80° C., and add 40 cc. of ammonium molybdate at room temperature. Allow to stand for one minute, shake or agitate for 3 minutes, filter on a 9 cm. paper, and wash very thoroughly (about 25 times) with acid ammonium sulphate. Dissolve the precipitate on the paper using 50 cc. of dilute ammonia. Add 10 cc. of H₂SO₄, sp.gr. 1.84, and immediately pass the solution through a Jones reductor, which has the reductor tube prolonged and reaching nearly to the bottom of the flask, dipping into 50 cc. of ferric-alum solution. Wash through the reductor with 150 cc. of distilled water, and follow with an additional 100 cc. of distilled water. Titrate with standard KMnO₄.

By this method the molybdenum in passing through the reductor is reduced entirely to the form Mo₂O₃, and is oxidized by the ferric alum to the form MoO₃, an equivalent amount of iron being reduced to the ferrous condition. As the yellow precipitate contains one atom of phosphorus to each twelve molecules of MoO₃, and as three atoms of oxygen oxidize two of molybdenum, eighteen oxygens or thirty-six irons are equivalent to one phosphorus. Therefore, the iron value of the permangante multiplied by the factor P/36 Fe (or 0.01540) gives the value of the permanganate in terms of phosphorus.

Accuracy: Duplicate determinations should check within 0.01 per cent of phosphorus.

NOTES. The ammonium-molybdate solution should be kept in a cool place and should always be filtered before using.

A blank determination should be made on corresponding amounts of acid and water, passing through the reductor into the usual amount of ferric-alum solution in the flask.

A small quantity of liquid should always be left in the reductor funnel, and air should never be allowed to enter the reductor.

Description of the Jones reductor is given on page 319, Volume I.

STANDARD METHODS OF CHEMICAL ANALYSIS OF BRASS INGOTS AND SAND CASTINGS,

A. S. T. M. Method

Determination of Copper by the Electrolytic Method

APPARATUS FOR ELECTROLYSIS

Electrodes. The electrodes recommended are of the stationary and not of the rotating type, as the stationary require less of the operator's time and there is less chance for erroneous results to be obtained than with the other kind. Rapid and accurate results are obtained with stationary electrodes made from platinum gauze.

Cathodes. Platinum cathodes may be formed either from plain or perforated sheets, or from wire gauze, and may be either open or closed cylinders. They should give a depositing surface, counting both sides, of approximately 100 sq. cm. Gauze cathodes are recommended, and are best made from gauze containing approximately 400 meshes per sq. cm. (50 meshes per linear inch). The cathode should be stiffened by doubling the gauze for about 3 mm. at the top and at the bottom of the cylinder. The cylinder should be approximately 30 mm. in diameter and 30 mm. in height. The stem should be made from 1.14 mm. or 1.29 mm. wire, flattened and welded the entire width of the gauze; the height over all should be approximately 130 mm., and the gauze should be sand blasted.

Anodes. Platinum anodes may be of the spiral type when used in the determination of copper by electrolysis, or in the electrolytic determination of lead when it is present in amounts not over 0.2%. When used in the electrolytic determination of copper and lead together in samples containing 0.2% of lead or over, the anodes should be of wire gauze. Spiral anodes should be made from 1.02 mm. or 1.14 mm. wire formed into a spiral of 7 turns having a height of approximately 51 mm. and a diameter of 16 mm., the length over all being approximately 145 mm. Platinum gauze used in making anodes should contain approximately 400 meshes per sq. cm. (50 meshes per linear inch). The gauze should be formed into closed cylinders approximately 12 mm. in diameter and 30 mm. in height. The cylinders should be stiffened by doubling the gauze for about 3 mm. at the top and at the bottom. The stem should be made from 1.02 mm. or 1.29 mm. wire, flattened and welded the entire width of the gauze; the height over all should be approximately 130 mm., and the gauze should be sand blasted.

METHOD

In a 150-cc. beaker, dissolve 1 g. of brass in 10 cc. of HNO_3 (sp.gr. 1.42). When the action has ceased, evaporate the solution to dryness, and bake thoroughly on the edge of a hot plate. Moisten thoroughly with HNO_3 (sp.gr. 1.42), and after digesting for a short time dilute to 50 cc. with hot distilled water, heat to boiling, and allow to stand and settle for about one hour, keeping the temperature just below the boiling point. Filter on double 7 cm. papers, keeping the solution hot, and receive the filtrate in a 200-cc. electrolysis beaker. Wash with boiling water. Add to the filtrate 5 cc. of H_2SO_4 (sp.gr. 1.84), and evaporate until copious fumes of H_2SO_4 are evolved.

7

Dilute to about 100 cc. with distilled water, add 1.5 cc. of HNO_3 (sp.gr. 1.42), insert electrodes, cover with a pair of split watch glasses and electrolyze. For each solution use a current over night of 0.5 ampere at approximately 10 volts, or else use a current of 4 amperes at approximately 10 volts continued for about $2\frac{1}{2}$ hours. The latter case requires the use of gauze cathodes. When the solution is colorless, wash down the cover glasses, electrodes, and sides of the beaker, raising the level of the liquid slightly, and continue the electrolysis about 15 minutes, noting whether or not copper is deposited on the newly exposed surface of the platinum. If no copper appears, transfer about 1 cc. of the colorless solution to the cavity of a porcelain test plate, and add a few drops of fresh H_2S water. If the slightest discoloration occurs, continue the electrolysis, repeating the test. Remove the cathode quickly, rinse it in distilled water and then dip it in two successive baths of alcohol. Shake off the excess alcohol and ignite the remainder by bringing it to the flame of an alcohol lamp. Keep the cathode moving continually as the alcohol burns. Weigh as metallic copper.

Accuracy. Duplicate determinations should check within 0.10% of copper.

NOTES

In alloys of this type which carry considerable iron, it is impossible to remove the tin quantitatively as meta-stannic acid (H_2SnO_3), notwithstanding the preliminary baking. Upon testing (by the addition of H_2S water), the liquid in the pits of the test plate may be colored yellow, due to the tin present, but there should be no darkening due to the presence of copper. If the cathode appears dark, as though tin had been deposited on it, dissolve the coating in 10 cc. of HNO_3 (sp.gr. 1.42), filter off the tin as before, add to the filtrate 5 cc. of H_2SO_4 (sp.gr. 1.84), and redeposit the copper by electrolysis. It is rarely necessary thus to purify the deposited copper.

A slight amount of copper is retained by the meta-stannic acid (H_2SnO_3), which should be recovered in very accurate work but is generally neglected in routine analysis.

[1] Ref. J. C. Chiiring, C.A., **18**, 1799 (June 20, 1924).

Determination of Lead by the Electrolytic Method

In a 250-cc. beaker, dissolve 1 g. of brass in 25 cc. of HNO_3 (sp.gr. 1.42). Allow the solution to bake dry on the edge of a hot plate or by standing over night on the steam bath. Add 17 cc. of HNO_3 (sp.gr. 1.42), and after digesting for a short time, add 85 cc. of hot water and heat to boiling for a few minutes. Allow the solution to stand for several hours at a temperature just below the boiling point. Filter off the precipitated H_2SnO_3 on double closely woven filter papers, being careful to keep the solution hot throughout the process of filtration. Wash with boiling water. Receive the combined filtrate and washings in a 250-cc. beaker. Dilute to about 150 cc. with distilled water and insert electrodes. In the positive terminal use a sand-blasted platinum gauze electrode such as is used for the cathode in the " Determination of Copper by the Electrolytic Method "; in the negative terminal insert an electrode such as is used for the anode in the " Determination of Copper by the Electrolytic Method." Cover with a pair of split watch glasses and electrolyze. For each solution use a current of 1.25 to 1.5 amperes at 10 volts continued for about one hour. Wash down the cover glasses, electrodes and sides of the beaker, raising the level of the liquid slightly, and continue the electrolysis for 15 minutes. If no darkening of the newly exposed surface of the platinum can be detected, the lead has been entirely deposited. Continue the electrolysis until no darkening of the platinum can be detected when the current has been passed for 15 minutes after the level of the liquid has been raised.

When the lead has been entirely deposited, remove the anode quickly, rinse it in distilled water and then in alcohol, and dry at 210° C. for 30 minutes. Weigh as PbO_2, using the factor for lead 0.8643 instead of the theoretical value.

Accuracy. Duplicate determinations should check within 0.01% of lead. Results obtained by this method are likely to be about 0.01% too high. For exceptionally accurate or investigation work, redissolve the coating from the electrode and determine the lead as sulphate. See the " Determination of Lead as Sulphate (Optional)."

NOTES

It is impossible to remove the tin quantitively as H_2SnO_3 in the case of alloys containing over 0.25% of iron, and traces of tin are sometimes found in the PbO_2 deposit.

In this and in the following method, a slight amount of lead may be retained by the H_2SnO_3. This should be recovered in very accurate work, but is neglected in a routine analysis.

Determination of Lead as Sulphate
(Optional)

SOLUTIONS REQUIRED

" **Lead Acid.**" Mix 300 cc. of H_2SO_4 (sp.gr. 1.84) and 1800 cc. of distilled water. Dissolve 1 g. of lead acetate, c.p. in 300 cc. of distilled water and add this to the hot solution, stirring meanwhile. Let stand at least 24 hours and siphon through a thick asbestos filter.

Dilute Alcohol for Washing. Mix equal parts of denatured alcohol and distilled water.

METHOD

In a 150-cc. beaker, dissolve 1 g. of brass in 10 cc. of HNO_3 (sp.gr. 1.42). Allow the solution to bake dry on the edge of a hot plate, or by standing over night on the steam bath. Add 10 cc. of HNO_3 (sp.gr. 1.42), and after digesting for a short time, add 50 cc. of hot water and heat to boiling for a few minutes. Allow the solution to stand for several hours at a temperature just below the boiling point. Filter off the precipitated H_2SnO_3 on double closely woven filter papers, being careful to keep the solution hot throughout the process of filtration. Wash with boiling hot water. To the combined filtrate and washings add 40 cc. of lead acid, and evaporate until copious fumes of H_2SO_4 are evolved. Cool, add 35 cc. of distilled water to dissolve the salts and to make the acid concentration the same as in lead acid, heat to boiling, and allow to cool and settle for 5 hours, or over night if convenient. Filter on a weighed porcelain Gooch crucible and wash with lead acid. Wash out the lead acid with dilute alcohol, set the Gooch crucible inside a porcelain crucible, dry and ignite for 5 minutes at the full heat of a Tirrill burner, cool and weigh as $PbSO_4$, which contains 68.29% of lead.

Accuracy. Duplicate determinations should check within 0.01% of lead. Results obtained by this method are likely to be about 0.01% too low.

NOTES

Copper and lead may be determined on the same samples if so desired. In such a case, after filtering off the lead sulphate and washing with lead acid, and before washing with dilute alcohol, remove the filtrate, add 3 cc. of HNO_3 (sp.gr. 1.42), dilute to 120 cc. and determine copper by electrolysis. See the "Determination of Copper by the Electrolytic Method."

It is impossible to remove the tin quantitatively as H_2SnO_3 in the case of alloys containing over 0.25% of iron, but by the preliminary baking and long standing, most of the H_2SnO_3 is precipitated.

Determination of Copper and Lead Simultaneously by the Electrolytic Method

METHOD

In a 150-cc. beaker, dissolve 1 g. of brass in 10 cc. of HNO_3 (sp.gr. 1.42). When the action has ceased, evaporate the solution to dryness, and bake thoroughly on the edge of a hot plate. Add 10 cc. of HNO_3 (sp.gr. 1.42), and after digesting for a short time add 50 cc. of hot distilled water, heat to boiling, and allow to stand and settle for about one hour, keeping the temperature just below the boiling point. Filter on double 7 cm. filter paper, keeping the solution hot, and receive the filtrate in a 200-cc. electrolysis beaker. Wash with boiling water, dilute to about 100 cc. and insert electrodes. In the positive terminal insert one of the platinum gauze anodes previously described, and in the negative terminal insert a platinum gauze cathode. Cover with a pair of split watch glasses and electrolyze, using a current of from 3 to 5 amperes at approximately 10 volts for each solution. After about 45 minutes, the lead will have been entirely deposited on the anode as PbO_2; without interrupting the current add to the electrolyte 3 to 4 cc. of H_2SO_4 (sp.gr. 1.84), and continue the electrolysis. When the solution is colorless, wash down the cover glasses, electrodes and sides of the beaker, raising the level of the liquid slightly, and continue the passage of the current for about 15 minutes, noting whether or not copper is deposited on the newly exposed surface of the platinum. If no copper appears, transfer about 1 cc. of the colorless solution to the cavity of a porcelain test plate, and add a few drops of fresh H_2S water. If the slightest discoloration occurs, continue the electrolysis until there is no discoloration whatever upon repeating the test. Remove the solution from the electrodes quickly without interrupting the current. Rinse the electrodes in distilled water and then dip them in two successive baths of alcohol. Dry the anode at 210° C. for 30 minutes. Weigh as PbO_2, using the factor for lead 0.8643 instead of the theoretical value. Shake off the excess alcohol from the cathode and ignite the remainder by bringing it to the flame of an alcohol lamp. Keep the cathode moving continually while the alcohol burns. Weigh as metallic copper.

Accuracy. Duplicate copper determinations should check within 0.10% of copper. Duplicate lead determinations should check within 0.02% of lead. Lead results obtained by this method are likely to be about 0.01% too high. See notes under the " Determination of Lead by the Electrolytic Method."

Determination of Tin

SOLUTIONS REQUIRED

Dilute Hydrochloric Acid. Mix 500 cc. of HCl (sp.gr. 1.20) and 500 cc. of distilled water.

Dilute Sulphuric Acid. Mix 300 cc. of H_2SO_4 (sp.gr. 1.84) and 600 cc. ot distilled water.

Dilute Ammonia. Mix 100 cc. of NH_4OH (sp.gr. 0.90) and 900 cc. of distilled water.

Ammonium Acetate Solution for Washing. Dissolve 10 g. of ammonium acetate in 300 cc. of distilled water. Make slightly acid with acetic acid and saturate with H_2S gas.

METHOD

In a 150-cc. beaker, dissolve 1 g. of brass in a mixture of 10 cc. of HCl (sp.gr. 1.20) and 5 cc. of HNO_3 (sp.gr. 1.42). Dilute to about 75 cc. with distilled water. Add NH_4OH (sp.gr. 0.90) until the basic salts of copper have dissolved and the solution has become a deep blue. Boil and allow to settle and filter on a closely woven filter paper. Wash with dilute ammonia and with hot water. Dissolve the precipitate on the filter with hot dilute HCl. Dilute the solution to about 100 cc. Add NH_4OH (sp.gr. 0.90) until a permanent precipitate forms. Heat the solution to boiling, allow to settle, filter and wash as before. Dissolve the precipitate on the filter with boiling hot dilute H_2SO_4, washing the paper very thoroughly with this acid. Add NH_4OH (sp.gr. 0.90) cautiously until the precipitate which forms at first dissolves rather slowly. Allow the solution to stand for some hours and if any lead sulphate forms filter it off. Dilute the solution to about 200 cc. and saturate it with H_2S gas. Filter the precipitated tin sulphide off on double papers and wash with ammonium acetate solution, retaining the filtrate and washings for the iron determination. Dry the precipitate and place it with the papers in a porcelain crucible which projects part way through a hole in a piece of asbestos board. Heat slowly until any free sulphur has been driven off, but without allowing the sulphur to burn. When the sulphur has been expelled, place the crucible on a triangle and ignite slowly at first and finally at the full heat of the burner. If the precipitate weighs more than 20 mg., heat to constant weight, using a blast lamp. Weigh as SnO_2, which contains 78.81% of tin.

Accuracy. Duplicate determinations should check within 0.06% of tin.

NOTES

If, during ignition, the sulphur is allowed to burn, some tin sulphate may be formed, causing high results. On the other hand, low results may be caused by too high heat, which causes spattering and volatilizes some tin sulphide.

Tin and iron are best determined on the same sample, retaining the filtrate from the tin sulphide precipitate to use for the iron determination.

In alloys containing an appreciable amount of antimony and in presence of a large excess of tin, the antimony, as determined by titration according to the method given below, should be calculated to Sb_2O_4, and a corresponding amount deducted from the weight of the ignited SnO_2 before calculating to tin.

Determination of Iron

SOLUTIONS REQUIRED

See " Determination of Tin."

Dilute Sulphuric Acid for Reductor. Mix 50 cc. of H_2SO_4 (sp.gr. 1.84) and 1000 cc. of distilled water. This solution is used boiling hot.

Potassium Permanganate. Dissolve 0.2 g. of $KMnO_4$ in water, filter through asbestos, and dilute to 1000 cc. with distilled water. Standardize against 0.020 g. portions of pure sodium oxalate. Each cubic centimeter is equivalent to approximately 0.00033 g. of iron.

METHOD

Proceed exactly as in the " Determination of Tin " through the filtration and washing of the precipitated tin sulphide. Combine the filtrate and washings from the tin sulphide precipitate and boil until all H_2S is expelled. Add HNO_3 (sp.gr. 1.42) until the iron is oxidized, which is shown by the solution becoming clear and of a yellowish color. Add about 5 g. of NH_4Cl, then NH_4OH (sp.gr. 0.90) until a permanent precipitate forms. Boil, allow to settle, filter on a loosely woven filter paper and wash with dilute ammonia and with hot water. Dissolve the precipitate on the paper with hot dilute HCl and add NH_4OH (sp.gr. 0.90) to the solution again until a permanent precipitate forms. Boil, allow to settle, filter on a loosely woven filter paper, and wash with dilute ammonia and with hot water until all NH_4Cl is removed. Dissolve the precipitate and wash the filter paper with 100 cc. of dilute H_2SO_4 for reductor. Pass the solution through a Jones reductor, wash first with 150 cc. of the H_2SO_4 for reductor and then with 100 cc. of distilled water. Titrate with the standard $KMnO_4$ solution.

Accuracy. Duplicate determinations should check within 0.03% of iron.

NOTES

A blank determination should be made on corresponding amounts of acid and water passed through the reductor and the results should be corrected accordingly. About 0.5 cc. of the permanganate will be required to give a permanent coloration to the solution.

A small quantity of liquid should always be left in the reductor funnel, and air should never be allowed to enter the body of the reductor. See pages 319, 320.

Determination of Antimony by the Volumetric Method

SOLUTIONS REQUIRED

Potassium Permanganate. Dissolve 0.3 g. of potassium permanganate in 1000 cc. of distilled water. Standardize by dissolving 25 mg. of pure antimony in 15 cc. of boiling sulphuric acid and proceed according to the method from this point.

METHOD

In a 250-cc. beaker, dissolve 5 g. of brass in 25 cc. of HNO_3 (sp.gr. 1.42)· When the action has ceased, boil until the oxides of nitrogen are expelled, add 125 cc. of boiling water and allow to stand and settle for one hour or longer, keeping the temperature just below the boiling point. Filter on double 9 cm. closely woven papers, keeping the solution hot. Wash with boiling water. Discard the filtrate.

Transfer the papers containing the tin and antimony to a 350-cc. Erlenmeyer flask and add 25 cc. of HNO_3 (sp.gr. 1.42), 5 g. of ammonium persulphate, and 15 cc. of H_2SO_4 (sp.gr. 1.84). Boil to strong fumes of SO_3. If the solution is brown, cool and add 5 cc. of HNO_3 (sp.gr. 1.42) and a little more (1 g. or less) persulphate, if necessary, and boil again to strong fumes of SO_3. When the solution is colorless, cool, add 20 cc. of distilled water, 20 cc. of HCl (sp.gr. 1.20) and 1 g. of sodium sulphite. Boil gently for 10 minutes to expel SO_2 completely. Dilute with 200 cc. of distilled water and cool to 10 to 12° C. in ice or under running water.

Titrate with standard permanganate solution until the appearance of a decided pink color.

NOTES

1. In alloys containing a large excess of tin, the antimony is precipitated quantitatively with the meta-stannic acid.

2. Ammonium persulphate and nitric acid are used to destroy the filter paper, and subsequent boiling with sulphuric acid effects the solution of the tin and antimony. A mixture of fuming nitric and sulphuric acids might be used to accomplish the same results, but the persulphate mixture is much more efficient.

3. If the solution becomes cool during the first filtration, some of the meta-stannic acid may dissolve.

4. If arsenic is present, correction should be made for it.

Determination of Sulphur

METHOD

Weigh out four 5 g. samples of brass into 250-cc. beakers. Dissolve each in 25 cc. of HNO_3 (sp.gr. 1.42) and boil until the disappearance of red fumes. Add 125 cc. of boiling water and settle for one hour or longer, keeping the temperature just below the boiling point. Filter on double 12.5 cm. closely woven papers, keeping the solutions hot. Wash with boiling water. Discard the meta-stannic acid precipitates, combine the four filtrates in a tall 700-cc. beaker, and add 0.5 g. of Na_2CO_3, and evaporate the solution until syrupy. Cool somewhat, then dilute to the lip with warm water. There should be present a layer about $\frac{1}{4}$ in. (6 mm.) in thickness, composed of basic salts of copper. Electrolyze, using stationary electrodes, at a current of 4 amperes, or using the Frary solenoid at a current of about 10 amperes. The lead must be removed at the anode as the copper is taken out at the cathode. When copper and lead are out, evaporate the electrolyte to small volume, cover the beaker, add 75 cc. of HCl (sp.gr. 1.20), and boil down to small volume. Add 75 cc. more HCl and evaporate to dryness to dehydrate any silica present. Moisten with about 0.5 cc. of HCl and take up with 20 cc. of hot water. Filter into a small beaker. Heat the filtrate to boiling and add 10 cc. of 5% $BaCl_2$ solution, drop by drop, with stirring. Allow to settle at least five hours, filter on a small ashless paper, and wash with hot water. Ignite cautiously in a small porcelain or platinum crucible, and then heat to bright redness for 20 minutes. Cool and weigh the $BaSO_4$ and calculate to sulphur.

NOTES

1. Throughout the entire analysis, the utmost precautions must be taken to prevent contamination by sulphur in any form, H_2SO_4 fumes, H_2S, and SO_2 gases especially. All heating with gas burners must be avoided. Run a blank with each analysis, adding all the reagents and subjecting it to the same operations as the beakers containing the drillings. Subtract the amount of $BaSO_4$ found in the blank from that in the determinations. If this blank amounts to 0.002 g., it is a sign of poor work or impure reagents, and the analysis should be repeated. Wash out all beakers, funnels, etc., with distilled water before using.

2. It is necessary to keep the solution containing the meta-stannic acid hot during filtration. If the solution becomes cool, some of the meta-stannic acid may dissolve.

STANDARD METHODS OF CHEMICAL ANALYSIS OF BRONZE BEARING METAL,

A. S. T. M. Method

GENERAL CONSIDERATIONS

Practically all of the following methods call for a preliminary separation of tin as meta-stannic acid by means of solution and digestion of the alloy in nitric acid. The meta-stannic acid so obtained is subject to contamination by such alloy constituents as copper and iron and will quantitatively contain such elements as phosphorus, arsenic and vanadium provided the ratio of tin to these elements in the alloy is high enough. In addition to the above drawbacks, tin is not always quantitatively precipitated as meta-stannic acid, particularly when the alloy contains more than 0.25% of iron. In ordinary analyses of material containing but little iron, correction or provision is made for antimony and phosphorus when they are present, and the contaminants and the slight solubility losses are ignored. This procedure results in compensating errors in the determinations of copper and tin; for the impurities make up for dissolved tin while the dissolved tin plates out to a considerable extent with the copper. In umpire analyses, or with alloys high in iron or antimony, the above weaknesses of the method must be taken into account and provision must be made for the complete recovery of all tin, as well as the complete recovery of all contaminating elements carried down with the tin.

A special method is given for the determination of tin in alloys containing considerable phosphorus.

Methods are given for the determination of the impurities, sulphur and antimony.

Determination of Copper by the Electrolytic Method

APPARATUS FOR ELECTROLYSIS

Electrodes. The electrodes recommended are of the stationary and not of the rotating type, as the stationary require less of the operator's time and there is less chance for erroneous results to be obtained than with the other kind. Rapid and accurate results are obtained with stationary electrodes made from platinum gauze.

Cathodes. Platinum cathodes may be formed either from plain or perforated sheets, or from wire gauze, and may be either open or closed cylinders. They should give a depositing surface, counting both sides, of approximately 100 sq. cm. Gauze cathodes are recommended, and are best made from gauze containing approximately 400 meshes per sq. cm. (50 meshes per linear inch). The cathode should be stiffened by doubling the gauze for about 3 mm. at the top and at the bottom of the cylinder. The cylinder should be approximately 30 mm. in diameter and 30 mm. in height. The stem should be made from 1.14 mm. or 1.29 mm. wire, flattened and welded the entire width of the gauze; the height over all should be approximately 130 mm., and the gauze should be sand blasted.

Anodes. Platinum anodes may be of the spiral type when used in the determination of copper by electrolysis, or in the electrolytic determination of lead when it is present in amounts not over 0.2%. When used in the electrolytic determination of copper and lead together in samples containing 0.2% of lead or over, the anodes should be of wire gauze. Spiral anodes should be made from 1.02 mm. or 1.14 mm. wire formed into a spiral of 7 turns having a height of approximately 51 mm. and a diameter of 16 mm., the length over all being approximately 145 mm. Platinum gauze used in making anodes should contain approximately 400 meshes per sq. cm. (50 meshes per linear inch). The gauze should be formed into closed cylinders approximately 12 mm. in diameter and 30 mm. in height. The cylinders should be stiffened by doubling the gauze for about 3 mm. at the top and at the bottom. The stem should be made from 1.02 mm. or 1.29 mm. wire, flattened and welded the entire width of the gauze; the height over all should be approximately 130 mm., and the gauze should be sand blasted.

METHOD

In a 150-cc. beaker, dissolve 1 g. of the bronze in 10 cc. of HNO_3 (sp.gr. 1.42). When the action has ceased, boil until the oxides of nitrogen are expelled, add 50 cc. of hot distilled water, and allow to stand and settle for about one hour, keeping the temperature just below the boiling point. Filter on double 7 cm. ashless papers, being careful to keep the solution hot throughout the process of filtration, and receiving the filtrate in a 200-cc. beaker of the tall type used in electrolysis. Wash with boiling hot water. Retain the papers containing the precipitate for subsequent use in the tin determination.

Add to the filtrate 5 cc. of H_2SO_4 (sp.gr. 1.84), and determine copper by electrolysis, retaining the electrolyte, after the removal of the copper, for the subsequent determination of zinc. See the " Determination of Copper by the Electrolytic Method," Standard Methods of Chemical Analysis of Manganese Bronze.

NOTES

Copper, zinc, and tin are conveniently determined on the same sample, tin being first removed, and any zinc tested for after copper has been deposited by electrolysis.

If the solution becomes cool during the first filtration, some of the meta-stannic acid (H_2SnO_3) may dissolve.

Determination of Tin

(For Samples Free from Phosphorus)

METHOD

See the " Determination of Copper by the Electrolytic Method."

Use the papers containing the meta-stannic acid which was filtered off in the " Determination of Copper by the Electrolytic Method." Ignite the papers with the precipitate while moist in a porcelain or platinum crucible, slowly at first, and finally at the full heat of the burner. If the precipitate weighs more than 20 mg., heat to constant weight, using a blast lamp. Weigh as SnO_2, and calculate to Sn.

NOTES

1. This method is not accurate for alloys which contain phosphorus, or which contain over 0.25% of iron.

2. The ignited tin oxide contains small amounts of iron and copper as well as any phosphorus, antimony or arsenic which may be present in the alloy. Qualitative tests should be made for phosphorus, antimony and arsenic. In the absence of antimony and arsenic the following "Qualitative Test for Phosphorus" is here made use of to detect phosphorus and to estimate its amount, if any is found.

Qualitative Test for Phosphorus

SOLUTIONS REQUIRED

Ferric Chloride. Dissolve 25 g. of ferric chloride in 100 cc. of distilled water, and add 25 cc. of HCl (sp.gr. 1.20).

METHOD

Dip a piece of the alloy into a few cubic centimeters of ferric chloride for about ten seconds, and rinse it in running water. Alloys containing phosphorus are darkened noticeably where they have been dipped; alloys containing over 0.25% of phosphorus are rendered almost black by this test.

In alloys containing up to 0.20% of phosphorus, a correction for its presence in the ignited tin oxide may be made according to the following empirical method. From the phosphorus content of the alloy, which has been determined on a separate sample, calculate the weight of P_2O_5 and subtract two thirds of this weight from the weight of the ignited tin oxide containing phosphorus. The remainder is considered as pure SnO_2. The factor for converting phosphorus to $\frac{2}{3} \times P_2O_5$ is 152.6%, or approximately $1\frac{1}{2}$ times the phosphorus content of the sample.

If the alloy contains over 0.20% of phosphorus, a special method for the determination of tin should be used.

In alloys which contain over 0.25% of iron, use the method for the " Determination of Tin " in the Standard Methods of Chemical Analysis of Manganese Bronze.

Determination of Tin for Samples Containing Phosphorus

SOLUTIONS REQUIRED

Yellow Ammonium Sulphide. Saturate 150 cc. of NH_4OH (sp.gr. 0.90) with H_2S gas, and then add 50 cc. more of NH_4OH. Dissolve in this solution 3 or 4 g. of sulphur flour, and about 1 g. of NH_4Cl. Make up this solution fresh, and filter immediately before using.

Dilute Yellow Ammonium Sulphide for Washing. Mix 20 cc. of yellow ammonium sulphide, prepared as above, and 400 cc. of distilled water.

Ammonium Acetate for Washing. Dissolve 10 g. of ammonium acetate in 300 cc. of distilled water, make slightly acid with acetic acid and saturate with H_2S gas.

METHOD

See the " Determination of Copper by the Electrolytic Method."

Use the papers containing the freshly filtered meta-stannic acid which was filtered off in the " Determination of Copper by the Electrolytic Method." Transfer the papers with the precipitate to a 150-cc. beaker, and cover with 40 to 50 cc. of yellow ammonium sulphide. Warm for about 15 minutes, or until the meta-stannic acid has dissolved. Filter and wash thoroughly with dilute yellow ammonium sulphide. Acidify the combined filtrate and washings cautiously with 50% acetic acid. Warm, and allow the precipitated tin sulphide and sulphur to settle. Filter on double papers and wash with ammonium acetate solution. Dry the precipitate, and place it with the papers in a porcelain crucible which projects part way through a hole in a piece of asbestos board. Heat slowly until the free sulphur has been driven off, but without allowing the sulphur to burn. When the sulphur has been expelled, place the crucible on a triangle and ignite slowly at first, and finally at the full heat of the burner. If the precipitate weighs more than 20 mg., heat to constant weight, using a blast lamp. Weigh as SnO_2, and calculate to Sn.

Accuracy. Duplicate determinations should check within 0.06% of tin.

NOTES

1. The ignited tin oxide will contain any arsenic or antimony that was present in the sample.

2. During the ignition, if the sulphur is allowed to burn, some tin sulphate may be formed, causing high results. On the other hand, low results may be caused by too high heat, which causes spattering and volatilizes some tin sulphide.

Determination of Lead by the Electrolytic Method

APPARATUS

Electrodes and other apparatus used in electrolysis; see the " Determination of Copper by the Electrolytic Method."

METHOD

In a 150-cc. beaker, dissolve 1 g. of the bronze in 10 cc. of HNO_3 (sp.gr. 1.42). When the action has ceased, boil until the oxides of nitrogen are expelled; add 50 cc. of boiling hot distilled water and allow to stand and settle for about one hour, keeping the temperature just below the boiling point. Filter on double 7 cm. ashless papers, being careful to keep the solution hot throughout the process of filtration. Wash with boiling hot water. Add to the filtrate 9 cc. of HNO_3 (sp.gr. 1.42) and dilute to about 150 cc. with distilled water. Insert a sand-blasted platinum gauze electrode in the anode terminal; this electrode may be one of the type used as cathode in the " Determination of Copper by the Electrolytic Method," or it may be one of the sand-blasted gauze anodes therein described. Insert in the cathode terminal one of the electrodes used as anode in the " Determination of Copper by the Electrolytic Method." Cover with a pair of split watch glasses and electrolyze. For each solution use a current of 2 amperes at 10 volts continued for about 2 hours. Wash down the cover glasses, electrodes, and sides of the beakers, raising the level of the liquid 5 or 6 mm., and continue the electrolysis for 15 minutes. If no darkening of the newly exposed surface of the platinum can be detected, the lead has been entirely deposited. If the newly exposed surface of the platinum is darkened, continue the electrolysis until no such darkening can be detected when the current has been continued for 15 minutes after the level of the liquid has been raised.

When the lead has been entirely deposited, remove the anode quickly and rinse it in distilled water and then in alcohol, and dry in an oven at 210° C. for 30 minutes. Weigh as PbO_2, using the factor for lead 0.8643 instead of the theoretical value.

NOTES

1. It is impossible to remove the tin quantitatively as H_2SnO_3 in the case of alloys containing over 0.25% of iron, and traces of tin are sometimes found in the PbO_2 deposit.

2. In this and in the following method, a slight amount of lead may be retained by the H_2SnO_3. This should be recovered in very accurate work, but is neglected in a routine analysis.

3. *Samples for Analysis.* When lead is less than 0.10%, a 5 or 10 g. sample is taken. The 5 g. sample should be dissolved in 25 cc. of HNO_3. The 10 g. sample should be dissolved in 45 cc. of HNO_3. When the lead content is greater than 15%, dissolve the sample in HNO_3 as described under Method, transfer the solution to a graduated flask and choose aliquot portions for analysis in order not to exceed the above-mentioned limit of lead to be deposited on the anode as PbO_2. The lead peroxide will tend to flake off the electrode when the amount deposited becomes excessive.

Determination of Lead as Sulphate

(Optional)

SOLUTIONS REQUIRED

" **Lead-Acid.**" Mix 300 cc. of H_2SO_4 (sp.gr. 1.84) and 1800 cc. of distilled water. Dissolve 1 g. of lead acetate, c.p. in 300 cc. of distilled water and add this to the hot solution with stirring. Let stand at least 24 hours, and siphon through a thick asbestos filter.

Dilute Alcohol for Washing. Mix equal parts of denatured alcohol and distilled water.

METHOD

In a 150-cc. beaker, dissolve 1 g. of the bronze in 10 cc. of HNO_3 (sp.gr. 1.42). When the action has ceased, boil until the oxides of nitrogen are expelled, add 50 cc. of boiling hot distilled water, and allow to stand and settle for about one hour, keeping the temperature just below the boiling point. Filter on double 7 cm. ashless papers, being careful to keep the solution hot throughout the process of filtration. Wash with boiling hot water. Add 40 cc. of lead-acid and evaporate until copious fumes of H_2SO_4 are evolved. Cool, add 35 cc. of distilled water to dissolve the salts. Heat to boiling and allow to cool and settle for 5 hours, or over night, if convenient. Filter on a weighed Gooch crucible and wash with lead-acid. Wash out the lead-acid with dilute alcohol, set the Gooch crucible inside a porcelain crucible, ignite for five minutes at the full heat of a Tirrell burner, cool and weigh as $PbSO_4$, and calculate to Pb.

NOTES

1. Copper and lead may be determined on the same samples if so desired. In such a case, after filtering off the lead sulphate and washing with lead-acid, and before washing with dilute alcohol, remove the filtrate, add 3 cc. of HNO_3 (sp.gr. 1.42), dilute to 120 cc. and determine copper by electrolysis. See the "Determination of Copper by the Electrolytic Method."

2. Copper and lead may also be determined simultaneously by the electrolytic method. See the Standard Methods of Chemical Analysis of Manganese Bronze.

Determination of Iron

SOLUTIONS REQUIRED

Yellow Ammonium Sulphide. Saturate 150 cc. of NH_4OH (sp.gr. 0.90) with hydrogen sulphide gas, and then add 50 cc. more of NH_4OH. Dissolve in this solution 3 or 4 g. of sulphur flour, and about 1 g. of NH_4Cl. Make up this solution fresh, and filter it immediately before use.

Dilute Yellow Ammonium Sulphide for Washing. Mix 20 cc. of yellow ammonium sulphide, prepared as above, and 400 cc. of distilled water.

Other Solutions. See the "Determination of Iron" in the Standard Methods of Chemical Analysis of Brass Ingots and Sand Castings.

METHOD

In a 150-cc. beaker, dissolve 1 g. of bronze in 10 cc. of HNO_3 (sp.gr. 1.42). When the action has ceased, boil until the oxides of nitrogen are expelled, add 50 cc. of boiling water, and allow to stand and settle for about one hour, keeping the temperature just below the boiling point. Filter on double 7 cm. papers, keeping the solution hot, and wash with boiling hot water. Retain both the filtrate and the precipitate. Transfer the papers with the precipitate to a 150-cc. beaker, and cover them with 40 to 50 cc. of yellow ammonium sulphide. Warm about 15 minutes, or until the meta-stannic acid is dissolved. Filter and wash thoroughly with hot, dilute yellow ammonium sulphide.

Dissolve the small black residue on the filter with hot dilute HCl, receiving the solution in a small beaker. Add 5 cc. of HNO_3 (sp.gr. 1.42) and boil to oxidize sulphur and iron. Add this small solution to the original filtrate from the meta-stannic acid. Add about 5 g. of NH_4Cl, then NH_4OH (sp.gr. 0.90) and proceed as in the "Determination of Iron" in the Standard Methods of Chemical Analysis of Brass Ingots and Sand Castings.

Determination of Nickel by the Dimethylglyoxime Method

SOLUTIONS REQUIRED

Dimethylglyoxime Solution.   Dissolve 5 g. of dimethylglyoxime in 500 cc. of grain alcohol, and filter before using.

Sodium Potassium Tartrate Solution.   Dissolve 200 g. of the salt in 1 liter of distilled water.

Dilute Ammonia for Washing.   Solution containing 10 cc. of NH_4OH (sp.gr. 0.90) per liter of water.

METHOD

In a 200-cc. electrolytic beaker, dissolve a 1 g. sample exactly as in the "Determination of Copper by the Electrolytic Method" and remove the copper by electrolysis.   Evaporate the solution to about 100 cc., filter, add about 1 g. of NH_4Cl, then 10 cc. of sodium potassium tartrate solution, and nearly neutralize with NH_4OH (sp.gr. 0.90).   Heat nearly to boiling, add 5 cc. of dimethylglyoxime solution for each 0.01 g. or fraction of nickel present and then NH_4OH in slight excess.   Let stand at least 30 minutes on the steam bath, filter and wash with dilute ammonia solution.   For accurate work, the precipitate should be dissolved in hot HCl (1 : 1) and reprecipitated as before. Filter on a weighed Gooch crucible, wash with dilute ammonia solution, and then with hot water; dry at 110 to 120° C. for about two hours and weigh as the glyoxime salt which contains 20.31% of nickel.   If it is preferred, instead of by weighing the glyoxime salt, the nickel can be determined electrolytically as follows: Dissolve the red precipitate of nickel glyoxime in hot HCl (1 : 1), add 10 cc. of H_2SO_4 (1 : 1) and evaporate to strong fumes.   Dilute, neutralize with NH_4OH (sp.gr. 0.90), and add 20 cc. in excess.   The final volume should be about 150 cc.   Electrolyze with a current of 0.3 ampere per solution.   Test the solution for completion of deposition with fresh H_2S water as is done in the " Determination of Copper by the Electrolytic Method." Remove the cathode, wash with water and dry with alcohol as in the " Determination of Copper by the Electrolytic Method."   Weigh the deposit as metallic nickel.

Determination of Zinc

After the copper has been completely deposited by electrolysis, quickly remove the cathode and wash it thoroughly with distilled water, catching the washing in the beaker containing the electrolyte.   Heat the solution and saturate with H_2S gas.   Filter off any precipitate, and boil the solution to expel H_2S.   Make the solution barely alkaline with NH_4OH, and add 25 cc. of 85% formic acid.   Dilute the solution with distilled water to 300 cc., heat to boiling, and saturate with H_2S gas.   Filter, wash with hot water and dissolve the precipitate with hot HCl (1 : 1) and transfer the solution to a weighed platinum or porcelain dish or crucible.   Add a few drops of H_2SO_4 (sp.gr. 1.84) and evaporate the solution until copious fumes escape.   If the solution is not clear and colorless, cool, add a few cubic centimeters of HNO_3 (sp.gr. 1.42) and again evaporate the solution until fumes of H_2SO_4 come off freely.   Repeat the treatment with HNO_3, if necessary, until the organic matter is destroyed, and the solution is colorless.   Remove the excess of H_2SO_4 by heating the dish cautiously, and finally heat to dull redness.   Weigh as $ZnSO_4$ and calculate Zn.

8

Determination of Phosphorus by the Alkalimetric Method

SOLUTIONS REQUIRED

Nitric Acid for Dissolving. Mix 1000 cc. of HNO_3 (sp.gr. 1.42) and 1200 cc. of distilled water.

Nitric Acid for Washing. Mix 20 cc. of HNO_3 (sp.gr. 1.42) and 1000 cc. of distilled water.

Ammonium Molybdate Solution No. 1. Place in a beaker 100 g. of 85% molybdic acid, mix it thoroughly with 240 cc. of distilled water, add 140 cc. of NH_4OH (sp.gr. 0.90), filter and add 60 cc. of HNO_3 (sp.gr. 1.42).

Ammonium Molybdate Solution No. 2. Mix 400 cc. of HNO_3 (sp.gr. 1.42) and 960 cc. of distilled water.

When the solutions are cold, add solution No. 1 to solution No. 2, stirring constantly; then add 0.1 g. of ammonium phosphate dissolved in 10 cc. of distilled water and let stand at least 24 hours before using.

Potassium Nitrate, 1% Solution. Dissolve 10 g. of potassium nitrate in 1000 cc. of distilled water.

Phenolphthalein Indicator. Dissolve 0.2 g. in 50 cc. of 95% ethyl alcohol and 50 cc. of distilled water.

Standard Sodium Hydroxide. Dissolve 3.3 g. of purified NaOH in 1000 cc. of distilled water, add a slight excess of 1% solution of barium hydroxide, let stand for 24 hours, decant the liquid, and standardize it against a steel of known phosphorus content as determined by the molybdate-magnesia method, so that 1 cc. will be equivalent to 0.01% of phosphorus on the basis a of 1 g. sample (see Notes). Protect the solution from carbon dioxide with a soda-lime tube.

Ferric Chloride. Dissolve 100 g. of ferric chloride (phosphorus free) in 100 cc. of distilled water.

Standard Nitric Acid. Mix 5 cc. of HNO_3 (sp.gr. 1.42) and 1000 cc. of distilled water. Titrate the solution against standardized NaOH, using phenolphthalein as indicator, and make it equivalent to the sodium hydroxide by adding distilled water.

METHOD

In a 400-cc. beaker, dissolve a 1 g. sample in 10 cc. of HNO_3 (sp.gr. 1.42) and heat until brown fumes are driven off; then add 15 cc. of HCl (sp.gr. 1.20) and evaporate to dryness. Add 10 cc. of HCl (sp.gr. 1.20) and again evaporate to dryness, but do not bake.

Add 15 cc. of HCl (sp.gr. 1.20) and heat to solution; dilute with 50 cc. of distilled water and bring to a boil. Take off the hot plate and wash down the cover glass and sides of the beaker, add 20-mesh c.p. zinc, 2 or 3 g. at a time until the solution becomes colorless, that is, until all the copper, tin and lead are precipitated. Filter, receiving the filtrate in a 400-cc. beaker, and wash well with hot water.

Add 3 cc. of the ferric chloride solution to this filtrate and make faintly ammoniacal; bring to a boil, let settle and filter. Dissolve this precipitate in hot dilute HCl and again make ammoniacal; heat to boiling, let settle and filter, washing well with hot water.

Dissolve this precipitate in as small a quantity of hot dilute HNO_3 as possible, receiving the solution in a 300-cc. Erlenmeyer flask; wash filter free of iron with hot dilute HNO_3 and hot distilled water. Evaporate to about 15 cc., cool, make ammoniacal, then neutralize with HNO_3 (sp.gr. 1.42) and add 5 cc. in excess.   Cool to 80° C., and add 60 cc. of the ammonium molybdate solution.   Let stand one minute, then shake three minutes and let settle. Filter on an 11 cm. filter (using a small quantity of paper pulp on the filter) and wash free of iron with 2% nitric acid wash, then free of acid with the 1% potassium nitrate solution.

Place the paper in the thoroughly washed acid-free flask in which the original precipitation was made, add 25 cc. of distilled water and an excess of the standard sodium hydroxide solution.   By using a long glass rod, the paper can be pulped and the yellow precipitate dissolved in a very few seconds. Wash off the rod and the sides of the flask and add a few drops of the phenolphthalein solution and titrate the excess of standard NaOH with the standard HNO_3.   The strength of the standard NaOH and the standard HNO_3 in terms of phosphorus can be determined by using a standard steel or preferably a standard phosphor bronze in which the phosphorus has been determined by the molybdate-magnesia method.

Accuracy.   Duplicate determinations should check within 0.01% of phosphorus.

NOTES

1. The ammonium molybdate solution should be kept in a cool place and should always be filtered before using.

2. All distilled water used in titration should be freed from carbon dioxide by boiling or otherwise.

3. Bureau of Standards Steel No. 19 (a) or a bronze of known phosphorus content are recommended as suitable materials for standardization of the sodium hydroxide solution.

4. (Gravimetric method, optional.)   It is considered by some that more accurate results can be obtained by a gravimetric determination of phosphorus as $Mg_2P_2O_7$. This can be carried out by dissolving the yellow molybdate precipitate in 20 cc. of NH_4OH (1 : 1) to which has been added 2 g. of citric acid, precipitating with magnesia mixture, and proceeding as usual, finally weighing as $Mg_2P_2O_7$.

5. Determination of phosphorus by the ferric alum method is optional.   See the Standard Methods of Chemical Analysis of Gun Metal.

Determination of Antimony by the Volumetric Method

SOLUTIONS REQUIRED

Potassium Permanganate. Dissolve 0.3 g. of potassium permanganate in 1000 cc. of distilled water. Standardize by dissolving 25 mg. of pure antimony in 15 cc. of boiling H_2SO_4 and proceeding according to the method from this point.

METHOD

In a 250-cc. beaker, dissolve 5 g. of bronze in 25 cc. of HNO_3 (sp.gr. 1.42). When the action has ceased, boil until the oxides of nitrogen are expelled, add 125 cc. of boiling water and allow to stand and settle for one hour or longer, keeping the temperature just below the boiling point. Filter on double 9 cm. closely woven papers, keeping the solution hot. Wash with boiling water. Discard the filtrate.

Transfer the papers containing the tin and antimony to a 350-cc. Erlenmeyer flask and add 25 cc. of HNO_3 (sp.gr. 1.42), 5 g. of ammonium persulphate, and 15 cc. of H_2SO_4 (sp.gr. 1.84). Boil to strong fumes of SO_3. If the solution is brown, cool and add 5 cc. of HNO_3 (sp.gr. 1.42) and a little more (1 g. or less) persulphate, if necessary, and boil again to strong fumes of SO_3. When the solution is colorless, cool, add 20 cc. of distilled water, 20 cc. of HCl (sp.gr. 1.20) and 1 g. of sodium sulphite. Boil gently for 10 minutes to expel SO_2 completely. Dilute with 200 cc. of distilled water and cool to 10 to 12° C. in ice or under running water.

Titrate with standard permanganate solution until the appearance of a decided permanent pink color.

NOTES

1. In alloys containing a large excess of tin, the antimony is precipitated quantitatively with the meta-stannic acid.
2. Ammonium persulphate and HNO_3 are used to destroy the filter paper, and subsequent boiling with H_2SO_4 effects the solution of the tin and antimony. A mixture of fuming HNO_3 and H_2SO_4 might be used to accomplish the same results, but the persulphate mixture is much more efficient.
3. If the solution becomes cool during the first filtration, some of the meta-stannic acid may dissolve.
4. If arsenic is present, correction should be made for it.

Determination of Sulphur

METHOD

Weigh out four 5 g. samples of bronze into 250-cc. beakers. Dissolve each in 25 cc. of HNO_3 (sp.gr. 1.42) and boil until the disappearance of red fumes. Add 125 cc. of boiling water and allow to settle for one hour or longer, keeping the temperature just below the boiling point. Filter on double 12.5 cm. closely woven papers, keeping the solution hot. Wash with boiling water. Discard the meta-stannic acid precipitates, combine the four filtrates in a tall 700-cc. beaker and add 0.5 g. of sodium carbonate, and evaporate the solution until syrupy. Cool somewhat, then dilute to the lip with warm water. There should be present a layer about 6 mm. in thickness, composed of basic salts of copper. Electrolyze, using large stationary electrodes, at a current of 4 amperes, or using the Frary solenoid at a current of about 10 amperes. The lead must be removed at the anode as the copper is taken out at the cathode. When copper and lead are out, evaporate the electrolyte to small volume, cover the beaker, add 75 cc. of HCl (sp.gr. 1.20) and boil down to small volume. Add 75 cc. more HCl and evaporate to dryness to dehydrate any silica present. Moisten with about 0.5 cc. of HCl and take up with 20 cc. of hot water. Filter into a small beaker. Heat the filtrate to boiling and add 10 cc. of 5% $BaCl_2$ solution, drop by drop, with stirring. Allow to settle at least five hours, filter on a small ashless paper, and wash with hot water. Ignite cautiously in a small porcelain or platinum crucible, and then heat to a bright redness for 20 minutes. Cool and weigh the $BaSO_4$ and calculate to sulphur.

NOTES

1. Throughout the entire analysis, the utmost precautions must be taken to prevent contamination by sulphur in any form, H_2SO_4 fumes, H_2S and SO_2 gases especially. All heating with gas burners must be avoided. Run a blank with each analysis, adding the reagents and subjecting it to the same operations as the beakers containing the drillings. Subtract the amount of $BaSO_4$ found in the blank from that in the determinations. If this blank amounts to 0.002 g., it is a sign of poor work or impure reagents and the analysis should be repeated. Wash out all beakers, funnels, etc., with distilled water before using.

2. It is necessary to keep the solution containing the meta-stannic acid hot during filtration. If the solution becomes cool, some of the meta-stannic acid may dissolve.

Determination of Arsenic

SOLUTIONS REQUIRED

Ammonium Carbonate. Dissolve 150 g. of ammonium carbonate in one liter of distilled water.

METHOD

Dissolve the sample (5.00 to 10.00 g.) in a 100-cc. beaker in 10 cc. of HNO_3 (sp.gr. 1.42) and 30 cc. of HCl (sp.gr. 1.19). When solution is complete, cool, add 35 cc. of H_2SO_4 (sp.gr. 1.84), evaporate to the appearance of copious fumes of H_2SO_4, and continue the fuming for from ten to fifteen minutes. Cool, take up in HCl (sp.gr. 1.19), transfer to an 800-cc. flask having a two-hole stopper with separatory funnel and outlet tube connecting with a vertical condenser outside. (The part of the outlet tube within the distilling flask should have a steam outlet hole about 1 cm. from the open end.) Rinse the beaker with HCl (sp.gr. 1.19) and dilute the solution with the acid to make a total volume of 350 to 450 cc. Add 10 g. of cuprous chloride (Cu_2Cl_2), connect the flask with the condenser, and gradually raise the contents of the flask to boiling. Catch the distillate in a tall 400-cc. beaker containing 100 cc. of cold water. The end of the condenser should extend several millimeters into the water in the beaker and the beaker should be surrounded with ice water in order to avoid any possible volatilization of arsenious chloride. After about 100 cc. of distillate has passed over, remove the flame from the distilling flask, pour 3 to 5 cc. of hypophosphorus acid through the separatory funnel into the distilling flask, and redistill as before, catching the distillate in the same beaker. The volume of the second distillate should be 50 to 100 cc. Pass a rapid current of H_2S through the distillate for one hour, allow to settle, and filter on a weighed Gooch crucible. Wash twice with HCl (1 : 1), four times with cold water, three times with alcohol, and four times with CS_2. Dry at 110° C. for 10 minutes, and weigh after cooling. Dissolve the As_2S_3 with $(NH_4)_2CO_3$ solution, wash thoroughly with water, dry for 30 minutes at 110° C. and reweigh after cooling. The difference in weights multiplied by 0.609 gives the weight of arsenic.

NOTE

1. Blank determinations should be made on the reagents carried along as in the method and the proper corrections made.

The Determination of Cadmium in Brass

GENERAL CONSIDERATIONS

From the results of a series of experiments on known synthetic mixtures, it was found that the following method is satisfactory even in the presence of moderate amounts of arsenic, lead, bismuth, tin and antimony.

METHOD

Prepare a sufficient amount of sawdust or drillings from the brass to be tested to furnish at least a twenty-gram sample. For the assay weigh ten grams of this sample into a 500-cc. Erlenmeyer flask and dissolve in concentrated nitric acid. Add 50 cc. conc. H_2SO_4 and fume strongly. Cool and dilute to 200 cc. with water, boil for a few minutes and allow to cool. After two or three hours filter off any insoluble matter, collecting the filtrate in a tall 600-cc. beaker. Discard the residue on the paper and dilute the filtrate to 400 cc. Heat to boiling and pass a rapid stream of H_2S through this hot solution for thirty minutes. (It is well to thoroughly mix the copper sulphide with the solution by means of rubber-tipped rod so as to keep the precipitate from being forced out of the solution by the gas.)

At the end of the half hour filter off the precipitated sulphides on an $18\frac{1}{2}$ cm. paper, receiving the filtrate in a tall 600-cc. beaker. Wash the sulphides once with hot water. If proper precipitation has been made, this filtration will be rapid and easy to make and the filtrate will have no blue color. Return the precipitated sulphides with the filter paper to the beaker in which precipitation was made and add 400 cc. of 10% H_2SO_4. Boil vigorously for a half hour and filter hot on a $19\frac{1}{2}$ cm. paper. Wash the residue thoroughly with boiling water. Discard the residue on the paper. All of the cadmium is now present in these two solutions.

Cool and pass a rapid stream of H_2S through the solution for ten minutes. Add ammonia slowly to each solution until zinc sulphide begins to precipitate. When this is certain, continue the passage of the gas for five minutes more and then filter off the precipitates separately on $12\frac{1}{2}$ cm. paper. Discard the filtrates. Combine the two papers containing mixed sulphides and boil with 100 cc. 10% H_2SO_4 for ten minutes, stirring frequently. Filter and wash. Cool and dilute to 300 cc. Pass in H_2S and add ammonia drop by drop until cadmium is entirely precipitated. Pass gas for about twenty minutes. Filter the precipitate on an 11 cm. close texture paper. Return the paper to the beaker and boil with 50 cc. 10% H_2SO_4. Filter and wash. Dilute to 300 cc. and pass in H_2S for twenty minutes. A drop or two of ammonia will be sufficient to start the precipitation of cadmium.

Filter the cadmium sulphides on a weighed gooch crucible. Wash twice with cold water. Dry at 110° C. for two hours and reweigh.

Weight $CdS \times 0.778 =$ Weight Cadmium.

The final cadmium sulphide precipitate will have characteristic bright yellow color and will be entirely free of other sulphides if the foregoing directions be carefully followed.

As a special precaution when arsenic or tin are suspected in the brass the final sulphide may be washed out of the crucible after weighing and treated with yellow ammonium sulphide. (The addition of NH_4Cl will tend to prevent cadmium sulphide being carried into the ammonium sulphide solution as a colloid.) Filter and wash the residue and dissolve the cadmium sulphide in 10% H_2SO_4, reprecipitate and weigh again.

DETERMINATION OF ALUMINUM IN NON-FERROUS ALLOYS [1]

(Routine Method)

SOLUTIONS REQUIRED

Sodium Hydroxide Solution (2.5%). Dissolve 25 g. of sodium hydroxide (free from aluminum) in water and dilute to 1000 cc.

Sodium Sulphide Solution. Dissolve 150 g. of sodium hydroxide (free from aluminum) in 1000 cc. of water, saturate 500 cc. of this solution with hydrogen sulphide and then mix with the remaining 500 cc. of solution.

Dilute Hydrochloric Acid (1 : 3). Mix 200 cc. of hydrochloric acid, sp.gr. 1.19, with 600 cc. of water.

Acidified Hydrogen Sulphide Water. Dilute 10 cc. of hydrochloric acid, sp.gr. 1.19, with 1000 cc. of water and saturate the solution with hydrogen sulphide.

Ammonium Chloride Solution (2%). Mix 30 cc. of hydrochloric acid, sp.gr. 1.19, with 200 cc. of water, add methyl red, neutralize with ammonia until the solution changes to a distinct yellow, and then dilute to 1000 cc. with water.

METHOD

Dissolve 2 g. of the sample in 20 cc. of hydrochloric acid, sp.gr. 1.19, and 5 cc. of nitric acid, sp.gr. 1.42. Boil the solution to expel chlorine and dilute with 50 cc. of water.

Nearly neutralize the cold solution with sodium hydroxide solution (2.5 % or stronger if much free acid is present) and pour it slowly, and with constant shaking, into a 500-cc. volumetric flask containing 100 cc. of sodium sulphide solution, dilute to the mark with sodium hydroxide solution (2.5%) and thoroughly mix the solution.

Filter on a dry No. 42 Whatman filter paper (or its equivalent), reject the first 20–25 cc., and catch exactly 250 cc., which will represent 1 g. of sample. With samples high in aluminum, the aliquot portion should be gathered in a 250-cc. volumetric flask; in ordinary analyses a graduate will suffice.

Transfer the aliquot portion to a 600-cc. beaker, carefully acidify the solution with dilute hydrochloric acid (1 : 3) and finally add 25 cc. in excess. Digest at 40–60° C. for one hour, filter, and wash the paper and precipitate with acidified hydrogen sulphide water.

Boil the filtrate and washings to expel hydrogen sulphide, add a few drops of methyl red indicator and then dilute ammonia (1 : 2) until the solution is just distinctly yellow. Boil for one to two minutes and filter at once. Wash the beaker, paper, and precipitate two or three times with hot ammonium chloride solution (2%) and discard the filtrate.

Dissolve the precipitate in 30–40 cc. of hot dilute hydrochloric acid (1 : 3), wash the filter thoroughly with hot water, and reserve it for ignition with the final precipitate or for the second filtration. Dilute the filtrate to 200 cc., add methyl red and precipitate with dilute ammonia (1 : 2) as before. Filter, wash with hot ammonium chloride solution (2%), and ignite.

[1] Method proposed by Dr. G. E. F. Lundell, Bureau of Standards.

The ignited residue is prone to carry silica and must be purified before weighing as follows: Add one or two drops of water, one drop of diluted sulphuric acid and 1–5 cc. of hydrofluoric acid. Evaporate to dryness, ignite (finally with a blast lamp or its equivalent) and weigh as Al_2O_3. The weight of Al_2O_3 multiplied by 52.94 gives the percentage of aluminum.

NOTES

1. The above method is reasonably accurate and has the advantage of actually showing the presence of aluminum. The retention of aluminum by the sodium sulphide precipitate is slight as is also the case with the arsenic group precipitate except where both tin and aluminum are high.

2. The method is somewhat similar in principle to certain methods which are used in alloy steel analysis as, for example, the determination of molybdenum in steel. It is apparent that the first precipitation eliminates copper, lead, zinc, iron, nickel, manganese and similar elements. The second precipitation separates tin, antimony, arsenic, and any other metals of the arsenic group. This leaves aluminum as the only possible remaining constituent in ordinary materials and its absence is assured, if no precipitate is subsequently obtained with ammonia. If the sodium hydroxide and sulphide solutions are free from aluminum, a precipitate is almost sure evidence of aluminum and the only ordinary contaminant is silica. Phosphorus, if present in the alloy, will come down with the precipitate as would also vanadium and two or three uncommon elements such as glucinum.

3. The first aluminum hydroxide precipitate will carry down sodium chloride and any silica that may be dissolved in the solution. Hence it is not safe to omit the second precipitation and the hydrofluoric acid treatment.

4. If phosphorus is known to be present, the method should be followed through the first addition of ammonia. If aluminum is indicated, re-acidify the solution with hydrochloric acid, add macerated paper, two drops of methyl orange, and 5 cc. of a solution of diammonium phosphate (10%). Render the solution just ammoniacal, then just restore the pink color with dilute hydrochloric acid (1 : 3), heat to boiling and add 30 cc. of a solution of ammonium acetate (25%). Boil for 5 minutes, filter on a 11 cm. No. 42 Whatman or similar paper and wash with hot ammonium nitrate solution (5%) until 5 cc. of the washings no longer give a test for chlorides with acidified silver nitrate. Ignite in platinum or porcelain, blast for ten minutes and weigh as $AlPO_4$. This method is not strictly accurate on account of the uncertain composition of the phosphate but is probably sufficiently accurate for all but the most painstaking analyses.

METHOD FOR THE CHEMICAL ANALYSIS OF NICKEL SILVER AND CUPRO NICKEL

Determination of Tin, Copper and Lead

SOLUTIONS REQUIRED

See " Analysis of Manganese Bronze."

METHOD

Proceed exactly as in the determination of these elements under "Analysis of Manganese Bronze."

Determination of Iron

SOLUTIONS REQUIRED

Stannous Chloride. Dissolve 450 g. of the salt in 380 cc. of concentrated HCl (sp.gr. 1.20) to which some water has been added and dilute to 2 liters.

Mercuric Chloride. Make a saturated solution of the salt in hot water, allow to cool to room temperature and filter.

Manganese Sulphate. Dissolve 160 g. of the salt in water and dilute to 1750 cc. To this add 330 cc. of phosphoric acid (sp.gr. 1.70) and 320 cc. of sulphuric acid (sp.gr. 1.84). This solution is to obviate the deleterious action of hydrochloric acid upon the standard potassium permanganate. The phosphoric acid allows the formation of iron phosphate, which, being nearly colorless, renders the end reaction more distinct.

Potassium Permanganate. Make a solution containing .3163 g. of salt per liter. This is approximately N/100.

Standardization of above Permanganate Solution. Take measured quantities of a carefully standardized ferric chloride solution, containing 5 g. of metallic iron and 100 cc. strong hydrochloric acid to a liter in No. 1 beakers. About 5 cc. of this solution should prove adequate. Add from a burette stannous chloride solution until the iron is almost reduced, told by the color change. Then heat to boiling and reduce iron completely with SnCl$_2$, using a slight excess of the reagent. Add 5 cc. of HgCl$_2$ solution to oxidize excess of SnCl$_2$. Pour solution into a 600-cc. beaker containing 6–8 cc. of the MnSO$_4$ solution in 400 cc. of water. Titrate with KMnO$_4$ immediately until a faint pink is obtained. Calculate potassium permanganate in terms of metallic iron.

Treatment of Sample. Weigh out a 5 g. sample of drillings from which all steel chips have been removed by a magnet and transfer to a 250-cc. beaker. Dissolve in as little nitric acid (sp.gr. 1.42) as possible (25 cc. should be sufficient), heat until all nitric oxide fumes have been driven off and then dilute to 100 cc. with distilled water. Add 3 to 4 g. of ammonium chloride crystals, heat to boiling, and add a slight excess of ammonia to precipitate all the iron as hydroxide.

A small amount of zinc is usually precipitated at this point as hydroxide and also, if manganese is present in the alloy, it will come down as manganese hydroxide.

After the precipitate has settled down, filter through filter paper and wash with 1-4 ammonium hydroxide until all soluble salts are removed (or until the blue copper color has been washed from the filter paper). Treat the precipitate on the filter paper with a little hot 1-1 hydrochloric acid, catching the resulting solution in original beaker. Wash the filter paper alternately with hot water and 1-1 hydrochloric acid until the iron has been completely removed. Dilute the hydrochloric acid solution in the beaker to about 75 cc. and add 3-4 g. of ammonium chloride. Heat to boiling and reprecipitate the iron with a slight excess of ammonium hydroxide. Filter and wash as before. (A double precipitation is usually sufficient to remove zinc, etc.) Dissolve the precipitate in a small amount of 1-1 hydrochloric acid. Add stannous chloride to reduce the iron—2 or 3 drops are usually sufficient.

Heat almost to boiling and add 1 or 2 drops more of stannous chloride to be sure an excess is present. Run in an excess of mercuric chloride solution (about 5 cc.) to oxidize the stannous chloride.

Pour into a 600-cc. beaker containing 6-8 cc. of the manganese sulphate solution in 400 cc. of water.

Titrate with standard potassium permanganate solution until a slight pink opalescence is obtained.

Determination of Manganese

SOLUTIONS REQUIRED

See " Determination of Manganese by the Persulphate Method " and " Determination of Manganese by the Bismuthate Method " under " Analysis of Manganese Bronze."

METHOD

Proceed exactly as in the " Determination of Manganese by the Persulphate Method " or " Determination of Manganese by the Bismuthate Method " under " Analysis of Manganese Bronze."

Determination of Nickel

Solutions Required

Standard Solution of Potassium Cyanide. Dissolve 26 g. of pure potassium cyanide in 1000 cc. distilled water and add 1.25 g. of silver nitrate. This solution is standardized against a solution of known metal content.

Potassium Iodide. Dissolve 100 g. of c.p. potassium iodide crystals in 1000 cc. distilled water.

Sodium Pyrophosphate. Make a saturated solution of c.p. sodium pyrophosphate crystals in distilled water.

Method

See the "Determination of Copper, Lead and Tin."

Transfer the electrolyte and washings from the electrolytic determination of copper to a 400-cc. beaker. Add 3 to 4 g. of ammonium chloride and then 50 to 75 cc. of a saturated solution of sodium pyrophosphate, depending upon the amount of zinc present. Neutralize solution with ammonium hydroxide (sp.gr. 0.90) and then add enough to make the solution only slightly but yet distinctly alkaline. A large excess of ammonia will hinder or entirely prevent the reaction. Cool, and do not let the temperature to get much above 20° C. or the result will be irregular. Add 2 cc. of a 10% solution of potassium iodide and titrate with a standard solution of potassium cyanide containing silver nitrate until the white cloud caused by the formation of silver iodide has entirely disappeared and one drop of the cyanide causes a clear solution. This is the end point which is very sharp and distinct.

Notes

The method of estimating nickel by means of adding potassium cyanide to an ammoniacal solution of nickel containing silver iodide in suspension so that the solution remained turbid until the nickel was all converted into the double cyanide of nickel and potassium, after which a single drop of the cyanide in excess cleared up the solution, was originally proposed by T. Moore and modified by W. B. Price for use in the determination of nickel in German silver, etc.

The following elements interfere with the method: Manganese, zinc, iron, aluminum and especially copper, which, owing to its forming cyanides, would render the method valueless. Cobalt, if present, will be estimated as nickel. The iron, aluminum and zinc may be kept in solution so that they do not interfere by the use of organic acids such as tartaric or citric or with sodium pyrophosphate.

Determination of Zinc

The actual determination of zinc in these alloys is not necessary as a rule. The difference between the sum of the percentages of the other constituents in the alloy and 100 is taken as the percentage of zinc in the sample.

In case an actual determination is desired, proceed exactly as in the "Determination of Zinc" under Standard Methods of Chemical Analysis of Bronze Bearing Metal.

METHODS OF CHEMICAL ANALYSIS OF ALUMINUM AND LIGHT ALUMINUM ALLOYS,

A. S. T. M. Method

The methods of analysis listed under " Analysis of Aluminum " contemplate the analysis of aluminum containing more than 98% aluminum and containing only silicon, titanium, iron, copper, carbon and traces of manganese as impurities.

Unless it is positively known that such elements as tin, antimony, zinc, lead, nickel, magnesium, sodium, nitrogen or oxygen (as aluminum oxide) are absent, the methods listed under the " Analysis of Light Aluminum Alloys " should be employed.

ANALYSIS OF ALUMINUM

(Not Less than 98% Aluminum)

A. DETERMINATION OF NON-GRAPHITIC SILICON, GRAPHITIC SILICON, TOTAL SILICON, TITANIUM AND IRON

Determination of Non-Graphitic Silicon

SOLUTIONS REQUIRED

" Acid Mixture." 1200 cc. of H_2SO_4 (25% by volume), 600 cc. HCl (sp.gr. 1.20) and 200 cc. HNO_3 (sp.gr. 1.42).

25% Sulphuric Acid. Pour 250 cc. of H_2SO_4 (sp.gr. 1.84) into distilled water, and dilute to 1000 cc.

METHOD

Dissolve 1 g. of the well-mixed sample in 35 cc. of the acid mixture in a covered flat-bottomed porcelain dish or casserole. When the drillings are completely dissolved, boil the solution to complete expulsion of HNO_3 and HCl and heat until copious fumes of H_2SO_4 have been given off for five minutes. Cool and take up the residue with 10 cc. of 25% H_2SO_4 and 100 cc. of water. Warm to complete solution of the sulphates and filter on an ashless filter paper. Wash the residue with hot water until free from sulphates, ignite in a platinum crucible and weigh. Treat the ash with HF and a few drops of 25% H_2SO_4, carefully evaporate, ignite and again weigh. The difference in the two weights multiplied by the factor 46.93 represents the percentage of non-graphitic silicon.

Determination of Graphitic Silicon

See " Determination of Non-Graphitic Silicon."

The non-volatile residue obtained above, especially if dark colored, may contain graphitic silicon. Treat the non-volatile residue with 5 cc. HNO_3, 5 cc. HF, carefully evaporate, and add 2 or 3 drops of 25% H_2SO_4 toward the end of the evaporation. Ignite and weigh. Reserve the residue for the " Determination of Titanium." The loss in weight multiplied by 100 represents the percentage of graphitic silicon.

Determination of Total Silicon

The total silicon is represented by the sum of the percentage of non-graphitic and graphitic silicon.

NOTES

Blanks should be carried along with all reagents and the proper correction made.

Graphitic silicon is only slightly and slowly oxidized to silica by the solution or ignition treatments, and to the extent in which it is not oxidized, it resists the action of HF and H_2SO_4. Graphitic silicon is, however, readily attacked and volatilized by a mixture of HNO_3 and HF. On account of the possibility of slight oxidation of graphitic silicon by the treatments involved in the method, the latter may not be absolutely exact, but it is the best that has been devised.

Determination of Titanum

APPARATUS AND SOLUTIONS REQUIRED

Nessler tubes or some form of colorimeter.

Hydrogen Peroxide U.S.P. This reagent must be free from HF.

Standard Titanium Solution. This solution is best prepared and standardized as follows:

" Potassium titanium fluoride, K_2TiF_6, best serves as the starting point for the preparation of the standard solution. A quantity of this is recrystallized from boiling water one or more times, dried, and preserved in a glass-stoppered bottle. Enough of it to make 0.5 to 1 liter of the standard sulphate solution is put into a platinum dish and evaporated several times with strong sulphuric acid without bringing to dryness, till the fluorine is completely expelled. The residue is then taken up with water containing enough sulphuric acid to make at least 5% of the latter when fully diluted. Two 50 to 100 cc. portions of the prepared solution are then further diluted, boiled, and precipitated with ammonia. The precipitates are collected on paper, washed with hot water till free from alkali, ignited moist in the filter, blasted, and weighed. Duplicates should agree almost exactly. From the weights found, the strength of the standard is calculated and the result affixed to the bottle containing it. The stopper of the bottle should be coated with vaseline and the needed quantities of solution should be withdrawn by a pipette, never poured. In a solution so prepared there is not enough alkali sulphate to weaken the color when peroxidized."

METHOD

See " Determination of Graphitic Silicon."

Fuse the non-volatile residue remaining after the graphitic silicon determination in a small amount of $K_2S_2O_7$, take up in a little 5% H_2SO_4 and add to the filtrate and washings from the silicon determination. Evaporate the solution to approximately 100 cc., and treat with 5 cc. H_2SO_4 (sp.gr. 1.84) and 3 g. of iron-free zinc. Heat until the zinc is nearly dissolved and the reduction of copper is complete. Decant the solution into another beaker, wash the zinc and copper with hot water and continue the evaporation of the solution to approximately 75 cc. Cool and transfer to a 100-cc. Nessler's comparison tube, add 5 cc. of 3% H_2O_2 and dilute to the 100 cc. mark. In another tube, place 88 cc. H_2O, 5 cc. of H_2SO_4 (sp.gr. 1.84) and cool. Add 5 cc. of 3% H_2O_2 and then from a burette add the standard titanium solution until the colors match. Reserve the tested solution for the determination of iron. The volume of the standard solution required multiplied by 100 times its titre represents the percentage of titanium in the sample.

NOTES

The filtrate and washings from the Silicon Determination should ordinarily be colorless. If light yellow owing to iron, the standard comparison solution should be brought to the same tint with ferric sulphate solution before adding the hydrogen peroxide.

In case the amount of titanium is high, the solution may be diluted to a definite volume and aliquot portions taken for the colorimetric test.

Determination of Iron

SOLUTIONS REQUIRED

Potassium Permanganate Solution (10%). Dissolve 10 g. of $KMnO_4$ in distilled water and dilute to 100 cc.

Dilute Sulphuric Acid for Reduction. Mix 50 cc. of H_2SO_4 (sp.gr. 1.84) and 1000 cc. of distilled water. This solution is used boiling hot.

Standard Potassium Permanganate Solution. Dissolve 1 g. of $KMnO_4$ in 1000 cc. H_2O, and allow to stand for several days in a glass-stoppered bottle in a dark closet. Filter the solution through prepared asbestos and standardize against 0.1000 g. portions of pure sodium oxalate. Each cubic centimeter is equivalent to approximately 0.0018 g. of iron.

METHOD

See " Determination of Titanium."

Transfer the solution used in the " Determination of Titanium " from the Nessler tube to a 400-cc. beaker, add 10% $KMnO_4$ solution to a good permanent pink tint and pass the solution through the reductor. Wash the beaker and reductor with 150 cc. of the H_2SO_4 for reduction and then with 100 cc. of distilled water. Titrate with the standard $KMnO_4$ solution.

The results of the titration should be corrected by a " blank " determination made on 100 cc. of a 7% H_2SO_4 solution which has been carried through as in the titanium and iron determinations, not omitting the treatment with iron-free zinc, hydrogen peroxide, and permanganate preliminary to the actual reduction. About 0.5 cc. of the permanganate solution will be required to give a permanent color to the blank.

Calculate the apparent percentage of iron. To obtain the true percentage, multiply the percentage of titanium by 1.161 and subtract.

NOTES

Air should never be allowed to enter the body of the reductor.

Titanium is reduced to the trivalent condition in the reduction process and afterwards oxidized to the quadrivalent condition by the permanganate. There is a slight tendency toward oxidation in the receiver, but this may be disregarded in the small amounts of titanium ordinarily involved.

In case titanium is present and iron alone is to be determined, proceed as follows: Place the H_2SO_4 solution of the sample in a 250-cc. flask, dilute to 100 cc. containing 2.5 cc. H_2SO_4 (sp.gr. 1.84) and treat with H_2S for 30 minutes in the cold and 15 minutes while warmed. If sulphides appear, filter and gas the filtrate 10 minutes more. Add 15 cc. H_2SO_4 (1 : 1) and boil vigorously until H_2S is expelled and the volume reduced to 50 cc. Fill the flask with distilled water, transfer to a beaker, and titrate with $KMnO_4$ solution.

Determination of Copper

(a) Electrolytic Method

APPARATUS FOR ELECTROLYSIS

See the " Determination of Copper by the Electrolytic Method " in the Standard Methods of Chemical Analysis of Manganese Bronze.

SOLUTIONS REQUIRED

Dilute Sulphuric Acid (1 : 1). Pour 500 cc. of H_2SO_4 (sp.gr. 1.84) into distilled water, cool and dilute to 1000 cc.

METHOD

Dissolve 10 g. of the sample in 100 cc. of dilute H_2SO_4 (1 : 1). When action has ceased add 25 cc. of HNO_3 (sp.gr. 1.42) and boil until oxides of nitrogen have been expelled. Filter into the tall form of beaker used in electrolysis and wash the residue with hot water. Dilute to 400 cc. and electrolyze. Use a weighed sand-blasted cathode and a current of from 3 to 5 amperes at approximately 10 volts. When the solution is colorless and 1 cc. of the solution gives no copper test with H_2S water on a porcelain plate, remove the solution from the electrodes quickly without interrupting the current. Quickly rinse the cathode in distilled water and then dip it in two successive baths of alcohol. Shake off the excess alcohol and ignite the remainder by bringing it to the flame of an alcohol lamp. Keep the cathode moving continually while the alcohol burns. Weigh as metallic copper.

NOTES

The electrolytic method is preferred for the determination of copper no matter what the percentage.

It is not anticipated that the aluminum will contain tin. In case tin has been found it will be preferable to precipitate with hydrogen sulphide as in the optional method. The sulphides are then to be dissolved, digested in HNO_3 (1 : 1), the metastannic acid filtered off and the electrolysis then carried out.

A staining of the anode indicates the presence of lead or manganese.

(b) Iodide Method. (Optional)

SOLUTIONS REQUIRED

Dilute Sulphuric Acid (1 : 1). Pour 500 cc. of H_2SO_4 (sp.gr. 1.84) into distilled water, cool and dilute to 1000 cc.

Wash Solution. Saturate 500 cc. of H_2SO_4 (1 : 99) with H_2S.

Nitric Acid (1 : 1). Pour 500 cc. of HNO_3 (sp.gr. 1.42) into distilled water, cool and dilute to 1000 cc.

Potassium Iodide Solution. Dissolve 30 g. of KI in water and dilute to 100 cc.

Sodium Thiosulphate Solution. Dissolve 19 g. of $Na_2S_2O_3.5H_2O$ in distilled water and dilute to one liter. After aging for 1 week or more in a glass-stoppered bottle, standardize against 0.1 g. portions of c.p. copper or suitable material of known copper content, carried through the operations of the method described below. One cubic centimeter should correspond to approximately 0.005 g. of copper.

Starch Solution. Grind 0.5 g. arrow-root starch in a mortar with a little water to a smooth paste and pour into 250 cc. of boiling water. Boil 3 minutes, cool, and allow to settle. The clear solution should be employed and it must be prepared frequently.

METHOD

Place 10 g. of the sample in a covered porcelain dish or casserole and dissolve in 80 cc. of dilute H_2SO_4 (1 : 1). When solution is complete, add 5 cc. of HNO_3 (sp.gr. 1.42) and evaporate the solution until dense fumes of H_2SO_4 are given off. Cool the solution and add 200 cc. of distilled water. Boil until the sulphates are in solution, filter and wash with hot water. Treat with hydrogen sulphide until the solution is cold. Filter, wash with the hydrogen sulphide wash solution and dissolve the precipitate in the smallest possible amount of hot HNO_3 (1 : 1). Digest the HNO_3 solution at near boiling for one hour unless the absence of tin is assured. Filter if necessary and evaporate to a syrupy consistency. Transfer the HNO_3 solution of the copper to a 250-cc. flask and add 5 cc. of strong bromine water and boil until all bromine and oxides of nitrogen are expelled. Add a slight excess of NH_4OH, add then $HC_2H_3O_2$ in slight excess. Cool, add 10 cc. of KI solution and titrate at once with the $Na_2S_2O_3$ solution until the free iodine is nearly removed, then add 5 cc. of starch solution and continue the titration cautiously until the color due to free iodine has entirely vanished. The volume of thiosulphate employed multiplied by ten times its copper titre represents the percentage of copper in the sample.

NOTE

Copper, when present in small amounts, may also be determined by potassium cyanide titration. See "Standard Methods of Chemical Analysis of Alloys of Lead, Tin, Antimony and Copper."

Determination of Manganese

(a) Persulphate Method. (For samples containing under 1.5% of Manganese)

SOLUTIONS REQUIRED

Dilute Sulphuric Acid (1 : 1). Pour 500 cc. of H_2SO_4 (sp.gr. 1.84) into distilled water, cool, and dilute to 1000 cc.

Silver Nitrate. Dissolve 1.33 g. of $AgNO_3$ in 1000 cc. of distilled water.

Stock Sodium Arsenite Solution. To 15 g. of arsenious oxide (As_2O_3) in a 300-cc. Erlenmeyer flask add 45 g. of Na_2CO_3 and 150 cc. of distilled water. Heat the flask and contents on the steam bath until the As_2O_3 is dissolved. Cool the solution, filter and make up to 1000 cc. with distilled water.

Standard Sodium Arsenite Solution. Mix 200 cc. of the stock sodium arsenite solution with 2500 cc. of distilled water, and standardize by the method described below against a steel or iron of known manganese content. One cubic centimeter of this solution should be equivalent to approximately 0.00050 g. of manganese.

Ammonium Persulphate. Dissolve 6 g. of ammonium persulphate in 100 cc. of distilled water. (This solution should be made up as needed as it deteriorates rapidly.)

METHOD

In a 250-cc. Erlenmeyer flask, dissolve 0.5 g. of the sample in 25 cc. of H_2SO_4 (1 : 1) by warming and adding a drop or two of HNO_3 (sp.gr. 1.42) occasionally until solution is complete. Boil until oxides of nitrogen are expelled. Dilute to 100 cc. with boiling hot water, remove the flask from the flame, add 20 cc. of $AgNO_3$ solution, and then 30 cc. of the persulphate solution. Let the solution stand on the steam bath until it has developed a full permanganate color and no bubbles can be seen to come off when the flask is given a whirling motion. Cool to below 25° C., and titrate with the standard arsenite solution to the disappearance of the pink color.

NOTES

Large amounts (above 0.01 g. of manganese per 100 cc. of solution) of permanganic acid are unstable; the method can, however, be used with satisfaction for alloys containing high percentages of manganese by decreasing the size of the sample.

The ammonium persulphate must be tested for its strength. A good grade should contain about 95% $(NH_4)_2S_2O_8$; some lots contain no more than 25% of the salt.

(b) Bismuthate Method. (For Samples containing less than 1.50% Manganese.) (Optional)

SOLUTIONS REQUIRED

Dilute Sulphuric Acid (1 : 1). Pour 500 cc. of H_2SO_4 (sp.gr. 1.84) into distilled water, cool and dilute to 1000 cc.

Nitric Acid (1 : 3). Pour 250 cc. of HNO_3 (sp.gr. 1.42) into distilled water and dilute to 1000 cc.

Dilute Nitric Acid (3%). Pour 30 cc. of HNO_3 (sp.gr. 1.42) into distilled water and dilute to 1000 cc.

Standard Permanganate Solution. Dissolve 1 g. of $KMnO_4$ in 1000 cc. of distilled water. Allow it to stand for at least one week and then filter through purified asbestos. Standardize against 0.1 g. portions of pure sodium oxalate. One cubic centimeter of this solution should be equal to approximately 0.00035 g. of manganese.

Standard Ferrous Ammonium Sulphate Solution. Dissolve 12.4 g. of ferrous ammonium sulphate crystals in 950 cc. distilled water and add 50 cc. of H_2SO_4 (sp.gr. 1.84).

METHOD

In a 250-cc. Erlenmeyer flask dissolve 0.5 g. of the sample in 10 cc. of H_2SO_4 (1 : 1), adding a drop or two of HNO_3 (sp.gr. 1.42) occasionally.

When solution is complete, heat to expel all oxides of nitrogen and cool. Dilute with 50 cc. of HNO_3 (1 : 3) and add 0.5 g. sodium bismuthate. Heat for a few minutes until the purple color has disappeared with or without the precipitation of manganese dioxide. Add a little ferrous ammonium sulphate solution until the solution becomes clear and boil until the oxides of nitrogen are expelled. Cool, add an excess of sodium bismuthate and agitate for a few minutes. Add 50 cc. of 3% HNO_3 and filter through an alundum crucible or an asbestos pad. Wash with 50 cc. of 3% HNO_3. Add from a pipette or a burette 10 to 50 cc. (depending on the amount of permanganic acid) of ferrous ammonium sulphate solution and titrate with the $KMnO_4$ solution.

In exactly the same manner carry through a blank determination, using the same amounts of H_2SO_4, HNO_3, and sodium bismuthate as was done with the regular sample. Finally add the exact volume of ferrous ammonium sulphate solution employed and titrate with the $KMnO_4$ solution.

The difference between the volumes required in the two titrations represents the manganese in the sample, and the percentage is found by multiplying this volume by 200 times the manganese titre of the permanganate solution.

NOTES

Large amounts (above 0.01 g. of manganese per 100 cc. of solution) of permanganic acid are unstable; the method can be used with satisfaction for alloys containing high percentages of manganese by decreasing the size of the sample.

The filtrate from the bismuthate must be perfectly clear, as the least particle of bismuthate carried into the filtrate will vitiate the results.

The solution must be cold at time of filtration and titration.

Instead of employing the method of reducing permanganic acid by means of standardized ferrous ammonium sulphate solution and titrating the excess of the reagent, it is possible to reduce the permanganic acid by standard sodium-arsenite solution. See " Determination of Manganese by the Persulphate Method."

Determination of Carbon

SOLUTIONS REQUIRED

Copper-Potassium Chloride Solution.   Dissolve 300 g. of $CuCl_2.2KCl.2H_2O$ in water, dilute to 1000 cc., filter through ignited asbestos and preserve in a glass-stoppered bottle.

METHOD

Place 3 g. of the sample in a 400-cc. beaker, add 200 cc. of the $CuCl_2.2KCl$ solution and 10 cc. of HCl (sp.gr. 1.20). Stir the solution constantly with a glass rod for some minutes and then occasionally until solution is complete. The solution may be warmed slightly but never above 50° C., and continuous mechanical stirring hastens the solution. When solution is complete, add a little ignited asbestos, wash down the sides of the beaker with a little acidulated $CuCl_2.2KCl$ solution and allow to settle. Filter on ignited asbestos in a Gooch crucible or, preferably, on a platinum boat. Transfer the carbonaceous matter completely with dilute acidulated $CuCl_2.2KCl$ solution and scrub the sides of the beaker. Finally wash with distilled water until chlorides are absent and then dry at 100° C. When dry, burn in a combustion tube through which is passed a current of oxygen freed from all organic compounds. The post train should contain a tube containing pumice soaked in sulphuric acid saturated with chromic acid to oxidize and retain any sulphur dioxide and a tube containing $CuSO_4$ dehydrated at 200° C. to catch any traces of HCl, in addition to the ordinary driers, carbon dioxide absorbers and protectors. The weight of carbon dioxide times 0.27273 represents the carbon in the sample.

ANALYSIS OF LIGHT ALUMINUM ALLOYS

Determination of Silicon (Non=Graphitic, Graphitic and Total Silicon)

Proceed as described under " Determination of Silicon " in Aluminum.

NOTE

In case lead sulphate is present (as evidenced by a white crystalline precipitate quickly settling after stirring to the bottom of the casserole), the filtered precipitate must be washed free from the sulphate with an $NH_4C_2H_3O_2$ wash solution made up as follows: Take 20 cc. NH_4OH (sp.gr. 0.90), add 20 cc. of distilled water and make slightly acid with glacial acetic acid. The final washing must be made with hot water.

Determination of Titanium

(a) In the Absence of Nickel

METHOD

Proceed as described under " Determination of Titanium " in Aluminum.

NOTE

Vanadium, which interferes in the test, should not be encountered in this class of material. Its presence would be betrayed by an "off" reddish-brown cast in the peroxidized solution.

(b) In the Presence of Nickel

METHOD

Dissolve 1 g. of the sample as described under " Determination of Tin and Antimony " below. If the nitric acid solution of the sodium hydroxide insoluble is not clear, it must be filtered, the residue burned in platinum, fused with a little $K_2S_2O_7$, dissolved in a little 5% H_2SO_4 and added to the nitric acid filtrate. Dilute the nitric acid solution to 200 cc., treat with NH_4OH (sp.gr. 0.90) until ammoniacal, boil 3 minutes, filter and wash. Dissolve the precipitate in hot dilute H_2SO_4 (25%), keeping the volume below 80 cc., cool and proceed with the colorimetric test as described under " Determination of Titanium " in Aluminum.

NOTES

The above method provides for the color interference of copper and nickel when they are present in large amounts.

Vanadium (see Notes above) and other elements which would cause color interferences are not apt to occur in this class of material.

Determination of Iron

METHOD

Proceed as described under " Determination of Iron " in Aluminum.

NOTES

In case the alloy contains high percentages of copper, lead, tin or antimony it is preferable to treat the combined filtrate and washings from the silicon determination with H_2S and filter off and wash the sulphide. The solution should then be boiled free from hydrogen sulphide, treated with 10% $KMnO_4$ solution to a pink tint and then reduced as directed.

Reducible elements other than iron and titanium must be absent. Such elements are chromium, vanadium, molybdenum, tungsten and uranium, and they ordinarily will not be found in this class of material.

For the determination of iron in the presence of titanium, see Notes under "Determination of Iron" in Aluminum.

Determination of Antimony, Tin, Lead and Copper

Preliminary Separation

SOLUTIONS REQUIRED

Sodium Hydroxide Solution (25%). Dissolve 250 g. of NaOH in distilled water and dilute to 1000 cc. If a sediment forms on standing, decant the solution and filter through an asbestos pad. The NaOH must be entirely free from organic matter.

Nitric Acid (1 : 1). Pour 500 cc. of HNO_3 (sp.gr. 1.42) into distilled water and dilute to 1000 cc.

METHOD

Dissolve 5 g. of the sample in a covered porcelain dish of suitable size in 125 cc. of (25%) NaOH solution. When solution is complete, dilute with 100 cc. of distilled water, decant off the clear solution and wash the residue well with hot dilute NaOH solution (2%). Treat the filtrate and washings with H_2S. If no precipitate appears, zinc is absent. In case a precipitate appears, zinc must be determined in a fresh sample as described further. Unfold the wet paper containing the NaOH insoluble and wash the residue back into the original vessel. Replace the paper in the funnel and pour 20 cc. of hot HNO_3 (1 : 1) over the paper and allow it to filter into the original vessel. Boil the residue until action ceases and oxides of nitrogen are expelled. Add 50 cc. of hot distilled water and allow to stand and settle for about one hour, keeping the temperature just below the boiling point. Filter on an ashless paper, being careful to keep the solution hot throughout the process of filtration, and receiving the filtrate in a 200-cc. beaker of the tall type used in electrolysis. Wash with boiling hot water. Retain the filtrate and washings for subsequent use in the copper and lead determination and treat the residue as described under " Determination of Antimony."

NOTES

Antimony will be quantitatively recovered with the tin provided it does not exceed one-fifth its amount. In the rare case of high antimony evaporate the nitric acid solution of the NaOH insoluble to dryness, bake at 105° C., take up in hot 10% by volume nitric acid, and proceed with the filtration and washing.

The meta-stannic acid precipitate will not contain enough copper to make a recovery worth while in ordinary work. As iron is determined in a separate portion and does not interfere in the determinations of antimony and tin, it may also be disregarded.

Determination of Antimony

SOLUTIONS REQUIRED

Standard Permanganate Solution. The solution prepared as under " Determination of Iron " may be employed. It must be standardized against weighed 0.05 g. portions of pure antimony or suitable material of known antimony content carried through the regular procedure after solution in acid and treatment in the Kjeldahl flask.

METHOD

See " Preliminary Separation."

Transfer the filter containing meta-stannic acid and antimony oxide to a 500-cc. Kjeldahl flask, add 10 to 12 cc. H_2SO_4 (sp.gr. 1.84) and 3 to 5 g. Na_2SO_4. Heat until all organic matter is decomposed. Dilute, when cool, with 20 cc. of water. Add 0.5 g. Na_2SO_3 and boil until all SO_2 is expelled from the flask. Dilute to about 250 cc., add 20 cc. of HCl (sp.gr. 1.20), cool to 10° C. and titrate with the $KMnO_4$ solution to the first definite shade of pink. Reserve the solution for the " Determination of Tin."

Determination of Tin

SOLUTIONS REQUIRED

Standard Iodine Solution. Dissolve 10.7 g. of iodine in 50 cc. of water containing 20 g. of KI in solution, and dilute to 1000 cc. *when the iodine is completely in solution.* Standardize against pure tin by the method described below.

Starch Solution. Prepare as described under " Determination of Copper, Iodide Method."

METHOD

See " Determination of Antimony."

Transfer the solution used in " Determination of Antimony " to a 450-cc. Erlenmeyer flask, add an excess of powdered antimony and 50 cc. of HCl (sp.gr. 1.20). Attach a reflux condenser and boil for 15 minutes on a hot plate. Cool in a current of CO_2, add 5 cc. of starch solution, and without disconnecting the stream of CO_2, titrate with iodine solution to the blue end point.

Determination of Copper and Lead Simultaneously by the Electrolytic Method

APPARATUS REQUIRED

See " Determination of Copper " under " Analysis of Aluminum."

METHOD

See " Preliminary Separation."

Dilute the filtrate and washings from the " Preliminary Separation " to about 150 cc. with distilled water and electrolyze, using weighed sand-blasted cathode and anode. Cover with a pair of split watch glasses and use a current of from 1.25 to 1.5 amperes, at approximately 10 volts for each solution. After about one hour the lead will have been entirely deposited on the anode as PbO_2; without interrupting the current, add to the electrolyte 3 to 4 cc. of H_2SO_4 (sp.gr. 1.84), wash down the cover glasses, electrodes and sides of the beaker and continue the electrolysis for 15 minutes. If no darkening of the newly exposed anode surface can be detected and if a few drops of H_2S water added to 1 cc. of the electrolyte on a porcelain plate gives no coloration, the electrolysis is complete. In this case, remove the solution from the electrodes quickly without interrupting the current. Rinse the electrodes in quick succession with distilled water and then twice with alcohol. Reserve the electrolyte and water washings for the nickel and magnesium determinations. Dry the anode at 210° C. for thirty minutes. Weigh as PbO_2, using the factor for lead 0.8643 instead of the theoretical value. Shake off the excess alcohol from the cathode and ignite the remainder by bringing it to the flame of an alcohol lamp. Keep the cathode moving continually while the alcohol burns. Weigh as metallic copper.

NOTE

The electrolyte and water washings may be diluted to 500 cc. and one 250-cc. portion taken for the "Determination of Nickel" and the other for the "Determination of Magnesium" as directed further. If the alloy contains copper and no tin, antimony or lead, the electrolytic method given under "Determination of Copper" in Aluminum may be employed.

Determination of Lead as Sulphate. (Optional)

SOLUTIONS REQUIRED

" **Lead Acid.**"   Mix 300 cc. of H_2SO_4 (sp.gr. 1.84) and 1800 cc. of distilled water.   Dissolve 1 g. of lead acetate c.p. in 300 cc. of distilled water and add this to the hot solution, stirring meanwhile.   Let stand at least 24 hours and siphon through a thick asbestos filter.

Dilute Alcohol for Washing.   Mix equal parts of denatured alcohol and distilled water.

METHOD

See " Preliminary Separation."

To the combined filtrate and washings from the " Preliminary Separation " add 120 cc. of lead acid, and evaporate until copious fumes of H_2SO_4 are evolved.   Cool, add 105 cc. of distilled water to dissolve the salts and to make the concentration the same as in the lead acid, heating to boiling, and allow to cool and settle for 5 hours, or over night if convenient.   Filter on a weighed porcelain Gooch crucible and wash with lead acid.   Set the filtrate and washings aside for the " Determination of Copper by the Iodide Method." Continue the washing and wash out the lead acid with dilute alcohol.   Set the Gooch crucible inside a porcelain crucible, dry and ignite for 5 minutes at the full heat of a Tirrill burner.   Cool and weigh as $PbSO_4$, which contains 68.32% lead.

Determination of Copper by the Iodide Method. (Optional)

METHOD

See " Determination of Lead as Sulphate."

Dilute the reserved filtrate and washings from the " Determination of Lead as Sulphate " with an equal volume of water, treat with H_2S and proceed as directed in " Determination of Copper by the Iodide Method " under " Analysis of Aluminum."

Determination of Nickel by the Dimethylglyoxime Method

SOLUTIONS REQUIRED

Sulphuric Acid (1 : 1). Pour 500 cc. of H_2SO_4 (sp.gr. 1.84) into distilled water, cool, and dilute to 1000 cc.

Hydrogen Sulphide Wash Water. Add 10 cc. of H_2SO_4 (sp.gr. 1.84) to 1000 cc. of distilled water and saturate with H_2S.

Tartaric Acid Solution (20%). Dissolve 20 g. of tartaric acid in distilled water, dilute to 100 cc. and filter if necessary.

Dimethylglyoxime Solution (1%). Dissolve 10 g. of the reagent in 1000 cc. of 95% alcohol.

METHOD

Dissolve 1 g. of the sample in 25 cc. of H_2SO_4 (1 : 1) as directed in " Determination of Manganese by the Persulphate Method." After oxides of nitrogen have been expelled, add 14 cc. NH_4OH in order to bring down the acidity to approximately 5 cc. H_2SO_4 (sp.gr. 1.84) per 100 cc. of solution. Treat with hydrogen sulphide. Filter off the sulphides, wash with hydrogen sulphide wash water and boil the filtrate until H_2S is expelled. Add a few crystals of $(NH_4)_2S_2O_8$ and boil thoroughly to destroy sulphur and oxidize iron. Add 20 cc. of tartaric acid solution and make slightly ammoniacal. If no precipitate appears, add HCl (sp.gr. 1.20) to slight acidity. If a precipitate appears, dissolve in HCl, add 10 cc. of tartaric acid and again make ammoniacal, repeating the operation, if necessary, to get a clear solution. To the weakly acid solution add dimethylglyoxime in such an amount that the ratio of the reagent to nickel is at least 4 : 1. Heat the solution to boiling, and make slightly ammoniacal. Allow to digest while cooling for two hours. Collect on a weighed Gooch crucible and wash thoroughly with hot water. Dry for forty-five minutes at 110 to 120° C. and weigh. The nickel dimethylglyoxime contains 20.32% of nickel.

NOTES

In case copper and lead have been determined electrolytically, nickel may be determined in one 250 cc. portion of the electrolyte and washings (see Notes), starting with the $(NH_4)_2S_2O_8$ treatment to oxidize iron and then proceeding as directed in the method above.

Nickel may be precipitated by glyoxime, filtered, dissolved in nitric acid, made ammoniacal and titrated with cyanide solution according to Frevert's method.

Determination of Magnesium

SOLUTIONS REQUIRED

Dilute Hydrochloric Acid (1 : 1). Pour 500 cc. of HCl (sp.gr. 1.20) into distilled water and dilute to 1000 cc.

Sulphuric Acid Wash Water. Saturate 500 cc. of a 1% H_2SO_4 solution with H_2S.

Ammonium Sulphide Wash. Take 10 cc. of NH_4OH, dilute to 500 cc., add 10 g. NH_4Cl and saturate with H_2S.

Microcosmic Salt Solution. Prepare a clear saturated solution as required.

Ammoniacal Wash Solution. Dissolve 50 g. of NH_4NO_3 in distilled water, add 50 cc. NH_4OH (sp.gr. 0.90), dilute to 1000 cc. and filter if necessary.

METHOD

Dissolve 10 g. of the sample and wash the residue as directed under the " Preliminary Separation Determination of Antimony, Tin, Lead and Copper." Dissolve the residue in 10 cc. hot HCl (1 : 1), using a little HNO_3 if necessary. If the hydrogen sulphide group of metals are present, neutralize with NH_4OH, make weakly acid with HCl, dilute to 100 cc., heat and precipitate with hydrogen sulphide. Filter off the sulphides and wash with the H_2SO_4 wash water. To this filtrate or to the HCl solution, if no H_2S treatment was required, add 5 cc. HCl (sp.gr. 1.20), make slightly ammoniacal and precipitate with H_2S. Let the solution stand for about two hours at a temperature of approximately 40° C. (at the side of the steam bath). Filter and wash with the $(NH_4)_2S$ wash. Acidify the filtrate with HCl, boil off H_2S, add $(NH_4)_2S_2O_3$ and boil to destroy sulphur if necessary. Add 1 g. of tartaric acid and 30 cc. of microcosmic salt solution. Cool, and add NH_4OH (sp.gr. 0.90) drop by drop while stirring vigorously until a crystalline precipitate begins to form. Continue the very slow addition of NH_4OH with stirring until a precipitate no longer forms and then add one-tenth the volume of NH_4OH (sp.gr. 0.90) and let stand over night. Filter and wash with cold ammoniacal wash solution. Ignite slowly under oxidizing conditions in a tared porcelain or platinum crucible and finally heat over the blast lamp or its equivalent. Weigh as $Mg_2P_2O_7$. The weight multiplied by 0.2185 represents magnesium.

NOTE

In case copper and lead were determined electrolytically, one reserved portion of the electrolyte and washings (see Notes) may be used for the determination of magnesium, starting in with the addition of 5 cc. HCl (sp.gr. 1.20) and the precipitation of the $(NH_4)_2S$ group.

Determination of Manganese

(a) Persulphate or Bismuthate Method (for Samples containing under 1.50% Manganese)

Proceed as directed in " Determination of Manganese " under " Analysis of Aluminum."

(b) Nitric Acid and Potassium Chlorate Method (for Samples containing over 1.50% Manganese)

SOLUTIONS REQUIRED

Hydrochloric Acid (1 : 1). Mix 500 cc. of HCl (sp.gr. 1.20) and 500 cc. of distilled water.

Sulphurous Acid. Pass SO_2 from a cylinder into 500 cc. of cold distilled water until saturated.

Bromine Water. Place 20 to 30 cc. of liquid bromine in a 500-cc. bottle, fill with cold distilled water, and shake thoroughly. *Avoid any contact with the skin.*

Dilute Hydrochloric Acid (1 : 3). Pour 250 cc. of HCl (sp.gr. 1.20) into distilled water and dilute to 1000 cc.

Sodium-Ammonium Phosphate Solution. Prepare this solution as needed by dissolving 1 part of the salt in 6 parts of cold water and filtering.

Ammonium Nitrate Solution. Dissolve 100 g. of NH_4NO_3 in distilled water, make slightly ammoniacal, dilute to 1000 cc. and filter if necessary.

METHOD

In a 250-cc. Erlenmeyer flask, dissolve 1 g. of the sample in 30 cc. of HCl (1 : 1). When solution is complete, add 25 cc. HNO_3 (sp.gr. 1.42) and evaporate until the solution is almost syrupy. Add 50 cc. of HNO_3 (sp.gr. 1.42) and 5 g. $KClO_3$. Heat the solution to boiling either on the hot plate or on a tripod with a thin piece of sheet asbestos about 1 in. (25 mm.) in diameter, on the center of the wire gauze. Boil the solution 15 minutes, remove from the heat, add 50 cc. HNO_3 (sp.gr. 1.42) and 5 g. $KClO_3$ and boil 15 minutes longer or until yellowish fumes are no longer given off. Cool the solution rapidly in cold water and filter through asbestos. Wash two or three times with HNO_3 (sp.gr. 1.42) (free from oxides of nitrogen which dissolve the dioxide).

Transfer the dioxide with the asbestos filter to the beaker in which the precipitation was made. Pour from 10 to 40 cc. of strong sulphurous acid through the filtering apparatus into the beaker. As soon as the precipitate has dissolved, filter from the asbestos into a 150-cc. beaker, wash with hot water, and add 5 cc. HCl (sp.gr. 1.20). Heat to expulsion of SO_2, add bromine water until the solution is strongly colored with it, and boil off all excess bromine. Add NH_4OH in slight excess, boil for a few minutes, and filter into a 600-cc. beaker. Wash with hot water, remove and reserve the filtrate, and dissolve the precipitate in dilute HCl (1 : 3), allowing the solution to run back into the beaker in which the precipitation was made. Wash the filter with hot water. Boil the solution for 10 minutes to drive off any chlorine and reprecipitate by NH_4OH as before, filter into the reserved filtrate and repeat the solution, precipitation and filtration, allowing all the filtrates from the $Fe(OH)_3$ to run into the 600-cc. beaker. Acidulate this solution, which will be about 300 or 400 cc. in volume, with acetic acid, heat to boiling and treat with H_2S for 10 minutes. Filter, wash with a little dilute acetic acid saturated with hydrogen sulphide and boil off the hydrogen sulphide after adding 5 cc. HCl (sp.gr. 1.20). Add from 5 to 20 cc. of a clear filtered solution of microcosmic salt, heat to boiling, and add NH_4OH drop by drop with constant stirring. When the precipitate begins to form, stop the addition of NH_4OH and stir until the precipitate becomes crystalline. When this change occurs, add one more drop of ammonia; the additional precipitate formed will be curdy, but a few seconds stirring will change it to the silky crystalline condition. Continue the addition of NH_4OH in exactly the same manner until the precipitate is all down and further additions of NH_4OH fail to change the silky appearance. Add a dozen drops of NH_4OH in excess and cool the beaker in ice water. Filter the precipitate on an asbestos filter, wash with the cold NH_4NO_3 solution until the filtrate gives no reaction for HCl. Dry, ignite and weigh as $Mn_2P_2O_7$ which contains 38.69% manganese.

NOTES

The Ford method is recommended only where extreme accuracy is desired; otherwise use the persulphate or bismuthate methods.

If a cylinder of SO_2 is not available, hydrogen peroxide will serve equally well for the solution of the hydrated manganese dioxide.

Determination of Zinc

(a) Samples Containing up to 3% of Zinc

SOLUTIONS REQUIRED

Dilute Hydrochloric Acid (1 : 1). Pour 500 cc. of HCl (sp.gr. 1.20) into distilled water and dilute to 1000 cc.

Acid Wash Water. Pour 10 cc. of H_2SO_4 (sp.gr. 1.84) into 1000 cc. of distilled water and saturate with H_2S.

Formic Acid Mixture. Treat 400 cc. of formic acid with 60 cc. of NH_4OH (sp.gr. 0.90) and dilute to 2000 cc.

Formic Acid Wash Water. Pour 25 cc. of formic acid mixture into 1000 cc. of distilled water and saturate with H_2S.

Dilute Hydrochloric Acid (1 : 10). Pour 100 cc. of HCl (sp.gr. 1.20) into distilled water and dilute to 1000 cc.

Bromine Water. See " Determination of Manganese, Nitric Acid and Potassium Chlorate Method."

METHOD

Dissolve 1 g. of the sample in a covered 400-cc. beaker in 25 cc. of dilute HCl (1 : 1), with the addition of 1 cc. of HNO_3 (sp.gr. 1.42) toward the end of the reaction. Boil to expel oxides of nitrogen and dilute to 200 cc. Precipitate the H_2S group, filter and wash with acid wash water. Boil thoroughly to expel H_2S, cool, and add 5 g. of citric acid crystals. Neutralize with NH_4OH, using methyl orange as an indicator, and then add 25 cc. of the formic acid mixture. Dilute to 300 cc., heat nearly to boiling and pass in H_2S until the solution is cold. Filter and wash with the formic acid wash water. Dissolve the zinc sulphide off the filter with warm dilute HCl (1 : 10) and wash the filter with hot water. Boil the solution to expel H_2S. Cool, add 1 g. of citric acid crystals, neutralize with NH_4OH, using methyl orange as an indicator, and then add 20 cc. of the formic acid mixture. Dilute to 200 cc. and proceed as before through the filtration on an ashless paper and washing of the sulphide. Dissolve the precipitate with hot dilute HCl, and transfer the solution to a weighed platinum or porcelain dish or crucible. Add a few drops of H_2SO_4 (sp.gr. 1.84) and evaporate the solution until copious fumes escape. If the solution is not clear and colorless, cool, add a few cubic centimeters of HNO_3 (sp.gr. 1.42) and again evaporate the solution until fumes of H_2SO_4 come off freely. Repeat the treatment with HNO_3 if necessary, until the organic matter is destroyed, and the solution is colorless. Remove the excess of H_2SO_4 by heating the dish cautiously, and finally heat at a temperature just below dull redness. Weigh as $ZnSO_4$, which contains 40.49% of zinc.

NOTE

The use of sodium hydroxide solution of the turnings is not recommended for the determination of zinc on account of uncertainty as to the completeness of the solution of the zinc in all cases.

(b) Samples Containing over 3% of Zinc

SOLUTIONS REQUIRED

Ferrous Sulphate Solution. Dissolve 3 g. of $FeSO_4.7H_2O$ in distilled water, add 10 cc. of HCl (sp.gr. 1.20) and dilute to 1000 cc.

Ferrocyanide Solution. Dissolve 44 g. of K_4FeCN_6 and 0.3 g. of K_3FeCN_6 in distilled water, dilute to 1000 cc. and age six weeks before standardization as follows: Dissolve 6 g. of zinc of known content in 40 cc. of HCl (sp.gr. 1.20) in a 2-liter flask. Cool and make up to the mark. Take 100 cc. portions, add 20 cc. of HCl (1 : 1) and add 13 cc. of NH_4OH (sp.gr. 0.90) and proceed with the titration as directed below.

METHOD

Proceed as in the previous method until the first zinc sulphide precipitate has been obtained. Return the paper and precipitate to the original beaker and add 20 cc. of HCl (1 : 1). When the sulphide has dissolved, filter off the paper together with some sulphur and possibly a little nickel sulphide. Boil the solution containing the zinc to expel H_2S, cool, and wash down. Add 13 cc. of NH_4OH (sp.gr. 0.90) and if the solution is not alkaline, add NH_4OH carefully until it is. Make the solution barely acid again with HCl (1 : 1) and add 3 cc. of HCl (sp.gr. 1.20) in excess. Add 1 cc. of $FeSO_4$ solution, dilute nearly to 200 cc., heat almost to boiling and titrate with the K_4FeCN_6 solution. The end point is a sharp change in the color of the solution from a turquoise blue to a " pea green " and with several more drops to a " creamy yellow."

NOTE

The end point occurs a little sooner than the one with uranium nitrate, and is easier to use, as the change is seen directly in the solution.

Determination of Carbon

Determine carbon as described under " Analysis of Aluminum."

Determination of Sodium

SOLUTIONS REQUIRED

Dilute Nitric Acid (1 : 2). Pour 250 cc. of HNO_3 (sp.gr. 1.42) into distilled water and dilute to 750 cc.

Saturated Ammonium Carbonate Solution. Small quantities made up as required.

METHOD

Dissolve 5 g. of the sample in a porcelain dish in 100 cc. of dilute HNO_3 (1 : 2) by continued digestion at 50 to 60° C. When solution is complete, evaporate the solution to dryness and heat on a sand bath for several hours to complete decomposition of aluminum nitrate, but without melting any sodium nitrate formed. Cool the residue, take it up in boiling distilled water, filter and wash thoroughly. Treat the water extract with saturated $(NH_4)_2CO_3$ solution, heat to boiling and filter if a precipitate forms. Evaporate the clear filtrate in a weighed platinum dish, treat the residue with sufficient H_2SO_4 to convert the nitrate to sulphate, continue the evaporation and finally heat at 300 to 400° C. to complete expulsion of H_2SO_4. Weigh as Na_2SO_4. A blank should be carried through all operations and the proper correction applied.

Determination of Nitrogen

SOLUTIONS REQUIRED

Sodium Hydroxide Solution (10%). Dissolve 100 g. of NaOH in distilled water, dilute to 1000 cc. and filter through asbestos if the solution develops a sediment upon standing.

Approximate N/10 Sulphuric Acid Solution. Pour 2.8 cc. of H_2SO_4 (sp.gr. 1.84) into 1000 cc. of distilled water and standardize by any standard method.

Approximate N/10 Sodium Hydroxide Solution. Dissolve 4.5 g. of NaOH in distilled water and dilute to 1000 cc. This solution should be standardized against the standard acid solution.

METHOD

Place 3 to 4 g. of the sample in a Kjeldahl flask fitted with a two-hole stopper carrying a separatory funnel and a trap connected with a condenser as in a Kjeldahl determination of nitrogen. Add 400 cc. of the NaOH solution through the separatory funnel, and allow the generated gas to bubble through 50 cc. of N/10 sulphuric acid solution. When the action has ceased, boil the alkaline solution to expel all ammonia Finally titrate the acid with N/10 sodium hydroxide in the usual manner and calculate nitrogen.

Determination of Aluminum and Aluminum Oxide

SOLUTIONS REQUIRED

Sodium Hydroxide Solution (10%). Dissolve 100 g. of NaOH in distilled water and dilute to 1000 cc. If a sediment forms on standing, decant the solution and filter through an asbestos pad.

Sodium Carbonate Solution. Dissolve 36 g. of Na_2CO_3 in distilled water, dilute to 1000 cc., and filter if necessary.

Barium Chloride Solution. Dissolve 90 g. of $BaCl_2.2H_2O$ in distilled water, dilute to 1000 cc., and filter if necessary.

Dilute Hydrochloric Acid. Dilute 500 cc. of HCl (sp.gr. 1.20) with 500 cc. of water.

Methyl Red Indicator. Dissolve 0.02 g. of the acid in 100 cc. of distilled water.

Ammonium Chloride Wash Solution. Dissolve 50 g. of NH_4Cl in distilled water, make sure the solution is just alkaline to methyl red, dilute to 1000 cc., and filter if necessary.

Dilute Nitric Acid (1 : 1). Dilute 500 cc. of HNO_3 (sp.gr. 1.42) with 500 cc. of distilled water.

Acid Wash Water. Add 5 cc. of H_2SO_4 (sp.gr. 1.84) to 500 cc. of water and saturate with H_2S.

PRELIMINARY TREATMENT

Place 2 g. of the sample in a suitable porcelain dish, add 60 cc. of the NaOH solution (10%), cover with a glass, and cool in water if the reaction proceeds too violently. When violent action ceases, wash the cover-glass and sides of the vessel, replace the glass and warm on a sand-bath or steam-box until reaction ceases. These operations should be carried on expeditiously. Filter and wash the residue with hot NaOH solution (10%). Reserve the residue and treat the filtrate and washings as below.

(a) Determination of Aluminum

Cool the filtrate and washings to room temperature, dilute to exactly 500 cc. and mix thoroughly. Transfer pipetted 50 cc. portions to 600-cc. beakers, add 10 cc. of HCl (sp.gr. 1.20), place on water bath and evaporate to dryness. When dry, continue the heating for one hour more. Take up the residue in cold distilled water, transfer to a flask and add a mixture of 50 cc. of the Na_2CO_3 solution and 50 cc. of the $BaCl_2$ solution. Shake thoroughly and allow to settle. Filter, wash with cold water, and then transfer the precipitate to the original flask by piercing the paper and washing down with boiling water, finally with dilute HCl, adding enough to dissolve the precipitate and avoiding mechanical loss. Evaporate the solution to one third volume, add a few drops of methyl red and then NH_4OH (sp.gr. 0.90) until the indicator just turns yellow. Boil for three minutes, filter and wash with warm 5% NH_4Cl solution. Bring the precipitate back into the beaker as before, dissolving all $Al(OH)_3$ on the paper and evaporate the solution to dryness. Drench with a little HCl (sp.gr. 1.20), add hot water and warm until salts are in solution. Filter in case a residue is present, reprecipitate $Al(OH)_3$

and wash as above. Place the wet paper and contents in a tared crucible (with cover and preferably of platinum), dry, ignite carefully in an oxidizing atmosphere and finally cover and blast strongly. Weigh as Al_2O_3 and calculate aluminum.

NOTES

This method is a modification of the method proposed by J. G. Rhodin, Faraday Society Trans., 14 (1918–19), pp. 135–7, and presupposes complete solubility of aluminum and insolubility of aluminum oxide in a 10% solution of NaOH.

It is important that the "50 cc." pipette deliver exactly one-tenth of the "500 cc." volume.

Two precipitations with NH_4OH are necessary to eliminate barium and the intervening evaporation to dryness is desirable in case silica is present.

(b) Determination of Aluminum Oxide

See "Preliminary Separation."

Transfer the residue insoluble in NaOH solution (10%) to a small flask and treat the paper with hot dilute HNO_3 (1 : 1). When solution of the residue is complete, dilute to 100 cc., neutralize with NaOH solution (10%), add 3 cc. HCl (sp.gr. 1.20) and treat with hydrogen sulphide. Filter, wash the sulphides with acid wash water and boil the filtrate and washings until H_2S is expelled, using a few crystals of $K_2S_2O_8$ if sulphur separates. Pour the hot solution slowly and with stirring into 50 cc. of boiling hot NaOH solution (10%). Filter and wash with a little hot NaOH solution (10%).

In case the precipitate is large, dissolve it and reprecipitate. Acidify the NaOH filtrate or filtrates with HCl (sp.gr. 1.20) and precipitate $Al(OH)_3$ as described in (a) above. A second precipitation should be carried out in case the precipitate is large, and always in accurate work. Ignite, weigh as Al_2O_3.

ANALYSIS OF MONEL METAL

Determination of Carbon in Monel Metal

The usual carbon combustion apparatus is used with a platinum combustion tube. In addition to the usual absorption train there is placed next to the platinum combustion tube a 5 inch "U"-tube filled with glass beads and moistened with chromic acid solution, with a loose plug of glasswool in the forward end. This serves to oxidize any sulphurous anhydride and to absorb the sulphuric anhydride formed from the sulphur in Monel Metal drillings during combustion. This tube is washed out daily and fress glasswood inserted. The forward end of the platinum combustion tube contains a plug of loosely wound platinum gauze, $5\frac{1}{2}$ inches long, completely filling the bore of the tube and a similar roll 2 inches long, fitted with a loop is pushed in after the boat.

Fill the alundum boat with ignited alumina and make a "V"-shaped depression in the middle with a spatula, pressing the material against the sides of the boat. Ignite the boat and its contents strongly to expel any carbon dioxide present and burn off any carbonaceous matter that the alumina may contain. Weigh out three grams of Monel Metal drillings which have been broken down so as to pass through a 10-mesh sieve and transfer it to the boat.

The absorption is made in potassium hydroxide 1.27 sp. gr. placed into a Geissler potash bulb with calcium chloride tube attached. Burn the carbon by starting a slow current of oxygen and lighting one of the burners at the forward end of the tube, and as soon as the tube is red hot increase the heat slowly by lighting the other burners. The valve controlling the supply of oxygen must be regulated so as to keep a slow current of gas passing through the absorption apparatus at all times, and not to exceed three bubbles in a second. Monel Metal containing manganese, or high in silicon, we burn at a temperature between 1125° C. and 1200° C., for twenty minutes.

Method of Determining Copper and Nickel in Monel Metal

Dissolve one gram Monel Metal drillings in 15 cc. of 1 to 1 nitric acid in a 200 cc covered beaker. Add 30 cc. of 1 to 1 sulphuric acid, and evaporate until fumes of sulphuric acid are given off. Dilute with 125 cc. water, heat on hot plate until sulphates are dissolved. Add 1½ cc. of nitric acid, cool and plate out copper over night with .3 amp. After copper is all plated out pour the solution and water used in washing off cathode, into a 500 cc. beaker. The cathode is dipped in alcohol and heated over an alcohol lamp and when cool, weighed. The increased weight is equal to copper. The solution in the beaker is covered, made alkaline with ammonia, and 75 cc. added in excess. To 30 cc. of cold water add about 2 grams of sodium peroxide. Add this solution to the alkaline nickel solution and let stand on the steam bath for one half hour. Repeat the addition of sodium peroxide solution, then cool the alkaline nickel solution, and when cold plate nickel over night with .5 amp. Wash the cathode with water and alcohol. Heat over an alcohol lamp and when cool weigh as nickel and cobalt. The nickel and cobalt contain a small amount of manganese, so dissolve the nickel and cobalt in nitric acid and determine the manganese by the bismuthate method. This is deducted, the result being nickel and cobalt.

As Monel Metal contains .28 per cent to .32 per cent cobalt, we deduct .30 per cent cobalt, the difference being nickel.

NOTE. In very accurate determinations the solution, after plating out the nickel and cobalt, is evaporated down, made acid with sulphuric acid, make alkaline with ammonia, sodium peroxide added and replated, same as above.

Determination of Iron in Monel Metal

Dissolve one gram Monel Metal drillings in 25 cc. 1 to 1 nitric acid, in a 300 cc. Griffin lip beaker, add 50 cc. cold water, make strongly alkaline with ammonia. Boil a few minutes, filter, wash precipitate with hot water two or three times. The precipitate is redissolved in 1 to 3 hot hydrochloric acid to which a few drops of sulphurous acid is added. After the precipitate is dissolved, boil the solution a few minutes, add a few drops of nitric acid, let solution cool for 5 or 10 minutes, then make alkaline with ammonia, filter and wash with hot water. Repeat redissolving and ammonia precipitation. After final reprecipitation, dissolve the iron hydrate in 30 cc. hot, 1 to 3 hydrochloric acid into a 24 oz. flask, cool and add 300 cc. cold distilled water and titrate with a standard cuprous chloride solution, using potassium sulfocyanate as inside indicator. The cuprous chloride solution is standardized each time before using, with standard ferric chloride.

The ferric chloride is made by dissolving 5 grams of standard iron wire in 100 cc. of 1 to 1 hydrochloric acid, then 5 grams of potassium chlorate is added to oxidize the iron. Boil until all the free chlorine is driven off, then cool and make the solution up to two liters.

NOTE. If the ferric hydrate is dissolved in dilute sulphuric acid and the iron reduced with zinc, the iron titrated with potassium permanganate is just as accurate as above method, providing 5 grams of the drillings are taken.

Determination of Manganese in Monel Metal, Bismuthate Method

Dissolve one gram of drillings in 10 cc. of strong nitric acid in a No. 2 Tall 250 cc. beaker. Add 30 cc. warm water and add about $\frac{1}{2}$ gram of sodium bismuthate, heat a few minutes, then add enough sulphurous acid to clear the solution and boil until nitrous oxide is all driven off. Cool to about 15° C., add an excess of sodium bismuthate and let stand a few minutes. Filter through asbestos felt on a Gooch crucible into a 500 cc. Erlenmeyer suction flask; apply suction gently, wash with 3% nitric acid. Run into the flask a measured amount of ferrous ammonium sulphate solution and titrate the excess at once with standard permanganate of potash, deducting $\frac{1}{2}$ cc. of permanganate, which is used in neutralizing the color of copper and nickel solution. The number of cc. of permanganate used less $\frac{1}{2}$ cc. is subtracted from the original amount of ferrous ammonium sulphate taken and the remainder multiplied by .001 gives the per cent of manganese.

Reagents

Ferrous Ammonium Sulphate.—35.6 grams per liter. Add about 1 cc. sulphuric acid. 1 cc. equals .001 gr. Mn.

Permanganate of Potash.—2.90 grams per liter. 1 cc. equals 1 cc. ferrous ammonium sulphate.

The ferrous ammonium sulphate solution changes rapidly, therefore, it is standardized against permanganate every day. Run 25 cc. of ferrous ammonium sulphate solution into a flask which contains a sample that has feen titrated, then titrate to a faint pink with permanganate. This gives the value in permanganate of the ferrous ammonium sulphate.

Method of Determining Sulphur in Monel Metal

Weigh duplicate 10-gram samples of drillings. Place each in an 800-cc. casserole and treat as follows:

Add 3 grams of potassium chlorate, cover and then add 200 cc. strong nitric acid. Place on steam bath until action has ceased, evaporate to dryness on the hot plate. Cool and then add 50 cc. hydrochloric acid and again evaporate to dryness, repeat this operation. Take up with 150 cc. water. Add 8 cc. hydrochloric acid. Heat to boiling. Filter and wash, taking care that the filtrate and washings do not exceed 300 cc. in volume. Heat the filtrate to boiling. Add 25 cc. of 20 per cent barium chloride solution. Allow it to stand in a warm place over night. Filter through a small double ashless paper and wash with very dilute hydrochloric acid, and finally with hot water. Ignite in a small platinum crucible and then heat to bright redness for twenty minutes. Cool and weigh the barium sulphate.

$$\frac{BaSO_4 \times .1373}{10 \text{ gm.}} \times 100 \text{ equals per cent sulphur.}$$

NOTE. Run a blank analysis, that is, take an 800-cc. casserole, adding to it all the reagents, and subject the contents to the same operations as the samples of drillings. Deduct any barium sulphate obtained from the result of the actual assay. If this blank amounts to .0040 gram, the reagents are unfit for the above analysis and the determinations should be repeated with other reagents.

FIXED OILS, FATS AND WAXES

It will be remembered that the *fixed oils* are those which leave a permanent stain on paper, whereas the essential or volatile oils evaporate. The fixed oils, if saponifiable, are glycerides of the higher fatty acids, oleic, $C_{17}H_{33}COOH$, stearic, $C_{17}H_{35}COOH$, palmitic, $C_{15}H_{31}COOH$; and if unsaponifiable, hydrocarbons, usually of the paraffin (C_nH_{2n+2}) and olefin (C_nH_{2n}) series. The *fats* differ from the oils in having a higher melting-point, caused by a larger percentage of stearic and palmitic acid. The *waxes* differ from the oils or fats in that the former are esters of monatomic alcohols. The oils are further divided according to their drying power on exposure to the air, into drying, semi-drying and non-drying oils.

The drying oils contain a large proportion of glycerides of the unsaturated acids, particularly linoleic and linolenic, whereas the semi-drying contain a smaller percentage, and the non-drying little or none of these esters.

Examination of an Unknown Oil

There being no specific tests for the various oils, as for their identification, the analyst should, in attacking an unknown oil, ascertain all possible facts about it, as the source, the use to which it is put, and the cost.

Certain physical properties too, may aid in the examination. The *color* is of little assistance, as oils may be colored by the use of oleates or butyrates of iron or copper. *Fluorescence* or "bloom" is valuable as indicating the presence of mineral oil; this can be shown by placing a few drops of the oil on a sheet of ebonite and observing the bluish color. The *odor* and *taste* are particularly valuable. Marine animal oils are detected, especially when warm, by their strong "fishy" odor, while neatsfoot, tallow, lard, rosin and linseed oils each have a well-marked and easily distinguishable smell. Whale oil is said to have a "nutty," and rape oil has a harsh, unpleasant "turnipy" taste. The *turbidity*, showing the presence of water, or of oils which imperfectly mix—as castor and mineral oils—and the *sediment*, either stearin or dirt, are also to be noted; these should be filtered out through paper before the oil is analyzed.

The **elaidin** test (page 1135) may be applied next, to allow time for the cake to form; it will be followed by the **Maumené** test (page 1135) both being done in duplicate. In making the elaidin test it is advisable to carry on an experiment under the same conditions with a known sample of lard oil. These two tests will show whether the sample under examination is a drying or non-drying oil and when the ingredients of the mixture are determined, the results of the Maumené test can be used for calculating their relative amounts. The **iodine** test can be employed to check this result.

Chapter contributed by Augustus H. Gill.

The **saponification** test, unless mineral or rosin oil be suspected, need rarely be resorted to; the reason being that it would show practically nothing regarding the nature of the oil. Except in the case of castor (Sapn. No. 181), rape (174), sperm (135) and cocoanut (260), this characteristic is about 193.

Finally, where the importance of the case will warrant, the analyst is advised to prepare a mixture of oils using the proper proportions indicated by the various tests, and subject it to the more rapid tests as the specific gravity, viscosity, Maumené and iodine number. In making out the report of analysis it should be borne in mind that, excepting in the case of the special test, the results of *one* test cannot be relied upon to determine the nature of an oil, but the evidence of all the tests here given should be carefully compared and weighed before rendering a final verdict: in consideration of the fact of the wide variation of the characteristics of the oils, it is futile to report the quantities of oil found in a mixture more closely than 1%.

PETROLEUM PRODUCTS

(a) Burning Oils

The tests or determinations to be made are, in the order of their importance, flash, fire, specific gravity, distillation, sulphur, free acid, sulphuric acid, cloud test, mineral salts and water. In some cases the color is determined as it is of commercial importance.

Flash Test or Point. By flash point we understand the lowest temperature to which an oil must be heated, to give off vapors which when mixed with air produce an explosive mixture. The results of this test will vary according to the quantity of air over the surface of the oil, and whether this be moving or still; also according to the distance of the testing flame from the surface of the oil. Furthermore, the size of this testing flame, the length of its time of action, its form and dimensions, and lastly, the manner of heating the oil, will all influence the result.[1]

Any cause producing the rapid evolution of a large amount of petroleum vapor tends to lower the flash point. Barometric changes are, for practical work, negligible, each 5 mm. causing a variation of but 0.1° C.

Determination by the " New York State Board of Health Tester." The apparatus, Fig. 86, consists of a copper oil cup, *D*, holding about 10 oz., the quantity usually contained in lamps, heated in a water bath by a small Bunsen flame. The cup is provided with a glass cover, *C*, carrying a thermometer, *B*, and a hole for the insertion of the testing flame—a small gas flame one-quarter of an inch in length.

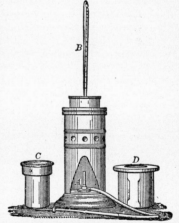

FIG. 86.—N. Y. Tester.

Manipulation. After describing the apparatus minutely, the regulations of

---

[1] Engler and Haase, Z. Anal. Chem., **20**, 3, 1881.

the New York State Board of Health say,[1] " (2) The test shall be applied according to the following directions:

" Remove the oil cup and fill the water bath with cold water up to the mark on the inside. Replace the oil cup and pour in enough oil to fill it to within one-eighth of an inch of the flange joining the cup and the vapor-chamber above. Care must be taken that the oil does not flow over the flange. Remove all air-bubbles with a piece of dry paper. Place the glass cover on the oil cup, and so adjust the thermometer that its bulb shall be just covered by the oil.

" If an alcohol lamp be employed for heating the water bath, the wick should be carefully trimmed and adjusted to a small flame. A small Bunsen burner may be used in place of the lamp. The rate of heating should be about two degrees per minute, and in no case exceed three degrees.

" As a flash torch, a small gas jet one-quarter of an inch in length should be employed. When gas is not at hand employ a piece of waxed linen twine. The flame in this case, however, should be small.

" When the temperature of the oil has reached 85° F. the testings should commence. To this end insert the torch into the opening in the cover, passing it in at such an angle as to well clear the cover, and to a distance about half-way between the oil and the cover. The motion should be steady and uniform, rapid and without any pause. This should be repeated at every two degrees' rise of the thermometer until the temperature has reached 95°, when the lamp should be removed and the testings should be made for each degree of temperature until 100° is reached. After this the lamp may be replaced if necessary and the testings continued for each two degrees.

" The appearance of a slight bluish flame which passes over the entire surface shows that the flashing-point has been reached.

" In every case note the temperature of the oil before introducing the torch. The flame of the torch must not come in contact with the oil.

" The water bath should be filled with cold water for each separate test, and the oil from a previous test carefully wiped from the oil cup."

For the determination with the open tester (Tagliabue's small) reference may be had to the author's " Short Handbook of Oil Analysis"; for the test with the closed tester, Abel's or Pensky-Martens, Holde-Mueller, " Examination of Hydrocarbon Oils "; or for the " Tag Tester " the " Tag Manual " (published by C. J. Tagliabue Co., N. Y.) or Proc. Am. Soc. Testing Mats. **18**.

Fire Test. The fire test of an oil is the lowest temperature at which it will give off vapors which when ignited will burn *continuously*. It is made by continuing to heat the oil (the cover being removed in the case of a closed tester without slipping out the thermometer) at the same rate after the flash test is made and noting the point as indicated above. The flame is extinguished by a piece of asbestos board and the heating discontinued. In the case of many illuminating oils this point is from 10° to 20° F. higher than the flash-point.

In the case of " Mineral Sperm " (300° F. fire test oil) these tests should be made with the Cleveland open cup. The heating should be at the rate of 10° F. per minute, and the testing flame first applied at 230° F. and then every seven degrees until the flashing-point is reached.

The most satisfactory way of making these tests is to place the watch upon the desk and read the thermometer at the expiration of every minute, noting down each reading in the proper column in the laboratory note-book.

[1] Report of the New York State Board of Health, 1882, p. 495.

Specific Gravity: (a) *By the Hydrometer.*   A hydrometer jar is four-fifths filled with the oil, a verified Baumé hydrometer introduced into it, and the depth read off to which the instrument sinks into the oil.   This may be effected by placing a strip of white paper back of the jar and noting the point at which the lower meniscus of the oil touches the scale.   The temperature of the oil is taken at the same time, and in case it be not 60° F. (15.5° C.), subtract 1° Baumé from the hydrometer reading, for every 10° F. it is higher than 60°, and add 1° Baumé for every 10° F. it is lower than 60° F.   In practice this can be done by Tagliabue's " Manual for Inspectors of Petroleum," which gives the readings at 60° F. for any gravity from 10 to 100° Baumé, between 20° and 109° F.   The specific gravity may be found by the formula [1] $\dfrac{141.5}{131.5+\text{Bé}}$, Bé representing the reading Baumé at 15.5° C.

   (b) *By the Westphal Balance.*   This is a specially constructed instrument, Fig. 87, with a glass plummet carrying a thermometer counterbalanced by a weight.

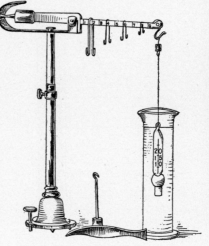

Upon immersing the plummet in a liquid the positions of the weights, which must be added to restore the equilibrium, represent the specific gravity directly.   The largest weight represents the first decimal place, the next the second, and so on.   The instrument is placed upon a level table, and by means of the leveling screw is brought into adjustment—i.e., so that the point upon the beam is exactly opposite the point upon the fixed part.

   The plummet is now placed in the vial or balance jar containing the oil, cooled to 15.5° C., hung upon the balance, being careful completely to immerse it in the oil, weights added to restore the equilibrium, and the specific gravity read off as above described.

   Care should be taken that the plummet does not touch the sides of the jar or vial.

Fig. 87.—Wesphal Balance.

For solid fats and some oils the specific gravity is taken at 100° C., using a special plummet.

Distillation Test:

Method 100.22.[2]—Kerosene

Apparatus

   1. Flask.   The standard 100-cc. Engler flask is shown in Figure 87a, the dimensions and allowable tolerance being as follows:

---

   [1] This formula is that of the American Petroleum Institute and the one used by the oil trade.   The older formula $\dfrac{140}{130+\text{Bé}}$ was used by the Bureau of Standards.

   [2] Bureau of Mines Technical Paper.

DIMENSIONS OF ENGLER FLASK

Description	Centimeters	Inches	Tolerances (cm.)
Diameter of bulb, outside.................	6.5	2.56	0.2
Diameter of neck, inside..................	1.6	.63	.1
Length of neck...........................	15.0	5.91	.4
Length of vapor tube.....................	10.0	3.94	.3
Diameter of vapor tube, outside...........	.6	.24	.05
Diameter of vapor tube, inside............	.4	.16	.05
Thickness of vapor tube wall..............	.1	.04	.05

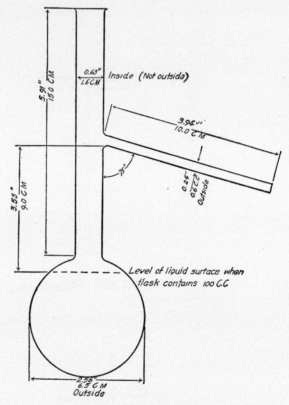

FIG. 87*a*.   Standard 100-cc. Engler flask for use in making distillation tests of gasoline and kerosene

The position of the vapor tube shall be 9 cm. (3.55 inches) ±3 mm. above the surface of the liquid when the flask contains its charge of 100 cc. The tube is approximately in the middle of the neck and set at an angle of 75° (tolerance ±3°) with the vertical.

2. Condenser.   The condenser (Fig. 87b) consists of a $\frac{9}{16}$-inch OD No. 20 Stubbs gage seamless brass tube 22 inches long.   It is set at an angle of 75° from the perpendicular and is surrounded with a cooling bath 15 inches long, approximately 4 inches wide by 6 inches high.   The lower end of the condenser tube is cut off at an acute angle, and curved downward for a length of 3 inches and slightly backward so as to insure contact with the wall of the graduate at a point 1 to $1\frac{1}{4}$ inches below the top of the graduate when it is in position to receive the distillate.

3. Shield.   The shield (Fig. 87b) is made of approximately 22-gage sheet metal and is 19 inches high, 11 inches long, and 8 inches wide, with a door on one narrow side, with two openings, 1 inch in diameter, equally spaced, in each of the two narrow sides, and with a slot cut in one side for the vapor tube.   The centers of these four openings are $8\frac{1}{2}$ inches below the top of the shield.   There are also three $\frac{1}{2}$-inch holes in each of the four sides, with their centers 1 inch above the base of the shield.

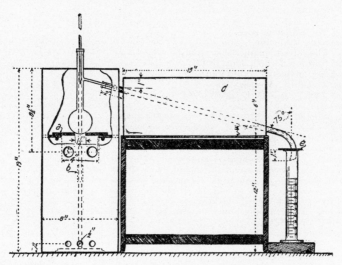

Fig. 87b.   Distillation outfit (A. S. T. M.) arranged for use of gas burner: *a*, 6 by 6 by $\frac{1}{4}$ inch asbestos board; *b*, Bunsen burner; *c*, $\frac{9}{16}$-inch OD No. 20 Stubbs gage brass tube; *d*, ice-water bath; *e*, blotting paper.

4. Ring Support and Hard Asbestos Boards.   The ring support is of the ordinary laboratory type, 4 inches or larger in diameter, and is supported on a stand inside the shield.   There are two hard asbestos boards, one 6 by 6 by $\frac{1}{4}$ inch, with a hole $1\frac{1}{2}$ inches in diameter in its center, the sides of which shall be perpendicular to the surface; the other, an asbestos board to fit tightly inside the shield, with an opening 4 inches in diameter concentric with the ring support.   These are arranged as follows: The second asbestos board is placed on the ring and the first or smaller asbestos board on top, so that it may be moved in accordance with the directions for placing the distilling flask.   Direct heat is applied to the flask only through the $1\frac{1}{4}$-inch opening in the first asbestos board.

5. Gas Burner or Electric Heater. (*a*) *Gas Burner.* The burner is so constructed that sufficient heat can be obtained to distil the product at the uniform rate specified below. The flame should never be so large that it spreads over a circle of diameter greater than $3\frac{1}{2}$ inches on the under surface of the asbestos board. A sensitive regulating valve is a necessary adjunct, as it gives complete control of heating.

(*b*) *Electric Heater.* The electric heater, which may be used in place of the gas flame, shall be capable of bringing over the first drop within the time specified below when started cold, and of continuing the distillation at the uniform rate. The electric heater shall be fitted with an asbestos board, top $\frac{1}{8}$ to $\frac{1}{4}$ inch thick, having a hole $1\frac{1}{4}$ inches in diameter in the center. When an electric heater is employed, the portion of the shield above the asbestos board shall be the same as with the gas burner, but the part below may be omitted.

6. Thermometer. A. S. T. M. high-distillation thermometer shall conform to the following specifications:

Type: Etched stem, glass.
Total length: 381 mm.
Stem: Plain front, enamel back, suitable thermometer tubing; diameter, 6 to 7 mm.
Bulb: Corning normal, Jena 16 III, or equally suitable thermometric glass; length, 10 to 15 mm.; diameter, 5 to 6 mm.
Actuating liquid: Mercury.
Range: 30° F. to 760° F., or 0° C. to 400° C.
Immersion: Total.
Distance to 30° F. or 0° C. mark, from bottom of bulb: 250 to 300 mm.
Distance to 760° F. or 400° C. mark, from top of stem: 30 to 45 mm.
Filled: Nitrogen gas.
Top finish: Glass ring.
Graduation: All lines, figures, and letters clear cut and distinct; scale graduated in 2° F. or 1° C. divisions and numbered every 20° F. or 10° C., the first and each succeeding 10° F. (5° C.) line to be longer than the others.
Special markings: "A. S. T. M. High Distillation," serial number, and manufacturer's trade-mark etched on the stem.
Accuracy: Error at any point on scale shall not exceed one smallest scale division up to 700° F. or 370° C.
Test for permanency of range: After being subjected to a temperature of 700° F., or 370° C., for 24 hours, the accuracy shall be within the limit specified.
Points to be tested for certification: 32°, 212°, 400°, 700° F., or 0°, 100°, 200°, 370° C.

7. Graduate. The graduate shall be of the cylindrical type, of uniform diameter, with a pressed or molded base and a lipped top. The cylinder shall be graduated to contain 100 cc. and the graduated portion shall be not less than 7 inches nor more than 8 inches long; it shall be graduated in single cubic centimeters, and each fifth mark shall be distinguished by a longer line. It shall be numbered from the bottom up at intervals of 10 cc. The distance from the 100 cc. mark to the rim shall be not less than $1\frac{1}{4}$ inches nor more than $1\frac{3}{4}$ inches. The graduations shall not be in error by more than 1 cc. at any point on the scale.

[1] Technical Paper 323A, p. 46; also A. S. T. M. method.

Procedure

8. (*a*) The condenser bath shall be filled with cracked ice [1] and enough water added to cover the condenser tube. The temperature shall be maintained between 32° and 40° F. (0° and 4.4° C.).

(*b*) The condenser tube shall be swabbed to remove any liquid remaining from the previous test. A piece of soft cloth attached to a cord or copper wire may be used for this purpose.

(*c*) One hundred cubic centimeters of the product shall be measured in the 100 cc. graduated cylinder at 55° to 65° F. (12.8° to 18.3° C.) and transferred directly to the Engler flask. None of the liquid shall be permitted to flow into the vapor tube.

(*d*) The thermometer provided with a cork shall be fitted tightly into the flask so that it will be in the middle of the neck and so that the lower end of the capillary tube is on a level with the inside of the bottom of the vapor outlet tube at its junction with the neck of the flask.

(*e*) The charged flask shall be placed in the 1¼-inch opening in the 6 by 6 inch asbestos board with the vapor outlet tube inserted into the condenser tube. A tight connection may be made by means of a cork through which the vapor tube passes. The position of the flask shall be so adjusted that the vapor tube extends into the condenser tube not less than 1 inch nor more than 2 inches.

(*f*) The graduated cylinder used in measuring the charge shall be placed, without drying, at the outlet of the condenser tube in such a position that the condenser tube shall extend into the graduate at least 1 inch but not below the 100 cc. mark. Unless the temperature is between 55° and 65° F. (12.8° and 18.3° C.), the receiving graduate shall be immersed up to the 100 cc. mark in a transparent bath maintained between these temperatures. The top of the graduate shall be covered closely during the distillation with a piece of blotting paper or its equivalent cut so as to fit the condenser tube tightly.

9. When everything is in readiness, heat shall be applied at a uniform rate, so regulated that the first drop of condensate falls from the condenser in not less than 5 nor more than 10 minutes. When the first drop falls from the end of the condenser, the reading of the distillation thermometer shall be recorded as the *initial boiling point*. The receiving cylinder shall then be moved so that the end of the condenser tube shall touch the side of the cylinder. The heat shall then be so regulated that the distillation will proceed at a uniform rate of not less than 4 nor more than 5 cc. per minute. The reading of the distillation thermometer shall be recorded when the level of the distillate reaches each 10 cc. mark on the graduate.

After the 90% point has been recorded the heat may be increased because of the presence of the heavy ends which have high boiling points. However, no further increase of heat should be applied after this adjustment. The 4 to 5 cc. rate can rarely be maintained from the 90% point to the end of the distillation, but in no case should the period between the 90% and the end-point be more than 5 minutes.

---

[1] Any other convenient cooling medium may be used, provided that means are readily available for determining the temperature.

The heating shall be continued until the mercury reaches a maximum and starts to fall consistently. The highest temperature observed on the distillation thermometer shall be recorded as the *maximum temperature* or end-point. Usually this point will be reached after the bottom of the flask has become dry.

The total volume of the distillate collected in the receiving graduate shall be recorded as the *recovery*.

The cooled residue shall be poured from the flask into a small cylinder graduated in 0.1 cc., measured when cool, and the volume recorded as *residue*.

The difference between 100 cc. and the sum of the recovery and the residue shall be calculated and recorded as *distillation loss*.

ACCURACY

10. With proper care and attention to detail, duplicate results obtained for initial boiling point and maximum temperature, respectively, should not differ from each other by more than 6° F. (3.3° C.).

CORRECTION FOR BAROMETRIC PRESSURE

11. The barometric pressure shall be observed and recorded. (Pressure A.) The average barometric pressure of the point where the gasoline is delivered to the consumer shall be ascertained (from records of the United States Weather Bureau). (Pressure B.) No correction shall be made unless the difference between pressures A and B exceeds 1 inch (25 mm.) of mercury, when the boiling range of the gasoline shall be corrected according to the following rule:

If pressure A is greater than pressure B, subtract the corrections according to the following table.

If pressure A is less than pressure B, add the corrections according to the following table.

Apparent boiling points				Correction for each inch (25 mm.) of difference between pressures A and B	
From—	To—	From—	To—	A	B
° C.	° C.	° F.	° F.	° C.	° F.
14	33	57	91	1.6	2.9
33	51	91	124	1.7	3.1
51	70	124	158	1.8	3.2
70	88	158	190	1.9	3.4
88	107	190	225	2.0	3.6
107	125	225	239	2.1	3.8
125	144	239	291	2.2	4.0
144	162	291	324	2.3	4.1
162	181	324	358	2.4	4.3
181	199	358	390	2.5	4.5
199	218	390	424	2.6	4.7
218	236	424	457	2.7	4.9
236	255	457	491	2.8	5.0
255	273	491	523	2.9	5.2
273	292	523	558	3.0	5.4
292	310	558	590	3.1	5.6

The lighter portions, for example, those between 150° and 200°, burn much better than those between 250° and 290°; the heavy portions of American petroleum burn much better than those of the Russian oils.

The end point shall not be higher than 625° F. For lighthouse kerosene (the highest grade) the U. S. requirements are as follows: first drop not lower than 160° C.; 10% over below 175°, 90% over below 270°, end-point not higher than 280° and 97% recovered as distillate in the receiver.

The averages from four samples of Caucasian and ten samples of American oils subjected to this test were as follows, in per cent by volume:[1]

	Below 150° C.	150–290°	Above 290° C.
Caucasian petroleum	8.0	86.6	5.4
American petroleum	16.9	57.1	26.0

Determination of Sulphur.[2] The deleterious effect of the oxides of sulphur upon hangings and bindings—as well as upon the human system—is well known, sulphuric acid being their ultimate product. The sulphur exists in combination, partly as compounds formed from the sulphuric acid used in refining and partly as alkyl sulphides. Its qualitative detection may be effected by heating the oil to its boiling-point with a bright piece of sodium or potassium. If sulphur compounds be present, a yellowish layer is formed upon the metal. After cooling add distilled water drop by drop until the metal is dissolved, and test for sulphides with sodium nitroprusside.

For the quantitative determination of sulphur, Method 520.1 (A. S. T. M. Method D90–21T) is employed

APPARATUS

Absorber of chemically resistant glass, about 150 cc. capacity, containing glass beads or short pieces of glass rod in the suction side as shown.

Chimney of chemically resistant glass connected with the absorber by a rubber stopper.

Spray trap of chemically resistant glass connected with the absorber by a rubber stopper.

Small lamp of about 25 cc. capacity. This lamp may conveniently consist of a 25- to 35-cc. Erlenmeyer flask and a cork carrying a short section of glass tubing about $\frac{1}{8}$ inch in inside diameter. The cork must be grooved along the sides so that air may enter the flask while the oil is being consumed.

Ordinary cotton wicking.

Filter pump or other means for continuous suction and rubber tubing to connect with spray trap

SOLUTIONS REQUIRED

Hydrochloric Acid. Solution containing 2.275 grams HCl per liter, carefully checked for accuracy.

Sodium Carbonate. Solution containing 3.306 grams Na_2CO_3 per liter. Exactly 10.0 cc. should be required to neutralize 10.0 cc. of the hydrochloric acid solution.

[1] Veith, "Das Erdoel," p. 244.

Methyl Orange.   Solution in distilled water, containing 0.004 gram methyl orange per liter.

PROCEDURE

Pass two strands of new cotton wicking about 4.5 inches long through the $\frac{1}{8}$-inch diameter wick tube so that they are not twisted but parallel in the wick tube.   Trim the wick with very sharp scissors.   Pour into the clean, dry lamp about 20 cc. of the oil to be tested, insert the wick, and cork and weigh the assembly with an accuracy of 0.001 gram.   It is advisable to make a blank determination at the same time and under the same conditions by burning sulphur-free alcohol in a similar lamp.

Rinse the absorber containing the glass beads thoroughly with distilled water and add exactly 10.0 cc. of the standard sodium carbonate solution from an accurately calibrated burette, allowing the burette to drain for 3 minutes before the reading is taken.   Rinse the chimney and the spray trap with distilled water, dry the chimney, and connect both to the absorber as shown in Fig. 87c.   Set up the apparatus for the blank determination in exactly the same manner, using exactly 10.0 cc. of the sodium carbonate solution. Apply gentle suction to both absorbers, light both the weighed oil lamp and alcohol lamp, and then place in position under the chimneys, so that the tops of the wick tubes extend into the chimneys not more than $\frac{1}{16}$ inch.   Adjust the wick height and the suction so that the flame is steady, free from smoke, and approximately $\frac{1}{4}$ inch high.   This requires that the wick be flush with the top of the wick tube for naphthas and a little higher for illuminating oils. The room must be free from drafts.   The suction on the blank should be so adjusted that air is drawn through both determinations at the same rate. Continue burning for about 2 hours, or less if the sulphur content of the oil is high.   During this time the oil should be consumed at the rate of about 1 gram per hour.

Extinguish the flames and stop the suction on both absorbers.   Weigh the oil lamp immediately and calculate by difference the weight of oil consumed. Working with the blank first, disconnect the spray trap and chimney and wash them thoroughly with the methyl orange solution, using a wash bottle with a very fine jet and collecting the washings in the absorber.   The amount of solution required for washing should not exceed 35 cc.   Carefully titrate the very faintly yellowish solution in the absorber with standard HCl, added to the suction side of the absorber from an accurately calibrated burette. During this titration the contents of the absorber should be agitated carefully, either by blowing through a rubber tube held between the operator's lips and connected at the other end with the chimney side of the absorber or else by the use of a suitable rubber syringe bulb.   As the end-point is approached, draw the liquid back into the chimney side between each addition of acid and then blow it into the suction side, agitating as before.   As soon as the first permanent pink color appears, the end-point has been reached.   Read and record the volume of HCl solution used.

Rinse the chimney and spray trap used in the actual determination into the absorber to which they were connected, exactly as prescribed for the blank.

[1] Tech. Paper 323A, p. 81.

If the methyl orange solution in the absorber has a pink color, too much oil has been burned and the determination must be repeated, burning for a shorter time. Titrate just as in the blank, making sure that the absorber is cold. Read and record the volume of HCl solution required.

Calculate the sulphur content of the oil by substituting the proper values in the following formula:

$$\text{Percentage of sulphur} = \frac{(\text{HCl for blank, cc.} - \text{HCl for sample, cc.}) \times 0.1}{\text{grams of oil burned}}.$$

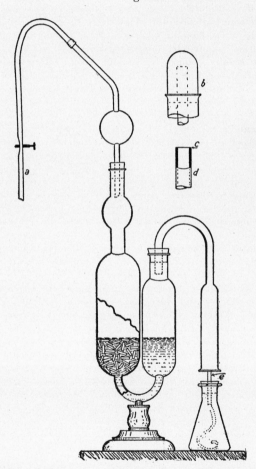

FIG. 87c. Apparatus for determination of sulphur in oils (A. S. T. M.): a, Suction tube; b, top of burner with glass cap in place; c, annealed top; d, part section of glass burner; e, glass burner.

If blank is not run, the formula is:

$$\text{Percentage of sulphur} = \frac{(Na_2CO_3, \text{ cc.}—HCl, \text{ cc.})\times 0.1}{\text{grams of oil burned}} .$$

These formulas are correct only for the standard solutions specified, 1 cc. of each being equivalent to 0.001 gram of sulphur. The use of solutions of other strength, such as N/10, involves more complicated calculation and is not advisable.

Or the barium sulphate can be precipitated and determined for rapid work by the Jackson Turbidimeter, p. 1119.

The percentage of sulphur in a kerosene should not exceed 0.05; the Pennsylvania oils contain usually 0.02 to 0.03, the Lima 0.04 to 0.05.[1]

Detection of Acidity. Shake equal quantities of oil and warm water in a test-tube, pour off the oil, and test the water with litmus paper. If the water be strongly acid, the quantity may be determined as in " Free Acid," page 596.

The acid in this case is most probably sulphuric, coming from the refining process.

Sulphuric Acid Test. The object of this test is to judge of the degree of refinement of the oil, a perfectly refined oil giving little or no color when submitted to the process. One hundred grams of oil and 40 grams of sulphuric acid, 1.73 specific gravity, are shaken together for two minutes in a glass-stoppered bottle and the color of the acid noticed. For comparative work this color is matched by solutions of Bismarck brown.[2]

Mineral Salts. Salts of calcium or magnesium when dissolved in the oil diminish its illuminating power; their action is to form a crust on the wick and prevent access of air.

Redwood[3] states that 0.02 gram of either of these salts in 1000 grams of oil diminishes the illuminating power 30 to 40% in eight hours.

They are determined by distilling 100 to 200 cc. of the oil down to about 20 cc., evaporating and igniting this residue, and subsequently treating with hydrochloric acid. The calcium and magnesium are then determined in the usual way.

Determination of Water. By rubbing the oil together with a little eosin on a glass plate the oil will take on a pink color if water be present.

The evaporation method is approximate and applicable only to heavy oils and greases. Its accuracy even with heavy greases is questionable.

Dilute[4] the oil with an equal volume of benzol, whirl it vigorously in a centrifuge until the separated layer of water does not appear to increase in volume. However, as water is somewhat soluble in any diluent used and also in oils, a portion of the water content will fail to appear, consequently the method in which a diluent is used cannot be considered accurate. It is advisable first to agitate the diluent vigorously with water and then to separate with the centrifuge in order to saturate it with water before using. See also Dean's test under Fuel Oil.

Groschuff[5] states that 100 grams of benzene will dissolve 0.03 gram of water at 3° C. and 0.337 gram of water at 77° C., whereas petroleum products (density 0.792) will dissolve from 0.0012 gram at 2° C. to 0.097 gram at 94° C.

[1] Kissling, Ch., Rev. Fett und Harz. Ind., **14**, 157, 1906.
[2] J. Soc. Chem. Ind., **15**, 678, 1896.
[3] Dingler, Pol. J., **255**, 427, 1887.
[4] Reported by Allen and Jacobs. Bureau of Mines Technical Paper No. 25, 1912.
[5] Groschuff, Chem. Abs., **5**, 2550, 1911.

While water to the extent even of 3 or 4% is apparently without influence on the viscosity, 1% extinguishes the flame when making the flash test.

Color. This test has lost its importance, since oils are sometimes satisfactory despite their yellow color. The determination is usually made with the Saybolt colorimeter,[1] in which the depth of the oil is changed in a cylinder until it matches the color of standard plates of uranium glass.

(b) Lubricating Oils

The tests to be made are, in the order of their importance, viscosity, specific gravity, evaporation, cold test, pour point, flash test, fire test, test for soap, carbon residue test, friction test. Saponification value, tarry matter insoluble in 88° naphtha, color and added impurities are also determined.

The office of a lubricant is to prevent the attrition of axle and journal box by interposing itself between them in a thin layer, upon which the shaft revolves. The ideal lubricant is that which has the greatest adhesion to surfaces and the least cohesion among its own particles, or, as the practical man expresses it, the most fluid oil that will do the work and stay in place. The determination of its viscosity or " body " is then of the first importance.

Viscosity is the degree of fluidity of an oil or its internal friction. It is independent of the specific gravity of the oil, although this in the pipette instruments influences the time of efflux. Within certain limits it may be taken as a measure of the value of oil as a lubricant, by comparing the viscosity of the oil under examination with that of other oils which have been found to yield good results in practice.

The instruments employed for its determination may be divided into two classes—pipette viscosimeters, giving the time of efflux, as those of Engler, Saybolt, and others, and torsion viscosimeters, giving the retardation due to the oil, those of Macmichael and Doolittle.

In expressing viscosity, consequently, it is necessary to give the name of the instrument with which it is determined. It is sometimes expressed as specific viscosity, that is, the time of the oil divided by the time of water; this is only comparative when done with instruments of the same name, that is, specific viscosity Engler is not the same figure as specific viscosity Saybolt. Besides this manner of expressing viscosity, it is measured in absolute (C.G.S.) units or dynes per cm. This unit of viscosity has received the name of Poise from Poiseuille, one of the first to express this property in absolute measure. This is possible when the diameter of the orifice, its length, the quantity and specific gravity of the oil, its time of efflux and change of head are known. Where it is impracticable to determine all these data by direct measurements, the readings of a viscosimeter may be changed into dynes by determining the viscosity in seconds of standard solutions of glycerine, the viscosity of these being determined in dynes from tables of physical constants. Or it may be done by use of the tables on pages 1117 and 1158.

Engler Apparatus. *Description.* The apparatus (Fig. 88) consists of a flat, brass cylindrical vessel, A, 106 mm. in diameter and about 62 mm. deep, holding 240 cc., provided with a jet 2.9 mm. in diameter and 20 mm. long. This vessel is gilt inside and the jet, in the standard instruments, is of platinum—ordinarily it is made of brass; the vessel is surrounded with a bath, B, either of water or

[1] Tech. Paper 323A, p. 30.

11

oil, provided with a stirrer and heated by a ring burner. The jet is closed by the wooden valve, F, passing through the cover, and a thermometer, c, shows the temperature of the oil; three studs show the height to which A is filled and at the same time when it is level. The oil ordinarily is discharged into the 200-cc. flask, although in case the oil or time be limited, 100 or 50 cc. may be used and the time of efflux multiplied by a suitable factor. The instrument is standardized with water, 200 cc. of which at 20° C. should run out in from 50 to 52 seconds.

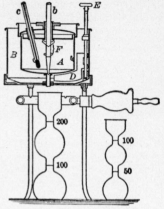

Fig. 88.—Engler Viscosimeter.

Manipulation. The instrument is thoroughly cleaned with alcohol and ether if necessary and dried; any suspended matter is removed from the oil, which is poured into it up to the level of the studs, stirred until 20° C. is reached and the bath adjusted to the same temperature. The flask is placed beneath the orifice, the plug raised and the time required for 200 cc. of oil to flow out is noted; this is divided by the water value of the instrument and gives then relative or specific viscosity. If only 50 cc. are allowed to run out the time must be multiplied by 5, and if 100 cc., by 2.35. If only 50 cc. were put in and 40 cc. allowed to run out, multiply this time by 3.62 to obtain the time for 200 cc.; if 66 cc. and 50 cc. run out, multiply by 2.79.[1] If it be desired to express the viscosity in absolute measure (C.G.S. units) it can be done by reference to the table on page 1158. It should be noted that specific viscosity obtained with a different type of instrument, e.g., the Saybolt, is not the same as with the Engler.

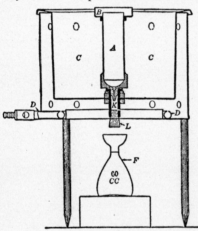

Fig. 89.—Saybolt Viscosimeter.

The Saybolt Viscosimeter.[2] 1. (a) Viscosity shall be determined[3] by means of the Saybolt Universal or Saybolt Furol viscosimeter.

(b) In general, the Saybolt Universal viscosimeter shall be used for lubricants and the Saybolt Furol viscosimeter for fuel oils and other oils of similar viscosity.

(c) The Saybolt Universal viscosimeter shall not be used for times of flow less than 32 seconds.

[1] Gans, Chem. Revue der Fett und Harz. Ind., **6**, 221, 1899.

[2] Redwood, J. Soc. Chem. Ind., **5**, 124, 1886. This was formerly made in three forms, A, B, C. Apparatus "A" was the standard for testing at 70° F. Atlantic Red, Paraffin, and other distilled oils; "B" for testing at 70° F. Black Oils of 0°, 15°, 25°, and 30°, Cold Test, and other reduced oils up to, but not including, Summer Cold Test Oil. Apparatus "C" was used for testing at 212° F. Reduced, Summer, Cylinder, Filtered Cylinder, XXX Valve, 26.5° Bé., and other heavy oils.

[3] Bureau Mines Tech. Paper 323A, p. 39.

DIMENSIONS OF OIL TUBES

Dimensions	Saybolt Universal viscosimeter			Saybolt Furol viscosimeter		
	Minimum	Normal	Maximum	Minimum	Normal	Maximum
	Centimeters	*Centimeters*	*Centimeters*	*Centimeters*	*Centimeters*	*Centimeters*
Inside diameter of outlet tube................	0.1750	0.1765	0.1780	0.313	0.315	0.317
Outside diameter outlet tube at lower end.....	0.28	0.30	0.32	0.40	0.43	0.46
Length of outlet tube [a] ..	1.215	1.225	1.235	1.215	1.225	1.235
Height of overflow rim above bottom of outlet tube [a]...............	12.40	12.50	12.60	12.40	12.50	12.60
Diameter of container [a] ..	2.955	2.975	2.995	2.955	2.975	2.995
Depth of cylindrical part of container [a]........	8.8	....	....	8.8	....	....

[a] This dimension is identical in the Saybolt Universal and the Saybolt Furol instruments.

APPARATUS

2. (*a*) The Saybolt viscosimeters (Fig. 89) are made entirely of metal. The oil tube *A* is fitted at the top with an overflow cup, *B*, and the tube is surrounded by a bath. At the bottom of the oil tube is a small outlet tube through which the oil to be tested flows into a receiving flask whose capacity at 20° C. (68° F.) to a mark on its neck is 60, ± 0.15 cc. The lower end of the outlet tube is enclosed by a larger tube, which when stoppered by a cork, *L*, acts as a closed air chamber and prevents the flow of oil through the outlet tube until the cork is removed and the test started. A looped string may be attached to the lower end of the cork as an aid to its rapid removal. The temperatures in the oil tube and in the bath are shown by thermometers. The bath may be heated by any suitable means. The oil tube shall be thoroughly cleaned, and all oil entering the oil tube shall be strained through a 60-mesh wire strainer. A stop watch shall be used for taking the time of flow of the oil and a pipette shall be used for draining the overflow cup.

(*b*) The oil tubes, which may be standardized by the United States Bureau of Standards, shall conform to the dimensions given in the table.

(*c*) The bath and oil tube thermometers shall conform to the following requirements. They cover two sets of four thermometers each, one set being graduated in Fahrenheit degrees and the other set in centigrade degrees, the ranges being chosen to include the temperatures commonly used in testing.

Type: Etched stem, glass.
Liquid: Mercury.
Ranges and subdivisions:
    Range 66–80° F., subdivision in 0.2° F. for tests at 77° F.
    Range 94–108° F., subdivision in 0.2° F. for tests at 100° F.

Range 120–134° F., subdivision in 0.2° F. for tests at 122° and 130° F.
Range 204–218° F., subdivision in 0.2° F. for tests at 210° F.

or—

Range 19–27° C., subdivision in 0.1° C. for tests at 25° C.
Range 34–42° C., subdivision in 0.1° C. for tests at 40° C.
Range 49–57° C., subdivision in 0.1° C. for tests at 50° C.
Range 95–103° C., subdivision in 0.1° C. for tests at 100° C.

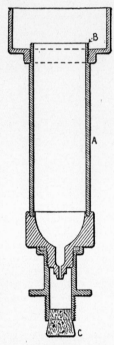

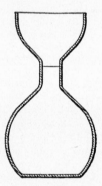

FIG. 89a.   Sectional view
of standard oil tube.

FIG. 89b.   Receiving
flask.

Total length: 252 to 256 mm. (9.92 to 10.08 in.).
Stem: Plain front, enamel back, suitable thermometer tubing. Diameter, 6 to 7 mm. (0.236 to 0.275 in.).
Bulb: Corning normal or equally suitable thermometric glass; length, 25 to 35 mm. (1.0 to 1.4 in.); diameter, not less than 5 mm. (0.197 in.) and not greater than that of stem.
Distance to lowest specified graduation from bottom of bulb: 135 to 150 mm. (5.3 to 5.9 in.).
Distance to highest specified graduation from top of stem: 20 to 35 mm. (0.8 to 1.4 in.).
Contraction chamber: To be of long narrow type, top to be not more than 60 mm. (2.36 in.) above bottom of bulb, mercury to stand in contraction chamber at 32° F. (0° C.).
Expansion chamber: To permit heating the thermometer 90° F. (50° C.) above highest temperature on scale, and in all cases to permit heating to 212° F. (100° C.).
Filling above mercury: Nitrogen gas.
Top finish: Glass ring.

Graduation: All lines, figures, and letters clear cut and distinct. The first and each succeeding 1° F. or 0.5° C. line to be longer than the remaining lines. Graduations to be numbered at each multiple of 2° F. or 1° C.

Immersion: Total.

Special marking: "A. S. T. M." Viscosity test points to be numbered in full figures and in red, other graduations and figures in black. A serial number and the manufacturer's name or trade-mark shall be etched on the stem.

Scale error: The error at any point of the scale shall not exceed 0.2° F. (0.1° C.).

Standardization: The thermometers are to be standardized for the condition of total immersion.

Case: Each thermometer shall be supplied in a suitable case on which shall appear the marking, "A. S. T. M., Saybolt Viscosimeter Thermometer," and the range.

TEMPERATURE OF TESTING

3. (*a*) With the Saybolt Universal viscosimeter, determinations shall be made at 100° F. (37.8° C.), 130° F. (54.4° C.), or 210° F. (98.9° C.).

(*b*) With the Saybolt Furol viscosimeter, determinations shall be made at 122° F. (50° C.).

(*c*) Viscosities shall be expressed as — seconds, Saybolt Universal (or Saybolt Furol), being the time in seconds for the delivery of 60 cc. of oil.

(*d*) Fuel oils and other oils of similar viscosity showing a time of less than 25 seconds, Saybolt Furol, at 122° F., shall be tested in the Saybolt Universal at 122° F. Oil showing a time of less than 32 seconds, Saybolt Universal, at 122° F., shall be measured in the Saybolt Universal at 100° F. (37.8° C.). These methods of test do not apply to fuels having a viscosity at 100° F. of less than 32 seconds, Saybolt Universal, which are not considered to be fuel oils.

PROCEDURE

4. The bath shall be held constant within 0.25° F. (0.14° C.) at such a temperature as will maintain the desired temperature in the oil tube. For viscosity determinations at 100°, 122°, and 130° F., oil or water may be used as the bath liquid. For viscosity determinations at 210° F., oil shall be used as the bath liquid. Viscosity determinations shall be made in a room free from draughts and from rapid changes in temperature. All oil introduced into the oil tube either for cleaning or for test shall first be passed through the strainer.

To make the test, heat the oil to the necessary temperature and clean out the oil tube Pour some of the oil to be tested through the cleaned tube. Insert the cork stopper into the lower end of the air chamber at the bottom of the oil tube, far enough to prevent the escape of air but not to touch the small outlet tube.

Heat the oil to be tested, outside the viscosimeter, to slightly below the temperature at which the viscosity is to be determined, and pour it into the oil tube until it ceases to overflow into the overflow cup. By means of the oil-tube thermometer, keep the oil in the oil tube well stirred, and also stir well the liquid in the bath. It is extremely important that the temperature of the bath be maintained constant during the entire time consumed in making the test. When the temperatures of the bath and of the oil in the oil tube are constant and the oil in the oil tube is at the desired temperature, withdraw the oil-tube thermometer: quickly remove the surplus oil from the overflow cup by means of a pipette, so that the level of the oil in the overflow cup is below the level of the oil in the tube proper; place the 60-cc. flask (Fig. 6) in position so that the stream of oil from the outlet tube will strike the neck of the flask so as to avoid foam.   Snap the cork from its position, and at the same instant start the stop watch.   Stir the liquid in the bath during the run and carefully maintain it at the previously determined proper temperature. Stop the watch when the bottom of the meniscus of the oil reaches the mark on the neck of the receiving flask.

The time in seconds for the delivery of 60 cc. of oil is the Saybolt Universal (or Saybolt Furol) viscosity of the oil at the temperature at which the test was made.

The tube should be cleaned out before each test with some of the oil to be tested.   Black oils or any oil containing sediment should be carefully strained before testing or " running," as it is technically termed.   The instruments should be carefully guarded from dust when not in use.

The results obtained with this instrument are not the same in many cases as those furnished by the A, B, and C instruments, but they seem to have been adopted by the trade generally.

It is worth noting that 3 or 4% of water are apparently without influence on the viscosity.

MacMichael's Viscosimeter.   This is an instrument of the torsion type in which a disk is suspended in a cup of fluid, the latter being rotated, and the torsion it produces on the disk noted.   The disk is suspended by a gold-plated, steel wire 10 inches long, held between two grooved pins at the top of the standard.   The brass cup is oil jacketed, the oil covering the wires $\frac{1}{2}$ inch and heated electrically, or it may be cooled by ice or brine.   A bent thermometer passing through the cover indicates the temperature, which may be controlled easily within a fraction of a degree.   The graduated dial at the top of the disk is rotary and may be easily set to 0°.   A dash pot filled with engine oil on the stem of the disk damps the action of the motor.   In operating, the instrument is levelled, the cup is filled to the mark with the fluid to be tested (about 100 cc.), the temperature adjusted, the cup rotated and the readings of the dial noted.   These are in degrees of angular deflection, 300 to the circumference, and noted as ° M. = 1/1000 poise.   Water at 20° should read 10° M.   The smallest, or "practical unit" is 1° M.: by changing the decimal point, practical units, absolute units or specific viscosity may be obtained at one reading of the dial, no calculations being required.   Three strengths of wire are supplied, giving water readings of 1°, 10°, and 100°, covering ranges of viscosity to 5000° M. or 5 poise.

The instrument should be calibrated by solutions of pure granulated sugar dried over sulphuric acid, the absolute viscosity of which is shown below. The accuracy of the instrument is well within 0.5 per cent.   The instrument is very rapid, the time required for a reading being very short.   It can be applied to colloidal or lumpy solutions or suspensions, as limes, clay, glues, gums, explosives, paints, catsups or even jams with fruit seeds in them.

VISCOSITY IN CENTIPOISES OF SUGAR SOLUTIONS[1]

Temp. 0 C.	Per cent Sugar by Weight			
	0	20	40	60
0	1.789	3.804	14.77	238
5	1.516	3.154	11.56	156
10	1.306	2.652	9.794	109.8
15	1.141	2.267	7.468	74.6
20	1.005	1.960	6.200	56.5
25	0.894	1.704	5.187	43.86
30	0.802	1.504	4.382	33.78

Absolute Viscosity. This expresses viscosity in dynes, that is, the force necessary to produce the acceleration of 1 cm. per second on the mass of a gram. It is independent of the instrument used; Engler numbers can be converted to absolute viscosity by the following factors:

Engler No.	Absolute Viscosity Dynes per Sq.Cm.[2]
1	$0.01006 \times$ specific gravity
2	$0.1146 \times$ specific gravity
5	$0.353 \times$ specific gravity
10	$0.726 \times$ specific gravity
20	$1.46 \times$ specific gravity
30	$2.19 \times$ specific gravity
60	$4.38 \times$ specific gravity

The Engler numbers of 5 or over are quite nearly proportional to the absolute viscosities.

Specific Gravity. See under Burning Oils, page 1111.

Evaporation Test.[3] The object of this test is to determine what percentage of an oil—more especially a spindle oil—is volatile when exposed to nearly the same conditions as it is on a bearing.

The oil is exposed upon annular disks of filter-paper $1\frac{5}{8}$ in. outside diameter, with hole $\frac{5}{8}$ in. in diameter, which have been standing in a sulphuric acid desiccator for several days, contained in a flat watch-glass.

Manipulation. The watch-glass and paper are weighed—to tenths of a milligram—and about 0.2 gram of oil brought upon it by dropping from a rod, and *accurately* weighed. The watch-glass is now placed in an air bath, the temperature of which remains nearly constant at 60° to 65° C. (140° to 150° F.), and heated for eight hours. It is then cooled and reweighed, the loss being figured in per cent. No oil should be passed which gives an evaporation of more than 4%.

The following table of results upon some spindle oils shows the relation of gravity, flash point, and evaporation:

Gravity.	Flash, °F.	Evaporation.	Gravity.	Flash, °F.	Evaporation.
....	298	7.0%	.862	352	0.9%
.846	318	4.4%	.866	366	1.7%
....	348	2.0%	.870	384	0.8%
.852	348	1.0%	.882	364	1.7%
.856	336	1.4%			

[1] Bingham & Jackson, Bureau Standards Bulletin, No. 298 (1917).
[2] Waidner, Proc. Am. Soc. Test. Mat., Pt. I, 293, 1915.
[3] Archbutt, J. Soc. Chem. Ind., **15**, 326, 1896.

NOTES.   The temperature employed, 65° C., is approximately that attained by a bearing (in a spinning frame) after running two hours, thus leaving the oil exposed to it for eight hours, assuming a ten-hour day.

The test is important to the insurance underwriter, because it measures the amount of inflammable material sent into the air, and hence the liability to cause or aid conflagrations; it is important to the mill-owner, as it indicates the quantity of oil left upon the bearing, hence serving its purpose.

The test is made upon other oils by heating them six hours in a shallow dish to 100°, 150°, 220, or 300°, sometimes in a draft of air.

Cold Test.   This may be defined as the temperature at which the oil will just flow.

Manipulation.   A 4-oz. vial is one-fourth filled with the oil to be examined, a short, rather heavy, thermometer inserted in it, and the whole placed in a freezing mixture.   When the oil has become solid throughout, let it stand one hour; the vial is removed, the oil allowed to soften, and thoroughly stirred until it will run from one end of the bottle to the other.   The reading of the thermometer is now taken by withdrawing it and wiping off the oil with waste to render the mercury visible.[1]

The chilling-point is the temperature at which flakes or scales begin to form in the liquid, and is determined similarly, by cooling the liquid 5° at a time.

Freezing Mixtures.   For temperatures above 35° F. use cracked ice and water; between 35 and 0° F. use two parts of ice and one part of salt; and from 0 to −30° F. use three parts of crystallized calcium chloride and two parts of fine ice or snow. A still more convenient means is by the use of solid carbonic acid dissolved in ether, giving −50° F. readily.

The preceding method is open to quite an error from the personal equation of each observer.   To obviate this Martens[2] proceeds as follows:

The oil is poured into a U-tube 1 cm. in diameter, 16 cm. high, with 3 cm. between the bends, to a depth of 3 cm.; it is then placed in a freezing mixture, cooled, and connected with a blast at a constant pressure of 3 cm.   The temperature at which the oil begins to flow under these conditions is considered as the cold test.

Cloud and Pour Points (A. S. T. M. Method D97–22T)[3]

1. (*a*) The cloud point of a petroleum oil is that temperature at which paraffin wax or other solid substances begin to crystallize out or separate from solution when the oil is chilled under certain definite specified conditions.

(*b*) The pour point of a petroleum oil is the lowest temperature at which this oil will pour or flow when it is chilled without disturbance under certain definite specified conditions.

2. (*a*) The test for cloud point shall be used only for oils which are transparent in layers 1½ inches thick.

(*b*) The test for pour point shall be used for all other petroleum oils and may be used for oils on which the test for cloud point is permitted.

APPARATUS

3. The test jar *a* shall be of clear glass, cylindrical form, flat bottom, approximately 1¼ inches in inside diameter and 4½ to 5 inches high (see Fig. 89*c*).

---

[1] Dudley and Pease, An. Eng. and R. R. J., **69**, 332, 1895.
[2] Mitt. kgl. tech. Versuchstation; abstr. J. Soc. Chem. Ind., **9**, 772, 1890.
[3] Bureau Mines Tech. Paper 323A, p. 36.

An ordinary 4-ounce oil sample bottle may be used if the test jar is not available.

4. The thermometer *b* shall conform to the following specifications:

Type: Etched stem, glass.
Total length: 222 mm.
Stem: Plain front, enamel back, suitable thermometer tubing; diameter, 7 to 8 mm.
Bulb: Corning normal, Jena 16 III, or equally suitable thermometric glass; maximum length, 9.5 mm.; diameter, not greater than stem.
Actuating liquid: Mercury.
Range: −36° to +120° F.
Immersion: 4¼ inches; the words "4¼ in. Immersion" shall be etched on tube, and a line etched around the stem to indicate the depth of immersion.
Distance to −36° line from bottom of bulb: 120 to 130 mm.
Distance to 120° line from top of stem: 19 to 25 mm.
Expansion chamber: To hold 212° F.

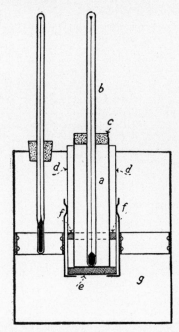

Fig. 89c. Apparatus for cloud and pour test: *a*, Test jar; *b*, thermometer; *c*, cork; *d*, jacket; *e*, disk of cork or felt; *f*, ring gasket; *g*, cooling bath.

Filled: Nitrogen gas.
Top finish: Plain.
Graduation: All lines, figures, and letters clear cut and distinct; scale graduated in 2° F. divisions; scale numbered every 20° F., starting at −20°. The − 30° line and each succeeding 10° line to be longer than the others.
Special markings: "A. S. T. M. Cloud and Pour," serial number, and manufacturer's name or trade-mark etched on the stem.
Accuracy: Error at any point on scale shall not exceed one smallest scale division.
Points to be tested for certification: − 28°, + 32°, + 92° F.

5. The cork *c* shall fit the test jar, and shall be bored centrally to take the test thermometer.

6. The jacket d shall be of glass or metal and shall be water-tight, of cylindrical form, flat bottom, about $4\frac{1}{2}$ inches deep, with inside diameter $\frac{1}{2}$ inch greater than outside diameter of the test jar.

7. A disk of cork or felt, e, $\frac{1}{4}$ inch thick and of the same diameter as the inside of the jacket will be required.

8. The ring gasket f shall be about $\frac{3}{16}$ inch thick, and made to fit snugly around the outside of the test jar and loosely inside the jacket. This gasket may be made of cork, felt, or other suitable material, elastic enough to cling to the test jar and hard enough to hold its shape. The purpose of the ring gasket is to prevent the test jar from touching the jacket.

9. The cooling bath g shall be of a type suitable for obtaining the required temperatures. The size and shape of the bath are optional but a support, suitable for holding the jacket firmly in a vertical position, is essential. The required bath temperatures may be maintained by refrigeration if available, otherwise by suitable freezing mixtures.

NOTE. The freezing mixtures commonly used are as follows:
For temperatures down to 35° F., ice and water.
For temperatures down to $-$ 5° F., crushed ice and sodium chloride.
For temperatures down to $-$ 25° F., crushed ice and calcium chloride crystals.
For temperatures down to $-$ 70° F., solid carbon dioxide and acetone.
The last-named mixture may be made as follows: In a covered metal beaker chill a suitable amount of acetone to 10° F., or lower, by means of an ice-salt mixture. Invert a cylinder of liquid carbon dioxide and draw off carefully into a chamois-skin bag the desired amount of carbon dioxide, which through rapid evaporation will quickly become solid. Then add to the chilled acetone enough of the solid carbon dioxide to give the desired temperature.

PROCEDURE FOR CLOUD POINT

10. The oil to be tested shall be brought to a temperature at least 25° F. above the approximate cloud point. Moisture, if present, shall be removed by any suitable method, as by filtration through dry filter paper until the oil is perfectly clear, but such filtration shall be made at a temperature at least 25° F. above the approximate cloud point.

The clear oil shall be poured into the test jar a to a height of not less than 1 nor more than $1\frac{1}{4}$ inches. The test jar may be marked to indicate the proper level.

The test jar shall be tightly closed by the cork c carrying the test thermometer b in a vertical position in the center of the jar with the thermometer bulb resting on the bottom of the jar.

The disk e shall be placed in the bottom of the jacket d and the test jar with the ring gasket f 1 inch above the bottom shall be inserted into the jacket. The disk, jacket, and inside of the jacket shall be clean and dry.

The temperature of the cooling bath g shall be adjusted so that it is below the cloud point of the oil by not less than 15° nor more than 30° F., and this temperature shall be maintained throughout the test. The jacket containing the test jar shall be supported firmly in a vertical position in the cooling bath so that not more than 1 inch of the jacket projects out of the cooling medium.

At each test thermometer-reading which is a multiple of 2° F. the test jar shall be removed from the jacket quickly but without disturbing the oil, inspected for cloud, and replaced in the jacket. This complete operation shall require not more than 3 seconds.

When such inspection first reveals a distinct cloudiness or haze in the oil at the bottom of the test jar, the reading of the test thermometer, corrected for error if necessary, shall be recorded as the cloud point.

PROCEDURE FOR POUR POINT

11. The oil to be tested shall be brought to a temperature of 90° F., or to a temperature 15° higher than its pour point if this pour point is above 75° F. The oil shall then be poured into the test jar a to a height of not less than 2 nor more than $2\frac{1}{4}$ in.[1]

The jar may be marked to indicate the proper level.

The test jar shall be tightly closed by the cork c carrying the test thermometer b in a vertical position in the center of the jar, with the thermometer bulb immersed so that the beginning of the capillary shall be $\frac{1}{8}$ inch below the surface of the oil.

The disk e shall be placed in the bottom of the jacket d and the test jar, with the ring gasket f 1 inch above the bottom, shall be inserted into the jacket. The disk, gasket, and inside of jacket shall be clean and dry.

After the oil has cooled enough to allow the formation of paraffin wax crystals, great care shall be taken not to disturb the mass of the oil nor to permit the thermometer to shift in the oil. Any disturbance of the spongy network of wax crystals will lead to low and fictitious results.

The temperature of the cooling bath g shall be adjusted so that it is below the pour point of the oil by not less than 15° nor more than 30° F., and this temperature shall be maintained throughout the test. The jacket containing the test jar shall be supported firmly in a vertical position in the cooling bath so that not more than 1 inch of the jacket projects out of the cooling medium.

At each test thermometer reading which is a multiple of 5° F. the test jar shall be removed from the jacket carefully and shall be tilted just enough to ascertain whether the oil around the thermometer remains liquid. As long as the oil around the thermometer flows when the jar is tilted slightly, the test jar shall be replaced in the jacket. The complete operation of removal and replacement shall require not more than 3 seconds. As soon as the oil around the thermometer does not flow when the jar is tilted slightly, the test jar shall be held in a horizontal position for exactly 5 seconds and observed carefully. If the oil around the thermometer shows any movement under these conditions, the test jar shall be immediately replaced in the jacket and the same procedure shall be repeated at the next temperature reading 5° F. lower. In determining the pour point of oils it shall be noted that the first movement of oil sometimes is not around the thermometer but from the sides of the test jar. In such cases this movement shall be considered in making the test. As soon as a temperature is reached at which the oil around the thermometer shows no movement when the test jar is held in a horizontal position for exactly 5 seconds, the test shall be stopped.

The lowest reading of the test thermometer, corrected for error if necessary, at which the oil around the thermometer shows any movement when the test jar is held in a horizontal position for exactly 5 seconds, shall be recorded as the pour point. It shall be noted that the pour point is the temperature 5° F. above the solid point or temperature at which the test is discontinued.

[1] Test jar and contents shall be immediately placed in the previously assembled apparatus.

Flash Point. Several forms of apparatus for testing the flash point of lubricating oils have been devised: Pensky-Martens's closed tester employing a stirrer is used in Germany. Martens states in a later article that stirring is unnecessary. In this country the open cup flash and fire test on all petroleum products except fuel oils and those having an open cup flash below 175° F. shall be determined in the Cleveland open cup.[1]

APPARATUS

2. The cup shall be heated by contact with a metal plate (Fig. 89d) $\frac{1}{4}$ inch (0.635 cm.) in thickness and 6 inches (15.24 cm.) in width. The plate shall

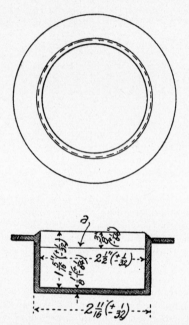

FIG. 89d. Cleveland open cup (A. S. T. M.): a, Filling mark.

be of brass, cast iron, wrought iron, or steel. In the center of the plate there shall be a plane depression $\frac{1}{32}$ inch (0.079 cm.) in depth and of just sufficient diameter to fit the cup. There shall be a circular opening $2\frac{3}{16}$ inches (5.50 cm.) in diameter, cut through the plate, centering with the center of the above-mentioned depression. The plate shall be covered with a sheet of hard asbestos board $\frac{1}{4}$ inch in thickness, and of the same shape as the metal plate. There shall be cut in the center of the asbestos board a circular hole just fitting the cup. Heat may be supplied from any convenient source. The use of a gas burner, electric heater, or alcohol lamp is permitted, but under no circumstances are products of combustion or free flame allowed to come up around

Bureau Mines Tech. Paper 323A, p. 61.

the cup. The source of heat shall be centered under the opening in the plate and shall be of a type that will not produce local superheating. If a flame heater is used, it may be protected from drafts or excessive radiation by any suitable type of shield that does not project above the level of the upper surface of the asbestos board.

3. The thermometer shall conform to the following specifications:

Type: Etched stem, glass.
Total length: 305 mm.
Stem: Plain front, enamel back, suitable thermometer tubing; diameter, 6 to 7 mm.
Bulb: Corning normal, Jena 16 III, or equally suitable thermometric glass; length, 13 mm., maximum; diameter, not greater than stem.
Actuating liquid: Mercury.
Range: + 20° to + 760° F.
Immersion: 1 inch. The words "1 in. Immersion" shall be etched on the stem and also a line around the stem to indicate the depth of immersion
Distance of 20° line from bottom of bulb: 40 to 50 mm.
Distance to 760° line from top of stem: 30 to 45 mm.
Filled: Nitrogen gas.
Top finish: Red glass ring.
Graduation: All lines, figures, and letters clear cut and distinct; scale graduated in 5° divisions; scale numbered every 20°, the first and each succeeding 10° F. line to be longer than the others.
Special marking: "A. S. T. M. Open Flash," serial number, and manufacturer's name or trade-mark etched on stem.
Accuracy: Error at any point on scale shall not exceed one-half smallest scale division up to 700° F.
Test for permanency of range: After being subjected to a temperature of 700° F. for 24 hours, the accuracy shall be within the limit specified.
Points to be tested for certification: 32°, 212°, 400°, 700° F.

PROCEDURE

4. (*a*) The thermometer shall be suspended or held in a vertical position by any suitable device. The bottom of the bulb shall be one-fourth inch (0.635 cm.) [1] from the bottom of the cup and above a point halfway between the center and back of the cup.

(*b*) The cup shall be filled with the oil to be tested in such a manner that the top of the meniscus is exactly at the filling line at room temperature. The surface of the oil shall be free from bubbles. There shall be no oil above the filling line or on the outside of the apparatus.

(*c*) The test flame shall be approximately $\frac{5}{32}$ inch (0.397 cm.) in diameter.

NOTE. For purposes of comparison it is recommended that a bead of suitable light-colored material be mounted in a convenient position so that the size of the test flame can be determined. The device for applying the flame may be of any suitable type, but it is suggested that the tip be approximately one sixteenth inch (0.159 cm.) in diameter at the end and that the orifice be one thirty-second inch (0.079 cm.) in diameter. If the device for operating the test flame be mounted in such a manner as to permit automatic duplication of the sweep of the test flame, the radius of swing shall be not less than 6 inches.

(*d*) The test flame shall be applied as the temperature read on the thermometer reaches each successive 5° F. mark. The flame shall pass in a straight line (or on the circumference of a circle having a radius of at least 6 inches) across the center of the cup and at right angles to the diameter passing through the thermometer. The test flame shall, while passing across

---

[1] The immersion line engraved on the thermometer stem will be $\frac{1}{16}$ inch (0.159 cm.) below the level of the rim of the cup.

the surface of the oil, be in the plane of the upper edge of the cup. The time for the passage of the test flame across the cup shall be approximately 1 second.

(e) The oil shall be heated at a rate not exceeding 30° F. per minute temperature rise, till a point is reached approximately 100° F. below the probable flash point of the oil. Thereafter the rate of heating shall be decreased, and for at least the last 50° F. before the flash point is reached, the rate shall be not less than 9 nor more than 11° F. per minute.

5. The flash point shall be taken as the temperature read on the thermometer when a flash appears at any point on the surface of the oil. The true flash must not be confused with a bluish halo that sometimes surrounds the test flame.

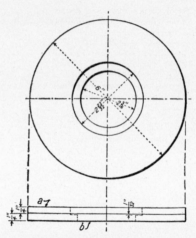

Fig. 90. Heating plate for use with Cleveland open cup (A. S. T. M.):
a, Asbestos disc; b, plate

6. After the flash point is determined the heating shall be continued at the specified rate of 9° to 11° F. per minute, and application of the test flame shall be made at the specified intervals until the oil ignites and continues to burn for a period of at least 5 seconds. The method of application of the flame shall be the same as for flash point. The temperature read at the time of the flame application which causes burning for a period of 5 seconds or more shall be recorded as the fire point.

7. The flash-point and fire-point tests shall be made in a room or compartment free from air drafts. The operator shall avoid breathing over the surface of the oil. It is desirable that the room or compartment be darkened sufficiently to make the flash readily discernible.

The method of recording is the same as in the case of the illuminating oils, one column for times and another for temperatures. Holde[1] finds that with oils flashing between 172° C. and 241° C. the exact quantity of oil used is of little importance. In these particular cases a difference of filling of 13 cc. altered the flash point only 1–1.5° C. For the effect of water see page 1115.

It is worthy of notice that the free fatty (oleic) acid contained in an oil lowers its flash point apparently in proportion to the quantity present.

[1] J. Soc. Chem. Ind., **16**, 322, 1897.

Detection of Soap. To increase the viscosity of an oil,[1] resort is had to the use of "oil pulp," "oil-thickener," or "white gelatin," usually an oleate of aluminum, though other bases may be present. Its disadvantages are that it causes the oil to chill more easily and to emulsify, thus increasing the friction. Furthermore, it is precipitated by contact with water or steam, causing clogging of the machinery.

The test depends upon the fact that the metaphosphates of the earthy and alkali metals and aluminum are insoluble in absolute alcohol.[2]

The test is applied as follows: five to 10 cc. of the oil to be tested are dissolved in about 5 cc. of 86° gasoline or ether, and about 15 drops of the phosphoric acid solution (Reagents, p. 1158) added, shaken and allowed to stand; the formation of a flocculent precipitate indicates the presence of soap. An idea of the kind of soap can be often gained by adding an alcoholic solution of $PtCl_4$. If the precipitate becomes crystalline, it is a potash soap; if it dissolves, soda, lime, or magnesia; if unchanged, alumina or iron.

For the accurate determination of these compounds a known weight of the oil must be ignited, the residue determined and quantitatively examined.

Caoutchouc. Holde[3] states that 1 to 2% of unvulcanized caoutchouc is sometimes added to oils to increase their viscosity. This may be detected by adding three parts of alcohol to four parts of the ethereal solution, whereby the rubber material is precipitated and may be dried and weighed.

Test for Fatty Oils. To detect small quantities of fatty oil ($\frac{1}{4}$ to 2%) Lux[4] recommends heating a few cubic centimeters of the oil for fifteen minutes with some bits of sodium in a test-tube in an oil bath; a similar test is made with sodium hydroxide. The temperature employed should be for light oils about 230°, for dark oils 250°.[5] In case fatty oil be present, the contents of one or both of the tubes solidify to a jelly of greater or less consistence according to the amount of fatty oil present.

The quantitative determination of these oils, as for example in cylinder oils, is effected after the manner of determining the saponification value (p. 1140) or the detection of unsaponifiable oils in fatty oils (page 1140b).

Schreiber[6] adopts a method similar to Sweetham and Henriques, in that he dissolves 5 grams of the oil in 25 cc. of benzole, adds 25–50 cc. N/2 alcoholic potash, and boils for half an hour on the water bath, using a 3-ft. glass tube as a condenser.

Gumming Test.[7] This is designed to give an idea of the amount of a change that may be expected in a mineral oil when in use. These resinified products increase the friction of the revolving or rubbing surfaces.[8] It is also a measure of the amount that an oil will "carbonize" in a gas or gasoline engine cylinder. It is applied after the manner of the elaidin test, by thoroughly mixing together 5 grams of the oil in a cordial glass with 11 grams of nitrosul-

---

[1] In a case which came to the writer's notice the oil would not flow out of the Saybolt "A" apparatus at 70°, at 85° required 1167'', and at 110°, 181''.
[2] Schweitzer and Lungwitz, J. Soc. Chem. Ind., **13**, 1178, 1894.
[3] "Examination of Hydrocarbon Oils," p. 202.
[4] Z. anal. Chem., **24**, 357, 1885.
[5] Holde, Examination of Hydrocarbon Oils, p. 76.
[6] J. Am. Chem. Soc., **29**, 74, 1907.
[7] Gill, J. Am. Chem. Soc., **24**, 467, 1902.
[8] Aisinman, J. Soc. Chem. Ind., **14**. 282, 1895.

phuric acid and cooling by immersion in a pan of water at 10–15°. Brownish spots or, in case of a bad oil, masses, form around the edges and become red in the course of two hours.

As shown by long practical experience, the oil showing the best tar or gum is the best oil; it also absorbs the least oxygen.

Carbon Residue Test: Conradson's Method.

APPARATUS

(a) Porcelain crucible, wide form, glazed throughout, 25 to 26 cc. capacity, 46 mm. diameter.[2]

(b) Skidmore iron crucible, 45 cc. (1½ ounces) capacity, 65 mm. in diameter, 37 to 39 mm. high with cover, without delivery tubes, and one opening closed.

(c) Wrought-iron crucible with cover, about 180 cc. capacity, 80 mm. diameter, 58 to 60 mm. high. At the bottom of this crucible a layer of sand is placed about 10 mm. deep, or enough to bring the Skidmore crucible with cover on nearly to the top of the wrought-iron crucible.

(d) Triangle, pipe stem covered, projection on side to allow flame to reach the crucible on all sides.

(e) Sheet-iron or asbestos hood provided with a chimney about 2 to 2½ inches high, 2⅛ inches in diameter, to distribute the heat uniformly during the process.

(f) Asbestos or hollow sheet-iron block, 6 to 7 inches square, 1¼ to 1½ inches high, provided with opening in center 3¼ inches in diameter at the bottom and 3½ inches in diameter at the top.

METHOD OF TESTING

The tests shall be conducted as follows: A sample [3] of the oil to be tested is weighed in a porcelain crucible, which is placed in a Skidmore crucible. These two crucibles are set in a larger iron crucible (Fig. 90a), being careful to have the Skidmore crucible set in the center of the iron crucible, covers being applied to the Skidmore and iron crucibles. Place on triangle and suitable stand with asbestos block, and cover with sheet-iron or asbestos hood in order to distribute the heat uniformly during the process.

Heat from a Bunsen burner or other burner is applied with a high flame surrounding the large crucible c until vapors from the oil begin to ignite over the crucible, when the heat is slowed down so that the vapor (flame) will come off at a uniform rate. The flame from the ignited vapors should not extend over 2 inches above the sheet-iron hood. After the vapor ceases to come off, the heat is increased as at the start and kept constant for 5 minutes, making the lower part of the large crucible red hot, after which the apparatus is allowed to cool somewhat before the crucible is uncovered. The porcelain crucible is removed, cooled in a desiccator, and weighed.

The entire process should require one-half hour to complete when heat is properly regulated. The time will depend somewhat upon the kind of oil

---

[1] Tech. Paper 323A, p. 79.

[2] A glazed silica crucible of the same dimensions may be used.

[3] When a carbon residue is not greater than 1.5%, a 10-gram sample of the oil shall be used; if the carbon residue is between 1.5 and 3.0%, a 5-gram sample; if above 3.0%, a 2-gram sample shall be used.

tested, as a very thin, rather low flash-point oil will not take as long as a heavy, thick, high flash-point oil.

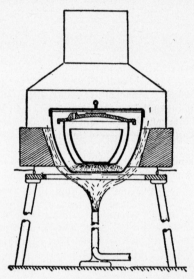

Fig. 90a.   Apparatus for determining carbon residue.

Motor oils, of light and medium grade, range in coke-like residue from 0.06 to 0.5%, the percentage of fixed carbon being roughly proportional to the viscosity of the oil. That is, the higher the viscosity, the higher will be the percentage of fixed carbon, provided the oils have been manufactured from the same grade of crude petroleum by the same general methods. The heavy and extra heavy motor oils range from 0.5 to 1.25%. As the percentage of fixed carbon varies with the viscosities of the oils, the viscosity should be taken into consideration. For illustration, it would not be fair to compare a motor oil having a viscosity of 200 at 100° F., Saybolt, with a motor oil having a viscosity of 400 at the same temperature. The carbon residue in the 200 viscosity oil would be in the neighborhood of 0.2%, where as the fixed carbon of the higher viscosity oil would be in the neighborhood of 0.75%.

Gasoline Test. This shows the presence of tar (still bottoms) or asphaltic matters.

Mix 10 cc. of the oil with 90 cc. 86°–88° gasoline (from Pennsylvania crude) B.pt. 30°–50° C., allow to stand one hour at 70° to 80° F.; not more than 10% of flocculent or tarry matter should have settled out. This settling can be

12

facilitated by whirling in a centrifuge in a graduated tube in which the volume of the precipitate can be read off. If the test be applied to the oil before making the flash test and then again after this test it shows the extent to which the oil is changed upon heating. Other things being equal the oil which is changed the least is the best oil.[1]

Microscopical Test. Put a few drops of the well-mixed oil on a slide and note the nature of the suspended matter—whether carbonaceous specks, flakes of paraffin which disappear on warming, or foreign matter. A good oil should be practically free from all these bodies.

Heat Test. Heat 20–25 cc. of the oil in an Erlenmeyer flask or beaker, nearly to the flashing point and keep it at this temperature for fifteen minutes; a satisfactory oil will darken, but remain clear even after standing a day. A poorly refined oil changes to jet black, and forms a carbon-like precipitate. This is usually indicative of an oil that has been refined by acid treatment.

Herschel's Demulsibility Test.[1] The test is applicable to non-emulsifying oils, such as are used with high speed engines and turbines, and in its present form does not apply to steam cylinder or other compounded oils. It is made as follows:

Twenty cc. of oil and 40 cc. of distilled water are placed in a 100 cc. cylinder having an inside diameter of 2.6 cm. and heated to 55°. The oil and water are then mixed or emulsified by stirring with a paddle for five minutes at a speed of 1500 R.P.M. The paddle is simply a metal plate 89 by 20 by 1.5 mm. thick, conveniently driven by an electric motor.

The rate at which the oil settles out from the emulsion, when it is allowed to stand at a temperature of 55° is a measure of the emulsibility of the oil. There is a tendency for the rate of settling out of the oil to increase up to a maximum and then decrease, and we may take readings every five minutes (or every minute if the oil separates out rapidly) and note the maximum rate. For example, the following readings were obtained for a certain oil:

Time	Time Since Stopping Paddle	Reading of Cylinder at Top of Emulsion	Cc. of Oil Settled Out	Rate of Settling Cc. per Hour
9.50.......	0	60	0	0
9.55.......	5	57	3	36
10.02.......	12	47	13	65
10.05.......	15	43	19	68
10.10.......	20	41	17	57

The maximum rate is here 68 cc. per hour, and this is called the "demulsibility." The best transformer, motor, and turbine oils settle out in one minute or less, so that if we take readings to even minutes and even cc., the rate would be 1200. Oils are found with rates all the way down from this maximum rate to zero.

It has been found necessary to shake the container holding the sample of oil if it has been allowed to stand for some time, or otherwise the oil poured off from the top may show a different rate of settling from the oil at the bottom. It is also necessary to protect the oil from sunlight which has the effect of decreasing the rate of settling.

[1] U. S. Bureau Standards, Bulletin **86** (1917).

With some oils, under certain conditions, part of the water does not enter into the emulsion and drops of oil adhere to the sides of the cylinder. When this phenomenon occurs, the rate of settling, indicated by the test, is apt to be incorrectly high. The adhering drops may be avoided by using a lower speed or less water, the total quantity of oil and water being kept equal to 60 cc. If part of the water does not enter into the emulsion, but we do not have the above described phenomenon, complete emulsification may sometimes be obtained by prolonging the stirring beyond five minutes, or by increasing the speed.

Friction Tests. The writer doubts if friction tests are worth the outlay for a machine and the time expended in their execution. Without question they do determine the relative efficiency as regards lubricating power of different oils, but the conditions under which the test is made seldom occur in practice; the bearings upon which the oil is tested are as nearly perfect as can be made, and the feed and load are as regular as is possible; in other words, the conditions are ideal.

The lubricating power of an oil is so closely related to its viscosity [1] that the author believes that results of more practical value can be obtained by the determination of the viscosity of the oils, and subsequent observation of their behavior in actual use than by the longer and more troublesome friction test. Recent experiments,[2] however, have shown that of two oils of the same viscosity and other constants the coefficient of friction of one was 14% less than the other.

In case, however, it be desired to make the friction test, the following machines, it is believed, will be found to be most satisfactory for the purpose:

For spindle oils and light lubricating oils, the machine [3] of the Thurston type which can be run at the highest speed and lowest pressure.

For heavy oils and railroad work, the large machine of the Thurston [4] type, described also in Redwood Treatise on Petroleum, III, 851 (1922); also in Archbutt and Deeley.[5]

Color. This is determined with the Union Colorimeter which uses standard glass plates, Tech. Paper 323A, p. 33.

LIQUID FUELS

(a) *Gasoline.* The tests usually made are color, doctor test, corrosion, distillation, acidity, and sulphur.

The color, acidity, and sulphur tests are made as with kerosene.

The doctor test (sodium plumbite) is made as follows: [6]

Doctor Test (Sodium Plumbite)

PREPARATION OF REAGENTS

(1) *Sodium plumbite (doctor solution).*—Dissolve approximately 125 grams of sodium hydroxide (NaOH) in 1 liter of distilled water. Add 60 grams of litharge (PbO) and shake vigorously for 15 minutes or let stand with occasional

---

[1] Brannt, "Petroleum and its Products," p. 510; Woodbury, *vide infra*.
[2] Trans. Am. Soc. Mech. Eng., **32**, 834, 1910.
[3] Made by Olsen or Riehlé Bros., Philadelphia, Pa.
[4] "Lubrication and Lubricants," 1907, pp. 332–348.
[5] Ibid., pp. 355, 359.
[6] Tech. Paper 323A, p. 85.

shaking for at least a day. Allow to settle and decant or siphon off the clear liquid. Filtration through a mat of asbestos may be employed if the solution does not settle clear. The solution should be kept in a tightly corked bottle and should be refiltered before use if not perfectly clear.

(2) *Sulphur.*—Pure, dry flowers of sulphur.

MAKING OF TEST

Shake vigorously together in a test tube 10 cc. of the sample to be tested and 5 cc. of sodium plumbite solution for about 15 seconds. Add a small pinch of flowers of sulphur, again shake for 15 seconds, and allow to settle. The quantity of sulphur used should be such that practically all of it floats on the interface between the sample and the sodium-plumbite solution.

INTERPRETATION OF RESULTS

If the sample is discolored, or if the yellow color of the sulphur film is noticeably masked, the test shall be reported as *positive* and the sample condemned as " sour." If the sample remains unchanged in color, and if the sulphur film is bright yellow or only slightly discolored with gray or flecked with black, the test shall be reported *negative* and the sample considered " sweet."

Corrosion Test (Copper Dish)

APPARATUS

A freshly polished hemispherical dish of spun copper approximately $3\frac{1}{2}$ inches in diameter.

MAKING OF TEST

Place 100 cc. of the gasoline to be examined in the dish and place the dish in an opening of an actively boiling steam bath, so that the steam comes in contact with the outer surface of the dish up to the level of the gasoline. Leave the dish on the steam bath until all volatile material has disappeared.

INTERPRETATION OF THE RESULTS

If the gasoline contains dissolved elementary sulphur or corrosive sulphur compounds, the bottom of the dish will be colored gray or black.

If the gasoline contains undesirable gum-forming constituents, there will be a weighable amount of gum deposited on the dish. Acid residues will show as gum in this test.

Corrosion Test[1] at 122° F. (A. S. T. M. Method D130–22T, Copper Strip)

1. This method of test shall be used for the detection of free sulphur and corrosive sulphur compounds in gasoline.

2. A clean strip of mechanically polished pure sheet copper about $\frac{1}{2}$ inch in width and 3 inches in length shall be placed in a suitable clean tube or sample bottle. Gasoline under test shall be added so that the copper strip is completely immersed. The test tube or sample bottle shall be closed with a loosely fitting cork and held in a suitable bath at 122° F. (50° C.).

[1] Tech. Paper 323A, p. 86.

At the end of 3 hours the gasoline-exposed strip shall be removed and shall be compared with a similar strip of freshly polished copper.

3. The presence of sulphur or corrosive sulphur compounds is indicated by the corrosion or discoloration of the gasoline-exposed strip when compared with the fresh copper strip.

4. (a) Gasoline shall be reported as passing the test when on examination the exposed strip shows no discoloration as compared with the fresh copper strip.

(b) Gasoline shall be reported as not passing the test when on examination the exposed strip shows discoloration as compared with the fresh copper strip.

Method 100.12.—Distillation of Gasolene

APPARATUS AND PROCEDURE

The apparatus and procedure are the same as given in method 10022, p. 1111, with the following exceptions:

Paragraph 4: The hard asbestos board, 6 by 6 by $\frac{1}{4}$ inch, shall have a hole $1\frac{1}{4}$ inches in diameter in its center.

Paragraph 6: The A. S. T. M. low-distillation thermometer shall conform to the following specifications:

Type: Etched stem, glass.
Total length: 381 mm.
Stem: Plain front, enamel back, suitable thermometer tubing; diameter, 6 to 7 mm.
Bulb: Corning normal, Jena 16 III, or equally suitable thermometric glass; length, 10 to 15 mm.; diameter, 5 to 6 mm.
Actuating liquid: Mercury.
Range: 30° F. to 580° F., or 0° C. to 300° C.
Immersion: Total.
Distance to 30° F., or 0° C. mark from bottom of bulb: 100 to 110 mm.
Distance to 580° F., or 300° C. mark from top of tube: 30 to 45 mm.
Filled: Nitrogen gas.
Top finish: Glass ring.
Graduation: All lines, figures, and letters clear cut and distinct; scale graduated in 2° F. or 1° C. divisions and numbered every 20° F. or 10° C., the first and each succeeding 10° F. (5° C.) to be longer than the others.
Special markings: "A. S. T. M. Low Distillation," serial number, and manufacturer's name or trade-mark etched on the stem.
Accuracy: Error at any point on scale shall not exceed one-half smallest scale division.
Tests for permanency of range: After being subjected to a temperature of 560° F. or 290° C. for 24 hours, the accuracy shall be within the limit specified.
Points to be tested for certification: 32°, 212°, 400°, 570° F. or 0°, 100°, 200°, 370° C.

FUEL OILS

The tests usually made are flash, viscosity, sulphur, water and sediment.

Flash Point by Means of the Pensky=Martens Closed Tester [1] (A. S. T. M. Method D93–22)

1. The A. S. T. M. standard Pensky-Martens closed tester shall be used for determining the flash point of fuel oil unless the use of the Tag closed tester is specified.

[1] Tech. Paper 323A, p. 46.

2. The Pensky-Martens tester, a diagram of which appears in Fig. 90*b*, shall include the following major parts:

(*a*) *Cup.* The cup of the A. S. T. M. Pensky-Martens flash tester shall be made of brass and shall satisfy the following dimensional specifications:

SPECIFICATION FOR CUP OF A. S. T. M. PENSKY–MARTENS FLASH TESTER

Dimensions	Minimum	Normal	Maximum	Minimum	Normal	Maximum
	Inches	*Inches*	*Inches*	*Cm.*	*Cm.*	*Cm.*
Inside diameter below filling mark..........	1.950	2.000	2.050	4.953	5.080	5.207
Difference, inside and outside diameters below filling mark.......	.120	.125	.130	.305	.318	.330
Inside height...........	2.150	2.200	2.250	5.461	5.588	5.715
Thickness of bottom.....	.070	.095	.120	.178	.241	.305
Distance from rim to filling mark..........	.845	.860	.875	2.146	2.184	2.223
Distance lower surface flange to bottom of cup	1.780	1.795	1.810	4.521	4.559	4.597

The inside of the cup may be turned to a slightly larger diameter above the filling mark and the outside may be tapered above the flange, but the wall thickness at the upper edge shall be not less than 0.04 inch (0.102 cm.). The flange should be approximately 0.5 inch (1.27 cm.) wide and approximately 0.125 inch (0.318 cm.) thick. It shall be equipped with devices for locating the position of the lid on the cup and the cup in the stove. A handle, attached permanently to the flange of the cup, is a desirable accessory.

(*b*) *Lid.* 1. *Stirring device.* The lid shall be equipped with a stirring device consisting of a vertical steel shaft, not less than 0.1 inch (0.254 cm.) nor more than 0.125 inch (0.318 cm.) in diameter, mounted in the center of the cup, and carrying two 2-bladed brass propellers. The blades of both propellers shall be approximately 0.313 inch (0.795 cm.) wide and shall be set at an angle of approximately 45°. The smaller (upper) propeller shall have an over-all diameter of approximately 0.75 inch (1.905 cm.). The larger (lower) propeller shall have an over-all diameter between 1.25 and 1.75 inches (3.175 and 4.445 cm.). The thickness of the propeller blades shall be not less than 0.057 inch (0.145 cm.) nor more than 0.081 inch (0.206 cm.), which limits correspond, respectively, to No. 15 and No. 12 B. and S. gage sheet brass. The collars on which the propeller blades are mounted shall have horizontal and vertical dimensions not greater than 0.4 inch (1.016 cm.).

The plane of the center of the upper propeller shall be 0.4 inch (1.016 cm.) below the level of the rim of the cup. The plane of the center of the lower propeller shall be 2 inches (5.08 cm.) below the level of the rim of the cup. The level of the rim of the cup is in effect the level of the plane part of the portion of the lower surface of the lid inside the rim.

2. *Cover proper.* The cover proper shall be of brass and shall have a rim

[1] Tech. Paper 323A.

projecting downward almost to the flange of the cup and fitting the outside of the cup closely. The thickness of the cover, measured just inside the rim, shall not be less than 0.031 inch (0.079 cm.) nor more than 0.078 inch (0.198

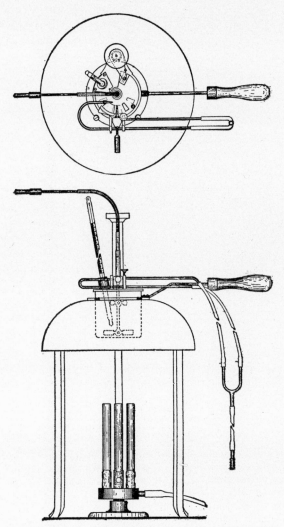

FIG. 90b. Pensky-Martens closed tester (A. S. T. M.)

cm.). There shall be a proper locating device engaging with a corresponding locating device on the flange of the cup.

There shall be four openings in the cover, as indicated in Fig. 90c.

Opening A is an area defined by arcs of two concentric circles and the intersected lengths of two radii. The radius of the outer circle shall be not less than 0.938 inch (2.383 cm.) nor more than 0.969 inch (2.461 cm.). The chord of the arc of the outer circle shall be not less than 0.500 inch (1.270 cm.) nor more than 0.540 inch (1.372 cm.).

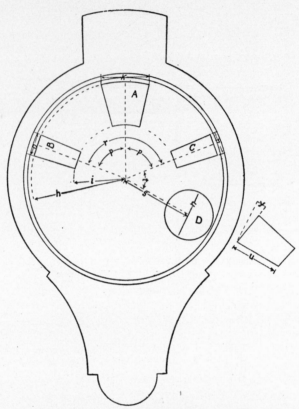

FIG. 90c.   Cover for Pensky-Martens tester (A. S. T. M.).

Openings B and C are equal areas, each of the same general form as opening A but of approximately half of the (angular) width. The radii of the defining inner and outer circles shall be within the limits specified for the radii of the two circles, arcs of which partly define opening A. The chord of the outer arc for opening B or opening C shall be not less than 0.187 inch (0.475 cm.) nor more than 0.219 inch (0.556 cm.). The sum of the areas of openings B and C shall be not less than 75% nor more than 100% of the area of opening A. Openings B and C shall be equally distant from opening A and radii drawn through each of their centers shall be at an angle of not less than 135° nor more than 140°.

Openings A, B, and C need not conform exactly to the shape of geometrical figures bounded by arcs of two concentric circles and intersected lengths of radii. Their boundaries must, however, fall on or between the lines indicated by the limiting values of the dimensional specification of the preceding text and of Fig. 90c.

Opening D is for a thermometer collar. Its center is approximately 0.75 inch (1.905 cm.) from the center of the lid and on a radius at an angle of not less than 50° nor more than 60° from a radius passing through the center of opening C. The thermometer collar shall have an inside diameter of approximately 0.5 inch (1.27 cm.). It shall be set at an angle of not less than 10° nor more than 15° from the perpendicular.

3. *Shutter.* The lid shall be equipped with a brass shutter, approximately 0.094 inch (0.239 cm.) thick operating on the plane of the upper surface of the lid. The shutter shall be so shaped and mounted that it rotates on the axis of the horizontal center of the lid between two stops so placed that when in one extreme position the openings A, B, and C of the lid are completely closed and when in the other extreme position these orifices are completely opened.

4. *Flame-exposure device.* The flame-exposure device shall have a tip with an opening 0.027 inch (0.069 cm.) to 0.031 inch (0.079 cm.) in diameter. The flame-exposure device shall be equipped with an operating mechanism which, when the shutter is in the "open" position, depresses the tip so that the center of the orifice is between the planes of the under and upper surfaces of the lid proper at a point on a radius passing through the center of the larger opening A and approximately 0.1 inch (0.254 cm.) from the outer edge of the opening.

NOTE. A pilot flame for automatic relighting of the exposure flame should be provided. A bead $\frac{5}{32}$ inch in diameter, of some suitable material, may be mounted on the lid so that the size of the test flame can be regulated by comparison.

The mechanism operating the shutter should be of the spring type and so constructed that when at rest the shutter shall exactly close the three openings. When operated to the other extreme the three openings in the lid shall be exactly open and the tip of the exposure tube shall be fully depressed.

(c) *Stove.* Heat shall be supplied to the cup by means of a properly designed stove which is equivalent to an air bath. This stove shall consist of (1) an air bath and (2) a top plate on which the flange of the cup rests.

1. *Air bath.* The air bath shall have a cylindrical interior 1.625 inches (4.128 cm.) to 1.656 inches (4.206 cm.) deep and a diameter not less than 0.125 inch (0.317 cm.) nor more than 0.156 inch (0.396 cm.) greater than the outside diameter of the cup. The air bath may be either a flame-heated metal casting or an electric resistance element.

NOTE. If the heating element is a flame-heated metal casting, it shall be so designed and used that the temperature of bottom and walls is approximately the same. On this account it should be not less than 0.25 inch (0.635 cm.) thick. The casting shall be so designed that products of combustion of the flame can not pass up and in contact with the cup.

If the air bath is of the electric-resistance type, it shall be so constructed that all parts of the interior surface are heated equally. This necessitates an even distribution of resistance wire over bottom and walls and a method of construction such that heat is given out from the whole core of the resistance element rather than directly from the wire.

2. *Top plate.* The top plate shall be of metal. The total distance from the upper surface of the plate to the bottom of the air bath shall exceed the distance from the under surface of the flange to the bottom of the cup by not less than 0.063 inch (0.160 cm.) nor more than 0.125 inch (0.317 cm.).

The top plate shall be mounted with an air gap between it and the air bath. The top plate may be attached to the air bath by means of three screws and spacing bushings. The spacing bushings should be of proper thickness to define the air gap, which shall be not less than 0.125 inch (0.317 cm.) nor more than 0.187 inch (0.475 cm.). The spacing bushings shall be not more than 0.375 inch (0.952 cm.) in diameter.

(d) *Thermometers.* Two standard thermometers shall be used with the A. S. T. M. Pensky-Martens tester. The low-range " P. M. and Tag " thermometers shall be used for tests when the indicated reading falls within the limits 20° to 200° F. The " P. M. high " thermometer shall be used for tests when the indicated reading falls within the limits 230° to 700° F. For the range 200° to 230° F. either thermometer may be employed, depending on the convenience of the operator. The thermometers shall comply with the specifications given in Table 3.

Thermometers shall be so mounted that the bottom of the bulb is 1.75 inches (4.445 cm.) below the level of the rim of the cup (which corresponds to the level of the lower surface of the portion of the lid inside the rim).

Procedure

3. (a) All parts of the cup and its accessories shall be thoroughly clean and dry before the test is started. Particular care shall be taken to avoid the presence of gasoline or naphtha used to clean the apparatus after a previous test.

(b) The cup shall be filled with the oil to be tested up to the level indicated by the filling mark.

(c) The lid shall be placed on the cup and the latter set in the stove. Care shall be taken to have the locating devices properly engaged. The thermometer shall be inserted. If it is known that the oil will flash above 220° F., the " P. M. High " thermometer may be selected; otherwise, it is preferable to start with the " P. M. and Tag " thermometer and change in case a temperature of 220° to 230° F. is reached.

(d) The test flame shall be lighted and so adjusted that it is of the size of a bead $\frac{5}{32}$ inch in diameter.

(e) Heat shall be supplied at such a rate that the temperature read on the thermometer increases not less than 9° nor more than 11° F. per minute. The stirrer shall be turned at a rate of from one to two revolutions per second.

(f) Application of the test flame shall be made at each temperature reading which is a multiple of 2° F. up to 220° F. For the temperature range above 220° F., application shall be made at each temperature reading which is a multiple of 5° F. The first application of the test flame shall be made at a temperature at least 30° F. below the actual flash point. Application of the test flame shall be made by operating the device controlling the shutter and test flame burner so that the flame is lowered in one-half second, left in its lowered position for 1 second, and quickly raised to its high position. Stirring shall be discontinued during the application of the test flame.

4. The flash point is taken as the temperature read on the thermometer at the time of the flame application that causes a distinct flash in the interior of the cup. The true flash must not be confused with the bluish halo that sometimes surrounds the test flame for the applications preceding the one that causes the actual flash.

TABLE 3.—*Specifications for thermometers for Pensky-Martens tester*

	Low range " P. M. and Tag "[1]	High range " P. M. High "
Type	Etched stem, glass	Etched stem, glass.
Total length	275 mm.	275 mm.
Stem	Plain front, enamel back, suitable thermometer tubing; diameter, 6 to 7 mm.	Plain front, enamel back, suitable thermometer tubing; diameter, 6 to 7 mm.
Bulb	Corning normal, Jena 16 III, or equally suitable thermometric glass; diameter, less than stem; length, 9 to 13 mm.	Corning normal, Jena 16 III, or equally suitable thermometric glass; diameter, less than stem; length, maximum, 10 mm.
Actuating liquid	Mercury	Mercury.
Range	20° F. to 230° F.	200° F. to 700° F.
Immersion	2¼ inches (57 mm.) from end of bulb. Words "2¼ in. Immersion" etched on the stem, also a line around the stem to indicate depth of immersion.	2¼ inches (57 mm.) from end of bulb. Words "2¼ in. Immersion" etched on the stem, also a line around the stem to indicate depth of immersion.
Distance to 20° line from bottom of bulb. }	75 to 90 mm	
Distance to 200° line from bottom of bulb. }		75 to 90 mm.
Distance to 230° line from top of stem. }	25 to 40 mm	
Distance to 700° line from top of stem. }		25 to 40 mm.
Expansion chamber	Required	None.
Filled	Nitrogen gas	Nitrogen gas.
Top finish	Glass ring	Glass ring.
Graduating	All lines, figures, and letters clear cut and distinct; scale graduated in 1° divisions; scale numbered every 10°, the first and each succeeding 5° line to be longer than the others.	All lines, figures, and letters clear cut and distinct; scale graduated in 5° divisions; scale numbered every 50°, the first and each succeeding 25° line to be longer than the others.
Special marking	"A. S. T. M., P. M., and Tag," serial number, manufacturer's name or trademark etched on the stem.	"A. S. T. M., P. M., High," serial number, manufacturer's name or trade-mark etched on the stem.
Accuracy	Error at any point in scale shall not exceed 1°.	Error at any point in scale shall not exceed one-half smallest scale division.
Test for permanency		After being subjected to a temperature of 680° F. for 24 hours the accuracy shall be within the limit specified.
Points to be tested	32°, 100°, 150°, 212° F.	212°, 450°, 700° F.

5. The barometric pressure shall be observed and recorded. No corrections shall be made except in case of dispute, when the flash-point figure shall be corrected according to the following rule:

For each inch (25 mm.) below 29.92 inches (760 mm.) barometric reading add 1.6° F. to the flash point.

[1] The low-range "P. M. and Tag" thermometer is the instrument specified for use with the Tag closed tester.

For each inch (25 mm.) above 29.92 inches (760 mm.) barometric reading subtract 1.6° F. from the flash point.

Viscosity is determined with the Saybolt Furol viscosimeter, p. 1116.

Sulphur[1] (A. S. T. M. Method D129–22T)

APPARATUS

1. The oxygen bomb shall have a capacity of not less than 300 cc. and shall be of a design or construction such that no leaks shall occur at any pressure or temperature generated during the test, and such that when the bomb is open the liquid contents can be easily and completely drained. The inner surfaces shall be of materials that are chemically and physically resistant to the process or products of combustion. The gaskets, insulating materials, etc., shall be, as far as possible, physically and chemically resistant and in no event shall they undergo any reaction which would increase or decrease the sulphur content of the bomb liquors.

2. The oil cup shall be of platinum, glazed silica, or other suitable material, with a capacity of not less than 2.5 cc. nor more than 5 cc.

3. If a platinum oil cup is used, the fuse wire shall be of platinum; if a glazed silica oil cup is used, the fuse wire may be of either platinum or iron. No. 35 (B. and S. gage) is a convenient size.

4. (*a*) The distilled water and all reagents should be sulphur free, but when it is necessary to employ reagents not sulphur free, blanks shall be run and the figures thus obtained used to correct the results of actual determinations.

(*b*) The barium chloride solution shall contain 100 grams of $BaCl_2.2H_2O$ per liter.

PROCEDURE

5. (*a*) Twenty cubic centimeters of distilled water shall be placed in the bottom of the bomb. From 0.6 to 0.8 gram of the oil to be tested shall be placed in the weighed oil cup and the weight of this charge shall be determined to an accuracy of at least ±0.002 gram. The cup shall be placed in the proper position in the bomb, the ignition mechanism arranged and the bomb closed. Oxygen shall be admitted slowly until a pressure is reached as indicated by the following table:

Capacity of bomb, cc.	Minimum gage pressure, atmospheres
300 to 350	40
350 to 400	35
400 to 450	30
450 to 500	27.5
Above 500	25

The leads from the firing circuit shall be attached, the bomb placed in a bucket of cold water, and ignited. The bomb shall be allowed to stand in the water for 10 minutes and shall then be removed. The valve of the bomb shall be opened, allowing the gas to escape at an approximately even rate so that the pressure is reduced to atmospheric in not less than 1 minute. The bomb shall be opened, and all parts of its interior, including the oil cup, rinsed with a fine jet of distilled water. All washings, which should not amount to more than 350 cc., shall be collected in a beaker. Particular care should be

[1] Tech. Paper 323A.

taken not to lose, by splashing or otherwise, any of the liquid contents of the bomb. The washings shall be filtered through a washed " qualitative " filter paper. The filter shall be washed thoroughly. Two cc. of concentrated HCl and 10 cc. of saturated bromine water shall be added to the filtrate. The solution shall be evaporated to about 75 cc. on a steam bath or hot plate. Ten cc. of hot barium chloride solution shall be added in a fine stream or drop-wise to the hot solution, stirring during the addition and for 2 minutes after-wards. The solution shall be allowed to stand over night, or shall be kept hot for 1 hour on the steam bath or hot plate, allowing the precipitate to settle for another hour while cooling. The supernatant liquid shall be filtered through an " ashless quantitative " filter paper and the precipitate washed with water, first by decantation, then on the filter, till free from chloride. The paper and precipitate shall be transferred to a suitable weighed crucible, dried at low heat till moisture is evaporated, the paper charred (without flaming), and finally ignited at a good red heat till the precipitate is just burned white. A satisfactory means of accomplishing these operations is to place the crucible containing the wet filter paper in a cold electric muffle furnace and to turn on the current. Drying, charring, and ignition will usually occur at the desired rate.

(b) After ignition is complete, the crucible shall be allowed to cool to room temperature and weighed. The use of a desiccator is not recommended.

(c) From the increase in weight of the crucible the percentage of sulphur shall be calculated from the formula:

$$\text{Percentage of sulpur} = \frac{\text{grams of BaSO}_4 \times 13.734}{\text{grams of oil used}}.$$

6. Duplicate determinations should agree to $\pm 2\%$ on the basis of the sulphur found.

The Jackson Turbidimeter for rapid work can be used, p. 1620.

Water and *Sediment* are determined as follows:

Water [1] (A. S. T. M. Method D95–23T)

1. This method of test determines the water in a sample of bituminous material by distilling the sample with a volatile solvent. This method is suitable for a variety of materials but is especially applicable to petroleum, fuel oil, road oil, coal tar, water-gas tar, coke-oven tar, and other petroleum products or bituminous materials.

APPARATUS

2. The apparatus shall consist of a metal still or glass flask, heated by suitable means and provided with a reflux condenser discharging into a trap connected to the still or flask. The trap serves to collect and measure the condensed water and to return the solvent to the still.

The type of distilling apparatus used is not an essential feature of this method, but glass has been generally used for petroleum products and the metal still for road materials and tars.

3. (a) The metal still (Fig. 91, a) shall be a vertical cylindrical vessel, preferably of copper, having a faced flange at the top to which the head is tightly attached by means of a clamp. The head shall be of metal, preferably

[1] Tech Paper 323A, p. 67.

of brass or copper, and be provided with a tubulation 1 inch in inside diameter.

(b) The glass flask (Fig. 91, b) shall be of the short-neck, round-bottom type, made of well-annealed glass, having an approximate capacity of 500 cc.

4. The burner used with the metal still shall be a ring gas burner 4 inches (100 mm.) in inside diameter. With the glass flask an ordinary gas burner or electric heater may be used as the source of heat.

5. The condenser shall be of the water-cooled, reflux, glass tube type, having a condenser jacket not less than 400 mm. (15¾ inches) in length with an inner tube 12 to 16 mm. (½ to ⅝ inch) in diameter. The end of the condenser to be inserted in the trap shall be ground off at an angle of 60°.

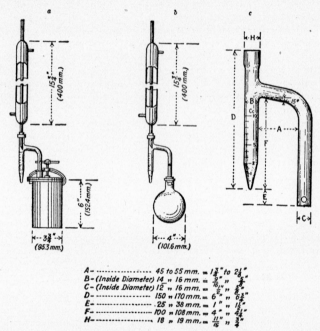

A- .... 45 to 55 mm. = 1¾" to 2⅛"
B- (Inside Diameter) 14 ″ 16 mm. = 9/16" ″ ⅝"
C- (Inside Diameter) 12 ″ 16 mm. = ½" ″ ⅝"
D- .... 150 ″ 170 mm. = 6" ″ 6¾"
E- .... .25 ″ 38 mm. = 1" ″ 1½"
F- .... 100 ″ 108 mm. = 4" ″ 4¼"
H- .... 18 ″ 19 mm. = 11/16" ″ ¾"

FIG. 91. Apparatus for determination of water.

6. The trap shall be made of well-annealed glass constructed in accordance with Fig. 91, c, and shall be graduated as shown from 0 to 10 cc. in 0.1 cc. divisions. The error of any indicated capacity shall not be greater than 0.05 cc. The outside diameters should preferably be 2.5 to 3.5 mm. (3/32 to ⅛ inch) greater than the inside diameters specified.

7. (a) The solvent used when testing petroleum products or bituminous materials derived from petroleum shall be gasoline free from water and shall conform to the following distillation requirements, determined in accordance with the "Tentative method of test for distillation of gasoline, naphtha, kerosene, and similar petroleum products"; 5 per cent shall distil at a temperature not below 194° F. (90° C.) nor above 212° F. (100° C.); 90 per cent shall distil below 410° F. (210° C.).

(b) The solvent used when testing bituminous materials derived from coal tar, water-gas tar, etc., shall be a coal-tar naphtha or a light oil and shall conform to the following distillation requirements, determined in accordance with the "Tentative method of test for distillation of gasoline, naphtha, kerosene, and similar petroleum products"; 98 per cent shall distil between 248° F. (120° C.) and 482° F. (250° C.).

SAMPLE

8. The sample shall be thoroughly representative of the material to be tested and the portion of the sample used for the test shall be thoroughly representative of the sample itself. Deviation from this requirement shall not be permitted.

NOTE. The difficulties in obtaining proper representative samples for this determination are unusually great, so that the importance of sampling can not be too strongly emphasized.

PROCEDURE

9. When the sample to be tested contains less than 10 per cent of water, exactly 100 cc. of the material to be tested shall be placed into the still or flask and thoroughly mixed with an equal volume of solvent by swirling, proper care being taken to avoid any loss of material. If the material is measured by volume, an accurate 100-cc. graduated cylinder shall be used and the contents transferred to the still by rinsing with one 50-cc. portion of solvent followed by two successive 25-cc. portions of solvent, the cylinder being allowed to drain each time. When the sample to be tested contains more than 10 per cent of water, the volume of material used shall be decreased to that which will yield somewhat less than 10 cc. of water.

NOTE. In special cases where the water content exceeds 10 per cent and it is not desirable to reduce the size of the sample to that which will yield somewhat less than 10 cc. of water, a distilling tube receiver graduated from 0 to 25 cc. may be used. This tube shall be graduated from 0 to 2 cc. in 0.1 cc., from 2 to 5 cc. in 0.2 cc., and from 5 to 25 cc. in 0.5 cc.

The connections between the still or flask, trap, and condenser shall be made by means of tight-fitting corks as shown in Fig. 91 (a and b). When the metal still is used, a heavy paper gasket moistened with the solvent shall be inserted between the lid and flange before attaching the clamp.

Heat shall then be applied and so regulated that the condensed distillate falls from the end of the condenser at the rate of from 2 to 5 drops per second. The ring burner used with the metal still should be placed about 3 inches above the bottom of the still at the beginning of the distillation and gradually lowered as the distillation proceeds.

The distillation shall be continued at the specified rate until no water is visible on any part of the apparatus except at the bottom of the trap. This operation usually requires less than an hour. A persistent ring of condensed water in the condenser tube shall be removed by increasing the rate of distillation for a few minutes.

10. The volume of condensed water measured in the trap at room temperature multiplied by 100 and divided by the volume of the sample used shall be the percentage of water and shall be reported as " — per cent water by volume, A. S. T. M. method."

11. The accuracy to be expected with this method is that duplicate determinations of water should not differ from each other by more than one division on the trap.

Sediment

Alundum (porous grade) thimbles,[1] 1 inch in diameter by $2\frac{3}{4}$ inches high, weighing not less than 15 nor more than 17 grams.

Extraction apparatus (see Fig. 91a) of such construction that the thimble is completely surrounded by the vapor of the boiling solvent. *Siphon extractors must not be used.*

Place approximately 10 grams of the sample in the previously extracted and dried, accurately weighed thimble and weigh to ±0.01 gram, place in the extraction apparatus, and extract with 90 per cent benzol until the solvent dropping from the thimble is colorless. Dry the thimble for 1 hour at 105° C., and weigh to ±0.0001 gram. Repeat the extraction until the weight of the dried thimble and sediment is constant.

NOTE. The rate of extraction shall be such that the mixture of oil and benzol in the thimble does not rise to within $\frac{1}{4}$ inch of the top.

Water and Sediment by Centrifuge (A. S. T. M. Method D96–21T)

1. This method may be used for crude mineral oils and fuel oils. A centrifuge method for " Water and Sediment " is not entirely satisfactory because the amount of water obtained is nearly always lower than the actual water content. Nevertheless, on account of the wide use of the centrifuge for this purpose, it is desirable that the method of making the determination be standardized as far as possible. It must be clearly understood that the reading of the centrifuge tube includes both the sediment and the precipitated water. Accurate determination of water content, if desired, should be made in accordance with method above.

2. The sample shall be thoroughly representative of the material in question and the portion used for the test shall be thoroughly representative of the sample itself. Deviation from this rule shall not be permitted. The difficulties in obtaining representative samples for this determination are unusually great; hence the importance of sampling can not be too strongly emphasized.

3. The centrifuge shall be capable of whirling at the required speed at least two 100-cc. centrifuge tubes filled with water. It shall be of sound design and rugged construction so that it may be operated without danger. The tube carriers shall be so designed that the glass centrifuge tubes may be cushioned with water, rubber, or other suitable material. The tube holders

---

[1] Alundum thimbles listed by the Norton Co., Worcester, Mass., as 5163 RA 98, have proved satisfactory.

shall be surrounded during the operation by a suitable metal shield or case, strong enough to eliminate danger if any breakage occurs.

The preferred form of centrifuge shall have a diameter of swing (tip to tip of whirling tubes) of 15 to 17 inches and a speed of at least 1500 r.p.m. or the equivalent. If the available centrifuge has a diameter of swing varying from these limits, it shall be run at the proper speed to give the same centrifugal force at the tips of the tubes as that obtained with the preferred form of centrifuge. The proper speed shall be calculated from the following formula in which d represents diameter of swing (tip to tip of whirling tubes) of the centrifuge used:

$$\text{r.p.m.} = 1500\sqrt{\frac{16}{d}}.$$

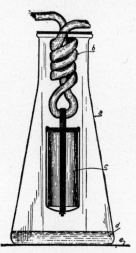

Fig. 91a. Extraction apparatus for determination of sediment: a, Extraction flask; b, condenser; c, extraction thimble; d, solvent; e, top of hot plate.

4. The centrifuge tubes, A. S. T. M. type, shall be made of suitable glass and thoroughly annealed. The total capacity shall be about 125 cc. and the mouth shall be suitably constricted for closing with a cork. The graduations shall be clear and distinct, reading upward from the bottom of the tube as follows:

Range	Scale of divisions	Limit of error	Numbered
Cc.	Cc.	Cc.	Cc.
0– 3	0.1	0.05	1, 2, 3
3– 5	.5	.2	4, 5
5– 10	1.0	.5	6, 8, 10
10– 25	5.0	1.0	15, 20, 25
50–100	50.0	1.0	50, 100

13

The shape is optional, provided it does not conflict with the other requirements. Satisfactory types are shown in Fig. 91b.

5. The water or oil bath shall be of sufficient depth for immersing the centrifuge tubes in a vertical position to the 100-cc. mark. Means shall be provided for heating this bath to 100° F.

PROCEDURE

6. (a) Exactly 50 cc. of 90% benzol shall be measured into each of two centrifuge tubes and exactly 50 cc. of the oil to be tested shall then be added to each. The centrifuge tubes shall be tightly stoppered and shall be shaken vigorously until the contents are thoroughly mixed. The temperature of the bath shall be maintained at 100° F., and the centrifuge tubes shall be immersed therein to the 100-cc. mark for 10 minutes.

(b) The two centrifuge tubes shall then be placed in the centrifuge on opposite sides and shall be whirled at a rate of 1400 to 1500 r.p.m., or the equivalent, for 10 minutes. The combined volume of water and sediment at the bottom of each tube shall be read and recorded, estimating to 0.1 cc. if necessary. The centrifuge tubes shall then be replaced in the centrifuge, again whirled for 10 minutes, and removed for reading the volume of water and sediment as before.

This operation shall be repeated until the combined volume of water and sediment in each tube remains constant for three consecutive readings. In general, not more than four whirlings will be required.

7. The combined total volume of water and sediment shall be read on each tube, estimating to 0.1 cc. if necessary. The sum of the two readings shall be recorded as percentage of water and sediment, centrifuge method.

ACCURACY

8. With care and proper attention to details, duplicate determinations of water and sediment by this method should not differ by more than 0.2 cc., provided the centrifuge tubes are accurate and readable to this degree.

Water by Centrifuge

APPARATUS

1. The apparatus shall be the same as in the preceding method.

PROCEDURE

2. Exactly 40 cc. of 90 per cent benzol shall be measured into each of two centrifuge tubes and exactly 20 cc. of the oil to be tested shall then be added to each. The centrifuge tubes shall be tightly stoppered and shall be shaken vigorously until the contents are thoroughly mixed.

3. The two centrifuge tubes shall then be placed in the centrifuge on opposite sides and shall be whirled at a rate of 1400 to 1500 r.p.m., or the equivalent, for 10 minutes. The volume of water at the bottom of each tube shall be read and recorded, estimating to 0.1 cc. if necessary. The centrifuge tubes shall then be replaced in the centrifuge, again whirled for 10 minutes as before, and removed for reading the volume of water as before. This

operation shall be repeated until the volume of water in each tube remains constant for three consecutive readings.

4. The volume of water shall be read on each tube, estimating to 0.1 cc. if necessary, and the average percentage of water in the sample calculated.

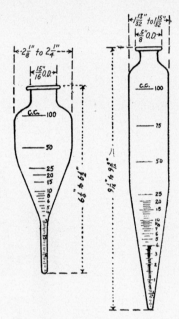

FIG. 91b.   Centrifuge tubes (A. S. T. M.).

ANIMAL AND VEGETABLE OILS

The tests most commonly employed for the identification of these oils are as follows: specific gravity, refractive index, Valenta test, elaidin test, Maumené test, iodine number, and saponification value.

In addition, certain special and commercial tests are applied, as Bechi test, Baudouin test, free acid, spontaneous combustion, and drying test.

Specific Gravity.   This is usually determined either by the Westphal balance (page 1111) or by the *picnometer*.

A two-necked flask of 50 cc. capacity, having a thermometer carefully ground into one neck, the second one being a narrow tube bearing the mark, is most suitable. This is filled with the oil to be examined, cooled to 15.5° C.,[1] the excess of oil removed and weighed. If the weighings be made to 0.5 milligram and a correction applied for the expansion of the glass by the difference in temperature $= 15.5 - 4 = 11.5° = -0.025\%$ of the value obtained, the determination is accurate to 0.00002.[2]

For the determination of the specific gravity of small quantities of oil, satisfactory results can be obtained by weighing 1 or 5 cc. of the oil carefully measured from an accurately calibrated pipette. Or a mixture of alcohol and water can be made until a drop of oil will stay in any position in it, and its specific gravity determined.

Refractive Index. This is of the same value as the determination of specific gravity: it has, however, the advantage that it is more rapid and uses only one or two drops of the oil.

The apparatus preferably employed is the Abbé refractometer, Fig. 92, the prisms of which are kept at constant temperature, usually 25° C., by circulating water.

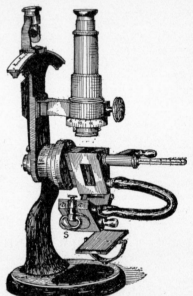

The illuminating mirror should light the cross hairs and the telescope should be sharply focused on them.

The double prism is opened by means of the screw heads, and after carefully cleansing the prisms with cotton and ether, a drop or two of the oil placed on the horizontal surface of the fixed prism. The prisms are then tightly closed. The telescope is brought into the position shown and the sector is firmly held and the alidade (the moving part) moved forward until the field of vision shows the boundary between light and shade just intersecting the cross hairs.

By means of the screw on the right of the instrument this boundary line should be made as sharp as possible. The index of refraction is read off directly from the sector, using a lens if necessary; the reading is accurate to .0002.

FIG. 92.—Refractometer.

After using, the prisms are again carefully cleansed and a piece of filter paper placed between them to prevent them from being scratched. The instrument is in correct adjustment when water at 18° gives a mean reading of 1.333. The temperature correction for oils and fats is 0.0004 for every degree rise.

Valenta Test.[3] Although considered by some to be unreliable, yet as the

---

[1] Allen (Organic Analysis, 33) states that a correction of 0.00064 can be made for each variation of 1° C.

[2] Wright, J. Soc. Chem. Ind., **11**, 300, 1892.

[3] Valenta, Dingler polyt. J., **253**, 418; also J. Soc. Chem., Ind., **3**, 643, 1884.

indication given by this test may be of value, it is barely worth the trouble of execution.   It depends upon the solubility of the oil in glacial acetic acid.

Enough oil is poured into a test-tube to fill it to the depth of about 1 in., the exact height being marked by the thumb; an equal quantity of glacial acetic acid is poured in, that is, until the acid reaches the point indicated by the thumb. A light thermometer is placed in the tube, and it is heated until the oil dissolves —shown by the liquid becoming homogeneous.   The tube is now allowed to cool, and the point noted at which it begins to become thoroughly turbid.

Castor oil is soluble at ordinary temperatures, while rape-seed and other cruciferous oils are usually insoluble even at the boiling-point of the acid.   The temperatures at which other oils become turbid are given on pages 1148 and 1149.

Elaidin Test.   Although this is not a quantitative test, yet its ease of application and the conclusions which may be drawn from it render it valuable.   It depends upon the change of the liquid olein into its solid isomer elaidin, and is especially applicable to olive and lard oils.

Manipulation.   Five grams of the oil are weighed [1]—within 2 drops—into a cordial glass, 7 grams of nitric acid, specific gravity 1.34, are then weighed into it,[1] and two pieces of copper wire (0.6 to 1.0 gram) added.   Place the glass in a pan of cold water at about 12° C., and stir with a short glass rod about 20 to 30 turns, not only with a rotary movement, but also with an up-and-down motion, so as to mix the oil and the evolved gas thoroughly.   When the wire has dissolved, add a second piece and stir as before.   This second addition should furnish gas enough if the liquid has been kept cool and the stirring has been thorough.

At the end of the first hour, pure lard oil will usually show flakes of a wax-like appearance, and upon standing without disturbance and at the same temperature for another hour, the oil will have changed to a solid white cake hard enough to bear several ounces' weight, or admit of lifting the glass and contents by the glass rod.

Most of the fish and seed oils yield a pasty or buttery mass separating from a fluid portion, whereas olive, almond, peanut, lard, sperm and sometimes neat's-foot oil, yield a solid cake.

Instead of using nitric acid and copper, sulphuric acid of 46° Baumé, containing a little nitric acid and saturated at 0° C. with nitric oxide, may be employed.

A test should always be made at the same time with an oil of undoubted purity.

NOTES.   If the oil be stirred too much or too frequently, or is too warm, it has no opportunity to form a hard cake.

Hübl states that all attempts to make the test a quantitative one have resulted in failure.

Mercury can be used instead of copper.

Cailletet's method,[2] in which a smaller quantity of oil is used, and sulphuric and nitric acids allowed to act upon it in a boiling water bath, cannot, in the experience of the writer, be depended upon to give reliable results.

Maumené Test.[3]   While this, like the preceding, is not a quantitative test, yet the indications afforded by it are of more value in many cases than those obtained by quantitative methods, as, for example, the saponification value. It depends upon the heat developed by the mixing of the oil with strong sul-

[1] Not on the analytical balance.
[2] Milliau, J. Am. Chem. Soc., **15**, 156, 1893.
[3] SO_2Cl gives similar results.

phuric acid. This takes place in a small beaker $7\frac{1}{2}$ to 9 cm. deep and of 150 cc. capacity, packed in an agate-ware cup with dry felt or cotton waste packing.

Manipulation. Fifty grams of the oil are weighed [1] into the beaker to within 2 drops, and its temperature noted by a thermometer. Ten cc. of sulphuric acid are now run gradually into the oil—allowing the graduate to drain five seconds—the mixture being stirred at the same time with the thermometer, and the stirring continued until no further increase in temperature is noted. The highest point at which the thermometer remains constant for any appreciable time is observed, and the difference between this and the initial temperature is the " rise of temperature." This varies with the strength of the acid employed, and to secure uniformity [2] the results should be expressed by dividing the rise of temperature with the oil by the rise of temperature with water, and multiplying by one hundred. This is called the " specific temperature reaction." The rise of temperature with water is determined in the same manner as with oil, using the same vessel.

NOTES. In performing this test it is important that the oil and acid be of the same temperature, attained by keeping them beside each other.

The strength of acid should be as far as possible the same; it should be determined not by specific gravity, but by titration, as 100% and 94.3% acid have the same specific gravity.

For concordant results the conditions should be the same, and the same apparatus should be used. In case the test is to be applied to a drying oil, it should be diluted one-half with a mineral oil, 25° paraffin, for example, thoroughly mixing them. The "rise of temperature" is then, the rise of temperature of mixture minus half the rise of temperature of 50 grams of mineral oil, multiplied by 2.

It is advisable to make a test at the same time with an oil of known purity. Results should agree within 2%. By the use of the Hübl formula, page 1130, substituting thermal values, results comparable with those obtained with the iodine value can be obtained.

Sherman, Danziger, and Kohnstamm [3] have studied this method with the idea of eliminating the errors. Rather than dilute the oil with a mineral oil they dilute the acid, using one of 89%. The results obtained are a little lower for vegetable oils and a little higher for animal oils than those usually found with the strong acid as employed by Thomson and Ballantyne. Mitchell [4] uses an inert diluent—carbon tetrachloride—in a vacuum-jacketed tube and one-fifth the quantities; all oils are diluted. He finds that the results obtained are in close agreement with the bromine thermal values; further, that the test may be of use in determining the degree of oxidation of fats and oils, the figures becoming greater with the age of the oil.

Data upon various oils will be found on pages 1152–1155.

References.

Maumené, Compt.-Rend., **35**, 572, 1852.
Ellis, J. Soc. Chem. Ind., **5**, 361, 1886.
Thomson and Ballantyne, J. Soc. Chem. Ind., **10**, 234, **1891**.
Richmond, Analyst, **20**, 58, 1895.
Munroe, Am. Pub. Health Ass'n, **10**, 236, 1884.

Iodine Number or Value. This is the percentage of iodine absorbed by an oil; the method depends upon the fact that different oils absorb different amounts of the halogens; the process is mainly one of addition, although small quantities

---

[1] Not on the analytical balance.

[2] Tortelli, J. Soc. Chem. Ind., **23**, 668, 1904, is unable to secure uniformity in this way.

[3] J. Am. Chem. Soc., **24**, 266, 1902.

[4] Analyst, **26**, 169, 1901.

of substitution products are formed. For example, the unsaturated body olein, $(C_{17}H_{33}COO)_3C_3H_5$, when brought in contact with iodine takes up 6 atoms and forms the *addition product*, di-iodo stearin, $(C_{17}H_{33}I_2COO)_2C_3H_5$. Palmitin, $(C_{15}H_{31}COO)_3C_3H_5$, when similarly treated, forms no addition product, but a small quantity of the *substitution product*, iodo-palmitin, $(C_{15}H_{30}ICOO)_3C_3H_5$, and the hydrogen displaced unites with the iodine to form hydriodic acid. The quantity of hydriodic acid thus formed is a measure of the amount of substitution.[1]

1. **Hanus's Method.**[2] *Manipulation.* From 0.12 to 0.15 gram of a drying oil, 0.2 to 0.3 gram of a non-drying oil, or 0.6 to 0.7 gram of a solid fat, is accurately weighed into a *dry* 200-cc. bottle. This should be of colorless glass and be provided with a well-ground stopper. This is best effected by pouring out about 5 grams of the oil into a No. 1 beaker containing a short stirring rod, and setting it into a watch-glass upon the pan of the analytical balance. The whole system is weighed, the beaker removed, and several drops of oil transferred to the bottle by dropping down the rod, being careful that no oil touches the neck. Eight drops are approximately 0.2 gram. The beaker is replaced in the watch-glass and the system again weighed, the difference in weight being the amount of oil in the bottle.

The oil is dissolved in 10 cc. of chloroform, 30 cc. of the iodine solution (Reagents) added—best from a burette—and allowed to stand with occasional shaking for exactly thirty minutes; with oils of an iodine number of less than 100, ten minutes suffices; 10 cc. of potassium iodide solution are added; shake thoroughly, add 100 cc. water, washing down any iodine on the stopper. Titrate the excess of iodine with N/10 sodium thiosulphate, adding the latter gradually, with constant shaking, until the yellow color of the iodine has almost disappeared. Add a few drops of starch solution, shake thoroughly to dissolve out the iodine from the chloroform solution, and titrate to the disappearance of the blue color. The blue color returns after a few minutes but the end-point is that of its first disappearance.

At the same time at which the oil is prepared, two " blanks " should be prepared similarly in every way to the actual tests, except in the addition of the oil, and treated in every respect like them; the strength of the thiosulphate solution should also be determined the same day on which this test is carried out.

Standardization of the Thiosulphate Solution. Ten cc. of potassium iodide and 100 cc. of water are poured into the Erlenmeyer flask; 20 cc. of the bichromate solution, equivalent to 0.2 gram of iodine, are now measured in with a pipette, and to this 5 cc. of strong hydrochloric acid added and the mixture shaken for three minutes. It is now titrated with the thiosulphate solution until the yellow color of the iodine has almost disappeared; starch paste is now added, and the titration continued until the deep-blue color of the solution changes to a sea-green—due to $CrCl_3$,—which is usually brought about by the addition of a single drop.

The reactions involved are:

$$K_2Cr_2O_7 + 14HCl = 2CrCl_3 + 2KCl + 7H_2O + 3Cl_2;$$

$$3Cl_2 + 6KI = 6KCl + 3I_2;$$

$$6Na_2S_2O_3 + 3I_2 = 3Na_2S_4O_6 + 6NaI.$$

NOTES. Wijs[3] uses iodine chloride instead of bromide; it is more troublesome to prepare and gives results about 1.2 points higher.[4] Either of these methods has the advantage over Hübl's—first, that the solutions keep better, remaining practically

---

[1] McIlhiney, J. Am. Chem. Soc., **16**, 275, 1894.   [2] This is the official A. S. T. M. method.
[3] Berichte, **31**, 752, 1898.   [4] Tolman and Munson, J. Am. Chem. Soc., 244, **25**, 1903.

unchanged for several months; secondly, that the action is about sixteen times as rapid, it being completed in fifteen minutes; thirdly, that the solutions are cheaper.

Acetic acid cannot be displaced by carbon tetrachloride as a solvent, as the last traces of iodine are difficult to remove from it. The acetic acid used should be at least 99.5% and show no reduction with potassium bichromate and sulphuric acid.

2. Hübl's Method. *Manipulation.* The oil is weighed out as in 1, into 300-cc. bottles, except that about 25% more may be used.

The oil is now dissolved in 10 cc. of chloroform, 30 cc. of iodine and mercuric chloride solution added, the bottle placed in a dark closet, and allowed to stand, with occasional gentle shaking, for four hours. If the solution becomes nearly decolorized after two hours, an additional quantity should be added. One hundred cc. of distilled water and 20 cc. of potassium iodide are added to the contents, and the excess of iodine titrated with sodium thiosulphate. If at this point a red precipitate (HgI_2) is formed, more potassium iodide should be added. As the chloroform dissolves some of the iodine, the titration can proceed until the chloroform layer is nearly colorless, then the starch solution is added, and the operation continued to the disappearance of the blue color.

" Blanks " should be titrated as with the foregoing process, page 1137.

NOTES. The method was proposed by Cailletet in 1857, made use of by Mills and Snodgrass [1] in 1883, using, however, bromine and carbon bisulphide, and described in almost its present form by Hübl.[2] The chief factors in its execution are (1) strength of the iodine solution; (2) the quantity used; and (3) the length of its time of action.

1. *The Strength of Iodine Solution.* According to Hübl's original memoir, the solutions can be kept indefinitely when mixed.

Fahrion [3] states that the solution deteriorated as much as from 17 to 23% in eight days. Ballantyne [4] confirms the deterioration, but finds it much less, 5 to 8% in thirty-eight days. This weakening of the solution is probably due to the hydriodic acid formed by the action of the iodine upon the alcohol.[5]

The mercuric chloride acts apparently as a carrier of iodine, as the reaction takes place very slowly without it. (Gantter.) [6] Waller [7] finds that the addition of 50 cc. HCl, specific gravity, 1.19, to the mixed iodine solution preserves it for months. Of the other metallic chlorides, $CoCl_2$ gives the highest true iodine value, $MnCl_2$, $MnBr_2$ and $NiCl_2$ cause practically no addition. (Schweitzer and Lungwitz.) [8]

2. *The Quantity of Iodine Solution Used.* The mixed iodine solution as made up should require about 53 cc. of the thiosulphate. Before using, a rough titration should be made, and if it be much weaker than this, a proportionately larger amount added. The action of a large excess of iodine is to increase the substitution rather than addition; increase in temperature or in time produces the same effect.[9]

The excess of iodine recommended is from 150 to 250%; some observers recommend from 400 [10] to 600%.[11]

3. *Length of Time.* Two hours is sufficient for olive oil, tallow, and lard, while for linseed oil, 18 hours, balsams, and resins 24 hours should be allowed.[12]

[1] J. Soc. Chem. Ind., **2**, 435, 1883.
[2] Dingler polyt. J., **253**, 281; also J. Soc. Chem. Ind., **3**, 641, 1884.
[3] J. Chem. Ind., **11**, 183, abstr., 1892.
[4] Ibid., **13**, 1100, abstr., 1894.
[5] J. Soc. Chem. Ind., **14**, 130, 1895.
[6] Ibid., **12**, 717, abstr., 1893.
[7] Chem. Ztg., **19**, 1786, 1831, 1895.
[8] J. Soc. Chem. Ind., **14**, 1031, 1895.
[9] J. Soc. Chem. Ind., **12**, 717, abstr., 1893.
[10] Ibid., **14**, 1031, 1895.
[11] Holde, Mitt. kgl. Techn. Versuchs., **9**, 81, 1891.
[12] Dieterich, J. Soc. Chem. Ind., **12**, 381, 1893.

Ingle[1] has shown that the free acid formed during the process is due to the action of water upon the iodochlorides. Some of these are reduced by potassium iodide with liberation of iodine and consequent reduction in the iodine absorption. Iodine chloride is the active agent, and not hypoiodous acid.

For the calculation of the percentage of adulteration of one oil by another, Hübl gives the following formula:[2]

" Let x = percentage of one oil and y = percentage of the other oil, further, m = iodine value of pure oil x, n of pure oil y, and I of the sample under examination, then

$$x = \frac{100(I - n)}{m - n}. \text{"}$$

He further states that the age of the oil, provided it be not rancid or thickened, is without influence on the iodine value. Ballantyne[3] finds that light and air diminish the iodine number.

As might be expected, the iodine value is inversely proportional to the cold test.

The method, as will be seen, is a conventional one, and the best results will be obtained by using measured quantities of reagents and carrying through the process in the same manner every time.[4]

The calculation is perhaps most easily made as follows: Subtract the number of cc. of thiosulphate used for the titration of the oil, from that obtained by titrating the blank—this gives the thiosulphate equivalent to the iodine absorbed by the oil. Multiply this number (of cc.) by the value of the thiosulphate in terms of iodine, and the result is the number of grams of iodine absorbed by the oil; this divided by the weight of oil used and multiplied by 100 gives the iodine number.

In case it be desired to recover the iodine used, reference may be had to an article by Dieterich, abstracted in the Jour. Soc. Chem. Ind., **15**, 680, 1896.

Oxidized Oils. Iodine Number of. To find the original iodine number of a semi-drying or non-drying oil which has been altered by atmospheric oxidation, add 0.8 to the iodine number found on the altered sample for each increase of 0.001 in the specific gravity $\left(\text{taken at } \dfrac{15.5° \text{ C.}}{15.5° \text{ C.}} \right)$[5]

Bromine Number or Value. The iodine method just described has, among others, the disadvantage that it fails to distinguish between addition and substitution; this is sometimes of importance, and to accomplish it McIlhiney[6] makes use of the bromine absorption.

Manipulation. From 0.2 to 0.3 gram of a drying oil, 0.4 to 0.5 of a non-drying oil, or 1.0 to 1.2 grams of a solid fat, are accurately weighed into the 300 cc. bottle, as in the iodine number (page 1137).

The oil is dissolved in 10 cc. of carbon tetrachloride, and 20 cc. of bromine solution (Reagents) added, best from a burette. After allowing it to stand two minutes by the watch, 20 or 30 cc. of potassium iodide are added, in the manner

---

[1] J. Soc. Chem. Ind., **21**, 587, 1902.
[2] Dingler polyt. J., **253**, 281, 1884.
[3] J. Soc. Chem. Ind., **10**, 31, 1891.
[4] If, for example, the water be added before the iodide solution, the iodine number is changed by 0.3 per cent.
[5] Sherman and Falk, J. Am. Chem. Soc., **27**, 608, 1895.
[6] J. Am. Chem. Soc., **21**, 1084, 1899.

described below, the amount depending upon the excess of bromine. To prevent loss of bromine and hydrobromic acid, a short piece of thin and wide rubber tubing—" bill tie tubing "—is slipped over the lip of the bottle, thus forming a well around the stopper; some of the iodide solution is poured into this and the bottle cooled in cracked ice. Upon removing the stopper the solution is sucked into the bottle, it is shaken to insure the solution of the vapors, and the remainder of the reagent added. The iodine liberated is titrated by sodium thiosulphate in the usual way.

When this titration is finished, 5 cc. of the potassium iodate solution are added and the titration repeated. The iodine liberated in this reaction is equivalent to the hydrobromic acid present. Blank determinations should be made with the reagents used, as with the iodine number.

NOTES. Oftentimes, particularly with resins, emulsification of the solution takes place, masking the end-point. This can be prevented by the addition of 50 or 100 cc. of a 10% solution of salt.

In case ice be not at hand, the vapors will probably be completely absorbed by passing through the iodine solution in the rubber well.

The reactions involved, in addition to those on page 1137 are:

Palmitin
$$(C_{15}H_{31}COO)_5C_3H_5 + 3Br_2 = (C_{15}H_{30}BrCOO)_3C_3H_5 + 3HBr.$$
$$3HBr + 3KI = 3KBr + 3HI.$$
$$6HI + KIO_3 = 3I_2 + 3H_2O + KI.$$

The calculation is similar to that followed in the iodine number (page 1137).

The percentage of bromine found as hydrobromic acid is called the bromine substitution figure, and the total percentage absorbed, less twice the bromine substitution figure, gives the bromine addition figure.

The method has the further advantages that it is rapid, the bromine solution is permanent and inexpensive. For data upon various oils, see table on page 1152.

Saponification Value. This is expressed by the number of milligrams of potassium hydrate necessary to saponify one gram of the oil. It is called from the originator " Koettstorfer [1] number or value," also " Saponification number," and must not be confounded with " Saponification equivalent " as proposed by Allen,[2] which is the number of grams of oil saponified by 56.1 grams of potassium hydrate.

Method. [3]

SOLUTIONS REQUIRED

Alcoholic solution for saponification. Dissolve 58 grams of potassium hydrate " purified by alcohol " in 500 cc. of 95 per cent purified ethyl alcohol. Allow the solution to settle in a dark place. Draw off the clear solution or filter through an asbestos filter and make up to 1 liter with 95 per cent alcohol. The solution so prepared shall stand at least 20 hours before it is standardized.

Alcohol. Purify 95 per cent ethyl alcohol with silver oxide in the following manner: [4]

Dissolve 1.5 grams of c.p. silver nitrate in about 3 cc. of water, add to 1 liter of alcohol in a glass-stoppered bottle, and mix thoroughly. Dissolve

[1] Z. anal. Chem., **18**, 199, 1879. [3] Tech. Paper 323A, p. 87.
[2] Commercial Organic Analysis, **2**, 40. [4] Dunlap, J. Am. Chem. Soc., **28**, 397, 1906.

3 grams of potassium hydrate (by alcohol) in 10 to 15 cc. of warm alcohol. After cooling, add slowly to the alcoholic silver nitrate solution, stirring slightly. Allow the precipitated silver oxide to settle, siphon off the clear solution, and distil on a steam bath.

Standard hydrochloric acid solution. One-half normal solution.

Phenolphthalein solution. One gram phenolphthalein in 100 cc. alcohol and water.

APPARATUS

The saponification shall be carried out in a wide-mouthed, flat-bottom extraction flask, or Erlenmeyer flask, of 250 to 300 cc. capacity, fitted to a reliable condenser properly connected with a good cork. The boiling shall preferably be carried on by means of an electric hot plate.

BLANK DETERMINATION

Determination shall be made in duplicate in the alcoholic potash solution in the following manner:

Measure accurately into the flask 25 cc. of alcoholic potash solution from a calibrated pipette. The tip and outside of the pipette shall be wiped off with a clean filter paper before the solution is delivered, then rinsed out with 25 cc. of neutral alcohol. If a standard burette is used, allow 60 seconds total time for drawing and draining. Connect the flask to a suitable condenser and boil for 3 hours. Before disconnecting the flask, wash out the condenser with a few cubic centimeters of neutral alcohol; if a Soxhlet is used as the condenser, the tip shall be washed off into the flask. Titrate while hot with N/2 HCl, using 3 drops of phenolphthalein as indicator. The total number of cubic centimeters of N/2 HCl required for the blank represents the strength of the alcoholic potash solution.

PROCEDURE

For straight fats or oils, use 2 or 3 grams of the material, for oils containing over 30 per cent of fatty oils, use about 5 grams, and for oils containing less than 30 per cent of fatty oils, use about 10 grams.

Weigh the oil accurately, by difference, p. 1137, from a small beaker into the saponification flask. Add 25 cc. of alcoholic potash solution and 25 cc. of neutral alcohol in the same manner as for the blank, connect to the condenser, and boil for 3 hours. Titrate while hot. Calculate the saponification number from the difference between the number of cubic centimeters of N/2 HCl required for the determination and the average of the two blanks, using the formula:

$$\text{Saponification number} = \frac{\text{difference, cubic centimeters} \times 28.05}{\text{weight of oil, grams}}.$$

Petrolic ether may be used with compounded cylinder oils in the quantity of 50 cc., providing a Soxhlet extraction flask is used to collect this petrolic ether periodically. The Soxhlet flask should be so adjusted, through the addition of glass rodding or beads when necessary, that it will just overflow with the full quantity of petrolic ether.

The percentage of fatty oil (or fat) in a compounded petroleum product can be calculated from the saponification number of such a product only when the saponification number of the fatty oil is known. If the saponification numbers of both fatty oil and compounded oil are known, the following formula should be used:

$$\text{Percentage of fatty oil} = \frac{100 \times \text{saponification number of compounded oil}}{\text{saponification number of fatty oil}}.$$

For this determination the following values of saponification number may be used:

Fatty oil	Saponification number	Fatty oil	Saponification number
Lard oil	192–198	Soya bean	189–197
Tallow	193–198	Peanut	186–197
Neat's-foot	193–204	Cottonseed	191–197
Fish	140–193	Blown rapeseed	195–216
Sperm	120–140	Blown cottonseed	210–225
Castor	176–187	Degras	110–210
Rapeseed	170–179		

NOTES. Many prefer to cork the flasks tightly and tie down the stoppers, thus saponifying under pressure; others make use of a return flow condenser, oftentimes merely a long glass tube.

McIlhiney [1] has applied the process to dark-colored substances by making use of the principle that when ammonium chloride is added to a neutral soap solution, and the mixture distilled, the amount of ammonia freed is equivalent to the quantity of alkali combined with the fatty acids. As a description of the process is beyond the scope of the present volume, reference must be had to the original article.

As ordinarily prepared, the alcoholic potash solution turns rapidly reddish brown, so that it is very difficult to note the end-point. This trouble can be partially avoided by adding a drop or two of the solution to the diluted indicator contained upon a tile after the manner of the titration of iron by bichromate. As the color is probably due to the polymerization of the aldehyde formed by the oxidation of the alcohol, it is more satisfactory to use for the preparation of the potash solution an alcohol which is practically aldehyde free. Alcoholic potash made up from this, using the so-called "potash by alcohol," will give a solution which will remain water-white for weeks.

The writer has found, if the stock solution be kept under an atmosphere of hydrogen, that the coloration by standing is almost entirely prevented.

Detection of Unsaponifiable Oils. The qualitative detection takes place by observing the behavior of the solution obtained by boiling the oil with alcoholic potash when diluted with warm water. Any unsaponifiable material will manifest itself as oily drops in the clear alcoholic solution, or as a whitish cloud on the addition of water.

The quantitative determination may take place in two ways: 1. From the saponification number. 2. By gravimetric methods.

1. *From the Saponification Number.* On pages 1152 and 1153 it will be noticed that, except for castor, rape, and sperm oils, the saponification number averages 193. If the number found be divided by this figure, the percentage of saponifiable matter will be obtained; this subtracted from 100 will give the unsaponifiable matter. This method gives no idea of the kind of saponifiable matter.

2. *By Gravimetric Methods.* The procedure is essentially that of Spitz and Hönig: [2] 10 grams of the oil are boiled fifteen minutes under a return-flow condenser with 50 cc. of 5% alcoholic potash; [3] 40 cc. of water are added and the

[1] J. Am. Chem. Soc., **16**, 409, 1894. For a discussion of the theory of the process, see Lewkowitsch, J. Soc. Chem. Ind., **17**, 1107, 1898.

[2] Z. ang. Chem., **19**, 565, 1891.

[3] The potash is made by dissolving purified potash in the smallest possible quantity of water and adding absolute alcohol.

boiling repeated.   The liquid is allowed to cool, washed into a separatory funnel with 50% alcohol and 50 cc. of 86° gasoline, thoroughly shaken and allowed to stand.   The gasoline layer should separate clearly and quickly from the soap solution and the latter is drawn off; the gasoline is washed 2 or 3 times with 50% alcohol to extract any soap, and these washings added to the soap solution.   This latter is extracted, until upon evaporation the gasoline leaves no stain upon paper, care being taken to wash the gasoline extracts each time with 50% alcohol; three extractions with gasoline are usually sufficient.

The gasoline is distilled from these extracts, the residue heated until the gasoline odor disappears, and weighed.   From the appearance of the residue some idea of the kind of unsaponifiable matter can be obtained.   This in the case of sperm oil will be mainly solid alcohols, probably of the ethylene series.

According to Schicht and Halpern [1] this method is open to the following errors: incomplete saponification, incomplete extraction, solubility of soaps in the solvent, and the solubility of the unsaponifiable matter in the washing solution.   Their improved method is as follows: 5 grams of fat [2] with 3 of grams solid caustic potash dissolved in a little water and 25 cc. of absolute alcohol are boiled half an hour under a reflux condenser.   After cooling 25 cc. of 10% KCl are added and the solution is then shaken four times with 200 cc. of petroleum ether distilling under 60°. The petroleum ether is evaporated and, without washing, the residue is dissolved in 25 cc. absolute alcohol and the solution made slightly alkaline with normal alkali; 25 cc. of 10% KCl are added and the shaking with petroleum ether repeated. The petroleum ether solution is shaken with 100 cc. of 50% alcohol and the wash solution with 100 cc. petroleum of ether, which is afterwards washed with 100 cc. of 50% alcohol.   After combining the extracts the petroleum ether is driven off and the residue dried and weighed.

NOTE.   Care should be taken to use gasoline which leaves no residue on evaporation at 100° C.

Identification of the Unsaponifiable Matter.   The unsaponifiable matter is either liquid or solid; in case it is liquid, it may be (1) *hydrocarbon oils*, either mineral, or formed by the distillation of waste fats, as wool grease, or (2) *tar oils,* " dead oils," etc., obtained by the distillation of coal tar; or (3) *rosin oils.* If it be a question of one of these three, the specific gravity will usually decide it; that of the hydrocarbon oils is 0.855 to 0.930, of the rosin oils 0.96 to 0.99, while the tar oils are heavier than water.   Rosin oils would be shown by the Liebermann-Storch test, p. 1144b; a mixture of mineral and tar oils would be identified by treatment with an equal quantity of nitric acid, sp.gr. 1.45, both previously cooled to 15° C., and noting the rise of temperature.   Mineral oils give a very slight rise, being paraffins, while the tar oils belong to the benzole series and are more easily nitrated.   Hydrocarbon oils from distilled grease oleins can be identified by their refractive index and rotatory power.[3]

Solid unsaponifiable matters may be:

(4) *Paraffin.*

(5) *Ceresene*—refined ozokerite.

(6) *Higher alcohols* of the paraffin series, as cetyl, $C_{16}H_{33}OH$, coming from the saponification of sperm oil and other waxes.

[1] Chem. Ztg., **31**, 279, 1907.
[2] For linseed and other oils, ten or twenty times this weight should be used, the alkali being correspondingly increased.
[3] Gill and Forrest, J. Am. Chem. Soc., **32**, 1071; Gill and Mason, J. Am. Chem. Soc., **26**, 665.

(7) *Cholesterol*, $C_{23}H_{43}OH$, and its isomers, phytosterol, sitosterol, isocholesterol, etc.

(8) *Lactones*, internal anhydrides of oxy acids as stearlactone,

$$C_{14}H_{29}CHOHCH_2CH_2COOH = C_{14}H_{29}CHCH_2CH_2COO + H_2O.$$

These may be separated by boiling for two hours with an equal quantity of acetic anhydride; if the substance dissolves and does not precipitate on cooling, higher alcohols are indicated; if a mass of crystals separates out on cooling, cholesterol and its isomers, or a mixture of these with the higher alcohols is indicated; if an oily layer remains on top, it is an indication of the presence of paraffin or ceresene. For the complete separation and identification of these reference must be had to Lewkowitsch, " Analysis of Fats, Oils, and Waxes," as it is beyond the limits of this chapter.

Test for Animal or Vegetable Oils. Animal oils contain cholesterol, $C_{25}H_{43}OH$, while vegetable oils contain the isomeric body phytosterol; hence the isolation and identification of these compounds enables one to say with certainty as to the presence of one class of oil or the other—for example as to the presence of fish oil in linseed. The quantity of these bodies varies from 0.2 to 1%. The method is essentially that of Börner.[1] Fifty grams of the oil are boiled in a flask with a return cooler with 75 cc. of 95% alcohol for five minutes and the alcoholic solution separated; this is repeated with another portion of alcohol. The alcoholic solutions are mixed with 15 cc. of 30% sodium hydroxide and evaporated on a water bath nearly to dryness in a porcelain dish and the residue shaken out with ether. The ether is evaporated, the residue taken up with a little ether, filtered, again evaporated, dissolved in 95% alcohol (by volume), and allowed to crystallize slowly. Börner states that the form of the crystals is more to be relied upon than a determination of their melting-point. Cholesterol crystallizes from alcohol or ether in leaflets or rhomboid tables containing one molecule of water of crystallization. Phytosterol crystallizes also from alcohol with one molecule of water in needles forming stars or bundles. As a further means of identification, some of the esters should be made and their melting-points determined.

To this end the crystals above obtained are heated over a low flame in a small porcelain dish covered with a watch-glass, with 2 or 3 cc. of acetic or other acid anhydride until it boils: the watch-glass is removed and the excess of anhydride evaporated on the water bath. The contents of the dish are treated with a small quantity of absolute alcohol to prevent crystallization, more alcohol added and the solution allowed to crystallize. The crystals are filtered off through a very small filter, washed with a small quantity of 95% alcohol, dissolved in absolute alcohol, and recrystallized until a constant melting-point is obtained.

The following table shows the corrected melting-points of these alcohols and their esters:

	Cholesterol.	Phytosterol.
Alcohol	148–150.8°	136–143.8°
Acetate	113–114°	120–137°
Benzoate	135–151 '	142–148°
Propionate	97–98°	104–105°

[1] J. Soc. Chem. Ind., **17**, 954, 1898; Tolman, J. Am. Chem. Soc., **27**, 590, 1905; Tolman, Bull. 107, U. S. Dept. Agriculture, 1907.
[2] Neuberg and Rauchwerger, abstr. J. Soc. Chem. Ind., **23**, 1163, 1904.

Notes. Some directions state, in isolating the cholesterol or phytosterol, to boil with the 30% sodium hydroxide until one-fourth of the alcohol is evaporated. As a result of repeated experiments this has been found to cut down the yield so much that on a large scale practically none of these bodies, particularly phytosterol, was obtained. This agrees with the observation of Lewkowitsch that by heating cholesterol with normal alcoholic potash, cholesterin hydrate is obtained.

The following test will serve to differentiate between cholesterol and phytosterol.[2] A very small quantity of cholesterol is warmed with 1.5 cc. absolute alcohol and a trace of isodulcit or rhamnose (δ-dimethylfurfural) added. After cooling, an equal volume of concentrated sulphuric acid is added, so as to form a layer below the solution, whereupon a raspberry-colored ring is produced at the zone of contact of the two liquids. On mixing the layers while the tube is cooled in a current of cold water, the mixture becomes intensely colored. With phytosterol the reaction fails or at most a pink color. Similar reactions are given by abietic acid. Or mix the pure unsaponifiable matter with an equal quantity of pure cholesterol; if the melting point be unchanged, the unsaponifiable matter is cholesterol; lowering of the melting point indicates phytosterol.

As little as 1% of cotton-seed has been found in lard, and 4% in any oil have been detected by this test.

For the means of distinguishing between drying and marine animal oils, see Halphen, J. Pharm. Chim., 14, 391 (1901), abstracted J. Soc. Chem. Ind., 21, 74, or Chem. Centralb., 72, ii, 1097 and 1323.

Tests for Antifluorescents.[1] It is often desired to remove the fluorescence or " bloom " from petroleum oils. This may be effected by refining with chromic acid, or more easily by the addition of a small quantity of nitro-naphthalene or nitro-benzene. The latter may often be detected by the odor.

The test is made by boiling about 1 cc. of the oil with 3 cc. of 10% alcoholic potash for one to two minutes. If either of the nitro compounds be present, a blood- or violet-red coloration is produced; a pure mineral oil is changed only to yellow or brownish-yellow by this treatment. In case the characteristic color does not appear the following test may be applied.[2] It depends upon the reduction of the nitro bodies to their amines.

A few cc. of the oil are heated with feathered tin and hydrochloric acid in an Erlenmeyer flask for ten minutes: this can be aided by the introduction of a piece of platinum wire. The oil is separated by a separatory funnel and filtration through a wet filter, the filtrate treated in another separatory with sodium hydrate until the tin hydrate redissolves and shaken out with 10–20 cc. of ether. The amines go into solution in the ether, giving to it a violet color and fluorescence in the case of α-naphthylamine. These can be recognized by their odor, that of naphthylamine being very characteristic. The latter may be recognized by dissolving in hydrochloric acid, evaporating the latter, and upon treatment with ferric chloride obtaining an azure-blue precipitate. This changes when filtered off to purple-red and the filtrate to violet.

Aniline can be recognized by solution in concentrated sulphuric acid and the red and then blue color which appears on the addition of a small crystal of potassium bichromate. Free aniline is also temporarily colored violet by a solution of bleaching powder.

Acetyl Value. The estimation of the acetyl value is seldom required in oil analysis, it being characteristic only when triglycerides are present. For a description of the method and its applications, reference must be had to the larger works, as Lewkowitsch or Allen.

[1] Holde, J. Soc. Chem. Ind., 13, 906, 1893.
[2] Holde, "Examination of Hydrocarbon Oils," p. 75.

Special Tests for Certain Oils

Lewkowitsch says:[1] " It should be distinctly understood that color reactions taken by themselves should not be relied upon as giving a decisive answer. At best they can only be used as a preliminary test, or as a confirmatory test. The ease with which this test can be carried out, and its apparent reliability, have led to an over-estimation of this very useful and important reaction; so much so, that grave errors may be committed by those who assign to this test an exclusive or even a paramount importance. It is altogether unjustifiable to look upon this test, as has been done, as permitting of quanti ative interpretation."

Bechi's Test for Cotton-seed Oil. This depends upon the supposition that a substance of an aldehydic nature which reduces silver nitrate is contained in the oil. The method is essentially that of Milliau.[2]

Fifteen grams of oil are weighed into a No. 6 porcelain dish, using the coarse scales, and heated for about ten minutes upon the water bath; a mixture of 10 cc. of 30% caustic soda and 10 cc. of the alcohol is slowly poured upon the oil. The whole is occasionally stirred until the mass becomes clear and homogeneous, and 150 cc. of hot distilled water slowly added so as not to decompose the soap, and the boiling continued until the alcohol is expelled. Dilute sulphuric acid (1:10) is added to acid reaction, and the separated fatty acids washed three times by decantation with cold water. A portion of these is brought into a large test-tube, 15 cc. of alcohol and 2 cc. of 3% silver nitrate solution are added, the tube is wrapped with brown paper, held in place by an elastic band, and heated, with constant stirring, in the water bath until one-third of the alcohol is expelled, which is replaced by 10 cc. of water. This heating is continued for a few minutes longer and the coloration of the insoluble fatty acids observed. The presence of cotton-seed oil in any appreciable proportion causes a mirrorlike precipitate of metallic silver, which blackens the fatty acids of the mixture.

NOTES. The alcohol should be proved free from aldehyde by a blank test. Unless the mixture in the test-tube be thoroughly stirred while heating, it will "bump" and eject the contents. Other methods of procedure consist in applying the test to the oil itself, often after treatment with dilute caustic soda and nitric acid. (Wesson.[3]) The writer had a case in which the *oil* gave the test while the *fatty acids* gave no blackening, showing there was something in the oil itself other than cotton-seed oil which reduced the silver nitrate. Students have no difficulty in detecting a 5% adulteration with cotton-seed oil.

Dupont[4] thinks that the reduction of silver nitrate is due rather to sulphur compounds contained in the oil; by passing steam over the oil he obtained a product containing sulphur and the oil still gave the Bechi test. This work has been repeated and confirmed by the author.[5] It is to be noted that while the fatty acids blacken silver nitrate they do not color cadmium, lead, or copper salts, but reduce mercury compounds. No indication of an aldehyde was noted by the fuchsine or ammonia tests. The supposition that the reducing substance is aldehydic in its nature finds support in the fact that if the oil be heated to 240°[6] or be kept for some time[7] it loses this peculiar property.

[1] "Chemical Technology and Analysis of Fats, Oils and Waxes," **2**, 203.
[2] J. Am. Chem. Soc., **15**, 164, 1893.
[3] J. Am. Chem. Soc., **17**, 723, 1895.
[4] Bull. Soc. Chem. (3), **13**, 696; J. Soc. Chem. Ind., **14**, 811, 1895; also Charabot and March, Bull. Soc. Chim., **21**, 252, 1899.
[5] Gill and Dennison, J. Am. Chem. Soc., **24**, 397, 1902.
[6] Holde, J. Soc. Chem. Ind., **11**, 637, 1892.
[7] Wilson, Chem. News, **59**, 99, 1889.

By purifying the acids by the lead salts Tortelli and Ruggeri [1] are able to detect as little as 10% of heated cotton-seed oil.

It is to be noted that pure lard, tung and olive oil are not infrequently met with which give the test, consequently its indications cannot be considered as conclusive.

Halphen's Test for Cotton-seed Oil. [2] This depends upon the observation that this oil contains an unsaturated fatty acid which combines with sulphur, giving a colored compound. [3]

Procedure. Ten cc. of the oil or melted fat are heated, in a large test-tube with a long glass condenser tube attached, with an equal volume of amyl alcohol and of carbon bisulphide solution of sulphur (Reagents), at first with frequent agitation, in a steam bath, and then, after the violent boiling has ceased, in a brine bath (105–110°) for forty-five minutes to three hours, according to the quantity of adulterant present, the tube being occasionally removed and shaken. As little as 1% will give a crimson wine coloration in twenty minutes. [4]

NOTES. If the mixture be heated for too long a time a misleading brownish-red color due to burning is produced. The reaction seems to be peculiar to this oil; it is more sensitive with fresh than old fats, and while, by comparison with a blank, $\frac{1}{16}$ of 1% is noticeable, $\frac{1}{4}$ of 1% is easily detected. Cotton-seed oil which has been heated to 250° does not give the test; the oil is then not available as food. Heating to 200° does not interfere with the test. [5]

The test is not given by an oil which has been oxidized with sulphuric acid and potassium permanganate, although such an oil gives the Bechi test. [6] This shows that the two tests are not produced by the same substance. Nor is this test or that of Bechi given by an oil which has been treated with chlorine or sulphurous acid. [7] If treated with the former it is no longer edible; an oil treated with sulphurous acid and washed with alcohol cannot be distinguished from ordinary cotton-seed oil and does not, as already stated, respond to either the Halphen or Bechi test. In this case the test for phytosterol is the only means of determining if it has been added to an animal oil. The test is also given by kapok oil, which is used as an edible oil in China, the East and West Indies, and in Africa; baobab oil also gives it.

Lard from hogs fed on cotton-seed meal shows this reaction strongly, as if it were 25% oil. [8] The butter from cows similarly fed also yields the reaction. [9]

The test may be applied to the soaps or fatty acids, provided they are not too deeply colored.

The amyl alcohol cannot be omitted nor substituted by ethyl alcohol without impairing the delicacy of the test. [10] The compound in the oil cannot be removed by treating with animal charcoal. [11]

Hexabromide Test for Linseed Oil. The object of the test is to determine the amount of insoluble bromides of the fatty acids contained in the oil. Linseed gives the highest percentage of bromides of any of the common oils, consequently its adulteration can be shown by the hexabromides

[1] J. Soc. Chem. Ind., **20**, 753, 1901.
[2] Halphen, J. Pharm. Chim., 390, 1897.
[3] Raikow, Chem. Ztg., **24**, 562, 583, 1900.
[4] Oilar, Am. Chem. J., **24**, 355; abstr. Anal., **26**, 22, 1901.
[5] Fischer and Peyan, Analyst, **30**, 131, 1905; Soltsien, Z. öffentl. Chem., **5**, 135, 1899; J. Soc. Chem. Ind., **18**, 865.
[6] Raikow, loc. cit.
[7] Petkow, Analyst, **32**, 123, 1907.
[8] Soltsien, Z. öffentl. Chem., **7**, 140, 1901.
[9] Wauters, J. Soc. Chem. Ind., **19**, 172, 1900.
[10] Soltsien, loc. cit., **25**, Oilar, loc. cit.
[11] Utz, Rev. Fett u. Harz. Ind., **9**, 125, 1902.

Fifteen grams of the oil are saponified by boiling with 15 cc. of potassium hydroxide solution, sp.gr., 1.35, and 15 cc. of alcohol in a flask under a reflux condenser; 300 cc. of warm water are added and the solution distilled with steam until the alcohol is removed. Dilute sulphuric acid is added to excess, the solution heated until the fatty acids are obtained as a clear oily upper layer; this is washed several times with hot distilled water until free from sulphuric acid, using methyl orange as an indicator. This does not react with fatty acids of low molecular weight which being soluble in water may redden litmus. This washing is effected in an atmosphere of inert gas, carbonic acid or hydrogen by stopping the flask with a three-holed stopper, carrying a siphon, an entrance and an exit tube for the gas. The acids are siphoned into a small Erlenmeyer flask and in case a few drops of water come over—an equal quantity of alcohol added and dried upon the water bath in a stream of dry inert gas.

In order to test for the presence of unsaponified fat, 3 cc. are dissolved in 15 cc. of 95% (by volume) alcohol, and 15 cc. of aqueous ammonia are added. If an appreciable amount of fat has escaped saponification, the mixture will become turbid (Geitel).

Two grams of mixed fatty acids [1] are dissolved in a flask in 27 cc. of dry ether, cooled down to 10° C., and 0.25 cc. of bromine allowed to run into the solution from a very finely-drawn-out pipette, the time allowed for this being about twenty minutes. The remaining 0.25 cc. of bromine is added somewhat more rapidly, within about ten minutes, the bromination thus occupying about thirty minutes. The authors attach great value to the exact observance of the time. The temperature should never be allowed to rise during bromination above 5°. The flask is corked and allowed to stand for two hours at 0°. The ethereal solution is next decanted through a weighed asbestos or paper filter (Lewkowitsch) and the precipitate is washed with five lots of 5 cc. each of dried and cooled ether. After complete draining, the precipitate is dried for two hours at 80° to 85°, and allowed to cool in a desiccator. The temperature is designedly kept below 100°, as the authors found that the color of the hexabromide becomes somewhat gray if the drying takes place at 100°. The melting-point of the hexabromides was 177°, whereas the melting-point of pure hexabromide has been found to be higher. No doubt the low melting-point is due to the drying having been carried out below 100°.

Nevertheless small traces of retained moisture cannot account for the much larger yield of hexabromide which the authors obtained.

The yields of hexabromide obtained by these authors are as follows:

Fatty Acids	Per cent.	Fatty Acids	Per cent.
Perilla oil...............	64.12	Tung oil................	nil
Linseed oil, Baltic.........	57.96	Soya bean oil...........	up to 7.78
Linseed oil, Dutch.........	51.73	Poppy seed oil..........	nil
Linseed oil, La Plata.......	51.66	Rape oil................	6.34
Linseed oil. Indian........	50.50		

Bailey and Baldsiefen, J. I. and E. Chem., **12**, 1189 (1920), have devised a modification which is more elaborate and may give more accurate results.

[1] Eibner and Muggenthaler, Farben Ztg., 1912.

Bellier's Qualitative Test. for Peanut Oil.

The necessary reagents are:

Alcoholic potash, made by dissolving 8.5 grams of pure potassium hydroxide in 70 per cent alcohol and making up to 100 cc.

Acetic acid of such strength that 1.5 cc. will neutralize 5 cc. of the alcoholic potash. (Acid having a specific gravity of 1.04 is approximately correct.)

Procedure. Weigh 1 gram of the oil into a dry test-tube, add 5 cc. of the alcoholic potash and boil gently over a small flame, avoiding evaporation as much as possible. Boil until the oil is completely saponified, which will take a little over 2 minutes. Add 1.5 cc. of acetic acid, or just sufficient to neutralize the alcoholic potash (use phenolphthalein as an indicator), mix well, cool rapidly by placing the test-tube in water at 17° to 19° C. and leave in the water at the stated temperature for not less than 30 minutes, shaking occasionally. Then add 50 cc. of 70 per cent alcohol containing 1 per cent by volume of hydrochloric acid (sp.gr. 1.16), shake well and again place in water at 17° to 19° for an hour. If no peanut oil be present, the liquid will remain clear or at most slightly opalescent; with 10 per cent, or more, of peanut oil a flocculent, crystalline precipitate forms.

Renard [1]-Tolman [2] Quantitative Test.

Weigh 20 grams of oil into an Erlenmeyer flask. Saponify with alcoholic potash, neutralize exactly with dilute acetic acid, using phenolphthalein as indicator, and wash into a 500-cc. flask containing a boiling mixture of 100 cc. of water and 120 cc. of a 20% lead acetate solution. Boil for a minute and then cool the precipitated soap by immersing the flask in water, occasionally giving it a whirling motion to cause the soap to stick to the sides of the flask. After the flask has cooled, the water and excess of lead can be poured off and the soap washed with cold water and with 99% (by volume) alcohol. Add 200 cc. of ether, cork, and allow to stand for some time until the soap is disintegrated, heat on the water bath, using a reflux condenser, and boil for about five minutes. In the oils most of the soap will be dissolved, while in lards, which contain much stearin, part will be left undissolved. Cool the ether solution of soap to 15° or 17° C. and let it stand until all the insoluble soaps have crystallized out (about twelve hours).

Filter and thoroughly wash the precipitate with ether. Wash the soaps on the filter back into the flask by means of a stream of hot water acidified with hydrochloric acid. Add an excess of dilute hydrochloric acid, partially fill the flask with hot water, and heat until the fatty acids form a clear oily layer. Fill the flask with hot water, allow the fatty acids to harden and separate from the precipitated lead chloride, wash, drain, repeat washing with hot water, and dissolve the fatty acids in 100 cc. of boiling 90 per cent (by volume) alcohol. Cool to 15° C., shaking thoroughly to aid crystallization.

From 5 to 10 per cent of peanut oil can be detected by this method, as it effects a complete separation of the soluble acids from the insoluble, which inter-

---

[1] Renard, Compt. rend., **73**, 1330, 1871; also Archbutt, J. Soc. Chem. Ind., **17**, 1124.
[2] Bull. 107, U. S. Dept. Agriculture, 1907, p. 145.

fere with the crystallization of the arachidic acid. Filter, wash the precipitate twice with 10 cc. of 90% (by volume) alcohol, and then with alcohol 70% (by volume). Dissolve off the filter with boiling absolute alcohol, evaporate to dryness in a weighed dish, dry and weigh. Add to this weight 0.0025 gram for each 10 cc. of 90% alcohol used in the crystallization and washing if done at 15° C.; if done at 20° add 0.0045 gram for each 10 cc. The melting-point of arachidic acid thus obtained is between 71° and 72° C. Twenty times the weight of arachidic acid will give the approximate amount of peanut oil present. No examination for adulterants in olive oil is complete without making the test for peanut oil. Arachidic acid has a characteristic structure and can be detected by the microscope.

Bach's Test for Rapeseed Oil. According to O. Bach,[1] the acids obtained from rape-seed oil are completely insoluble in David's alcoholic acetic acid, in the proportion of 1 to 15, by volume; those from cottonseed, peanut, sesame, and sunflower oil dissolve on heating. Those from the last oil separate as a granular precipitate at 15°, while from the other three they gelatinize. The acids from olive oil are completely soluble at the ordinary temperature. David's acid is made by mixing 22 cc. of 50% acetic acid (by volume) with 30 cc. of alcohol, sp.gr. 0.817, 92.07% (by weight.)

NOTE. The author has found that Bach's observation cannot be implicitly relied upon, as some rape-seed oils yield acids which are soluble in David's mixture.

Liebermann-Storch Test for Rosin Oil. One or 2 cc. of the oil are shaken with an equal quantity of acetic anhydride and gently warmed. When cool the acetic anhydride is pipetted off and tested by the addition of 1 drop of concentrated sulphuric acid. A fine violet color is produced in the presence of rosin oil. Tung oil and also cholesterol, which is contained in the animal fats, produce a similar coloration; the latter can be removed by saponifying the oil as completely as possible and shaking out the somewhat dilute soap solution with ether or petroleum ether. The soap solution is then acidified, setting free the fatty acids, and these treated with acetic anhydride as if they were the oil.

Baudouin's, or Camoin's Test for Sesame Oil.[2]

Dissolve 0.1 gram of finely powdered sugar in 10 cc. of hydrochloric acid (sp.gr. 1.18), add 10 cc. of the oil to be tested, shake thoroughly for 1 minute and allow to stand for 10 minutes. In the presence of even a very small admixture of sesamé oil, the aqueous solution is colored crimson. It should be observed that some olive oils, especially those of African or Spanish origin, give pink or crimson colors which can be readily differentiated from that due to sesamé oil by applying the following modification of the Villavecchia method.

Villavecchia Test

Add 2 cc. of furfural to 100 cc. of 95 per cent alcohol by volume and mix thoroughly 0.1 cc. of this solution with 10 cc. of hydrochloric acid (sp.gr. 1.18) and 10 cc. of the oil to be tested by shaking them together for $\frac{1}{4}$ of a minute. Allow the mixture to stand 10 minutes, observe the color, add 10 cc. of water, shake and again observe the color.

[1] Allen, "Commercial Organic Analysis," **2**, pt. 1, 128, 1899.
[2] Official.

The furfurol may be replaced by 0.1 g. of sugar in 10 cc. HCl, sp.gr. 1.18, and twice the quantity of oil used.

Milliau[2] saponifies as in the Bechi test and dries the acids at 105° and tests them instead of the oil. Lewkowitsch[3] states that this is a needless complication. Da Silva[4] states that this test has given colors with certain Portuguese olive oils; also those of Bari, Brindisi and Lecce. Kreis[5] states that the active or color-giving constituent is probably phenolic in its nature. The reaction is given by other substances,[6] as vanillin, oil of cloves, and cinnamon; this should be borne in mind in testing oils which have been extracted from confectionery. Rancid fats prevent the coloration; it can, however, be brought about even in rancid fats by the addition of an equal quantity of cotton-seed oil.[7]

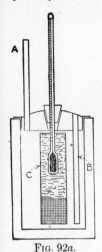

Free Acid Test.[8] About 10 grams of oil are weighed (to centigrams) into a 250-cc. Erlenmeyer flask, 60 cc. of neutral alcohol (Reagents) added, the mixture warmed to the boiling point, shaken thoroughly, and titrated with N/6 potassium hydrate, using phenolphthalein, the flask being frequently and thoroughly shaken. The result is conventionally reported in per cent of oleic acid; 1.0 cc. N/6 KOH is equivalent to 0.047 gram oleic acid. Or it can be reported like the saponification number, in milligrams of KOH per gram of oil. For mineral oils use alcohol diluted with its own volume of water.

Spontaneous Combustion Test.   Mackey's Apparatus. The apparatus,[9] Fig. 92a, consists of cylindrical copper water bath 7 in. high and 4 in. in diameter (inside measurements), surrounded with a ½-in. water-jacket. The cover is packed with asbestos and carries the draft tubes A and B, ½ in. in diameter and 6 in. long, which cause a current of air to be sucked down B and up A, thus ensuring a circulation of air in the apparatus: C is a cylinder made of 24-mesh wire gauze

Fig. 92a.

Mackey's Apparatus.

6 in. high and 1½ in. in diameter and supported upon a projection from the bottom of the bath. A thermometer projects down into the center of the cylinder; if a metal condenser be connected to the water bath it can be used indefinitely without refilling and without danger of burning out.

Seven grams of ordinary bleached cotton wadding or " absorbent cotton " are weighed out in a porcelain dish or on a watch-glass, and 14 grams of the oil to be tested poured upon the cotton and thoroughly worked into it, care being

[1] Ibid., 1893, 505; abstr. Analyst, **19**, 47.   [4] J. Soc. Chem. Ind., **17**, 275, 1898.
[2] J. Am. Chem. Soc., **15**, 162, 1893.   [5] Chem. Ztg., **27**, 316, 1903.
[3] "Oils, Fats and Waxes."   [6] Gerber, Analyst, **32**, 90, 1907.
[7] Lauff and Hinsmann, Chem. Ztg., **31**, 1023, 1908.
[8] Tech. Paper 323A.
[9] Mackey, J. Soc. Chem. Ind., **15**, 90, 1896; Gill, ibid., **26**, 185, 1907.

taken to replace any oil that is lost. The cotton is then placed in the cylinder, packed about the thermometer so that it occupies the upper $4\frac{1}{4}$ in. of the cylinder, and put into the boiling water bath. After the expiration of an hour, the bath having been kept in active ebullition, the temperature is read. Any oil which shows a temperature exceeding 100° C. in one hour, or 200° C. in two hours, should be regarded as a dangerous oil, or liable to produce spontaneous combustion. The following tables show the results obtained in using this apparatus.[1]

Oil.	Temperature °C. in		
	1 hr.	1¼ hrs.	1½ hrs.
Olive (neutral)........................	97–98	100	101
Cotton-seed..........................	112–128	177–242	194–282
Elaine...............................	98–103	101–115	102–191
Olive fatty acids.....................	102–114	....	196

Other values obtained were:

Oil.	Temp. °C.	Time Minutes.	Iodine, No.	Free Acid, per cent.
Olive.............................	234	130	85.4	5.3
Lard..............................	234	75	75.2	Trace
Oleic acid........................	158	188	60.5	....
Cotton-seed.......................	234	70	108.9	Neutral
Linseed...........................	234	65	168.1	Neutral
25° Paraffin......................	97	135	16.2	....

Besides being used for testing oils it can be applied to testing other materials, oily waste, sawdust, or any mixtures suspected of causing spontaneous combustion.

" The results [1] of the greatest practical value obtained in the use of this apparatus have been, first, determining the cause of fires; and, second, determining the degree of safety of the various oils used in manufacturing. Mineral oil, as is well known, is not liable to spontaneous combustion; and a certain percentage of animal or vegetable oil may be added to mineral oil without materially increasing the danger under ordinary circumstances. This percentage varies according to the oil; with neat's-foot and first quality lard oil some 50 to 60% may be used, with cotton-seed not over 25% is allowable. The claim so often made for so-called ' safe ' oils, said to have been changed by special and secret processes of refining so as to be no longer dangerous, is easily exposed by this test."

Drying Test Upon Glass.[2] A few drops of oil are brought upon a glass plate inclined at about 30° from the horizontal. A test of the oil is made from time to time by touching it with the fingers, the time at which it does not soil them being noted as the point when it is dry. Good oil should dry in three days.

Archbutt [3] makes this test as follows: A piece of polished plate-glass 7 cm. square by 4 mm. thick is cleaned and counterpoised on the balance; it is then heated for an hour at 200° C. in an air bath to thoroughly dry it. It is taken out,

---

[1] Small percentages (0.5–2.0) of iron, sodium, magnesium or zinc salts in "red" or olive oil may cause a degree of heating which may be dangerous. Gill, Ind. and Eng. Chem., **16**, 23, 1924.   [2] Richards, Tech. Quarterly, 4, 346, 1891.
    [3] Amsel, J Soc. Chem. Ind., **15**, 222, 1896.   [4] Id., **18**, 347, 1899.

laid on a non-conductor, allowed to cool for three or four minutes, and the hot glass thinly painted with the oil to be tested by means of a camel's-hair brush. When the glass is cold it is weighed and sufficient oil added to make it up to 0.1 gram. Two glasses are coated with the sample and two with a standard oil, all placed on a level surface in a large air bath at 50° C. and heated for nine hours; one set of plates is withdrawn, cooled, and tested by the finger. Good raw linseed is tacky, when tested by the finger when cold, in nine hours and dry in twelve; corn oil is practically dry in fifteen hours, though slightly tacky; cottonseed, partially dry in eighteen hours and fully dry in twenty-one. Refined rape oil dried in forty-eight hours, and olive oil was sticky after thirteen days.

Titer Test. Under this rather misleading title is expressed the solidification point of the fatty acids derived from a fat or oil; it has nothing at all to do with titration, as might be expected. The test is extensively used for the evaluation of fats, and according to the method provisionally adopted by the Association of Official Agricultural Chemists is carried out as follows:[1]

(a) *Standard Thermometer.* The thermometer must be graduated in tenth degrees from 10° to 60°, with a zero mark, and have an auxiliary reservoir at the upper end, also one between the zero mark and the 10° mark. The cavity in the capillary tube between the zero mark and the 10° mark must be at least 1 cm. below the 10° mark, the 10° mark to be about 3 or 4 cm. above the bulb, the length of the thermometer being about 15 in. over all. The thermometer is annealed for 75 hours at 450° C., and the bulb is of Jena normal 16‴ glass, moderately thin, so that the thermometer will be quick acting. The bulb is about 3 cm. long and 6 mm. in diameter. The stem of the thermometer is 6 mm. in diameter and made of the best thermometer tubing, with scale etched on the stem, the graduation to be clear-cut and distinct, but quite fine.

(b) *Determination.* Saponify 75 grams of fat in a metal dish with 60 cc. of 30% sodium hydroxide (36° Baumé) and 75 cc. of 95% (by volume) alcohol or 120 cc. of water. Boil to dryness, with constant stirring to prevent scorching, over a very low flame or over an iron or asbestos plate. Dissolve the dry soap in a liter of boiling water, and if alcohol has been used, boil for forty minutes in order to remove it, adding sufficient water to replace that lost in boiling. Add 100 cc. of 30% sulphuric acid (25° Baumé) to free the fatty acids, and boil until they form a clear, transparent layer. Wash with boiling water until free from sulphuric acid, collect in a small beaker, and place on the steam bath until the water has settled and the fatty acids are clear; then decant them into a dry beaker, filter, using the hot-water funnel, and dry twenty minutes at 100° C. When dried, cool the fatty acids to 15 or 20° C. above the expected titer and transfer to the titer tube, which is 25 mm. in diameter and 100 mm. in length (1 by 4 in.) and made of glass about 1 mm. in thickness. Place in a 16-oz. salt-mouth bottle of clear glass, about 70 mm. in diameter and 150 mm. high (2.8 by 6 in.), fitted with a cork, which is perforated so as to hold the tube rigidly when in position. Suspend the thermometer, graduated to 0.1° C., so that it can be used as a stirrer, and stir the mass slowly until the mercury remains stationary for thirty seconds. Then allow the thermometer to hang quietly, with the bulb in the center of the mass, and observe the rise of the mercury. The highest point to which it rises is recorded as the titer of the fatty acids.

Test the fatty acids for complete saponification as follows:

[1] U. S. Dept of Agriculture, Bureau of Chemistry Bulletin No. 107, p. 135, 1907.

Place 3 cc. in a test-tube and add 15 cc. of alcohol (95% by volume). Bring the mixture to a boil and add an equal volume of ammonium hydroxide (0.96 sp.gr.). A clear solution should result, turbidity indicating unsaponified fat. The titer must be made at about 20° C. for all fats having a titer above 30° C. and at 10° C. below the titer for all other fats.

References

Hefter, G. Technologie der Fette, Oele, und Wachsarten des Pflanzen und Tier-reichs. 4 volumes, 1906+

Ubbelohde, L. Chemie, Analyse und Gewinnung der Oele, Fette und Wachse. 4 volumes, 1908+

EDIBLE FATS

These include butter, lard and hardened oils.

Butter is examined for water, fat, ash, curd, and salt; these are usually present in the following proportions:

	Per cent.	Average per cent
Fat.	78. –90	82
Water.	5. –20	12
Salt.	0. 4–15	5
Curd.	0. 1– 5	1

These are determined as follows: weigh about 2 grams of butter into a platinum Gooch crucible half filled with ignited fibrous asbestos, and dry it at 100° C. to constant weight. The loss is the amount of *water*. Dissolve out the fat by repeated treatment with petroleum ether and again dry to constant weight. The loss represents the amount of *fat*. Ignite the crucible with a low flame or in a muffle, being careful not to volatilize the salt, until a light-gray ash is obtained. The loss represents *curd* and the residue *ash*. By extraction of the ash with water, and neutralization with calcium carbonate, the salt can be titrated with silver nitrate.

Examination of the Fat. Butter is adulterated with oleomargarine, renovated butter, and cocoanut oil. The first may be detected by testing for cottonseed or sesamé oil either by the color tests or by the index of refraction; this at 25° is for butter 1.459–1.462, for oleo. 1.465–1.470. Owing to the fact that butter contains a large per cent of volatile fatty acids (butyric, caproic, caprylic and capric acids, in all about 8%), adulterants may be detected by determining the amount of these. The process usually employed is that of Reichert modified by Meissl.

Five grams of the clear fat, filtered through absorbent cotton, are weighed into a 250-cc. round-bottomed flask and saponified by 2 cc. potassium hydroxide 1 : 1 and 10 cc. of 95% alcohol, under a return flow condenser for twenty-five minutes. The alcohol is rapidly evaporated off on the water bath until no odor of alcohol is perceptible. Add slowly 160 cc. of recently boiled distilled water which has been cooled to 50° or 60°; warm the flask until a clear solution of the soap is obtained. Cool to about 60° and add 8 cc. sulphuric acid 1 : 4 to liberate the fatty acids. Drop into the flask two bits of pumice (about the size of peas) which have been heated and quenched in water, and tie in a well-fitting cork; warm the flask until the fatty acids have melted and are floating on the liquid. Cool to about 60° and attach the flask to a condenser, using a trap to prevent the sulphuric acid from being mechanically carried over; 110 cc. are distilled into a graduated flask in as nearly thirty minutes as possible. Thoroughly mix the distillate, pour through a dry filter, and titrate 100 cc. with N/10 NaOH, using phenolphthalein as an indicator. Multiply the cc. of alkali by 1.1 and calculate them to 5 grams of fat. The Reichert-Meissl value for butter is from 24 to 34, the average is about 28.8; cocoanut oil gives 6–8 and other fats less than 1.

The procedure is a conventional one and should be followed as exactly as possible. Cocoanut and other vegetable oils would be shown by the fact that the unsaponifiable matter would contain phytosterol; also by the Polenske number.[1] Renovated butter is best shown by the "Spoon or Foam Test." This consists in melting a third of a teaspoonful of the sample in a tablespoon over a small flame and stirring with a match. Increase the heat until the fat boils briskly, stirring thoroughly several times. Oleomargarine and renovated butter boil noisily, sputtering like a mixture of grease and water and produce no foam. Butter boils with less noise and much foam sometimes rising over the sides of the spoon. The pieces of curd in butter are much smaller than in either of the others.

Preservatives. benzoic, boric and salicylic acids, may be examined according to the procedure given in Woodman and Norton, "Air, Water and Food," pp. 154 and 196.

Color may be detected according to Allen, "Commercial Organic Analysis," 4th Ed., Vol. II, or Leach's "Food Analysis."

Lard is adulterated with water, 25% being added in some cases, with cottonseed oil or stearine and beef stearine.

Water is determined as with butter; *cottonseed oil* or stearine by the usual tests. It should be borne in mind, however, that hogs fed on cottonseed meal yield a lard which will give the Halphen test as strongly as if it contained 25% of the oil. The iodine number and the presence of phytosterol will confirm this test; the iodine number varies widely according to the source of the fat, but in general it may be said it should be between 46 and 66.

Beef stearine is very difficult if not impossible of detection. For this, reference may be had to Lewkowitsch, 5th Ed., Vol. II.

HARDENED OILS

As the name denotes, these are oils which have been changed to more or less solid fats by the addition of hydrogen, in the presence of a catalyst, usually a compound of nickel. This betrays their presence and may be tested for as follows:[2]

Ten grams of the fat are heated on the water bath with 10 cc. of hydrochloric acid (sp. gr. 1.12) with frequent shaking for two or three hours. The fat is removed by filtering through a wet filter, receiving the filtrate in a porcelain dish; after partial evaporation of the filtrate 2 or 3 cc. of strong nitric acid are added and the evaporation continued to dryness to ensure the destruction of the organic matter. The residue is dissolved in a few cc. of distilled water, a few drops of a

[1] Z. Nahr. Genussm., 7, 193, 1904, also Leach, "Food Analysis."
[2] Kerr, J. Ind. and Eng. Chem., 6, 207, 1914.

1% solution of dimethyl glyoxime in alcohol added, and a few drops of dilute ammonia. The presence of nickel is shown by the appearance of the red-colored nickel dimethyl glyoxime. The amount of nickel can be determined colorimetrically by comparison with solutions containing known quantities.

The quantity of nickel is very minute, not as much as the fats take up when cooked in nickel or nickeled dishes and need cause no apprehension.

Hydrogenation destroys all the characteristics, particularly the color tests, by which the different oils may be sometimes detected.

WAXES

These, as will be remembered, contain no glycerine; the tests applied to them are the same as to the oils. The characteristics of the more commonly occurring waxes are given in the table, p. 1150; sperm oil, which is really a liquid wax, is included among the oils.

MISCELLANEOUS OILS AND LUBRICANTS

PROPERTIES OF SOME OF THE MINERAL OILS

Oil.	Specific gravity, deg. Baumé at 60° F.	Flash point, °F.	Viscosity (Saybolt), at 70° F.	Cold test, deg. Fahr.
Black...................	29	325	100–120	5–15
Ice machine...............	26–27	325–360	60–100	0–4
Crank case..............	26–27	455	100	
Transformer..............	....	340–380	400	25
Turbine..................	30	420	160	
Spindle..................	30–35	320–390	58–156	....
Loom....................	28	360	203	....
Engine..................	27–30	410	190–210	....
Cylinder................	23–25	525	200–300*	....
Cylinder.................	26–28	400–575	....	....

* At 212° F.

Belt Dressings are (1) mixtures of fats, waxes, degras or tallow with castor or fatty oils; (2) vulcanized corn or cottonseed oil thinned with naphtha; (3) preparations containing wood tar; or (4) preparations containing rosin, which is undesirable. Black oils, car oils, well oil or reduced oils are crude oils from which the naphthas and burning oils have been separated by distillation. Crank-case oils are pure mineral oils which emulsify but little with water. Milling-machine or soluble oils are lard, sulphonated oils or mineral oils held in suspension in water by soaps or alkalies, as borax or soda; the soaps used are either ammonium, sodium or potassium with resin, oleic or sulphofatty acids. Rosin oils are obtained by distilling or "running" rosin, each distillate being called a "run" and numbered according to the times it has been distilled. They oxidize quite rapidly and should not be used as lubricants except as soaps in lubricating greases. Screw-cutting oils are often mixtures of 27° Bé. paraffin and 25% fatty oil, preferably cottonseed, although lard oil was formerly used. Stainless oils are spindle or loom oils mixed with fatty oils—lard or neatsfoot. Transformer oils should be either pure mineral or rosin oils and as free as possible from water.

acid, alkali and sulphur.   Turbine oils should be of excellent quality, free from acid and tendency to resinify, and low in sulphur.   Watch oil is obtained from the porpoise, dolphin, or blackfish, where it exists in cavities in the jaw and in the brain or " melon " of the fish.   Lubricating greases are mixtures of soaps of palm oil, tallow or rosin oil (with lime or soda as bases) with various oils or fats such as rosin, tallow or mineral oil.   The best are those made from tallow by saponification with caustic soda.   They may also contain finely powdered talc or graphite. Non-fluid oils are oils or their greases stiffened with " oil pulp " or "dope," i.e., aluminum oleate or palmitate.

The source, preparation and uses of the various oils and greases are described in Rogers and Aubert's Industrial Chemistry, Chapters XXII, XXIV, XXV and XXVII.

For the guidance of the analyst, the characteristics of the more frequently occurring oils are given, the usual figures being given in italic.

The animal and vegetable oils may be classified into

Drying.   Linseed, Chinese wood, poppyseed, sunflower and menhaden.

Semi-drying.   Corn, cottonseed, sesamé, rape, black mustard and horse.

Non-drying.   Castor, almond, peanut, olive, cocoanut, palm, seal, cod-liver, elaine, lard, neatsfoot, tallow, sperm and whale.

References

Lewkowitsch, "Technology and Analysis of Oils, Fats and Waxes."   3 vols.
Gill, "A Short Handbook of Oil Analysis."
Battle, "Industrial Oil Engineering."
Lockhart, "American Lubricants."

United States Government Specifications for Petroleum Products

SPECIFICATIONS FOR LUBRICANTS AND LIQUID FUELS. REVISED MARCH 18, 1924

Gasoline

Name and grade	Color, darkest allowed (Saybolt No.)	Doctor test	Corrosion test	First drop, maximum °C	5 per cent minimum °C	5 per cent minimum °F	5 per cent maximum °C	5 per cent maximum °F	20 per cent maximum °C	20 per cent maximum °F	50 per cent maximum °C	50 per cent maximum °F	90 per cent maximum °C	90 per cent maximum °F	96 per cent maximum °C	96 per cent maximum °F	End point, maximum °C	End point, maximum °F	Recovery, minimum (P.d.)	Distillation loss, maximum (P.d.)	Acidity test	Sulphur, maximum	Special tests and requirements
Aviation gasoline:																							
Fighting	25	Required	Required		50	122	65	149			95	203	125	257	150	302	165	329	96	2	Required	0.10	Red dye
Domestic	25	do.	do.		50	122	75	167			105	221	155	311	175	347	190	374	96	2	do.	.10	
U. S. Government motor gasoline	16	do.	do.	55					105	221	140	284	200	392			225	437	95			.10	

(First drop, maximum for U. S. Government motor gasoline: 55 °C / 131 °F)

Burning Oils

Name and grade	Color, darkest allowed (Saybolt No.)	Flash point, Tag (°F)	Sulphur, maximum (Per cent)	Flock test	End point, maximum (°F)	Cloud test, maximum (°F)	Doctor test	Burning test (Hours)	Photometric test	Reaction test	Flash point, Cleveland, minimum (°F)
Marine kerosene	16	115	0.125	Required	625	5		16			
Marine kerosene (U. S. Navy)	16	115	.125	do.	625	5		16			
Kerosene	16	100	.125	do.	625	5		16	May be required		
Long-time burning oil	21	115	.10	do.	600	Zero	Required	168			
300° mineral seal	16			do.		32		Special		Required	250

Fuel Oils for Use in Oil Burners

Name and grade	Flash point, Pensky-Martens, minimum	Water, maximum	Sediment, maximum	Water and sediment, maximum	Furol viscosity at 77° F., maximum	Furol viscosity at 122° F., maximum	Sulphur, maximum
	°F.	Per cent	Per cent	Per cent	Seconds	Seconds	Per cent
Navy standard	150			1.0	100		1.5
Bunker A	150			1.0	100		
Bunker B	150			1.0		100	
Bunker C	150	a1.75	a0.25			300	

a A deduction in quantity will be made for all water plus sediment in excess of 1.0 per cent.

Greases

Name and grade	Viscosity at 100° F. of mineral oil, minimum	Calcium soap content, approximate	Moisture, maximum	Corrosion test	Ash	Soda soap content, minimum	Free alkali. NaOH	Color	Water, glycerin, and impurities, maximum of dry soap content
	Saybolt seconds	Per cent	Per cent		Per cent	Per cent	Per cent		Per cent
Cup grease No. 0	100	13	3	Required	1.7				
Cup grease No. 1	100	14	3	..do..	1.8				
Cup grease No. 2	100	16	3	..do..	2.0				
Cup grease No. 3	100	18	3	..do..	2.3				
Cup grease No. 4	100	24	3	..do..	3.5				
Cup grease No. 5	180	18	3	..do..	2.3				
Recuperator grease						40	0.5-2.5	Yellowish	33⅓
Crank-pin grease						45	.5-2.5	Greenish	33⅓
Driving-journal compound						40	.5-2.5	Yellowish	33⅓
Rod-cup grease									

Waxes

Name and grade	Color of melted wax	Melting point
	Saybolt No.	°F.
Paraffin:		
130 to 132	25	130–132
124 to 127	25	124–127
117 to 120	25	117–120

SPECIFICATIONS FOR LUBRICANTS AND LIQUID FUELS. REVISED MARCH 18, 1924—Continued

Lubricating Oils

Name and grade	Flash, minimum (°F.)	Fire, minimum (°F.)	Viscosity, Saybolt seconds 100° F. Minimum (Seconds)	100° F. Maximum (Seconds)	210° F. Minimum (Seconds)	210° F. Maximum (Seconds)	A.S.T.M. color, undiluted	A.S.T.M. color, diluted 85 per cent	Pour, maximum (°F.)	Acidity, maximum mg. KOH per gram	Corrosion test	Emulsion test	Demulsibility, minimum	Carbon residue, maximum (Per cent)	Precipitation, maximum (No.)	Compounding (Per cent)	Special tests required
Class A, extra light	315	355	135	165			7		35		Required						
Class A, light	325	365	180	220			7		35		do.						
Class A, medium	335	380	270	330			7½		40		do.						
Class A, heavy	345	390	360	440			8		45		do.						
Class A, extra heavy	355	400	450	550			8		50		do.						
Class B, extra light	315	355	135	165			7		35		do.	Required	300				
Class B, light	335	365	180	220			7		35		do.	do.	300				
Class B, medium	335	380	270	330			7½		40		do.	do.	300				
Class B, heavy	345	390	360	440			8		45		do.	do.	300				
Class B, extra heavy	355	400	450	550			8		50		do.	do.	300				
Class C, extra light	315	355	135	165			7		35	0.10	do.	do.	300				
Class C, light	325	365	180	220			7		35	.10	do.	do.	300				
Class C, medium	335	380	270	330			7½		40	.10	do.	do.	300				
Class C, heavy	345	390	360	440			8		45	.10	do.	do.	300				
Class C, extra heavy	355	400	450	550			8		50	.10	do.	do.	300				
Class D, light	315	355	135	165	55	65	7		35	.30	do.	do.		0.10			
Class D, medium	325	365	180	220	75	85	7		35	.30	do.	do.		.20			
Class D, heavy	335	380	270	330	90	100	7½		40	.30	do.	do.		.45			
Class D, extra heavy	345	390	360	440	110	120	8		45	.30	do.	do.		.55			
Class D, ultra heavy	355	400	450	550			8		50	.30	do.	do.		.70			
Class D, tractor	360	410						5	45	.30	do.	do.		.10			
Class D, tractor, heavy	390	430						6	50	.30	do.	do.		.20			
Class D, motor cycle	400	440						7	50	.30	do.	do.		.45			
Aircraft machine gun	200	450	80	115	65	75		8	-45	.10	do.	do.		.55			
Buffer	265		65	75	120	150			Zero	.10		do.		.70			
Car and locomotive engine	300								45			do.		1.50	0.5		
Compounded steam cylinder	475								60	.80		do.		2.00	.5	5–7	Reaction test

SPECIFICATIONS FOR LUBRICANTS AND LIQUID FUELS. REVISED MARCH 18, 1924—*Continued*

Lubricating Oils

Name and grade	Flash, minimum °F.	Fire, minimum °F.	Viscosity, Saybolt seconds 100° F. Minimum	Viscosity, Saybolt seconds 100° F. Maximum	Viscosity, Saybolt seconds 210° F. Minimum	Viscosity, Saybolt seconds 210° F. Maximum	A.S.T.M. color, undiluted	A.S.T.M. color, diluted 85 per cent	Pour, maximum °F.	Acidity, maximum mg. KOH per gram	Corrosion test	Emulsion test	Demulsibility, minimum	Carbon residue, maximum Per cent	Precipitation, maximum No.	Compounding Per cent	Special tests required
Diesel engine	360				55	65			45	.30	Required	Special		.80			Protection test
Gear, chain, and wire rope					900	1100					do.	Required					
Gun and ice machine No. 100	290		95	115					5	.10		do.	330	1.5	.5		
Gun and ice machine No. 125	290		120	135					5	.10		Special	300	2.0	.5		
Liberty Aero, grade 1	400				75	85			15	.10		do.		2.5	.5		
Liberty Aero, grade 2	400				90	100			30	.10		do.		2.5	.5		
Liberty Aero, grade 3	450				90	100			45	.10		do.					
Liberty Aero, grade 4	450				115	125			45	.10		do.					
Marine engine No. 1				850	65	75			32	3.00	Required	do.					Wick-feed test
Marine engine No. 2				850	65	75			45	3.00	do.						Do.
Mineral steam cylinder No. 1	475				135	165			60		Required			4.5	.5	10–20	
Mineral steam cylinder No. 2	525				180	220			60		do.			4.5	.5	10–20	
Recoil oil, light	225	250	40	45					−5	.10	do.						
Recoil oil, medium	315	355	140	160					−5	.10	do.						
Recoil oil, heavy	345	390	385	430					−5	.10	do.						Heat, breakdown and unsaturation tests
Electric switch	290		95	110					20								
Transmission	460				135	165											

Class A covers grades of petroleum oil used for general lubrication where a highly refined petroleum oil is not required; only refined petroleum oils without admixture will be considered.

Class B covers grades of petroleum oil for lubrication of turbines, dynamos and high-speed steam engines using circulating and forced-feed systems.

Class C covers the grades used for lubricating *both* turbine and internal combustion engines.

Class D covers the grades of petroleum oils used by the government for lubrication of internal combustion engines, except aircraft, and Diesel engines.

CHARACTERISTICS OF THE FATTY ACIDS FROM SOME OILS

Oil.	Refr. Ind. at 60° C.	M.pt. °C.	Solidifn. Pt. °C.	Iodine Per cent.
Almond................	1.4461	13–14	9–11.8	93.5–96.5
Castor.................	1.4546	13	3	86–88
Chinese wood............	—	40–43.8	31.2	145–159.4
Cocoanut................	1.4295	24–27	15–20	8.4–9
Codliver, Medicinal........	—	—	17–18 (titer)	164–171
Corn....................	—	18–21.6	14–16	113–125
Cottonseed..............	1.446	34–40	32–35	105–112
Elaine.................				
Horse..................		37.5–39.5	33.6–37.7	84–87
Lard...................		35		
Linseed................	1.4546	17–24	13–17	179 209.8
Menhaden..............	No figures available.			
Black Mustard...........	1.4665 at 20°	9–17	6–8	108–126.5
Neatsfoot...............	—	28.5–29.8	16–26.5 (titer)	62–77
Olive...................	1.4410	19–31	17–24.6	86–90
Palm...................	—	47.7–50	36–46 44	53.3
Peanut.................	1.4461	27–35	22–32.5	95–103
Poppyseed..............	1.4506	20–21	16.5	139
Rape...................	1.4491	16–22	16–18	99–105
Seal...................	—	14–33	13–17	186–202
Sesamé.................	1.4461	23–32	18–26	109–112
Sperm..................	—	13–21	16	83–99
Sunflower..............	1.4531	17–24	17–18	124
Tallow.................				
Whale..................	—	14–27	23–24	130–132

CHARACTERISTICS OF SOME OILS

Oil.	Sp.Gr. 15° C.	Refr. Ind. 15° C.	Valenta °C.	Elaidin.	Maumené °C.	Sap. No. ng.	Iodine %	Composition.	Common Adulterants.	Visc. U. Sec. 100° F.	Flash °F.[1]
Almond	0.914–.920 / .918	1.4738	110	Solid	53	190–195.4	93–101 / 97	Olein, linolein.	Peach and apricot kernel, cottonseed, peanut, lard, olive, sesamé and poppyseed.		
Castor	0.959–.968	1.4795–.4803	Soluble	Solid	46–47	176–186	81–90	Ricinolein, stearin, dihydroxy stearin.	Blown oils, linseed, rape, cottonseed and rosin.	1485	505
Chinese wood or tung oil	0.940–.944	1.503 at 19°	40–47	Liquid and solid	—	190–197	156–176	Olein, elacomargarin.			
Cocoanut	0.926 / 0.874 at 99° C.	1.4573	—	—	—	225–268	8–10	Caproin, caprylin, caprin, olein, laurin, myristicin, palmitin, stearin.	Rarely adulterated.		
Codliver, medicinal	0.922–.941	1.478–1.481	—	Liquid and solid	100–116	183–188	135–198	Palmitin, stearin, jecolein, therapin	Salmon, seal, whale, shark liver; oils from other Gadidæ are not, commercially speaking adulterants.		
Corn or maize	0.921–.927 / 922	1.4768	80	Pasty	56–88 / 85	189–193 / 191	111–123 / 115	Palmitin, arachidin, olein, linolein.	Rarely adulterated.	187	480
Cottonseed	0.921–.930 / 922	1.4737–.4757	90–110	Pasty	70–90 / 76	191–196	101–117 / 108	Stearin, palmitin, olein, linolin, arachidin.	Rarely adulterated.		
Elaine or Red	0.899–.908	1.4631 at 25° C.	—	Solid	—	200	90	Oleic, palmitic and stearic acids.	Cottonseed and mineral.		
Horse	0.916–.922	1.4652–.4704	54–80	—	46–55	195–197	75–86	Similar to lard but dries.	Rarely adulterated.		
Lard	0.914–.916	1.4694	54–98	Very solid	39–47 / 43	190–196	60–88	Olein, stearin, palmitin.	Cottonseed, tallow, corn and mineral.	214	565
Linseed	0.9315–.9371 / 0.932–.996	1.4835	57–79	Liquid and solid portion	103–126 / 90	187–195.2 / 189–194	167.6–205.4 / 178–190	Isolinolein, linolein, linolin, olein, stearin, palmitin.	Corn, cottonseed, fish and rosin.		
Maize	See Corn										

[1] With covered tester.

15

	Specific gravity	Refractive index		As linseed				Constituents	Mineral and rosin.		
Menhaden	0.927–.936 / 0.930	1.4783	64		123–128	189–193	139–193	Linolein, myristin, asellin, and acetin, clupanodonin.	Mineral and rosin.		440
Bl'k Mustard	0.917–.919	1.4672	Insoluble	Pasty	42–43 / 126	173–176 / 190	98–110 / 154	Like rapeseed.	Sesamé.		
Neatsfoot	0.915–.916 / 916	1.4695–.4705	62–75	Solid at times	42–49.5	194–199	66–76	Olein, palmitin and stearin.	Other hoof oils, fish, poppy seed, rape, cottonseed and mineral oils.	224	
Olive	0.915–.920 / 916	1.4703 .4713	85–111	Very Solid	35–47 / 41	185–203 / 190	77–94 / 82	Olein, palmitin, arachidin and linolin.	Cottonseed, peanut, rape, sesamé, poppyseed and lard.		
Palm	0.920–.924 / 0.859 at 99° C.	1.451 at 60°	—	—	—	196–202	53–57	Palmitin, palmitic acid and stearin.	Water, sand and dirt.		
Peanut or Arachis	0.916–.925 / 917	1.4731	87–112	Solid	46–75 / 51	185–197 / 194	83–105 / 98	Palmitin, l i n o l i n, olein, arachidin and lignoerin.	Cottonseed, rape, sesamé and poppyseed.		
Poppyseed	0.924–.927 / 925	1.4773	—	Pasty	87	190–197 / 193	133–143 / 138	Linolin, linolein and isolinolein, olein, stearin, palmitin.	Sesamé.		
Rape or Colza	0.913–.917 / 916	1.472– .4757	Insoluble	Pasty	49–64 / 55	168–178 / 174	94–106 / 101	Stearin, olein, erucin, rapin, and arachidin.	Cottonseed, poppyseed, hempseed, linseed, fish oil.	247	455
Seal	0.924–.933	1.477	—	Pasty	—	178–196 / 188	127–193 / 147	Palmitin, olein, hypogaein.	Mineral and rosin.	164	515
Sesamé	0.922–.924	1.4748– .4762	87–107	Pasty	63–72	187–194	103–115	Stearin, palmitin, olein and linolin	Cottonseed, peanut, rape and poppyseed		
Sperm	0.844–.884 / .880–.884	1.4664– .4673	Insoluble	Solid at times	45–51	123–147	70–96	Contains no glycerin, palmitic acid.	Whale, mineral, rape, liver and arctic sperm.	115	455
Sunflower	0.924–.926	1.4762	—	Pasty	72–75	188–194	119–133	Linolin, olein.			
Tallow	0.916	1.4660 at 25° C.	71–75	Solid	35	197	56	Similar to lard.			
Turpentine	See page 617.										
Whale	.917–.927 / .916	1.4691 at 25°	—	Pasty	88	188–193	110–136	Palmitin.	Seal oil.	184	515

CHARACTERISTICS OF SOME WAXES

Wax	Sp.Gr. 15° C.	Ref. Index at 40°	M.pt.	Solid Pt.	Sapn. Value.	Acid Value.	Iodine Value.	Composition.	Common Adulterants.
Carnauba	0.99–.999	65–69°	83–91	80–87	79–88	0.3–7.0	5–13.2.	Ceryl and myricyl cerotate, carnaubate and a hydrocarbon.	Stearic acid, ceresin and paraffin.
Candelilla	0.969–.993	At 71.5° 1.455	65–68	63–68	46–65	10–21	14–36.8	Hydrocarbon, myricyl alcohol	Like carnauba wax.
Beeswax	0.959–.970	At 75° 1.439–1.445	62–70	60–63	87–107	16.8–21	7.9–11	Cerotic and melissic acids, myricin, ceryl and myricyl, alcohols, hydrocarbons.	Water, mineral matter, flour, starch, tallow, stearic acid, other waxes, rosin.
Chinese or Insect	0.970	—	80–81	80–83	80–93	51% fatty acids	1.4	Ceryl cerotate.	
Spermaceti	0.905–.960	—	41–46	41–47	120–134.6	49–53% fatty acids	3.8	Cetyl palmitate.	Stearic acid, beeswax, tallow, paraffin.
Woolfat or wax	0.941–.97	—	Acids 31–42	Acids 40	82–130	—	15–29	Ceryl and carnaubyl alcohols, cholesterol, lanoceric, lanopalmic, myristic, and carnaubic acids.	
These two below are really fats but are called waxes.									
Japan	0.975	—	50–51	48–50.8	217–237.5	—	4.2–15.1	Palmitin and palmitic acid.	Water, starch, other fats.
Myrtle	0.995	At 80° 1.436	40–48	39–45	205–217	1.9–3.9	—	Palmitin.	

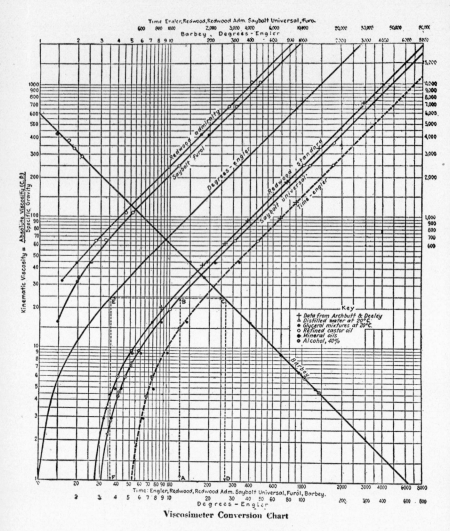

Viscosimeter Conversion Chart

DEGREES–ENGLER

FIG. 92b.   Viscosimeter Conversion Chart[1]

(Directions for Use of Chart)

OBJECT: To find the viscosity reading of a particular oil on any of the standard viscosimeters when its reading on one of the viscosimeters has been determined by experiment *at the same temperature.*

SCALES: There are two sets of scales which must not be confused with each other.

X: The scales at bottom and left hand side go together.   They are the ones regularly used in practice applying to all ordinary oils.

Y: The scales at top and on right hand side go together.   They are rarely used, applying only to very viscous products beyond range of other scales.

[1] Power (1922), 377.

NOTE: There are two lines of scales at the bottom: (a) The lower scale applying only to degrees Engler. (b) The upper scale applying to all other readings, including Engler-time. In simply changing from one viscosimeter to another the scales at left and right are not used. The scales at top must never be used in connection with those at the bottom.

APPLICATION OF CHARTS: X: For ordinary cases.—GIVEN: Saybolt Universal Viscosity = 120″. DESIRED: Case (a) Barbey reading. Case (b) Engler-Degree reading. PROCEDURE: Find point on bottom scales for Saybolt Universal corresponding to 120″ (A). Follow up vertically to curve marked Saybolt Universal (the known instrument) (B). (a) To get Barbey reading: Follow horizontally to curve marked Barbey (C). Drop down to bottom scale for Barbey and read (C). Reading = 265 deg. (b) To get Engler-Degree reading: Follow horizontally to curve marked Degrees-Engler (E). Drop down to lower of the two bottom scales for Engler-Degrees and read (F). Reading = 3.62 deg., i.e., 120″ Saybolt = Barbey 265 deg. = Engler 3.62.

Y: For very viscous fluids beyond range of other scales. GIVEN: Engler-Degrees = 1,100 deg. DESIRED: Saybolt Furol reading. PROCEDURE: Find point on upper scales under Degrees-Engler corresponding to 1,100 deg. Follow vertically down to Degrees-Engler curve. Follow horizontally to curve marked Furol. Rise vertically to scales under Furol and read. Reading = 3,800″, i.e., 1,100 deg. Engler = 3,800″ Furol.

MULTIPLYING FACTORS TO REDUCE SAYBOLT TIMES TO ENGLER NUMBERS OR TO REDWOOD TIMES [1]

Saybolt Times Seconds.	Factor Saybolt Time to Engler Number.	Factor Saybolt Time to Redwood Time.	Saybolt Times Seconds.	Factor Saybolt Time to Engler Number.	Factor Saybolt Time to Redwood Time.
28	0.0357	0.95	75	0.0289	0.86
30	.0352	.95	80	.0286	.86
32	.0346	.94	85	.0284	.86
34	.0342	.94	90	.0282	.85
36	.0337	.94	95	.0280	.85
38	.0334	.93	100	.0279	.85
40	.0330	.93	110	.0276	.85
42	.0327	.92	120	.0274	.84
44	.0323	.92	130	.0272	.84
46	.0320	.91	140	.0271	.84
48	.0317	.91	160	.0269	.84
50	.0314	.90	180	.0268	.84
55	.0308	.90	200	.0267	.84
60	.0302	.89	....	.....	....
65	.0297	.88	1800	0.0267	0.84
70	0.0293	0.87			

The Engler number is the quotient of Engler Time divided by the water value of the instrument at 20° C. in seconds.

Reagents

The reagents used in oil analysis are few and easily obtained. A list and their method of preparation is here given.

Acetic Acid, Glacial. Baker and Adamson's C. P., 99.5% pure. The determination of its strength should be made by titration and not by specific gravity, as the 98% and 80% acid have the same specific gravity, 1.067. The determination of the melting-point gives results equally good with those obtained by titration and requires less time.[2] It is made after the manner of the "titer test" (p. 598), the tube being half filled, chilled to 10 to 11° C., and further chilled by placing the outside bottle in ice-water; the temperature of the super-cooled acid rises to its melting-point, where it remains stationary for some time. The melting-points of acids of various strengths are as follows: 100%, 16.75° C.; 99.5%, 15.65°; 99%, 14.8°.

For Hanus's solution it must not reduce potassium bichromate and sulphuric acid.

Acetic Anhydride.

Alcohol. Commercial "Cologne Spirits." For the preparation of alcohol free from aldehyde for alcoholic potash, cologne spirits are treated with silver oxide as follows: 1½ grams of silver nitrate are dissolved in 3 cc. of water, added to 1 liter of alcohol and thoroughly shaken; 3 grams of potassium hydrate are dissolved in 15 cc. warm alcohol and, after cooling, added to the alcoholic silver nitrate and thoroughly shaken again, best in a tall bottle or cylinder. The silver oxide is allowed to settle, the clear liquid siphoned off and distilled, a few bits of pumice, prepared by igniting it and immediately quenching under water, being added to prevent bumping. Alcohol for use in the free acid determination is prepared by placing 10 to 15 grams of dry sodium carbonate in the reagent bottle, taking care to filter it before use.

Alcohol, Amyl.

Bromine. The commercial article; also a N/3 solution, made by dissolving 26.6 grams bromine in 1 liter carbon tetrachloride.

Calcium Chloride. The dry and also the crystallized salt.

Calcium Sulphate. Plaster of Paris.

Carbon Tetrachloride. Baker and Adamson's C. P. or Kahlbaum's "Tetrachlor-kohlenstoff."

Chloroform. Squibb's, U. S. P.

Copper. Copper turnings or clippings, used for the generation of nitric oxide.

Copper Wire. Cut in pieces of 0.3 to 0.5 gram.

Ether. Squibb's, U. S. P.

Gasoline. Gasoline, 86° Baumé.

Hydrochloric Acid, C. P.—Specific gravity 1.2. For N/2 HCl dilute 39 cc. of the above acid to 1 liter and standardize.

Iodine Solution. Fifty grams of iodine to 1 liter of alcohol. For Hanus's solution dissolve by warming 13.2 grams iodine in 1 liter glacial acetic acid; cool and add 3 cc. of bromine.

Lead Acetate. One hundred grams of the salt to 1 liter.

Lacmoid. Three grams per liter of dilute alcohol.

Lacmoid Paper. Unsized paper dipped in above solution.

Litmus Paper.

Mercuric Chloride. Sixty grams of the salt to 1 liter of alcohol.

Nitric Acid. Specific gravity 1.34.

Phenolphthalein. One gram of the substance to 500 cc. of alcohol.

Meta-Phosphoric Acid. A saturated solution of the commercial "stick phosphoric acid" in absolute alcohol.

Potassium Bichromate. Dissolve 3.8633 grams of the C. P. salt in 1 liter of water; 1 cc. is equivalent to 0.01 gram of iodine. The solution should be tested against iron wire containing a known percentage of iron.

---

[1] Proc. Am. Soc. Test. Mat., **15**, 1, 288, 1915.
[2] McIlhiney, et al., J. Am. Chem. Soc., **29**, 1224, 1907.

Potassium Hydroxide. N/2: Dissolve 30 grams of "potash by alcohol" in 1 liter of alcohol. N/6: Dissolve 10 grams of "potash by alcohol" in 1 liter of water and dilute to proper strength. The solution should be protected by "stick potash" from the carbon dioxide in the air. *Ten per cent:* Dissolve 100 grams of "stick potash" in 1,100 cc. of alcohol.

Potassium Iodate. A 2% solution.

Potassium Iodide. One hundred fifty grams of the commercial salt are dissolved in water and made up to 1 liter of water. This should be free from iodate, shown by yielding no coloration when acidified with strong HCl.

Silver Nitrate. Thirty grams to 1 liter+0.4 cc. HNO₃.

Sodium.

Sodium Chloride. Ordinary " coarse fine " salt for freezing mixtures.

Sodium Hydrate. 36° Baumé. Dissolve 300 grams of caustic soda in 1 liter of water.

Sodium Nitroprusside. The commercial salt.

Sodium Thiosulphate. N/10: Dissolve 26 grams of "sodium hyposulphite" in 1 liter of water.

Starch Solution. Rub up in a mortar 1 gram of potato starch, with 10 to 15 cc. of water, pour this into 200 cc. of water which is boiling actively, and continue the boiling for a few minutes.

Sugar. Ordinarily granulated sugar.

Sulphur. A 1.5% solution in carbon bisulphide.

Sulphuric Acid. C. P. This should be at least 99.5% pure, and its strength be determined by titration, as 100% and 94.3% acid have the same specific gravity.

Dilute. One part acid to ten parts water.

Nitrosulphuric Acid, for the Elaidin Test. A liter of sulphuric acid of 46° Baumé (1.47 specific gravity) is prepared by diluting 560 cc. commercial sulphuric acid to 1 liter; a few drops of nitric acid are added and nitric oxide (generated from copper and nitric acid) passed in until it is saturated. The acid is then cooled in ice-water and the gas passed in until it is saturated at 0° C. This is called Roth's liquid.

The author wishes to acknowledge his indebtedness to Mr. Thomas T. Gray for his careful review of this chapter. Mr. Gray's broad experience in petroleum products as Chief Chemist of Tidewater Oil Company, makes his criticism and suggestions of special value.

[1] Richmond, J. Soc. Chem. Ind., 9, 479, 1890.

JUNKER'S CALORIMETER FOR LIQUID FUELS

Directions for Working

1. Filling the lamp: Loosen the wing screw *b*, remove the arm with the gauge and pour about 150–200 cm.³ of fuel into the recipient. Then put the gauge arm on again and close the opening by again tightening the screw.

2. Setting up: Place the balance by the side of the calorimeter so that the burner of the lamp hangs exactly in the center of the combustion chamber of the calorimeter, after which the lamp with its appendage *g* is hung from one arm of the scales and counterbalanced by putting weights on the other scale. By using a mirror the right position to be obtained can be easily controlled. The lamp can be turned round the appendage *e*, when the nut *f* is loosened.

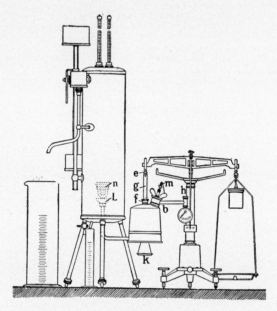

Fig. 92c.

3. Starting: Remove the lamp again from the balance, fill the cup *L* beneath the burner heat with spirit and light it. Then take the hood *m* and screw the air hose of the air-pump to the valve. When the spirit of small cup is nearly burnt out, press air into the recipient by vigorously pushing the air piston, the air acting upon the fuel, it will rise into the burner and gasify on its hot surface. The gas streaming out of the nozzle ignites itself on the spirit flame and feeds the gasification, even when the spirit is completely burnt out.

If no gas streams out, the nozzle n is obstructed; it must be cleaned by means of the special pin included with the apparatus. An ordinary pin must not be used as in doing so damage would be done to the nozzle.

4. Regulation: Press as much air into the apparatus that a uniform and free burning flame is obtained. (The development of heat should be about 1000 calories per hour, thus about 100 grams of petroleum benzine or lubricating oil, or 130 grams of spirit must be burnt per hour.)

If the flame is too large, the screw h should be slightly slackened so as to let some air escape. When the flame is well regulated, the small wing screw of the valve is tightened again, the pump is removed and the small hood m is screwed on the thread.

5. Measuring: Now introduce the burner into the combustion chamber beneath the calorimeter and hang the lamp on one arm of the balance as indicated but *not before having filled the calorimeter with water so that it flows out at the outlet.*

After having introduced the lamp, the thermometer at the water outlet begins to rise. By means of the regulating cock of the calorimeter the water supply must be regulated thus, that the difference between the inflowing and outflowing water is about 10–20°. After having reached the state of permanency, *i.e.*, when the thermometer does not rise any more, put a small weight on the scale k so that the arm of the balance goes down. The balance will only reach its state of equilibrium when a certain amount of fuel has been burnt.

The moment when the pointer of the balance reaches the point of zero, the hose must be turned over the gauge. At the same time the cup k is charged with 10–20 grams. After this, begin reading the two thermometers, doing this preferably at regular intervals. The trapping of the water and the reading is interrupted the moment where the lamp again starts rising and the hand goes again through o. At this point 10–20 grams of fuel have been burnt.

The higher heating value is calculated according to

$$H = \frac{W}{G} T,$$

where H is the heating value in calories per gram,

W the quantity of the water trapped in kilos or liters,
G the quantity of fuel consumed, in grams,
T the difference of temperature between inflowing and outflowing water.

Heating value of a kilogram $= 1000H$.

In order to ascertain the lower heating value, the condensed water flowing off is caught in a small gauge, the number of cubic centimeters of collected condensed water obtained from 10 grams of burnt fuel is multiplied by 60 and the number thus obtained is deducted from the upper heating value of a kilogram of fluidity, found in the calorimeter.

6. Stopping the calorimeter: Slacken the screw h of the lamp whereby the pressure of air will cease at once and the flame will be extinguished.

Annotations: The burner head with the small nozzle is designed for fuels rich in carbon (as petroleum, benzine, etc.), that with the large nozzle for fuels containing water (spirit). The more carbon, the smaller the bore.

Spirit requires the smallest pressure of air, under 200 millimeters; mineral and lubricating oil the highest. Vegetable and animal oils must be used for combustion only if they are completely volatilized at a boiling point of 250° at the highest. Thus, several oils cannot be used, for instance, neat's foot oil, rape oil, olive oil.

Mineral lubricating oils may be used, if they evaporate completely at 250°.

If the preliminary warming is not sufficient, or the pressure of the air is too high, the burning is subject to sudden shocks; by slackening the screw h and warming up again, this inconvenience will be done away with.

When lubricating oil has been burnt, the lamp must be well cleaned with petroleum followed by benzine. Then the lamp should be soaked with a quantity of the liquid fuel which is to be tested. Only when this has been done, the liquid fuel for a new measuring may be poured into it.

There is no danger whatever of explosion, even with benzine, as the flame will never get back into the recipient, as the pipe and the small nozzle are always filled with fluid. Naturally benzine should not be poured into the recipient in the proximity of the burning lamp.

This equipment may be purchased from Junkers and Co., Dessau, Germany.

Determination of Lead Tetra Ethyl in Motor Spirit

When bromine fumes or chlorine are passed into a spirit containing a lead tetra alkyl a bulky white precipitate is produced probably of the type $Pb(CH_3)_3Cl$. This dissolves in dilute hydrochloric acid, but before the lead can be precipitated by the usual reagents it is necessary to boil the acid extract, when complete conversion into lead chloride appears to result.

Procedure. 100 cc. of the spirit are saturated by bubbling in chlorine gas. The precipitate coagulates and the supernatant solution becomes a bright yellow. The product is transferred to a separatory funnel, washing out with dilute hydrochloric acid. The mixture is shaken once or twice with additional hydrochloric acid and the combined extracts boiled in a reflux condenser for half an hour. An excess of sodium acetate followed by potassium dichromate are added, the solution being kept hot until the lead chromate coagulates. The lead compound is filtered into a Gooch crucible and weighed as usual.

Notes. The results on weighed quantities of lead tetra ethyl are very consistent, but about 7 per cent low on the laboratory sample. In case of lead methyl the results are 4 per cent low. These results seem to conform to the sulphuric acid method, where the results given are 4 per cent low. It is probable that these figures indicate the degree of purity of the lead alkyl samples. A determination requires less than two hours.

The presence of carbon tetrachloride does not effect results. Solutions of lead methyl or ethyl on standing in a corked bottle exposed to light deposits a bulky light colored precipitate.[1]

[1] W. R. Ormandy, Journ. Inst. Petr. Tech., **10**, 47, 954, Dec. 1924.

Determination of Nitrobenzine in Oils Used for Oiling Floors.

Procedure.—Shake 20 cc. of oil with 1 cc. of concentrated HOAc until homogeneous, add about 0.2 g. of Zn powder, heat until the odor of $PhNO_2$ is gone, cool, decant into a separating funnel, wash the excess Zn 3 times with 1 cc. of diluted HOAc and after filtering these washings add them to the funnel, shake, let stand, separate the red-brown lower layer and divide into 2 parts. (1) To 1 part add 2–3 vols. of Et_2O and a "pinch" of PbO_2. The liquid immediately turns violet and on agitation the Et_2O absorbs this color. (2) To the second part also add Et_2O as before and then a few drops of aqueous $K_2Cr_2O_7$. The aqueous layer becomes green, then yellow-red, and in the Et_2O the same violet color appears as with PbO_2. By means of standard color tubes which are prepared under the same conditions with known amounts of $PhNO_2$ in a hydrocarbon oil the amount of $PhNO_2$ in the oil under investigation can be estimated. About 0.05 per cent $PhNO_2$ is the minimum which can be detected. The intensity and tone of the colors are influenced by the conditions of the reactions, so that both the amounts of liquids and the conditions must be carefully controlled. The use of a colorimeter serves to increase the precision of the test.[1]

[1] Pietro Biginelli, Atti congresso naz. chim. ind. **1924**, 274–6. C. C. Davis, C. A. **19**, 1391, May, 1925.

THE TESTING OF PETROLEUM AND ITS PRODUCTS, INCLUDING THE INTERPRETATION OF RESULTS[1]

The modern refining methods with the growing demand of greater efficiency, better products and the reclaiming of former waste products places petroleum chemistry in a very important place in the chemical industry. The testing of crude oils and their products determines the methods used in refining and gives an accurate evaluation of the oils to be refined.

Petroleums may be classed as paraffin, asphaltic and mixed base crude. The paraffin base petroleum is made up of the straight chain hydrocarbons having a formula C_nH_{2n+2}. They are saturated hydrocarbons and are not acted upon by sulphuric acid. The asphaltic base contains the naphthenes (C_nH_2n) or cyclic compounds and acomatic hydrocarbons. The mixed crudes are a combination of paraffin and asphaltic compounds.

Petroleums frequently have other compounds than the hydrocarbons mentioned, such as the compounds containing oxygen, nitrogen, and sulphur. These may be of industrial significance but are generally considered as the undesirable qualities which should be removed. Foreign matter such as water, sand, clay and asphalt may be found as suspensions and emulsions. The information as to their presence may avoid much trouble in the distillation as they often form the emulsifying agents for permanent emulsions or decrease the temperatures in which " cracking " begins.

The increased demand for gasoline has increased the " cracking " of the higher molecules and has made the tests for unsaturates, carbon in colloidal form, fixed gases and gases containing gasoline, of great importance in most commercial plants.

The reclaiming of the waste matters and the making of by-products by the treating of the fractions containing the sulphur and nitrogen compound makes a careful and accurate testing of these compounds of greatest importance.

The examination and evaluation of the petroleums and their products should be done in an accurate and systematic manner, so that the combined results will give a workable knowledge. The complexity of the petroleums or their fractions makes most tests have little value or they may be very misleading unless accompanied by other data. The conclusions arrived at should be verified by other tests and a complete report made as to the results.

The following tests mentioned will be found in detail in other parts of this text. Each test should have a definite point to determine and all data recorded in a logical manner.

Tests Made on Crude Petroleum and its Products, Including the Interpretation of Results

Crude Oils

The Physical Tests. The color of petroleum gives little information unless other than green or black. Other colors may indicate contamination with clays, sands or water.

Odor. The odor of petroleum may indicate in a general way the fields from which the oil came. A gasoline odor indicates a pure paraffin base crude with high gasoline content. The aromatic and pyridine odors are common to

---

[1] Contribution by Robert C. Beckstrom.

some of the crude oils from California, Texas, Rumania, Russia, and is found in shale oils. The odor of pyridine is more pronounced if the sample is agitated with potassium hydroxide solution. A slight terpene odor may be detected in some of the Gulf Coast oils.

The specific gravity or Baumé gravity [1] of a crude indicates the approximate amount of light oils. This test should be followed by the distillation of the crude oil for an accurate determination.

The test for sediment and water (page 1132b) determines the need of dehydration, the types of stills used for refining or whether it will be accepted for pipe line transportation. In the heavier crudes, water may be in such small droplets that considerable care must be taken to complete the separation.

The fractional distillation of petroleum as outlined by the United States Bureau of Mines [2] gives a fair determination of the amounts of gasoline, kerosene, fuel oil, and lubricating oil. It is found that any one method of distillation for the different kinds of petroleums is unsatisfactory when fractions are identified by their boiling points alone. These results should be supplemented with other tests. The asphaltic and mixed base petroleums begin to crack at lower temperatures than the paraffin base petroleums and the products of distillation will be found to be much different. A crude oil with emulsions or finely dispersed particles of water in it must first be dehydrated before a distillation can successfully be made.

Sulphur may be detected by the odor of hydrogen sulphide or the mercaptans when a crude is heated. The sulphur tests as outlined on page 1130 give the quantitative measurements. The fact that sulphur is found in a petroleum does not follow that it will be equally divided in the distilled fractions. The author has found sulphur in varying amounts in the 10% fractions of the same crude oil with a slight variation in the method of refining. The importance of sulphur tests is not in the crude oil but in the products of distillation.

Gasoline, Naphtha

The specific gravity, Baumé or A.P.I., is taken with a hydrometer (page 1111). This information without other data, such as the distillation curve or the knowledge of its being a straight run, natural gasoline, or blended product, is of little value in the determination of the quality of the gasoline.

The yellow color in a gasoline (test, page 1115) indicates improper treatment with acid or sodium plumbate solution. A dark color may be caused by contamination with heavier hydrocarbons in pipe line or tank cars, and should not be confused with colors caused by other methods.

The sweet ethereal odors of gasoline are characteristic of the gasolines from low sulphur paraffin base crude oil. Sour or " cracked " odor is characteristic of a gasoline incompletly refined and it is probably made from a high temperature cracking process.

The distillation test (page 1112) should be made with great care as a change in the rate of distillation, rapid or slow heating during the process gives inaccurate results. The distillation curve indicates a straight run, natural

[1] The specific gravity $= \dfrac{141.5}{131.5 + \text{Bé.}}$.

[2] Bulletin 207, Bureau of Mines.

gasoline or blended product.   The distillation range of a motor gasoline should conform to the following: [1]

The sodium plumbate test (page 1124) when positive indicates sulphur compounds that will cause the gasoline to turn yellow in storage.   The gasoline giving a negative test may upon standing in the sunlight later give a positive test.   This shows that the treatment of the gasoline has been incomplete and further treatment is needed.   The sodium plumbate treatment may not decrease the sulphur content and may increase it.   It does, however, cause the sulphur compounds to become more stable so as not to cause the gasoline to become yellow.

The testing for unsaturates (tests, pages 1135–1136) or the test by the United States Bureau of Mines [2] may be used.   The Maumene (page 1135) test is to be used only as a check as it is unreliable for highly unsaturated mixture.

U. S. Bureau of Mines Test.   Five cc. of the gasoline are run into a clean, dry Babcock cream bottle and when cooled in ice water 200% by volume of sulphuric acid (1.84 sp.gr.) is added.   A rubber stopper is then placed in the bottle and shaken with a rotary motion for several minutes.   The gasoline and sulphuric acid then are separated by adding sulphuric acid until the surface is about level with the upper graduation mark on the neck of the bottle.   The bottle is allowed to stand twelve hours or it can be placed in a centrifuge and whirled at the rate of 500 to 1000 R.P.M. for three minutes.   A reading of the volume of gasoline remaining is then made and the loss to sulphuric acid is calculated.

The unsaturation gives information as to the amount of acid needed for the acid treatment.   A highly unsaturated finished product may cause the deposition of carbon and gummy matter in the cylinder of the motor.   This point is not accepted by all authorities.

Corrosion and gumming test (page 1126) indicates elementary sulphur compounds in the gasoline.   The gummy material may be acid residues, polymerization of highly unsaturated compounds or asphaltic bodies.

Vapor Pressure determinations give direct information as to the probable behavior of motor fuels as regards easy starting and " flexibility."   It indicates, if the pressure is high, the blending of natural gasoline with a straight run product.   It is important in the shipping of gasoline in tank cars [3] and must conform with interstate shipping laws.

Kerosene, Mineral Seal and Gas Oil

Specific Gravity.   The specific gravity, Baumé or A.P.I., is determined by the same methods as described under gasoline.   The test indicates approximately where the fraction has been cut during the distillation of the crude oil.

[1] Bulletin 323A, United States Bureau of Mines.

> Overpoint not more than 131° F.
> 20% recovered in receiver not more than 221° F.
> 50% recovered in receiver not more than 284° F.
> 90% recovered in receiver not more than 392° F.
> End point not higher than   437° F.
> At least 95% of distillate recovered.

[2] Tech. paper 181.
[3] Bureau of Explosive Circular MCL, No. 147.

This must be comfirmed by other data such as the distillation curve, flash and fire points.

The dark colors show incomplete acid treatment, percolation or contact filtration. A " cracked " odor is the result of high temperatures or pressures during distillation, but may be removed with acid treatment.

The viscosity tests (page 1116) must conform to the specification for fuel oils under working temperatures. The oils should be free from water, dirt, and tarry matter which may clog the burners.

The cloud test (page 1118) indicates too deep a cut into the lubricating fraction and the settling out of crystals of paraffin. A fuel oil showing a cloud test will solidify when in storage during cold weather.

The distillation test determines the cause for the decrease of the illuminating power of the oil after burning for a time. In absorbing oils for " casing head gas " the distillation curve may determine its usefulness as an absorbing oil. A fraction having an over point much higher than the end point of the gasoline is desirable.

The flash and fire tests (page 1127) must meet the specifications of illuminating and burning oils. A low flash and a high fire indicates a mixture of light fractions with the heavy fractions, making a poor fuel for the burners. The flame will not be uniform and the higher fractions will not burn but change into a vapor in the fire box, causing explosive mixtures. The test determines the fire hazard and is the real measure of inflammability. Most states have a law stating the minimum flash and fire points of illuminating oils.

The sulphur determinations (pages 1112e, 1130) are of great importance in illuminating oil as they produce disagreeable odors during the burning period, and cause a charring of the wicks. The amount should not exceed .1%. Fuel oils when atomized with steam form sulphuric acids which cause rapid deterioration of boilers and pipe stills.

Lubricants

The determination of specific gravity of a lubricating oil (page 1116) may give information as to the nature of the petroleum from which it is made. A high Baumé gravity and a very high viscosity may indicate a lubricant that has been mixed with soaps, resins, or oils other than mineral oils.

The color of lubricating oils indicates the source of the oil. A turbid oil indicates finely divided droplets of water, or if cooled an amorphous wax. A dark-colored oil should be examined under a microscope for suspended carbon. When the oil is diluted with naphtha, the foreign matter held in suspension settles out.

The viscosity test (page 1116) has been regarded as a most important test of lubricants. The working temperature of the bearing should determine the temperature at which the test is made. Most lubricants have the same viscosity at 300° F. A lubricating oil functions only when a continuous film of oil separates the wearing surfaces and the oil is efficient when its viscosity allows this film to be continuous without a break in the film. The true test for a lubricating oil under working conditions is the machine for which it is to be used.

The cloud test (page 1118) indicates the temperature at which the paraffin wax separates from the oil solution. It shows whether the process for the separation of wax has been well done and gives the quality of the wax which is separated out.   If the wax is amorphous in character, the oil must either be redistilled or centrifuged to remove this wax.

The pour test (page 1118) indicates the temperature under which an oil will flow.   Knowing the working temperatures that the oil will be used will determine whether it will be an efficient lubricant.

The flash and fire test (page 1118d) should be above the working temperatures of the bearing.   High flash and burning points indicate good quality and careful refining.   Too low flash and fire test results in a large loss from evaporation under working conditions.

The carbon residue test (page 1122) gives information in the laboratory approximating working conditions with the lubricants, producing more or less carbon deposits.   A large per cent of residue indicates oils thickened by other matter or badly refined.

The demulsibility test (page 1124) determines the value of a lubricant which is to be used in forced feed lubrication and motor cylinders.   A high degree of emulsification indicates an oil containing an emulsifying agent such as sulphur compounds, salts of napthenic and other organic acids.

The fatty acid test (page 1121) when more than 15 per cent, unless found in a cutting oil, will cause the formation of metallic soaps which clog the lubricating channels.

The test for rosin (page 1144b) when found positive indicates an adulterated lubricating oil and is always objectionable.

Free sulphuric acid indicates poor refining methods and should not exceed .01% in transformer oils.

The evaporation test (page 1115) is used in testing lubricating oils used in high vacuum machines, transformer oils and air compressor oils.   A high evaporation loss indicates light oils used in blending.   It may be used in testing the dilution of " crank case " oil.

Waxes

The melting point of mineral waxes may indicate its origin and determines its classification.   A wide range of temperature in the melting shows a mixture of waxes and incomplete refining methods.

Heavy Oils and Asphalts

The heavy oils may be crude oils with a low Baumé gravity or residues from the distillation of mixed or asphaltic base crudes.   They are used for fuel oil, dust laying oils and road oils.   Asphalts may be found in nature in a semi-liquid (Baumé gravity 10) or a mixture of sand and limestone.   Artificial asphalts are the residues of asphaltic base crude oils and may be polymerized into a hard asphalt by blowing air through the residues at high temperatures.

The testing of fuel oils is of little value unless the specifications for the individual oil are given.   The many types of burners and the various conditions under which fuel oils are used make any one set of specifications impossible to use.   The term fuel oil as now used is broad in meaning and may range from a mineral seal distillate to heavy residues or a mixture of oils having no other apparent use.

The gravity of fuel oils gives little information unless other information is obtainable. The flash point is important and should be higher than the temperature at which the oil is sufficiently fluid for the particular apparatus for which it is desired. A low flash shows a naphtha and should not be used in open burners. The viscosity of an oil must be low enough so that it will flow readily at low temperatures. Water and sediment (page 1132b) choke the burners and freeze in the pipes during low temperatures. The fuel [1] should not contain grit, acid, fibrous or other foreign matter and shall pass through a filter of wire gauze 16 meshes to the inch.

The sulphur content when high (over 2.5%) indicates a residue of a high sulphur crude or a mixture of fuels obtained from acid recovery plants. A high sulphur fuel causes rapid corrosion of all exposed metal parts of stills and boilers.

The determination of the calorific value is made by the oxygen or Parr bomb calorimeter. Care must be taken to make corrections before reporting the higher and lower calorific values.

Road Oils

Road oils may be used as dust-laying oils, binders for sand, sandy loam and gravel roads. The value of a road oil depends upon its penetration into the soil, the binding qualities of the oil, and its resistance to weather and wear.

The tests on road oils are important in as much as the importance of the specifications for the particular duty for which they are intended. Road oils are often placed on roads without any study as to the adaptability of the oil for the soil or base on which it is placed.

Gravity is a common test made on road oils but has little value. The asphalt in a road oil acts as the binder and weather-resisting element. The total bitumen (page 1317) is determined to give the value of the oil as a binder. The penetration of the asphalt into the road bed determines its wearing qualities. The viscosity should be low enough to enable to penetrate the soil and to flow with ease and uniformly when applied. A heavy asphalt oil mixed with a lighter oil will give greater penetration, the lighter oil slowly evaporating, leaving a layer of high asphaltic content in the soil. The asphalt should contain little or no paraffin wax. The wax particles combine with the soil and form little dry particles which soon wear loose and blow away leaving small pits in the surface which soon wear away forming large holes and ruts in the finished roads.

Asphalts either native or artificial when used for paving should be tested for total bitumen, penetration (page 1299), viscosity (page 1297) and carbene (page 1318) content. If asphalts are made from petroleum residues, the wax content should be determined. Petroleum with a carbene content over .5% (part insoluble in carbon tetrachloride) indicates that the residue had been overheated or overblown, making a brittle product.

Shale Oils

The testing of shale oils is much the same as the testing of petroleums. Shale oils are made by the retorting of the oil shales changing the pyrobitumens into the bitumens. The bitumens formed vary in chemical and physical

[1] U. S. Bureau of Mines Bulletin 323A.

16

properties as the methods of retorting.   High temperatures cause " cracking " with a resulting polymerization.   The nitrogen and sulphur content being high gives a different reaction to heat than petroleums of the same gravity.

The waxes made from shales have a higher melting point than the paraffin from petroleum.   They may be separated into a white flake wax by washing the re-run lubricating distillate with acetone.   This method can be used as a quantitative test for waxes in shale oils.

The different finished products, gasolines, kerosenes, fuel oils, lubricants and waxes, are tested in the same manner as similar petroleum products.

ANALYSIS OF PAINTS

In reporting the results of an examination of a paint, it is advisable to give all the analytical data as well as a résumé showing the probable composition of the paint. This is shown in the following example:

RESULTS OF ANALYSIS

Total Pigments or Solids.................................... 60%
Total Vehicle or Liquids................................... 40

Analysis of Pigment Portion

Lead Oxide (PbO)....................................... 37.47%
Zinc Oxide (ZnO)....................................... 44.50
Alumina, iron, lime.................................... 2.90
Magnesia (MgO).. 1.90
Silica (SiO_2)....................................... 4.63
Carbon Dioxide (CO_2)................................ 2.50
Sulphuric Anhydride (SO_3)........................... 5.02
Water (combined)...................................... .73

                                                        99.15%

Analysis of Vehicle Portion

Vehicle contained 20% volatile matter.
Volatile matter consisted of equal parts of turpentine and mineral spirits.
Non-volatile matter had:

Iodine Number.. 175
Acid Number... 2.4
Saponification Number................................. 188

and contained .02% ash consisting of lead and manganese oxides.

Probable Composition of Paint.

Pigment.. 60%
Liquid... 40

Pigment

Basic Carbonate—White Lead............................ 22%
Basic Sulphate—White Lead............................. 25
Zinc Oxide... 43
Asbestine.. 10

                                                        100%

Liquid

Raw Linseed Oil.. 80%
Mineral Spirits.. 10
Turpentine and Drier.................................. 10

                                                        100%

Chapter contributed by Henry A. Gardner and John A. Schaeffer.

ANALYSIS OF PAINT VEHICLES

Composition of Liquid Part. The vehicle or liquid portion of paints may contain various fixed animal, vegetable or mineral oils, oleo-resinous varnishes, turpentine, mineral distillates, benzol and driers.

It is always advisable to determine the total percentage of liquids in a paint. The container should be thoroughly shaken so that the contents will be uniform throughout. A portion of 4 or 5 ounces may then be removed and placed in a screw-cap bottle. The original can of paint should then be set aside so that settling of the pigments will take place. Unless the paint is in paste form, this will usually be accomplished in twenty-four hours. A portion of the clear liquid floating over the pigments may then be removed and directly examined as outlined under Separation of Vehicle Components.

Percentage of Liquid by Ignition Method. The percentage of vehicle in the uniform sample of paint previously obtained may be found by placing a weighed portion in a porcelain crucible and slowly igniting it to burn off the organic constituents. By carefully regulating the heat, the oil and volatile thinners will be slowly burned off, leaving the pigment behind, which may then be weighed, calculating the vehicle by difference. This method is a rapid one and works well with some pigments. When pigments are present which show an appreciable loss on ignition, or blacks or blues, this method is not to be relied upon.

Percentage of Liquid by Extraction Methods. Another good method of separating the vehicle from a paint is to place a portion in a large tube, adding a considerable quantity of benzol, petroleum ether, or that portion of gasoline distilling below 120° C., subsequently centrifuging. Pigments which settle slowly are thrown down very rapidly by this method. The process is repeated three or four times in order thoroughly to free the pigment from oil. After drying, the pigment is weighed and the percentage of vehicle determined by difference. In case a centrifuge is not available, the vehicle of many paints may be separated by simply shaking a portion of the paint in a long test-tube with benzol, allowing the pigment to settle, repeating the extraction until the oil is thoroughly removed.

Some operators have from time to time used a Soxhlet extractor for the determination of the vehicle of a paint. This method is rather slow and does not always give satisfactory results.

It must be remembered that no method of extraction of the oil from a paint will give absolute results. The last traces of oil cannot be removed from the pigment, which is probably due to the fact that many pigments such as lead and zinc react with the oil, producing small quantities of insoluble soaps which are not completely dissolved by the solvent.

In the extraction of paints, the choice of a solvent is important. When benzol (90°) is not available, it may be replaced by gasoline that has been redistilled, using the light fraction coming over below 120° C. This cannot be used, however, when varnish resins other than rosin are present, as they are insoluble therein.

There are some pigments which by reason of their low specific gravity, colloidal nature or partial solubility can never be completely separated from oil, either by settling, centrifuging or extraction. Of these the most commonly met with are lampblack and other forms of carbon, zinc oxide and Prussian blue. Colloidal pigments such as zinc oxide are very troublesome in this respect. When these pigments, however, are present in a paint in considerable percentage, the difficulty of their separation may be avoided by adding to the paint three or four times its volume of fuller's earth, diluting the mixture in a large test-tube with gasoline or petroleum ether and either centrifuging or placing in a rack to settle. The fuller's earth carries down the colloidal pigments and the separation is sharp and easy. This method, of course, is simply used to extract the vehicle present. The pigment resulting from the separation cannot be used for analysis on account of admixture with the fuller's earth.

In some cases the pigments in paste colors made of lampblack and Prussian blue cannot be separated from the vehicle portion. The amount of Prussian blue present, however, may be determined by making a Kjeldahl-Gunning determination on a portion of the entire paint, multiplying the nitrogen found by 4.4. For the determination of the lampblack present, a portion of the entire paint may be boiled with an excess of alcoholic potash until all of the oil is saponified. The mixture is then decanted through a filter and washed, first with hot alcohol and then with hot water. This affords a very good separation of the vehicle from the pigment of such paints. By this method, the Prussian blue which may be present is partially destroyed, the iron content remaining admixed with the black pigment on the filter.

Separation of Vehicle Components. Whenever possible, it is advisable to determine the constituents of the vehicle upon that sample that has been removed from the top of the settled can of paint. A weighed portion of this vehicle may be placed in a tared flask and attached to a Liebig condenser. Heating to 180° C. or lower will drive off nearly all the volatile constituents. The composition of the distillate may be determined by the methods given under the Examination of Turpentine. A portion of the residue in the flask, which consists of oil, driers, gums, etc., may be transferred to a crucible and ignited. The residue may then be weighed and calculated to ash. The ash should be analyzed for lead, manganese and other driers.

Another portion of the original vehicle may be evaporated in an atmosphere of CO_2 (prevents oxidation) to remove the volatile constituents. A portion of the oil residue may then be examined for iodine number and other constants. In some instances it would be advisable to make a saponification and extraction of the fatty acids from this residue, determining the iodine number on the fatty acids.

Water. For a direct determination of the percentage of water in a paint, the analyst may place a weighed quantity (approximately 100 grams) of the paint in a metal still, mixing it with an equal quantity of sand. Distillation will drive off the water and other volatile constituents which will separate into two layers in the graduate.

Direct Distillation for Volatiles. For a direct determination of the volatile constituents in a paint, a sample may be distilled *in vacuo*. This is easily managed wherever a vacuum pump is available and avoids the necessity of overheating the oil. When distilling by this method, a sample of the clear vehicle from a settled paint, in order to obtain the fixed oils for analysis, it should not be heated above 150° C. and neither should the solvent be volatilized in such a way as to allow the oil to be in contact with air, as it will oxidize rapidly while warm and its iodine number be very much lowered. The volatile may also be separated by steam distillation.

Detection of Resinates. To determine whether the drier in a paint is of the resinate type or linoleate type, a few drops of the oil vehicle may be mixed on a porcelain plate with one or two drops of acetic anhydride, subsequently adding a drop of sulphuric acid.   Upon the addition of the sulphuric acid, a flash of purple color, turning to dark brown, will be shown where rosin is present.   If rosin should be present in the vehicle to a considerable extent, the oil will have a very high acid number.   The approximate percentage of rosin present may be determined by shaking a portion of the vehicle with 95% alcohol in a separatory funnel, subsequently separating the alcoholic extract, evaporating and weighing the residue.

Detection of Various Oils.   Chinese wood oil may be detected in the vehicle by mixing the oil with an equal volume of a saturated solution of iodine in petroleum ether, allowing the mixture to stand in direct sunlight.   Under these conditions, a peculiar, insoluble, spongy polymer of one of the fatty acids of Chinese wood oil is shown.   Fish oil can usually be detected by its odor and the dark red color during saponification.   The presence of soya bean and other vegetable oils is in some cases difficult to detect.   The iodine numbers of these oils, however, are all lower than that of linseed oil.   It must be remembered, however, that the iodine number of boiled linseed oil is lower than that of raw oil and that the iodine number of oils extracted from many paints is usually lower than shown by the original oil.   In the presence of considerable quantities of drier, it is always advisable to extract the fatty acids from oil and make the iodine determination upon them.

The distillate from the paint vehicle may consist of turpentine, mineral distillates, benzol and similar solvents.   The presence of benzol is readily detected by adding a few drops of the distillate to a small quantity of a mixture of concentrated nitric and sulphuric acids.   Upon heating this mixture, the characteristic odor of nitro-benzol will be recognized if benzol is present.   Mineral distillates from petroleum are easily detected by the polymerization method given under the Examination of Turpentine.

ANALYSIS OF PAINT OILS

Although linseed oil is used to the greatest extent in paints, some other oils occasionally find application in the manufacture of special paints.   The following have been used for this purpose: soya bean oil, perilla oil, corn oil, cottonseed oil, sunflower oil, lumbang oil and similar vegetable oils; menhaden oil, whale oil, herring oil, and similar marine animal oils of relatively high iodine number.

There are given below methods for the analysis of linseed oil, in accordance with the latest practice developed by the U. S. Government Interdepartmental Committee on standardization of paint specifications.   These methods may be followed in examining any of the other oils mentioned above.

Iodine Number.   Weigh in a small glass capsule from 0.2 to 0.3 gram of oil, transfer to a 500-cc. bottle having a well-ground stopper, dissolve the oil in 10 cc. of chloroform and add 30 cc. of Hanus solution; let it stand with occasional shaking for one hour, add 10 cc. of a 10 per cent solution of potassium iodide and 150 cc. of water, and titrate with standard sodium thiosulphate, using starch as indicator.   Blanks must be run each time.   From the difference between the amounts of sodium thiosulphate required by the blanks and the determination, calculate the iodine number (centigrams of iodine to 1 gram of oil).   The iodine number of raw linseed oil varies from 175 to 193.   Make the Hanus solution by dissolving 13.2 grams of iodine in 1000 cc. of glacial acetic acid which will not reduce chromic acid, and adding 3 cc. of bromine.

Analysis of Linseed Oil

Loss on Heating at 105° to 110° C. Place 10 grams of the oil in an accurately weighed 200 cc. Erlenmeyer flask; weigh. Heat in an oven at a temperature between 105 and 110° C. for 30 minutes; cool and weigh. Calculate the percentage loss. This determination shall be made in a current of dry carbon dioxide gas.

Foots. With all materials at a temperature between 20° and 27° C. mix, by shaking in a stoppered flask for exactly one minute, 25 cc. of the well-shaken sample of oil, 25 cc. of acetone and 10 cc. of the acid calcium chloride solution. Transfer the mixture to a burette where settling can take place for 24 hours. The temperature during this period should be between 20° and 27° C.

The volume of the stratum lying between the clear calcium chloride solution and the clear acetone and oil mixture is read in tenths of a cubic centimeter or a fraction thereof. This reading multiplied by four expresses the amount of foots present as percentage by volume of the oil taken.

Specific Gravity. Use a pyknometer accurately standardized and having a capacity of at least 25 cc., making the test at 15.5° C., water being unity at 15.5° C.

Acid Number. Weigh from 5 to 10 grams of the oil. Transfer to a 350 cc. Erlenmeyer flask. Add 50 cc. of neutral 95 per cent ethyl alcohol. Put a condenser loop inside the neck of the flask. Heat on a steam bath for 30 minutes. Cool and add phenolphthalein indicator. Titrate to a faint permanent pink color with the standard sodium hydroxide solution. Calculate the acid number (milligrams KOH per gram of oil).

Saponification Number. Weigh about 2 grams of the oil in a 350 cc. Erlenmeyer flask. Add 25 cc. alcoholic sodium hydroxide solution. Put a condenser loop inside the neck of the flask and heat on the steam bath for one hour. Cool, add phenolphthalein as indicator, and titrate with half normal sulphuric acid. Run two blanks with the alcoholic sodium hydroxide solution. These should check within 0.1 cc. $N/2$ H_2SO_4. From the difference between the number of cubic centimeters of $N/2$ H_2SO_4 required for the blank and for the determination, calculate the saponification number (milligrams KOH required for 1 gram of oil).

Unsaponifiable Matter. Weigh 8 to 10 grams of the oil. Transfer to a 250 cc. long-neck flask. Add 5 cc. of strong solution of sodium hydroxide (equal weights of NaOH and H_2O), and 50 cc. 95 per cent ethyl alcohol. Put a condenser loop inside the neck of the flask and boil for two hours. Occasionally agitate the flask to break up the liquid but do not project the liquid onto the sides of the flask. At the end of two hours remove the condenser and allow the liquid to boil down to about 25 cc.

Transfer to a 500 cc. glass-stoppered separatory funnel, rinsing with water. Dilute with water to 250 cc., add 100 cc. redistilled ether. Stopper and shake for one minute. Let stand until the two layers separate sharp and clear. Draw all but one or two drops of the aqueous layer into a second 500 cc. separatory funnel and repeat the process using 60 cc. of ether. After thorough separation draw off the aqueous solution into a 400 cc. beaker, then the ether solution into the first separatory funnel, rinsing down with a little water. Return the aqueous solution to the second separatory funnel and shake out again with 60 cc. of ether in a similar manner, finally drawing the aqueous solution into the beaker and rinsing the ether into the first separatory funnel.

Shake the combined ether solution with the accumulated water rinsings and let the layers separate sharp and clear. Draw off the water and add it to the main aqueous solution. Shake the ether solution with two portions of water (about 25 cc. each). Add these to the main water solution.

Swirl the separatory funnel so as to bring the last drops of water down to the stopcock, and draw off until the ether solution just fills the bore of the stopcock. Wipe out the stem of the separatory funnel with a bit of cotton on a wire. Draw the ether solution (portionwise if necessary) into a 250 cc. flask and distill off. While still hot, drain the flask into a small weighed beaker, rinsing with a little ether. Evaporate this ether, cool and weigh. (*The unsaponifiable oil from adulterated drying oils is volatile and will evaporate on long heating. Therefore heat the beaker on a warm plate, occasionally blowing out with a current of dry air. Discontinue heating as soon as the odor of ether is gone.*)

Iodine Number. Place a small quantity of the sample in a small weighing burette or beaker. Weigh accurately. Transfer by dropping about 0.15 grams (0.10 to 0.20 grams) to a 500 cc. bottle having a well-ground glass stopper, or an Erlenmeyer flask having a specially flanged neck for the iodine test. Reweigh the burette or beaker and determine the amount of sample used. Add 10 cc. of chloroform. Whirl the bottle to dissolve the sample. Add 10 cc. of chloroform to each of two empty bottles like that used for the sample. Add to each bottle 25 cc. of Hanus solution and let stand with occasional shaking for one-half hour. Add 10 cc. of the 15 per cent potassium iodide solution and 100 cc. of water, and titrate with standard sodium thiosulphate using starch as indicator.

The titrations on the two blank tests should agree within 0.1 cc. From the difference between the average of the blank titration and the titration on the samples and the iodine value of the thiosulphate solution, calculate the iodine number of the samples tested. (Iodine number is centigrams of iodine to 1 gram of sample.)

Ash. Take a porcelain crucible or dish. Add 10 to 25 cc. of oil, carefully weighing the amount added. Place on a stone slab on the floor of a hood. Ignite by playing the flame of a burner on the surface of the oil and allow to burn quietly until most of the oil is burned off; then transfer to a muffle or over a flame and continue heating at a very low temperature (not over a dull red) until all carbonaceous matter is consumed. Cool, weigh, and calculate the percentage of ash. Moisten the ash with a few drops of water and test with litmus paper. Record whether neutral or alkaline. Wash any ash adhering to the test paper back into the crucible. Dissolve the ash in dilute nitric acid to which a little hydrogen peroxide has been added. After solution is complete make up the volume to about 50 cc. with nitric acid and water so that the final volume will contain about 1 volume of concentrated nitric acid and 3 volumes of water. Boil to remove excess of hydrogen peroxide. Determine manganese by the bismuthate method.

Ash another portion of the oil and dissolve the ash as above in nitric acid and hydrogen peroxide. Transfer to a 250 cc. beaker and dilute to about 200 cc. This volume of solution should contain 15 to 20 cc. of concentrated nitric acid. Electrolyze this solution using platinum electrodes (the anode being previously weighed) with a current density of about 0.5 amperes and

2 to 2.5 volts. It is best to pass the current overnight (about 15 hours). On removing the anode, it is carefully washed in clear water, dried in a steam oven, transferred to an oven where it is heated to 180° C., cooled and weighed. The increase in weight of the anode multiplied by 0.86 gives the weight of lead in the sample. Calculate to percentage. If desired, the lead may be determined by the sulphate or any other accurate method in place of the electrolytic method given above.

Time of Drying on Glass. Flow the oil over a perfectly clean glass plate and allow to drain in a vertical position in a well-ventilated room at a temperature between 15° and 39° C. After about 2 hours the film is tested at intervals with the finger at points not less than $2\frac{1}{2}$ cm. from the edges. The film will be considered dry when it adheres no longer to the finger and does not rub up appreciably when the finger is rubbed lightly across the surface. With boiled linseed oil this usually occurs in from 5 to 18 hours.

Reagents for Testing

The following reagents will be required:

Acetone that will pass the specification of the United States Pharmacopoeia.

Acid Calcium Chloride Solution. Saturate with calcium chloride a mixture of 90 parts water and 10 parts concentrated hydrochloric acid (specific gravity 1.2).

Standard Sodium Thiosulphate Solution. Dissolve pure sodium thiosulphate in distilled water that has been well boiled to free it from carbon dioxide in the proportion so that 24.83 grams crystallized sodium thiosulphate will be present in 1000 cc. of the solution. It is best to let this solution stand for about two weeks before standardizing. Standardize with pure resublimed iodine. This solution will be approximately decinormal, and it is best to leave it as it is after determining its exact iodine value, rather than to attempt to adjust it to exactly decinormal strength. Preserve in a stock bottle provided with a guard tube filled with soda lime.

Starch Solution. Stir up 2 to 3 grams of potato starch or 5 grams soluble starch with 100 cc. of 1 per cent salicylic acid solution, add 300 to 400 cc. boiling water, and boil the mixture until the starch is practically dissolved. Dilute to 1 liter.

Standard Iodine Solution. Dissolve 13 grams of resublimed iodine and 18 grams of pure potassium iodide (free from iodates) in 50 cc. of distilled water, and dilute to 1000 cc. Determine its exact value by titrating with the standard sodium thiosulphate solution.

Potassium Iodide Solution. Dissolve 150 grams of potassium iodide free from iodate in distilled water and dilute to 1000 cc.

Hanus Solution. Dissolve 13.2 grams of iodine in 1000 cc. of glacial acetic acid (99.5 per cent) that will not reduce chromic acid. Add enough bromine to double the halogen content, determined by titration (3 cc. of bromine is about the proper amount). The iodine may be dissolved by the aid of heat, but the solution should be cold when the bromine is added.

Standard Sodium Hydroxide Solution. Prepare a stock concentrated solution of sodium hydroxide by dissolving sodium hydroxide in water in the proportion of 200 grams NaOH to 200 cc. water. Allow this solution to cool and settle in a stoppered bottle for several days. Decant the clear liquid from the precipitate of sodium carbonate into another clean bottle. Add clear barium hydroxide solution until no further precipitate forms. Again allow to settle until clear. Draw off about 175 cc. and dilute to 10 liters with freshly boiled distilled water. Preserve in a stock bottle provided with a large guard tube filled with soda lime. Determine the exact strength by titrating against pure benzoic acid (C_6H_5COOH) using phenolphthalein as indicator. This solution will be approximately one-fourth normal, but do not attempt to adjust it to any exact value. Determine its exact strength and make proper corrections in using it.

Alcoholic Sodium Hydroxide Solution. Dissolve pure sodium hydroxide in 95 per cent ethyl alcohol in the proportion of about 22 grams per 1000 cc. Let stand in a stoppered bottle. Decant the clear liquid into another bottle, and keep well stoppered. This solution should be colorless or only slightly yellow when used; it will keep colorless longer if the alcohol is previously treated with NaOH (about 80 g. to 1000 cc.), kept at about 50° C. for 15 days, and then distilled.

Half Normal Sulphuric Acid Solution. Add about 15 cc. sulphuric acid (1.84 specific gravity) to distilled water, cool and dilute to 1000 cc. Determine the exact strength by titrating against freshly standardized sodium hydroxide or by any other accurate method. Either adjust to exactly half normal strength or leave as originally made, applying appropriate correction.

Standards are given below for raw and boiled linseed oil obtained from South American flax. The same specifications obtain for linseed oils from North American flax except that the minimum iodine number of such oil should be 178 for the raw and 176 for the boiled.

Raw Linseed Oil

	Maximum	Minimum
Loss on heating at 105 to 110° C. (per cent)	0.2	....
Foots by volume (per cent)	2.0	....
Specific gravity 15.5/15.5° C.	.936	0.932
Acid number	6.0	....
Saponification number	195.0	189.0
Unsaponifiable matter (per cent)	1.5	....
Iodine number (Hanus)	....	170.0
Color	Not darker than a freshly prepared solution of 1.0 gram potassium bichromate in 100 cc. pure strong (1.84 specific gravity) sulphuric acid.	

Boiled Linseed Oil

	Maximum	Minimum
Loss on heating at 105° to 110° C. (per cent)	0.2	....
Specific gravity at 15.5/15.5° C.	.945	0.937
Acid number	8.0	....
Saponification number	195.0	189.0
Unsaponifiable matter (per cent)	1.50	....
Iodine number (Hanus)	....	168.0
Ash (per cent)	.7	.2
Manganese (per cent)	....	.03
Lead (per cent)	....	.1
Time of drying on glass (hours)	20.0	....

Examination of Tung Oil (Chinese Wood Oil)

The methods given above for the analysis of linseed oil and similar oils may be used for the examination of tung oil except that the iodine number must be determined by the Wijs method.

Properties and Tests

PROPERTIES

Raw tung oil shall conform to the following requirements:

	Maximum	Minimum
Specific gravity at $\dfrac{15.5°\ C.}{15.5°}$	0.943	0.940
Acid number (Alcohol-Benzol)	8	....
Saponification number	195	190
Unsaponifiable matter, per cent	0.75	....
Refractive index at 25° C.	1.520	1.5165
Iodine number (Wijs)	....	163
Heating test, minutes	12	....

Heating Test. Test tubes containing the oil should be 15 cm. by 16 mm., with a mark near the bottom to indicate 5 cc., and closed by a cork so perforated that a glass rod 3 mm. in diameter can move freely.

Fill an 800-cc. glass beaker (height, 13 cm.; diameter, 10 cm.) with cottonseed oil or soya bean oil to a height of 7.5 cm. Place a thermometer so as to be 1.5 cm. from the bottom of the bath. (See Fig. 1.)

Use a nitrogen-filled, chemical thermometer; engraved stem; total length 4 to $4\frac{1}{2}$ in., graduated from 210 to 310° C. in 2° intervals; the length between 210 and 310° C. not less than $2\frac{1}{2}$ in. Thermometer glass shall be well annealed.

When the bath temperature is 293° C. (560° F.) and very slowly rising at this point, place the tube containing 5 cc. of the oil to be tested and the tube containing 5 cc. of a control sample of known value, so that the bottom of each tube is level with the lowest part of the bulb of the thermometer. If desired, the collars may be omitted and the tubes allowed to rest upon a piece of wire gauze placed in the bottom of the oil bath so that the tubes will be 1.5 cm. from the bottom of the bath. Note the time. Remove the source of heat for about 45 seconds and then reapply. Before 2 minutes have elapsed the temperature of the bath will have fallen to 282° C. (530° F.), at which point it should be kept as steady as possible. When the samples have been in the bath 9 minutes, raise the glass rods at intervals of $\frac{1}{4}$ minute. Note the time when each sample becomes firmly set. At this period the oil will be so stiff that the entire tube may be lifted by aid of the rod if the collar is omitted from the apparatus. As setting or jellying takes place within a few seconds of fluidity, a good end determination is afforded. Remove the specimens. Heat the bath again to 293° C., and repeat the experiment with fresh portions of the sample.

No stirrer is used in the bath. A screen round the bath enables the temperature to be more easily reached. When the bath oil has become tarry and viscid, it should be renewed; otherwise heating may be irregular.

Quality Test.[1]   Into an ordinary agateware casserole, having a bottom diameter of 3 in., weigh 150 g. of the tung oil to be tested, and set the casserole on a wide-flanged tripod having a 3-in. opening.   The object of the flange is to prevent super-heating of the sides of the casserole.   Heat rapidly with a full Bunsen flame, stirring with a thermometer, until the heat reaches 540° F. (282.2° C.).   Turn down the flame and hold the heat as near 540° F. (282.2° C.) as possible, stirring with the thermometer, until on lifting the latter the oil drops with a pronounced string, showing that polymerization has started.   The time required after reaching 540° F. (282.2° C.), until the string is noted, is the time of the heat test.   For pure tung oils this will not exceed eight minutes. As soon as the oil strings, remove the lamp and the thermometer, and stir with a stiff spatula until the oil is solid.   After stringing, a pure tung oil will require not over 40 seconds more to become solid.   When solid, allow to stand just one minute, then turn out, upside down, on clean paper and cut with a clean spatula.   Pure tung oil gives a gel that is dry, not adhering to the spatula when cut, that is firm, crumbling under pressure of the spatula without sticking, and the cut portions should crumble under pressure like dry bread crumbs. Adulterated tung oil gives a gel that is soft, sticky, and which will not crumble.

[1] Furnished by R. S. Worstall for A. S. T. M.

ANALYSES OF VARIOUS OILS

	Sp. Gr.	Iodine No.	Sapon. No.	Acid No.	Refrac. Index.
Raw Linseed Oil...............	.931	186	188	2.0	1.4867
Soya Bean Oil.................	.924	129	189	2.3	1.4813
Menhaden Oil..................	.932	158	187	3.9	1.4850
Raw Tung Oil.................	.942	166	183	3.8	1.5200
Perilla Oil....................	.94	200	188	2.0	1.4874
Heavy Bodied Linseed Oil......	.968	133	189	2.8	1.4966
Lithographic Linseed Oil........	.97	102	199	2.7	1.4978
Whale Oil.....................	.924	148	191	9.2	1.4820
Boiled Linseed Oil.............	.941	172	187	2.7	1.4895
(Linolcate Drier)					
Corn Oil......................	.921	124.8	190.1	4.1	1.4800
Cottonseed Oil.................	.920	111.7	194.3	0.9	1.4781
Rosin Oil.....................	.964	68.9	35.5	32.4	....
Treated Tung Oil [1]...........	.882	56.4	101.3	7.7	1.4764
Lumbang Oil..................	.927	152	189	1.0	1.4789
Sunflower Oil.................	.924	124.6	189.3	7.5	1.4796
Hempseed Oil.................	.927	149.4	191.1	3.9	1.4822
Shark Oil.....................	.910	132.8	158.9	5.2	1.4815
Sardine Oil...................	.919	134.6	177.3	10.4	1.4800
Petroleum Mixing Oil...........	.851	28.2	52.9	1.1	1.4773
Boiled Linseed Oil.............	.936	184.2	187.6	7.3	1.4895
(Resinate Drier)					
Peanut Oil....................	.932	102.2	188.0	2.2	1.4790

Boiled linseed oil from North American seed should conform to the following requirements, A. S. T. M.:

	Maximum.	Minimum.
Specific gravity at $\frac{15^\circ.5}{15^\circ.5}$ C.................	0.945	0.937
Acid number............................	8	
Saponification number....................	195	189
Unsaponifiable matter, per cent.............	1.5	
Refractive index at 25° C..................	1.484	1.479
Iodine number (Hanus).....................	....	178
Ash, per cent.............................	0.7	0.2
Manganese, per cent.........................	....	0.03
Calcium, per cent..........................	0.3	
Lead, per cent.............................	....	0.1

Raw linseed oil from North American seed should conform to the following requirements, A. S. T. M.:

	Maximum.	Minimum.
Specific gravity at $\frac{15^\circ.5}{15^\circ.5}$ C.................	0.936	0.932
or		
Specific gravity at $\frac{25^\circ}{25^\circ}$ C...................	0.931	0.927
Acid number.............................	6.00	....
Saponification number....................	195	189
Unsaponifiable matter, per cent..............	1.50	....
Refractive index at 25° C..................	1.4805	1.4790
Iodine number (Hanus).....................	....	180

[1] Contained 30% volatile matter, largely high boiling-point petroleum spirits.

Examination of Turpentine

RECOMMENDED METHODS OF THE A. S. T. M.

Color. Fill a 200-mm., perfectly flat-bottom colorimetric tube graduated in millimeters to a depth of from 40 to 50 mm. with the turpentine to be examined. Place the tube in a colorimeter and place on or under it a No. 2 yellow Lovibond glass. Over or under a second graduated tube in the colorimeter, place a No. 1 yellow Lovibond glass and run in the same turpentine until the color matches as nearly as possible the color in the first tube. Read the difference in depth of the turpentine in the two tubes. If this difference is 50 mm. or more the turpentine is " Standard " or better.

Specific Gravity. Determine specific gravity at any convenient temperature with a plummet, the displacement of which has been accurately determined for that temperature, or by an equally accurate method, using the factor 0.00082 for each degree centigrade that the temperature of determination differs from 15°.5 C.

Refractive Index. Determine refractive index at any convenient temperature with an accurate instrument, and calculate the results to 15°.5 C., using the factor 0.00045 for each degree that the temperature of determination differs from 15°.5 C.

Distillation. Use an ordinary Engler flask and condenser,[1] and heat the flask by placing it in a glycerine or oil bath of the general type described in Bulletin No. 135, Bureau of Chemistry. Fit the flask with a thermometer reading from 145 to 200° C. in such a way that the mercury bulb shall be opposite the side tube of the flask and the 175° mark below the cork. Place 100 cc. of the turpentine to be examined in the flask, connect with the condenser, insert stopper bearing thermometer, and heat until distillation of the turpentine begins. Conduct the distillation so that the distillate passes over at the rate of 2 drops per second. Note the initial distilling temperature and the percentage distilling below 170° C.

Polymerization. Place 20 cc. of exactly 38/N (100.92 per cent[2]) sulphuric acid in a graduated, narrow-neck Babcock flask, stoppered, and place in ice-water and cool. Add slowly 5 cc. of the turpentine to be tested. Gradually mix the contents, cooling from time to time, and not allowing the temperature to rise above about 60° C. When the mixture no longer warms up on shaking, agitate thoroughly and place the bottle in a water bath and heat from 60 to 65° C. for about ten minutes, keeping the contents of the flask thoroughly mixed by vigorous shaking five or six times during the period. Do not stopper the flask after the turpentine has been added, as it may explode. Cool to room temperature, fill the flask with concentrated sulphuric acid until the unpolymerized oil rises into the graduated neck. Centrifuge at about 1200 R.P.M. from four to five minutes, or allow to stand for twelve hours. Read unpolymerized residue, notice its consistency and color, and determine its refractive index.

[1] Stillman, " Engineering Chemistry," p. 503.
[2] 4% free SO_3.

Standards for Turpentine

Turpentine should be clear and free from suspended matter and water, and should conform to the following requirements:

The color shall be " Standard " [1] or better.

The specific gravity shall be not less than 0.862 nor more than 0.872 at 15°.5 C.

The refractive index at 15°.5 C. shall be not less than 1.468 nor more than 1.478.

The initial boiling-point shall be not less than 150 nor more than 160° C.

Ninety per cent of the turpentine shall distill below 170° C.

The polymerization residue shall not exceed 2% and its refractive index at 15°.5 C. shall not be less than 1.500.

ANALYSIS OF VARNISH

The testing of varnish should largely be of a physical nature. Such properties as odor, consistency, clarity, flowing, time of drying, character of finish, hardness, resistance to moisture and abrasion, elasticity, etc., point out the real value of a varnish. Chemical tests that give additional information, sometimes of a valuable nature, are as follows: Flash point, acid number, ash, character of solvent, fixed oil and resins.

Flash Point. A nickel or iron crucible of 60 mm. diameter and 40 mm. height is filled with the varnish to within 20 mm. of the top. It is then supported in a water bath in such a manner as to be about two-thirds immersed in the water. The water should be from 15° to 20° C. at the start and should be heated slowly so that the temperature of the varnish, as indicated by a thermometer suspended in it, will show a rise of about 1 degree per minute. Test for flash at each half degree, using a very small flame.

Acid Number. Ten to 20 grams of the varnish are weighed into a small Erlenmeyer flask, 50 cc. neutral alcohol added, and a small funnel inserted in the neck. Heat on the water bath for one-half hour, with occasional shaking. Allow to cool somewhat, add two drops of phenolphthalein indicator and titrate with tenth-normal potassium hydroxide solution. The acid number is the number of milligrams of KOH required to neutralize each gram of the varnish.

Ash. Weigh in a porcelain or fused silica crucible several grams of the varnish. Burn off over a small Bunsen flame, using great caution to avoid boiling over and spattering. When all combustible matter is destroyed, weigh the ash and if desired analyze it.

Solvent. Steam distillation of a portion of the varnish will remove the solvents, leaving a residue of fixed oils and varnish resins, which may be weighed after driving off the water. The distillate should be examined as recommended under Methods for the Examination of Turpentine. The amount of mineral spirits and turpentine may thus be determined.

Fixed Oils and Resins. In the above determination, the total amount of fixed oils and resins is obtained. It is a difficult matter, however, to determine the exact

[1] The term " Standard " refers to the color recognized as standard by the " Naval Stores Trade." Turpentine is of " Standard " color when a depth of 50 mm. in a perfectly flat polished bottom tube, approximately matches a No. 1 yellow Lovibond glass.

percentage and character of resins that have been used in the manufacture of the varnish. This is due to the fact that during the process of heating oils in the presence of resins many intricate chemical changes are brought about, a considerable portion of the resins being distilled off in the form of vapors and combinations of the oil brought about that are difficult of separation. One of the best methods, however, of separating the fixed oils and varnish resins is carried out in the following manner.

A portion of about a half ounce of the varnish resin should be placed in a 300-cc. tared beaker. There should then be added about 200 cc. of ice-cold petroleum ether and the beaker should be covered and allowed to stand, preferably in a dish containing ice. In an hour's time the resinous ingredients will be found precipitated at the bottom of the beaker or adhering to the side thereof (with the exception of rosin, which is largely soluble in petroleum ether). The precipitated resins should be washed with fresh portions of cold petroleum ether two or three times, pouring the decanted portions into a large bottle. The combined portions of petroleum ether may then be filtered through a tared filter, adding by the aid of a stirring rod the resins contained in the beaker. The filter paper and the beaker with the resins may then be dried at 100° C. and weighed. The combined filtrates may be distilled to obtain the fixed oil which may be examined for constants. (This fixed oil may contain rosin.) The amount of rosin contained in a varnish may be roughly ascertained by thoroughly shaking in a separatory funnel a portion of the varnish with a large quantity of absolute alcohol. The rosin may be obtained by evaporation of the alcoholic extracts. The fixed oils after oxidation or polymerization, as caused by the heating of the varnish during manufacture, are not readily soluble in alcohol.

Separation of Polymerized Oils and Resins. In the making of varnish, some oils become oxidized or polymerized to a condition resembling resins. For instance, when a varnish is examined for resins by the above method, it will often be found that a considerable amount of matter insoluble in petroleum ether will be obtained even when hard resins are absent. The insoluble substance is oxidized or polymerized oil. It may be differentiated from varnish resins by the fact that it is readily saponified by alcoholic potash. The following method by Boughton (Technologic Paper No. 65, U. S. Bureau of Standards), though involving considerable work, is probably the most accurate method for the separation of polymerized oils and resins.

To about 4 grams of varnish in a flask add about 25 cc. of water and boil until the volume is about 10 cc. This removes nearly all of the volatile. Add 25 cc. half normal alcoholic potash and 25 cc. benzol and boil under a reflux condenser for one-half hour. Evaporate the solution to about 15 cc. and add about 10 cc. of alcohol. Transfer completely to a separatory funnel, washing the flask with water and ether and using a policeman if necessary. Dilute with water to about 100 cc., add 100 cc. of ether, and shake. Add a few cc. of alcohol if necessary to make the layers separate. Draw off the aqueous layer and wash the ether three times with water and transfer to a tared flask for future use.

To the combined soap solution and washings, add an excess of hydrochloric acid and extract twice with 50 cc. of ether. Discard the aqueous layer, wash the combined ether extracts with water, transfer to a flask and distill off the ether. To the dry residue add 20 cc. of absolute alcohol and 20 cc. of a mixture of 1 volume of sulphuric acid and 4 volumes of absolute alcohol and boil for two minutes under a reflux condenser. Completely transfer the contents of the flask to a separatory funnel, washing the flask with water and ether. Add 100 cc. ether and after agitation add 100 cc. of 10 per cent sodium chloride solution and again shake. Draw off the aqueous layer, extract it with 50 cc. of ether, combine the ether solutions and wash with water. Add 50 cc. of a fifth-normal potassium hydroxide solution and 10 cc. of alcohol, shake and draw off the lower layer into a second funnel. Wash the ether layer with 50 cc. of water containing 5 cc. of the potassium hydroxide solution and 5 cc. of alcohol.

Extract the combined aqueous portions with two 50-cc. portions of ether and finally wash the combined ether solutions (containing the ethyl esters of the fatty acids) with water.

Distill off the ether and boil the residue with 25 cc. of half-normal alcoholic potash for one-half hour under a reflux condenser. Transfer completely to a separatory funnel and extract the soap four times with ether. Wash the combined ether solution twice with water and add it to the first ether solution of unsaponifiable matter obtained.

Unite the solution and washings containing the soaps, add an excess of hydrochloric acid, and extract twice with ether. Transfer to a tared flask the combined ether solutions, after washing them with water, distill off the ether, dry the residue to constant weight at 110° C. and weigh as " fatty acids."

Report the percentage of fatty acids as percentage of oil and calculate the percentage of resin by difference.

OTHER MATERIALS

For detailed methods other than those given in this book for the examination of shellac, resins, bitumens, and other like materials for the vehicle portion of paints and varnishes, the following references may be consulted:

Proceedings of the American Society for Testing Materials, Committee D-1, 1910 to 1923.
Manufacture of Varnishes. Livache & McIntosh. Vols. 1–3, Scott, Greenwood & Sons, London.
Mixed Paints. Holley & Ladd. John Wiley & Sons, New York.
Physical and Chemical Examination of Paints, Varnishes, and Colors. Gardner. P. H. Butler, 1845 B St., N.W., Washington, D. C.
Interdepartmental Committee on Standardization of Paint Specifications. Specifications published as circulars of the Bureau of Standards, Washington, D. C., as follows:

Bureau of
Standards
Circular

No. 82—2d Edition—Linseed Oil.
  84—2d Edition—B a s i c   Carbonate White Lead.
  85—2d Edition—Basic S u l p h a t e White Lead.
  86—2d Edition—Turpentine.
  87—2d Edition—Zinc Oxide.
  88—2d Edition—Leaded Zinc Oxide.
  89—2d Edition—White and Tinted Paints (Exterior).
  90—2d Edition—Red Lead.
  91—2d Edition—Ocher.
  93—2d Edition—Iron Oxide Paints.
  94—2d Edition—Black Paint.

Bureau of
Standards
Circular

No. 97—3d Edition—Green Paint.
  98—2d Edition—Mineral Spirits.
 102—1st Edition, corrected—Composite Thinner.
 103—3d Edition—Spar Varnish.
 104—2d Edition—Asphalt Varnish.
 105—2d Edition—Liquid Paint Drier.
 111—2d Edition—Flat Interior Lithopone Paint.
 117—2d Edition—Interior Varnih.
 146—Sept., 1923—Water-resisting Red Enamel.
 147—Sept., 1923—Gloss Interior Lithopone Paint.

17

THE ANALYSIS OF PAINT PIGMENTS

The vehicle having been extracted from the paint under examination, by the previously outlined methods, the pigment is left ready for analysis. The pigment can be readily classified under one of the following heads by its color, thus shortening any preliminary examination. Many of the colors have a white base which necessitates a determination of both the colored portion of the pigment and any white base which may have been used.

The general analysis of colored pigments is carried out according to the specific method outlined for the individual colored pigments, together with the methods for a composite white paint, provided a qualitative examination does not directly reveal the identity of the pigment.

The pigments used in the manufacture of paints are classified as follows, in certain instances the trade names being given by which the particular pigments are known.

White Pigments

Lead Pigments

Sublimed White Lead—Basic Sulphate of Lead—Basic Sulphate—White Lead.
Super Sublimed White Lead.
Corroded White Lead—Basic Carbonate of Lead.
     Old Dutch Process White Lead.
     Quick Process White Lead.
     Mild Process White Lead.
  Zinc Lead.
  Leaded Zinc.

Zinc Pigments

  Zinc Oxide—Zinc White.
  Lithopone—Ponolith—Beckton White—Charlton White—Orr's White.

Other Opaque White Pigments

Titanium Oxide (Titanox).
Antimony Oxide.

Silica Pigments

  Silica—Silex.
  Asbestine—Talcose.
  China Clay—Kaolin—Tolamite.

Calcium Pigments

Whiting—Paris White—Chalk—Alba Whiting—Spanish White.
Gypsum—Plaster of Paris—Terra Alba—Agalite.

Barium Pigments

Barytes—Barite—Blanc Fixe—Barium Sulphate.
Barium Carbonate—Witherite.

Red and Brown Pigments

Red Lead—Orange Mineral.
Vermilion.
Ochres—Tuscan Red—Indian Red—Venetian Red.
Umbers—Siennas.

Blue Pigments

Sublimed Blue Lead.
Ultramarine Blue.
Prussian Blue—Antwerp Blue—Chinese Blue.

Yellow and Orange Pigments

Chrome Yellow—Lemon Yellow—Medium Chrome Yellow.
American Vermilion—Orange Chrome—Basic Lead Chromate.
Orange Mineral.

Green Pigments

Chrome Green.
Chromium Oxide.
Green Earth.

Black Pigments

Graphite.
Carbon Black—Bone Black—Lamp Black—Drop Black—Ivory Black—Mineral Black.
Willow Charcoal.
Black Oxide of Iron.

ANALYSIS OF WHITE PIGMENTS

SUBLIMED WHITE LEAD

SUPERSUBLIMED WHITE LEAD

Basic Sulphate of Lead.   Basic Sulphate—White Lead

This pigment, embracing the daily analysis by the manufacturers of the product of over five months' time, shows the following average composition:

Lead sulphate 76.68%
Lead oxide... 17.23
Zinc oxide... 5.79
                                                       _____
                                                       99.70

The remaining .3 of 1 per cent consists of moisture and ash which are rarely determined.

The analysis of this pigment based on the following method,[1] which depends upon the above average composition, together with the volumetric determination of the total lead and zinc contents, is rapid and accurate.

[1] Jour. of Ind. and Eng. Chem., **6**, 3, 200, March, 1914.

Volumetric Determination of Lead [1]

One gram of the sample is dissolved in 100 cc. of an acid ammonium acetate solution made up as follows:

Eighty per cent acetic acid.............................. 125 cc.
Concentrated ammonium hydroxide.................... 95 cc.
Water... 100 cc.

Add this solution hot, dilute with 50 cc. water and boil until a clear solution is obtained. Dilute to 200 cc. and titrate with standard ammonium molybdate solution, using a freshly prepared solution of tannic acid as an outside indicator. A solution of ammonium molybdate containing 8.67 grams per liter usually gives a solution where,

One cc. = 0.01 gram Pb.

Standardize against pure PbO, pure $PbSO_4$, or clean lead foil.
For further details of this method see p. 239.

Volumetric Determination of Zinc [2]

Boil 1 gram of the sample with the following solution:

Water... 30 cc.
Ammonium chloride................................. 4 grams
Concentrated hydrochloric acid..................... 6 cc.

If the sample is not quite dissolved, the result is unaffected, as the residue is lead sulphate or precipitated lead chloride.

Dilute to 200 cc. with hot water. Add 2 cc. of a saturated sodium hyposulphite solution and titrate with a standard solution of potassium ferrocyanide, using a 5% solution of uranium nitrate as an outside indicator. Calculate the zinc to zinc oxide.

Using the average total of 99.70%, the total lead found and the zinc oxide content, the composition of this pigment is determined by the following calculation:

Total percentage of lead compounds present
= total percentage found of ZnO, PbO and $PbSO_4$ − percentage of ZnO.

Total percentage of lead compounds present
= 99.70% (average total) − percentage ZnO.

Atomic weight lead................................. 207.1
Molecular weight lead oxide......................... 223.1
Molecular weight lead sulphate..................... 303.1

As a hypothetical case, we can assume the presence of a 4.70% ZnO and 69.00% metallic lead.

[1] Modification of Low's Method, " Technical Methods of Ore Analysis," p. 149.
[2] Low's Method, " Technical Methods of Ore Analysis," p. 284.

$$\frac{\left(\dfrac{\text{Mol. wt. PbSO}_4}{\text{At. wt. Pb}} \times \% \text{ Pb found}\right) - \% \text{ Pb constituents}}{\dfrac{\text{Mol. wt.PbSO}_4 - \text{mol. wt. PbO}}{\text{Mol. wt. PbO}}} = \% \text{ PbO present}$$

$$\frac{\left(\dfrac{\text{Mol. wt. PbO}}{\text{At. wt. Pb}} \times \% \text{ Pb found}\right) - \% \text{ Pb constituents}}{\dfrac{\text{Mol. wt. PbO} - \text{Mol. wt. PbSO}_4}{\text{Mol. wt. PbSO}_4}} = \% \text{ PbSO}_4 \text{ present.}$$

Determining the percentage of lead oxide and lead sulphate present by the above formulas we find:

$$\frac{\left(\dfrac{303.1}{207.1} \times 69.00\right) - 95.00}{\dfrac{303.1 - 223.1}{223.1}} = \text{per cent PbO} = 16.68$$

$$\frac{\left(\dfrac{223.1}{207.1} \times 69.00\right) - 95.00}{\dfrac{223.1 - 303.1}{303.1}} = \text{per cent PbSO}_4 = 78.32.$$

If it is necessary actually to determine the percentage of lead sulphate present, the following procedure may be followed:

Total Sulphate

Mix 0.5 gram of the sample with 3 grams of sodium carbonate. Add 30 cc. of water and boil gently for ten minutes. Allow to stand for four hours. Dilute with hot water, filter and wash thoroughly. All the lead sulphate is here changed to lead carbonate, the sodium carbonate being transposed to sodium sulphate, which is found in the filtrate.

. The sulphate is determined in the filtrate by precipitation as $BaSO_4$. Calculate the $BaSO_4$ to $PbSO_4$. Determine the total lead as above outlined, deduct the lead found as $PbSO_4$ and calculate the residual lead to PbO.

The foregoing method is the one generally used in the commercial estimation of lead and yields excellent results to the analyst who is familiar with it. However, in laboratories where only occasional lead determinations are made, the well-known gravimetric methods for lead and zinc will sometimes be found preferable. The time required for gravimetric determinations is not much greater and the chance of error is reduced.

The method referred to consists in weighing the lead as sulphate[1] and the precipitation of the zinc from the filtrate with sodium carbonate, igniting it, and weighing as zinc oxide.

[1] As outlined under Basic Carbonate of Lead, p. 625.

Super Sublimed White Lead

Super Sublimed White Lead is a new basic sulphate of lead pigment recently developed. It is extremely white. Chemically, it shows the presence of no zinc oxide, being a true basic sulphate of lead showing approximately 25% lead oxide, the balance being lead sulphate. Its physical properties are similar to sublimed white lead, its distinguishing characteristics being its extreme whiteness.

The analysis of this pigment is an exceedingly simple procedure. If it is desired to determine the sulphate present, the method as outlined under sublimed white lead can be used. All the sulphate is calculated as lead sulphate after determination of total lead and sulphate, the difference between the lead present as lead sulphate and the total lead present being calculated as lead oxide.

The analysis of this pigment can be further simplified by a simple determination of the total lead present and the calculation followed for the determination of the lead sulphate and lead oxide as outlined under sublimed white lead. In this latter calculation, however, it must be remembered that the total sum of the lead constituents present represents 100%, instead of the difference between 99.70% and the percentage of zinc oxide present in sublimed white lead. This is due to the fact that super sublimed white lead shows the presence of no zinc oxide or insoluble residue. By the simple substitution of 100.00 in place of the determined per cent Pb constituents in the formula and the determination of the total lead present, the analysis can be completed in a rapid way.

CORRODED WHITE LEAD

Basic Carbonate of Lead[1]—Old Dutch Process White Lead—Quick Process White Lead—Mild Process White Lead

Corroded white lead contains approximately 80% metallic lead and 20% carbonic acid and combined water with traces sometimes of silver, antimony and other metals. The formula for this compound is $2PbCO_3 \cdot Pb(OH)_2$.

Total Lead (Gravimetric)

Dissolve 1 gram in 20 cc. of HNO_3 (1:1) in a covered beaker, heating till all CO_2 is expelled; wash off cover, add 20 cc. of H_2SO_4(1:1) and evaporate to fumes of SO_3, cool, add about 150 cc. of water and 150 cc. of ethyl alcohol; let stand in cold water one hour, filter on a Gooch crucible, wash with 95% ethyl alcohol, dry at 110° C., and weigh the $PbSO_4$. Calculate to PbO or to basic carbonate.[2] Instead of determining the lead as sulphate, the sample may be dissolved by boiling with acetic acid; then dilute to about 200 cc. with water, make alkaline with NH_4OH, then acid with acetic acid, heat to boiling and add 10 to 15 cc. of a 10% solution of potassium dichromate; heat till the yellow precipitate assumes an orange color. Let settle and filter on a Gooch crucible, washing by decantation with hot water till the washings are colorless, finally transferring all of the precipitate. Then wash with 95% ethyl alcohol and then ether; dry at 110° C. and weigh $PbCrO_4$. (Any insoluble matter should be filtered out before precipitating the lead.)

Total Lead (Volumetric)

Dissolve 0.5 gram of sample in 10 cc. of concentrated hydrochloric acid, boil till solution is effected, cool, dilute to 40 cc. and neutralize with ammonium hydroxide. Add acetic acid until distinctly acid, dilute to 200 cc. with hot water, boil and titrate with ammonium molybdate as follows:

Dissolve 4.25 gram of ammonium molybdate in water and make up to one liter. To standardize this solution, dissolve about 0.2 gram of pure lead foil in nitric acid (pure PbO or $PbSO_4$ may also be used), evaporate nearly to dryness, add 30 cc. of water, then 5 cc. H_2SO_4 (sp.gr. 1.84), cool, and filter.

Drop filter with $PbSO_4$ into a flask, add 10 cc. concentrated HCl, boil till completely disintegrated, add 15 cc. of HCl, 25 cc. of water, and NH_4OH till alkaline. Acidify with acetic acid, dilute to 200 cc. with hot water and boil. Titrate, using an outside indicator of one part of tannic acid in 300 parts of water.

It should be noted that when calcium is present, it forms a more or less insoluble molybdate, and results are apt to be high. With samples containing less than 10% of lead, the lead should be precipitated as $PbSO_4$, filtered, redissolved and titrated as in the process of standardizing.

Carbon Dioxide

Determine by evolution with dilute hydrochloric acid absorbing in soda-lime or KOH solution. Calculate CO_2 to $PbCO_3$, subtract PbO equivalent from total PbO and calculate residual PbO to $Pb(OH)_2$.

[1] Tentative Methods for the Routine Analysis of White Pigments. Report of Commission D-1, American Society for Testing Materials, 1915.

[2] This method of weighing lead sulphate is not accurate in the presence of calcium compounds.

Acetic Acid [1]

Place 18 grams of the pigment in a 500-cc. flask, add 40 cc. of sirupy phosphoric acid, 18 grams of zinc dust and 50 cc. of water. Connect to a straight Liebig condenser, apply heat and distill down to a small bulk. Then pass steam into the flask until it becomes about half full of condensed water, shut off the steam and distill down to a small bulk—this operation being conducted twice. To the total distillate which was collected in a larger flask add 1 cc. of sirupy phosphoric acid, connect to a Liebig condenser, using a spray trap, and distill to a small volume—about 20 cc. Pass steam through till about 200 cc. of water condense in the distillation flask, shut off steam and continue the distillation. These operations of direct and steam distillations are conducted until 10 cc. of the distillate require only 1 drop of 0.1 N alkali to give a change in the presence of of phenolphthalein. Then titrate the total distillate with 0. 1 N sodium hydroxide and phenolphthalein and calculate the total acidity as acetic acid. It will be found convenient to titrate each 200-cc. portion of the distillate as collected.

Metallic Lead [1]

Weigh 50 grams of the sample into a 400-cc. beaker, add a little water and add slowly 60 cc. of 40% acetic acid and after effervescence has ceased, boil on hot plate. Fill the beaker with water, let settle, and decant the clear solution. To the residue add 100 cc. of a mixture of 360 cc. of strong NH_4OH, 1080 cc. of water, 2160 cc. of 80% acetic acid, and boil until all solution is complete. Fill the beaker with water, let settle and decant the clear solution. Collect residue on a watch-glass, floating off everything but metallic lead. Dry and weigh. Result $\times 2$ = percentage of metallic lead in sample.

The following method of A. N. Finn (unpublished) gives total basicity of a pure white lead: Place 2 grams of pigment in an evolution flask, add a little CO_2-free water, connect with a separatory funnel and condenser (Knorr type), add through the funnel, finally washing down, 100 cc. of N/4 nitric acid, boil and absorb the CO_2 in a soda lime tube in the usual manner (having H_2SO_4 and $CaCl_2$ drying tubes in train) and weigh. To the solution in the evolution flask, add about 20 cc. of neutral sodium sulphate solution and titrate with N/4 sodium hydroxide solution (carbonate-free), using phenolphthalein. CO_2 is calculated to $PbCO_3$. The amount of N/4 acid corresponding to the CO_2 is calculated and deducted from the total amount of N/4 acid neutralized by the sample and the difference calculated to combined H_2O, from which $Pb(OH)_2$ is computed.

ZINC LEAD AND LEADED ZINC

Zinc lead and leaded zinc are varying compounds containing zinc oxide and lead sulphate, the former showing approximately 50% zinc oxide and 50% lead sulphate, while the latter contains on an average 25% lead sulphate and 75% zinc oxide. See also pp. 277, 600, Vol. I.

These pigments may be analyzed by the following procedure:

Moisture. Heat 2 grams at 105° C. for two hours.

[1] Thompson's Method, Jour. Soc. Chem. Ind., **24**, 487 1905.

Lead and Zinc. Determine the lead directly by the volumetric molybdate method and the zinc by the volumetric ferrocyanide method as outlined under Sublimed White Lead. See also pages 277 and 600, Vol. I.

Total Soluble Sulphates[1] (in the absence of $BaSO_4$). Treat 0.5 gram of the sample with 5 cc. of water, 3 grams of NH_4Cl and 5 cc. of HCl saturated with bromine; digest (covered) on the steam bath about fifteen minutes, add 25 cc. of H_2O, neutralize with dry Na_2CO_3 and add about 2 grams more. Boil ten to fifteen minutes; let settle, dilute with hot water, filter and wash with hot water; redissolve in HCl, reprecipitate as above and wash thoroughly with hot water. Acidify the united filtrates with HCl and add a slight excess of 10% $BaCl_2$ solution. Let stand on steam bath for one hour, filter, wash with hot water, ignite and weigh the $BaSO_4$. Calculate to SO_3 (includes SO_3 formed from SO_2).

Total Soluble Sulphate (in the presence of $BaSO_4$). Treat 1 gram in a 600-cc. beaker with 10 cc. of H_2O, 10 cc. of strong HCl, saturated with bromine, and 5 grams of NH_4Cl, heat on a steam bath in a covered beaker for five minutes, add hot water to make about 400 cc., boil for five minutes and filter to separate any insoluble material. (A pure pigment should be completely dissolved.) Wash with hot water, ignite and weigh the insoluble. Remove lead with Na_2CO_3 as above, making a double precipitation, acidify, and to the boiling hot filtrate add slowly, with stirring, 20 cc. of a 10% $BaCl_2$ solution; let stand for two hours on the steam bath, filter, wash, ignite, and weigh as $BaSO_4$. (Includes SO_3 formed from SO_2.)

Soluble Zinc Sulphate. Boil 2 grams of the sample with 150 cc. of water and 50 cc. of alcohol for thirty minutes, filter and wash with a mixture of alcohol and water (1:3). Heat the filtrate to boiling and expel most of the alcohol; then determine SO_3 by the usual method of precipitation with $BaCl_2$. Calculate to $ZnSO_4$ and to SO_3.

Sulphur Dioxide. Digest 2 grams of the sample with frequent stirring in 100 cc. of freshly boiled cold water and 5 cc. of concentrated HCl; let stand ten to fifteen minutes, add an excess of 0.01 normal iodine solution and titrate back with 0.01 normal sodium thiosulphate solution, using starch indicator. Report as SO_2. Run blank on reagents and make corrections.

Calculations. Report soluble SO_3 as $ZnSO_4$. Deduct ZnO equivalent of the $ZnSO_4$ from total ZnO and report residue as ZnO. Deduct soluble SO_3 and SO_3 equivalent to SO_2 from total SO_3, calculate remainder to $PbSO_4$; subtract PbO equivalent of $PbSO_4$ from total PbO and report remainder as PbO.

ZINC OXIDE [2]

Moisture. Weigh 10 grams on watch-glass and dry for two hours at 105 to 110° C. Cool and weigh.

Carbon Dioxide. Place 10 grams in a 4-ounce Erlenmeyer flask, moisten with water, add solution of $KMnO_4$ to oxidize SO_2, insert a two-hole rubber stopper, with an acid delivery tube and connect to a carbon dioxide apparatus. This apparatus consists of a tube containing KOH solution, preceding the flask with

---

[1] Report of Sub-committee VIII of Committee D–1, Proceedings of American Society for Testing Materials, **14**, 271–2, 1914.

[2] Frank G. Breyer, Chief, Testing Department, The New Jersey Zinc Co.

sample, to absorb any CO_2 from the air drawn in. The flask is followed by a tube with concentrated H_2SO_4 to absorb moisture, a calcium chloride tube, and next is a weighed Geissler [1] bulb with KOH solution, to absorb the CO_2 from the sample; this is followed by another calcium chloride tube which is connected to a suction line. The acid delivery tube contains 25 cc. H_2SO_4 (1 : 1) and before opening the stopcock the suction is applied to insure that the connections are all air-tight; if there is no leak the acid is allowed to flow into the flask and the suction regulated so that the bubbles in the Geissler bulb may easily be counted. The flask is heated cautiously to boiling for a minute or two, the flame removed and the suction allowed to proceed from thirty to forty minutes. The Geissler [1] bulb is then disconnected, placed in the balance for fifteen minutes together with the end calcium chloride tube and then weighed. The KOH solution used for absorption is of the same strength as for carbon in steel.

Insoluble. Treat 10 grams in a 250-cc. beaker with 50 cc. concentrated HCl, evaporate to dryness, take up residue with HCl and water, filter and wash thoroughly with HCl (1 : 4) and hot water. Ignite filter paper and contents in a weighed platinum crucible.

Sulphuric Anhydride; Total S as SO_3. Treat 10 grams with 50 cc. strong HCl and a few cc. of bromine water; boil to expel bromine, filter from insoluble, wash with hot water. Neutralize the excess of HCl with ammonia, keeping the solution slightly acid, heat to boiling and add about 15 cc. of hot $BaCl_2$. Let stand overnight, filter on a weighed Gooch crucible, wash well with hot water, ignite in a muffle, cool and weigh as $BaSO_4$.

Lead Oxide

Gravimetric Method. Treat 10 grams with 50 cc. strong HCl and 50 cc. H_2SO_4 (1 : 1), evaporate on a hot plate, and finally over a Bunsen burner to strong fumes of SO_3.

Cool, and add 100 cc. water, heat again to dissolve the soluble sulphates, cool, add 25 cc. 95% alcohol, let stand overnight, filter on a Gooch crucible and wash with dilute H_2SO_4, and finally with alcohol. Dry at 110° C., ignite for five to ten minutes, cool and weigh. Dissolve the $PbSO_4$ in the Gooch crucible with a hot solution of ammonium acetate, slightly acidify with acetic acid, wash with hot water, dry at 110° C., ignite and weigh again. The loss in weight is $PbSO_4$, from which the PbO is calculated.

Electrolytic Method. 9.330 grams of the sample are dissolved in a 250-cc. beaker with 40 cc. concentrated HNO_3 and about 50 cc. of distilled water. The solution is boiled for a few minutes until all red fumes are expelled. Add enough silver nitrate solution to precipitate all chlorides (an excess of silver nitrate does not interfere) and dilute to about 200 cc.

Electrolyze for two hours, using about .5 ampere current. The solutions are tested for lead before turning off the current by raising the liquid in the beaker, and allowing to continue for twenty minutes. If there is no fresh deposit of PbO_2, the electrode is washed three times with distilled water (current still on) and then after removal from the electrolytic stand, with alcohol. After drying one hour at 110° C. the electrode is weighed. The weight of PbO_2 in milligrams divided by 100 gives the percentage of PbO.

[1] See Procedure for CO_2 determination in the chapter on Carbon, p. 103.

Chlorine. Treat 10 grams of sample with 50 cc. strong HNO_3, add 10 cc. N/10 $AgNO_3$, boil, cool, add 10 cc. ferric nitrate (1 : 3), and titrate the excess of $AgNO_3$ with NH_4CNS (9 grams per liter of solution). A blank determination is conducted in a similar manner and from the amount of N/10 $AgNO_3$ required the chlorine is calculated.

Ferric Oxide. Treat 10 grams with 50 cc. strong HCl, add about 1 gram $KClO_3$, and boil down to a syrupy consistency. Cool, add water and a large excess of ammonia. Allow to stand until the ferric oxide separates, and filter; wash with dilute ammonia water and then with hot water. Dissolve the precipitate of ferric oxide in an Erlenmeyer flask with warm dilute H_2SO_4. Wash the filter paper thoroughly with hot water, dilute the solution in the Erlenmeyer flask to about 200 cc. and pass in hydrogen sulphide for five minutes. Place a funnel in the neck of the flask and boil until all H_2S is expelled. Cool and titrate with dilute $KMnO_4$. A blank determination is carried out in a similar manner and the number of cc. of $KMnO_4$ required to give a pink color is subtracted from the total number required on the sample.

Manganese Oxide. Treat a 10-gram sample in a 16-oz. Erlenmeyer flask with 100 cc. of HNO_3 (1:3), heat to boiling and add a pinch of sodium bismuthate, when the pink color of permanganic acid is produced; now add a few cc. of dilute $Na_2S_2O_3$ solution to destroy the pink color, and continue boiling to drive off all nitrous oxide fumes. Cool thoroughly and add 50 cc. of a 3% solution of HNO_3, and a very small pinch of sodium bismuthate to restore the pink color again. Filter the solution through a Gooch crucible to remove the excess of sodium bismuthate, rinsing the flask and Gooch with 50 cc. of 3% HNO_3 solution to which a small amount of sodium bismuthate has been added. Now add 10 cc. of ammonium ferrous sulphate solution, and titrate the excess of ammonium ferrous sulphate with standard $KMnO_4$ whose iron value has been determined. One gram of $KMnO_4$ per liter is a convenient strength; and 12.4 grams of ammonium ferrous sulphate, and 50 cc. strong H_2SO_4 to the liter gives a solution which is almost equal to the permanganate solution. A blank determination is carried out in exactly the same manner as with the sample of oxide, and the difference in the number of cc. of $KMnO_4$ required to give a pink color with the blank determination and the sample of oxide is equal to the amount of MnO present. The manganese value of the $KMnO_4$ is calculated from the iron value, according to the ratio of Mn : Fe, or 55 : 279.5 or 0.1968 : 1.

Arsenous Oxide. Weigh 10 grams of oxide in a 16-ounce Erlenmeyer flask, add about 10 grams of $FeSO_4$, place a rubber stopper with an acid delivery tube and an exit tube, which is immersed in a beaker containing about 200 cc. distilled water. The beaker of water is placed in a pan of cold water, the pan having an inlet and overflow. Now add 100 cc. strong HCl from the delivery tube, and heat the flask to boiling so as to distill the arsenic into the beaker of water. Continue boiling until about two-thirds of the acid has been distilled, remove from the flame, rinse the delivery tube, add 10 cc. strong HCl to the solution in the beaker, warm and pass in H_2S to precipitate the arsenic, as As_2S_3. Let stand in a warm place for some time and filter in a Gooch crucible, wash the precipitate of As_2S_3 with alcohol and then with carbon bisulphide and several times with dilute alcohol. Dry at 105° C. for one hour and weigh. Dissolve the As_2S_3, in the Gooch crucible with dilute ammonia water, wash well with hot water, and dry at 105° C. and reweigh. The loss in weight is As_2S_3, from which the As_2O_3 may be calculated. See procedure for arsenic distillation, p. 37.

SO₂ Equivalent. Treat 10 grams in a 250-cc. beaker with 25 cc. cold water, 25 cc. hot water, add some starch solution and titrate with N/10 iodine solution, gradually adding 25 cc. HCl until a permanent blue color appears.

Zinc Oxide. The percentage of ZnO is found by adding together all the percentages of impurities, except the SO_2 equivalent, and subtracting this sum from 100.

LITHOPONE

Albalith—Ponolith—Beckton White—Charlton White, Etc.

This pigment is a chemically precipitated pigment containing approximately from 69 to 70 per cent barium sulphate, the remainder consisting of zinc sulphide, with occasional impurities of zinc oxide and carbonate.

Moisture. Heat 2 grams for two hours at 105° C.

Barium Sulphate. Treat 1 gram with 10 cc. conc. HCl and 1 gram of potassium chlorate, added in small amounts. Evaporate to one-half its volume, add 100 cc. hot water and a few cc. of dilute H_2SO_4. Boil, filter, wash and weigh the insoluble residue, which should show only the presence of barium sulphate. Examine the residue for silica and alumina.

Total Zinc. Determine the total zinc in the filtrate by the volumetric method as outlined under Sublimed White Lead.

Zinc Sulphide. Digest 1 gram at room temperature for one-half hour with 100 cc. of 1% acetic acid. Filter and determine the zinc in the precipitate by solution in HCl as under Sublimed White Lead.

Zinc soluble in acetic acid is reported as zinc oxide, zinc insoluble as zinc sulphide. The filtrate from the acetic acid treatment, after precipitating the zinc as zinc sulphide and subsequent removal, should be examined for barium which might be present as carbonate, and calcium, present as either sulphate or carbonate. The zinc sulphide may also be determined by the method as outlined under Tentative Methods for Analysis of Pigments by Committee D-I [1] as follows:

Zinc Sulphide.[2] Place 0.5 gram of the pigment in an evolution flask [3] with about 10 grams of " feathered " or mossy zinc, add 50 cc. of water; insert the stopper carrying a separatory funnel and an exit tube. Run in 50 cc. of concentrated HCl from the funnel, having previously connected the exit tube to two absorption flasks, in series; first flask contains 100 cc. of alkaline lead nitrate solution, second flask, 50 cc. of same as a safety device. After all of the acid has run into the evolution flask, heat slowly, finally boiling until the first appearance of steam in the first absorption flask. Disconnect, let the lead sulphide settle, filter, wash with cold water, then with hot water till neutral to litmus paper and washings give no test for lead. The PbS precipitate in dissolved in hot, dilute HNO_3, evaporated to fumes with H_2SO_4 and finally weighed as $PbSO_4$. Calculate PbS or $PbSO_4$ to ZnS.

The alkaline lead solution is made as follows: Into 100 cc. of KOH solution (56 grams in 140 cc. of H_2O) pour a saturated solution of lead nitrate (250 grams in 500 cc. of H_2O) until the precipitate ceases to redissolve, stirring constantly

---

[1] American Society for Testing Materials, 1915.
[2] Evolution Method of W. G. Scott, " White Paints and Painting Material," p. 257; see also p. 398, chapter on Sulphur by W. W. Scott.
[3] See Apparatus on p. 399.

while mixing. About three volumes of the lead solution will be required for one of the alkali.

Instead of absorbing the evolved H_2S in alkaline lead-nitrate solution, a solution of 8 grams of cadmium chloride in 250 cc. of water and 150 cc. of NH_4OH (sp.gr. 0.90) may be used. The CdS precipitate may be filtered on a weighed Gooch, washed with water containing a little NH_4OH, dried at 100° C., and weighed. Calculate to ZnS. It is better to filter the CdS on a small filter and wash as above, then place filter and precipitate in a beaker and dissolve in HCl and $KClO_3$ (keeping at room temperature at first). Filter out any paper pulp or insoluble matter, make filtrate alkaline with NH_4OH, then just acid with HCl, heat to boiling and precipitate with $BaCl_2$ in the usual manner. Filter, wash, ignite, and weigh the $BaSO_4$. Calculate to ZnS.

For very rapid work the contents of the absorption flask, after all H_2S has been absorbed, may be washed into a vessel with cold water and diluted to about 1 liter, acidified with concentrated HCl and titrated with standard iodine solution, using starch indicator. (The precipitate should be completely dissolved.) The iodine solution is prepared by dissolving about 12.7 grams of pure resublimed iodine and 18 grams of KI in a little water and then diluting to 1 liter.

Soluble Salts. Digest 2 grams with hot water and examine the filtrate for soluble salts.

SILICA OR SILEX—CHINA CLAY—ASBESTINE

These pigments, while all true silica pigments, are widely different from the standpoint of physical structure. A microscopic examination is of great value, showing silica or silex to consist of small, sharp particles, china clay to be tabloid in appearance and asbestine to consist of long, rod-like fibrous particles.

The following procedure taken from the outlined method published by Sub-Committee VIII of Committee D-I [1] will well serve for the analysis of these pigments.

Moisture. Heat 2 grams at 105° for two hours.

Loss on Ignition. Ignite 1 gram to constant weight in a platinum crucible.

Insoluble Matter. Boil 2 grams for thirty minutes with 50 cc. HCl (1 : 1), add 50 cc. of water, wash, ignite, and weigh insoluble residue.

In the case of China clay, or asbestine, a sodium carbonate fusion should be resorted to, with the subsequent dehydration of the silica.

The insoluble residue in either case is volatilized with H_2SO_4 and HF in the usual manner, any loss in weight being considered silica. Any residue is fused with sodium carbonate, the fusion being added to the original filtrate. Should $BaSO_4$ be present, the melt is digested with warm water, the $BaCO_3$ filtered off, washed, dissolved in hot dilute HCl and precipitated and determined as $BaSO_4$.

The filtrates, combined from the preceding filtrations, are examined for alumina, iron, manganese, calcium and magnesium in the usual way.

Should it be necessary to determine the alkalies present, a separate sample is treated according to the method of Mr. J. Lawrence Smith as in Bulletin No. 422, U. S. Geological Survey. See page 416, Vol. I.

Carbon Dioxide. Determine by evolution with HCl, weighing in soda-lime, KOH solution, or by absorbing in $Ba(OH)_2$ solution and titrating or weighing as $BaCO_3$. See p. 121, Vol. I.

[1] Proceedings of American Society for Testing Materials, **14,** 279, 1914.

Any excess of calcium is reported as oxide. The magnesium is calculated as MgO, unless the carbon dioxide is in excess of the amount of calcium present, in which case it is reported as $MgCO_3$, and the remainder as MgO.

WHITING—PARIS WHITE

Gypsum—Plaster of Paris

These pigments are of the following composition:

Whiting. The natural form of calcium carbonate.

Paris White. The artificial form of calcium carbonate.

Gypsum. The hydrated form of calcium sulphate, of formula $CaSO_4 \cdot 2H_2O$. These pigments are analyzed in the following manner:

Moisture. Heat 2 grams at 105° C. for two hours.

Loss on Ignition. Ignite 1 gram at a high heat to constant weight. The loss will be water, if carbonates are absent.

Calcium. Treat 1 gram with dilute HCl and a few drops of HNO_3. Evaporate to dryness, dehydrate, moisten with a few drops of concentrated HCl, dilute with hot water and determine the insoluble residue. Examine for $BaSO_4$. The residue should consist of silica.

In the filtrate, precipitate and determine the iron hydroxide and aluminum hydroxide in the usual manner. The calcium is precipitated in the boiling ammoniacal filtrate with 30 cc. of saturated ammonium oxalate solution, allowing the solution to boil for one-half hour. A double precipitation is here advisable to remove the last traces of magnesium. The calcium oxalate is filtered off, thoroughly washed and determined volumetrically by the permanganate method, p. 92.

Magnesium. Determine in the filtrates after removal of the calcium by precipitation as magnesium ammonium phosphate and ignition to magnesium pyrophosphate in the usual manner, p. 293, Vol. I.

Carbon Dioxide. Determine as outlined under Silica.

Sulphates. Dissolve 1 gram in concentrated HCl, remove any insoluble residue, heat to boiling and precipitate any sulphate as $BaSO_4$, determining in the usual manner. See p. 497, Vol. I.

BARYTES AND BLANC FIXE

Of these two barium pigments used in the manufacture of paints, barytes is the natural barium sulphate, while blanc fixe is precipitated barium sulphate. Their barium sulphate content should be not less than 95%.

The following method may be used for the analysis of these pigments:

Moisture. Heat 2 grams at 105° C. for two hours.

Loss on Ignition. Ignite 1 gram to constant weight. The loss will be reported as loss on ignition, and will consist of free and uncombined water, carbon dioxide and organic matter.

Barium Sulphate. Boil 1 gram with dilute HCl, evaporate to dryness, moisten with HCl, add water, boil, filter and wash. Should lead be present in the insoluble residue, as shown by the action of H_2S, treat the insoluble residue with a little (1 : 1) HCl and several drops of H_2SO_4. Filter, wash and weigh the residue. Treat the ignited residue with H_2SO_4 and HF, evaporate to dryness and ignite. The residue should show no loss as silica. The filtrate is examined for alumina, iron, calcium and magnesium in the usual manner.

Soluble Sulphates. Treat 1 gram with 20 cc. conc. HCl, dilute to 200 cc. with hot water, boil, filter, wash, add NH_4OH until neutral, make acid with HCl and precipitate any sulphate as $BaSO_4$. Determine in the usual manner. Calculate to $CaSO_4$. If carbonates are present, calculate the remaining CaO to $CaCO_3$. Any excess of oxide is reported as CaO.

Carbon Dioxide. Determine as outlined under silica. If any barium carbonate is present, it is determined in the filtrate from the preliminary HCl treatment, by precipitation and weighing, as $BaSO_4$. Any excess of carbon dioxide over the barium is reported as calcium carbonate.

ANALYSIS OF A COMPOSITE WHITE PAINT

A white paint may consist of a mixture of any of the preceding pigments, excepting that it is understood that lead pigments and lithopone are seldom found together, owing to their tendency to blacken with the formation of lead sulphide.

After separation from the oil and other liquids as outlined above, the white pigment mixture may be rapidly analyzed by the following method. It is, however, often advisable to resort to a qualitative examination before beginning the quantitative analysis.

Insoluble Residue. Boil 1 gram of the sample with 20 cc. (1 : 1) HCl. Evaporate to dryness, moisten the residue with a few cc. of concentrated HCl, allow to stand a few minutes, dilute with hot water, boil, filter and wash the insoluble residue thoroughly with hot water. Treat the insoluble residue with (1 : 1) HCl and 2 cc. H_2SO_4 to remove the last traces of lead. Filter, wash and weigh the insoluble residue. Determine the silica by volatilization with H_2SO_4 and HF. Any loss is reported as silica. Determine the $BaSO_4$ in the residue by boiling with dilute HCl or making a potassium bisulphate fusion. The residue remaining after either of these treatments is reported as barium sulphate.

Total Lead. This constituent can be best determined on a separate sample. To 1 gram add 10 cc. of conc. HNO_3, boil, add, after cooling, conc. H_2SO_4 and evaporate to strong SO_3 fumes. Dilute with water, allow to stand several hours, filter, wash slightly, dissolve and determine the lead volumetrically as outlined under Sublimed White Lead.

Lead can also be determined on the combined filtrates from the insoluble residue. Precipitate the lead in an acid solution with H_2S and determine volumetrically in the above outlined manner.

To determine whether both sublimed white lead and corroded white lead are present, treat a separate portion of the paint with boiling acetic acid, filter and collect the insoluble residue. Determine the lead either in the filtrate or in the insoluble residue by the volumetric method. The lead soluble in acetic acid is the basic carbonate of lead and the lead oxide from the sublimed white lead, while the lead sulphate from the sublimed white lead remains insoluble.

Alumina and Iron Oxide. Remove the H_2S from the filtrate by boiling, after removal of the lead, and precipitate the hydroxides in an ammoniacal solution after boiling with the addition of a few drops of HNO_3. Determine and separate in the usual manner.

Zinc. Precipitate the zinc in the filtrate from the alumina and iron pre-cipitation, after acidifying with acetic acid, and determine the zinc as outlined under Sublimed White Lead on p. 1179.

Calcium and Magnesium. Determine the calcium and magnesium in the filtrate from the precipitation of zinc sulphide in the usual manner, testing, how-ever, first for the presence of barium.

Sulphate. Determine as outlined under Zinc Lead and Leaded Zincs.

Sulphide. Should lithopone be present, separate the zinc oxide and zinc sulphide as outlined under Lithopone, p. 1186.

Carbon Dioxide. Determine as outlined under Silica, p. 1187.

Calculations. Silica is reported as silica, except where alumina is present, showing the presence of China clay. In this case, calculate the alumina to clay by the method of Scott.

Weight of $Al_2O_3 \times 2.5372 =$ weight of clay.

Weight of clay $\times 0.4667 =$ weight of SiO_2 in clay.

Any difference greater than 5% may be considered silica.

Barium sulphate is reported as barium sulphate or as lithopone, if zinc sul-phide is present, according to the given composition of lithopone, 70% barium sulphate and 30% zinc sulphide.

Lead is reported as Basic Carbonate of Lead on the formula $2PbCO_3 \cdot Pb(OH)_2$.

Calculate lead soluble in acetic acid, after determining CO_2 to basic lead car-bonate and any residual lead to lead oxide which, together with the lead sulphate is reported as Sublimed White Lead.

Should calcium sulphate be present the portion soluble in water is examined for lime or sulphuric acid and calculated to calcium sulphate, any residual lime being calculated to calcium carbonate and any residual sulphuric acid being cal-culated to lead sulphate. Any residual CO_2 after calculating calcium carbonate is calculated to white lead and any residual lead is calculated to lead oxide.

Lead oxide should not be reported except in the presence of lead sulphate. Any large percentage of magnesium denotes the presence of asbestine.

TITANIUM PIGMENTS

Titanox [1]

The recent advent of titanium oxide as a constituent of white paints should be of interest to analytical chemists, since special methods are necessary for the determination of the titanium present. There is given below L. E. Barton's method for the analysis of dry titanium oxide pigment such as is made in the United States and which usually contains 75% barium sulphate and 25% titanium oxide. There is also given a method for the separation of zinc and lead from mixtures containing titanium. (See also Titanium, Vol. I.)

Determination of Barium Sulphate. Weigh $\frac{1}{2}$ gram sample into 250-cc. Pyrex glass beaker; add 20 cc. concentrated sulphuric acid and 7 or 8 grams sodium sulphate. Mix well and heat on hot plate until fumes of sulphuric anhydride are evolved and then heat directly over flame to boiling for five minutes or until solution is complete. Traces of silica, if any, remain as an insoluble residue.

[1] Physical and Chemical Examination of Paints, Varnishes and Colors. Gardner, pp. 174–6.

Cool, take up with 100 cc. of water, boil and filter off barium sulphate and silica, washing with 5% sulphuric acid to free residue from titanium.

Determination of Titanium. The volumetric method used for determination of titanium is essentially that described by P. W. and E. B. Shimer (Proc. Eighth Internat. Congress of Applied Chem.); the method hereafter described differing principally in the form of reductor and also in a few details of operation.

Reagents. Standard ferric ammonium sulphate solution. Dissolve 30 grams of ferric ammonium sulphate in 300 cc. water acidified with 10 cc. of sulphuric acid; add potassium permanganate drop by drop as long as the pink color disappears, to oxidize any ferrous to ferric iron; finally dilute the solution to one liter.

Standardize this solution in terms of iron. The iron value multiplied by 1.4329 gives the value in titanic oxide (TiO_2); and iron value multiplied by .86046 gives the value of the solution in terms of metallic titanium.

Indicator. Saturated solution of potassium thiocyanate.

Reductor. As a reductor a 500-cc. dispensing burette is used. The internal dimensions of the burette are $1\frac{5}{8}$ inches by 22 inches.

The reductor is charged with 1200 grams of 20-mesh amalgamated zinc, making a column about 12 inches high and having an interstice volume of about 135 cc. This form of reductor is convenient, and when used as hereafter described is adapted to maintaining hot solutions, which is essential for complete reduction of the titanium.

The reductor is connected to a liter flask for receiving the reduced titanium solution through a three-hole rubber stopper, which carries also an inlet tube for carbon dioxide supply and an outlet tube for connecting with a suction pump.

The reductor is prepared for use by first passing through it a little hot dilute sulphuric acid followed by hot water, finally leaving sufficient hot water in the reductor to fill to the upper level of the zinc.

The hot filtrate from the barium sulphate determination is now introduced; about 10 cc. of water being drawn from the reductor into the original beaker to bring the solution to about the upper level of the zinc. The water thus removed will not contain any titanium if the operation has been conducted as described, but it serves as a safeguard and is also convenient to acidify this water with 10 cc. sulphuric acid and reserve it on the hot plate to be used as an acid wash after the reduction of the sample solution.

The titanium solution is allowed to remain in the reductor for 10 minutes. While the solution is being reduced, the receiving flask is connected to the reductor and the air completely displaced by carbon dioxide, conveniently drawn from a cylinder of the liquified gas.

When the reduction is complete, the receiving flask is connected with the suction pump, and while still continuing the flow of carbon dioxide the reduced solution is drawn out, followed by the reserved acid wash and then three or four 100-cc. washes with hot water. The displacement of the sample solution and washing of the zinc is so regulated by means of the stopcock that the reductor is always filled with solution or water to the upper level of the zinc.

When the washing is complete, gradually release the suction to prevent air being drawn back into the receiving flask.

Disconnect the flask, add 5 cc. of potassium thiocyanate solution as indi-

18

cator and titrate immediately with standard ferric ammonium sulphate solution, adding the solution rapidly until a brownish color is produced, which will remain for at least one minute.

Bureau of Standards Method for Titanox Pigment

Moisture. Place 1 g. of the sample in a wide-mouth, short weighing tube provided with a glass stopper. Heat with stopper removed for two hours at a temperature between 100° and 105° C. Insert stopper, cool, and weigh. Calculate loss in weight as moisture.

Matter Soluble in Water. Transfer 2.5 g. of the pigment to a graduated 250-cc. flask, add 100 cc. of water, boil for 5 minutes, cool, fill to mark with water, mix, and allow to settle. Pour the supernatant liquid through a dry filter paper and discard the first 20 cc. Then evaporate 100 cc. of the clear filtrate to dryness in a weighed dish, heat for one hour at 105–110° C., cool, and weigh.

Titanium Oxide. Transfer 0.5 g. of the dried sample to a 250-cc. Pyrex beaker, add 20 cc. of concentrated sulphuric acid and 7 to 8 g. of ammonium sulphate. Mix well and heat on hot plate until fumes of sulphuric acid are evolved, and then continue the heating over a strong flame until solution is complete (usually takes not over five minutes of boiling) or it is apparent that the residue is composed of silica or siliceous matter. Caution should be observed in visually examining this hot solution. Cool the solution, dilute with 100 cc. of water, stir, heat carefully to boiling while stirring, settle, filter through paper and transfer the precipitate completely to the paper. Wash the insoluble residue with cold 5% (by volume) sulphuric acid until titanium is removed.

Dilute the filtrate to 200 cc. and add about 10 cc. of ammonia, sp.gr. 0.90, to lower the acidity to approximately 5% sulphuric acid (by volume).

Wash out a Jones reductor with dilute 5% by volume sulphuric acid and water, leaving sufficient water in the reductor to fill to the upper level of the zinc. (These washings should require not more than one or two drops of 0.1 N potassium permanganate solution to obtain the pink color.) Empty the receiver, and put in it 25 cc. (measured in a graduate) of ferric sulphate solution (see Reagents). Reduce the prepared titanium solution as follows:

(1) Run 50 cc. of the 5% sulphuric acid solution through the reductor at a speed of about 100 cc. per minute.

(2) Follow this with the titanium solution.

(3) Wash out with 50 cc. of 5% sulphuric acid.

(4) Finally run through about 100 cc. of water.

Care should be observed that the reductor is always filled with solution or water to the upper level of the zinc.

Gradually release the suction, wash thoroughly the glass tube that was immersed in the ferric sulphate solution, remove the receiver, and titrate immediately with 0.1 N potassium permanganate solution (see Reagents).

$$1 \text{ cc. } 0.1 \text{ N } KMnO_4 = 0.0048 \text{ g. Ti}$$
$$= 0.00801 \text{ g. } TiO_2.$$

Run a blank determination, using the same reagents, washing the reductor as in the above determination. Subtract this permanganate reading from the original reading and calculate the final reading to titanium dioxide (TiO_2)

(which will include iron, chromium, arsenic, and any other substance which is reduced by zinc and acid).

Determination of Barium Sulphate. Ignite and weigh the precipitate of $BaSO_4$ obtained in separating the titanium.[2]

ANALYSIS OF PAINTS CONTAINING TiO₂ [3]

After the pigment has been extracted and dried, a sample is weighed out and decomposed by the ordinary acid treatment. Weigh 1 gram into a 250-cc. Pyrex beaker; add 40 cc. concentrated sulphuric acid and 15 grams sodium sulphate. Mix well and heat on a hot plate until fumes of SO_3 are evolved, and then continue heat to boiling for five minutes. Silica, if present, will, of course, remain undissolved. Cool, take up with 200 cc. water, boil and filter off lead sulphate, barium sulphate, silica, and similar acid-insoluble inert pigments. Separate as usual. The filtrates should contain the titanium and zinc in solution as sulphates.

To the filtrate ammonia is added in excess, which precipitates the titanium with the iron group. For the complete separation of zinc from the iron group, the hydroxide precipitate should be redissolved in acid and a second precipitation with ammonia should be made. Zinc may then be determined in the combined filtrate.

Titanium should be determined on a separate sample, as described in the above method for dry TiO_2 pigments.

ANTIMONY OXIDE

Antimony trioxide (Sb_2O_3), a fume pigment that has recently been introduced, may be occasionally found in certain classes of mixed paints. After being brought into solution, it may be quantitatively estimated by oxidation with permanganate or iodine. (See Vol. I, pages 27 and 28.)

RED AND BROWN PIGMENTS

These pigments are grouped under these heads:

The Lead Oxide Pigments—The Iron Oxide and Manganese Oxide Pigments—The Mercury Oxide Pigments

RED LEAD AND ORANGE MINERAL

These pigments in the pure form are oxides of lead, of the generally accepted form, Pb_3O_4, being probably mixtures of lead monoxide, and lead dioxide.

Two methods are given for the analysis of this pigment.

Moisture. Dry 2 grams at 105° for two hours.

[1] Any other accurate method of determining titanium oxide may be used. See Vol. I, chapter on Titanium, by Scott and Barton.

[2] If sample is impure it may be necessary to purify this precipitate, using appropriate methods.

[3] Physical and Chemical Examination of Paints, Varnishes and Colors. Gardner.

Organic Color. Boil 2 grams with 25 cc. of 95% ethyl alcohol, let settle, decant off the supernatant liquid; boil residue with water, decant as before and boil residue with very dilute NH_4OH. If either the alcohol, water or NH_4OH is colored, organic coloring matter is indicated.

Total Lead and Insoluble Residue. Treat 1 gram with 15 cc. of HNO_3 (1 : 1) and sufficient hydrogen dioxide to dissolve all the PbO_2 on warming. If any insoluble matter is present, add 25 cc. of water, boil, filter and wash with hot water. Insoluble contains free SiO_2, and should be examined for $BaSO_4$ and silicates, if appreciable. To the original solution or filtrate from insoluble, add 20 cc. of conc. H_2SO_4 and evaporate to SO_3 fumes; cool and determine lead as lead sulphate either gravimetrically or volumetrically. If the sample contains soluble barium salts, the $PbSO_4$ will contain $BaSO_4$ and should be treated with acid-ammonium acetate solution, the lead being determined in the filtrate.

Determination of Lead Peroxide (PbO_2) and True Red Lead (Pb_3O_4). (Method of Diehl,[1] modified by Topf [2]—not applicable when substances are present, other than oxides of lead, that liberate iodine under conditions given.)

Weigh 1 gram of finely ground sample into a 200-cc. Erlenmeyer flask, add a few drops of distilled water and rub the mixture to a smooth paste with a glass rod flattened on end. Mix in a small beaker 30 grams of C.P. " Tested Purity " crystallized sodium acetate, 2.4 grams of C.P. potassium iodide, 10 cc. of water and 10 cc. of 50% acetic acid; stir until all is liquid, warming gently; if necessary add 2 to 3 cc. of H_2O, cool to room temperature and pour into the flask containing the red lead. Rub with the glass rod until nearly all the red lead has been dissolved; add 30 cc. of water containing 5 or 6 grams of sodium acetate, and titrate at once with decinormal sodium thiosulphate, adding the latter rather slowly and keeping the liquid constantly in motion by whirling the flask. When the solution has become light yellow, rub any undissolved particles up with the rod until free iodine no longer forms, wash off rod, add the sodium thiosulphate solution until pale yellow, add starch solution and titrate until colorless, add decinormal iodine solution until blue color is just restored and subtract the amount used from the volume of thiosulphate that had been added.

Calculation. The iodine value of the sodium thiosulphate solution multiplied by $0.94193 = PbO_2$; the iodine value multiplied by $2.69973 = Pb_3O_4$; the PbO_2 value multiplied by $2.86616 = Pb_3O_4$.

Sodium Thiosulphate Solution (decinormal). Dissolve 24.83 grams of C.P. sodium thiosulphate, freshly pulverized and dried between filter paper, and dilute with water to 1 liter at a temperature at which the titrations are to be made. The solution should be made with well-boiled H_2O, free from CO_2, or let stand eight to fourteen days before standardizing. Standardize with pure, resublimed iodine, as described in the chapter on Iodine, page 204, and also against pure potassium iodate. The two methods of standardization should agree within 0.1% on iodine value.

Starch Solution. Two to 3 grams of potato starch are stirred up with 100 cc. of 1% salicylic acid solution, and the mixture boiled till the starch is practically dissolved and then diluted to 1 liter.

The red lead may also be examined for zinc, carbon dioxide, and soluble sulphate.

[1] Dingl. Polyt. Jour., **246**, 196.
[2] Zeitschrift für analytische Chemie, **26**, 296.

The second method for determination of the lead peroxide or true red lead content is somewhat shorter.[1]

Treat 1 gram in a beaker with 15 cc. of nitric acid, sp.gr. 1.2 (110 cc. nitric acid, sp.gr. 1.42 to 100 cc. of water). Stir the sample until all trace of red color has disappeared. Add from a calibrated pipette or burette exactly 10 cc. of dilute hydrogen dioxide (1 part of 3% hydrogen dioxide to 3.5 parts of water). Add about 50 cc. of hot water and stir until all the lead dioxide has passed into solution. In the case of some coarsely ground oxides the contents of the beaker may have to be gently heated to effect complete solution. After the oxide has completely passed into solution, dilute with hot water to about 250 cc. volume and titrate directly with a standard potassium permanganate solution, having an iron value of 0.005. Titrate to the faint pink permanganate color. A blank titration on the hydrogen dioxide solution must now be made.

Into a beaker pour 15 cc. of nitric acid of above strength and add exactly the same amount of hydrogen dioxide (10 cc.). Dilute to 250 cc. with hot water and titrate with standard potassium permanganate solution to a faint pink color.

The difference between the number of cc. of potassium permanganate required for the blank titration and the number required for the red lead titration is the amount required for the hydrogen dioxide which was reacted on by the red lead. The difference between the two amounts of potassium permanganate required multiplied by 3.058 grams gives the percentage of red lead present. The difference multiplied by 1.067 gives the percentage of PbO_2 present.

VERMILION

The following portion of Walker's [2] method, will suffice for the examination of this pigment. Should the analyst desire to determine the sulphide of mercury present or make a more complete examination—reference may be made to the original method.

True vermilion, or, as it is generally called, English vermilion, is sulphide of mercury. On account of its cost it is rarely used in paints, and is liable to gross adulteration. It should show no bleeding on boiling with alcohol and water and no free sulphur by extraction with carbon disulphide. A small quantity mixed with five or six times its weight of dry sodium carbonate and heated in a tube should show globules of mercury on the cooler portion of the tube. The best test for purity is the ash, which should be not more than one-half of 1%. Make the determination in a porcelain dish or crucible, using 2 grams of the sample. Ash in a muffle or in a hood with a very good draft, as the mercury fumes are very poisonous. It is seldom necessary to make a determination of the mercury.

Genuine vermilion is at the present time little used in paints. Organic lakes are used for most of the brilliant red, scarlet and vermilion shades. These organic coloring matters are sometimes precipitated on red lead, orange mineral or zinc oxide; but as a usual thing the base is barytes, whiting or china clay. Paranitraniline red, a compound of diazotized paranitraniline and beta-naphthol, is largely employed; but a number of colors may be used.

Paranitraniline red is soluble in chloroform. It is also well to try the solvent

[1] " Analysis of Lead and Its Compounds," Schaeffer and White, pp. 25–27.
[2] P. H. Walker, Bulletin 109, Revised, Bureau of Chemistry, U. S. Dept. of Agri., pp. 31–33.

action on different reds, of sodium carbonate, etc. The amount of organic pigment present in such reds is generally very small, and when it cannot be determined by ignition owing to the presence of lead, zinc or carbonate, it is best determined by difference.

IRON OXIDES

The iron oxides and manganese oxide pigments include the ochres, umbers, siennas, Venetian red, metallic brown, Indian red and Tuscan red.

In analyzing these pigments, the following constituents are sought; moisture, loss on ignition, insoluble residue, iron oxide, manganese dioxide, calcium and magnesium oxides and sulphur trioxide.

Owing to the similarity of the methods used for the analysis of these pigments to those used in the analysis of iron ores, the analyst is referred to p. 247 on the Analysis of Iron Ores, or to the method of Walker.[1]

BLUE PIGMENTS

In examining blue pigments, only three are found of commercial importance in the manufacture of paints; namely, Prussian blue, ultramarine blue and sublimed blue lead.

Sublimed blue lead is the fume product resulting from the smelting of lead ores. In composition it consists of lead sulphate, lead sulphide, lead sulphite, lead oxide and zinc oxide, with occasional traces of carbon. It is finding its greatest use as an inhibitive pigment for the protection of iron and steel. Its color is a bluish gray.

Prussian blue is the double iron and potassium salt of hydroferrocyanic and hydroferricyanic acids.

Ultramarine blue is essentially a silicate and sulphide of sodium and aluminum.

ULTRAMARINE BLUE

Moisture. Heat 2 grams at 105° C. for two hours.

Silica. Digest 1 gram with 30 cc. of concentrated HCl, taking care to avoid spattering. Evaporate to dryness, dehydrate, moisten with conc. HCl, dehydrate a second time, dilute, filter, and determine the silica by volatilization with H_2SO_4 and HF.

Aluminum Oxide. In the filtrate from the silica, precipitate the aluminum hydroxide and determine in the usual manner. Report as aluminum oxide.

Sodium Oxide. The filtrate, after the removal of the aluminum hydroxide is acidified with H_2SO_4. Evaporate to dryness, ignite at a low red heat, and weigh the sodium sulphate. Calculate to sodium oxide.

Total Sulphur. Fuse 1 gram with a mixture of KNO_3 and Na_2CO_3. Dissolve the fused mass in HCl, boil with conc. HNO_3 for one-half hour, remove the insoluble residue and determine the sulphuric acid in the usual way.

Sulphur Present as Sulphate. Dissolve 1 gram in dilute HCl and boil until all the hydrogen sulphide is removed. Filter off the insoluble residue and determine the sulphate in the filtrate.

---

[1] Bulletin 109, Revised, Bureau of Chemistry, U. S. Dept. Agri., pp. 33–34.

PRUSSIAN BLUE—(CHINESE BLUE)—ANTWERP BLUE

Moisture. Heat 2 grams at 105° C. for two hours. Dry Prussian blue should contain less than 7% moisture.

Nitrogen. Determine the nitrogen present by the Kjeldahl-Gunning method.

Iron and Aluminum Oxides. Ignite 1 gram at a low temperature, sufficient to decompose all the blue, but not to render the iron difficultly soluble. Digest the residue with (1 : 1) HCl. Any insoluble residue is examined for silica, barium sulphate and alumina. A pure Prussian blue should show no insoluble residue. The filtrate is examined for alumina, iron and calcium in the usual way.

An aliquot portion of the filtrate after the removal of the calcium is examined for the alkaline metals. Calculate any alkaline metal present to sulphate.

Sulphuric Acid. Determine the sulphuric acid in an aliquot portion after removal of the calcium.

Commercial Analysis. The method of Parry and Coste [1] is sufficiently accurate to determine the Prussian blue in most instances.

By multiplying the percentage of iron by 3.03 or the percentage of nitrogen by 4.4, the percentage of Prussian blue is directly determined.

In the case of Chinese blue, tin salts are frequently found. The presence of these salts should be sought by a qualitative examination.

SUBLIMED BLUE LEAD [2]

Total Lead. The total lead content is determined by the volumetric method for lead as outlined under Sublimed White Lead.

Total Sulphur. Treat 0.5 gram with 10 cc. of water and a few cc. of bromine water. Boil gently until all the bromine has passed off. Dilute with water, add another portion of bromine water, boil, and continue the treatment until the sediment has become white in color. Add 8 cc. of nitric acid, evaporate until the brown fumes of nitric acid have disappeared, dilute with water and add an excess of sodium carbonate. Determine as outlined under Zinc Lead and Leaded Zinc.

Lead Sulphate. On a separate sample determine the sulphate directly as outlined under Zinc Lead and Leaded Zinc, without any preliminary treatment for the oxidation of sulphites and sulphides.

Lead Sulphite. Boil 1½ grams with 3 grams of sodium carbonate. Allow to stand, filter and thoroughly wash. Treat the filtrate with bromine water as outlined under Total Sulphur and determine the combined sulphur present as sulphate and sulphite. Deduct the amount present as sulphate and calculate to sulphite.

Lead Sulphide. Deduct the sulphur present as sulphate and sulphite from the total sulphur and report the difference as lead sulphide.

Lead Carbonate. Determine any CO_2 present by the evolution method and calculate to lead carbonate. See p. 121, Vol. I.

Lead Oxide. Deduct the lead present as sulphate, sulphite, sulphide and carbonate from the total lead and report the difference as lead oxide.

[1] The Analyst, **21**, 225–230, 1896.
[2] "The Chemical Analysis of Lead and its Compounds," Schaeffer and White, pp. 22–24.

Zinc Oxide. Determine the zinc volumetrically as outlined under Sublimed White Lead and report as zinc oxide.

Carbon and Volatile Matter. Ignite the sample in a partially covered crucible at a low heat for two hours. Report the difference in weight as carbon and volatile matter.

YELLOW AND ORANGE PIGMENTS

Chrome Yellows—American Vermilion—Basic Lead Chromate

The pigments under this class all contain chromates, with the exception of orange mineral, which is analyzed as under Red Lead. Frequently they contain lead sulphate and sometimes lead carbonate. A pure chrome yellow should contain only lead chromate and insoluble lead compounds. Owing to the frequent use of organic colors to brighten up the pigment, it is essential that a test be made for organic colors as outlined under Vermilion.

The analysis of these pigments is carried out in the following manner:

Moisture. Heat 2 grams at 105° C. for two hours.

Insoluble Residue. Treat 1 gram with 25 cc. of concentrated HCl, boil and during the boiling add a few drops of alcohol, one at a time. The solution is diluted to 100 cc., the boiling is continued for ten minutes and any insoluble residue is filtered off, thoroughly washed and examined for silica, barium sulphate and alumina.

Lead. The solution is nearly neutralized with NH_4OH and the lead is precipitated as PbS with H_2S. Filter off the precipitate of PbS, dissolve in HNO_3, add H_2SO_4, boil to strong fumes and determine as outlined under Sublimed White Lead or weigh as $PbSO_4$.

Chromium. The filtrate from the lead precipitation is boiled until all the H_2S is driven off. The solution is rendered alkaline with NH_4OH and the chromium is precipitated and determined as chromic oxide. Calculate to chromic anhydride.

Zinc, Calcium and Magnesium. Precipitate the zinc in the filtrate with H_2S and determine as previously outlined, either volumetrically or gravimetrically.

In the filtrate from the zinc precipitation, determine the calcium and magnesium in the usual manner.

If any carbonates are present, determine by the evolution method.

Sulphuric Acid. Determine the total sulphate as outlined under Zinc Lead and Leaded Zinc on p. 1183.

Calculations. Any chromic anhydride is calculated to lead chromate, sulphuric acid to lead sulphate, if calcium sulphate is absent, and any residual lead is calculated to lead oxide.

GREEN PIGMENTS

Chrome Green

Green pigments are usually mixtures of chrome yellow and Prussian blue, though organic color is sometimes present, which may be determined by an extraction with alcohol.

A microscopic examination should be made to determine whether the green is a combined precipitation product, which is of the greater value, or one mixed after separate precipitation. A good green will show the presence of green and blue particles, while a poor green will show yellow and blue particles mixed with green. The analysis may be carried out as follows: [1]

Moisture. Heat 2 grams at 105° C. for two hours.

Insoluble Residue. Heat 1 gram at a low heat until the blue color has been decomposed, keeping the temperature sufficiently low so as not to render any of the iron or lead chromate insoluble. Determine the insoluble residue as outlined under Yellow Pigments, on p. 1195.

Lead. Determine as outlined under Yellow Pigments.

Iron, Alumina and Chromium. All the H_2S is expelled from the filtrate after the lead precipitation by boiling. Add a few drops of HNO_3, boil a few minutes and precipitate the aluminum, iron and chromium hydroxides with NH_4OH. Filter, wash, dissolve the precipitate in HCl, and make up the solution to a definite volume.

In one portion the three hydroxides are precipitated together with NH_4OH and weighed. Another portion is treated in a flask with an excess of KOH and bromine water until the iron hydroxide has assumed its characteristic reddish-brown color. Dilute with water, filter, wash and determine the iron in the usual way. Render the filtrate from the iron precipitation acid with HNO_3, precipitate the aluminum hydroxide with NH_4OH and weigh as Al_2O_3.

Chromium is determined in the filtrate by reduction to a chromic salt with HCl and alcohol, precipitated with NH_4OH and weighed as oxide. Any method for the separation of the above hydroxides may be used in place of the one outlined.

Calcium and Magnesium. These constituents are determined in the filtrate from the precipitation of the above hydroxides.

Sulphuric Acid. One gram after ignition until all the blue has been decomposed, is dissolved in 30 cc. of conc. HCl, diluted with water, boiled, filtered, and washed. The sulphuric acid is determined in the filtrate.

Nitrogen. Determine as outlined under Prussian Blue.

Calculation. The Prussian blue is determined by multiplying the iron found by 3.03 or the nitrogen formed by 4.4. The sulphate is calculated to lead sulphate and calcium sulphate, should calcium be present, and the chromium to lead chromate.

BLACK PIGMENTS

The black pigments include those which contain carbon as their essential constituent. The introduction of many black pigments which are made from asphaltic and coal-tar mixtures complicates their chemical analysis. For those pigments which contain coal-tar mixtures, recourse may be had to works [2] covering this matter thoroughly.

The analysis of the simple black pigments may be carried out in the following way:

Moisture. Dry 2 grams at 105° C. for two hours.

Oil. Extract 2 grams, with ether in a fat-extraction apparatus.

Carbon. Determine the carbon by difference after determining the moist-

[1] " The Analysis of Paints," Gardner and Schaeffer, pp. 36–37.

[2] Allen's "Commercial Organic Analysis," 4th Edition; " The Analysis of Paints," Gardner and Schaeffer.

ure, oil and ash.   For an exact determination of carbon make a combustion test, absorbing the carbon dioxide in soda-lime or caustic potash as usual.

Ash.   Ignite 2 grams to a bright red heat until all the carbon is driven off. If graphite is present, the ignition must be carried out with the aid of oxygen. Should carbonate be present, mix the ash with a small amount of ammonium carbonate and again ignite, thus reconverting to carbonate any oxide which may have been decomposed.

Analysis of Ash.   The ash is boiled with concentrated HCl and the insoluble residue determined in the usual manner.   The filtrate is examined for calcium, magnesium and phosphoric acid.

Calculate the magnesium to phosphate, any residual phosphoric acid to calcium phosphate and any residual calcium to carbonate.

Standard Definitions of Terms Relating to Paint Specifications

These definitions are issued by the A. S. T. M. under the fixed designation D 16; the final number indicates the year of original adoption as standard, or in the case of revision, the year of last revision.

ADOPTED IN AMENDED FORM, 1922

Size.   In the painting art, a liquid coating material, intended to close the pores, used to prepare a surface for further treatment.

It is not regarded as a finishing material.

Varnish.   A liquid coating material, containing no pigment, which flows out to a smooth coat when applied and dries to a smooth, glossy, relatively hard, permanent solid when exposed in a thin film to the air.

Some materials possessing the other characteristics dry without the usual gloss and are termed "flat varnish."

Enamel.   A special kind of paint which flows out to a smooth coat when applied and dries to a smooth, glossy, relatively hard, permanent solid when exposed in a thin film to the air.   An enamel always contains pigment and has considerable hiding power and color.   Some enamels dry to a flat or eggshell finish instead of a gloss finish.

Filler.   A special kind of paint used for filling pores or other small breaks in the continuity of a surface to render it smooth preparatory to further treatment.   When applied and exposed to the air, a filler should dry to a relatively hard, permanent solid capable of properly supporting subsequent coats.

Toner.   An organic pigment which does not contain inorganic pigment or inorganic carrying base.

Lake.   A special type of pigment consisting essentially of an organic soluble coloring matter combined more or less definitely with an inorganic base or carrier.   It is characterized generally by a bright color and a more or less pronounced translucency when made into an oil paint.

Under this term are included two (and perhaps three) types of pigment: (a) the older original type composed of hydrate of alumina dyed with a solution of the natural organic color, (b) the more modern and far more extensive type made by precipitating from solution various coal-tar colors by means of a metallic salt, tannin, or other suitable reagent, upon a base or carrier either previously prepared or coincidently formed, and (c) a number combining both types in varying degree, might be regarded as a third class.

Drying Oil. An oil which possesses to a marked degree the property of readily taking up oxygen from the air and changing to a relatively hard, tough, elastic substance when exposed in a thin film to the air.

Semi-Drying Oil. An oil which possesses the characteristics of a drying oil but to a less degree.

There is no definite line of demarcation between drying and semi-drying oils.

Non-Drying Oil. An oil which does not of itself possess to a perceptible degree the power to take up oxygen from the air and lose its liquid characteristics.

COMPLEX COMPOUNDS—FERRO AND FERRI CYANIDES

Hydroferrocyanic Acid

One gram of the hydroferrocyanide in 100 cc. of water acidified with 10 cc. of sulphuric acid is titrated in a casserole with standard potassium permanganate to a permanent pink color. The end-point is poor, so that it is advisable to standardize the permanganate against pure potassium ferrocyanide.

Reaction: $2H_4Fe(CN)_6 + O = H_2O + 2H_3Fe(CN)_6$

One cc. N $KMnO_4 = 0.3683$ gram $K_4Fe(CN)_6$.

Hydroferricyanic Acid

Ten grams of hydroferricyanide are dissolved in water, the solution made alkaline with KOH and heated to boiling and an excess of ferrous sulphate solution added. The yellowish brown ferric hydroxide turns black with excess of ferrous salt. The solution is diluted to exactly 500 cc. and 50 cc. of a filtered portion titrated with potassium permanganate.

One cc. N $KMnO_4 = .3292$ gram $K_3Fe(CN)_6$.

CEMENT

ANALYSIS AND TESTING OF CEMENTS

The tests ordinarily applied to Portland cement are as follows:

Fineness.
Specific gravity.
Setting time.
Soundness.
Tensile strength.

Chemical analysis is also made, particular attention being paid to the determination of magnesia, sulphur trioxide, and loss on ignition. As a general rule, however, it may be said that so far as the consumer is concerned, more attention is paid to the physical tests than to chemical analysis.

Standard specifications covering the requirements for cement, both chemical and physical, have been adopted by the American Society for Testing Materials, and by the U. S. Government. The former are generally recognized by cement users as the standard requirements, while the latter are used by the various branches of the federal government.

The specifications and methods of making these tests follow.

Specifications [1]

Definition. Portland cement is the product obtained by finely pulverizing clinker produced by calcining to incipient fusion an intimate and properly proportioned mixture of argillaceous and calcareous materials, with no additions subsequent to calcination excepting water and calcined or uncalcined gypsum.

Chemical Limits. The following limits shall not be exceeded:

Loss on ignition, per cent................................. 4.00
Insoluble residue, per cent............................... 0.85
Sulphuric anhydride (SO_3), per cent..................... 2.00
Magnesia (MgO), per cent................................. 5.00

Physical Properties. The specific gravity of cement shall be not less than 3.10 (3.07 for white Portland cement). Should the test of cement as received fall below this requirement a second test may be made upon an ignited sample. The specific gravity test will not be made unless specifically ordered.

The residue on a standard No. 200 sieve shall not exceed 22 per cent by weight.

[1] Approved March 31, 1922, as "American Standards" by the American Engineering Standards Committee.

Chapter by Richard K. Meade, chemical and industrial engineer, Baltimore, Md.

A pat of neat cement shall remain firm and hard, and show no signs of distortion, cracking, checking, or disintegration in the steam test for soundness.

The cement shall not develop initial set in less than 45 minutes when the Vicat needle is used or 60 minutes when the Gillmore needle is used. Final set shall be attained within 10 hours.

The average tensile strength in pounds per square inch of not less than three standard mortar briquettes composed of one part cement and three parts standard sand, by weight, shall be equal to or higher than the following:

Age at Test, days	Storage of Briquettes	Tensile Strength, lb. per sq. in.
7	1 day in moist air, 6 days in water.........	200
28	1 day in moist air, 27 days in water........	300

The average tensile strength of standard mortar at 28 days shall be higher than the strength at 7 days.

Packages and Marking. The cement shall be delivered in suitable bags or barrels with the brand and name of the manufacturer plainly marked thereon, unless shipped in bulk. A bag shall contain 94 lb. net. A barrel shall contain 376 lb. net.

The cement shall be stored in such a manner as to permit easy access for proper inspection and identification of each shipment, and in a suitable weather-tight building which will protect the cement from dampness.

Inspection. Every facility shall be provided the purchaser for careful sampling and inspection at either the mill or at the site of the work, as may be specified by the purchaser. At least 10 days from the time of sampling shall be allowed for the completion of the 7-day test, and at least 31 days shall be allowed for the completion of the 28-day test. The cement shall be tested in accordance with the methods hereinafter prescribed. The 28-day test shall be waived only when specifically so ordered.

Rejection. The cement may be rejected if it fails to meet any of the requirements of these specifications.

Cement shall not be rejected on account of failure to meet the fineness requirement if upon retest after drying at 100° C. for one hour it meets this requirement.

Cement failing to meet the test for soundness in steam may be accepted if it passes a retest using a new sample at any time within 28 days thereafter.

Packages varying more than 5 per cent from the specified weight may be rejected; and if the average weight of packages in any shipment, as shown by weighing 50 packages taken at random, is less than that specified, the entire shipment may be rejected.

Sampling

Number of Samples. Tests may be made on individual or composite samples as may be ordered.   Each test sample should weigh at least 8 lb.

(*a*) *Individual Sample.*   If sampled in cars, one test sample shall be taken from each 50 bbl. or fraction thereof.   If sampled in bins, one sample shall be taken from each 100 bbl.

(*b*) *Composite Sample.*   If sampled in cars, one sample shall be taken from one sack in each 40 sacks (or 1 bbl. in each 10 bbl.) and combined to form one test sample.   If sampled in bins or warehouses, one test sample shall represent not more than 200 bbl.

Method of Sampling.   Cement may be sampled at the mill by any of the following methods that may be practicable, as ordered:

(*a*) *From the Conveyor Delivering to the Bin.*   At least 8 lb. of cement shall be taken from approximately each 100 bbl. passing over the conveyor.

(*b*) *From Filled Bins by Means of Proper Sampling Tubes.*   Tubes inserted vertically may be used for sampling cement to a maximum depth of 10 ft. Tubes inserted horizontally may be used where the construction of the bin permits.   Samples shall be taken from points well distributed over the face of the bin.

(*c*) *From Filled Bins at Points of Discharge.*   Sufficient cement shall be drawn from the discharge openings to obtain samples representative of the cement contained in the bin, as determined by the appearance at the discharge openings of indicators placed on the surface of the cement directly above these openings before drawing of the cement is started.

Samples preferably shall be shipped and stored in air-tight containers. Samples shall be passed through a sieve having 20 meshes per linear inch in order to thoroughly mix the sample, break up lumps and remove foreign materials.

Specific Gravity.   The determination of specific gravity shall be made with a standardized Le Chatelier apparatus which conforms to the requirements illustrated in Fig. 93.   This apparatus is standardized by the U. S. Bureau of Standards.   Kerosene free from water, or benzine not lighter than 62° Baumé, shall be used in making this determination.

The flask shall be filled with either of these liquids to a point on the stem between zero and one cubic centimeter, and 64 g. of cement, of the same temperature as the liquid, shall be slowly introduced, taking care that the cement does not adhere to the inside of the flask above the liquid and to free the cement from air by rolling the flask in an inclined position.   After all the cement is introduced, the level of the liquid will rise to some division of the graduated neck; the difference between readings is the volume displaced by 64 g. of the cement.

The specific gravity shall then be obtained from the formula:

$$\text{Specific gravity} = \frac{\text{Weight of cement (g.)}}{\text{Displaced volume (cc.)}}.$$

The flask, during the operation, shall be kept immersed in water, in order to avoid variations in the temperature of the liquid in the flask, which shall not exceed 0.5° C.   The results of repeated tests should agree within 0.01.

The determination of specific gravity shall be made on the cement as received; if it falls below 3.10, a second determination shall be made after igniting the sample.

Fineness. Wire cloth for standard sieves for cement shall be woven (not twilled) from brass, bronze, or other suitable wire, and mounted without distortion on frames not less than $1\frac{1}{2}$ in. below the top of the frame. The sieve frames shall be circular, approximately 8 in. in diameter, and may be provided with a pan and cover.

A standard No. 200 sieve is one having nominally an 0.0029 in. opening and 200 wires per inch standardized by the U. S. Bureau of Standards, and conforming to the following requirements:

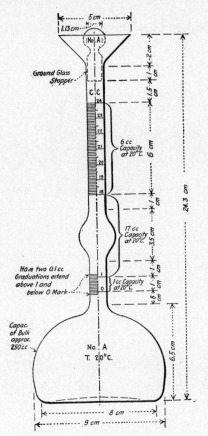

FIG. 93.   Le Chatelier Apparatus

The No. 200 sieve should have 200 wires per inch, and the number of wires in any whole inch shall not be outside the limits of 192 to 208.   No opening between adjacent parallel wires shall be more than 0.0050 in. in width.   The diameter of the wire should be 0.0021 in. and the average diameter shall not be outside the limits 0.0019 to 0.0023 in.   The value of the sieve as determined by sieving tests made in conformity with the standard specifications for these tests on a standardized cement which gives a residue of 25 to 20 per cent on the No. 200 sieve, or on other similarly graded material, shall not show a variation of more than 1.5 per cent above or below the standards maintained at the Bureau of Standards.

The test shall be made with 50 g. of cement.   The sieve shall be thoroughly clean and dry.   The cement shall be placed on the No. 200 sieve, with pan and cover attached, if desired.   The sieve shall be held in one hand in a slightly inclined position so that the sample will be well distributed over the sieve, at the same time gently striking the side about 150 times per minute against the palm of the other hand on the up stroke.   The sieve shall be turned every 25 strokes about one-sixth of a revolution in the same direction.   The operation shall continue until not more than 0.05 g. passes through in one minute of continuous sieving.   The fineness shall be determined from the weight of the residue on the sieve expressed as a percentage of the weight of the original sample.

Mechanical sieving devices may be used, but the cement shall not be rejected if it meets the fineness requirement when tested by the hand method described.

Mixing Cement Pastes and Mortars.   The quantity of dry material to be mixed at one time shall not exceed 1000 g. nor be less than 500 g.   The proportions of cement, or cement and sand, shall be stated by weight in grams of the dry materials; the quantity of water shall be expressed in cubic centimeters (1 cc. of water = 1 g.).   The dry materials shall be weighed, placed upon a non-absorbent surface, thoroughly mixed dry if sand is used, and a crater formed in the center, into which the proper percentage of clean water shall be poured; the material on the outer edge shall be turned into the crater by the aid of a trowel.   After an interval of $\frac{1}{2}$ minute for the absorption of the water the operation shall be completed by continuous, vigorous mixing, squeezing and kneading with the hands for at least one minute.[1]   During the operation of mixing, the hands should be protected by rubber gloves.

The temperature of the room and the mixing water shall be maintained as nearly as practicable at 21° C. (70° F.).

Normal Consistency.   The Vicat apparatus consists of a frame A (Fig. 94) bearing a movable rod B, weighing 300 g., one end C being 1 cm. in diameter for a distance of 6 cm., the other having a removable needle D, 1 mm. in diameter, 6 cm. long.   The rod is reversible, and can be held in any desired position by a screw E, and has midway between the ends a mark F which moves under a scale (graduated to millimeters) attached to the frame A. The paste is held in a conical, hard-rubber ring G, 7 cm. in diameter at the base, 4 cm. high, resting on a glass plate H about 10 cm. square.

In making the determination, 500 g. of cement, with a measured quantity of water, shall be kneaded into a paste, as described above, and quickly

[1] In order to secure uniformity in the results of tests for the time of setting and tensile strength, the manner of mixing above described should be carefully followed.   At least one minute is necessary to obtain the desired plasticity which is not appreciably affected by continuing the mixing for several minutes.   The exact time necessary is dependent upon the personal equation of the operator.   The error in mixing should be on the side of over mixing.

formed into a ball with the hands, completing the operation by tossing it six times from one hand to the other, maintained about 6 in. apart; the ball resting in the palm of one hand shall be pressed into the larger end of the

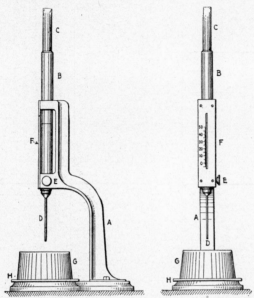

Fig. 94.   Vicat Apparatus

rubber ring held in the other hand, completely filling the ring with paste; the excess at the larger end shall then be removed by a single movement of the palm of the hand; the ring shall then be placed on its larger end on a glass plate and the excess paste at the smaller end sliced off at the top of the ring by a single oblique stroke of a trowel held at a slight angle with the top of the ring.   During these operations care shall be taken not to compress the paste.   The paste confined in the ring, resting on the plate, shall be placed under the rod, the larger end of which shall be brought in contact with the surface of the paste; the scale shall be then read, and the rod quickly released. The paste shall be of normal consistency when the rod settles to a point 10 mm. below the original surface in $\frac{1}{2}$ minute after being released.   The apparatus shall be free from all vibrations during the test.   Trial pastes shall be made with varying percentages of water until the normal consistency is obtained. The amount of water required shall be expressed in percentage by weight of the dry cement.

The consistency of standard mortar [1] shall depend on the amount of water required to produce a paste of normal consistency from the same sample of cement.   Having determined the normal consistency of the sample, the

[1] Probably the majority of cement testers determine normal consistency by the ball test.   This consists in forming the paste into a ball and dropping it onto the table from a height of 18 ins.   If of normal consistency the ball will neither flatten nor crack —the former if too wet and the latter if too dry.   Most cements require about 20 to 24% of water for normal consistency.

19

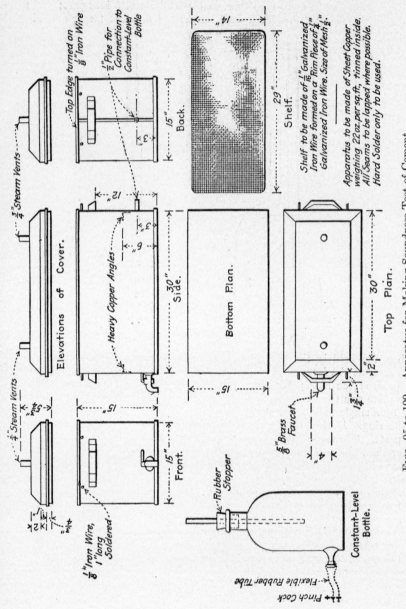

FIGS. 95 to 100. Apparatus for Making Soundness Test of Cement

consistency of standard mortar made from the same sample shall be as indicated in Table I, the values being in percentage of the combined dry weights of the cement and standard sand.

Soundness. A steam apparatus, which can be maintained at a temperature between 98° and 100° C., or one similar to that shown in Fig. 95, is recommended. The capacity of this apparatus may be increased by using a rack for holding the pats in a vertical or inclined position.

A pat from cement paste of normal consistency about 3 in. in diameter, ½ in. thick at the center, and tapering to a thin edge, shall be made on clean glass plates about 4 in. square, and stored in moist air for 24 hours. In molding the pat, the cement paste shall first be flattened on the glass and the pat then formed by drawing the trowel from the outer edge toward the center. (Fig. 101.)

The pat shall then be placed in an atmosphere of steam at a temperature between 98° and 100° C. upon a suitable support 1 in. above boiling water for 5 hours.

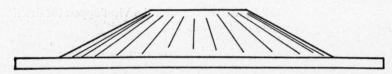

FIG. 101.   Pat for Determining Setting Time and Soundness

At the end of this time the pats should show no signs of cracking, distortion, or disintegration.   Distortion has not taken place if the pat sticks to the

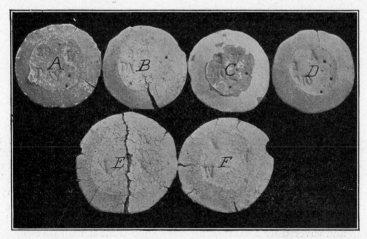

FIG. 102.   Appearance of Pats Made from Sound and Unsound Cement after Steaming

glass plate. Should it leave the plate, however, distortion may be detected by applying the edge of a ruler to the under side of the pat.

Fig. 102 shows six pats which have been steamed.   Pats *E* and *F* have almost entirely disintegrated, while *B* is somewhat better and *A* and *D* almost sound. Pat *C* has stood the test successfully.

The cracks due to disintegration should not be confused with those due to drying of the pat. The former are wedge shaped and radiate from the center of the pat, while the latter are usually running across the middle of the pat or around its edges. Shrinkage cracks due to drying are usually developed in a day, and are due to too thin (wet) a paste. The cracking of the glass to which the pat is attached during boiling means nothing to condemn the cement, and is due merely to unequal expansion of the pat and glass by the heat and a firm adhesion of the one to the other.

Where only a few tests have to be made, a convenient form of boiler consists of a tin bucket provided with a tin top. A few holes to permit exit of the steam are made in the top and a shelf of wire net or perforated tin is placed in the bucket. The pats are set on this and should be at least 2 in. above the water.

Setting Time. The following are alternate methods, either of which may be used as ordered:

The time of setting shall be determined with the Vicat apparatus described (refer to Normal Consistency). (See Fig. 94.)

TABLE I.—PERCENTAGE OF WATER FOR STANDARD MORTARS

Percentage of Water for Neat Cement Paste of Normal Consistency	Percentage of Water for One Cement, Three Standard Ottawa Sand	Percentage of Water for Neat Cement Paste of Normal Consistency	Percentage of Water for One Cement, Three Standard Ottawa Sand
15	9.0	23	10.3
16	9.2	24	10.5
17	9.3	25	10.7
18	9.5	26	10.8
19	9.7	27	11.0
20	9.8	28	11.2
21	10.0	29	11.3
22	10.2	30	11.5

A paste of normal consistency shall be molded in the hard-rubber ring *G* as described, and placed under the rod *B*, the smaller end of which shall then be carefully brought in contact with the surface of the paste, and the rod quickly released. The initial set shall be said to have occurred when the needle ceases to pass a point 5 mm. above the glass plate in $\frac{1}{2}$ minute after being released; and the final set, when the needle does not sink visibly into the paste. The test pieces shall be kept in moist air during the test. This may be accomplished by placing them on a rack over water contained in a pan and covered by a damp cloth, kept from contact with them by means of a wire screen; or they may be stored in a moist closet. Care shall be taken to keep the needle clean, as the collection of cement on the sides of the needle retards the penetration, while cement on the point may increase the penetration. The time of setting is affected not only by the percentage and temperature of the water used and the amount of kneading the paste receives, but by the temperature and humidity of the air, and its determination is therefore only approximate.

The time of setting shall be determined by the Gillmore needles. The Gillmore needles should preferably be mounted as shown in Fig. 103.

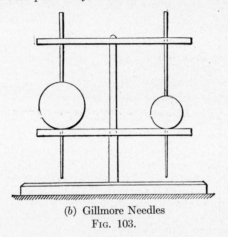

(b) Gillmore Needles
Fig. 103.

The time of setting shall be determined as follows: A pat of neat cement paste about 3 in. in diameter and $\frac{1}{2}$ in. in thickness with a flat top (Fig. 101), mixed to a normal consistency, shall be kept in moist air at a temperature maintained as nearly as practicable at 21° C. (70° F.). The cement shall be

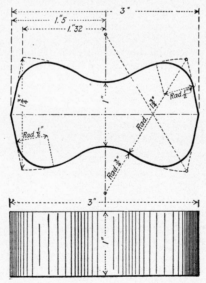

Fig. 104.   Details for Briquette

considered to have acquired its initial set when the pat will bear, without appreciable indentation, the Gillmore needle $\frac{1}{12}$ in. in diameter, loaded to weigh $\frac{1}{4}$ lb. The final set has been acquired when the pat will bear, without appreciable indentation, the Gillmore needle $\frac{1}{24}$ in. in diameter, loaded to weigh 1 lb. In making the test, the needles shall be held in a vertical position and applied lightly to the surface of the pat.

Tension Test. The form of test piece shown in Fig. 104 shall be used. The molds shall be made of non-corroding metal and have sufficient material in the sides to prevent spreading during molding. Gang molds when used shall be of the type shown in Fig. 105. Molds shall be wiped with an oily cloth before using.

The sand to be used shall be natural sand from Ottawa, Ill., screened to pass a No. 20 sieve and retained on a No. 30 sieve. This sand may be obtained from the Ottawa Silica Co., at a cost of three cents per pound, f. o. b cars, Ottawa, Ill.

This sand, having passed the No. 20 sieve, shall be considered standard when not more than 5 g. passes the No. 30 sieve after one minute continuous sieving of a 500-g. sample.

The sieves shall conform to the following specifications:

The No. 20 sieve shall have between 19.5 and 20.5 wires per whole inch of the warp wires and between 19 and 21 wires per whole inch of the shoot wires. The diameter of the wire should be 0.0165 in. and the average diameter shall not be outside the limits of 0.0160 and 0.0170 in.

The No. 30 sieve shall have between 29.5 and 30.5 wires per whole inch of the warp wires and between 28.5 and 31.5 wires per whole inch of the shoot wires. The diameter of the wire should be 0.0110 in. and the average diameter shall not be outside the limits 0.0105 to 0.0115 in.

Immediately after mixing, the standard mortar shall be placed in the molds, pressed in firmly with the thumbs and smoothed off with a trowel without ramming. Additional mortar shall be heaped above the mold and smoothed off with a trowel; the trowel shall be drawn over the mold in such a manner as to exert a moderate pressure on the material. The mold shall then be turned over and the operation of heaping, thumbing and smoothing off repeated.

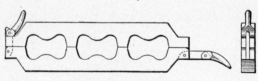

FIG. 105.   Gang Mold

Tests shall be made with any standard machine. The briquettes shall be tested as soon as they are removed from the water. The bearing surfaces of the clips and briquettes shall be free from grains of sand or dirt. The briquettes shall be carefully centered and the load applied continuously at the rate of 600 lb. per minute.

Testing machines should be frequently calibrated in order to determine their accuracy.

Briquettes that are manifestly faulty, or that give strengths differing more than 15 per cent from the average value of all test pieces made from the same sample and broken at the same period, shall not be considered in determining the tensile strength.

The moist closet may consist of a soapstone, slate or concrete box, or a wooden box lined with metal. If a wooden box is used, the interior should be covered with felt or broad wicking kept wet. The bottom of the moist closet should be covered with water. The interior of the closet should be provided with non-absorbent shelves on which to place the test pieces, the shelves being so arranged that they may be withdrawn readily.

Unless otherwise specified, all test pieces, immediately after molding, shall be placed in the moist closet for from 20 to 24 hours.

The briquettes shall be kept in molds on glass plates in the moist closet for at least 20 hours. After from 20 to 24 hours in moist air the briquettes shall be immersed in clean water in storage tanks of non-corroding material.

The air and water shall be maintained as nearly as practicable at a temperature of 21° C. (70° F.).

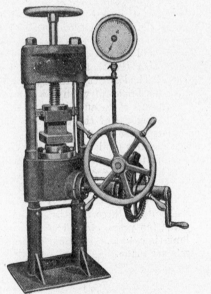

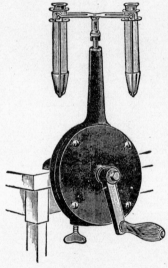

FIG. 105a. Olsen's Cement Hydraulic Compression Testing Machine.

FIG. 105b. Hand Power Centrifugal Machine.

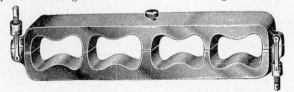

FIG. 105c. Brass Cement Briquette Gang Moulds.

The briquettes are then removed from the water at intervals and *immediately* broken by means of some form of testing machine. Fig. 106 shows the Fairbanks cement-testing machine. In this machine the briquette is held in the clips, N and N, and a stress is applied to it through the levers, C and R, by the weight of fine shot falling into the bucket, F. After the specimen breaks the stress required to rupture it is found by weighing the shot; the beam, R, being graduated for this purpose. In placing the briquette in the clips great care must be exercised to center it properly, as cross strains tend to lower the breaking strength. The briquettes must be broken as soon as they are removed from the water and the flow of shot into the bucket should be so regulated as to represent a load of about 600 lbs. per minute.

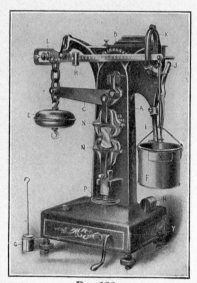

FIG. 106.
Fairbanks Cement-testing Machine.

Fig. 107 shows the Riehlé automatic cement-testing machine. This is a new type of machine which is coming into general use for cement testing, as it does away with some of the errors in the older form. In this type, the initial load is avoided by balancing a bucket of shot against a weight and the load is applied to the test specimen by allowing the shot to run out of the bucket. The load acting through the levers breaks the briquette when the shot is cut off by means of an automatic valve. The shot flowing out of the bucket are caught in a large cup resting on a spring scale which registers the load. This can be read as soon as the briquette breaks. The beam should be kept horizontal by means of the lever and worm gear as shown by the pointer on the beam.

Briquettes are usually broken in series from two to five each. The periods of breaking are after seven days, twenty-eight days, three months, six months, one year, two years, three years, five years, ten years, etc. The tests of one year and upwards are usually called long-time tests. In some laboratories only seven-day and twenty-eight-day tests are made.

The standard specifications require a minimum strength of 200 lbs. with sand after seven days, and 300 with sand after twenty-eight days, and also that the average figures in each case must be higher for the latter than for the former period.

The standard specifications now do not require a neat test to be made, but it is usually done for information.

Notes. After use, the moulds should be scraped free of hardened cement with a piece of soft metal (such as copper or zinc), brushed off with a stiff blacking brush, and wiped with a cloth and a little machine oil.

Neat briquettes should be marked with a stencil so as to identify them, and the sand briquettes placed in the water below the neat ones in such a manner as to identify the former. Usually the sand briquettes are placed edgewise in the water, and the corresponding neats are placed edgewise on top of the sand.

Small troughs or tanks consisting merely of galvanized iron pans, 3 ins. deep, may be purchased and will answer where only a few tests are to be made. Otherwise shallow wooden troughs lined with zinc will be found convenient. They may be placed one above the other.

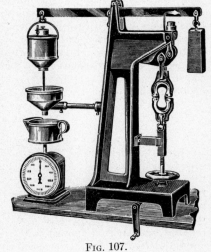

Fig. 107.
Riehlé Automatic Cement-testing Machine.

Apparatus Needed for Cement Testing. The following apparatus will be needed for cement testing:

1. Apparatus for specific gravity, Le Chatelier's.
2. Scale for fineness.
3. Sieve—100 mesh, standard.
4. Sieve—200 mesh, standard.
5. Vicat apparatus (or Gilmore needles).
6. Trowel—8 ins.
7. Rubber gloves.
8. Measuring glass—500 cc. capacity.
9. Slab of glass (or brass), 24×24 ins.
10. Scale, capacity, 1000 grams.
11. Weights for above scale.
12. Glass plates—4×4 ins.
13. Moulds.
14. Testing machine.
15. Standard sand.
16. Galvanized iron pan, 24×24×13 ins.

STANDARD METHOD FOR CHEMICAL ANALYSIS OF PORTLAND CEMENT [1]

Solution

One-half gram of the finely powdered substance is to be weighed out and, if a limestone or unburned mixture, strongly ignited in a covered platinum crucible over a strong blast for fifteen minutes, or longer if the blast is not powerful enough to effect complete conversion to a cement in this time. It is then transferred to an evaporating dish, preferably of platinum for the sake of celerity in evaporation, moistened with enough water to prevent lumping, and 5 to 10 cc. of strong HCl added and digested with the aid of gentle heat and agitation until solution is complete. Solution may be aided by light pressure with the flattened end of a glass rod.[2] The solution is then evaporated to dryness, as far as this may be possible on the bath.

Silica (SiO_2)

The residue without further heating is treated at first with 5 to 10 cc. of strong HCl, which is then diluted to half strength or less, or upon the residue may be poured at once a larger volume of acid of half strength. The dish is then covered and digestion allowed to go on for ten minutes on the bath, after which the solution is filtered and the separated silica washed thoroughly with water. The filtrate is again evaporated to dryness, the residue, without further heating, taken up with acid and water and the small amount of silica it contains separated on another filter paper. The papers containing the residue are transferred wet to a weighed platinum crucible, dried, ignited, first over a Bunsen burner until the carbon of the filter is completely consumed, and finally over the blast for fifteen minutes and checked by a further blasting for ten minutes or to constant weight. The silica, if great accuracy is desired, is treated in the crucible with about 10 cc. of HFl and 4 drops of H_2SO_4, and evaporated over a low flame to complete dryness. The small residue is finally blasted, for a minute or two cooled and weighed. The difference between this weight and the weight previously obtained gives the amount of silica.[3]

Alumina and Iron Oxide

The filtrate, about 250 cc., from the second evaporation for SiO_2, is made alkaline with NH_4OH after adding HCl, if need be, to insure a total of 10 to 15 cc. of strong acid, and boiled to expel excess of NH_3, or until there is but a faint odor of it, and the precipitated iron and aluminum hydrates, after settling, are washed once by decantation and slightly on the filter. Setting aside the filtrate, the precipitate is dissolved in hot dilute HCl, the solution passing into the

---

[1] Method Suggested for the Analysis of Limestones, Raw Mixtures, and Portland Cements by the Committee on Uniformity in Technical Analysis with the Advice of W. F. Hillebrand.

[2] If anything remains undecomposed it should be separated, fused with a little Na_2CO_2, dissolved and added to the original solution. Of course a small amount of separated non-gelatinous silica is not to be mistaken for undecomposed matter.

[3] For ordinary control in the plant laboratory this correction may, perhaps, be neglected; the double evaporation, never.

beaker in which the precipitation was made. The aluminum and iron are then reprecipitated by NH_4OH, boiled and the second precipitate collected and washed on the same filter used in the first instance. The filter paper, with the precipitate, is then placed in a weighed platinum crucible, the paper burned off and the precipitate ignited and finally blasted five minutes, with care to prevent reduction, cooled and weighed as $Al_2O_3+Fe_2O_3$.[1]

Iron Oxide (Fe_2O_3)

The combined iron and aluminum oxides are fused in a platinum crucible at a very low temperature with about 3 to 4 grams of $KHSO_4$, or, better, $NaHSO_4$, the melt taken up with so much dilute H_2SO_4 that there shall be no less than 5 grams absolute acid and enough water to effect solution on heating. The solution is then evaporated and eventually heated till acid fumes come off copiously. After cooling and redissolving in water, the small amount of silica is filtered out, weighed and corrected by HFl and H_2SO_4.[2] The filtrate is reduced by zinc, or preferably by hydrogen sulphide, boiling out the excess of the latter afterwards while passing CO_2 through the flask, and titrated with permanganate.[3] The strength of the permanganate solution should not be greater than .0040 gram Fe_2O_3 per cc.

Lime (CaO)

To the combined filtrate from the $Al_2O_3+Fe_2O_3$ precipitate a few drops of NH_4OH are added, and the solution brought to boiling. To the boiling solution 20 cc. of a saturated solution of ammonium oxalate are added, and the boiling continued until the precipitated CaC_2O_4 assumes a well-defined granular form. It is then allowed to stand for twenty minutes, or until the precipitate has settled, and then filtered and washed. The precipitate and filter are placed wet in a platinum crucible, and the paper burned off over a small flame of a Bunsen burner. It is then ignited, redissolved in HCl, and the solution made up to 100 cc. with water. Ammonia is added in slight excess, and the liquid is boiled. If a small amount of Al_2O_3 separates, this is filtered out, weighed, and the amount added to that found in the first determination, when greater accuracy is desired. The lime is then reprecipitated by ammonium oxalate, allowed to stand until settled, filtered, and washed,[4] weighed as oxide by ignition and blasting in a covered crucible to constant weight, or determined with dilute standard permanganate.[5]

Magnesia (MgO)

The combined filtrates from the calcium precipitates are acidified with HCl and concentrated on the steam bath to about 150 cc., 10 cc. of saturated solution

---

[1] This precipitate contains TiO_2, P_2O_5, Mn_3O_4.

[2] This correction of $Al_2O_3Fe_2O_3$ for silica should not be made when the HFl correction of the main silica has been omitted, unless that silica was obtained by only one evaporation and filtration. After two evaporations and filtrations 1 to 2 milligrams of SiO_2 are still to be found with the $Al_2O_3Fe_2O_3$.

[3] In this way only is the influence of titanium to be avoided and a correct result obtained for iron.

[4] The volume of wash-water should not be too large; vide W. F. Hildebrand.

[5] The accuracy of this method admits of criticism, but its convenience and rapidity demand its insertion.

of $Na(NH_4)HPO_4$ are added, and the solution boiled for several minutes. It is then removed from the flame and cooled by placing the beaker in ice water. After cooling, NH_4OH is added drop by drop with constant stirring until the crystalline ammonium-magnesium ortho-phosphate begins to form, and then in moderate excess, the stirring being continued for several minutes. It is then set aside for several hours in a cool atmosphere and filtered. The precipitate is redissolved in hot dilute HCl, the solution made up to 100 cc., 1 cc. of a saturated solution of $Na(NH_4)HPO_4$ added, and ammonia drop by drop, with constant stirring until the precipitate is again formed as described and the ammonia is in moderate excess. It is then allowed to stand for about two hours, when it is filtered on a paper or a Gooch crucible, ignited, cooled and weighed as $Mg_2P_2O_7$. Portland cement must not contain more than 4% magnesia.

A permissible variation of 0.4 will be allowed, and all results in excess of the specified limit but within this permissible variation shall be reported as 5.00 per cent.

Alkalies (K_2O and Na_2O)

For the determination of the alkalies, the well-known method of Prof. J. Lawrence Smith is to be followed, either with or without the addition of $CaCO_3$ with NH_4Cl.

Loss on Ignition

One gram of cement shall be heated in a weighed covered platinum crucible, of 20 to 25 cc. capacity, as follows, using either method (a) or (b) as ordered:

(a) The crucible shall be placed in a hole in an asbestos board, clamped horizontally so that about three-fifths of the crucible projects below, and blasted at a full red heat for 15 minutes with an inclined flame; the loss in weight shall be checked by a second blasting for 5 minutes. Care shall be taken to wipe off particles of asbestos that may adhere to the crucible when withdrawn from the hole in the board. Greater neatness and shortening of the time of heating are secured by making a hole to fit the crucible in a circular disk of sheet platinum and placing this disk over a somewhat larger hole in an asbestos board.

(b) The crucible shall be placed in a muffle at any temperature between 900° and 1000° C. for 15 minutes and the loss in weight shall be checked by a second heating for 5 minutes.

A permissible variation of 0.25 will be allowed, and all results in excess of the specified limit but within this permissible variation shall be reported as 4 per cent.

Insoluble Residue

To a 1 g. sample of cement shall be added 10 cc. of water and 5 cc. of concentrated hydrochloric acid; the liquid shall be warmed until effervescence ceases. The solution shall be diluted to 50 cc. and digested on a steam bath or hot plate until it is evident that decomposition of the cement is complete. The residue shall be filtered, washed with cold water, and the filter paper and contents digested in about 30 cc. of a 5 per cent solution of sodium carbonate, the liquid being held at a temperature just short of boiling for 15 minutes. The remaining residue shall be filtered, washed with cold water, then with a few drops of hot hydrochloric acid, 1 : 9, and finally with hot water, and then ignited at a red heat and weighed as the insoluble residue.

A permissible variation of 0.15 will be allowed, and all results in excess of the specified limit but within this permissible variation shall be reported as 0.85 per cent.

Sulphuric Anhydride

One gram of the cement shall be dissolved in 5 cc. of concentrated hydrochloric acid diluted with 5 cc. of water, with gentle warming; when solution is complete, 40 cc. of water shall be added, the solution filtered, and the residue washed thoroughly with water. The solution shall be diluted to 250 cc., heated to boiling, and 10 cc. of a hot 10 per cent solution of barium chloride shall be added slowly, drop by drop, from a pipette and the boiling continued until the precipitate is well formed. The solution shall be digested on the steam bath until the precipitate has settled. The precipitate shall be filtered, washed, and the paper and contents placed in a weighed platinum crucible and the paper slowly charred and consumed without flaming. The barium sulphate shall then be ignited and weighed. The weight obtained multiplied by 34.3 gives the percentage of sulphuric anhydride. The acid filtrate obtained in the determination of the insoluble residue may be used for the estimation of sulphuric anhydride instead of using a separate sample.

A permissible variation of 0.10 will be allowed, and all results in excess of the specified limit but within this permissible variation shall be reported as 2.00 per cent.

RAPID METHOD FOR CHEMICAL ANALYSIS OF PORTLAND CEMENT [1]

Before submitting the cement to a chemical analysis it should be passed through a No. 100 test sieve to free it from pieces of clinker too large to be quickly attacked by the acid.

Silica. Weigh 0.5 gram of cement into a wide platinum or porcelain dish. The former is the more expensive of the two, but it is a better conductor of heat and there is no danger of contaminating the solution with silica, etc., from the dish, if the evaporation is conducted in platinum. The silica can also be entirely removed from a platinum dish. Now stir up the sample of cement in the dish with 10 cc. of cold water until all lumps are broken up, and add immediately 10 cc. of cold dilute hydrochloric acid (1 : 1). Place the dish on a water bath and evaporate to dryness, stirring occasionally. The water bath will evaporate as fast as anything else and there is no danger of the silica's spattering, which it is apt to do, unless the operation is very carefully watched, when a hot plate is used. As soon as the contents of the dish are dry, cool, add 10 cc. of dilute hydrochloric acid and 30 cc. of water, digest five or ten minutes on the hot plate, filter and wash ten times with hot water. Evaporate the filtrate to dryness. Cool, add 10 cc. of dilute hydrochloric acid and 50 cc. of water to the contents of the dish, cover with a watch-glass and digest on the hot plate for five or ten minutes. Filter off the slight residue of silica on a 9-cm. filter, wash well (seven to ten times) with hot water and put in a weighed platinum crucible together with the silica obtained from the first filtration. Ignite over the Bunsen burner until all the filter paper is consumed and then ignite strongly over a blast lamp for ten minutes. Cool in a desiccator and weigh as SiO_2; multiply the weight by 200 for per cent of silica, SiO_2.

Alumina and Iron Oxide. Heat the filtrate to boiling and add a faint but distinct excess of ammonia. This can be most conveniently done by means of a bottle, fitted with a siphon tube, the end of which terminates in a jet, connected to it by a short piece of rubber tubing, which is closed by a pinchcock. The bottle stands on a shelf over the reagent table, and the siphon extends to within six inches of the surface of the table. The beaker is placed under the jet, and the ammonia can be very carefully and conveniently added by pressing the pinchcock. After adding the ammonia replace the beaker on the hot plate and boil for five minutes. Remove from the hot plate and allow the precipitate to settle. Filter onto an 11-cm. filter paper and wash once with hot water to collect the precipitate in the cone of the filter. Invert the funnel over the beaker in which the precipitation was made and wash practically all of the precipitate into this, allowing the filter to remain in the funnel. Dissolve the precipitate in 20 cc. of 10% nitric acid (1 : 10) and dilute the solution to 100 cc. Heat to boiling and reprecipitate with ammonia as before. Boil for five minutes, allow the precipitate to settle and filter through the same filter paper as used for the first precipitation. Wash once with hot water. Ignite carefully in a weighed crucible over a Bunsen burner and finally blast for five minutes. Cool and weigh as combined oxides of iron and alumina, Fe_2O_3 $+Al_2O_3$. This precipitate also contains manganese dioxide, phosphoric and titanic acids, all of which are present in small quantities in the cement. Deter-

[1] Method used in the laboratories of most cement companies and for routine work.

mine the iron oxide as directed further on, and deduct from the combined weights for the alumina, Al_2O_3 (phosphoric acid, titanic acid, etc.).

Lime. Make the filtrate from the iron and alumina alkaline with ammonia; boil and add 20 cc. of boiling saturated ammonium oxalate solution (or better, 3 grams of solid ammonium oxalate dissolved in 25–50 cc. of boiling water just prior to use). Stir well, allow fifteen minutes to settle, filter on an 11-cm. filter, and wash ten times with hot water, using as little as possible (about 100–125 cc.) to do the work well. Proceed as in A or B.

A. Gravimetric. Place the precipitate in a weighed platinum crucible, ignite, and weigh, after ignition over a blast-lamp to constant weight, as calcium oxide, CaO. Report as such.

B. Volumetric. Transfer the paper and precipitate to the beaker in which the latter was formed, and opening, spread it out against the upper side of the beaker. Wash the precipitate off the paper with a jet of hot water, fold the paper over, add 50 cc. of dilute (10%) sulphuric acid (1 : 10) to the contents of the beaker, dilute to 150 cc. and heat until the liquid is between 60 and 90° C. Titrate with permanganate solution until the pink color is produced. All this time the paper should be sticking to the walls of the beaker. Now drop this into the solution and stir. The pink color of the latter will be discharged. Finish the titration very carefully by adding permanganate, a drop at a time, and calculate the lime.

Magnesia. If the filtrate from the lime measures over 250 cc., acidify and evaporate until this bulk is reached. This can be rapidly done by using a large (8 in.) porcelain dish in the following manner: Place a piece of wire gauze on a tripod and in the center of this a round piece of thin asbestos paper about the size of a silver dollar. Now place the dish on this and a Bunsen burner turned fairly low under the asbestos dish. The contents of the dish can then be made to evaporate rapidly, without boiling, by regulating the flame. When the solution measures 250 cc., transfer to a beaker. If necessary, cool and, when perfectly cold, add 15 cc. of a 10% solution of sodium phosphate and 25 cc. of strong ammonia. Stir thoroughly and set aside in a cool place for at least six hours. Filter, wash with a mixture of water 800 cc., ammonia (0.96 sp.gr.) 200 cc., and ammonium nitrate 100 grams; place in a weighed platinum or porcelain crucible and ignite over a low flame until all carbon is burned off. (Do not use the blast lamp.) Cool in a desiccator and weigh as magnesium pyrophosphate, which weight multiplied by 72.38 gives the percentage of magnesia, MgO.

Iron Oxide. Weigh 1 gram of finely ground cement into a small beaker and add 15 cc. of dilute hydrochloric acid, heat from ten to fifteen minutes and add a little water. Heat to boiling and filter [1] through a small filter, washing the residue well with water and catching the filtrate and washings in a small beaker. Add to the solution 5 cc. of dilute hydrochloric acid and bring to a boil. Add carefully, drop by drop, stannous chloride solution (25 grams in 100 cc. of dilute 1 : 3 hydrochloric acid) until the last drop makes the solution colorless. Add 3 drops in excess. Remove from the burner and cool the liquid by setting in a vessel of cold water. When nearly cold, add 15 cc. of saturated mercuric chloride solution and stir the liquid with a glass rod. Allow the mixture to stand for a few minutes, during which time a slight

[1] May be omitted if the cement practically all dissolves. Most cements do.

white precipitate should form. Run in standard bichromate solution carefully from a burette until a drop of iron solution tested with a drop of 1% solution of potassium ferricyanide no longer shows a blue, but instead a yellow color. Multiply the number of cc. of bichromate used by the ferric oxide equivalent per cc. of the bichromate and divide the product by the weight of the sample. The result multiplied by 100 gives the per cent of the ferric oxide in the cement. The most convenient strength for the standard bichromate solution is 3.074 grams of the salt to the liter. One cc. of this solution is equivalent to 0.005 gram ferric oxide. It should be standardized against iron wire or ferrous ammonium sulphate.

Sulphuric Anhydride. Weigh 1 gram of the sample into a small dry beaker and stir it up with 10 cc. of cold water until all lumps are broken up and the lighter particles are in suspension. Add 7.5 cc. of dilute (1 : 1) hydrochloric acid and heat until solution is complete. Filter through a small paper and wash the residue thoroughly. Dilute the filtrate to 250 cc., heat to boiling, and add 10 cc. of boiling 10% barium chloride solution. Stir well and allow to stand overnight. Filter, ignite, and weigh as $BaSO_4$, which, multiplied by 34.29, gives the percentage of SO_3.

Loss on Ignition. Place one-half gram of the cement in a clean platinum crucible which has been previously ignited to redness and cooled in a desiccator. Cover with the lid and weigh. Ignite for fifteen minutes over a good blast lamp. Rinse off the crucible lid with hot water to remove volatile salts condensed on the latter. Ignite the lid to redness and cool the crucible and lid in a desiccator. Weigh and the loss in weight multiplied by 200 is " loss on ignition."

RAPID METHOD FOR CHECKING THE PERCENTAGE OF CALCIUM CARBONATE IN CEMENT MIXTURE

The following rapid method is generally used in the cement industry for checking the composition of the ground mixture of raw materials before these are fed into the kiln.

Standard Alkali

This should be exactly 2/5 normal and may be prepared in any convenient manner. Usually 8 or 10 liters are made up at one time and kept in a bottle provided with a siphon tube and with a layer of coal oil on top of the solution about $\frac{1}{2}$ in. thick to prevent the absorption of carbon dioxide by the caustic soda.

Phenolphthalein should be used as an indicator. A 1% solution of this is employed.

One cc. of 2/5 N alkali is equivalent to exactly 0.02 gram of $CaCO_3$ or to 2% where 1-gram sample is used.

Standard Acid

Take the specific gravity of a bottle of hydrochloric acid, using a hydrometer for the purpose. Refer to a table of specific gravities of hydrochloric acid and calculate from this the quantity of acid necessary to contain 97.0 grams of HCl.

Measure this quantity of the acid into a liter flask and dilute to the mark, pour into an 8-liter bottle and add 7 liters of water, measuring with the flask. Mix the contents of the bottle well by shaking. Ten cc. of this solution should be equivalent to from 8.1 to 8.5 cc. of the 2/5 N alkali when checked by adding a drop of phenolphthalein solution and running in the alkali to a purple red color. If its value does not lie between these figures add acid or water to make it of this strength.

Standard Sample

A standard sample of raw material is necessary to standardize the acid and alkali for actual use. This sample should be ground in the same manner as the daily run of samples to be checked by the acid and alkali. It should all pass a 100-mesh sieve and be freed from hygroscopic moisture, by drying for some hours, at 110° C. Three or four pounds of this sample should be prepared and kept in air-tight jars or bottles. A small sample (1 or 2 oz.) of this should be placed in a 2-oz. bottle and stoppered with a rubber cork when not in use. This small sample can then be redried for an hour at 100–110° C. and used for standardizing, avoiding the frequent opening and mixing of the contents of the large jars or bottles.

After drying, the standard sample should be carefully analyzed. It should contain approximately the quantity of carbonate of lime which it is desired to have in the mix, and the amount of magnesia should also be normal. When the magnesia varies at different times, fresh standard samples should be prepared to contain these varying percentages of magnesia; otherwise the lime will be reported incorrectly.

20

Standardizing the Acid

Weigh 1 gram of the standard sample into a 600-cc. Erlenmeyer flask and run in from a pipette 50 cc. of standard acid. Close the flask with a rubber stopper, having inserted through it a long glass tube 30 ins. long and about ⅜ in. internal diameter. Heat the flask on a wire gauze over a burner as shown in Fig.107a until steam *just begins* to escape from the upper end of the tube. The heating should be so regulated that the operation requires very nearly two minutes, from the time the heat applied, until steam issues from the tube. Remove the flask from the heat, as soon as the steam escapes from the tube, and rinse the tube into the flask, in the following manner. Rest the flask, still stoppered, on the table and grasp the tube between the thumb and forefinger of the left hand. Direct a stream of cold water, from a wash-bottle in the right hand, down the tube, holding the latter inclined at an angle of 45°, and rolling the flask from side to side on the table, in sweeps of 2 or 3 ft., by twirling the tube between the finger and thumb. Unstopper the flask and rinse off the .ides and bottom of the stopper, into the flask, and wash down the sides of the latter. Add a drop or two of phenolphthalein and run in the standard alkali, from a burette, until the color changes to purple red. This color is often obscured until the organic matter settles, so it is necessary to hold the flask to the light and observe the change by glancing across the surface. A little practice will easily enable the operator to carry on the titration with accuracy and precision.

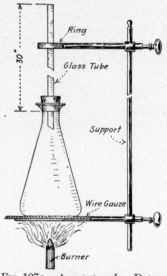

Fig. 107a.—Apparatus for Determining Calcium Carbonate with Acid and Alkali.

If the standard sample contains L per cent carbonate of lime and d cc. of alkali are required to produce the purple red color, then, to find the carbonate of lime in other samples it is only necessary to subtract the number of cc. of alkali required in their case from d, multiply the difference by 2, and add to L for the percentage of carbonate of lime in them; or the number of cc. is greater than d, subtract d from this number, multiply by 2, and subtract from L for the carbonate of lime.

In order to avoid all calculations, prepare a table giving the various percentages of carbonate of lime corresponding to different quantities of alkali.

Determination

Weigh 1 gram of the sample, which has been ground to pass a 100-mesh sieve, into the flask, add 50 cc. of the standard acid and proceed as directed under standardizing the acid. The percentage of carbonate of lime may be found from the number of cc. of alkali used either from the preceding table or by the formula

$$\text{Per cent } CaCO_3 = L + (d - S) \times 2,$$

where L and d have the same values as in the paragraph on "Standardizing the Acid" and S represents the number of cc. required for the sample whose composition is desired.

ANALYSIS OF LIMESTONE, CEMENT ROCK, LIME, ROSENDALE CEMENT, ETC.

Dr. Porter W. Shimer, of Easton, Pa., modifies the standard limestone scheme by fusing the sample with half its weight of sodium carbonate. By this means the silicates are decomposed, and yet the quantity of sodium carbonate introduced into the solution is so small that the lime and magnesia precipitates are not contaminated with sodium salts. Below is the method.

Silica, etc. Mix thoroughly 0.5 gram of the finely ground sample with $\frac{1}{4}$ gram of sodium carbonate. Place over a low flame for a few minutes, then gradually raise the flame. Heat over the full flame for five minutes and then over the blast lamp for five minutes. There will be no complete fusion, only a sintering. Put the crucible in a small beaker or casserole and add 30 cc. of water and 10 cc. of hydrochloric acid (sp.gr. 1.10). When the mass is dissolved out of the crucible, rinse the latter off into the beaker and remove any adhering matter with a rubber-tipped rod. To the solution in the beaker or casserole add a little bromine water or a few drops of nitric acid, evaporate to dryness and proceed as directed in the analysis of Portland cement.

For loss on ignition, weigh into a tared platinum crucible 0.5 gram of the sample. Heat at first over a low flame, then gradually raise the temperature and finally ignite over a blast lamp until it ceases to lose weight on reheating. Report such loss in weight as "loss on ignition."

To determine iron and alumina separately, fuse the precipitated ferric oxide and alumina with caustic potash in a silver crucible or dish. Treat with water, boil, and filter. Ignite the residue after washing and weigh as ferric oxide. This weight subtracted from the combined weight of the ferric oxide and alumina gives the weight of the alumina, Al_2O_3.

To determine alkalies in limestone use the method described for clay, employing 8 grams of the sample and 1 gram of ammonium chloride, but no calcium carbonate.

CEMENT

Portland Cement	SiO₂	Insol. M.	Al₂O₃	Fe₂O₃	CaO	MgO	SO₃	CO₂	H₂O	Alkalies, etc.
Typical sample	22.0	1.0	7.5	3.5	62.0	1.0	1.5	0.5	0.5	0.5
Extremes	18 to 27	—	5 to 10	0 to 7+	58 to 67	0–3	x to 2.75	variable	variable	x to 2
Kent-Essex	19.62	5.86	10.20	7.44	44.54	2.92	2.61	3.42	0.25	1.46 MnO = 1.57
Natural Cement	19 to 28	—	2.5 to 9	1 to 6.5	35 to 62	0.4 to 20	—	CO₂ + Loss = 0.3 to 15 +		

Natural Cement, raw product: See magnesian limestone under raw materials below.

CEMENT RAW MATERIALS

	Sand	Comb. SiO₂	Al₂O₃	Fe₂O₃	CaO	MgO	SO₃	CO₂	H₂O	Alkalies and Loss
Chalk	0.93	0.43	0.48		42.90	0.42		34.16	19.03	1.65
Clay	28.42	30.30	15.49	7.74	2.04	1.96	1.96		12.07	
Limestone	0.20		0.08	0.08	56.02	0.24		43.38	0.18	
Magnesian limestones		60.22	27.20		trace	1.62		4.54		6.42
Marl		22.77	10.43		34.54	21.85	1.44	2.84	2.50	3.63
Shale		15.10	7.30		42.16	0.34		33.51		1.59

ANALYSIS OF INDUSTRIAL GASES

Determination of the Calorific Value and of Operating Conditions from Analysis of Industrial Gases [1]

Industrially, the word GAS is restricted to substances which are used for burning for either light, heat or power, and while we speak of illuminating gas, or of fuel gas, we must remember that any industrial gas is a complex mixture of a number of diverse constituents.

There may be a vast difference between one gas and another gas, and there is a possibility of even vaster differences between mixtures of gases when the mixtures are made up of a number of constituents, and the nature of any such mixture can be profoundly effected by changes in the relative percentages of its component parts.

The importance of an analysis of the many forms of gas either produced or consumed in ordinary industrial processes is not thoroughly appreciated. If the great economic value of the light shed upon the condition of the machines, the fires, the retorts, the furnaces, the engines, or other gas-making or gas-using apparatus by a gas analysis were better understood, and if the simplicity and economy of the apparatus, and the ease of the process of analysis were more apparent, this form of research and this aid to station operations would be more nearly universal.

A deficit of air in boiler firing will result in the incomplete burning of fuel to carbon monoxide and the production of 4500 heat units to the pound instead of to carbon dioxide and the production of 14,500. An excess of air will overflow a fire, dilute and chill the flue gases and cause the needless heating of large quantities of air which escape up the stack. Too much or too little air will often cause boilers to work at a lower efficiency than can be offset by superior fuel, patented grates, damper regulators or high-priced settings.

An analysis of chimney or flue gas will tell definitely and accurately the conditions as to the air supply of a boiler.

An analysis of the exhaust from a gas engine will tell whether there is too little air and incomplete combustion which lowers the efficiency of the engine and affects the power bill, or whether there is an excess of air which takes the place of the mixture of gas in the cylinder, and thus lowers the available horse power.

In gas works, in iron and steel plants, with gas producers, in all forms of furnaces and for ventilating purposes, an analysis of the gas will give information upon the condition of the apparatus, will detect leaks of air, or gas, and will serve as an index to the character of the changes taking place inside of the apparatus. All of which knowledge can be turned by the manager to most advantageous economical account.

The chemical and physical examination of gas is in and constitutes a branch of chemistry and of physics peculiar to itself. The very nature of the gas business makes the requirements peculiar.

In other branches of analytical chemistry there is always some stock of material on hand from which a second sample can be drawn, or a check analysis of the sample already taken can be made, but under ordinary conditions

[1] Abstracted from a paper written for the fifth annual meeting of the American Gas Institute, 1910, by J. M. Morehead.

there is never any considerable stock of gas on hand, and to have any value at all a gas analysis must be finished and reported within a very few hours of the time when the sample is taken, otherwise the gas of which the sample was a part is gone, and while the results may have some interest as a record of what the plant *has* done, it can be of no value as an indication of what the plant *is* doing and to have such value a method which can be carried out in a short time must be available, and dispatch in the performance of the analysis is an essential.

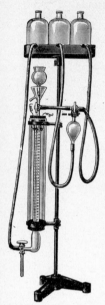

There is practically only one method of gas analysis. This was worked out many years ago by Bunsen, Hempel and Winkler, and consists in the successive absorption with different chemicals of the various constituents of the gas. Various modifications of this method are used with the different types of apparatus now employed.

The principal designs of gas-analyzing apparatus may be grouped into two classes. First, those which keep the reagents in what may be called a stationary position and pass the gas through the reagents, using the same chemicals over and over, and second, those which keep the gas in a stationary position and pass the chemicals through the gas, using the chemicals in this case only once.

The apparatus of the first class has the advantage of greater economy in chemicals and is not so sloppy in use, but these advantages are more than offset by the fact that the analyst never knows just when the solutions are exhausted below a point where they will give accurate results.

Fig. 107*b*. The Morehead Gas Burette in Use.[1]

There can be no such uncertainty with apparatus of the second class as fresh solutions are always being used and there is no possibility of the chemical having been weakened or exhausted by previous analyses.

As examples of apparatus of the first class we may mention the many forms of the Hempel type and also the many modifications of the original apparatus devised by Orsat and which usually bear his name compounded with that of the modifier. There are also many examples of the second class the best of which are undoubtedly the Elliott and Morehead systems—the latter being by far more recent has had the opportunity to avoid the bad or undesirable features of the former and we shall confine ourselves to this type only.

All modern designs of gas-analyzing apparatus come under these two heads and are modifications of what might be called these two standard types.

The Morehead apparatus consists of a single graduated, water-jacketed burette which is also provided with explosion points. The measuring, absorption, explosion and in fact the entire analysis being performed in the one burette, without necessity for movement of the sample. This apparatus is quite simple in design, economical in first cost, requires little training for its use and is quite rapid. As there is only the one burette, the necessity of shifting the sample is obviated, and an entire analysis of seven determinations can be

[1] By courtesy of E. H. Sargent and Co., Chicago.

made in from 30 to 40 minutes. Results obtained by different sets of this apparatus in the hands of different analysts working on the same gas, or results obtained by the same analyst working at different times on the same gas, are quite consistent and the calculations of calorific value from analyses made with this apparatus agree remarkably closely with determinations of the calorific value made with Junker's calorimeter.

Constituents

By analysis industrial gases are usually divided into their seven constituents, as follows:

Carbon dioxide...	CO_2
Illuminants...	Ill.
Oxygen..	O_2
Carbon monoxide.......................................	CO
Hydrogen..	H_2
Methane...	CH_4
Nitrogen...	N_2

The order in which the constituents are given being that in which the determinations are made.

These constituents exist in varying and in widely different proportions in different industrial gases, and in the same industrial gas proportions vary from day to day and with every change of operation. The characteristics of these constituents vary widely, but they may be grouped into a number of classes. Three of them—O_2, H_2 and N_2—are chemical elements, two—CO_2 and CO—are combinations of C and O; two—CH_4 and the Ill—are a combination of C and H. Five of the seven—O_2, CO, H_2, CH_4 and N_2—are permanent gases, one—CO_2—is usually termed a gas, but as it can be liquefied at ordinary temperatures it must be classified as a vapor, while one—Ill—consists of part permanent gases and part vapors. Four of the seven—Ill, CO, H_2 and CH_4—contribute all of the lighting and heating value, while three—CO_2, O_2 and N_2—will not burn, are direct impurities and detract from the thermal and illuminating value made up by the others. Of the four—Ill, CO, H_2 and CH_4—which form the bulk of a gas and give it its value, two—CO and H_2—burn with a rather low heating value and no light, one—CH_4—contributes very largely to the heating value but does not raise the candle-power, while one—Ill—increases the heating value and contributes practically all of the open flame illuminating value.

Separately considered, these constituents exhibit the following principal characteristics:

All figures given are for dry gases at 60° F. and 30" of mercury.

The percentages are for volume—not weight—and the same applies for combustion in air—not oxygen.

CARBONIC ACID OR CARBON DIOXIDE

Formula.................................	CO_2
Composition by weight....................	72.73% O—27.27% C
Density or specific gravity, air = 1	1.519
Lbs. per cubic foot.......................	0.1162
Cubic feet per lb.........................	8.606
Cubic feet air necessary to consume one cubic foot...................................	Non-combustible
Gross B.t.u. per cubic foot................	Non-combustible
Solubility, vols. absorbed in 1 vol. water......	1.005

Carbon Dioxide or Carbonic Acid is one of the commonest of all gases. It is the product of combustion, of fermentation, of decay, of putrefaction, or of animal or human respiration in the presence, if not of an excess, certainly of a sufficiency, of air or of oxygen. Carbon dioxide occurs in the air to the extent of about five parts in 10,000 unless the air is polluted, then the proportion is higher. CO_2 is the gas which absorbed in water gives soda or sparkling water. It is also the "After Damp," "Choke Damp" or "Black Damp" found in mines after an explosion. While small quantities of this gas are not poisonous and may be taken into the stomach or into the lungs with impunity, 0.1% of CO_2 in air is about the limit for breathing with comfort, 5% will cause headache and languor, 4% to 6% will affect a candle flame, 8% to 10% will eventually cause death from suffocation, 12% to 15% will extinguish a candle flame.

In CO_2 the carbon has all of the oxygen with which it can combine, it is already completely burned and incapable of further combustion.

Carbon dioxide is an impurity and its presence is a detriment to any industrial gas which is intended for further burning. Air added to the gas before it is out of the fire will increase the CO_2, or steam which passed through the fire will produce CO_2 in a water gas process by reaction with the CO. Its presence shows that some of the gas or of the fuel is already consumed, and in a way CO_2 in a gas is analogous to ashes in a coal pile. Owing to its high specific heat CO_2 will lower the candle-power of illuminating gas between 2% and 4% for each 1% present.

Carbon dioxide is an acid and almost any alkali will absorb, neutralize and remove it. Potassium hydroxide is the best absorbent unless very small quantities of this gas are being dealt with, as in air analysis, or where extreme accuracy is required, when the more expensive barium hydroxide is to be preferred.

ILLUMINANTS OR HEAVY HYDROCARBONS

FORMULA	Ethylene C_2H_4
Composition by weight	Ethylene 85.62% C—14.38% H
Density or sp. gr., air = 1	Ethylene 0.985
Lbs. per cubic foot	Ethylene 0.074
Cubic feet per lb	Ethylene 13.38
Cu. ft. air necessary to consume one cu. ft.	Ethylene 14.34
Solubility, vols. absorbed in 1 vol. water	Ethylene 0.15

"Illuminants" is a term used to designate a group of different gases and vapors, and is unlike carbon dioxide, carbon monoxide, etc., which refer to single definite chemical compounds.

Illuminants are derived for the most part from the decomposition or "cracking" due to the moderate heating of organic compounds or mixtures, such as coal, petroleum, oils, fats, resins, etc., and to a large extent consist of so-called "unsaturated" compounds, or compounds which have the ability to unite or add to themselves certain elements or other compounds.

"Heavy hydrocarbons" are mainly dense and complex combinations of carbon and hydrogen which upon being heated readily break up into hydrogen and relatively large amounts of carbon. The carbon set free by the illuminants in a gas flame is to a great measure the cause of luminosity or candle-power of that flame.

The heavy hydrocarbons are for the most part poisonous if inhaled or swallowed, but they are so widely among themselves that no definite figures can be given as to the percentages which carry toxic properties. It may be said of them, however, that in their physiological effect they resemble the vegetable rather than the mineral poisons, i.e., the effect is soporific or stupefying rather than violently active, as is the case of carbon monoxide or cyanogen.

Illuminants vary in percentage in any one gas, and differ widely in composition and in characteristics in different gases. The illuminants of a carburetted water gas consist mainly of ethylene with other members of the olefine series and various other complex hydrocarbons existing either as gases or vapors. The illuminants will also vary in percentage and in composition in the same gas upon standing, on account of the fact that many members of the family in such a gas are vapors which gradually condense into liquid form and hence change the general quantity and nature of the residual mixture of heavy hydrocarbons.

Ether, Turpentine, Petroleum, Olive Oil, Fuming Sulphuric Acid or Bromine will each absorb illuminants and may be used for this purpose, but the last named is the most satisfactory.

Acetylene behaves as an illuminant. Pure bromine will absorb 100% of it.

Oxygen

FORMULA..O_2
Composition by weight...........................100% O_2
Density or specific gravity, air = 1.............. 1.105
Lbs. per cubic foot............................. 0.0845
Cubic feet per lb............................... 11.83
Cubic feet air necessary to consume one cubic foot..Non-combustible
Gross B.t.u. per cubic foot.....................Non-combustible
Solubility, vols. absorbed in 1 vol. water.......... 0.039

Oxygen occurs free and forms 23.2% by weight and 20.8% by volume of the atmosphere—the rest being nitrogen—and it is the supporter of combustion and of animal and of vegetable life. Straight oxygen of 100% purity may be breathed without deleterious effect other than temporary giddiness and headache from over-stimulation. While air containing as low as $7\frac{1}{2}$% of oxygen—the remainder being pure nitrogen—will sustain human life.

Free oxygen found in gases in almost every instance comes from air which is mixed, intentionally or otherwise, with the gas, and when from this source it carries along with it four times its volume of inert nitrogen. The presence of oxygen itself is not detrimental to a gas, in fact, if the quantity of oxygen was not sufficient to carry an explosive hazard, its presence would be a benefit. A mixture of pure oxygen with gas would give a sharper, cleaner explosion in a gas engine, would have a higher candle-power in an open flame burner, and a much higher flame temperature and candle-power when used with a mantle than would be the same gas without oxygen, but oxygen keeps very bad company and of the fourfold volume of nitrogen with which it is always accompanied, and of whose presence it is an indication, not one single word of commendation can be said.

It is almost impossible to get any industrial gas absolutely free from oxygen. This element along with its partner may come into gases from air dissolved in the water, or in the oil used in the processes, or from air held in the pores or interstices of the fuel, bricks, carbide, purifying material, etc. The presence of considerable quantities of free oxygen, if accompanied by nitrogen in approximately the proportion of air, is always evidence of an air leak, or of the use of excessive quantities of air, though the absence of free oxygen does not necessarily imply that there is no such leak because oxygen is so energetic that it may be absorbed, or if mixed before the gas is cooled below its ignition point, it will combine with hydrogen and disappear as water vapor, or combine with the carbon and appear as carbonic acid or carbonic oxide leaving the nitrogen.

A high percentage of oxygen is an indication of a leak after the gas has passed out of the hot parts of the process, or the use of too much air for purification or for other purposes, or what is very often the case, of carelessness in taking the sample or in performing the analysis. Oxygen may be absorbed by yellow phosphorus, or by an alkaline solution of pyrogallic acid, of which the latter is the better.

Carbonic Oxide or Carbon Monoxide

FORMULA................................CO
Composition by weight..................... 42.85% C—57.15% O
Density or specific gravity, air = 1.......... 0.967
Lbs. per cubic foot........................ 0.07394
Cubic feet per lb.......................... 13.53
Cubic feet air necessary to consume one cubic
  foot.................................... 2.38
Gross B.t.u. per cubic foot.................323
Solubility, vols. absorbed in 1 vol. water...... 0.0256

Carbon Monoxide or Carbonous Oxide found in gases comes from the incomplete combustion of fuel. If there is a sufficiency of air, almost every fuel will burn to CO_2, water and ash, while a deficit of oxygen results in partial combustion of carbon to CO instead of in complete combustion to CO_2. The CO thus produced is half-burned carbon and will burn to CO_2 if subsequently supplied with additional air or oxygen and ignited. CO is produced also if a gas flame, either luminous or Bunsen, comes in contact with a cold or a sooty surface.

CO is the poisonous constituent of gases, 0.05% being sufficient to cause giddiness, 0.1% will bring about inability to walk, 0.2% loss of consciousness and 1% will produce death after a few minutes of inhalation.

CO like hydrogen is valuable principally on account of the volume which it gives to an industrial gas, and as a carrier for the vapors, etc., forming the illuminants. It possesses no candle-power but its 323 B.t.u. per foot contribute to the calorific value.

In gases for burning, a high percentage of CO is evidence of good working conditions, especially if there is at the same time little or no CO_2.

The best absorbent for carbon monoxide is a hydrochloric acid solution of copper monochloride.

HYDROGEN

FORMULA	H_2
Composition by weight	100% H
Density or specific gravity, air = 1	0.0692
Lbs. per cubic foot	0.005321
Cubic feet per lb.	187.9
Cubic feet air necessary to consume one cubic foot	2.39
Gross B.t.u. per cubic foot	326
Solubility, vols. absorbed in 1 vol. water	0.019

Hydrogen, generally known as a gas, is in reality a metal and is the lightest of all known substances. It does not exist free in nature. In industrial gases it is produced by the breaking up of water by hot carbon or by the excessive heating of some of the hydrocarbons introduced in the shape of oil or coal for the purpose of adding illuminants, or by the action of some acid on certain metals. Excessive temperatures in a gas machine will result in the breaking down of any illuminant or other hydrocarbon into lampblack and hydrogen.

The presence of steam in the carburetter or superheater of a water gas machine, or of wet coal in a retort, will produce hydrogen by combination with CO according to the formula:

$$CO + H_2O = CO_2 + H_2.$$

Like CO, hydrogen adds to the volume of a gas and acts as a carrier of the other constituents. It is without candle-power itself but its 326 B.t.u. per cubic foot contribute to the calorific value.

Hydrogen is without physical effect and probably stands next to nitrogen for inertness from this standpoint.

There is no satisfactory liquid absorbent for hydrogen. To determine its percentage it is caused to burn in an excess of oxygen with which it combines to the extent of one half its volume and forms water—H_2O—this condenses and from the contraction the percentage of hydrogen is calculated.

Hydrogen can be determined also by use of a "Palladium Tube." This method has to be used where the gas has, in addition to methane, ethane or other bodies of the methane series which have to be separated from the methane. It is also useful as a check on the other method but for ordinary use it is too cumbersome and costly, and requires too long a time and too high a degree of analytical ability to make it preferable to the regular explosion method.

METHANE OR MARSH GAS

FORMULA	CH_4
Composition by weight	74.86% C—25% H
Density or specific gravity, air = 1	0.553
Lbs. per cubic foot	0.04233
Cubic feet per lb.	23.62
Cubic feet air necessary to consume one cubic foot	9.5617
Gross B.t.u. per cubic foot	1009
Solubility, vols. absorbed in 1 vol. water	0.0386

Methane or " Marsh Gas." In industrial gases this constituent comes from the distillation of oil or of coal at fairly high temperatures. This hydrocarbon is the active element of natural gas and of "Fire Damp" found in mines, and was probably produced at some remote geological period when measures of soft coal or oil deposits were subjected to excessive temperatures. It is produced in nature by decay out of the presence of oxygen or of air, such as the slow decay of animal or of vegetable matter under water, hence the name of marsh gas.

Methane is without physiological effect and mixtures of it in air up to even 45% or 50% may be breathed and the discomfort experienced even then is probably more due to the want of oxygen than to the presence of methane.

After the illuminants have been distilled off of oil or of coal, or when the temperatures are too high for their production, methane is produced, or it may result from a partial breaking down of illuminants due to excessive temperatures which are not quite high enough to effect complete decomposition into lampblack and hydrogen. Methane having a c.p. of from 2 to 7 does not add especially to the illuminating value of a gas, but owing to its high calorific value it is of very great value in raising the B.t.u. of any gas in which it appears.

There is no known absorbent of methane but when this hydrocarbon combines with oxygen it produces its own volume of CO_2 which may be subsequently absorbed by KOH, and from the contraction the volume of methane originally contained may be calculated.

NITROGEN

FORMULA..N_2
Composition by weight.........................100% N
Density or specific gravity, air = 1.............. 0.971
Lbs. per cubic foot............................ 0.07413
Cubic feet per lb.............................. 13.49
Cubic feet air necessary to consume one cubic foot...Non-combustible
Gross B.t.u. per cubic foot.....................Non-combustible
Solubility, vols. absorbed in 1 vol. water.......... 0.105

Nitrogen is the dead, inert, effete or worn-out member of the family of elements. It exists free in nature, forming 77% by weight and 79% by volume of the atmosphere, the rest being oxygen. It is not poisonous, but will not support life or combustion. Nitrogen of 100% purity may be inhaled with perfect impunity until distress comes about from want of oxygen, or nitrogen may be swallowed or injected into the cavities of the body without effect. Nitrogen has only a few combinations with the other elements, and can not be made to form these without a good deal of difficulty, and when it is in combination it comes out with great emphasis upon very small provocation. Practically all modern explosives consist of nitrogen held in some form of unstable combination, and a dynamite, nitro-glycerine, guncotton, or gunpowder explosion is nothing more or less than this element dissociating from some unwilling union.

Nitrogen is not affected by extremes of temperature, or by ordinary chemical reagents. It passes into the stomach or lungs of animals, or into the fire of the gas engine, gas furnace, or of a gas burner as nitrogen and comes out again as nitrogen. In the analysis of gases every other constituent is absorbed, dissolved or burned, and what is left unchanged after the drastic treatment with a number of diverse chemicals and an explosition with pure oxygen is nitrogen.

The presence of some nitrogen in gas is unavoidable and like oxygen is usually evidence of air. Nitrogen like other incombustible impurities in gas lowers the calorific value just in proportion to its presence, but affects the candle-power to a greater extent. It may come from the same sources as those mentioned for oxygen, or in coal or in water gas is left from the air added for purposes of revivification. As there is no practical absorbent for nitrogen, it is determined by difference; the difference between the sum of the percentages of the other constituents and 100 is taken to be the percentage of this element.

AIR

FORMULA.................................Mixture O_2 and N_2
Composition by weight....................76.83% N—23.17% O_2
Density or specific gravity, air = 1........... 1.000
Lbs. per cubic foot......................... 0.07657
Cubic feet per lb..........................11.91
Cubic feet air necessary to consume one cubic
  foot...................................Non-combustible
Gross B.t.u. per cubic foot.................Non-combustible
Solubility, vols. absorbed in 1 vol. water...... 0.0178

Air is a mechanical mixture of oxygen and nitrogen. It usually contains small and varying percentages of moisture, dust, CO_2 and other impurities, though not in quantities which may be detected without special apparatus and methods.

An analysis of a typical sample of mountain or of sea air would be about as follows:

	Per cent
Nitrogen, N_2	78.35
Oxygen, O_2	20.77
Water vapor, H_2O	0.83
Carbon dioxide, CO_2	0.05
	100.00

Deducting the H_2O and CO_2, we would have:

Oxygen by volume, 20.96% By weight, 23.17%
Nitrogen by volume, 79.04% By weight, 76.83%

The ratios of the constituents by volume are:

Vol. oxygen $\times 4.77$ = vol. air.
Vol. oxygen $\times 3.77$ = vol. nitrogen.
Vol. nitrogen $\times 1.26$ = vol. air.
Vol. nitrogen $\times 0.265$ = vol. oxygen.
Vol. air $\times 0.791$ = vol. nitrogen.
Vol. air $\times 0.209$ = vol. oxygen.

No exact figures can be given which indicate definitely the proportion of the deficit of oxygen or the content of CO_2 in air at which point the air becomes dangerous to breath. If the oxygen is abstracted chemically, or pure CO_2 added, mixtures covering a very wide range indeed may be inhaled with impunity. But oxygen is almost invariably extracted and CO_2 added by some process by which other impurities are added at the same time, and these are very apt to render the air unfit for breathing before this condition would become evident from an analysis showing merely the oxygen, nitrogen and CO_2 content of the sample taken. From a hygienic standpoint, however, it is always wise to regard with grave suspicion any air showing from 0.5% to 2% of CO_2 or 5% less than the normal amount of oxygen, while air showing as much as 5% of CO_2 or any appreciable percentage of any other impurity—especially CO—is positively poison.

Air affects the calorific value of a gas as do other non-combustible impurities, just to the extent and in direct proportion to the percentage present, but like the other impurities in the same class it affects the candle-power to a far greater extent. Comparatively low candle-power illuminating gases such as coal gas of about 16 c.p. suffer more from an air admixture than does a higher c.p. water gas. 1% of air mixed with coal gas will take off about 8% of its candle-power, 4% of air 25%, and 45% of air will render the flame practically non-luminous.

With a good quality of water gas of 25 candle-power the admixture has a fairly constant effect of removing from 2% to 2.5% of the candle-power for each 1% of air present.

The analysis of air for its three constituents which may be determined by ordinary methods, and with ordinary apparatus, consists of the absorption of CO_2 with KOH, or with barium hydroxide, and of the oxygen by pyrogallate of potassium or with yellow phosphorus, the nitrogen being the difference.

ACETYLENE

FORMULA	C_2H_2
Composition by weight	92.29% C—7.71% H
Density or specific gravity, air = 1	0.898
Lbs. per cubic foot	0.0687
Cubic feet per lb.	14.56
Cubic feet air necessary to consume one cubic foot	11.91
Gross B.t.u. per cubic foot	1474
Solubility, vols. absorbed in 1 vol. water	1.11

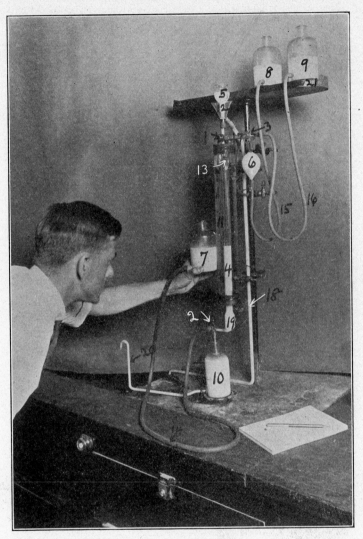

FIG. 107c. Morehead Gas Burette in Use.

Acetylene is an absolutely fixed, definite, chemical combination of carbon and hydrogen.   It may be prepared in a state of chemical purity and in this respect differs from all other artificial illuminants.   Acetylene is without physiological action and may be inhaled or swallowed with impunity just as could be hydrogen or nitrogen. Except for possibly traces in coal gas, acetylene does not occur in ordinary gases and in America it is never mixed with other industrial gases.   In its commercial form it is rarely free from 2% to 8% admixture of air which comes into it from the water in the generator, or is introduced when the generator is charged, or comes from the interstices of the carbide.   In chemistry acetylene behaves as an illuminant and may be absorbed with either an ammoniacal solution of cuprous chloride or with bromine, the latter is the better.

Method of Gas Analysis

These instructions apply specifically to the type of apparatus in use for the past six years in the laboratories of The Peoples Gas Light & Coke Company of Chicago, and by a number of other gas companies. Deductions, etc., are built upon deductions drawn from results obtained with this apparatus.

The seven constituents which compose most industrial gases, and which are ordinarily analyzed for, are:

Carbon dioxide...CO_2
Illuminants...Ill.
Oxygen...O_2
Carbon monoxide...CO
Hydrogen..H_2
Methane...CH_4
Nitrogen..N_2

Of these, the first four are determined by absorption, the next two by explosion and the last by difference.

The gas-analyzing apparatus as shown in Fig. 107c consists of a graduated burette (4) fitted with platinum electrodes (13) and a storage bulb (6). Three aspirator bottles (7, 8 and 9) with rubber tubing (14, 15, 16 and 17), and an electric sparking outfit are also required. Both glass pieces are fitted with three-way cocks (1, 2 and 3). The measuring, explosion, washing, and the entire analysis is made in the graduated burette; the bulb (6) is used only for storage of the reserve supply of gas after the CO absorption in case the explosion is unsatisfactory. The burette (4) is usually provided with a water-jacket (11) consisting of a large glass tube confining by large rubber stoppers at the ends clear distilled water. A bottle or beaker (10) is placed under cock (2) to form a seal and catch waste reagents and wash water. A removable funnel or cup (5) is attached to burette capillary tube at the top by a ground joint. A secondary funnel (12) beneath (5) serves to drain away excess reagent or wash water by means of drain tube (18).

In preparing the apparatus for an analysis, first fill the aspirator and seal bottles (8, 9 and 10) and the leveling bottle (7) with distilled water previously saturated at the temperature of the water-jacketed burette with the gas to be analyzed, and place aspirator bottles (7, 8 and 9) on shelf (21). By manipulating cock (3) displace all air from rubber tubing (15, 16 and 17) until water entirely free of bubbles flows upward through ground joint into cup (5). Then open cock (2) to seal bottle (10) and purge all air out of tube (14) through cock (2) into seal bottle (10). Similarly open cock (2) to burette (4) and fill same with water up to funnel. When the apparatus is quite full of water, as described, remove cup (5), open cock on sampling can or pipe from which the sample is to be taken, allow the gas to blow through the hose for a few seconds to insure the expulsion of all air, and then attach hose to the ground joint end of the capillary tube at the top of the burette. Turn cock (2) so that the water in burette (4) communicates with the leveling bottle (7), held level with funnel (5). Now, open cock (1) so that the gas sample enters burette only, and as the surface of water in the burette (4) is depressed, slowly lower the leveling bottle (7), keeping the surface of water in same slightly above that in the burette in order to insure no inward leaks of air through loosely attached tubing, etc. When the gas has displaced nearly all water to about a point (19) in the burette, close cock (1), remove rubber tubing at top of burette and replace cup (5). Open cock (3) for a few seconds and expel gas from capillary tubes until water flows into cup (5) and fills it about one quarter full. If the sample is taken from the house piping, or where there is an abundant sample, it is well to allow the gas to flow entirely through the burette and out at the lower stop-cock for a few seconds, care, of course, being taken to purge out excess gas from stem of cock (2) into bottle (10) before securing the 100-cc. sample for analysis.

If the gas sample be at a different temperature than the burette, allow it to remain in the burette for a few minutes before proceeding to secure the desired 100 cc. When the gas has assumed the temperature of the burette, raise leveling bottle (7) so that the water level is sufficiently above the 100 cc. graduation of the burette to force small bubbles of the confined sample through the water into cup (5), when the cock (1) is slightly opened. Bubble excess gas sample slowly outward in this manner until upon closing cock (1) and lowering bottle (7), its water level and that in the burette are at the 100 cc. mark. If the zero mark of the burette be at the cock (1), then the 100-cc. mark is taken for a leveling point as just described, but if the zero graduation be at the point of capillary retention, where the capillary tube immediately below cock (1) widens into the burette proper, then excess gas is bubbled outward, until the water levels in the bottle (7) and burette (4) are at a mark equal to 100 cc., minus the previously determined volume (usually 0.3 or 0.4 cc.) of the capillary tube between cock (1) and the zero graduation at the point capillary retention. In the latter case, after adjusting the burette water level at 99.7 or 99.6, as the case may be, bottle (7) is placed on a level with (10) and the cock (1) is slightly opened until the water in cup (5) slowly enters the burette capillary tube at the top to the point of capillary retention, when it will be found upon raising bottle (7) that the water level corresponds with the one in the burette which will be at the 100 cc. graduation.

When there is just 100 cc. in the burette, the analysis may be started.

Turn the cock (2) so as to connect the burette with the bottle (10), raise the funnel (5) until it is just off of its ground joint and drain, leaving about $\frac{1}{4}$ in. of water in the bottom. Lower the funnel on to its seat and put into it about 20 cc. of potassium hydrate solution. Be sure that cock (2) is set so that the burette is connected with (10). Now open cock (1) and let the potassium hydrate solution *drain* very slowly into the burette. When it has nearly all gone into the burette, close cock (1) and open cock (3) and let water from bottle (8) or (9) through into the funnel (5) for about ten seconds. Rinse the funnel and fill it with about 50 cc. of distilled water previously saturated with the gas being analyzed. Pass this wash water *slowly* through the burette, and when nearly all has entered burette, close cock (1). Wait two minutes for water to drain down the sides of the burette. Then turn cock (2) so that burette is connected with bottle (7), and read the contraction of the gas, at the same time holding the bottle (7) with the surface of the water in the bottle level with the surface of the water to the burette; also note the reading on the burette graduations coinciding with the bottom of the meniscus of the water level in the burette. The amount absorbed as indicated. by the contraction in cc., or difference in cc., between the 100 and the burette reading, equals the per cent of carbon dioxide.

Turn cock (2) to connect the burette with the bottle (10), and with a 1-cc.

pipette put about two drops of bromine into the funnel (5) which should contain about 20 cc. of distilled water. Drain this *slowly* into the burette, as in the previous operation, until the entire gas space in the burette is filled with reddish brown bromine fumes, then admit the rest of the bromine and most of the water in the funnel. Next pour into the funnel about 30 cc. of potassium hydrate solution and drain part of this solution in slowly until the water ceases to rise and the burette and the surface of the water are quite free from bromine fumes. Wash with about 75 cc. of aerated distilled water. Wait two minutes and measure as explained above. The amount absorbed in cc. equals the per cent of illuminants.

Now place in cup (5) about 20 cc. of pyrogallic acid solution, and add 20 cc. of KOH solution and allow mixing to take place naturally for about ten seconds, then drain this through, wash out the burette with about 75 cc. of distilled water and measure in the way previously explained, after waiting at least two minutes for gas to resume temperature of burette jacket. The resulting contraction in cc. equals the per cent of oxygen.

Next place about 40 cc. of copper monochloride solution in the funnel and drain through very slowly until no further contraction is observed. Then if no reagent remains in cup (5), add 10 cc. of same reagent and pass it through the burette. Pass in about 50 cc. of distilled water and after this 10 cc. KOH solution, drain through and wash out with about 100 cc. of distilled water. The amount absorbed in cc. equals the per cent of carbon monoxide. This reagent should be added rather slowly and several minutes allowed for its action on the CO.

The carbon monoxide is the last constituent to be determined by absorption. Of the remaining three, two must be determined by an explosion and the third by difference.

Make a careful note of the reading of the burette after the CO absorption, as this figure has to be used in the H_2 and CH_4 calculation.

Turn cock (2) so as to give connection between bottle (7) and burette, and cock (3) so as to connect (7) through burette (4) and bulb (6) with (8). Place (8) on the table level with (10) and hold (7) so that its water level is opposite the graduation indicating 10 cc. Now open cock (1) carefully and allow gas to pass very slowly through cocks (1) and (3) into the storage bulb (6). When all but exactly 10 cc. has passed into the bulb (6), close cocks (1) and (3) and place bottle (7) on a level with (10). Pass a little water from (9) directly into the cup (5) so as to get all of the gas out of the passages between the bulb (6) and the cup (5). Also open cock (1) slightly and allow water to pass from cup (5) into burette to zero mark. By manipulating (7) have the amount of gas in the burette exactly 10 cc. A small excess may be gotten rid of through cock (1) and the funnel (5). Turn cock (2) so as to connect burette (4) and bottle (10). Remove funnel (5) and connect oxygen hose to top capillary (2). Then open cock (1) and let about 20 cc. of oxygen enter. Remove oxygen tubing and allow about 10 cc. of air to enter burette, exact proportion of oxygen and of air admitted to burette are not essential. Close cock (1), allow water to pass from (9) through (3) and (1) into cup (5), and with bottle (7) lowered, open cock (1) until water passes into burette to zero mark. Then read contents of the burette accurately. The quantity of the mixture in the burette should be in the neighborhood of 40 cc. Attach wires to the electrodes on the sides of the burette, turn cock (2) so that the burette is connected to the bottle (7), see that tubing is straight and cause a spark to pass between the electrodes. After the explosion allow the gases to stand at least three minutes before reading the burette. Measure the contraction. This contraction is known as the " 1st contraction." Make a note of this, then place about 20 cc. of potassium hydrate solution in the funnel (5) and drain the burette. Wash with about 100 cc. of air-saturated distilled water and measure. The contraction due to absorption by the KOH solution is known as the " 2d contraction." The amount of gas left after the absorption for CO_2, divided by the amount taken for the explosion, is called the "constant."

The amount of hydrogen in the original mixture is equal to the first contraction multiplied by two, minus four times the second contraction divided by three and multiplied by the constant.

Formula for H_2

$$\text{Per cent by vol. of } H_2 = \frac{2 \times (\text{1st contraction}) - 4 \times (\text{2d contraction})}{3} \times \text{constant.}$$

Per cent by vol. $CH_4 = $ 2d contraction $\times$ constant.

The above formula is volumetric, not gravimetric, and is based on Avoagadro's law which states: " Under the same conditions of temperature and of pressure, equal volumes of all gases contain the same number of molecules." Since the analyses are made under the same conditions of temperature and of pressure, this law applies.

A clearer understanding of the derivation of the formula can probably be had by a graphic representation, and Fig. 107d is referred to.

Consider A, B and C to be the burette, A being before the explosion, B being after the explosion, and C after the second contraction. According to the formulae:

$$H_2 + \tfrac{1}{2}O_2 = H_2O$$

and

$$CH_4 + 2O_2 = CO_2 + H_2O.$$

Two volumes of H_2 will combine with one half volume of O_2 and leave no residue which will occupy space in the burette. That is to say, that for every two volumes of hydrogen consumed, three volumes disappear of which two volumes were hydrogen and one was oxygen. Or in other words, two thirds of a contraction due to an explosion of the hydrogen was hydrogen.

Now a given volume of methane when burned produces its own volume of CO_2 but at the same time causes the disappearance of two volumes of O. That is, there will be as much CO_2 after the explosion of the methane as there was of methane before the explosion, but twice this volume of oxygen will have disappeared. Or there will be a disappearance as contraction due to combination of the oxygen with the hydrogen of the methane equal to twice the volume of the original methane.

Thus after the explosion the only thing left in the burette to represent the original hydrogen and methane is a certain volume of carbon dioxide equal to the original volume of methane, all of the hydrogen along with two and one half volumes of the excess oxygen having disappeared.

If there was no methane at all present, the percentage of hydrogen in the original mixture would be equal to two thirds of the contraction due to the explosion of the hydrogen, but at the same time there is a contraction due to the combination of the hydrogen with oxygen. Here is also a contraction due to the combination of the methane with oxygen, and hence the first

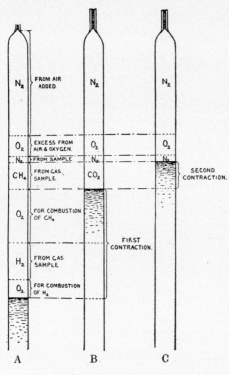

FIG. 107d

contraction is a gross contraction due to the combination of both the hydrogen and the methane. The next step is to determine what proportion of this gross contraction is due to the hydrogen and what to the methane.

We have seen that for every volume of carbon dioxide present before the absorption with KOH two volumes of oxygen have disappeared. The "second contraction" gives us this volume of carbon dioxide so that by multiplying it by two we get the total contraction due to the methane, and subtracting this from the gross contraction due to the hydrogen and the methane, we get the net contraction due to the hydrogen alone, two thirds of which would be the volumetric percentage of this hydrogen in the portion taken, and this multiplied by "constant" gives the percentage in the original gas.

The volume of carbon dioxide as given by the second contraction is equal to the volume of methane in the portion of the sample exploded, which multiplied by the "constant" gives the percentage in the original gas.

The constituent which we call "methane"—CH_4—often contains in addition ethane—C_2H_6—especially in rich gases and in natural gas from wells which are approaching exhaustion.

The ethane present is burned in the explosion and is reported as methane, increasing the per cent of methane slightly, and lowering to the same extent the percentage of hydrogen and of nitrogen, but in ordinary work and in the calculation of the calorific value of a gas the effect of the presence of small quantities of ethane is negligible.

Ethane may, however, be readily determined separately if it is desired. The hydrogen must first be separately removed by means of a palladium tube. This is done by adding to 10 cc. of the residual gases oxygen and air just as directed above for the explosion.

The palladium tube is installed between the burette and the storage bulb. A beaker containing water, which is kept at the boiling-point by a Bunsen lamp, is so placed as to have the loop of the tube immersed in the hot water. An accurate reading of the amount of mixture is then taken and the mixture passed very slowly through the tube into the storage bulb and then back. Care must be taken not to pass the gas through the tube too rapidly, or the heat generated is apt to break up some of the methane. The palladium does not really absorb the hydrogen from the mixture, but by a catalytic action causes it to combine with the oxygen present and form water, and hence two thirds of the contraction due to passage of the mixture over the palladium is the percentage of hydrogen. The known volume of mixture after the hydrogen absorption is then exploded and the contraction noted. A second contraction due to the absorption of the carbon dioxide by KOH formed is also noted.

The volumes of the methane and ethane may then be calculated from the following formulae, where:

First contraction, due to condensation of water vapor formed, and
Second contraction, due to absorption of carbon dioxide formed.

$$\text{Per cent by vol. of } CH_4 = \frac{4\times(\text{1st contraction})-5\times(\text{2d contraction})}{3}\times\text{constant.}$$

Per cent by vol. of C_2H_6

$$\frac{4\times(\text{2d contraction})-2\times(\text{1st contraction})}{3}\times\text{constant.}$$

The difference between the sum of all these percentages found by the above determinations and 100 is the percentage of nitrogen.

Solutions

1. The potassium hydrate, or hydroxide solution, is made by dissolving 5 parts by weight of chemically pure potassium hydroxide (purified sticks) in 100 parts by weight of distilled water. This solution should be kept in well-stoppered bottles, using rubber stoppers to prevent sticking and deterioration due to absorption of carbon dioxide from the air. The same hydrate solution is used for the absorption of CO_2, or bromine fumes, and with the pyrogallic acid for oxygen, and of CO_2 after methane. The potassium hydroxide purified by lime is better for this purpose than that purified by alcohol.

2. The pyrogallic acid solution is made by dissolving 10 parts by weight of chemically pure pyrogallic acid in 100 parts by weight of distilled water. To every 1000 parts by weight of this solution add 5 parts by weight of oxalic acid as a preservative.

Do not mix the pyrogallic acid solution with the potassium hydrate solution except in the funnel and until quite ready for use, as the potassium pyrogallate thus formed will absorb oxygen from the air and lose its strength. At least two minutes should be given the oxygen absorption with potassium pyrogallate when flue gases or engine exhaust is being analyzed.

3. The copper monochloride solution is made by dissolving 75 parts by weight of chemically pure copper monochloride in 720 parts by weight of concentrated hydrochloric acid, to which has been added 400 parts by weight of distilled water. Ten or twenty grams or more of clean bare copper wire or foil should be added and kept constantly in the bottle with the mixture to prevent deterioration. When a small quantity of the solution is added to a large amount of water, a cloudy white precipitate of copper monochloride appears. When no cloudiness is thus produced, and the mixture shows a blue tint, the preparation has become oxidized and is unreliable.

4. Gas-saturated distilled water may be prepared at a temperature not less than, and preferably a few degrees above, that at which it is to be used so as to avoid evolution of the dissolved gases in the burette.

5. Distilled water may be sufficiently aerated by shaking it vigorously for two or three minutes in a large bottle three quarters full of distilled water.

Apparatus

6. The apparatus may be cleaned from time to time by running through it a solution of potassium bichromate in sulphuric acid. This is useful when the platinum points become coated with carbon. This cleaning solution should be used with care, as sudden mixing of the sulphuric acid solution with the water in the burette generates considerable heat which may break the burette.

7. For constant use it is well to install the water-jacketed burette, as shown in plate, by means of clamps attached to a permanent pipe stand, supporting a shelf over a sheet lead drain. The electrodes (13) leading from burette (4) are insulated from water-jacket (11) by rubber tubing, containing copper wires fused to the platinum leads and leading to the terminals of a one fourth inch spark coil, operated by at least two ordinary dry batteries (not shown in plate). A drain funnel (12) connected by rubber tubing to a glass tube (18) of one fourth inch bore extending to sink or drain pipe will be found of great convenience in a permanent installation for getting rid of waste from funnel or cup (5). A drain tube (20) leading from bottom of bottle (10) upward and curved in a semi-circle at the top so that the outlet is level with the desired water level in the bottle (10) will be found advantageous in securing cleanliness.

8. Rubber tubing (14), (15), (16) and (17) should be of the heavy-wall, pure gum variety, and of such internal diameter as to give tight joints over the glass tubing, etc. The joints should be wired to insure freedom from leaks incident to loosely attached tubing.

9. By keeping the apparatus and all of the bottles filled with water, especially when not in use, and the reagent bottles in immediate proximity, the entire outfit acquires about the temperature of the room, and the error arising from the source of temperature changes in the sample is eliminated.

10. The explosions take place in the measuring burette. A coil which will give a one fourth inch spark is ample. Too strong a spark is apt to crack the glass as is a continuous play of sparks between the points, or a play of sparks when the burette is dry. If the explosion does not occur simultaneously with the first spark, the spark need not be continued. Something else is wrong. The usual trouble is that the confined

mixture is not an explosive one and the proportion of air or oxygen to gas residual must be changed.

11. The reagent funnel (5) and top ground joint of burette should be washed well after the completion of each analysis to prevent sticking at the ground joint, due to any potassium hydrate solution which may be present. This rule is applicable also to other movable parts such as cocks which are likely to stick.

12. The bulb (6) which is not graduated is used to hold the excess of gas when the explosion is being made. The analyst occasionally loses an explosion, and were it not for the gas held in this bulb, the entire analysis would have to be made over. By putting into the bulb all of the gas that is left after the CO_2 absorption, except the 10 cc. which is used for the explosion. Several explosions may be made as checks on one another, or in case the first one is lost.

13. If the cocks stick, they can usually be loosened by a little hot water on the outside. They should be well lubricated with a mixture of equal parts of vaseline, tallow and paraffine.

14. For getting samples, it is best to get four sample cans. The Fig. 107e will show what these are. In getting the sample the can is placed in an upright position and filled quite full of water, perfectly saturated with the gas to be sampled in order to expel all of the air. A tube connected with the upper stopcock is then introduced into the space from which the gas sample is to be drawn, and the lower stopcock is opened, allowing the water to run out, and thus the sample is aspirated into the can. In drawing samples

FIG. 107e

from places which have a suction instead of a pressure, such as the inlet of an exhauster, or at the base of a stack, or in the breeching of a boiler, the water should be allowed to flow out through a U-shaped glass tube attached by a piece of rubber hose to the lower stopcock. If this is not done, after the water is all out, air will enter and spoil the sample. It is essential to draw out all of the water, even if only a small sample is required, as a number of constituents, illuminants and CO_2 for example, are soluble in water. If the gas to be sampled is under pressure, it is well enough to allow it to flow through the can for a few seconds after all the water has run out.

To get the sample out of the can, the lower stopcock is connected by a hose with a source of water under pressure such as an aspirator bottle filled with water and placed at a level above that of the sampling can, and as the water runs into the can the gas will be displaced and may be led by means of a hose to the burette.

15. The principal precaution necessary in gas analysis is to see that the temperature of the appratus and of the water used, and of any additional water which may be added, as well as the temperature of the sample undergoing examination, does not change during the analysis. A change of 5.2° F. will cause a change of about one per cent in the volume of any gas at an ordinary temperature of 60°. The temperature at which an analysis is made is immaterial but that temperature MUST remain constant.

16. In reading the burette, hold leveling bottle (7) in front and just to one side of the burette, so that the eye of the analyst can sight along the under surface of the water level in (7) and bring it in the horizontal plane with the bottom of the meniscus in the burette, as shown in Fig. 107c.

Analysis

The quantities of reagents and wash water described in the foregoing method of analysis are intended mainly for the analysis of carburetted water gas, hence in the analysis of any other gas the quantities specified should be changed if it is found to be necessary in order to insure complete absorption of the various constituents. This is also true of the oxygen and air required for explosion.

18. Introduce potassium hydrate solution slowly for first absorption as the tendency otherwise is to secure too high a percentage for the carbon dioxide.

19. Care should be taken in handling bromine. Keep it always under water, and do not allow it to come in contact with the skin. Bromine is an exceedingly energetic reagent and will cause painful chemical burns. If bromine fumes are breathed, relief from the irritation caused to the throat can be obtained by inhaling alcohol or steam. The slick feeling caused by getting potassium hydrate on the hands may be removed by a little dilute hydrochloric acid.

20. The absorption of illuminants by bromine is a heat-producing reaction, and the increased temperature is apt to cause the sample to expand unduly and may cause the loss of a part of the sample by forcing it out through cock (1) and thus vitiate the analysis. If it is seen that the expansion is becoming excessive, a little water may be added from (8). The bulb at the lower end of the burette is provided for this contingency, however. In the analysis of acetylene, which contains over 90 per cent of illuminants, this is especially apt to occur. If the percentage of illuminants is high, it is well to admit a little water from (8) during the absorption with bromine to restore the normal temperature of the gas.

21. 20 cc. of potassium pyrogallate solution when mixed with 20 cc. of potassium hydrate solution produces a rise in the temperature of the mixture of about 5° F. over that of the original solutions. The heat gained by the gas in the burette due to this cause should be taken into consideration and sufficient time allowed the burette gases to resume initial temperature before reading. This solution should be passed into the burette very slowly, as the absorption of oxygen is rather sluggish. The absorption may be considered complete when no further discoloration to purple or brown occurs upon introduction of the clear reagent.

22. The absorption of the last traces of CO is attended with difficulty, and hence the analyst should be careful to add sufficient copper monochloride solution and allow plenty of time for the complete absorption. The reagent being strongly acid, about 10 cc. of potassium hydrate solution should always be added after passing in about 50 cc. of wash water to insure removal of all fumes of hydrochloric acid and followed with the customary wash water.

23. When carburetted water gas is being analyzed, double quantities of residual gases, oxygen and air may be taken for the explosion in order to secure higher accuracy.

24. Prior to all explosions sufficient time, at least two minutes, should be allowed for the gases to thoroughly diffuse through the oxygen and air added so as to give homogeneous explosive mixture and insure the combustion of all the oxidizable gases.

25. No special care need be taken in measuring the amount of air, or of oxygen added for the explosion, though the amounts taken should not be less than those stated in the " Method." Care must be taken, however, to measure accurately the amount of gas taken for the explosion, and the total amount of the gas, air and oxygen just before the explosion.

26. Air is added to the mixture to be exploded merely to lessen the jar. If the gas is very poor or contains large quantities of nitrogen, no air need be added, and on the other hand, if the gas is quite rich no oxygen need be added, air being sufficient, although if oxygen is available it is best added to insure

combustion.   An excess of oxygen used with a very rich gas such as acetylene or a high candle-power Pintsch, Water or Coal gas may result in the oxydization of some of the nitrogen, but this is not very apt to occur.   With extremely poor gas such as blast-furnace gas and the like, no explosion will take place even when oxygen is used and no air added.   Oxyhydrogen gas may be necessary in such cases.   This is made by the electrolysis of water slightly acidulated with sulphuric acid.   Five to 10 cc. of the oxygen and hydrogen mixture added in addition to the oxygen will always insure an explosion.   As it recombines to water no especial reading or note of the volume added need be made.

27. Use only c.p. chemicals.

General Notes

28. Never allow the funnel to become entirely empty; always keep about one fourth inch of water or other liquid in the bottom to prevent the suction of air into the burette.

29. In acetylene, flue gas, engine exhaust air and gasoline gas, there is no hydrogen or methane, and hence the analysis need not be carried beyond the absorption with copper monochloride for CO, and the oxygen tank or apparatus, the electric coil batteries, etc., need not be provided.   In analyses of these gases the sum of the first four contractions subtracted from 100 gives the percentage of nitrogen.

30. Where many analyses are to be made, or where dispatch is an important element, it will be more satisfactory to obtain a cylinder of compressed oxygen for use in the hydrogen and methane determinations, but where the apparatus is to be moved from place to place, or is to be used only occasionally, or where the analyses are confined for the most part to gases which do not contain hydrogen or methane, such as flue gases, acetylene, air, engine exhaust, etc., a cheaper and quite satisfactory substitute can be had in a small retort by means of which oxygen can be generated on the spot as needed.

To generate oxygen this retort is filled not more than half full with a pulverized thoroughly mixed charge of potassium chlorate and manganese dioxide in the proportions of 20 of the first to one of the latter by weight.   This is heated gently over a Bunsen lamp.   The evolution of oxygen begins at once and it may be led to the burette by means of a rubber tube.   As 100 grams of potassium chlorate will produce 27,000 cc. of oxygen and only about 20 cc. of oxygen are used for one analysis, a very small spoonful of the mixture will suffice for a great many explosions.

31. The method of analysis is so laid out that each determination must be made in its turn.   With the exception of the absorption of CO_2 with KOH, and possibly that of CO with cuprous chloride, no isolated determination of any one constituent can be made with anything approaching accuracy without starting at the beginning and making all of the absorptions down to that constituent.

Careful readings of the burette should be taken before and after each determination, and especial care should be taken in making the analysis to thoroughly absorb each constituent in its turn.   Partial absorption, or errors in the readings, will not only introduce an error in the percentages of the constituent in question, but the remaining portions of this constituent will affect the latter determinations in the analysis and thus have a doubly vitiating effect upon the accuracy.

Any CO_2 left after the first absorption will be absorbed by the KOH following the bromine and will be reported as illuminant, or if by chance it is not absorbed by the KOH following the bromine, it will be absorbed by the alkaline pyrogallate solution used for oxygen absorption and will appear as O_2.

Any illuminant not absorbed will remain and burn to approximately $3\frac{1}{2}$ times its volume of CO_2 when the explosion is made and will appear as CH_4.   A very small proportion of illuminant left and burned and calculated to CH_4 will be sufficient to run the total of the analysis to more than 100 per cent.   Any bromine vapors left after the absorption with bromine will be absorbed by the pyrogallate solution and will be reported as O_2.

Any unabsorbed CO will be burned to CO_2 in the explosion and will decrease the percentage of H_2 and CH_4 and increase the percentage of N_2 to the same extent.

Any unabsorbed O_2 left would decrease the percentage of H_2 and CH_4 and increase the percentage of N_2 to the same extent.

Any unabsorbed CO_2 after the explosion will decrease the percentage of CH_4 and increase that of the H_2 and N_2.

The N_2 being determined by differences will necessarily show the net effect of any and all errors in either readings of the burette or in the performance of the analysis.

Interpretation

To draw any trustworthy conclusions from a gas analysis, it is necessary to consider the analysis as a whole, rather than to base conclusions merely on the variation of the proportion of some one constituent from a standard figure that practice has taught to be normal.

For example, the candle-power of a coal gas or of a water gas may be said in a general way to vary with its percentage of illuminants, but it is not unusual to have a gas showing a high illuminant content, and at the same time a low candle-power on account of the percentage of carbon dioxide, oxygen or nitrogen, which neutralize the effect of the illuminants, and, conversely, a low illuminant content may co-exist with a high candle-power if the percentage of the impurities is low.

The statements in regard to inferences to be drawn from the excess of deficit of any one constituent in an otherwise normal analysis must be taken with the understanding that the analysis is otherwise normal, and that the good or bad effect of the excess or the deficit of any one constituent is not neutralized by the undue presence or absence of one or more of the other constituents.

	Coal gas (16 c.p.) Per cent	Pintsch gas Per cent
Carbon dioxide......................	2.5	0.5
Illuminants..........................	4	23.5
Oxygen..............................	0.5	0.5
Carbon monoxide....................	7.5	1.0
Hydrogen...........................	45	18.5
Methane............................	35	52.5
Nitrogen............................	5.5	3.5
	100.0	100.0
B.t.u. per cubic foot..................	616	1200
Specific gravity.....................	0.45	0.71

The carbon dioxide in coal gas or Pintsch gas comes either from an air leak in some hot part of the process, the oxygen of the air, burning the illuminants, CH_4, etc., to carbon dioxide, or to a leak in a retort or connection through which stack gases from the bench fire are drawn. Carbon dioxide constituent should be kept as low as possible.

The illuminants come from the distillation of the coal or of the oil and to this constituent is due a large part of the calorific and practically all of the illuminating value. An excess of it would mean—especially along with a deficit of methane—too low heats or too short a time of carbonization. An excess would show a good gas but would evidence an underload, or underheated condition and an uneconomical operation. A deficit of illuminants if accompanied with excess methane would show too high heats, or if with an excess of hydrogen very excessive heats.

An excess of oxygen would mean an air leak at some part of the process after the gas was cooled below the ignition point. It might mean a leaky exhauster connection or too much air for purification. A small percentage of free oxygen should be present as evidence of sufficient air for purification, but aside from this the lower the oxygen content the better, especially as oxygen almost invariably comes from the air and carries with it four times its volume of inert nitrogen. A deficit or total absence of any free oxygen means insufficient air for purification.

Carbon monoxide comes from the partial combustion of carbon with oxygen mixed or entrained with the coal or oil, or from water or moisture which breaks up and forms carbon monoxide and hydrogen. An excess would mean an air leak in some hot part of the process, or more likely water or moisture. As water would form this blue gas at the expense of the best part of the illuminants, the presence of an excess of carbon monoxide, especially if accompanied with high hydrogen, may be regarded as an indication of uneconomical conditions. A deficit of carbon monoxide would mean too low heats.

Hydrogen in coal gas or Pintsch gas may come from either the breaking up of water by hot carbon or from the breaking down of hydrocarbons by heat. An excess of hydrogen if accompanied by an excess of carbon monoxide would mean wet coal or water mixed with the oil, if not so accompanied would mean too long carbonization, insufficient charge or excess heats, as any hydrocarbon will break down into hydrogen and lampblack if heated sufficiently high. A deficit of hydrogen would mean low heats or an underloaded condition of the retorts.

Methane comes from hydrocarbons which have been subjected to temperatures too high to result in the formation of illuminants and not high enough to produce free hydrogen. An excess would mean too high heat or too long carbonization, especially if accompanied with high hydrogen.

Nitrogen comes from the air for the most part and its presence is evidence of a leak or of some other condition which should not eixst. A certain percentage is unavoidable, especially as some air must be added to the gas for purposes of purification, but the proportion should be kept as low as practicable. An excess of nitrogen would mean an air leak; if accompanied with high carbon dioxide or low hydrogen it would mean air or products of combustion mixed while the gas was hot, if accompanied by high oxygen it would mean air mixed after gas was cold.

PRODUCER GAS

	Per cent
Carbon dioxide	6.0
Illuminants	....
Oxygen	....
Carbon monoxide	30.0
Hydrogen	11.0
Methane	3.0
Nitrogen	50.0
	100.0
B.t.u. per cubic ft.	162
Specific gravity	0.89

Carbon dioxide is to be avoided in producer gas. Its presence is evidence of too low a fire, of a cold fire or one with dead spots in it, of an overloaded machine or of an excess of air. An absence or a great deficit of carbon dioxide would show that the machine was underloaded and not operating up to its capacity.

Carbon monoxide and hydrogen are produced when the conditions are best, resulting in a high carbon monoxide and hydrogen content. Low hydrogen with high nitrogen shows an excess or leak of air, as the hydrogen in the gas combines with the oxygen in the air and disappears as water vapor leaving the nitrogen. Methane is produced when the heats are low or the machine is underloaded, and, while it adds greatly to the value of the gas, its presence may be taken as evidence that the full capacity is not being gotten from the producer and that either there is not sufficient steam and air, or the fire is too cold or too shallow. Between 50% and 60% of nitrogen is unavoidable in producer practice, although as in every industrial gas the presence of nitrogen is a detriment. An excess of nitrogen especially if accompanied by an excess of carbon dioxide or carbon monoxide, or a deficit of hydrogen is evidence of an excess of air.

WATER GAS
(Carburetted, 24 c.p.)

	Per cent
Carbon dioxide	3.0
Illuminants	12.0
Oxygen	0.5
Carbon monoxide	29.0
Hydrogen	33.0
Methane	18.0
Nitrogen	4.5
	100.0
B.t.u. per cu. ft.	672
Specific gravity	0.68

There are a number of chemical reactions taking place in a water gas set, some beneficial, some the reverse, and it is only by keeping these properly balanced that the best results can be obtained.

First, the water in the form of steam is broken up by the hot carbon into monoxide and hydrogen, forming what is commonly called "Blue Gas." If steam passes through the fire and is mixed with this blue gas, a further reaction between the steam and some of the carbon monoxide takes place forming carbon dioxide and hydrogen.

If air is mixed with the hot blue gas, either a part of the hydrogen combines with the oxygen and disappears as water vapor or a part of the monoxide combines with the oxygen forming dioxide, in either event leaving the nitrogen of the air.

In the carburetter the changes in the oil depend very largely upon the temperature. If there is not sufficient heat, the oil is in a large measure merely volatilized to recondense upon becoming cold instead of being dissociated or cracked into a permanent gas. When the temperature is at the most economical point, the oil is broken up into what we call illuminants and what we call methane and a small volume of hydrogen. As the temperature gets too high the illuminants are broken up into methane, carbon and hydrogen. With excessive temperatures the methane and all of the proportions added as oil will break down into their elements of carbon in the shape of lampblack and free hydrogen.

The extent and the mutual balance of these reactions can be told by a study of the analysis.

An excess of carbon dioxide or "Acid" would show an excess of steam or poor fuel, or an overloaded machine, a low fire, a cold fire, a shallow fire, an uneven fire or a fire with dead spots in it. An excess may be due also to a steam leak in the "up and down" valve or incomplete purging of the machine after the blast.

A deficit or absence of carbon dioxide while being an advantage in the finished gas is evidence of too little steam for the temperature and the amount of fire, and shows an uneconomical condition of operation on account of the machines being underloaded, and not giving their output. A small fire and too little blue gas along with excessive heat in the checkerwork will result in a gas showing very little if any dioxide, the dioxide produced in the generator being reduced to monoxide with the oil as fuel which is not at all economical. Very low dioxide is evidence of conditions which produce naphthalene, and, while dioxide is an impurity and to be kept low, it will not do to crowd it too far toward extinction.

An excess of illuminants show too little blue gas or too much oil, cold checkerwork or a poor fire and show a gas which while possessing a high candle-power and calorific value at the station will not stand transmission.

A deficit of illuminants shows an excess of blue gas or too little oil, or if accompanied with excess hydrogen, shows too much heat in the checkerwork.

Excess oxygen shows air added by leak or otherwise after the gas is cold. It may show also an excess of air for purification, insufficient purging after blast, a leaky exhauster or connection, too little water in seal pot, leaks in valves of secondary air system and, especially, it may mean carelessness in getting the sample.

An absence of oxygen would mean insufficient air for purification other than its room is much better than its company.

An excess of carbon monoxide would mean a good fire. When accompanied with excess hydrogen, it means steam mixed with the oil gas.

A deficit of monoxide when accompanied with excess dioxide and, especially, an excess of nitrogen shows an air leak while the gas is still hot.

An excess of hydrogen would show overheated checkerwork and breaking up of oil, especially when lampblack appears on the water of the seal pot.

A deficit of hydrogen shows insufficient steam, or too little fire, or, if accompanied with excess nitrogen, it shows an air leak while the gas is hot.

An excess of methane would mean a low or dirty fire, too little steam, dirty checkerwork or overload, or a cold machine.

A deficit shows excess temperature which breaks up the oil, especially when accompanied with excess hydrogen.

An excess of nitrogen would show air added or mixed or leaked, also insufficient purging, leaky air valves or excess air for purification.

Deficit of nitrogen—there is no such thing as too little of this inert constituent.

GAS ANALYSIS

SAMPLING

The process[1] consists in the insertion of a suitable tube into the flue or duct, and the withdrawal of the gas sought, by some sort of pump.

Tubes. The tube employed varies with the nature of the gas and its temperature. Ordinarily, a combustion tube a meter long of 16–17 mm. outside diameter, which has been drawn down to 7 mm. at one end, to facilitate the attachment of rubber tubing, is used. These soften at about 500° C. For higher temperatures we have a choice of quartz, porcelain tubes of about the same dimensions, or water-cooled metal tubes. Uncooled metal tubes cannot be employed above 250° without danger of reduction of the oxides of the metals composing the tube, by the carbonic oxide contained in the gases.[2] If porcelain

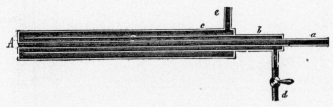

FIG. 108.

tubes be used, they should be glazed within and without, to prevent the transfusion through them of the lighter gases like methane and hydrogen: they, as well as glass tubes, should be warmed before insertion into a hot flue. The construction of the water-cooled tubes will be evident from Fig. 108.

For cooling the gas, the tube should not be inserted to its full length. Rolls of wire gauze can be inserted near the cool, drawn-out end of the tube: these will serve for the removal of soot and dust. The removal of dust may be further effected by the use of plugs of asbestos or glass wool.

The place from which the gas is collected should be so chosen as to give a representative sample, and all openings except those intended for the inlet of air, stopped up. In a circular duct or chimney the average velocity of the gases is usually at a point one-third the distance from the wall to the center. In case of a boiler, the setting should be carefully inspected, all cracks filled with mortar, and the clean out doors made tight. The fact that bricks themselves are porous must not be lost sight of, and new settings should be sized and given a coat of whitewash. If possible the tube should be inserted below the damper to avoid

[1] See also Bureau Mines Bulletin, No. 97, "Sampling and Analyzing Flue Gases," and General Outline for Sampling Gases, p. 1515.

[2] Fischer, "Technologie der Brennstoffe," 1880, p. 221, cites an instance in which CO_2 was changed from 1.5 in the mixture to 26% by the passage through an iron tube heated to dull redness.

Chapter contributed by Augustus H. Gill.

leakage from that source. A second hole should be made for the introduction of an oil tube for the thermometer. The joints around these tubes should be made tight with mortar, plaster of Paris, or in the case of a temporary connection, putty or wet cotton waste. Care should be taken not to insert the tube so close to the source of heat as to withdraw the gases in a dissociated or partially decomposed condition. For sampling the gases from different zones of a blast furnace, water-cooled tubes are made which can be screwed together to produce the desired length.

Pumps. Where a sufficient head of water (15 or 20 lbs. is enough for our purpose) is available, the Richards jet pump, Fig. 109, may be used. This can be easily constructed in glass as shown in Fig. 110 and the glass jets drawn down to suit the water pressure. It may be noted that the pump may be operated with steam equally as well as with water.

In case a head of water be not accessible, pumps employing a fall of water — the Bunsen pump, Fig. 111, may be used. This consists essentially of a quarter-inch tee, one branch of which is connected with the water supply, another with the vessel to be evacuated, while the third is connected with 10[1] or 15 ft. of quarter-inch pipe, preferably lead. The water in this acts as a moving piston and draws the gas in after it.

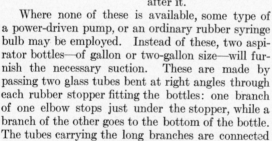

Fig. 109.　　　Fig. 110.

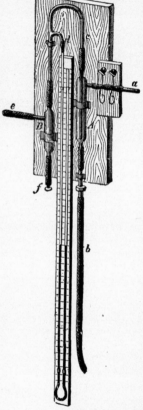

Fig. 111.

Where none of these is available, some type of a power-driven pump, or an ordinary rubber syringe bulb may be employed. Instead of these, two aspirator bottles—of gallon or two-gallon size—will furnish the necessary suction. These are made by passing two glass tubes bent at right angles through each rubber stopper fitting the bottles: one branch of one elbow stops just under the stopper, while a branch of the other goes to the bottom of the bottle. The tubes carrying the long branches are connected by a 3- or 4-foot piece of quarter-inch rubber tubing provided with a screw pinchcock. Upon setting one bottle higher than the other and blowing into its shorter tube, water siphons through the longer into the lower bottle, producing suction in the upper. This is sometimes used for taking a continuous sample extending

---

[1] For the highest vacuum over 32 ft.—the height of the water barometer.

over several hours. Strong brine is a suitable solution for the bottles, since it possesses the advantage over water in absorbing less carbon dioxide.

Containers for Samples. These are of glass, preferably of the shape shown in Fig. 112. Being pear shaped, the vessel is completely emptied, leaving no liquid to exercise a solvent action on the gas. The tubing shown in the figure is of lead, which can be safely used for chimney gases after it becomes attacked by them. Its obvious advantage is found in the fact that it bends rather than breaks. Glass bottles—parts of the aspirator just described—may be used; the rubber connection should be thick, carefully wired on and provided with screw pinch-cocks. The long tube should carry a short piece of rubber tubing within the bottle reaching to its side; by tipping it the water can be more completely run out through this tube. The use of metal containers in general is not recommended, as those of zinc or galvanized iron are attacked by carbon dioxide; where the gases do not act upon the metals they may of course be advantageously employed. To ensure tightness, the rubber stoppers used should be held in by screws which fit into a brass plate on top of the stopper and into wire loops about the neck of the bottle. This compresses the stopper about the tubes and into the bottle neck, making a thoroughly tight joint. Or the brass plate may be replaced by a piece of sole leather and wire passed over this after the manner of wiring down the bottles containing carbonated waters.

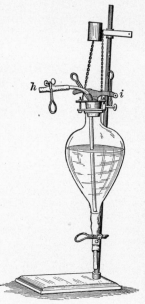

Fig. 112.

The use of rubber bags is not to be recommended, as they absorb certain gases and are oxidized by others: the most satisfactory containers are glass tubes provided with drawn-out ends which can be sealed in the lamp flame.

In connecting up the sampling tube, container and pump, the use of rubber tubing is to be avoided as much as possible for the reason just given.

MEASUREMENT OF GAS IN LARGE QUANTITIES. METERS

Several types of instruments are available for this purpose.

The wet meter } Measure total gas passed—not for acid gases.
The dry meter }

The Pitot tube or Davis anemometer } For all gases par-
The Rotameter or Thorp gauge } ticularly acid

The Capometer } All these measure
The Thomas electric meter } velocity simply
The orifice meter }
The anemometer }

The first two meters show all the gas passing through the system while the others simply measure the rate of flow: with these the size of the pipe must be known. Of all these instruments, the wet meter and Thomas meter are probably the most accurate. They, however, like some of the others, cannot be used with corrosive gases, being constructed of metal; hence the Pitot tube, rotameter and capometer are the ones to be employed in chemical works.

The **wet meter** consists of a cylindrical drum divided into four spiral compartments, suspended in a bath of water, surrounded by a tight casing: the pressure of the gas causes the drum to rotate, emptying a drumful of gas into the casing and pipes. It must be set level, the water level carefully adjusted to the mark on the glass gauge, with its top open, as well as the inlet and outlet pipes of the meter. The higher the water level the faster the meter. The **dry meter** consists of a pair of metal bellows, with sides of leather soaked in oil, on either side of a diaphragm, and connected with slide valves so that a bellowsful of gas is alternately emptied into the upper part of the meter and piping. The vibrations of the bellows produced by the gas pressure are transmitted to clockwork and indexes. It is to be noted that the indexes apparently read one-tenth of the actual volume passed: the index must make a complete circuit to register the amount stamped on the dial. A small index and dial are usually present for testing the meter, and a tolerance of 2% is allowed by law. This testing is done by meter-provers, carefully calibrated gas holders kept at constant temperature and the rate determined at different speeds. The meter-provers are, in their turn, calibrated by a cubic foot, standardized at the Bureau of Standards. It should be noted that all this calibration is corrected, not to standard conditions (0° C. and 760 mm.), but to the cubic foot as fixed by law—gas saturated with moisture at 60° F. and 30 inches.

The Pitot Tube. Fig. 113. This consists of two glass-tubes, D, of about $\frac{3}{16}$ inch internal diameter, inserted in the gas stream: one is bent at right angles and is set so that it receives the impact of the gas movement; the other merely registers the pressure of the gas in the pipe. The point of insertion of these tubes in the chimney or duct should be in a long straight run of pipe, so as to be as free from eddies as possible. Davis [1] says that authorities differ as to whether the tubes should be a third or one-sixth of the diameter from the circumference to show the mean speed: he states further that each flue or chimney is a separate problem and as a result of hundreds of measurements there seems to be "no settled proportionate distance corresponding to the mean velocity."

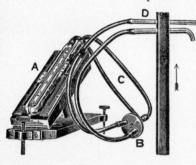

FIG. 113.

The glass tubes are connected by rubber tubing, C, through a reverser, B, with a U-tube A, which is either set vertically, inclined 30°, or one in ten—this carries a vernier reading to hundredths of an inch so that readings to thousandths are feasible. The U tube is filled with solutions of different specific gravity, although ether of 0.74 sp.gr. is the one commonly employed. The difference between the arms of the U tube represents the difference between the kinetic and static pressures of the gas in the flue or chimney.

[1] "Handbook of Chemical Engineering," **1, 197,** also for the tables for its use.

The formula for calculating the velocity recommended by W. W. Scott is

$$V = 1290 \sqrt{\frac{\frac{1}{2}h(1+.002176t)}{BM}},$$

where $h =$ vertical differential of gauge reading in terms of inches of water. $\frac{1}{2}$ the reading is taken as the actual reading is double that due to flow pressure alone. $B =$ barometric pressure of the gas in inches of mercury (29.92''). $M =$ specific gravity compared with $H = 1$. Air $= 14.39$. $t =$ temperature of the gas. $V =$ velocity in feet per second. The formula $V = 42\sqrt{h}$ gives fairly accurate results. Davis formula is

$$V_0 = \sqrt{\frac{h459+t°}{519}} \times 28.55.$$

The Rotameter, Fig. 114. This is a German instrument depending upon the height to which a float is carried in a glass tube by the velocity of the stream of gas. A modification of it was used by some of the gas-lighting companies under the name of the Thorp gauge.

It consists of a graduated glass tube fixed upon a tripod and provided with a plumb line so that it can be set vertically: gas passes in at the lower end, raises the clay or talc float to a certain height and passes out at the top. The height to which the float is raised is noted on the graduations of the tube. The formula for its use is

$$V_1 = V\sqrt{\frac{M}{M'}}.$$

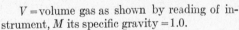

FIG. 114.

$V =$ volume gas as shown by reading of instrument, M its specific gravity $= 1.0$.

$V =$ volume desired, $M_1 =$ sp.gr. of gas.

It is made in all capacities from 0.2 cu.ft., per hour up.

The Capometer. Fig. 115. This consists of a series of capillary tubes of different sizes through which the gas is made to pass and the pressure thus produced noted in the U-tube A. Each capillary is calibrated and curves of gas flow are made corresponding to different pressures in the U-tube and various capillaries. An instrument made with capillaries 1–4 mm. in diameter has a capacity of 0.004 to 70 cu.ft. per hour.

The Thomas Electric Gas Meter. This depends upon the principle that if the specific heat of the gas be known, and an amount of energy be put into it, by means of a coil, sufficient to keep a certain difference

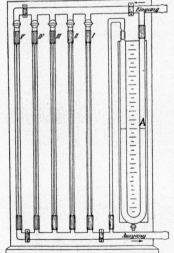

FIG. 115.

22

of temperature between two thermometers, one before and one after the coil, this energy is a direct measure of the volume of gas flowing. Two electrical thermometers are placed in the stream of gas with a heating coil between them: 2° difference of temperature is automatically maintained between the thermometers and the energy to preserve this difference of temperature (.0127 watt hour per standard unit of gas) is read off on the meter as cubic feet of gas. It is independent of temperature or pressure changes in the gas, and is used up to gas pressures of 180 lbs. per square inch. This is used in a Western gas works measuring 200,000 ft. of gas per hour.

The Orifice Meter. In this the same principle is used as in measuring water, by determining the diminution in pressure as registered on delicate gauges before

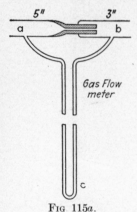

Fig 115a.

and after the gas has passed through a standard orifice. It is largely used for measuring natural gas.

The Anemometer is used ordinarily for measuring currents of air leaving or entering a room, analogous to its employment in meteorology.

The Gas Flow Meter.[1] This consists of a tube a, into which capillaries b of different sizes can be inserted by a rubber stopper (one at a time). On either side of the capillary is a T, the stems of which are joined together, making a U gauge c. This, when filled with water shows the difference in pressure of the gas before and after passing through the capillaries. The apparatus is calibrated by a wet or dry meter. It has a capacity of from 0.5 to 500 liters (0.0176 to 17.6 cu. ft.) per hour. See Fig. 115a.

MEASUREMENT OF GAS IN SMALL QUANTITIES. GAS BURETTES

Here may be mentioned the Hempel gas burette, made for accurate work with a compensation tube; the bulbed Orsat or Bunte burette; the separatory funnel and graduate. Fuwa and Shattuck[2] measure quantities of 30–200 cc. per minute by bubbling through water or dilute sulphuric acid.

The Hempel Gas Burette, Fig. 122, consists of a 100-cc. burette graduated in fifths of a cubic centimeter, provided with a short capillary at the top and closed with a rubber connector and pinch-cock, and a wider tube at the bottom, over which the $\frac{3}{16}$-in. rubber tube is drawn, which connects it with the leveling tube of similar size and length to the burette. It is manipulated by filling the leveling tube completely with water, opening the pinch-cock on the top of the burette and filling it with water. The gas to be analyzed is sucked in and measured as with the Orsat apparatus, p. 1241. Both burettes must be calibrated as is customary in volumetric analysis.

Separatory Funnel and Graduate, Fig. 130. From the water which has flowed out, the quantity of gas can be determined. See p. 1265.

[1] Benton, J. I. and Eng. Chem., **11**, 623 (1919).
[2] Id., **15**, 230 (1923).

ABSORPTION APPARATUS, TUBES, AND PIPETTES

These are quite varied according to the purpose for which they are intended. A very efficient form is the Friedrichs Spiral Gas Washing bottle, Fig. 116; here the gas has to pass through a long spiral path. Dennis[1] recommends this for the absorption of sulphur dioxide. The gas is run through a solution until a color change takes place. Were the reagent to be washed out and titrated it would not seem so well adapted on account of the difficulty of thoroughly washing it.

The Varrentrapp and Will bulbs, Fig. 117, the use of which is evident from the figure, are used for the absorption of ammonia in illuminating gas. The Wolff

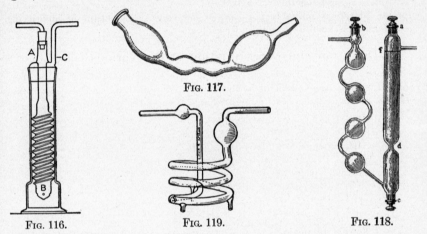

FIG. 117.

FIG. 116.   FIG. 119.   FIG. 118.

absorption tube, Fig. 118, the empty arm of which is filled with beads or broken glass is used for the absorption of carbon monoxide by blood. The bulbed tube, provided with a small jet, is generally used for containing standard solutions of acid, alkali, or potassium permanganate or, in general, a solution which is to be titrated after absorption. Where the presence of a gas as, for example, water vapor, is to be determined by the increase of weight of the reagent used, Winkler's spiral, Fig. 119[2], may be employed.

Pipettes—Particularly for the Orsat Apparatus. These are ordinarily filled with glass tubes, but various modifications have been proposed: these are the bubbling type of Hankus, the spiral bubbling variety of Nowicki-Heinz and a combination of the Friedrichs wash bottle proposed by Dennis. All these suffer from the very serious disadvantage of a glass three-way stopcock at the top, which it is practically impossible to prevent from sticking, unless the apparatus be used by one person and that one exceptionally careful and painstaking. Dennis[3] has shown that one variety is no more rapid than the original and some of the others but little more so. When it is further considered that they cost four times as much,[4] their use would seem of doubtful expediency.

[1] " Gas Analysis," p. 274, 1913.
[2] Called " Winkler's Bulbs " in the apparatus catalogs.
[3] Ibid., p. 83.
[4] Ten dollars.

It is interesting to note further that Anderson [1] has shown that with the modified potassium pyrogallate which he uses, the original Orsat slightly modified, to allow the precipitate to settle, is the best.

EXAMINATION OF THE GASES

The qualitative examination of a gaseous mixture is rarely resorted to in technical work: a sufficiently close idea of the gases present can be obtained by a consideration of the reactions involved in the various operations. It is, however, not safe to rely upon this in matters of importance, as conditions may change: for example if the gases be dry or dilute, hydrogen sulphide and sulphurous anhydride can exist together. Similarly in sewage gases, all the gas absorbed by cuprous chloride is probably not carbon monoxide. The means of identifying the different gases will be found under each gas.

Detection and Determination of the Various Gases

Clemens Winkler divided the gases into seven groups according to their behavior with various solvents. These were contained in suitable absorption tubes or vessels and the gases passed through them. His scheme was as follows

Gases absorbed by

I. H_2SO_4 1.7 sp.gr.; NH_3, (N_2O_3), N_2O_4.

II. KOH 1.3 sp.gr.; Cl_2, HCl, $(CN)_2$, HCN, SO_2, H_2S, SiF_4, CO_2.

III. $AgNO_3$; PH_3, AsH_3, SbH_3.

IV. Pyro; O_2, (O_3).

V. CuCl; CO.

VI. Acid $FeSO_4$ 1:2; NO.

VII. Unabsorbed; H_2, CH_4, C_2H_2, C_2H_4, N_2O, N_2, COS, and the noble gases.

The following tables give the specific gravity referred to air, the solubility in water at 20°, the qualitative tests and quantitative methods of determination of these gases: additional means will be found mentioned under the several gases themselves.

GROUP I

Gases Absorbed by H_2SO_4 1.7 sp.gr.

Name..............	Ammonia.	Nitrous anhydride.	Nitrogen tetroxide.
Gravity, air = 1......	0.589		1.590
Qualitative Tests....	Fumes w. HCl on a rod. Nessler's reagent.	Acts like a mixture of NO and NO_2.	Absorb in KOH, test for nitrites.
Quantitative Det'n..	Absorption in standard acid. Or $3NaBrO + 2NH_3$ $= N_2 + 3NaBr + 3H_2O$. Or absorption in water and Nesslerization. pp. 291, 537.		Absorption in N/10 $KMnO_4 \cdot 2KMnO_4$ $+ 10NO_2 + 3H_2SO_4$ $+ 2H_2O = 10HNO_3$ $+ K_2SO_4 +$ $2MnSO_4$. Or in standard alkali.
Solubility 20° C., 1 cc. water absorbs cc...	678		Forms HNO_3, HNO_2.

[1] J. Ind. and Eng. Chem., 8, 131–3, 1916.

GROUP II
Gases Absorbed by KOH 1.3 *sp.gr.*

Name.............	Chlorine.	Hydrochloric acid.	Cyanogen.
Gravity, air =1......	2.449	1.259	1.799
Qualitative Test.....	KI starch paper.	Fumes w. NH_3.	Pass through mixture of $FeSO_4$ 1 : 10+KOH, 1 : 3. and ppt. as Prussian blue w. ferric alum and H_2SO_4.[1]
Quantitative Det'n..	$2KI+Cl_2 = 2KCl + I_2$. Or absorption w. KOH.	Absorption in standard alkali or silver nitrate.	
Solubility 20° C., 1 cc. water absorbs cc..	2.15	442	4.5

Hydrocyanic acid	Sulphur dioxide.	Hydrogen sulphide.	Silicon fluoride.	Carbon dioxide.
0.936	2.213	1.177	3.60	1.520
Absorption in KOH and $FeSO_4$ and $FeCl_2$ = Prussian blue. Absorption w. KOH or acid $AgNO_3$.[2]	Fuchsine paper bleached or KIO_3 starch paper. $SO_2+2I+2H_2O = H_2SO_4+2HI$.	$PbAc_2$ paper, absorption by I solution. $H_2S+2I = 2HI+S$.	None $3SiF_4+4H_2O = SiO_4H_4 + 2H_2SiF_6$.	BaO_2H_2 on black rod. Absorption w. KOH or BaO_2H_2 and titration.
Very sol........	36.4	2.67	Decomposed.	0.892

GROUP III
Gases Absorbed by $AgNO_3$.

Name.............	Hydrogen phosphide, Phosphine.	Hydrogen arsenide, arsine.	Hydrogen antimonide, stibine.
Gravity, air =1......	1.175	2.696	4.330
Qualitative Test.....	Neutral H_2O Solution $KI+HgI_2$ = cryst. orange yel. ppt. PHg_3I_3.[3]	Blk. ppt. of $AsAg_3$ w. $AgNO_3$.	Blk. ppt. of $SbAg_3$ w. $AgNO_3$.
Quantitative Det'n..	Pass through Br water and ppt. H_3PO_4 as usual.	Absorb w. NaClO cont. 3% Cl.[4]	Decompose w. tartaric acid and det. Sb.
Solubility 20° C., 1 cc. water absorbs cc...	0.02	about 5	Slight.

[1] Nauss, J. Gasbeleuchtung, **43**, 969, 1900.
[2] Rhodes, J. Ind. and Eng. Ch., **4**, 652, 1912.
[3] Lemoult, Compt. rend, **139**, 478, 1904.
[4] Reckleben, Z. ang. Ch., **19**, 275, 1906.

	GROUP IV		GROUP V	GROUP VI
	Absorbed by potassium pyrogallate		*Absorbed by cnprous chloride*	*Absorbed by $FeSO_4$ 1 : 2 acidulated w. H_2SO_4*
Name........	Oxygen.	Ozone.	Carbon monoxide.	Nitric oxide.
Gravity, air $=1$	1.105	1.62	0.967	1.038
Qualitative Test.......	Darkening of light brown "pyro."	$MnCl_2$ paper; KI Starch paper, N_2O_4 and H_2O_2 being removed by $KMnO_4$.	Absorb in blood, and examine w. spectroscope.	Oxidize, absorb in KOH and test for nitrites.
Quantitative Det'n......	By "Pyro." CuCl in absence of CO.		Absorption w. CuCl.	Absorb in $FeSO_4$ 1 : 2 acidulated w. H_2SO_4 or with $KMnO_4$ as N_2O_4.
Solubility 20° C., 1 cc. water absorbs cc....	0.028	0.6 at 0°	0.023	0.267

GROUP VII
Unabsorbed

Name..........	Hydrogen.	Methane.	Ethylene (ethene).	Acetylene (ethine).
Gravity, air $=1$...	.0696	0.554	0.968	0.899
Qualitative Test..	None.	None.		Red ppt. w. am. CuCl (explosive!).
Quantitative Det'n	By combustion or explosion w. O_2.	By combustion or explosion w. O_2.	Absorption w. Br water or $H_2S_2O_7$	As C_2H_4, which see.
Solubility 20° C., 1 cc. water absorbs cc....	0.0182	0.035	0.15	1.03

Nitrous oxide.	Carbon oxysulphide.	Nitrogen.	The noble gases.
1.523	2.074	0.970	Helium, Neon, Argon, Krypton, Xenon.
None. By explosion with H_2 or combustion w. CuO.	None. Alcoholic KOH 1 : 3 in 66% alcohol by weight.	None. By absorption or combustion of all other gases and measuring the residue which also contains the noble gases.	
0.670	0.3	0.014	

NOTES. GROUP I: NaBrO is made by saturating a 10% solution of caustic soda with bromine.

GROUP II: Chlorine can be removed from hydrochloric acid by passing the gases over finely powdered antimony: hydrochloric acid can be removed from chlorine by means of manganese dioxide or zinc oxide.

The following reactions will serve to discriminate between HCN and $(CN)_2$:

$(CN)_2 + 2H_2O + (HCl) = 2CO(NH_2)_2 + (HCl)$ oxamide.

$HCN + 2H_2O + (HCl) = HCOOH + NH_3 + (HCl)$ formic acid.

Cyanogen is not absorbed by acid silver nitrate solution, from which it can be separated by drawing air through it: hydrocyanic acid is precipitated under these conditions.

GROUP IV: Ozone can be determined by Wurster's [1] method, consisting in passing the gas over paper moistened with *fresh* para phenylene diamine [2] and comparing the depth of color produced with a standard paper. In large quantities it can be determined according to Treadwell and Anneler [3] by passing through standard neutral potassium iodide and titration of the liberated iodine with N/10 sodium thiosulphate.

Analysis of Gaseous Mixtures

The analysis of a gaseous mixture is effected by absorbing the various constituents and observing the diminution in volume: in case the gas be unabsorbable, as for example methane (CH_4), it is burned and the carbon dioxide and water determined.

(a) *Analysis of mixtures for carbon dioxide, oxygen and carbon monoxide* (e.g. *chimney gases, producer and blast furnace gas*) can be done with any of the apparatus to be described. The Orsat, or Elliott are the forms usually employed.

(b) *Analysis of mixtures as in* (a) and also containing *combustible gases* as *hydrogen and methane*, e.g., illuminating gas.

The Orsat Apparatus. Description. The apparatus, Fig. 120, is enclosed in a case to permit of transportation from place to place; furthermore, the measuring-tube is jacketed with water to prevent changes of temperature affecting the gas-volume. The apparatus consists essentially of the leveling-bottle A, the burette B, the pipettes P', P'', P''', and the connecting tube T. Pipette P' is filled with potassium (or sodium) hydroxide solution (see Reagents) so that when it is drawn up into the front arm about half an inch in depth is left in the rear arm. Pipettes P'' and P''' are similarly filled with potassium (or sodium) pyrogallate and cuprous chloride solutions respectively. These reagents require to be pro-

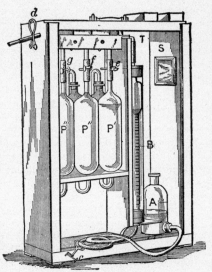

FIG. 120.

[1] Berichte, **20**, 921 (1888).
[2] Obtainable from Schuchardt, Görlitz.
[3] Treadwell-Hall, " Quantitative Analysis. "

tected from the oxygen of the air by collapsible rubber bags. As the oxygen in the air over the reagent is absorbed, a diminution in pressure takes place rendering it difficult to bring the reagent to the point on the stem: the obvious remedy is to remove the bag temporarily and adjust the reagent. When the apparatus is is first set up, one or two blank analyses should be made, to saturate the water and reagents with the gases. For example the potassium hydroxide absorbs carbon dioxide, it also absorbs about 3 cc. of oxygen, 2 cc. of carbon monoxide and 1.5 cc. of nitrogen, by virtue of the 100 cc. of water which it contains. A change of temperature of 1° makes a change of 0.36% of the volume of the gas: a change of pressure of 1 mm. produces 0.13% change in the volume.

Manipulation. The reagents in the pipettes should be adjusted in the capillary tubes to a point on the stem about midway between the top of the pipette and the rubber connector. This is effected by opening wide the pinchcock upon the connector, the bottle being on the table, and very gradually lowering the bottle until the reagent is brought to the point above indicated. Six inches of the tubing used correspond to but 0.1 cc., so that an error of half an inch in adjustment of the reagent is without influence upon the accuracy of the result. The reagents having been thus adjusted, the burette and connecting tube are completely filled with water by opening d and raising the leveling-bottle. The apparatus is now ready to receive a sample of gas (or air for practice). In case a flue-gas is to be analyzed d is connected with i, Fig. 112, A lowered and about 102 cc. of the gas forced over by opening h; or d may be connected with a T-joint in the gas-stream; the burette after filling is allowed to drain one minute by the sandglass, c snapped upon its rubber tube, and the bottle A raised to the top of the apparatus. By gradually opening c the water is allowed to run into the burette until the lower meniscus stands upon the 100 or 0 mark (according to the graduation of the apparatus). The gas taken is thus compressed into the space occupied by 100 cc., and by opening d the excess escapes. Open c and *bring the level of the water in the bottle to the same level as the water in the burette* and take the reading, which should be 100 cc. Special attention is called to this method of reading: if the bottle be raised, the gas is compressed; if lowered, it is expanded.

Determination of Carbon Dioxide. The gas to be analyzed is invariably passed first into pipette P', containing potassium hydroxide for the absorption of carbon dioxide, by opening e and raising A. The gas displaces the reagent in the front part of the pipette, laying bare the tubes contained in it, which being covered with the reagent present a large absorptive surface to the gas; the reagent moves into the rear arm of the pipette, displacing the air over it into the flexible rubber bag which prevents its diffusion into the air. The gas is forced in and out of the pipette by raising and lowering A, the reagent finally brought approximately to its initial point on the stem of the pipette, the burette allowed to drain one minute, and the reading taken. The difference between this and the initial reading represents the cubic centimeters of carbon dioxide present in the gas. To be certain that all the carbon dioxide is removed, the gas should be passed a second time into P^1 and the reading taken as before; these readings should agree within 0.1%, and are called " check readings."

Determination of Oxygen. The residue from the absorption of carbon dioxide is passed into the second pipette, P'', containing an alkaline solution of potassium pyrogallate, until no further absorption will take place. The difference between the reading obtained and that after the absorption of carbon dioxide, represents the number of cubic centimeters of oxygen present.

Determination of Carbon Monoxide. The residue from the absorption of oxygen is passed into the third pipette, P''', containing cuprous chloride, until no further absorption takes place; that is, in this case until readings agreeing exactly (not merely to 0.1) are obtained. The difference between the reading thus obtained and that after the absorption of oxygen, represents the number of cubic centimeters of carbonic oxide present.

Determination of Hydrocarbons. The residue left after all absorptions have been made may consist, in addition to nitrogen, the principal constituent, of hydrocarbons and hydrogen.

Accuracy. The apparatus gives results accurate to 0.2 of 1%, hence figures obtained by division to 0.01 should not be reported.

Time Required. About twenty minutes are required for an analysis; two may be made in twenty-five minutes, using two apparatus.

NOTES. The method of adjusting the reagents is the only one which has been found satisfactory: if the bottle be placed at a lower level and an attempt made to shut the pinchcock c upon the connector at the proper time, it will almost invariably result in failure.

The process of obtaining 100 cc. of gas is exactly analogous to filling a measure heaping full of grain and striking off the excess with a straightedge; it saves arithmetical work, as cubic centimeters read off represent per cent directly.

It often happens when e is opened, c being closed, that the reagent P' drops, due not to a leak, as is usually supposed, but to the weight of the column of the reagent expanding the gas.

The object of the rubber bags is to prevent the access of air to the reagents, those in P'' and P''' absorbing oxygen with great avidity, and hence if freely exposed to the air would soon become useless.

Carbon dioxide is always the first gas to be removed from a gaseous mixture. In the case of air the percentage present is so small, 0.08 to 0.1, as scarcely to be seen with this apparatus. It is important to use the reagents in the order given; if by mistake the gas be passed into the second pipette, it will absorb not only oxygen, for which it is intended, but also carbon dioxide; similarly if the gas be passed into the third pipette, it will absorb not only carbonic oxide, but also oxygen as well.

The use of pinchcocks and rubber tubes, original with the author, although recommended by Naef, is considered by Fischer to be inaccurate. The experience of the author, however, does not support this assertion, as they have been found to be fully as accurate as glass stopcocks, and very much less troublesome and expensive.

In case any potassium hydroxide or pyrogallate be sucked over into the tube T or water in A, the analysis is not spoiled, but may be proceeded with by connecting on water at d, opening this cock, and allowing the water to wash the tubes out thoroughly. The addition of a little hydrochloric acid to the water in the bottle A will neutralize the hydroxide or pyrogallate, and the washing may be postponed until convenient.

After each analysis the number of cubic centimeters of oxygen and carbonic oxide should be set down upon the ground-glass slip provided for the purpose. By adding these numbers and subtracting their sum from the absorption capacity (see Reagents) of each reagent, the condition of the apparatus is known at any time, and the reagent can be renewed in season to prevent incorrect analyses.

Elliott Apparatus. Description. The apparatus Fig. 121 consists of a burette holding 100 cc. graduated in tenths of a cubic centimeter and bulbed like the Bunte apparatus—the bulb holding about 30 cc.; it is connected with a leveling-bottle similar to the Orsat apparatus. The top of the burette ends in a capillary

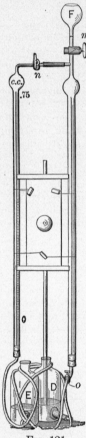

stopcock, the stem of which is ground square to admit of close connection with the "laboratory vessel," an ungraduated tube similar to the burette, except of 125 cc. capacity. The top of this "vessel" is also closed with a capillary stopcock, carrying by a ground-glass joint, or better a rubber stopper, a thistle-tube F, for the introduction of the reagents. The lower end of this "vessel" is closed by a rubber stopper carrying a three-way cock o, and connected with a leveling bottle D. The burette and vessel are held upon a block of wood—supported by a ring stand—by fine copper wire tightened by violin keys.

Manipulation. The ground-glass joints are lubricated with stopcock grease, p. 1269. The leveling-bottles are filled with water, the stopcocks opened, and the bottles raised until the water flows through the stopcocks m and n. m is connected with the source whence the gas to be analyzed is to be taken, n is closed, D lowered and rather more than 100 cc. drawn in, and m closed. n is opened, D raised and E lowered, nearly 100 cc. of gas introduced, and n closed; by opening m and raising D the remainder of the gas is allowed to escape, the tubes being filled with water and m closed. n is opened and the water brought to the reference mark; the burette is allowed to drain one minute, the level of the water in E is brought to the same level as in the burette, and the reading taken.

Determination of Carbon Dioxide. By raising E, opening n, and lowering D, the gas is passed over into the laboratory vessel; F is filled within half an inch of the top with potassium hydroxide, o closed, m opened, and the reagent allowed slowly to trickle in. A No. 3 evaporating dish is placed under o, and this turned to allow the liquid in the laboratory vessel to run into the dish. At first this is mainly water, and may be thrown away; later it becomes diluted reagent and may be returned to the thistle-tube. When the depth of the reagent in the thistle-tube has lowered to half an inch, it should be refilled either with fresh or the diluted reagent and allowed to run in until the absorption is judged to be complete, and the gas passed back into the burette for measurement. To this end close o and then m, raise E, open n, and force some pure water into the laboratory vessel, thus rinsing out the capillary tube. Now raise D and lower E, shutting n when the liquid has arrived at the reference-mark. The burette is allowed to drain a minute, the level of the water in the bottle E brought to the same level as the water in the burette, and the reading taken.

Determination of Oxygen. The manipulation is the same as in the preceding determination, potassium pyrogallate being substituted for potassium hydrate; the apparatus requiring no washing out.

Fig. 121.

Determination of Carbonic Oxide. The laboratory vessel, thistle-tube, and bottle if necessary, are washed free from potassium pyrogallate and the absorption made with acid cuprous chloride similarly to the determination of carbon dioxide. The white precipitate of cuprous chloride may be dissolved by hydrochloric acid.

Accuracy and Time Required. The apparatus is as accurate for absorptions as that of Orsat; it is stated to be much more rapid—a claim which the writer cannot substantiate. It is not as portable, is more fragile, and more troublesome to manipulate, and as the burette is not jacketed, it is liable to be affected by changes of temperature.

NOTES. In case at any time it is desired to stop the influx of reagent, o should be closed first and then m; the reason being that the absorption may be so rapid as to suck air in through o, m being closed.

The stopcock should be so adjusted as to cause the reagent to spread itself as completely as possible over the sides of the burette.

By the addition of an explosion tube it is used for the analysis of illuminating gas,[1] bromine being used to absorb the "illuminants," Winkler[2] states that this absorption is incomplete; later work by Treadwell and Stokes, and also Korbuly,[3] has shown that bromine water, by a purely physical solution, does absorb the "illuminants" completely; Hempel[4] states that explosions of hydrocarbons made over water are inaccurate, so that the apparatus can be depended upon to give results upon methane and hydrogen only within about 2%. It is, however, very rapid, a complete analysis of illuminating gas can be made with it in fifty-five minutes.

Hempel's Apparatus. Description. The apparatus, Figs. 122 and 123, is very similar in principle to that of Orsat; the burette is longer, admitting of the reading of small quantities of gas, and the pipettes are separate and mounted in brass clamps on iron stands. P shows a "simple" pipette[5] provided with a rubber bag; this form, after twenty-five years of use, can be said satisfactorily to take the place of the cumbersome "compound" pipette.

The pipette for fuming sulphuric acid[6] is shown at F, and differs from the ordinary in that vertical tubes after the manner of those in the Orsat pipettes replace the usual glass beads. This prevents the trapping of any gas by the filling, which was so common with the beads and glass wool. E represents the large explosion pipette,[7] of about 250-cc. capacity, with walls half an inch thick; the explosion wires enter at the top and bottom to prevent short-circuiting; mercury is the confining liquid. The small explosion pipette holds about 110 cc. and is of glass, the same thickness as the simple pipettes. Water is here used as the confining liquid, and also usually in the burette.

A "Ford" induction coil capable of giving a fourth-inch spark, with three dry cells, four "simple" pipettes and a mercury filled burette, complete the outfit.

The burette should be carefully calibrated and the corrections may very well be etched upon it opposite the 10-cc. divisions.

In working with the apparatus the pipettes are placed upon the adjustable stand S and connection made with the doubly bent capillary tube.

Manipulation. To acquire facility with the use of the apparatus before proceeding to the analysis of illuminating gas, it is well to make the following

[1] Mackintosh, Am. Chem. Jour., 9, 294.
[2] Zeit. f. Anal. Chem., 28, 286.
[3] Treadwell-Hall's "Quantitative Analysis," p. 569.
[4] "Gasanalytische Methoden," p. 102.
[5] Gill, Am. Chem. J., 14, 231, 1892.
[6] Ibid., J. Am. Chem. Soc., 18, 67, 1896.
[7] Gill, J. Am. Chem. Soc., 17, 771, 1895.

determinations, obtaining " check-readings " in every case: I. Oxygen in air, by (1) absorption with phosphorus; (2) absorption with potassium (or sodium) pyrogallate;[1] (3) by explosion with hydrogen.

I. DETERMINATION OF OXYGEN IN AIR

(1) By Phosphorus. 100 cc. of air are measured out as with the Orsat apparatus, the burette being allowed to drain two minutes. The rubber connectors upon the burette and pipette are filled with water, the capillary tube inserted, as far as it will go, by a twisting motion, into the connector upon the burette, thus filling the capillary with water; the free end of the capillary is inserted into the

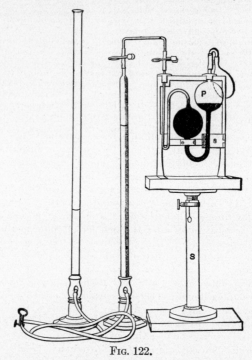

Fig. 122.

pipette connector, the latter pinched so as to form a channel for the water contained in it to escape, and the capillary twisted and forced down to the pinchcock. There should be as little free space as possible between the capillaries and the pinchcock. Before using a pipette, its connector (and rubber bag) should be carefully examined for leaks, especially in the former, and if any found the faulty piece replaced.

The pinchcock on the burette and pipette are now opened, the air forced over into the phosphorus, and the pinchcock on the pipette closed; action immediately

---

[1] The writer finds after an experience of more than twenty-five years in the laboratory with hundreds of students, that sodium pyrogallate can be used with practically the same results as the potassium compound. The absorption is complete, as shown by subsequent treatment with cuprous chloride.

ensues, shown by the white fumes; after allowing it to stand fifteen minutes the residue is drawn back into the burette, the latter allowed to drain and the reading taken. The absorption goes on best at 20° C., not at all below 15° C.; it is very much retarded by small amounts of ethane and ammonia. It cannot be used to absorb commercial oxygen. No cognizance need be taken of the fog of oxides of phosphorus.

(2) **By Pyrogallate of Potassium.** 100 cc. of air[1] are measured out as before, the carbon dioxide absorbed with potassium hydrate and the oxygen with potassium pyrogallate, as with the Orsat apparatus; before setting aside the pyrogallate pipette, the number of cubic centimeters of oxygen absorbed should be noted upon the slate *s* on the stand. This must never be omitted with any pipette save pos-

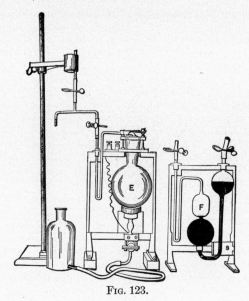

FIG. 123.

sibly that for potassium hydroxide, as failure to do this may result in the ruin of an important analysis. The reason for the omission in this case is found in the large absorption capacity—four to five liters of carbon dioxide—of the reagent.

(3) **By Explosion with Hydrogen.** Forty-three cc. of air and 57 cc. of hydrogen are measured out, passed into the small explosion pipette, the capillary of the pipette filled with water, the pinchcocks and glass stopcock all closed, a heavy glass or fine wire gauze screen placed between the pipette and the operator, the spark passed between the spark wires, and the contraction in volume noted. *The screen should never be omitted, as serious accidents may occur thereby.* The oxygen is represented by one-third of the contraction. For very accurate work the sum of the combustible gases should be but one-sixth that of the non-combustible gases, otherwise some nitrogen will burn and high results will be obtained;[2] that is, $(H+O) : (N+H) :: 1 : 6$.

[1] See Anderson's work, J. Ind. and Chem., **7,** 587, 1915.
[2] This is shown in the work of Gill and Hunt, J. Am. Chem. Soc., **17, 987, 1895.**

II. ANALYSIS OF ILLUMINATING GAS

One hundred cc. of gas are measured from the bottle containing the sample into the burette.

Determination of Carbon Dioxide. The burette is connected with the pipette containing potassium hydroxide and the gas passed into it with shaking until no further diminution in volume takes place.

Illuminants, C_nH_{2n}, C_nH_{2n-6} Series. The gas is passed into saturated bromine water and thoroughly shaken, the bromine fumes removed, with the potassium (or sodium) hydroxide, like the CO_2, and the treatment with bromine and hydroxide repeated until check readings are obtained. The difference between this last reading and that after the absorption of the carbon dioxide represents the volume of " illuminants " or " heavy hydrocarbons " present.

Or fuming sulphuric acid can be employed instead of bromine water, removing the sulphuric and sulphurous anhydrides by potassium hydroxide as in the case of the bromine fumes. Fuming nitric acid is not recommended, as it is liable to oxidize carbonic oxide.

Oxygen. This is absorbed, as in the analysis of air, by potassium or sodium pyrogallate.

Carbonic Oxide. The gas is now passed into ammoniacal cuprous chloride, until the reading is constant to 0.2 cc.; it is then passed into a second pipette, which is fresh, and absorption continued until constant readings are obtained. The second pipette should not have absorbed more than 10 cc. of CO.

Gautier and Clausmann[1] have shown that some carbonic oxide escapes solution in cuprous chloride, so that for very accurate work it may be necessary to pass the gas through a U-tube containing iodic anhydride heated to 70° C.

This is done by interposing this tube between the burette and a simple pipette filled with potassium hydrate. The reaction is $5CO + I_2O_5 = 5CO_2 + 2I$. The diminution in volume represents directly the volume of carbonic oxide present.

The volume of air contained in the tube should be corrected for as follows: One end of the tube is plugged tightly and the other end connected with the gas burette partly filled with air. A bath of water at 9° C. is placed around the U-tube and the reading of the air in the gas burette recorded when constant; the bath is now heated to 100° and the burette reading again recorded when constant. The increase in reading represents one-third the volume of the U-tube, $273 : 273 + (100 - 9) :: 3 : 4$.

Methane and Hydrogen. (*a*) *Hinman's Method.*[2] The gas left from the absorption of carbonic oxide is passed into the large explosion pipette. About half the requisite quantity of oxygen (40 cc.) necessary to burn the gas is now added, mercury introduced through the T in the connector sufficient to seal the capillary of the explosion pipette, all rubber connectors carefully wired, the pinchcocks closed, and the pipette cautiously shaken. A screen of heavy glass or fine wire gauze is interposed between the operator and the apparatus, the explosion

[1] Bull. Soc. Chem., **35**, 513; Abstr. Analyst, **31**, 349, 1906.
[2] Gill and Hunt, J. Am. Chem. Soc., **17**, 987, 1895.

wires are connected with the induction coil, a spark passed between them and the pinchcocks opened, sucking in the remainder of the oxygen. The capillary is again sealed with mercury, the stopcock opened and closed, to bring the contents of the pipette to atmospheric pressure, and the explosion repeated as before, and the stopcock opened.

It may be found expedient to increase the inflammability of the mixture, to introduce 5 cc. of "detonating gas," the hydrolytic mixture of hydrogen and oxygen. The gas in the pipette containing carbon dioxide, oxygen, and nitrogen is transferred to the mercury burette and accurately measured. The carbon dioxide resulting from the combustion of the marsh gas is determined by absorption in potassium hydroxide; to show the presence of an excess of oxygen, the amount remaining is determined by absorption with potassium pyrogallate.

The calculation is given on page 1250. For very accurate work a second analysis should be made, making successive explosions, using the percentages of methane and hydrogen just found as a basis upon which to calculate the quantity of oxygen to be added each time. The explosive mixture should be so proportioned that the ratio of combustible gas (i.e., CH_4, H and O) is to the gases which do not burn (i.e., N and the excess of CH_4 and H) as 100 is to about 50 (from 26 to 64);[1] otherwise the heat developed is so great as to produce oxides of nitrogen, which, being absorbed in the potassium hydroxide, would affect the determination of both the methane and the hydrogen. The oxygen should preferably be pure, although commercial oxygen, the purity of which is known, can be used; the oxygen content of the latter should be tested from time to time, especially with different samples.

(b) *Hempel's Method.*[2] From 12 to 15 cc. of the gas are measured off into the burette (e.g., 13.2 cc.) and the residue is passed into the cuprous chloride pipette for safe keeping. That in the burette is now passed into the small explosion pipette; a volume of air more than sufficient to burn the gas, usually about 85 cc., is accurately measured and also passed into the explosion pipette, and in so doing water from the burette is allowed partially to fill the capillary of the pipette and act as a seal. The rubber connectors upon the capillaries of the burette and pipette are carefully wired on, both pinchcocks shut, and the stopcock closed. The pipette is cautiously shaken, the screen interposed, the explosion wires connected with the induction coil, a spark passed between them, and the stopcock immediately opened. The gas in the pipette, containing carbon dioxide, oxygen, and nitrogen, is transferred to the burette, accurately measured, by reading immediately, to prevent the absorption of carbon dioxide, and carbon dioxide and oxygen determined in the usual way.

Calculation. (a) *Hinman's Method.* 56.2 cc. of gas remained after the absorption; 77.4 cc. of oxygen were introduced, giving a total volume of 133.6 cc.

Residue after explosion.............................	46.9 cc.
Residue after CO_2 absorption.......................	28.2
Carbon dioxide formed.............................	18.7
Contraction.........................133.6 − 46.9 =	86.7
Residue after O absorption.........................	25.6
Oxygen in excess....................28.2 − 25.6 =	2.6

[1] Bunsen, "Gasometrische Methoden," 2d ed., 73, 1877.
[2] Hempel, "Gas Analytische Methoden," 3d ed., 245, 1901.

The explosion of marsh gas or methane is represented by the equation

$$\boxed{CH_4} + \boxed{O_2} \ \ \boxed{O_2} = \boxed{CO_2} + \boxed{H_2O} + \boxed{H_2O}.$$

From this it is evident that the volume of carbon dioxide is equal to the volume of methane present; therefore in the above example, in the 56.2 cc. of gas burned, there were 18.7 cc. methane.

The total contraction is due (1) to the disappearance of oxygen in combining with the hydrogen of the methane, and (2) to the union of the free hydrogen with oxygen. The volume of the methane having been found, (1) can be ascertained from the equation above, equals twice the volume of the methane; hence

$$86.7 - (2 \times 18.7) = 49.3 \text{ cc.,}$$

contraction which is due to the combustion of hydrogen. This takes place according to the following reaction:[1]

$$\boxed{H_2} + \boxed{H_2} + \boxed{O_2} = \boxed{H_2O} + \boxed{H_2O}.$$

Hydrogen then requires for its combustion half its volume of oxygen, hence this 49.3 cc. represents a volume of hydrogen with $\frac{1}{2}$ its volume of oxygen, or $\frac{3}{2}$ volumes; hence the volume of hydrogen is 32.9 cc.

(b) *Hempel's Method.* Of the 82 cc. of gas remaining after the absorptions, 13.2 cc. were used for the explosion; 86.4 cc. air introduced, giving a total volume of 99.6 cc.

Residue after explosion............................ 78.0 cc.
Residue after CO_2 absorption...................... 73.2
                                                     ——
Carbon dioxide formed............................ 4.8
Contraction..........................99.6 − 78.0 = 21.6
Residue after O absorption........................ 70.2
Oxygen in excess....................73.2 − 70.2 = 3.0

The carbon dioxide being equal to the methane present, in the 13.2 cc. of gas burned there were 4.8 cc. of methane. The volume of methane is found by the proportion 13.2 : 82 :: 4.8 : x, whence $x = 29.8$ cc.

The hydrogen is calculated similarly.

Another method for the estimation of hydrogen is by absorption with palladium sponge;[2] it, however, must be carefully prepared, and it is the author's experience that one cannot be sure of its efficacy when it is desired to make use of it. A still better absorbent of hydrogen [3] is a 1% solution of palladous chloride at 50° C.; when fresh this will absorb 20–50 cc. of hydrogen in ninety minutes. A proportionately longer time is required if more hydrogen be present or the solution nearly saturated. The methane could then be determined by explosion or by mixing with air and passing to and fro over a white-hot platinum spiral in a tubulated pipette called the grisoumeter [4] (grisou = methane).

Nitrogen. There being no direct and convenient method for its estimation with this apparatus, the percentage is obtained by finding the difference between the sum of all percentages of the gases determined and 100%.

[1] H_2O being as steam at 100° C. At ordinary temperatures this is condensed, giving rise to " total contraction."
[2] Hempel, Berichte, 12, 636 and 1006, 1879.
[6] Campbell and Hart, Am. Chem. J., 18, 294, 1896.
[4] Winkler, Fres. Zeit., 28, 269 and 288.

New [1] determined nitrogen in illuminating gas directly after the method of Dumas in organic substances; 150 cc. of gas are used, the hydrocarbons partially absorbed by fuming sulphuric acid and the remainder burned in a combustion tube with copper oxide; the carbon dioxide is absorbed and the residual nitrogen collected and measured.

Accuracy and Time Required. For the absorptions the apparatus is accurate to 0.1 cc.; for explosions by Hinman's method [2] the methane can be determined within 0.2%, the hydrogen within 0.3%; by Hempel's method within 1% for the methane and 7.5% for the hydrogen. The time required for the analysis of illuminating gas is from three to three and one-half hours; for air, from fifteen to twenty minutes.

NOTES. The object in filling the capillaries of the explosion pipettes with water or mercury before the explosion is to prevent the bursting of the rubber connectors on them. With mercury this is effected by introducing it through the T-joint in the connector. After testing for oxygen with the pyrogallate a small quantity of dilute acetic acid is sucked into the burette to neutralize any alkali which by any chance may have been sucked over into it. The acid is rinsed out with water and this is forced out by mercury before the burette is used again.

The water in the burette should be saturated with the gas which is to be analyzed —as illuminating gas—before beginning an analysis. The reagents in the pipettes should also be saturated with the gases for which they are not the reagent. For example, the bromine water should be saturated with oxygen, carbon monoxide, methane, hydrogen, and nitrogen; this is effected by making a blank analysis, using illuminating gas.

The method of analysis of the residue after the absorptions have been made by explosion is open to two objections· 1st, the danger of burning nitrogen by the violence of the explosion; and 2d, the danger of breakage of the apparatus and possible injury to the operator. These may be obviated by employing the apparatus of Dennis and Hopkins,[3] which is practically a grisoumeter with mercury as the confining liquid; or that of Jaeger,[4] who burns the gases with oxygen in a hard-glass or quartz tube filled with copper oxide. By heating to 250° C. nothing but hydrogen is burned; higher heating of the residue burns the methane. Recent work shows this procedure to be very slow and not very accurate. Or the mixture of oxygen and combustible gases, bearing in mind the ratio mentioned at the bottom of page 1247, can be passed to and fro through Drehschmidt's [5] capillary heated to a bright redness. This consists of a platinum tube 20 cm. long, 2 mm. thick, 1.7 mm. bore, filled with three platinum or palladium wires. The ends of the tube are soldered to capillary brass tubes and arranged so that these can be water cooled. It is inserted between the burette and a simple pipette, mercury being the confining liquid in both cases. The air contained in the tube can be determined as in the case of the tube containing iodic anhydride, page 1248.

To the method of explosion by the mixture of an aliquot part of the residue with air, method (*b*), there is the objection that the carbon dioxide formed is measured over water in a moist burette, giving abundant opportunities for its absorption, and that the errors in analysis are multiplied by about six, in the example by $\frac{820}{132}$.

[1] J. Soc. Chem. Ind., **11**, 415, 1892.
[2] Gill and Hunt, loc. cit.
[3] J. Am. Chem. Soc., **21**, 398, 1899.
[4] J. Gasbeleuchtung, **41**, 764. Abstr. J. Soc. Chem. Ind., **17**, 1190, 1898.
[5] Berichte, **21**, 3242, 1888.
23

APPLICATIONS OF GAS ANALYSIS AND INTERPRETATION OF RESULTS

It is only within comparatively recent times that Gas Analysis has assumed any importance. The reasons are that the substances with which it deals are so intangible, the apparatus is complicated and fragile, and until lately, competition has not compelled manufacturers to seek every possible source of loss.

Some of its applications are to:

I. Chimney and flue gases;   IX. Natural Gas.
II. Producer and fuel gases;
III. Illuminating gas;
IV. Sulphuric acid gases;
V. Mine gases;
VI. Electrolytic gases;
VII. Acetylene;
VIII. Atmospheric air.

I. CHIMNEY AND FLUE GASES

Here the object is to keep the carbonic acid (CO_2) as high as possible, and to avoid the formation of carbon monoxide: in large plants every additional per cent of carbonic acid means the saving of tons of coal. Savings of 20 to 33% by the use of gas analysis alone, have frequently come to the writer's notice. A satisfactory procedure is to post in the fire-room the percentage of carbonic acid obtained by each stoker, and stimulate a rivalry among the men—a bonus in the pay envelope is also effective. The determinations to be made are:

Analysis of Chimney Gases. Determination of carbon dioxide, oxygen, carbon monoxide, nitrogen, and in some case hydrocarbons. For this purpose the Orsat apparatus is widely employed: the hydrocarbons may be determined by the Hempel apparatus.

Usually a few determinations of carbonic acid will suffice, but for regular work the installation of some form of registering carbonic acid indicator should be installed.

Carbonic Acid Indicators.[1] These usually depend upon the principle of collecting 100 cc. of the gas, causing it to pass through a suitable absorber and collecting the residue in a bell which floats to a greater or less height according to the residual volume. The fluctuations of this bell are recorded after the usual manner of self-registering barometers or thermometers: the usual time for this analysis and record is five minutes.

By modifying this apparatus slightly, it can be applied to the determination of any absorbable gas as, for example, sulphurous acid or chlorine. It has been adapted to carbon monoxide absorption, but it is not usual or easy.

Haber[2] employs the refractive index of gases to determine the amount of carbonic acid in chimney gas; it gives results within half of 1%;[3] it has also been

---

[1] These can be obtained from the following: Combustion Appliance Co., Chicago; Precision Instrument Co., Detroit; Uehling Instrument Co., Passaic. See Bureau of Mines Bulletin No. 91, "Instruments for Recording Carbon Dioxide in Flue Gases."

[2] Z. Ang. Chem., **19**, 1418, 1906; ibid., **23**, 1393, 1910.

[3] Mohr, ibid., **25**, 1313, 1912.

applied to other gaseous mixtures. The instrument is called the Interferometer or Gas Refractometer and is made by Zeiss of Jena.[1]

The Determination of Temperature. This is done by inserting a thermometer, mounted in a metal tube, on the chimney side of the gas sampling tube. These resemble those used for determining steam temperatures or for "running" varnish. It should register to 360° and, under certain circumstances, one showing 550° may be desirable. A chemical thermometer with long stem may also be employed; it should never be inserted naked into the flue—as a sudden hot blast may break it—but always in a tube of cotton-seed oil or sea sand.[2] These thermometers should be tested for accuracy by comparison with a standard, in a carefully stirred oil bath. The standard should be kept exclusively for the purpose and be allowed to stay in the bath until cool. Sudden cooling of a thermometer changes the zero point. The standard can be certified by the makers or the United States Bureau of Standards.

Electric pyrometers are also of course available for these measurements. An error of five degrees (5°) in the reading of the thermometer affects the final result by about 20 calories.

In case none of these appliances be at hand, the maximum temperature can be determined by utilizing the melting-points of certain pure salts or metals; as tin 232°, bismuth 270°, cadmium 302°, lead 327°, zinc 419°, cadmium chloride 541°, antimony 630°, etc. These can be suspended in the chimney in small covered cast-iron boxes.

Composition of the Coal. This is determined by the usual methods of organic combustion and is required only for very accurate work.

Calculation:

a. Heat passing up chimney;

b. Pounds of air per pound of coal.

(a) *Heat Passing up Chimney.* The accurate calculation resolves itself into finding what volume of gas of the composition determined by analysis would be produced by a kilo of the coal used, and whose analysis is known. The temperature of the escaping chimney gases being also known, and their specific heat, the quantity of heat they carry off can be calculated: this divided by the calorific power of the coal gives the per cent of heat lost in the chimney gases. The calculation is rather long and will be found in detail in the author's book.[3]

The formula of Shields.[4]

$$\text{Per cent heat lost} = \frac{\text{Per cent carbon in coal}}{\text{Heating value of coal}} \times \frac{200 + \text{per cent } CO_2}{\text{Per cent } CO_2 + \text{per cent } CO} \times \text{rise in temperature in °C.} \times 0.2864,$$

gives results usually 0.5% low, as no cognizance has been taken of the water vapor.

Another formula[5] in which only the carbon dioxide and its temperature enters was proposed by Bunte and gives close results.

For every per cent of carbonic acid present 43.43 calories per cubic meter of

[1] Bureau of Mines Technical Paper 185, "Use of the Interferometer in Gas Analysis," 1918.

[2] With *rounded* grains, not river sand, as it would make scratches.

[3] "Gas and Fuel Analysis for Engineers," Wiley.

[4] "Power," **30**, 1121, 1909.   [5] J. f. Gasbeleuchtung, **43**, 637, 1900.

flue gases have been developed $= W$; $C =$ specific heat of the flue gases per cubic meter; then W/C represents the initial temperature (which is never attained) the ratio of which to the actual exit temperature of the flue gases shows the heat lost. If $T =$ this initial temperature and t the rise of temperature of the flue gases, then t/T represents the heat lost in the chimney gases.

The following table gives the data for the calculation for both pure carbon and coal of average value:

Per Cent of CO_2 in Chimney Gas.	Specific Heat of Chimney Gas.	Initial Temperature, W/C. Degrees C.		
		For Carbon $= T$.	For Coal $= T$.	Diff. for 0.1% CO_2.
1	0.308	141	167	16
2	0.310	280	331	16
3	0.311	419	493	16
4	0.312	557	652	15
5	0.313	694	808	15
6	0.314	830	961	15
7	0.315	962	1112	15
8	0.316	1096	1261	15
9	0.318	1229	1407	15
10	0.319	1360	1550	14
11	0.320	1490	1692	14
12	0.322	1620	1830	14
13	0.323	1750	1968	14
14	0.324	1880	2102	13
15	0.324	2005	2237	13
16	0.325	2130	2366	13

If there were 11.5% carbonic acid, the initial temperature T would be 1762°; the rise of temperature in the chimney gases is 250°, the loss is $\frac{250}{1762}$ or 14.2%. The accurate calculation gives 14.1.

Finally, for very rapid work, Bunte's Chart, Table V, may be used. The results are within 2% for about 12% of carbonic acid. It is used by noting the point where the diagonal line representing CO_2 cuts the ordinate of temperature—the abscissa corresponding to this point represents the per cent loss.

The following table shows roughly the excess of air, and per cent of heat lost in the chimney gases, their temperature being 518° F.

Per cent CO_2..	2	3	4	5	6	7	8	9	10	11	12	13	14	15
Vol. air more than theory $= 1.0$.......	9.5	6.3	4.7	3.8	3.2	2.7	2.4	2.1	1.9	1.7	1.6	1.5	1.4	1.3
Per cent loss of heat.....	90	60	45	36	30	26	23	20	18	16	15	14	13	12

If the oxygen be from 1.5% to 2% with the temperature of escaping gases at 400–500° F., the fires are too thick; if it be more than 8% they are too thin.

(b) *Pounds of Air per Pound of Coal.* This can be determined by calculating the ratio of carbon to oxygen in the carbonic acid and carbon monoxide and oxygen of the chimney gases, or by the formula of Shields.[1]

---

[1] Loc. cit.

$$\text{Pounds of air per pound of coal} = 2.31\ \frac{\text{Per cent of carbon in coal}}{\text{Per cent } CO_2 + \text{per cent } CO}.$$

Loss Due to Carbonic Oxide. For every gram of carbon burned to carbonic oxide there is a loss of 5.66 calories.

Smoke. For the determination of the amount of smoke in the chimney gases, use may be made of the Ringelmann smoke scale. This consists [1] of a series of rectangles $\frac{3}{4}$ in. $\times \frac{1}{2}$ in. filled with cross-hatching lines a greater or less distance apart, with which the density of the smoke can be compared. Or the Eddy smoke recorder [2] may be employed; this consists of a tube of standard length through which the smoke gases are drawn. A standard electric light is fixed at one end of the tube and viewed through the smoke; its density is measured by the extent to which the light is obscured.

II. PRODUCER AND FUEL GASES. BLAST=FURNACE GAS

Here the object is the reverse of that in the chimney gases, to keep the percentage of carbon monoxide as high as possible and, for gas-engine purposes, the per cent of hydrogen constant.

The determinations made are the same as in chimney gas—CO_2, O, CO,[3] N, and oftentimes hydrogen and hydrocarbons; the quantity of *dust* is sometimes important. The heating value is determined as in illuminating gas, p. 713. The efficiency of conversion would be found by measuring the number of cubic feet of gas made per ton of coal gasified; the calorific power of each (gas and coal) being known, their quotient represents the efficiency. The heat contained in the gas due to its sensible heat, found after the manner of calculating the loss in chimney gases (i.e., volume gas$\times$weight$\times$rise of temperature$\times$specific heat) is to be added to this for accurate work.

As showing producer gas practice, the following typical analyses are cited:

	Anthra-cite.[5]	Bitu-minous.[5]	BlueWater Gas.[5]	Lignite.[5]	Peat.[6]	Tan.[4,5]	Wood.[5]
CO.............	27.0	27.0	45.0	22.0	30.6	14.2	13.3
H_2.............	12.0	12.0	45.0	9.6	6.1	8.7	21.0
CH_4.............	1.2	2.5	2.0	1.6	5.1	5.6	2.6
C_2H_4.............	.....	0.4	.....	0.7	.....	.....	0.3
CO_2.............	2.5	2.5	4.0	6.4	5.7	15.0	16.0
N_2.............	57.0	55.3	2.0	58.9	52.5	56.0	46.7
O_2.............	0.3	0.3	0.5	0.8	......	0.4	0.1
B.t.u.............	137	157	322	......	......	132	140

[1] Power, **40**, 66.   [2] Made by the Hamler-Eddy Smoke Recorder Co., Chicago.
[3] Tech. Paper 106, Bureau of Mines, "Asphyxiation from Blast Furnace Gas."
[4] With 38.7% H_2O, 3.2% ash.
[5] From "Gas Producers and Producer Gas Power Plants," R. D. Wood & Co., 1906.
[6] Richards, J. W., J. Frank. Inst., 415, 1900, quoted from V. Ihering, "Gas Maschinen."

GAS FROM DIFFERENT KINDS OF PRODUCERS

	Down Draft.[3]	Up Draft.[3]	Suction.[1]	Pressure, Taylor.[1, 2]	Mond.[1]	Blast Furnace.[4]	Siemens.[4]
CO...............	17.5	18.3	26.0	22–30	16.0	24	28
H₂..............	11.8	12.9	18.5	15–7	24.0	2	2
CH₄.............	1.1	3.1	0.5	3–1.5	2.2		
C₂H₄............	.04	0.2				2	2
CO₂.............	9.2	9.8	8.0	6–1.5	12.4	12	3
N₂..............	60.1	55.6	47.0	54–60	45.4	60	65
O₂..............	0.2	.04			0.		
B.t.u...........	110		145	138	146	106	122

Determination of Dust. Liddell[5] recommends the following: lump sugar is crushed, and that which is retained by a 90-mesh sieve packed in a 2-in. layer upon copper or brass gauze contained in a glass tube. The sugar is slightly moistened and the gas sucked through it: it is then dissolved in water and the dust collected upon a tared Gooch crucible and weighed. Another procedure and apparatus recommended by the Sargent Steam Meter Co., of Chicago,[6] consists in sucking the gas through a diaphragm consisting of a weighed filter 4½ ins. in diameter, drying and noting the increase in weight.

III. ILLUMINATING GAS [7]

The determinations usually made are as follows:

a. Candle power;	*e.* Analysis;
b. Calorific power;	*f.* Carbon dioxide;
c. Sulphur;	*g.* Specific gravity;
d. Ammonia;	*h.* Tar.

(a) Candle Power. This can be very satisfactorily found using a 60-in. open-bar photometer and Leeson contrast disc. The gas should be burned from a burner commercially obtainable which gives the highest candle power; for gas from 14 to 21 candle power, Sugg's London argand burner, sizes C to F, should be used; for richer gases, Sugg's table top or the Bray slit burner. For a standard of comparison, the sperm candle is convenient, satisfactory, and very extensively used: the Elliott kerosene and Hefner amyl acetate lamps are also employed.

For accurate work the Lummer-Brodhun disc and electric standards, or the Hefner lamp should be used. For the determination of candle power, reference

---

[1] From "Gas Producers and Producer Gas Power Plants," R. D. Wood & Co., 1906.

[2] With anthracite buckwheat.

[3] "Résumé of Producer Gas Investigations," Bureau of Mines Bulletin 13, Fernald & Smith.

[4] Richards, J. W., J. Frank. Inst., 415, 1900, quoted from V. Ihering, "Gas Maschinen."

[5] Power, **38**, 93.   [6] Power, **27**, 331.

[7] Circular 48, Bureau of Standards, "Standard Methods of Gas Testing," 1916.

may be had to Circular No. 48 of the Bureau of Standards on "Standard Methods of Gas Testing," 1914, or Stone, "Practical Testing of Gas and Gas Meters."

Carburetted water gas shows from 20–28 candle power, coal gas 14–20, oil gas 45–60, oil-air gas 30–35, gasolene 12–17, acetylene 170–200.

Inasmuch as 85 per cent of the gas now made is used for its heating power (mantle burners), the candle power is infrequently determined.

(b) **Calorific Power.** (a) *Direct Determination.* This is most commonly

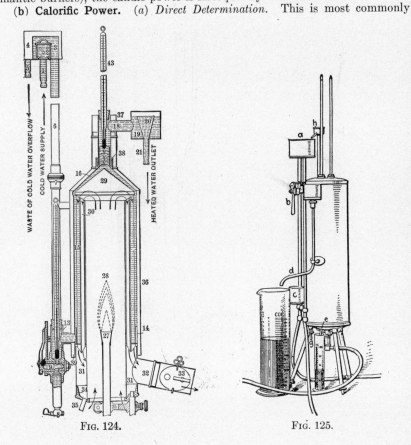

FIG. 124.   FIG. 125.

determined by the Junkers calorimeter, although others in use are the Sargent, Doherty, and in England the Boys and Simmance-Abady.

The original form is shown in section in Fig. 124 and the later modification in Fig. 125. As seen in Fig. 124 it consists of a combustion-chamber, 28, surrounded by a water-jacket, 15 and 16, this being traversed by a great many tubes. To prevent loss by radiation this water-jacket is surrounded by a closed annular air-space, 13, in which the air cannot circulate. The whole apparatus is constructed of copper as thin as is compatible with strength. The water enters the jacket at 1, passes down through 3, 6, and 7, and leaves it at 21, while the hot combustion gases enter at 30 and pass down, leaving at 31. There is therefore not only a very large surface of thin copper between the gases and the water, but the two move in opposite directions, during which process all the heat generated by the flame is transferred to the water, and the waste gases leave the apparatus approximately at atmospheric temperature. The gas to be burned is first passed through a meter, Fig. 126, and then, to insure constant pressure, through a pressure-regulator. The source of heat in relation to the unit of heat is thus rendered stationary; and in order to make the absorbing quantity of heat also stationary, two overflows are provided at the calorimeter, making the head of water and over-

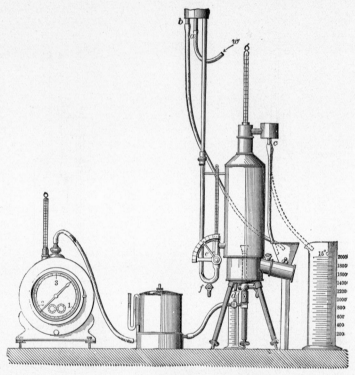

FIG. 126.

flow constant. The temperatures of the water entering and leaving the apparatus can be read by 12 and 43; as shown before, the quantities of heat and water passed through the apparatus are constant. As soon as the flame is lighted, 43 will rise to a certain point and will remain nearly constant.

Manipulation. The calorimeter is placed as shown in Fig. 126, so that one operator can simultaneously observe the two thermometers of the entering and escaping water, the index of the gas-meter, and the measuring-glasses.

No draft of air must be permitted to strike the exhaust of the spent gas.

The water-supply tube *w* is connected with the nipple *a* in the center of the upper container; the other nipple, *b*, is provided with a waste-tube to carry away the overflow, which latter must be kept running while the readings are taken.

The nipple c, through which the heated water leaves the calorimeter, is connected by a rubber tube with the large graduate. d empties the condensed water into the small graduate.

The thermometers being held in position by rubber stoppers and the water turned on by e until it discharges at c, no water must issue from d or from 39, Fig.124, as this would indicate a leak in the calorimeter.

The cock e is now set to allow about two liters of water to pass in a minute and a half, and the gas issuing from the burner ignited. Sufficient time, about twenty minutes, is allowed until the temperature of the inlet-water becomes constant and the outlet approximately so; the temperature of the inlet-water is noted, the reading of the gas-meter taken, and at this same time the outlet-tube changed from the funnel to the graduate. Ten successive readings of the outflowing water are taken while the graduate (2-liter) is being filled and the gas shut off.

A better procedure is to allow the water to run into tared 8-liter bottles, three being used for a test, and weighing the water. The thermometer in the outlet can then be read every half-minute.

Example.—Temp. of incoming water, 17.2°
Temp. of outgoing water, 43.8°
Increase, 26.6°

Gas burned, 0.35 cu.ft.

$$\text{Heat} = \frac{\text{Liters water} \times \text{Increase of temp.}}{\text{Cu.ft. gas}} = \frac{2 \times 26.6}{0.35} = 152.3 \text{ C.}$$

From burning 1 cu.ft. of gas 27.25 cc. of water were condensed. This gives off on an average 0.6 C. per cc.

$27.25 \times 0.6 = 16.3$ C.; $152.3 - 16.3 = 136$ C. per cubic foot; $136 \times 3.968 = 540$ B.t.u.

NOTES. After setting up the apparatus the *first* thing to be done is to turn on the *water*—(*not the gas*). Similarly, the *water* should be shut off *last*. All connections and the meter should be tested for leaks before each test. The water level in the meter should be checked daily. Slight drafts caused by moving suddenly near the apparatus will vary outlet readings and vitiate the test. The instrument should not be set up near a window or heating apparatus where radiant heat might affect the readings.

If 0.2 cu.ft. of gas are burned, then an error of 0.1° F. in temperature of water means an error of 4 B.t.u.; an error of 0.01 lb. water, 0.9 B.t.u.; 1° F. in gas temperature, 1.8 B.t.u.; 0.1 in. (barometer), 2 B.t.u.; 1 in. water pressure of gas, 1.5. B.t.u.[1]

The calorific power obtained without subtracting the heat given off by the condensation of the water represents the *total* heating value of the gas. This is the heat given off when the gas is used for heating water or in any operation where the products of combustion pass off below 100° C. The *net heating value* represents the conditions in which by far the greater quantity of gas is consumed, for cooking, heating and gas engines, and is one which should be reported. It should, however, be corrected,[2] to the legal cubic foot, that is, measured at 30 ins. barometric pressure, and 60° F. saturated with moisture.

The apparatus has been tested for three months in the German Physical Technical Institute with hydrogen, with but a deviation of 0.3% from Thomson's value. This

[1] Rept. Joint Committee on Calorimetry Public Service Commission and Gas Corporations in the Second Public Service District of New York State, p. 81, 1910.

[2] A difference of 1° C. or of 3 mm. pressure makes a change of 0.3% in the volume. Pfeiffe, J. Gasbeleucht., **50**, 67, 1907.

value may vary nearly that amount from the real value owing to the method which he employed.

The chief sources of error are,[1] in adjusting the meter, in measuring the temperature—rise of the water, and in changing over the outflow water to the weighed vessels.

(b) *By Calculation.*[2] Let us suppose an illuminating gas gave the following analysis: Illuminants 15, carbon monoxide 25.3, methane 25.9, hydrogen 27.9%; the heating value of these gases according to Table 3, page 737 is as follows:

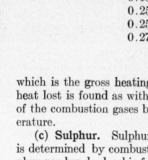

$$0.15 \times 2000 = 300.0 \text{ B.t.u.}$$
$$0.253 \times 341 = 86.3$$
$$0.259 \times 1065 = 276.0$$
$$0.279 \times 345 = 96.3$$

$$758.6 \text{ B.t.u.}$$

which is the gross heating value of the gas. The correction for the heat lost is found as with chimney gases, by multiplying the volume of the combustion gases by their weight × specific heat × rise of temperature.

(c) **Sulphur.** Sulphur, being present in gas in so many forms, is determined by combustion and usually reported in grains of sulphur per hundred cubic feet.

One of the most easily portable and satisfactory forms is that of Hinman and Jenkins described as follows:[3] The upper vessel, Fig. 127, is a " bead glass " 300 mm. long and 60 mm. in diameter; this is filled with large cut-glass beads, held up by a suitable fluted glass, giving a large condensing surface without obstructing the draft. To this bead glass is attached, by a rubber connector, the adapter, 410 mm. long and 50 mm. lower internal diameter. To the upper adapter is attached, by means of the " connecting piece," the lower adapter, 400 mm. long and 40 mm. lower diameter. The connecting piece projects 12 mm. above the top of a rubber stopper, fitting the upper adapter, and is surmounted by a watch-glass deflector carried on platinum wires. An overflow tube carries the condensation to the Erlenmeyer flask hung on the stopper as shown; this tube is so adjusted that some liquid remains on the stopper to keep it cool and to absorb some of the ascending gases. The Bunsen burner is fitted with a lava tip having a 5-mm. hole; surrounding the burner is a glass tube 20 mm. in diameter, forming the inner wall of an annular chamber, of which the outer wall is a glass ring 50 mm. in diameter. Into this chamber, which serves to contain 10% ammonium hydroxide, the lower adapter dips 10 mm.

Fig. 127.

The lower adapter is joined to the " connecting piece " by a short cork-lined metal tube. Although radically different in form, this apparatus is very similar to the Referees' in general principle and in method of use, the principal difference

[1] Technologic Papers of the Bureau of Standards No. 36. " Gas Calorimetry," Waidner and Mueller, page 100, 1914.

[2] U. S. Geol. Survey Paper No. 48; Part III, page 1005.

[3] Jenkins, J. Am. Chem. Soc., **28**, 543, 1906, also Technologic Paper No. 20, Bureau of Standards, McBride and Weaver " Determination of Sulphur in Illuminating Gas," 1913, also Stone, op. cit.

being the use of ammonium hydroxide instead of dry ammonium carbonate as a source of ammonia. About 10 cc. of concentrated ammonium hydroxide is placed in the reservoir about the burner at the beginning of the test and about 5 cc. more added every fifteen or twenty minutes. The gas is consumed at the rate of 0.4 to 0.6 cu.ft. per hour, and 2.5 to 3 ft. burned, if the sulphur is to be estimated gravimetrically, otherwise 1 cu.ft. is enough. When the run is completed the apparatus is allowed to cool and is then flushed four times by pouring 50 cc. portions of water in at the top of the bead tube. To the solutions and washings are added 2–3 cc. bromine water, and it is evaporated to 30 or 40 cc.; an excess of a hydrochloric acid solution of barium chromate is added to the hot solution, it is gently boiled, an excess of dilute ammonia added, again boiled for a minute, filtered and washed. The ammonium chromate in the filtrate (the chromic acid being equivalent to the sulphuric acid in the original solution) after being boiled in a stout flask, with a Bunsen valve, to expel the air, is cooled and titrated directly with stannous chloride (3.25 grams Sn per liter) using starch and potassium iodide to accentuate the end point.

The equations are:

$$(NH_4)_2SO_4 + BaCrO_4 = BaSO_4 + (NH_4)_2CrO_4,$$

$$2(NH_4)_2CrO_4 + 2HCl = (NH_4)_2Cr_2O_7 + 2NH_4Cl + H_2O,$$

$$3SnCl_2 + (NH_4)_2 Cr_2O_7 + 14HCl = 3SnCl_4 + 2NH_4Cl + 2CrCl_3 + 7H_2O.$$

The strength of the stannous chloride should be determined at the same time by standard bichromate of potassium.

Or the sulphuric acid can be determined with the turbidimeter as for sulphur in coal (see chapter). The amount of sulphur is usually from 20 to 30 grains per 100 cu. ft.

Sulphuretted Hydrogen.[1] The test is made by hanging a strip of paper moistened with lead acetate solution (1 : 20) in a bell-jar or tube through which the gas is passing at about 5 cu.ft. per hour and allowing it to act for one minute. Usually several tests are made. The gas should be taken fresh from the main and care should be taken not to confound any black tarry spots with lead sulphide. A properly purified gas should give no test.

It is quantitatively determined by drawing a known volume of the gas through standard iodine solution. Tutweiler[2] measures the gas in a modified Bunte burette over mercury, and having added starch solution, runs in a known quantity of standard iodine solution until it is in slight excess. If 100 cc. of gas were taken, the number of cubic centimeters of solution gives the grains of H_2S per 100 cu.ft., 1 cc. iodine = 0.0017076 gram iodine = 100 grains H_2S per 100 cu.ft.

(d) Ammonia.[3] This is determined by absorption in standard acid colored with cochineal: 10 cc. of HCl are placed in the bulb, Fig. 117, 2–3 drops cochineal solution added, and the gas allowed to bubble through it until the yellow color changes to a deep purple; the meter is now read. The acid is made by diluting 38.2 cc. N/10 HCl to 1 liter, 10 cc. = 0.01 grain of NH_3; the cochineal solution is made by treating 3 grams of the ground insect with 250 cc. 20% alcohol, allowing to stand forty-eight hours and filtering. The bubble tube is inserted in series

---

[1] Tech. Paper No. 41, Bureau of Standards, "Lead Acetate Test for Hydrogen Sulphide in Gas." [2] J. Am. Chem. Soc., **23**, 173, 1901.
[3] Tech. Paper No. 34, Bureau of Standards, "Determination of Ammonia in Illuminating Gas."

with the gas supply to the sulphur apparatus, Fig. 127, (c) so that both determinations are run at one time: the gas is passed through at the rate of 0.6 to 0.8 cu.ft. per hour. Massachusetts law limits the amount of ammonia to 10 grains per 100 cu.ft.

(e) **Analysis.** The volumetric analysis is carried out according to pages 704; either bromine water or fuming sulphuric acid can be used to absorb the "illuminants." Besides ethylene, it may be desirable to determine benzol: this is best done according to Dennis, O'Neill and McCarthy [1] by absorption in an ammoniacal solution of nickel cyanide.

Naphthalene. This is determined in purified gas by passing it through N/20 picric acid solution. White [2] determines it in raw gas by precipitation of the picrate and subsequent recovery of the naphthalene.

COMPOSITION OF COMMERCIAL GASES [3]

	CO_2	] Ill'ts.	O_2.	CO.	H_2.	CH_4.	C_2H_6.	N_2.	Candle Power.	B.t.u.
Coal...........	1.6	4.0	0.4	8.5	49.8	29.5	3.2	3.2	16.1	622
Carb. water......	3.0	13.3	0.4	30.4	37 7	10.0	3.2	2.1	22.1	643
Blue water......	3.4	0.0	0.9	40.9	50 8	0.2	0.	3.5	......	299
Pintsch.........	0.2	30.0	0.	0.1	13 2	45.0	9.0	1.6	43.0	1276
Blau...........	0.	51.9	0.	0.1	2.7	44.1	0.	1.2	48.2	1704
Oil-water........	2.6	7.0	0.2	9.2	39.8	34.6	....	6.6	19.7	680
Oil............	0.3	31.3	0.	2.4	13.5	46.5	3.9	1.1	38.0	1320
Gasolene........	..	1.5	18.5	..	..	C_6H_{14}	$= 10.3$	69.7	16.0	514
Acetylene	..	96.0	0.8	..	..	....	....	3.2	225.0	1350
Natural.........	0.3	0.3	0.3	0.5	2.3	92.6	....	3.5	$\dfrac{H_2S}{0.2}$	840–1174

(f) **Carbon dioxide.** This is best determined by Rudorff's method [5] which consists in titrating about a liter of the gas with standard potassium hydroxide. The arrangement and manipulation of this apparatus will be evident from Fig. 128: the capacity of the Woulff bottle must be known and if the gas contains hydrogen sulphide, it must be absorbed by passage over manganese dioxide.

(g) **Specific Gravity.** The readiest method depends upon the time of efflux of the gas compared with air; sp.gr. $= \dfrac{G_2}{A_2}$ G and A represent the times of efflux in seconds of gas and air. The apparatus is obtainable from the dealers, or may be constructed according to Jenkins [6] as follows:

"It consists, Fig. 129, of two large rubber stoppers, each having a brass tube, projecting laterally near the large end, and connecting with the hole in the stopper. A glass piece A in the form of a truncated cone fits tightly over one stopper; it is 9 ins. long, $1\frac{1}{2}$ ins. diameter at the base and 1 in. at the top. A similarly shaped piece B 9 ins. long by $1\frac{1}{2}$ ins. diameter at the lower end fits over the second stopper; 2 ins. above the latter the tube has a constriction 1 in. in diameter, and at its

[1] J. Am. Chem. Soc., **30**, 236, 1908.
[2] Proc. Mich. Gas Association, **83**, 1904, 1905.
[3] Fulweiler, Rogers, "Industrial Chemistry," 3d Ed., 474.
[4] Orton, Geol. of Ohio, VI, 137.   [5] Hempel, op. cit., 262.
[6] Stone, op. cit., 261. See also Bureau of Standards, Tech. Papers 89 and 94, by J. S. Edward.

upper part is narrowed to a neck $\frac{5}{16}$ in. in diameter which is ground on the inside to receive the end of a tube $7\frac{1}{2}$ ins. long and $\frac{1}{4}$ in. in diameter, in the upper end of which is fitted a platinum plate containing the emission orifice. One and three-fourths inches below this plate is a three-way glass stopcock, and 3 ins. below the latter a scratch surrounds the tube and serves as the upper mark in the escape of the gas.

"Fitted into the hole in the stopper is a hollow cylinder of brass to which is soldered a curved piece of brass wire pointed at the end, which rises $1\frac{1}{2}$ ins. above the surface of the stopper. The two brass tubes projecting from the outside of the stoppers are joined by a piece of rubber tubing 15 to 18 ins. long.

"In using this instrument the larger tube B is filled with water, of the temperature of the room, nearly to the top, the stopcock being turned so that egress

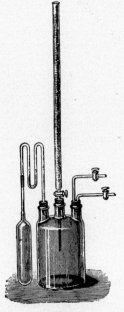

FIG. 128.

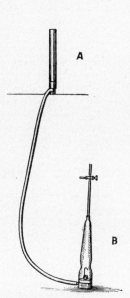

FIG. 129.

of air from the smaller tube is prevented. The larger tube is placed on an elevated surface just high enough so that its bottom is above the level of the scratch on the narrow outlet tube, the cock is turned so that the air may escape through the orifice in the platinum plate, and on the second, when the point of the brass wire breaks the surface of the rising water, a stop watch is started. The latter is stopped when the water exactly reaches the scratch.

"The large tube is lowered, and the stopcock turned so that air may enter through its hollow point. When the water is again all in the large cylinder, the cock is turned to connect the small vessel with the outside air through the platinum tip, the large cylinder is replaced on the elevation and the operation repeated. Results should be obtained which check within one-fifth second.

"Now connect a rubber tube to the gas supply and to the tip of the stopcock, lower the large cylinder and force the water into the latter by means of the gas pressure. Thoroughly saturate the water with the gas to be tested; this may be done by shaking gas and water together and by forcing the water up and down in the small vessel in contact with the gas. Repeat the operation with gas in in the same manner as described for air. The calculation is made in accordance with the formula.

"The advantages of this apparatus are its portability, its cheapness, its rapidity and accuracy. When set up, the cylinders are inclined to be a trifle unstable; this may be overcome by fastening a lead plate to the base of each stopper. Four precautions in connection with its use should be emphasized: (1) The water must be of the room temperature; (2) the water must be thoroughly saturated with the gas; (3) the platinum tip, stopcock, and upper part of the tube must be kept dry and clean; (4) the large cylinder must always, in any one determination, be placed at the same height."

Another method consists in the use of the Lux gas balance. This consists of a balanced globe into which the gas previously filtered through cotton, passes and its specific gravity is read off directly on a scale.

The knowledge of the specific gravity is important, as it is involved in the formula for the calculation of the flow of gas in pipes; it also enables the gas manager to ascertain the weight of gas produced from the coal, and to get an idea of the nature and amount of impurities in the gas, all these being heavier.

(h) **Tar.** For the estimation of tar, Clemens Winkler [1] recommends the procedure of Tieftrunk: This consists in passing the gas through 25% alcohol and collecting and weighing the tar on a tared filter.

IV. SULPHURIC ACID GASES,

the gases involved in the manufacture of sulphuric acid:

    a. Burner gases;
    b. Nitrogen gases;
    c. Oxygen;
    d. Gases involved in the contact process.

(a) Burner Gases. Sulphur Dioxide

This gas may be determined by the method of Reich. It consists in aspirating the gas through standard iodine solution (N/10 is suitable) until it is decolorized. The amount of iodine used in the test and the volume of the aspirated gas being known, the percentage of SO_2 can readily be calculated.

Fig. 130 shows a form of apparatus for making this determination. The standard iodine, 5 to 25 cc. N/10 I, diluted to 150 to 200 cc., is placed in the bottle, about 400 cc. capacity, and starch indicator added.[2] The gas to be tested is aspirated through the iodine until the color of the starch blue fades completely. Water which flows out from the graduated cylinder by lowering the aspirating bottle, produces the suction, and the amount measures the volume of the aspirated gas. From the quantity of iodine used and the volume of the gas required to decolorize the solution the per cent of sulphur dioxide is calculated.

[1] "Die Industrie Gase," page 52, also Hempel, op. cit., 239.
[2] Starch indicator may be omitted if the light is good for observing the fading out of the iodine color.

Should the contact gas contain SO_3, this is absorbed by passing the gas through 50 to 100 cc. of strong H_2SO_4, to avoid the action of SO_3 on the rubber tubing of the apparatus. A rapid current of the gas is passed through the acid to saturate it with SO_2 before making the tests.

The Reich method is more applicable for determining small amounts of SO_2. A 12–15-liter graduated aspirating bottle is used in works tests of exit gases for measuring the gas. Since these volumes are under standard conditions (760 mm. and 0° C.), it will be necessary to convert the volumes obtained in the tests to these conditions, using the formula $V = V° \dfrac{P° - w}{760 (1 + 0.00367t)}$, where $V° =$ measured volume, $P° =$ observed barometric pressure, $t =$ temperature of the gas, and $w =$ aqueous vapor pressure at temperature of the test.

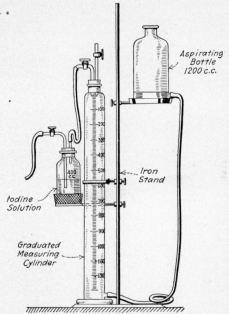

FIG. 130. Portable Reich Apparatus.

TABLE FOR REICH'S TESTS FOR PERCENTAGE SO_2. USING TENTH NORMAL IODINE SOLUTION

Volume Per cent SO_2	25 cc. N/10 Iodine.	10 cc. N/10 Iodine.	5 cc. N/10 Iodine.
12	205 cc. gas	. . . . . .	. . . . . .
11.5	215 " "	. . . . . .	. . . . . .
11	226 " "	. . . . . .	. . . . . .
10.5	238 " "	. . . . . .	. . . . . .
10	252 " "	. . . . . .	. . . . . .
9.5	265 " "	. . . . . .	. . . . . .
9	283 " "	. . . . . .	. . . . . .
8.5	300 " "	. . . . . .	. . . . . .
8	321 " "	. . . . . .	. . . . . .
7.5	344 " "	. . . . . .	. . . . . .
7	371 " "	148 cc. gas	. . . . . .
6.5	402 " "	161 " "	. . . . . .
6	438 " "	175 " "	. . . . . .
5.5	. . . . . .	192 " "	. . . . . .
5	. . . . . .	212 " "	. . . . . .
4.5	. . . . . .	237 " "	. . . . . .
4	. . . . . .	268 " "	. . . . . .
3.5	. . . . . .	308 " "	154 cc. gas
3	. . . . . .	361 " "	181 " "
2.5	. . . . . .	436 " "	218 " "
2	. . . . . .	. . . . . .	274 " "
1.5	. . . . . .	. . . . . .	367 " "
1.4	. . . . . .	. . . . . .	393 " "
1.3	. . . . . .	. . . . . .	424 " "
1.25	. . . . . .	. . . . . .	442 " "

Sulphur Dioxide in Exit Gases.[1] Sulphur dioxide is seldom above 1% in exit gases leaving the absorption tower of the sulphuric acid plant. Generally the loss is below 0.2% on a carefully regulated unit. The Reich method is sufficiently accurate for this determination, for all practical purposes. If 10 cc. of N/10 iodine are used the percent SO_2 may be calculated by the formula:

$$\frac{11.17}{V_0+11.17} = \%SO_2.$$

$V_0 =$ volume of the gas reduced to standard condition 0° C and 760 mm.
11.17 = cc. of SO_2 gas equivalent to 10 cc. of N/10 iodine.

The following table is calculated on the assumption that the gas is under a pressure of 760 mm.+vapor pressure of 17 mm., at room temperature of 20° C.

Measured Vol.	Per cent SO_2	Measured Vol.	Per cent SO_2
1000 cc	1.22	3200 cc	.38
1100 cc	1.09	3400 cc	.36
1200 cc	1.01	3600 cc	.34
1300 cc	.93	3800 cc	.32
1400 cc	.87	4000 cc	.31
1500 cc	.81	4200 cc	.29
1600 cc	.76	4400 cc	.28
1700 cc	.72	4600 cc	.27
1800 cc	.67	4800 cc	.26
1900 cc	.64	5000 cc	.25
2000 cc	.61	5500 cc	.22
2100 cc	.58	6000 cc	.20
2200 cc	.55	6500 cc	.18
2300 cc	.53	7000 cc	.17
2400 cc	.51	7500 cc	.16
2500 cc	.49	8000 cc	.15
2600 cc	.47	8500 cc	.14
2700 cc	.45	9000 cc	.14
2800 cc	.44	9500 cc	.13
2900 cc	.42	10000 cc	.12
3000 cc	.41		

Sulphur Dioxide in the Inlet Gases of the Sulphuric Acid Contact System [1]

Apparatus. *Burette.* This should be of the bulb type with a graduated capacity of 100 cc., the bulb holds about 87 cc.; the stem is graduated in tenths of a cubic centimeter from 0 to 12 cc. The diameter of this graduated portion is such that each cubic centimeter occupies approximately 18 mm. in length. The total length of the burette is 45 to 50 cc.

There is a constriction at the lower end of the burette, or the rubber tube connecting the burette with the leveling tube may be pinched down so that it requires 10 to 15 seconds to pass 100 cc. of mercury in or out of the burette.

The burette has a water jacket of sufficient capacity to include the chamber of the burette and its graduated portion. The diameter should be sufficient to accommodate the bulbed portion of the burette and a thermometer suspended by its side. Distilled water boiled free of air is used in this water jacket.

[1] Communicated by W. W. Scott

A thermometer registering from 5 to 35° graduated in tenths of a degree is left suspended in the water jacket next to the bulb.

Leveling Tube. This is preferably a straight glass cylinder constricted at lower end to accommodate the heavy-walled rubber tubing, connecting the tube with the burette. This tube is about 52 cm. long and has a diameter of 18 to 25 mm. The lower portion of the tube, where this is held by the hand, has a covering either of rubber, or of a heat-insulating material, to prevent warming of the mercury while making the test.

Capillary Tube. The tube connecting the burette with the pipettes and the

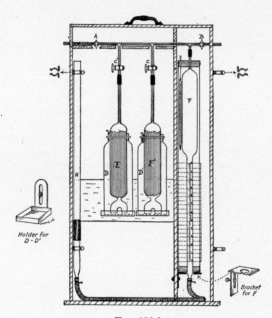

FIG. 131.[1]

sampling pipe should have a fine capillary—the entire internal capacity should not exceed 1 cc. Details of construction shown in the figure.

Pipette. The cylinder of the pipette has a capacity of 150 to 175 cc. The pipette reservoir of 500 to 550 cc. capacity is recommended.

Reagents. *Mercury.* Mercury is used in the measuring burette. This should be kept bright and clean and "drag no tail." To keep the gas saturated with moisture the burette should contain about 0.2 cc. of distilled water over the mercury.

Water Solution of Chromic Acid. A 50% solution is recommended, although a weaker solution may be used. The strength of the reagent, however, should be over 25% CrO_3.

Sampling. The iron pipes carrying the gas to and from the testing apparatus have a diameter of $\frac{1}{2}$ in. to $\frac{3}{4}$ in. The line is run from the positive pressure

[1] Orsat apparatus modified by T. L. Briggs and W. W. Scott

flue near the blower to the testing apparatus and back to the minus pressure flue entering the blower, and the gas allowed to flow continuously through this shunt line.

Making the Test. A volume of 100 cc. of the gas is drawn into the chamber burette (Fig. 131), by opening the stopcock A (B being closed) and lowering the leveling-tube—Stopcock A is closed, B opened and the gas expelled into the air by raising the leveling tube H, using care to prevent mercury bumping at the top of the reservoir. (Mercury carried into the chromic acid will reduce this reagent.) A second 100 cc. of the gas is taken and expelled as before. Finally a third 100 cc., carefully measured, is taken for the test. The top of the mercury columns in the burette and leveling tubes should be exactly level. The water surface should be at the 0 mark on the burette. Stopcock B is always closed during the drawing in of the gas. The temperature of the water jacket is now observed. Stopcock A is closed and stopcock C leading to the absorption pipette opened. The leveling tube is raised as before and the gas completely passed into the pipette. The gas is drawn back into the measuring burette by lowering the leveling tube and measured. The mercury columns should stand at the same level, the reading being taken at the surface of the water over the mercury. A second pass into the pipette is now made and, if no further contraction of the gas occurs, the reading taken. The temperature is observed and a correction made of 0.36 cc. per degree (centigrade) rise or fall of temperature. This correction is added if the temperature rises, or is subtracted if the temperature falls.

The contraction of the gas, due to absorption of SO_2, in terms of cc. gives the direct per cent reading.

Example:

> 100 cc. gas taken.
> Final reading 91.5, i.e., direct $=8.5$ cc.
> Temperature change $=0.4°$ rise.
> Then $8.5+(.4\times.36) =8.6\%$ SO_2.

Tests should be made in duplicate, each Orsat having two pipettes. Very little more time is required to run the check test if the following method is observed. The first sample is taken and passed into one of the pipettes; a second sample, immediately taken, is passed into the second pipette. The first sample is now again measured and then returned to the first pipette and then the check sample measured and returned to its pipette. The first sample is again measured and if a further contraction is observed it is again passed into its pipette and the process repeated with the second sample. By thus alternating the tests and allowing the gas to stand in the pipettes the second pass will cause complete absorption of SO_3, third pass seldom being necessary.

Notes and Precautions. *Burette.* The constriction preventing a rapid flow of mercury accomplishes the following:

1. It prevents the wave motion of mercury, which results from a rapid flow. This wave motion makes it exceedingly difficult to draw in 100 cc. of gas accurately, and makes it necessary to hold the tube several seconds until the motion has ceased before taking a reading.

2. The constriction prevents mercury bumping into the capillary and from being thus carried into the absorption reagent.

3. It minimizes the danger of drawing the absorption reagent into the chamber burette.

Water in the Burette. The burette should, as stated, always contain about 0.2 cc. of water, over the mercury to saturate the gas with moisture. Results 1 to 4% low will be obtained if the burette is allowed to become dry, the amount of error depending upon the temperature of the gas. One hundred cc. of dry gas expand upon absorbing moisture to 101.2 cc. at 10°; 101.7 cc. at 15°; 102.3 cc. at 20°; 103.1 cc. at 25° and 104.1 cc. at 30°.

Leveling Tube. The covering recommended prevents warming of the mercury with the hand. When the apparatus is kept stationary, practically no change of temperature takes place during the test if the mercury is thus protected, so that a temperature correction will not be required. If the apparatus is moved from a warm to cold zone or vice versa, temperature corrections will become necessary.

Pipette. The form of pipette shown in the illustration is simple and compact. The bottle affords both protection and acts as a water jacket. The pipette is filled with thin-walled tubes having a small bore. The pipette should be tightly packed as loose packing and large-bored tubes both lessen the efficiency of the pipette, cutting down the surface for absorption.

Rubber Tube Connection. Since sulphur gases act on rubber, in presence of these gases, rubber tubing for connecting the testing apparatus to the sampling pipe should not be used, except in flush connections with the pipe in contact with the inlet tube of the apparatus.

Cleaning the Burette upon Accidental Drawing in of Chromic Acid. Should the reagent be accidentally sucked into the capillary or into the burette, it may be easily washed out with distilled water by drawing this through stopcock *B* and flushing out several times by lowering and raising the leveling tube. The excess water may be removed from the capillary by opening stopcock *C* and allowing to flow out. If mercuric oxide is formed in the burette it may be dissolved by flushing with sodium hydroxide solution.

Chromic Acid Reagent. Theoretically, a charge of 50% aqueous chromic acid solution (100 g. CrO_3 + 100 g. H_2O) amounting to 300 cc., is sufficient to absorb the SO_2 of over 12,000 determinations. In practice, however, the reagent should be renewed long before the chromic acid has been used up by the sulphurous acid.

Number of Passes. Although two passes are generally sufficient to completely absorb the SO_2, it is necessary to make a third pass and observe whether any further contraction takes place. If the reagent is effective and there are no leaks in the apparatus the third pass will show no change.

Lubrication of Stopcocks. A mixture of beeswax and vaseline or wool grease (1 : 2) has been found excellent for this purpose. Not only does it lubricate the stopcock, but it prevents leaks. Eighty parts rubber melted with 20 parts beeswax is also good and is acid resisting.

Rubber Tube Connections. Coating the glass tube with a viscous solution of sealing wax, dissolved in alcohol, or etching it with hydrofluoric acid, on the portion covered by the rubber will make a tight joint so that wiring the joint will not be necessary.

Parallel Leveling Lines are placed behind the burette to enable more accurate leveling of the mercury columns.

(b) Nitrogen Oxides

Nitrogen tetroxide, N_2O_4, and nitrous acid, N_2O_3, can best be determined by absorption in standard permanganate (acidulated with sulphuric acid) according to p. 1238.

Nitric oxide can be determined by passing the gases through soda lye, then by adding air to the collected volume, converting it to nitrogen tetroxide and determining it as above indicated.

Nitrous oxide is determined in the acid-free gases by explosion with hydrogen.

(c) **Oxygen** is usually determined by acid or ammoniacal cuprous chloride—phosphorus is also employed. The percentage of oxygen should not exceed six; a larger amount means that heat is being lost from the chambers by the exhaust gases. Knowing their temperature, the loss of heat can be calculated as with chimney gases.

V. MINE GASES [1]

The gases to be sought are those found in illuminating gas and for most purposes the procedure on p. 1248 can be followed. For small quantities of methane the apparatus of Haldane, modified and described by Burrell and Seibert [2] should be used. This is practically an Orsat, using mercury as the confining liquid and with a compensating tube and grisoumeter for burning the methane.

For determination of **methane** alone, the apparatus of Shaw [3] may be recommended. This determines first the per cent of illuminating gas necessary to make an explosion of definite strength with ordinary air; when this has been done, mine air is used in place of the ordinary air and a smaller percentage of illuminating is required—smaller by the amount of combustible gas in the mine air. The strength of the explosion is measured by noting by the ear the force with which the plunger is driven out from the explosion cylinder against a bell.

In case this apparatus be not at hand, Brunck's [4] method can be employed. This consists in burning the methane in a 2-liter Erlenmeyer flask by means of an electrically heated platinum spiral. The flask carrying the spiral in the stopper is sunk inverted in a vessel of water and the current allowed to pass for half an hour, which is sufficient to burn the methane. It is then cooled and 25 cc. BaO_2H_2 (1 cc. $= 1$ cc. CO_2) added, time allowed for absorption of the carbon dioxide and the excess of BaO_2H_2 determined, p. 1272, and the quantity of methane calculated.

Clowes and Redwood [5] have worked out a method for the detection of inflammable gas in air, employing the " flame cap." When an inflammable atmosphere is brought in contact with a candle or better a hydrogen flame, the gas burns, forming a " cap," like the colorless flame above the blue cone in a Bunsen burner: the length of the flame is a measure of the percentage of gas, and as little as 0.1% is visible using the hydrogen flame.

Carbon Monoxide. Besides combustible gases or " fire damp," it is sometimes necessary to get an idea of the amount of carbon monoxide (" white damp ")

[1] See Technical Paper 14, Bureau of Mines, " Apparatus for Gas Analysis Laboratories at Coal Mines."
[2] Bull. 42, U. S. Bureau of Mines, 17, 42, 1913, also Technical Paper 39, 13.
[3] Berichte, **27**, 692.
[4] O. Brunck, " Die Chem. Unters. d. Grubenwetter," 1908.
[5] " Detection and Estimation of Inflammable Gas and Vapor in the Air," 1896, also Clowes, J. Soc. Arts, **41**, 307. Also McTrusty, " Mine Gases and Gas Testing," 1916.

in the mine air after an explosion or in the " after damp "; chemical methods, p.1248, being too slow, use is made of the behavior of birds and mice when exposed to such an atmosphere. To this end they are carried in cages by the rescuing party and their behavior noticed. Canaries show distress in an atmosphere containing 0.15% of CO in five to twelve minutes, or with 0.20% in half this time: Mice are less sensitive,[1] and men may display distress when carbon monoxide is as little as 0.1%, whereas animals may be unaffected. In case either is overcome by the gas, resuscitation can be effected by bringing them out into the open air again. Repeated exposure of the gas would seem to be without influence.

VI. ELECTROLYTIC GASES

Gases from electrolytic chlorine, hydrogen and oxygen generators. The following are to be sought for:

(a) Chlorine, (b) oxygen, (c) carbon dioxide, (d) carbon monoxide, (e) hydrogen.

(a) Chlorine. Hempel[2] recommends measuring the gas quickly in his burette over water and then sucking in 5 cc. of 50% potassium iodide solution through the capillary and shaking; the diminution in volume gives the chlorine.

The other gases are determined in the usual way. As phosphorus cannot be used for pure oxygen, a specially prepared potassium pyrogallate, p.1279, is employed; cuprous chloride or ammoniacal cuprous carbonate in the absence of carbon monoxide is very satisfactory.

VII. ACETYLENE

Commercial acetylene may contain the following gases:

1. Oxygen;
2. Hydrogen;
3. Methane;

4. Nitrogen;
5. Sulphur-containing gases;
6. Phosphine.

Oxygen is estimated after the absorption of the acetylene itself in fuming sulphuric acid, in the usual way with potassium pyrogallate. Methane and hydrogen would be determined in this residue, after treatment with ammoniacal cuprous chloride to complete the removal of acetylene, by the ordinary explosion methods, p.1248. Nitrogen would be left as a residue.

Sulphur-containing gases. These are most likely organic sulphides, as hydrogen sulphide is probably absent, since the solution is strongly alkaline from which the acetylene escapes. They can be determined by combustion, as in illuminating gas, p. 1260, and best be reported as " total sulphur."

Phosphine is also similarly estimated and the phosphoric acid determined in the usual way: the quantity of PH_3 rarely exceeds 0.05%. Acetylene can be purified by passing over bleaching powder, through acid cuprous chloride or chromic acid: The candle power is usually given as fifty per cubic foot, or 180–200, when burned at the rate of 5 cu.ft. per hour. The explosive limits are, according to Clowes[3] 3 to 82%, to Burrell and Oberfell, 2.5 to 73%.[4]

[1] Burrell, Seibert and Robertson, Bureau of Mines Technical Paper 62, 1914, "Relative Effects of Carbon Monoxide on Small Animals." Also Tech. Paper 11.
[2] "Gas-Analytische Methoden," 4th Ed., 1913, p. 278. [3] Op. cit.
[4] Bureau of Mines Tech. Paper 112, "Explosibility of Acetylene."

VIII. ATMOSPHERIC AIR

(a) Moisture; (b) Carbon dioxide; (c) Ozone; (d) Carbon monoxide; (e) Bacteria.

(a) **Moisture** [1] by chemical means, see p. 1275. The amount of moisture can be determined by the sling psychrometer, or wet- and dry-bulb thermometer or by the hair hygrometer. The sling psychrometer is the most rapid and accurate— the wet- and dry-bulb thermometers are so arranged that they can be rapidly whirled for fifteen or twenty seconds, stopped and quickly read, the wet bulb first; this is repeated until closely agreeing readings are obtained. The humidity is determined in the usual manner from the meteorological tables.

The amount of moisture in the air is probably indirectly responsible for our sensations of comfort or discomfort, rather than the amount of carbon dioxide, as was formerly thought. This moisture controls the heat loss from the body, which loss must be normal—neither too high nor too low. The greater the humidity the less the evaporation, consequently the less the cooling.

For comfort, the higher the temperature the less should be the humidity; the following shows the relation between the two:

Temp., °F	60	68 [2]	70	80	90
Relative humidity, per cent	67	40	49	31	16

(b) **Carbon Dioxide.** One of the most satisfactory methods is that of Hesse.[3] This consists in absorbing the carbon dioxide from a definite volume of air with standard barium hydroxide and determining its loss of strength.

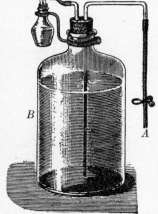

The air is collected in heavy Erlenmeyer flasks of 100–500 or 1000 cc. capacity, or clear glass bottles; these are stoppered with doubly perforated rubber stoppers carrying glass plugs and the capacity of the flask or bottle noted to the depth of the stopper. A 10-cc. pipette and a 15-cc. glass-stoppered burette graduated in cc./10 with an 8-cm. tip, complete the outfit; a solution of 1.7 grams of barium hydroxide and chloride (20 : 1) in a liter of water, B Fig. 132, and of oxalic acid 5.6325 grams per liter (1 cc. = 1 cc. CO_2), with phenolphthalein 1 : 250, are required.

The bottles are filled with steam by exposure for three minutes and the vaselined stoppers inserted, or they may be filled with distilled water and opened in the place the air of which is to be examined.

FIG. 132.

In all this work, it should be remembered that the exhaled breath contains about 400 parts carbon dioxide per 10,000, consequently care should be taken not to contaminate the samples, nor should they be warmed with the hand.

The 10-cc. pipette is partly filled from the tube A, Fig. 132, by means of the rubber connector and sucking the liquid into the pipette: it is rinsed, filled and

[1] Benedict, "The Composition of the Atmosphere with Special Reference to its Oxygen Content," Carnegie Institution of Washington, 1912, Publication No. 166.
[2] For indoor work. [3] Eulenberg's Vierteljahrschr. f. ger. Med. u. San. N. F., **31**, 2.

inserted through one of the holes in the rubber stopper of the bottle, the other plug being momentarily opened. The plugs are replaced and the bottles allowed to rest on their sides, with occasional rolling, for twenty minutes. Not more than one-fifth of the solution should be used up by the carbon dioxide present.

During this time, the barium hydroxide should be standardized; to this end a few drops of phenolphthalein and a quantity of the oxalic acid almost sufficient to neutralize the hydroxide should be run into a 100-cc. Erlenmeyer flask from the burette; this should be passed through the doubly perforated stopper; 10 cc. of the barium hydroxide solution are run into the flask as above described, and also the oxalic acid until a pink color appears.

Phenolphthalein is added to the bottles containing the samples, the oxalic acid burette inserted through the stopper and the excess of barium hydroxide titrated.

The barometric pressure and temperature in the laboratory are noted and the volume of the bottle less 10 cc. (BaO_2H_2) calculated to standard conditions; the difference in the titer of the barium hydroxide solution gives the volume of carbon dioxide in the bottle; this is calculated into parts per 10,000.

Other methods for this determination are more strictly gasometric, measuring the diminution in volume by absorption: Benedict [1] used Sonden's, and Anderson [2] recommends a shortened form of the Pettersson-Palmquist apparatus.

This may be described as an Orsat apparatus using mercury instead of water and with a 25-cc. burette the lower part of which is graduated to 0.0025 cc.; this is connected to a pipette of potassium hydroxide, a delicate manometer and compensating tube. The apparatus is delicate and rapid, but requires a skilled operator to manipulate it.

The amount of carbon dioxide in the outdoor air in the city is about 3.1 parts per 10,000, in the house, 3.7–3.9; with 6–7 parts in a room, the ventilation may be considered as excellent, with 10 parts as about the upper limit. In some theaters which were lighted by gas it approached 50 parts.

(c) **Ozone.** Probably most conveniently determined by Wurster's method, p. 1241.

Determination of Ozone, Iodide Method of Schönbein. [3] The method depends upon the reaction

$$2KI + O_3 + H_2O = I_2 + O_2 + 2KOH.$$

Procedure. A glass bulb of 300 cc. to 400 cc. capacity (the exact capacity being determined by weighing empty, then full of water) with two tubes at opposite sides, closed by stopcocks, one of which was a three-way cock, is filled with water. The ozone tested is introduced into the vessel, displacing the water. The gas is brought to atmospheric pressure by quickly opening and closing one of the cocks. A solution of 2N potassium iodide is introduced in excess of that required, through the three-way cock by means of a second bulb connected by rubber tube to the vessel, after displacing the air in the rubber connection through the cock. The mixture is well shaken and allowed to stand half an hour. The contents of the bulb are washed out with additional iodide solution followed by distilled water and the liberated iodine titrated with standard thiosulphate.

$$1 \text{ cc. } N/10 \text{ } Na_2S_2O_3 = 0.0024 \text{ g. } O_3.$$

---

[1] Op. cit., also Haldane's.   [2] J. Am. Chem. Soc., **35**, 162, 1913.

[3] Further details of this method may be found in Treadwell and Hall, "Quantitative Analysis."

(d) Carbon Monoxide. The qualitative detection is most certainly effected by the blood test; to this end the gas is drawn through a solution of blood contained in a Wolff, Fig. 118, or similar absorption tube and examined for its absorption spectrum. The blood solution is made by mixing ox blood which has been defibrinated by whipping, with an equal quantity of a cold saturated solution of borax; this can be kept (as a side-shelf reagent) in the laboratory for months. This solution is diluted with 19 volumes of water, giving a solution of blood of 1 in 40 which is placed in the absorption tube. The air is drawn through it at a rate of 3 liters per hour, requiring 10 liters in some cases; the solution is put in a thin flat-sided bottle and spectroscopically examined.

Pure diluted blood, Fig. 133, shows two dark absorption bands, spectrum 2, between the D and E line; these are welded into one broad band by reducing agents as NH_4SH, spectrum 4; blood which has absorbed carbon monoxide shows two broader bands in the same place, spectrum 3, which are unaffected by reducing agents. The quantitative determination depends upon the equation,

$$5CO + I_2O_3 = 5CO_2 + I_2.$$

This has been studied by Kinnicutt and Sanford and recently by Morgan and McWhorter and by the writer. The process consists in sucking the air through the iodine pentoxide contained in a U-tube heated in cottonseed oil or glycerin bath to 150°, passing the iodine into potassium iodide solution and then absorbing

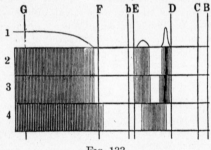

Fig. 133.

the carbon dioxide in standard barium hydroxide. Both the iodine and barium hydroxide solutions are titrated. The last two investigators call particular attention to the ease with which iodine pentoxide at 150° is decomposed by organic matter, particularly stopcock grease; the pentoxide should be sealed into the U-tube, as glass stopcocks cannot be used. The writer can substantiate this statement, and would suggest further that the U-tube be chemically cleaned with cleaning solution ($Na_2Cr_2O_7 + H_2SO_4$) before filling with I_2O_5, as well as the tubes through which the gas is sucked before reaching the U-tube; rubber connections should, if possible, be avoided, and the tubing should have been cleansed by warming with dilute soda lye and washing. The U-tube should be drawn down to the same size as the connecting glass tubing and the two butted closely together in the cleansed rubber connector.

The iodine is titrated with N/1000 thiosulphate and every 2.27 mg. of iodine corresponds to 1 cc. of carbon monoxide under standard conditions; the carbon dioxide is absorbed in the hydroxide contained in a long test-tube 24×2.5 cm. and titrated with oxalic acid (1.1265 grams crystallized acid to 1 liter) using phenolphthalein; 5 cc. of the acid are equivalent to 1 cc. of carbon dioxide.

Katz and Bloomfield [3] find that as little as 0.07% CO can be determined by " Hoolamite," a mixture of iodine pentoxide and fuming sulphuric acid on granular pumice stone. The mixture is kept in sealed glass tubes the ends of which are broken and connected up with a tube of activated charcoal through which the air to be tested is drawn by means of a measured rubber bulb. The amount of carbon monoxide is shown by comparing the color produced with a set of standards.

Haldane [4] states that as little as .01% of carbon monoxide can be determined colorimetrically by absorbing in diluted blood and comparing it with standard carmine solution; carbon monoxide turns the brownish yellow color of the blood to pink.

IX. NATURAL GAS

The determinations to be made are for carbon dioxide, oxygen, methane, ethane, gasolene content and helium.

Burrell and Seibert [1] state that the accurate determination of the constituents of natural gas has proven a stumbling block to gas analysts not familiar with the work. Technical forms of gas-analysis apparatus and established rules for bringing a gas mixture in contact with the absorbents for different constituents are not effective in all cases. Many samples contain absorbable constituents, such as carbon dioxide and oxygen, in extremely small quantities. The fact that oxygen may be a constant constituent of natural gas as it leaves a well has not been determined absolutely. The writers believe that traces of oxygen reported in some samples were due to the contamination of the samples with air. F. C. Phillips [2] detected only minute quantities of oxygen in natural gas from western Pennsylvania after the gas had bubbled continuously for many hours or days through reagents.

Olefin hydrocarbons and carbon monoxide have not been identified in the samples already received at the bureau's Pittsburgh laboratory. Because of the absorption of higher members of the paraffin series by fuming sulphuric acid and cuprous chloride, a natural gas that does not contain olefin hydrocarbons or carbon monoxide but does contain these higher members of the paraffin series will, when treated with these solutions, undergo a reduction in volume and lead the analyst to a wrong conclusion.

Natural gas as a rule contains a large proportion of paraffin hydrocarbons, in some instances as much as 99 per cent, so that if the paraffins are determined by explosion methods, in which a small quantity (8 or 10 cc.) of gas is used, a slight error of manipulation will be multiplied ten or twelve times in calculating results to a percentage basis. The only hydrocarbon that some natural gases contain is methane; but if a small quantity of sample is taken for the combustion analysis, errors are magnified. The relation between the volume of carbon dioxide and the contraction produced by the combustion may indicate hydrogen, although hydrogen is not present. Though the error in the observed data may be small, yet by the calculation to a percentage basis it may amount to several per cent of hydrogen. Many published analyses of natural gas are undoubtedly much in error owing to such causes.

The paraffin hydrocarbons that are gaseous at ordinary temperatures are methane, ethane, propane, and butane. Since the last two are liquefied [3] at ordinary temperatures by pressures below those found in most producing wells, quantities other than very small proportions carried by the permanent gases would scarcely be found in natural gases coming from wells under much pressure. On the other hand, gases drawn from wells by means of a partial vacuum may contain these and higher paraffins in considerable quantity.

[1] Bull. 42, Bureau Mines (1913).
[2] Phillips, F. C., "Composition of Natural Gas; Researches upon the Phenomena and Chemical Properties of Gases," Am. Chem. Jour., **16**, 1894, p. 411.
[3] Tech. Paper 10, Bureau of Mines.

Method of Sampling

Some samples of gas taken by the bureau's investigators are collected by air displacement in bottles with ground glass stoppers. At the wells or supply pipes a stopper is removed and the gas is allowed to run into a bottle until air has been entirely displaced. Usually a few minutes is sufficient. While the bottle is still in place, the stopper is inserted. As a precaution against leakage, melted paraffin is poured over the stopper. The bottles are then well packed in suitable wooden boxes, and mailed to the bureau's Pittsburgh laboratory. When received at the laboratory the stoppers are removed under mercury and the gas is transferred to and analyzed in an apparatus that contains mercury as the confining fluid. Some samples have been received in strong iron cylinders at the full pressure of the well. Other samples have been collected by a method devised by G. A. Hulett, chief chemist of the bureau, and at present used for collecting some of the bureau's natural gas samples. The method is as follows:

Glass tubes about 17 cm. long and 6 cm. wide are provided at one end with a glass tube extension about 15 cm. long and having a 6 mm. bore. The tube is left open. Natural gas is directed into the sampling tube through the orifice by means of a long slender brass tube. When the air originally in the tube has been displaced, the brass tube is withdrawn and the glass tube orifice closed by placing the finger over it. The sampling tube is then carried to a small alcohol flame and the glass tube extension sealed off.

Simplified Apparatus Used in Analyzing Natural Gas

The apparatus used to analyze natural gas is shown in Fig. 133a. The pipette a contains potassium hydroxide solution; pipettes b and d contain alkaline pyrogallate solution. The pipette c is the slow combustion pipette. The burette f has a capacity of 100 cc. and is graduated to 0.1 cc.

Procedure of Analysis

Natural gas is analyzed at the bureau's Pittsburgh laboratory in the following manner:

Oxygen or other gas left in the horizontal capillary train is displaced by drawing a few cubic centimeters of nitrogen from the pipette d (Fig. 133a) into the burette. This mixture is then allowed to escape into the atmosphere.

About 100 cc. of the gas sample is then drawn by mercury displacement from the sample container into the burette. The sample is measured in the burette against the pressure existing in the compensating tube f by bringing the mercury in the manometer tube exactly to the mark g. The sample is then passed successively into the potassium hydroxide and alkaline pyrogallate solutions for the removal of *carbon dioxide* and *oxygen,* burette measurements being made in the same manner as with the original sample.

The residual gas left after the carbon dioxide and oxygen have been determined is discarded and a fresh part of the sample taken for the combustion analysis. The capillary connections are cleared of combustible gas by dilution with air, and about 100 cc. of oxygen is measured into the burette and passed into the combustion pipette. About 35 cc. of the gas sample is then drawn into the burette from the sample container and measured. The platinum wire in the combustion pipette is then heated to a white heat and the gas sample passed at the rate of about 10 cc. per minute into the combustion pipette containing the oxygen. *The paraffins* burn as fast as they enter, so that an explosion consequent upon an accumulation of gas and oxygen can not follow. In analyzing natural gas the authors have obtained the best results by passing the oxygen into the pipette first. When the natural gas is passed in first, the mixture does not always burn as satisfactorily.

After burning, which requires about four or five minutes, the combustion pipette is allowed to cool, and the contraction in volume due to the combustion is measured. The carbon dioxide produced by the combustion is determined by absorption in the potassium hydroxide solution. Finally, the gas is passed into the alkaline pyrogallate solution to make sure that sufficient oxygen has been present for the complete oxidation of the paraffins. Some samples may contain such a large proportion of the higher paraffin hydrocarbons that 100 cc. of oxygen will not be sufficient for the complete oxidation of 35 cc. of natural gas. For such samples a smaller quantity of the gas must be used for the combustion. This statement has especial reference to those natural gases that are used for gasoline manufacture and contain a large percentage of the higher paraffins.

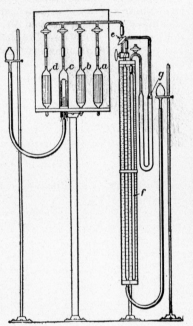

FIG. 133a. Laboratory apparatus for natural gas analysis

In no case is the burette mercury raised above the upper burette stopcock. The gas remaining in the capillary tubing at any stage of the analysis is brought in contact with the solutions by passing it back and forth several times between the burette and the pipette. After combustion, for instance, some carbon dioxide will remain in the capillary tubing between the combustion pipette and the burette when the gas is drawn back into the burette to record the contraction in volume. After most of the carbon dioxide has been absorbed by the passage of the gas into the potassium hydroxide pipette, the small quantity of carbon dioxide in the capillary tubing is swept out of the tubing into the potassium hydroxide pipette. This operation is repeated in order to insure the complete removal of the carbon dioxide. If this precaution were not taken, an error of considerable magnitude would result.

The apparatus may be used also for the analysis of other industrial gases, such as producer gas and blast furnace gas, when all three of the combustible constituents, carbon monoxide, hydrogen, and methane, can be determined simultaneously by triple combustion.

Qualitative Tests for Carbon Monoxide and Olefin Hydrocarbons in Natural Gas

The blood test for carbon monoxide and the iodine pentoxide and palladium chloride tests for carbon monoxide and olefin hydrocarbons are used at the bureau's Pittsburgh laboratory in analyzing natural gases.

A dilute solution of palladium chloride undergoes reduction in the presence of olefin hydrocarbons, hydrogen sulphide, or carbon monoxide.[1] The reaction is marked even when traces of these constituents are present in a gas mixture. Palladium separates out as a black cast or as particles suspended throughout the liquid. The authors found that 0.1% of ethylene in a mixture of ethylene and air could be detected by the appearance of precipitated palladium when 200 cc. of the mixture was passed through a 0.5% solution of palladium chloride at the rate of 10 cc. per minute. The reaction becomes more marked when the gas is shaken in a test tube for about 10 minutes with the palladium chloride solution.

Carbon monoxide, when present in a gas mixture in the same proportion and under the same conditions, produces a precipitation of the palladium from palladium chloride. Carbon monoxide combines with palladium chloride according to the following reaction:

$$PdCl_2 + CO + H_2O = 2HCl + CO_2 + Pd$$

The reaction of palladium chloride on ethylene does not produce carbon dioxide.

Calculations from Combustion Data

If the contraction and the volume of carbon dioxide from the combustion of the gas indicate methane, only this constituent is reported. But if the data indicate higher members of the paraffin series, a calculation is made that gives the two predominating constituents. The gaseous hydrocarbons react with oxygen as follows:

$$CH_4 + 2O_2 = CO_2 + 2H_2O$$
$$C_2H_6 + 3.5O_2 = 2CO_2 + 3H_2O$$
$$C_3H_8 + 5O_2 = 3CO_2 + 4H_2O$$
$$C_4H_{10} + 6.5O_2 = 4CO_2 + 5H_2O$$

But since the fact that some gases deviate somewhat from the gas laws has been shown by the experiments of Rayleigh, Leduc, Baumé and Perrot, and others, corrections must be made in the case of some gas analyses where this deviation is greater than the experimental error.

On the next page is a table of the theoretical and observed specific gravities of the gases involved in the calculations taken from Landolt and Börnstein.[2]

Below are given the equations for the reactions of methane and ethane with oxygen in which corrections have been made according to the specific gravity determinations shown in this table.

$$0.999\ CH_4 + 2.000\ O_2 = 0.994\ CO_2 + 2H_2O$$
$$0.990\ C_2H_6 + 3.500\ O_2 = 1.988\ CO_2 + 3H_2O$$

[1] Phillips, F. C., "Researches upon the Oxidation and Chemical Properties of Gases," Am. Chem. Jour., **16**, 1894, p. 267.

[2] Landolt, H., and Börnstein, R., Physikalisch-chemische Tabellen, 3d ed., 1905, pp. 222–223; Jour. Chem. Phys., **7**, 1909, p. 367.

THEORETICAL AND OBSERVED SPECIFIC GRAVITIES OF CERTAIN GASES *

| Gas | Mol. wt. | Specific gravity | | Observer | Theoretical |
		Theoretical	Observed		Observed
CH_4......	16.03	0.5539	0.5544	Baumé & Perrot.....	0.999
C_2H_6.......	30.05	1.0381	1.0494	do..........	.990
C_4H_{10}.....	58.05	2.0065	2.01	Frankland.........	.998
CO........	28.00	.9673	.96702	Leduc.............	1.000
CO........	28.00	.9673	.96716	Rayleigh..........	1.000
CO_2.......	44.00	1.5201	1.52874	Leduc............	.994
CO_2.......	44.00	1.5201	1.52909	Rayleigh..........	.994
N_2.........	28.08	.9680	.96737	do.............	1.001
N_2.........	28.08	.9680	.96717	Leduc............	1.001
O_2........	32.00	1.1055	1.10535	Rayleigh..........	1.000
O_2........	32.00	1.1055	1.10523	Leduc............	1.000

* At 0° C. and 760 mm. pressure.

As the partial pressure of gases in a mixture decreases, the gases more nearly conform in behavior to the gas laws; consequently a table is herein included showing the correct molecular volume to use in the case of carbon dioxide for different partial pressures. The partial pressure of the carbon dioxide has reference to the ratio of the volume occupied by the carbon dioxide found after the combustion to the total volume of residual gas found after the combustion; that is, if the total volume after combustion is found to be 70 cc. and the carbon dioxide is 40 cc., then the partial pressure of the carbon dioxide will be $\frac{40 \times 760}{70} = 434$ mm., and the proper molecular volume, namely, 0.997, will be found from the table.

The foregoing equations have reference to their use at 0° C. and 760 mm. pressure. The following table shows the correct molecular volumes for carbon dioxide at 20° C. and different partial pressures.

MOLECULAR VOLUME OF CARBON DIOXIDE CORRESPONDING TO DIFFERENT PARTIAL PRESSURES AT 20° C.

Mm. of mercury.	Molecular vol.
100	0.9993
200	.9986
300	.9980
400	.9972
500	.9965
600	.9958
700	.9951
760	.9950

In compiling this table advantage was taken of the work of Rayleigh,[1] Leduc[1] and Chappius[1] having to do with the determination of the specific gravity and coefficient of expansion of carbon dioxide. The specific gravity determinations were given by Rayleigh and Leduc for carbon dioxide at 0° C. and 760 mm. pressure. Values for 20° C. and 760 mm. pressure were determined from the coefficient of expansion of carbon dioxide between 0° C. and 20° C. A graph was plotted from two values, the deviation from the gas laws at 760 mm. pressure and at 380 mm. pressure.

[1] See Landolt and Börnstein, Phys.-chem. Tabellen, 1912, p. 14.

The coefficient of expansion of ethane between 0° and 20° C. has not been determined, consequently the same molecular volume was used at 20° C., the laboratory working temperature, as was reported by Baumé and Perrot [1] at 0° C. The error resulting from this usage can be disregarded without introducing any appreciable error in the analyses, judging from the molecular volume of carbon dioxide which at 20° C. is only 0.001 different from the value at 0° C.

Below are given the molecular volumes to be used in the case of ethane for different partial pressures.

Molecular Volume of Ethane Corresponding to Different Partial Pressures

Mm. of mercury	Molecular vol.
0	1.000
100	.999
200	.997
300	.996
400	.995
500	.993
600	.992
700	.991
760	.990

Although the individual paraffins in a mixture of several can not be exactly determined, one will know with a sufficient degree of accuracy which value in the above column to use by accepting the value that corresponds to the percentage of ethane determined from the combustion analysis. It is also true that in natural gas from many places the partial pressure of ethane is so low that only a small deviation from the gas laws occurs. A slight error arises from the probable percentage of propane or butane in a mixture when the combustion analysis indicates only methane and ethane. In most cases the partial pressures of the propane and butane will also be so low that errors in molecular volumes due to their presence can be disregarded.

Methane conforms so closely to the gas laws that no deviation from the given molecular volume need be made for different partial pressures.

The proper equations to use can be determined only from the partial pressures obtained from the analyses. For the purpose of determining the approximate percentage of ethane the theoretical equations can be used.

Application of the Use of Corrected Equations to the Analyses of Natural Gas and Other Gas Mixtures

Although the combustion analysis does not show an accurate distribution of hydrocarbons in a natural gas mixture, it does show the true total paraffin content. The heating value calculated from such an analysis is also correct.

Determinations by the slow combustion method show that the natural gas supplied to Pittsburgh from the Appalachian fields contains about 83% CH_4, 16% C_2H_6, and 1% nitrogen. The proportions vary from time to time during the year.

This gas is almost all methane but contains small amounts of ethane and propane and some of the higher homologues.

[1] See Landolt and Börnstein, Physikalisch-chemische Tabellen, 1912, p. 148.

A typical analysis with the calculation from the analytical data is given herewith:

TYPICAL ANALYSIS AND CALCULATION

	Burette readings (cc.)
Sample taken...	30.70
Volume after CO_2 absorption............................	30.70
Portion taken for combustion............................	30.70
Oxygen added..	74.85
Total volume..	105.55
Volume after burning...................................	42.30
Contraction..	63.25
Volume after CO_2 absorption............................	7.20
Carbon dioxide..	35.10

CH_4 and C_2H_6 are calculated from the theoretical equations as follows:

Let $x = $ methane,
and $y = $ ethane.
Then $2x + 2.5y = $ total contraction,
and $x + 2.0y = CO_2$ produced.
$C_2H_6 = 15.1\%$.
$CH_4 = 84.1\%$.

Total paraffins $= 99.2\%$.

They are calculated from the corrected equation as follows:

Let $x = $ methane,
and $y = $ ethane.
Then $2.004x + 2.5y = $ total contraction,
and $0.996x + 2.0y = CO_2$ produced.
$C_2H_6 = 15.7\%$.
$CH_4 = 83.1\%$.

Total paraffins $= 98.8\%$.

Gasolene content is determined according to the method on p. 1275.

Helium

Cady and McFarland proceed as follows:[1] "The apparatus is shown diagrammatically in Fig. 133b. *A* is a condensing bulb in which, when surrounded by liquid air, the greater part of the methane and other hydrocarbons contained in the natural gas can be liquefied. *B* and *C* are bulbs containing 20 grams each of cocoanut charcoal. *D* and *G* are U-shaped glass tubes which when immersed in liquid air hold back water and mercury vapors. This is by far the simplest and most effective method of preventing the diffusion of mercury vapor into the spectral tubes used. The actual apparatus is so made that *D* and *G* may both be immersed in the same vacuum tube. *H* is an automatic Sprengel air pump, the mercury being returned to the reservoir in the form of small drops by the suction of a Chapman water pump. *I* is the receiver for collecting helium, *F* and *E* are Plücker spectral tubes,

[1] J. Am. Chem. Soc., **29**, 1526, 1907.

F is a permanent part of the apparatus; E is filled with the gas and sealed off for later examination with a large spectrometer.

To prepare the apparatus for an analysis, a good water pump was connected to the charcoal bulbs at (J), and dry air drawn through the apparatus to remove all gases left from the previous analysis. The connection with the outer air was then cut off and the whole exhausted as thoroughly as possible with the water pump, heating the charcoal bulbs strongly at the same time. When exhaustion had been carried to the limit of the water pump, the Sprengel pump was put into operation, and the pumping continued until practically all the air had been removed. The charcoal bulbs were allowed to cool and then immersed in liquid air. The vacuum quickly became so good that a spark would not pass through the Plücker tubes. The apparatus was then ready for use.

Method of Analysis. The gas for analysis was taken from the gasometer containing it, and the amount used was determined from the weight of water

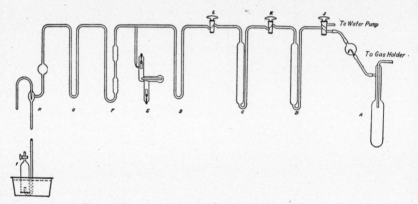

FIG. 133b. Apparatus for Determination of Helium

which displaced it, making all necessary corrections for temperature and pressure. The bulb (A) was first filled with water, inverted, and the water displaced by the gas. It was then surrounded with liquid air and put into connection with the gas holder. If the gas did not contain more than 50 per cent of nitrogen, from 12 to 15 liters would quickly pass into the bulb. A large amount of nitrogen seems to dissolve in the liquid methane. When the desired amount of gas had passed into (A), the connection with the gas holder was closed and after standing for several minutes the stopcock leading into (B) was opened for a moment, that between (B) and (C) being closed. The gas was held in B for five minutes to allow the absorption of everything except the helium. Stopcock (L) being closed, the gas was passed into C and allowed to stay there another five minutes and finally admitted to the Plücker tubes and pump. Here it was examined with the spectroscope, removed by means of the pump, and collected in I. When the pressure in the system became low, stopcock K was closed and more gas admitted into B from A, allowed to stand, passed into C, and finally after standing there the required time, the connection to the pump was again opened. This entire series of operations was repeated until no more helium could be obtained. It has been repeatedly proven by our experience that practically all the helium could be removed by this process. Towards the end of the operation when the pressure in the entire system was low, the liquid methane solution in *A* could be made to boil even when surrounded by liquid air, and this insured the removal of all the helium from the bulb. It might be mentioned in passing that the freezing point of the methane was lowered by the nitrogen, etc., so that only part of it solidified in *A*.

With care all the helium could be transferred to the charcoal bulb without permitting so much nitrogen to pass over as to saturate the charcoal. The purity of the gas could be insured by watching the spectrum as for a new analysis, and the gas run through again. The operation was tedious but not more so than most gravimetric determinations.

The purity of the helium may be determined by its specific gravity, using the Edward specific gravity apparatus, p. 1262, footnote 6.

R. B. Moore [1] proceeds as follows for the detection of helium:

Two or three glass tubes containing 20 grams of charcoal are connected together by glass tubing and arranged so that they can be readily heated to 300° by means of electric heaters, and the evolved gases completely pumped. When this condition is attained, the tubes are immersed in liquid air, and at the temperature of liquid air the charcoal will adsorb nitrogen, hydrocarbons and other heavy gases, but will not adsorb the helium, provided a sufficiently low vacuum is kept in the tubes. Stopcocks are placed between the charcoal tubes, and it is advisable to have a by-pass between alternative tubes, so that any particular tube can be eliminated from the train if desired. The gas to be analyzed is run slowly through the train, the stopcocks giving the proper control, and everything but the helium is adsorbed. The latter gas is pumped by a Sprengel pump into a graduated tube over mercury, and the volume of the helium finally obtained is measured and corrected for pressure and temperature. The purity of the gas can be determined at any time during the analysis by observing the spectrum in a Plückers tube attached between the pump and last charcoal tube.

Very concordant results can be obtained by this method. If the pressure be allowed to build up too much, some helium is retained by the charcoal, but this is not true at the low pressures worked with.[1]

The spectrum is characterized [2] by a yellow doublet line at D_3, wave-length 5876, and also a green line, wave-length 5015.

[1] Moore, J. Frank. Inst., **191**, 191, 1921.
[2] Travers, Proc. Roy. Soc., **60**, 449 (1897).

DETERMINATION OF MOISTURE IN GASES

The gas to be tested is passed through a dehydrating agent such as phosphorus pentoxide, P_2O_5, alumina, Al_2O_3, or lime, CaO, contained in a weighed U-tube,

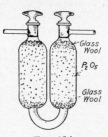

FIG. 134.

Fig. 134. The following facts should be borne in mind in selecting the dehydrating agent: (a) It should not absorb the gas; (b) it should not react chemically with the gas. For example—lime or alumina could not be used for determining moisture in sulphur dioxide, nor could phosphorus pentoxide be used in determining moisture in ammonia. For the former, phosphorus pentoxide is best, and for the latter, lime. Alumina that has been carefully heated to 1400° is useful for determining moisture in neutral gases. It should be remembered that gases dried over calcium chloride will give up moisture to strong sulphuric acid, and these in turn will give up moisture to phosphorus pentoxide: Professor Morley has even determined the amount of moisture that is left after this latter treatment.

Procedure. The volume of the gases required for the test varies widely according to the percentage of moisture in the gas, 1000 cc. to 10,000 cc. are generally required. For minute amounts of moisture it may be necessary to lead the gas over the dehydrating agent for a given length of time, using a manometer or difference gauge, or a gas meter. The absorption tube is weighed before and after the test and the increase in weight taken as the moisture content of the gas.

Method of Determining Gasolene Vapor in Gaseous Mixtures.[1] Fig. 135 shows the apparatus for the gasolene-vapor determination. The bulb a contains phosphorus pentoxide for removing water vapor. If the latter were not removed it would also be retained at low temperatures and would subsequently exert pressure when measurement was being made of the pressure exerted by the gasolene vapor.

To start a determination the apparatus is connected to a vacuum pump and its air exhausted. The mixture of gasolene vapor and air is then introduced at atmospheric pressure, the barometer is read, and the two bulbs are immersed in liquid air contained in a Dewar flask. After about ten minutes, the air is removed from the apparatus with a vacuum pump. The stopcock on the apparatus is then closed, the liquid air in the Dewar flask removed, the gasolene allowed to vaporize, and its pressure read on the mercury manometer attached to the apparatus. The ratio of this pressure to the pressure of the atmosphere gives the percentage of gasolene vapor originally in the air.

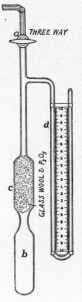

FIG. 135.

[1] U. S. Bureau of Mines, Technical Paper No. 115, Burrell and Boyd.

DETERMINATION OF NITROGEN BY THE NITROMETER [1]

The nitrometer, Fig. 136, consists of a gas-generating bulb fitted at the top with a two-way cock leading to a dissolving cup and a gas-exit tube, and which has at the bottom a connection for a rubber tube leading to a leveling tube, the whole being filled with mercury to a level just below the upper cock; a cylindrical glass measuring tube graduated from 0–100 cc. connected to a leveling tube through

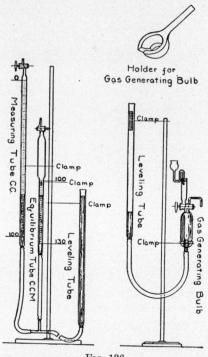

Fig. 136.

a T-tube leading to an equilibrium tube. The latter is shaped like an inverted 100-cc. pipette graduated downward below the bulb from 100–130 cc. The whole system is filled with mercury so that the measuring tube may be completely discharged by raising the leveling tube.

Adjusting the Equilibrium Tube. The volume of 100 cc. of dry air at 0° C. and 760 mm. under the temperature and barometric conditions prevailing at the time is calculated, 3 drops of 98% sulphuric acid are drawn into the tube and the level of the mercury fixed in accordance with the calculation. The cock of the tube is then closed and sealed with melted paraffin. The volume in this tube may be confirmed at any time by opening the measuring tube and adjusting the leveling tube so that the level is the same in the three tubes. The volume of gas in the equilibrium tube is then read and compared with the calculated volume

[1] Joyce and La Tourette, J. Ind. and Eng. Chem. 5, 1017, 1913.

at the time, a correction in the subsequent gas readings in the measuring tube being made accordingly.

Nitrogen in Potassium Nitrate. Approximately 0.4 gram potassium nitrate is placed in a weighing tube, dried two hours at 110° C., desiccated twenty-four hours over sulphuric acid and weighed exactly by difference into the cup of the gas-generating bulb. This is dissolved in 9 cc. 95% sulphuric acid, added through a siphon thistle tube, entering the top of the dissolving cup through a tight-fitting rubber stopper. When the salt is dissolved it is drawn into the gas-generating bulb and followed by two washings 1.5 cc. each of 95% acid. The bulb is then shaken with a motion normal to its long dimension until the volume of gas determined by a rough paper scale pasted on the leveling tube becomes constant, this operation taking from three to five minutes.

The gas is passed into the measuring tube, and after standing five minutes the leveling and measuring tubes are so adjusted that the level in the equilibrium tube reads 100 cc. and is the same as the level in the measuring tube. The reading of the latter is then taken. As the temperature and barometric conditions, in so far as they affect the measured volume of the gas, are automatically compensated by the equilibrium tube, and as the gas is washed with sulphuric acid and is, therefore, dry, the percentage of nitrogen may be calculated directly, correcting only for the calibration of the equilibrium and measuring tubes. Seventeen determinations made when the room temperature ranged from 20–28° gave 13.71% nitrogen, the theoretical being 13.84%.

The nitrometer gives reliable results within 0.02% in nitrate nitrogen, using 0.4–0.5 gram sample. It is not available for the determination of nitrogen in celluloid or other substances containing carbon ring compounds which appear to prevent the complete liberation of nitric oxide in the presence of sulphuric acid and mercury.

Besides the corrections for calibration and standardization of the nitrometer in accordance with temperature and barometer, the gas readings should be corrected for solubility of nitric oxide, which diminishes when the temperature goes above 28° C., and the formation of other gases by the breaking up of the cellulose molecule which increases.

The following table gives the algebraic sum of these two corrections for temperatures ranging from 20° to 35° C.

Temp.	Cc.	Temp.	Cc.
20.0–27.5	+0.90	30.0	−0.14
28.0	+0.74	30.5	−0.70
29.0	+0.34	31.0–35.0	−0.94

REAGENTS AND TABLES

The reagents used in gas analysis, particularly in the absorption apparatus, are comparatively few and easily prepared.

Hydrochloric Acid, Sp. gr. 1.10. Dilute " muriatic acid " with an equal volume of water. In addition to its use for preparing cuprous chloride, it finds employment in neutralizing the caustic solutions which are unavoidably more or less spilled during their use.

Fuming Sulphuric Acid. Saturate " Nordhausen oil of vitriol " with sulphuric anhydride. Ordinary sulphuric acid may be used instead of the Nordhausen; in this case about an equal weight of sulphuric anhydride will be necessary. *Absorption capacity,* 1 cc. absorbs 8 cc. of ethene (ethylene).

Acid Cuprous Chloride. The directions given in the various text-books being troublesome to execute, the following method, which is simpler, has been found to give equally good results: Cover the bottom of a two-liter bottle with a layer of copper oxide or " scale " $\frac{3}{8}$ in. deep, place in the bottle a number of pieces of rather stout copper wire reaching *from top to bottom,* sufficient to make a bundle an inch in diameter, and fill the bottle with common hydrochloric acid of 1.10 sp.gr. The bottle is occasionally shaken, and when the solution is colorless, or nearly so, it is poured into the half-liter reagent bottles, containing copper wire, ready for use. The space left in the stock bottle should be immediately filled with hydrochloric acid (1.10 sp.gr.).

By thus adding acid or copper wire and copper oxide when either is exhausted, a constant supply of this reagent may be kept on hand.

The absorption capacity of the reagent per cc. is, according to Winkler, 15 cc. CO; according to Hempel 4 cc. The author's experience with Orsat's apparatus gave 1 cc.

Care should be taken that the copper wire does not become entirely dissolved and that it extend from the top to the bottom of the bottle; furthermore the stopper should be kept thoroughly greased the more effectually to keep out the air, which turns the solution brown and weakens it.

Ammoniacal Cuprous Chloride. The acid cuprous chloride is treated with ammonia until a faint odor of ammonia is perceptible; copper wire should be kept in it similarly to the acid solution. This alkaline solution has the advantage that it can be used when traces of hydrochloric acid vapors might be harmful to the subsequent determinations, as, for example, in the determination of hydrogen by absorption with palladium. It has the further advantage of not soiling mercury as does the acid reagent.

Absorption capacity, 1 cc. absorbs 1 cc. CO.

Cuprous chloride is at best a poor reagent for the absorption of carbonic oxide; to obtain the greatest accuracy where the reagent has been much used, the gas should be passed into a fresh pipette for final absorption, and the operation continued until two consecutive readings agree exactly. The compound formed by the absorption—possibly Cu_2COCl_2—is very unstable, as carbonic oxide may be freed from the solution by boiling or placing it *in vacuo;* even if it be shaken up with air, the gas is given off, as shown by the increase in volume and subsequent diminution when shaken with fresh cuprous chloride.

Hydrogen. A simple and effective hydrogen generator can be made by joining two 6-in. calcium chloride jars by their tubulatures. Pure zinc is filled in as far as the constriction in one, and the mouth closed with a rubber stopper carrying a capillary tube and a pinchcock. The other jar is filled with sulphuric acid 1 : 5 which has been boiled and cooled out of excess of air. The mouth of this jar is closed with a rubber stopper carrying one of the rubber bags used on the simple pipettes.

Mercury. The mercury used in gas analysis should be of sufficient purity as not to "drag a tail" when poured out from a clean vessel. It may perhaps be most conveniently cleaned, except from gold and silver, by the method of J. M. Crafts, which consists in drawing a moderate stream of air through the mercury contained in a tube about 3 ft. long and 1¼ ins. internal diameter. The tube is supported in a mercury-tight V-shaped trough, of size sufficient to contain the metal if the tube breaks, one end being about 3 ins. higher than the other. Forty-eight hours' passage of air is sufficient to purify any ordinary amalgam. The mercury may very well be kept in a large separatory funnel under a layer of strong sulphuric acid.

Or Meyer's method [1] may be used. A separatory funnel is used to hold the mercury. The delivery tube of the funnel is slightly narrowed 0.5 cm. from the lower end. Over this side is bound with twine a piece of rather closely woven muslin. The mercury is allowed to flow through the cloth into a solution of mercury nitrate contained in a tall cylinder, with stopcock at the lower end. The tip of the funnel with the muslin dips under the surface of the cleaning solution. The purified mercury is drained off from the bottom of the cylinder. It can also be purified except from traces of zinc by distillation.

Palladous Chloride. Five grams palladium wire are dissolved in a mixture of 30 cc. hydrochloric and 2 cc. nitric acid, this evaporated just to dryness on a water bath, redissolved in 5 cc. hydrochloric acid and 25 cc. water, and warmed until solution is complete. It is diluted to 750 cc. and contains about 1% of palladous chloride. It will absorb about two-thirds of its volume of hydrogen.

Phosphorus. Use the ordinary white phosphorus cast in sticks of a size suitable to pass through the opening of the tubulated pipette.

Potassium Hydroxide. (a) For carbon dioxide determination, 500 grams of commercial hydroxide are dissolved in 1 liter of water

Absorption capacity. One cc. absorbs 40 cc. CO_2.

(b) For the preparation of potassium pyrogallate for special work, 120 grams of the commercial hydroxide are dissolved in 100 cc. of water.

Potassium Pyrogallate. Except for use with the Orsat or Hempel apparatus, this solution should be prepared only when wanted. The most convenient method is to weigh out 5 grams of the solid acid upon a paper, pour it into a funnel inserted in the reagent bottle, and pour upon it 100 cc. of potassium hydroxide (a) or (b). The acid dissolves at once, and the solution is ready for use.

If the percentage of oxygen in the mixture does not exceed 28, solution (a) may be used; [2] if this amount be exceeded, (b) must be employed. Otherwise carbonic oxide may be given off even to the extent of 6%.

Attention is called to the fact that the use of potassium hydroxide purified by alcohol has given rise to erroneous results.

Absorption capacity. One cc. absorbs 2 cc. O.

---

[1] J. H. Hildebrand, J. Am. Chem. Soc., **31**, 934.
[2] Clowes, Jour. Soc. Chem. Industry, **15**, 170.

Sodium Hydroxide. Dissolve the commercial hydroxide in three times its weight of water. This may be employed in all cases where solution (a) of potassium hydroxide is used. The chief advantage in its use is its cheapness. Sodium pyrogallate is, however, a trifle slower in action than the corresponding potassium salt.

TABLE 1

TABLE SHOWING THE TENSION OF AQUEOUS VAPOR AND ALSO THE WEIGHT IN GRAMS CONTAINED IN A CUBIC METER OF AIR WHEN SATURATED

From 5° to 30° C.

Temp.	Tension, mm.	Grams.	Temp.	Tension, mm.	Grams.	Temp.	Tension, mm.	Grams.
5	6.5	6.8	14	11.9	12.0	23	20.9	20.4
6	7.0	7.3	15	12.7	12.8	24	22.2	21.5
7	7.5	7.7	16	13.5	13.6	25	23.6	22.9
8	8.0	8.1	17	14.4	14.5	26	25.0	24.2
9	8.5	8.8	18	15.4	15.1	27	26.5	25.6
10	9.1	9.4	19	16.3	16.2	28	28.1	27.0
11	9.8	10.0	20	17.4	17.2	29	29.8	28.6
12	10.4	10.6	21	18.5	18.2	30	31.5	29.2
13	11.1	11.3	22	19.7	19.3			

Moisture in the Air.[1] Twenty tests made on different days extending from October 17th to November 10th, 1916, at a period agreeing closely with the average atmospheric conditions, gave results varying from 0.1510 gram to 0.5031 gram water vapor per standard cubic foot. The average of the results was 0.2469 gram moisture per cubic foot of air. Omitting three rainy days of this period the average moisture of the air in the laboratory (75° F.) was found to be 0.2141 gram per cubic foot.

It is an interesting fact that at 75° F., 52 per cent sulphuric acid (recommended as a standard) is in equilibrium with air containing 0.2137 gram moisture per cubic foot, according to an average of results by W. W. Scott and a calculation from Sorel's table on tension of aqueous vapor in mixtures of sulphuric acid and water.

TABLE 2

SPECIFIC HEATS OF GASES AT CONSTANT VOLUME

		Volumetric.[2]
Air	0.243	0.019
Carbon dioxide	0.234	0.027
Carbonic oxide	0.245	0.019
Hydrogen	3.41	0.019
"Illuminants"	0.404[3]	0.040
Methane	0.593	0.027
Nitrogen	0.244	0.019
Oxygen	0.217	0.019
Aqueous vapor	0.480	.....

The "volumetric" specific heat is the quantity of heat necessary to raise the temperature of 1 cu.ft. of gas from 32° F. to 33° F.

[1] Communicated by W. W. Scott.
[2] H. L. Payne, Jour. Anal. and Applied Chem., **7**, 233.
[3] Ethylene.

TABLE 3

CALORIFIC POWER OF VARIOUS GASES [1] IN BRITISH THERMAL UNITS PER CUBIC
FOOT

Name.	Symbol.	60° F. Initial.	32° F. Initial. 32° F. Final.	Ignition Point °F.
Hydrogen	H_2	326.2	345.4	1085 [4]
Carbonic oxide	CO	323.5	341.2	1200 [4]
Methane	CH_4	1009.2	1065.0	1230
Illuminants [2]	....	......	2000.0	......
Ethane	C_2H_6	1764.4	1861.0	1140
Propane	C_3H_8	2521	2657.0	1015
Butane	C_4H_{10}	3274	3441.0	......
Pentane	C_5H_{12}	......	4255.0	......
Hexane [3]	C_6H_{14}	......	5017.0	1400
Ethylene	C_2H_4	1588	1674.0	1010 [4]
Propylene	C_3H_6	2347.2	2509.0	940
Benzene	C_6H_6	3807.4	4012.0	......
Acetylene	C_2H_2	1476.7	1477.0	788 [4]

TABLE 4

1 pound	=453.59 grams	1 calorie	=3.969 B.t.u.
1 cubic inch	=16.39 cc.	1 cubic meter	=35.31 cu.ft.
1 cubic foot	=28.315 liters		
1 B.t.u. per cu.ft.	=8.89 calorie per cubic meter	1 calorie per cu. meter	=0.1124 B.t.u. per cu.ft.
1 in. H_2O pressure	=1.87 mm. Hg pressure	1 mm. Hg pressure	=0.535 in. H_2O pressure

Acetylene

Absorbents—Fuming sulphuric acid. Ammoniacal cuprous chloride produces a red color. Used as qualitative test.

Ethylene (in presence of Acetylene)

Absorbent—Fuming sulphuric acid absorbs Acetylene and Ethylene. Cold bromine or iodine sol. Ethylene not attacked. Hence determined both by $H_2SO_4+SO_3$ and Ethylene by Br. Diff. =Acetylene.

Benzene

Absorbent—Fuming sulphuric acid. Bromine water +Br. CO_2 is first absorbed by KOH (saturated with benzene vapor), then benzene in fuming sulphuric acid.

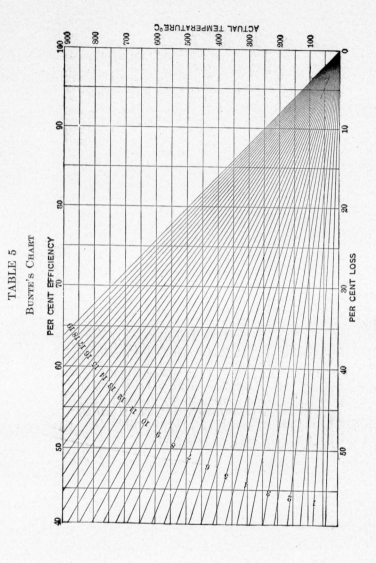

TABLE 5
BUNTE'S CHART

DETERMINATION OF SULPHUR DIOXIDE IN THE ATMOSPHERE[1]

This method is used for the determination of less than 10 and will detect as little as 0.1 part of sulphur dioxide per million by volume.

Determinations can be made in the field at the rate of one every 5 minutes.

The method depends upon measuring the bleaching effect of the sample of atmosphere on starch iodide solution by the amount of standard iodine solution required to restore the tint to that of an equal quantity of the same solution which has been treated mechanically in a barren atmosphere in the same way and under the same conditions in respect to temperature, light, kind and surface area of glassware.

Two aspirator bottles of 20 to 24 liters capacity each are employed; one (B), the exact volume of which is known, is the holder in which the sample is measured and treated with starch iodide solution; the other (A) is a check bottle in which a barren atmosphere is treated with an equal portion of the starch iodine solution. The two bottles should be of the same sort of glass and of approximately the same capacity.

Bottle A, the check bottle, has a solid rubber stopper in the upper tubulure and in the lower, a rubber stopper with a $\frac{3}{8}$-inch hole (b) which is closed by a glass plug (a). The glass plug should fit so it will retain liquid in the bottle but can be removed with little effort.

Bottle B, the sample bottle, has the upper tubulure fitted with a rubber stopper having a $\frac{3}{8}$-inch hole closed permanently by a glass stopcock (c) tube. The lower tubulure is outfitted in a similar manner, but the stopcock (g) tube must fit not so firmly in the hole (b) that it cannot be easily pulled out.

The titrating bottles (C & D) should be alike and of clear white glass. Bottles $2\frac{7}{8}$ inches diameter, $6\frac{3}{4}$ inches high and fitted with No. 8 rubber stoppers are suitable. The stopper to each of these bottles have each a 2 or 3 mm. bore vent tube (d), a $\frac{3}{8}$-inch L tube (e) which must not extend beyond the surface of the stopper inside of the bottle and must fit the holes (b) in the lower tubulures of the aspirator bottles. The $\frac{3}{8}$- to $\frac{1}{2}$-inch hole (f), which is closed by the forefinger or by a glass plug during a part of the process of determination, may have inserted in it a $\frac{1}{2}$-inch glass tube as the finger seat. These bottles should be marked in some way to distinguish the one from the other.

The mixing bottle (E) of about 500 cc. capacity is kept free of dust by a rubber stopper.

The 10 or 15 cc. burette for the iodine solution should have a long delivery tube so that the iodine may be discharged through the hole (f) clear of the stopper.

The vacuum pump is the type having a plunger barrel $2\frac{1}{8}$ by 16 inches.

The vacuum gauge should be provided with a scale upon which are marks indicating the vacuum to be attained corresponding to the temperature prevailing.

The method of making this calculation so that burette readings may be converted directly to parts per million by volume is formulated as follows:

$$F = \frac{I}{\dfrac{MV}{B} \times \dfrac{B}{B'} \times \dfrac{T'}{T' \div T}},$$

[1] Report of the Selby Smelter Commission, Bulletin 98, Bureau of Mines.

where F = Fraction of volume it is desired that each cc. of the iodine solution shall correspond to in terms of cc. or SO_2 at $0/760$.

I = Volume equivalent of 1 cc. of the iodine solution in terms of cc. of SO_2 at $0/760$.

M = Volume in cc. of the space for gas in the aspirator bottle in which the sample of atmosphere is taken.

B = Barometer reading in mm. of mercury.

B' = 760.

V = Vacuum in mm. of mercury.

T = Temperature, Centigrade.

T' = 273.

Examination of the equation shows that barometric pressure is without influence in the calculation. The simplified equation is

$$\frac{FMVT'}{B'(T' \div T)} = I. \quad \text{Since } \frac{T'}{B'} = \frac{273}{760} = 0.36, \text{ then } \frac{0.36FMV}{T' \div T} = I.$$

When the gas capacity of the aspirator bottle is, for example, 21000 cc., $7560FV = I(T' \div T)$.

When the fraction desired to be represented by 1 cc. of the iodine solution is the equivalent in volume of SO_2 to 2 parts per million, then 0.000002 $(7560FV) I(T' \div T)$, then $0.01512V = I(T' \div T)$.

By substituting 380 for V and the average temperature in degrees Cent. for T in this equation, the strength of iodine solution suitable to the size of aspirator bottle and fraction may be found.

When the fraction desired is 2 parts per million and the aspirator has a volume of 20 to 28 liters, it is convenient to use the $N/500$ solution.

When $N/500$ iodine solution is used, $0.01512V = 0.0224T' \div 0.0224T = 6.1152$ $+0.0224T$, then $V = 405 - 1.48T$.

Because of the tediousness of the operation and possible injury by a collapsed bottle it is not good practice to evacuate above 500 mm.

To establish uniform reducing conditions internally, the bottles should be prepared for analytical work by washing their inner surfaces and the plugs with sulphuric acid-bichromate of potassium solution (300 cc. of O.V. plus a few grams of $K_2Cr_2O_7$) and then with distilled water until free of the oxidizing fluid. Both tubulures are now closed to the atmosphere by their corresponding plugs. 300 to 400 cc. of starch solution are poured into the mixing bottle (which must be kept closed and free of dust), and given a light lavender tint by the addition of 1 to 2 cc. of $N/500$ iodine solution. (Note: The quality of the starch solution is a matter supreme importance in the operation of this method. Made in the following manner, it retains its sensitiveness throughout a working day: 1 gram of soluble starch is made into a paste by triturating with a few cc. of cold water and this paste is added to 1 liter of cold distilled water which contains 2 grams of potassium iodide. The liquid is brought just to boiling and then quickly cooled by setting the beaker into cold water. It is the practice to make up a fresh batch each day.) The starch solution is divided equally between the two titration bottles and from each transferred to the corresponding aspirator. The transfer is made by pulling out the glass rod or stopcock tube from the hold (b), inserting (e), closing (f) tightly with the forefinger or with a glass plug, inverting the titration bottle by turning (*e*) around in the hole (*b*) and at the same time tilting back somewhat the aspirator. The appropriate glass rod and tube plugs are then replaced and both aspirators shaken for an equal length of time (2 minutes) under the same conditions respecting light and so that every portion of each bottle receives an equal amount of wetting. Each solution is now transferred to its titration bottle by tilting back the aspirator, pulling the plug in the hole (*d*), inserting (*e*) and with (*f*) open tilting forward the aspirator until all of the starch solution has run into the titration bottle. The hole (*b*) is then closed with its corresponding glass plug. If, on comparing the solutions against a white background, both are of the same tint, the aspirators are considered ready for use in the field. If the colors are not the same, the test solutions are mixed (more iodine added if the bleaching has been great), halved and transferred to the aspirators in the same manner as before. The aspirators are shaken and the solutions again compared. The operation should be repeated until the iodine consumption factor is the same for both bottles.

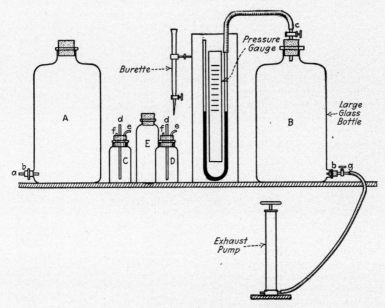

Fig. 137. Apparatus for Testing SO_2 in Air.

Immediately before making a determination, a 300 to 400 cc. portion of starch solution in the mixing bottle is colored with iodine to a shade which experience indicates is suitable to the character of atmosphere to be analyzed and distributed in equal amounts to the aspirators in the same way as in the preliminary procedure. From this point to the operation of titration care is taken that both aspirators have the same exposure to sunlight.

The sample aspirator is now connected to the vacuum pump and gauge in the manner illustrated and evacuated to the extent determined by the conditions of strength of iodine solution, volume of aspirator bottle and temperature. Refer to formula on page 1284. For instance: Assuming that gas capacity of sample bottle is 19600 cc., the temperature to be 20° C. and that N/500 is the strength of the iodine solution, when the evacuation is carried close to 465 mm., each 0.05 cc. of the iodine solution required to bring the portion of starch iodide solution from the sample bottle to the same shade as that from the check bottle represents one tenth part per million of SO_2 by volume.

The sample is taken by letting the air in through the stopcock (c) while shaking the bottle so that its entire inner surface is kept wet with the starch iodide solution. When the internal pressure becomes that of the atmosphere the stopcock is closed and the bottle is shaken vigorously 60 to 80 times. The check bottle is shaken in the same manner, the same length of time and under the same condition of light.

The starch iodide solutions are returned to their corresponding titration bottles in the same manner as in the preliminary procedure, their colors compared and sufficient N/500 iodine solution added from the burette through the hole (f) to the solution from the sample bottle to make its shade that of the check.

Whenever it is evident that the color of the solution in the sample bottle is completely discharged, N/500 iodine is added through the hole (b) until the tint is near that of the check and the bottles again shaken for a minute. Several additions of iodine in this way may be required when the operator has misjudged the character of atmosphere. The solutions are finally compared in the titration bottles, the color intensity of the sample solution made that of the check and the SO_2 content of the sample calculated from the net amount of iodine added.

The operator may allow for a relatively high concentration of SO_2 in the sample by adding a noted quantity of iodine to the sample solution before its transfer to the aspirator bottle. In case the bleaching effect of the sample has not been sufficient to make the shade as light as that of the check solution, the SO_2 content can be calculated from the difference between the noted quantity of iodine added and that required to make the color of the check that of the sample solution.

It is apparent that each determination prepares the aspirator for the next provided that not a very long interval of time elapses between determinations. When a half hour or more has elapsed a trial should be made as in the preliminary procedure to determine whether the iodine consumption factor remains the same for both bottles.

The starch iodide solution can be used repeatedly but must be discarded as soon as it becomes in the least dirty.

REFERENCES

Dennis, Gas Analysis.
White, Gas and Fuel Analysis.
Beam test for suspended matter in gas. See page 1763.
Determination of suspended matter in gas. See page 1763.

PROPERTIES OF DRY AIR

Barometric Pressure 29.921 Inches

Temperature Degrees Fahr.	Weight per Cu. Ft. Pounds	Per Cent. of Volume at 70° F.	B. t. u. Absorbed by One Cu. Ft. Dry Air per Degree F.	Cu. Ft. Dry Air Warmed One Degree per B. t. u.	Temperature Degrees Fahr.	Weight per Cu. Ft. Pounds	Per Cent. of Volume at 70° F.	B. t. u. Absorbed by One Cu. Ft. Dry Air per Degree F.	Cu. Ft. Dry Air Warmed One Degree per B. t. u.
0	.08636	.8680	.02080	48.08	130	.06732	1.1133	.01631	61.32
5	.08544	.8772	.02060	48.55	135	.06675	1.1230	.01618	61.81
10	.08453	.8867	.02039	49.05	140	.06620	1.1320	.01603	62.31
15	.08363	.8962	.02018	49.56	145	.06565	1.1417	.01592	62.82
20	.08276	.9057	.01998	50.05	150	.06510	1.1512	.01578	63.37
25	.08190	.9152	.01977	50.58	160	.06406	1.1700	.01554	64.35
30	.08107	.9246	.01957	51.10	170	.06304	1.1890	.01530	65.36
35	.08025	.9340	.01938	51.60	180	.06205	1.2080	.01506	66.40
40	.07945	.9434	.01919	52.11	190	.06110	1.2270	.01484	67.40
45	.07866	.9530	.01900	52.64	200	.06018	1.2455	.01462	68.41
50	.07788	.9624	.01881	53.17	220	.05840	1.2833	.01419	70.48
55	.07713	.9718	.01863	53.68	240	.05673	1.3212	.01380	72.46
60	.07640	.9811	.01846	54.18	260	.05516	1.3590	.01343	74.46
65	.07567	.9905	.01829	54.68	280	.05367	1.3967	.01308	76.46
70	.07495	1.0000	.01812	55.19	300	.05225	1.4345	.01274	78.50
75	.07424	1.0095	.01795	55.72	350	.04903	1.5238	.01197	83.55
80	.07356	1.0190	.01779	56.21	400	.04618	1.6230	.01130	88.50
85	.07289	1.2083	.01763	56.72	450	.04364	1.7177	.01070	93.46
90	.07222	1.0380	.01747	57.25	500	.04138	1.8113	.01018	98.24
95	.07157	1.0472	.01732	57.74	550	.03932	1.9060	.00967	103.42
100	.07093	1.0570	.01716	58.28	600	.03746	2.0010	.00923	108.35
105	.07030	1.0660	.01702	58.76	700	.03423	2.1900	.00847	118.07
110	.06968	1.0756	.01687	59.28	800	.03151	2.3785	.00782	127.88
115	.06908	1.0850	.01673	59.78	900	.02920	2.5670	.00728	137.37
120	.06848	1.0945	.01659	60.28	1000	.02720	2.7560	.00680	147.07
125	.06790	1.1040	.01645	60.79	1200	.02392	3.1335	.00603	165.83

By courtesy of the Chemical Equipment Co.

GAS ANALYSIS

Properties of Saturated Air

Weights of Air, Vapor of Water, and Saturated Mixture of Air and Vapor at Different Temperatures, Under Standard Atmospheric Pressure of 29.921 Inches of Mercury

Temperature Degrees Fahr.	Vapor Pressure Inches of Mercury	Weight in a Cubic Foot of Mixture			B. t. u. Absorbed by One Cubic Foot Sat. Air. per Degree F.	Cubic Foot Sat. Air Warmed One Degree per B. t. u.
		Weight of the Dry Air Pounds	Weight of the Vapor Pounds	Total Weight of the Mixture Pounds		
1	2	3	4	5	6	7
0	.0383	.08625	.000069	.08632	.02082	48.04
10	.0631	.08433	.000111	.08444	.02039	49.05
20	.1030	.08247	.000177	.08265	.01998	50.05
30	.1640	.08063	.000276	.08091	.01955	51.15
40	.2477	.07880	.000409	.07921	.01921	52.06
50	.3625	.07694	.000587	.07753	.01883	53.11
60	.5220	.07506	.000829	.07589	.01852	54.00
70	.7390	.07310	.001152	.07425	.01811	55.22
80	1.0290	.07095	.001576	.07253	.01788	55.93
90	1.4170	.06881	.002132	.07094	.01763	56.72
100	1.9260	.06637	.002848	.06922	.01737	57.57
110	2.5890	.06367	.003763	.06743	.01716	58.27
120	3.4380	.06062	.004914	.06553	.01696	58.96
130	4.5200	.05716	.006357	.06352	.01681	59.50
140	5.8800	.05319	.008140	.06133	.01669	59.92
150	7.5700	.04864	.010310	.05894	.01663	60.14
160	9.6500	.04341	.012956	.05637	.01664	60.10
170	12.2000	.03735	.016140	.05349	.01671	59.85
180	15.2900	.03035	.019940	.05029	.01682	59.45
190	19.0200	.02227	.024465	.04674	.01706	58.80
200	23.4700	.01297	.029780	.04275	.01750	57.15

By courtesy of the Chemical Equipment Co.

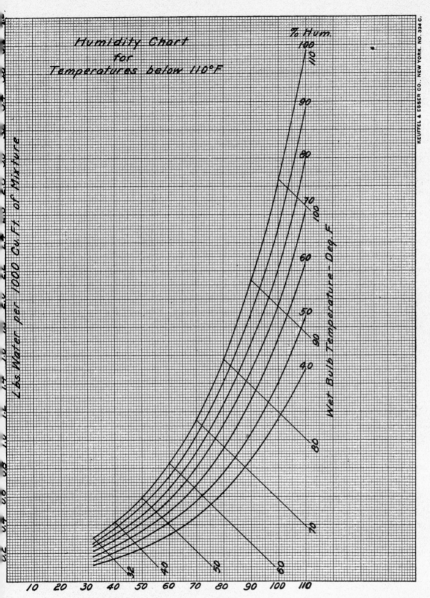

By courtesy of the Chemical Equipment Co.

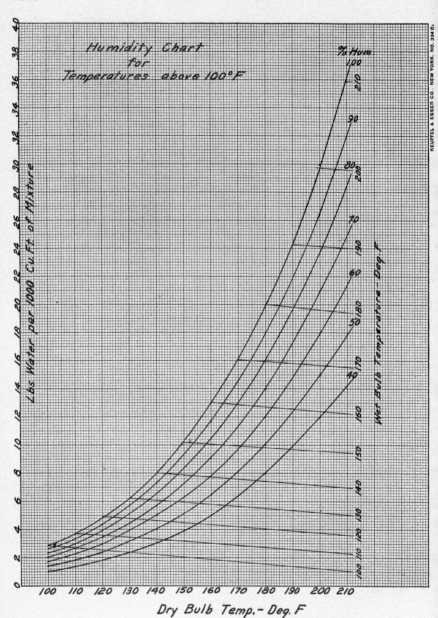

By courtesy of the Chemical Equipment Co.

Burrell Precision Gas Analysis Apparatus

This apparatus is one of our most popular types, combining as it does a broad range of usefulness with simplicity, accuracy and speed.

It has been designed to fill the need for an apparatus that will handle both simple and complex gas mixtures and give a degree of accuracy not found in the ordinary types. While it is particularly well adapted for work on natural gas, artificial gas and other complex gas mixtures containing carbon dioxide, unsaturated hydrocarbons, carbon monoxide, hydrogen, oxygen and nitrogen, it lends itself equally well to all varieties of the more simple gas mixtures and provides the laboratory with an apparatus capable of handling a full range of gas analyzing work.

It has superseded other types in the U. S. Bureau of Mines Gas Laboratory for high class work. School and college laboratories are using it extensively for class room demonstrations and in the handling of the wide variety of gas analyzing problems that are frequently presented. It has proven a most popular type of industrial laboratory apparatus not only because it adapts itself so well to so many specific kinds of work but also provides the facility in one apparatus for handling any job that might arise aside from the regular routine. For this latter reason it has filled a real need in commercial laboratories where the range of work is apt to cover the entire field of gas analysis.

Description

Three absorption pipettes are provided. These are made of soft glass or Pyrex and are filled with glass tubes to increase the absorption surface.

Pipette B is filled with caustic potash and is used for carbon dioxide absorption. A fuming sulphuric acid pipette or bromine water C removes unsaturated hydrocarbons. Oxygen is absorbed in alkaline pyrogallol in the pipette D.

E is a slow combustion pipette for determining paraffin hydrocarbons and can be made of transparent fused quartz.

A distinctive feature of the apparatus is the use of the copper oxide method for determining carbon monoxide and hydrogen. This is recognized as the most accurate method and is much to be preferred over the cuprous chloride method for carbon monoxide in point of accuracy and speed.

The copper oxide is contained in an inverted U-tube (f) passing through the top platform and heated to the required temperature by means of the electric heater G. The residual gas containing carbon monoxide, hydrogen and paraffin hydrocarbons is passed through the U-tube at 280° C. to 300° C. with the resultant oxidation of the carbon monoxide to carbon dioxide and the hydrogen to water. The carbon dioxide thus formed is determined in the pipette B and the hydrogen by difference. The paraffin hydrocarbons are not oxidized at the temperature at which the U-tube is held and are determined in the slow combustion pipette E over mercury.

The burette is 100 cc. capacity graduated in 1/10 cc. It is equipped with a compensator J for accurately compensating for atmospheric pressure and temperature changes during the period of the analysis.

In case any potassium hydroxide or pyrogallate be sucked over into the tube and the burette A, the analysis is not spoiled, but may be proceeded with by connecting with water at a, opening this cock, and allowing the water to wash the tubes out thoroughly. The addition of a little hydrochloric acid to the water in the bottle B will neutralize the hydroxide or pyrogallate, and the washing may be postponed until convenient.

Details of Construction

Each pipette is mounted upon an adjustable support. This arrangement found only in Burrell apparatus enables the operator to remove pipettes for cleaning or replacement easily and quickly and to adjust the pipette to the branch with minimum danger of breakage.

The burette is mounted upon a solid wood frame. The complete burette assembly, including water jacket and compensator, is mounted firmly upon a wood frame which may be fastened permanently in place on the laboratory bench. This provides a strong, rigid support in contrast to the rod and ring supports ordinarily used.

The electric heater is built especially for this service. It fits over the copper oxide tube and has a thermostat for controlling and holding the temperature. It rests on a separate adjustable platform and has a hole in the top for the thermometer. The heater is solidly and well built and will give the utmost in satisfying service. It is connected to a convenient lighting circuit.

A combined rheostat and transformer is provided for heating the slow combustion coil. This is connected to a convenient lighting circuit and in turn is wired to the platinum terminals of the slow combustion pipette. It enables the operator to control and hold the temperature of the coil in a most convenient manner.

Standardized Parts. All glass parts are made to specifications and users are assured that renewal parts will fit.

Finish and Workmanship. All glass parts are carefully made and annealed. The stopcocks are of the zigzag bore type and are warranted gas tight. The metal supports are nickeled and the wooden frames built of hard wood highly finished.

The apparatus is thoroughly well built for hard service, accuracy in results, convenience in manipulation and has an extra degree of finish in all of its parts.

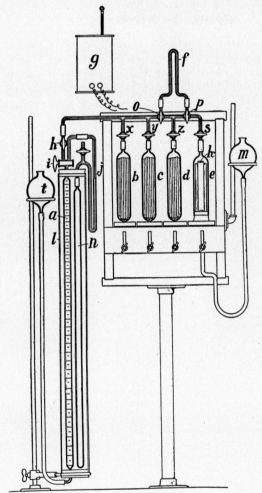

FIG. 137a. Burrell Precision Gas Analysis Apparatus

PROCEDURE FOR ANALYZING GAS MIXTURES CONTAINING CARBON DIOXIDE, UNSATURATED HYDROCARBONS, OXYGEN, CARBON MONOXIDE, HYDROGEN, PARAFFINS AND NITROGEN, BY THE BURRELL APPARATUS [1]

In the analysis of natural gas by means of the Burrell apparatus the carbon dioxide, unsaturated hydrocarbons and oxygen are first removed and then the residual gas is passed slowly back and forth through the copper oxide tube (f), which is heated to about 300° C. until no further contraction in volume occurs.   The last measurement is made after the copper oxide tube has cooled to the temperature of the air.   The contraction in volume is noted and then the gas is passed into the KOH pipette to remove the carbon dioxide.   This loss in volume is recorded.

The reactions are:

$$2H_2 + O_2 = 2H_2O,$$

therefore two thirds of the contraction = H;

$$2CO + O_2 = 2CO_2,$$

therefore CO_2 formed = CO in gas, and contraction = one half of CO, i.e., 3 vols. = 2 vols.

$CO = CO_2$ formed by combustion and H = (total contraction $- \frac{1}{2}CO_2)\frac{2}{3}$.

Next the residual gas is passed into the slow combustion pipette and the platinum spiral thermo heated to a white heat.   Oxygen is then slowly passed into combustion pipette whereupon the hydrocarbons burn slowly to carbon dioxide and water.

The reactions are:

$$CH_4 + 2O_2 = CO_2 + 2H_2O,$$
$$2C_2H_6 + 7O_2 = 4CO_2 + 6H_2O,$$

or

$$C_2H_6 + 3.5O_2 = 2CO_2 + 3H_2O.$$

The nitrogen is determined by difference.

Analysis of Natural Gas

The apparatus devised by the writer for the Bureau of Mines to analyze natural gas or any other of the commercial gas mixtures such as artificial illuminating gas made from coal and oil, producer gas, blast furnace gas, etc., is shown in figure.   It consists of the burette a of 100 cc. capacity and graduated to 0.1 cc. for measuring the sample, the absorption pipette b containing caustic potash solution for absorbing carbon dioxide, the pipette c containing fuming sulphuric acid for absorbing unsaturated hydrocarbons (saturated bromine water can also be used and is more rapid) the pipette d containing alkaline pyrogallate for absorbing oxygen, the electrically heated copper oxide tube f for burning hydrogen and carbon monoxide and the slow combustion pipette e for burning the paraffin hydrocarbons.   The electric furnace g is used to heat the tube f.   A sensitive manometer tube j is used to assist in making burette measurements.

In analyzing natural gas the fuming sulphuric acid pipette and the copper oxide tube are not used for the reason that unsaturated hydrocarbons, hydrogen and carbon monoxide are not found in natural gas.   Fuming sulphuric acid

[1] By George A. Burrell, Chemical Engineer, Pittsburgh, Pa.

will, however, absorb an appreciable quantity of the paraffin hydrocarbons, hence if the gas is passed into the pipette containing this acid, a pronounced reduction in volume will occur, leading to the wrong conclusion that unsaturated hydrocarbons are present. If a gas analysis apparatus be used which contains cuprous chloride as the absorbent for carbon monoxide, and a natural gas sample be passed into the pipette containing same, another reduction in volume will occur, because cuprous chloride solution also absorbs the higher paraffin hydrocarbons to a certain extent. This is one reason why gas analysts in the past have reported the presence of unsaturated hydrocarbons and carbon monoxide in natural gas. They did not know that these solutions, ordinarily used in gas analysis for absorbing the gases in question, also absorb appreciable quantities of the higher paraffin hydrocarbons. The alkaline pyrogallate pipette for the oxygen determination is used in all natural gas analyses to determine if air has entered the sample either through faulty sampling or, if the sample is taken from a gas main which carries the gas at a pressure lower than atmospheric pressure, to determine if pipe connections are leaky and allow air to enter the gas main. Air may also enter a gas or oil stratum which is under a pressure lower than atmospheric due to vacuum pumps working on the lease. It may enter one or more wells in a field and be found in the strata, especially if the formation is a porous or shattered one causing the wells to be in underground communication with each other. In the great majority of cases, however, air will not be found in natural gas. It is doubtful if oxygen is ever present except in minute traces of no practical significance.

Procedure for Analysis of Natural Gas for Carbon Dioxide, Oxygen and Paraffin Hydrocarbons

Oxygen or other gas left in the horizontal capillary train from the previous analysis is displaced by drawing a few cubic centimeters of nitrogen (prepared beforehand by passing air into the alkaline pyrogallate pipette and absorbing the oxygen) from the pipette *d* into the burette. This mixture is then allowed to escape into the air.

About 100 cc. of the gas sample are then drawn from the sample container into the burette. The sample is measured in the burette against the pressure existing in the compensating tube by bringing the mercury in the manometer tube exactly to the mark thereon. The sample is then passed successively into the potassium hydroxide solution to remove carbon dioxide, and the alkaline pyrogallate solution to remove oxygen, the burette measurements being made in the same manner as with the original sample.

The residual gas left after the carbon dioxide and oxygen have been determined is discarded. The capillary connections are cleared of combustible gas by dilution with air, and 100 cc. or slightly less of oxygen is measured into the burette and passed into the combustion pipette. About 35 cc. of the gas sample is then drawn into the burette from the sample container and measured. The platinum wire in the combustion pipette is then heated electrically to a white heat and the gas sample passed, at the rate of about 10 cc. per minute, into the combustion pipette containing the oxygen. The paraffins burn as fast as they enter, so that an explosion consequent upon the accumulation of gas and oxygen cannot follow. In analyzing natural gas the author has obtained the best results by passing the oxygen into the pipette first. When the natural gas is passed in first, the mixture does not always burn satisfactorily. Sometimes an accumulation of oxygen and natural gas occurs and an explosion follows, shattering the pipette.

After the paraffins are burned, which requires about four or five minutes, the combustion pipette is allowed to cool and the contraction in volume due to combustion is measured. The carbon dioxide produced by the combustion is determined by absorption in the potassium hydroxide solution. Then the gas is passed into the alkaline pyrogallate solution to make sure that sufficient oxygen has been present for the complete combustion of the paraffins. Some samples of natural gas, especially casinghead gas, may contain such a large proportion of the higher paraffin hydrocarbons that 100 cc. of oxygen will not be sufficient for the complete oxidation of 35 cc. of natural gas. For such samples a smaller quantity of the gas must be used for the combustion.

In no case is the mercury in the burette raised above the upper stopcock. The gas remaining in the capillary tubing at any state of the analysis is brought in contact with the solutions by passing it back and forth several times between the burette and the pipette. After combustion, for instance, some carbon dioxide will remain in the capillary tubing between the combustion pipette and the burette when the gas is drawn back into the burette to record the contraction in volume. After most of the carbon dioxide has been absorbed by the potassium hydroxide, the small quantity that remains in the capillary tubing is swept out of the tubing into the potassium hydroxide pipette and the operation is repeated in order to insure the complete absorption of the carbon dioxide. If this precaution is not taken, an error of considerable magnitude will result. Finally the residual gas is burned again in the combustion pipette, and the amount of contraction and the volume of carbon dioxide are measured. This second burning is often necessary in order to burn the natural gas completely.

EXAMPLE OF A TYPICAL ANALYSIS

A typical analysis with the calculations from the analytical data is given herewith.

	Burette readings, cc.
First sample	
Volume of sample taken for absorption	30.70
Volume after CO_2 absorption	30.70
CO_2 absorbed	.00
Volume after O_2 absorption	30.70
O_2 absorbed	.00
Fresh sample	
Volume of oxygen taken for combustion	74.85
Volume of sample taken for combustion	30.70
Total volume	105.55
Volume after burning	42.30
Contraction	63.25
Volume after CO_2 absorption	7.20
CO_2 contraction	35.10

Methane (CH_4) and ethane (C_2H_6) are calculated from the following equations:

Calculation:

$$CH_4 + 2O_2 = CO_2 + 2H_2O$$

1 vol. 1 vol. 1 vol. 2 vols. contraction

$$C_2H_6 + 3.5O_2 = 2CO_2 + 3H_2O$$

1 vol. 3.5 vols. 2 vols. 2.5 vols. contraction.

CO_2 produced with $CH_4 = 1$ vol.,
CO_2 produced with $C_2H_6 = 2$ vols.

Let $x = CH_4$ and $y = C_2H_6$. Then $x + 2y =$ total CO_2 produced and $2x + 2.5y =$ total contraction due to combustion.

In the example above total sample is 35.1 cc., CO_2 produced is 35.1 cc., and the total contraction is 63.25 cc.

Substituting (a) $x + 2y = 35.1$. (b) $2x + 2.5y = 63.25$. Eliminating x by multiplying (a) by 2 and subtracting (b) from (a), we get $1.5y = 6.95$ cc. or $y = 4.633$ cc.

Substituting the value of y in equation (a), $x = 35.1 - 9.26 = 25.83$ cc.

The percentages therefore would be

4.63×100 divided by 30.7% y,
25.83×100 divided by 30.7% x,

whence

$$CH_4 = 84.1\% \quad \text{and} \quad C_2H_6 = 15.1\%.$$

In gases containing hydrogen and carbon monoxide, the CO_2 produced by the combustion of the two by passing over heated copper oxide is measured and the total contraction noted. The gases are computed as follows:

Carbon monoxide is equal to the volume of CO_2 produced.

Hydrogen is equal to the total constraction minus the contraction due to the combustion of methane and the result multiplied by $\frac{2}{3}$ or

$$H = \tfrac{2}{3}(\text{total contraction} - \tfrac{1}{2}CO_2 \text{ formed})$$

The complete analysis of the natural gas follows:

Carbon dioxide, CO_2	.0[1]
Oxygen, O_2	.0
Methane, CH_4	84.1
Ethane, C_2H_6	15.1
Nitrogen, N_2	.8
	100.00

These results should be checked by the flow calorimeter. Specific gravity can be checked by the diffusion method.

The specific gravity is calculated from the known specific gravity of the constituents that comprise the natural gas. These are as follows:

SPECIFIC GRAVITIES OF CONSTITUENTS OF NATURAL GAS

Constituent	Specific Gravity (Air = 1)
Methane	0.5545
Ethane	1.0494
Nitrogen	0.9674
Carbon dioxide	1.5291
Oxygen	1.1054

[1] Less than .10 %.

The specific gravity of the natural gas sample then becomes:

$$0.841 \times 0.5545 = 0.456$$
$$.151 \times 1.0494 = \ \ .158$$
$$.008 \times \ .9674 = \ \ .007$$
$$\text{Total, } \ .621$$

CALCULATIONS OF HEATING VALUE

The heating value of natural gas is calculated by using the heating values of the combustible constituents. These heating values follow:

HEATING VALUES OF CONSTITUENTS OF NATURAL GAS

Constituent	Heating value, B.t.u. per cubic foot at 760 mm. pressure	
	0° C.	60° F.
Methane............. ..1065	1065	1008
Ethane................1861	1861	1761

The gross heating value of the natural gas sample at 0° C. and 760 mm· pressure becomes:

$$0.841 \times 1065 = \ \ 896 \text{ B.t.u.}$$
$$151 \times 1861 = \ \ 281 \text{ B.t.u.}$$
$$\text{Total, } 1177 \text{ B.t.u.}$$

EXAMINATION OF BITUMINOUS SUBSTANCES, INCLUDING ASPHALTS, TARS AND PITCHES

CLASSIFICATION OF BITUMINOUS SUBSTANCES

Table I contains a list of the principal commercial bituminous substances with a brief description of their origin or mode of production.

Although the methods included in this chapter are intended primarily for examining native asphalts, asphaltites, tars, pyrogenous asphalts and pitches, many of them may likewise be used for testing asphaltic pyrobitumens, native and pyrogenous waxes. Methods for examining petroleums are given in chapter on fixed oils, fats and waxes, and for testing non-asphaltic pyrobitumens (*e.g.*, coal) in chapter on analysis of coal.

CHEMICAL COMPOSITION OF BITUMINOUS SUBSTANCES

Bituminous substances are complex mixtures of saturated and unsaturated hydrocarbons, often associated with oxygenated, sulphurated and nitrogenous derivatives, and frequently admixed with mineral constituents in varying amounts.

The non-mineral constituents are accordingly composed of the elements carbon and hydrogen, with more or less oxygen, sulphur and nitrogen. It is a comparatively simple matter to ascertain by analytical methods the percentage by weight of the elements present. This is termed the *ultimate analysis*, in contra-distinction to the *molecular composition*.

The mineral constituents may be present in one or more of the following typical forms:

1. As consolidated mineral particles consisting of a porous rock impregnated with the bituminous constituents. This type is exemplified by the so-called "rock asphalts," which are usually composed of a fine-grained limestone or sandstone matrix, carrying the asphalt in its voids.

2. As unconsolidated mineral particles admixed mechanically with the bituminous constituents. This is typified by the numerous deposits of impure native asphalts and asphaltites, in which the bituminous constituents are associated with more or less detritus derived from the surrounding soil; also blast-furnace tar and pitch which carry a proportion of mineral dust carried over mechanically by the furnace gases.

3. As colloidal mineral particles held in suspension by the bituminous constituents. Trinidad Lake asphalt is typical of this group, and is characterized by the presence of colloidal clay and silica.

4. As mineral matter held in chemical combination by the non-mineral (*i.e.*, pure bituminous) constituents. This group differs from the foregoing, inasmuch as it relates to a *chemical* union of the mineral and non-mineral components. Many native asphalts carry small percentages of iron and aluminum, but it is as yet a mooted question whether these are present as colloidal particles, or united chemically with the bituminous matter. Most residual and blown petroleum asphalts contain a trace of iron, derived from the stills in which they are refined.

Chapter by Herbert Abraham, B.S. of Chemistry, The Ruberoid Co., N. Y.

1289

TABLE I.—BITUMINOUS SUBSTANCES

Genus	Species	Member	Remarks
Bitumens	Petroleums	Non-asphaltic petroleum.........	Contains an appreciable quantity of crystallizable paraffine and no asphalt.
		Mixed-base petroleum	Contains crystallizable paraffine also asphalt.
		Asphaltic petroleum .	Contains an appreciable quantity of asphalt and no crystallizable paraffine.
	Native mineral waxes	Ozokerite...........	A paraffinaceous mineral, called ceresine when refined.
		Montan wax........	The wax extracted from lignite or pyropissite by means of solvents.
	Native asphalts	Pure or fairly pure...	Comparatively free from associated mineral matter (less than 10 per cent on the dry weight)
		Associated with mineral matter ("Rock Asphalt").........	Containing a substantial proportion of sand, sandstone, limestone, clay or shale.
	Asphaltites	Gilsonite..........	Extremely pure ⎫ Have a higher fusing point than asphalt —derived from petroleum.
		Glance pitch........	Pure to moderately pure
		Grahamite.........	Pure to quite impure ⎭
Pyro-bitumens	Asphaltic pyrobitumens	Elaterite..........	Rubbery — partly saponifiable ⎫ Generally pure. Infusible and insoluble Derived from petroleum.
		Wurtzilite.........	Depolymerizes on heating, becoming fusible and soluble
		Albertite..........	Depolymerizes partially on heating
		Impsonite.........	Does not depolymerize on heating ⎭
		Asphaltic pyrobituminous shales.......	Mineral matters predominate Infusible and insoluble.
	Non-asphaltic pyrobitumens	Peat..............	Pure or fairly pure. Infusible and insoluble. Contain more or less oxygenated bodies Derived from vegetable growths. Gradual transition from peat to lignite to coal
		Lignite............	
		Bituminous coal.....	
		Anthracite coal......	
		Lignitic and coal shales...........	Mineral matters predominate otherwise the same as the foregoing.

Genus	Species	Member	Remarks
	Pyrogenous waxes	Wax tailings.........	Distillate from petroleum obtained immediately prior to coking.
		Petroleum paraffine..	Solid paraffine obtained from non-asphaltic petroleum.
		Peat paraffine.......	Solid paraffine obtained from peat tar.
		Lignite paraffine.....	Solid paraffine obtained from lignite tar.
		Shale paraffine......	Solid paraffine obtained from shale tar.
Pyrogenous distillates	Tars	Oil-gas tar..........	Produced by cracking petroleum vapors in manufacturing oil gas.
		Water-gas tar.......	Produced by cracking petroleum vapors in manufacturing carburetted water gas.
		Pine tar............	Produced by the destructive distillation of the wood and roots of coniferae.
		Hardwood tar.......	Produced by the destructive distillation of hardwoods.
		Peat tar............	Produced by the destructive distillation of peat.
		Lignite (brown coal) tar...............	Produced by the destructive distillation of lignite brown coal
		Shale tar...........	Produced by the destructive distillation of pyrobituminous shales.
		Gas-works coal-tar...	Produced from gas-house retorts in manufacturing gas from bituminous coal.
		Coke-oven coal-tar...	Produced from by-product coke-oven in manufacturing coke from bituminous coal.
		Blast-furnace coal-tar	Produced from blast-furnaces upon smelting metals with bituminous coal.
		Producer-gas coal-tar	Produced from gas-producers in manufacturing producer gas from coal.
		Bone tar...........	Produced by the destructive distillation of bones.
Pyrogenous residues	Pyrogenous asphalts	Residual oils........	Produced by the dry distillation of non-asphaltic petroleum, the dry or steam distillation of mixed-base petroleum, or the steam distillation of asphaltic petroleum.
		Blown petroleum asphalts..........	Produced by blowing air through heated residual oils.
		Residual asphalts....	Produced by the steam distillation of mixed-base and asphaltic petroleums.

Genus	Species	Member	Remarks
	Pyrogenous asphalts	Sludge asphalts......	Produced from the acid sludge obtained in the purification of petroleum distillates with sulphuric acid.
		Wurtzilite asphalt....	Produced by depolymerizing wurtzilite in closed retorts.
Pyrogenous residues	Pitches	Oil-gas-tar pitch..... Water-gas-tar pitch... Wood-tar pitch...... Peat-tar pitch....... Lignite-tar pitch..... Shale-tar pitch...... Gas-works coal-tar pitch............. Coke-oven coal-tar pitch............. Blast-furnace coal-tar pitch............. Producer-gas coal-tar pitch............. Bone-tar pitch......	Residues obtained by the partial evaporation or distillation of the corresponding tars.
		Rosin pitch.........	Residue obtained by the partial distillation of the resinous sap of coniferae.
		Fatty-acid pitch.....	Residue obtained by the steam distillation of fatty-acids.

Fatty-acid pitch, wood-tar pitch, bone-tar pitch and rosin pitch carry a substantial amount of iron or copper depending upon whether they have been produced in an iron or copper still. Sludge asphalts bear a trace of combined lead derived from the lead containers in which they have been treated.

Native asphalts often contain non-mineral impurities in the form of decayed vegetable substances of peat-like nature, which were originally present in the soil, now associated with the asphalt. These substances are derivatives of humic, or ulmic, crenic, etc., acids.

Certain tars and pitches as well as residual asphalts which have been overheated in their process of manufacture, will carry variable amounts of so-called "free carbon." This in reality consists of hydrocarbon derivatives, polymerized under the influence of heat to an insoluble modification, similar in certain respects to bituminous coal. It is probable that the "free carbon" may under certain conditions consist in part of amorphous carbon, similar to lampblack.

Every member of the bituminous family is a homogeneous or heterogeneous mixture, consisting of a multitude of chemical substances, each having a definite molecular composition. These constituent substances may be associated as a simple solution of liquids in liquids or solids in liquids; or in the form of a colloidal solution; or as a solid solution of amorphous or crystalline solids; or as an emulsion of immiscible liquids; or as a suspension of insoluble substances in a more or less liquid matrix; or combinations of two or more of the foregoing phases.

At the present time but a comparatively small number of distinct chemical substances have been identified in bituminous complexes. A vast amount of research work must yet be accomplished. Although hundreds of non-mineral substances of definite molecular composition have been identified in petroleums, native mineral waxes, pyrogenous waxes and certain tars, comparatively little is known regarding the innumerable non-mineral molecular substances present in native asphalts, asphaltites, asphaltic pyrobitumens, non-asphaltic pyrobitumens, pyrogenous asphalts and pitches.

The chemistry of bituminous substances is further complicated by the fact that commercial specimens of any given material are rarely alike in composition. In some, certain chemical bodies predominate; in others, they may be present in smaller amounts; while in still others they may be absent. Thus two shipments of any given member of the bituminous family are apt to fluctuate widely in composition and physical properties, even when emanating from the same source. Again, a native bituminous substance derived from a single deposit will often vary, depending upon the degree of exposure and extent of metamorphosis. Native bituminous substances are in a constant state of transition, as the result of their age and environment. Pyrogenous bituminous substances show a marked variation in composition and physical properties, depending upon the raw materials used in their production and the exact conditions to which they have been subjected in their processes of manufacture, including the temperature, length of treatment, etc.

Bituminous substances should not therefore be compared to vegetable or animal fats or oils, which in the case of any given material will run fairly uniform in composition and physical properties.

In certain instances, comparatively simple tests have been devised for identifying single chemical bodies present, whereas in other cases the ultimate analysis of the material will furnish a clue to the identity of the substance under examination.

PART I

EXAMINATION OF CRUDE, REFINED AND BLENDED BITUMINOUS SUBSTANCES

The methods ordinarily used for examining bituminous substances and their mixtures may be grouped under four headings, viz.:

(1) Physical characteristics.   (2) Heat tests.

(3) Solubility tests.   (4) Chemical methods of examination.

In general, these tests may have one or more of the following objects in view:

(a) To serve as a means of identification.

(b) To ascertain the value of the substance for a given purpose.

(c) To gauge its uniformity of supply.

(d) As an aid to factory control in its preparation, refining or blending.

(e) As a criterion of its quality.

The most important methods of testing are given in Table II.

TABLE II

Description	For Purposes of Identification	Adaptibility for a Given Purpose	Gauging the Uniformity of Supply	Purposes of Factory Control	As a Criterion of the Quality[1]
Physical Characteristics:					
Fracture	YES	....	....	....	....
Streak on Porcelain	YES	Yes	....	....	....
Specific gravity	YES	....	Yes	Yes	....
Viscosity	....	YES	Yes	Yes	....
Hardness or consistency	YES	YES	YES	YES	....
Susceptibility factor	YES	YES	YES	YES	....
Ductility	....	YES	Yes	Yes	....
Heat Tests:					
Fusing-point	YES	YES	YES	YES	....
Volatile matter	Yes	YES	Yes	Yes	....
Flash-point	....	YES	Yes	Yes	....
Fixed carbon	YES	....	....	....	....
Distillation test (for tars)	Yes	YES	Yes	Yes	YES
Solubility Tests:					
Solubility in carbon disulphide	YES	YES	YES	....	YES
Carbenes	Yes	....	Yes	Yes	YES
Solubility in 88° petroleum naphtha	YES	Yes	Yes	Yes	....
Chemical Tests:					
Water	Yes	....	....	....	YES
Carbon	YES	....	....	....	....
Hydrogen	YES	....	....	....	....
Sulphur	YES	....	....	....	....
Nitrogen	YES	....	....	....	....
Oxygen	YES	....	....	....	....
Free carbon in tars	YES	Yes	Yes	....	....
Solid paraffines	YES	....	....	....	....
Sulphonation residue	YES	....	:....	....	....
Unsaponifiable matter	YES	....	Yes	....	YES
Diazo reaction	YES	....	....	....	....
Anthraquinone reaction	YES	....	....	....	....

[1] (a) Purity; (b) Care exercised in its preparation; (c) Intrinsic value.

PHYSICAL CHARACTERISTICS
Fracture

This is ascertained upon cleaving the specimen by subjecting it to a sharp blow, and examining the cleavage surface. Only hard and "brittle" bituminous substances will yield to this test, including the hard asphalts and asphaltites. The fracture may either appear conchoidal (rounded and curved like a shell), or hackly (jagged, irregularly and rough).

Streak on Porcelain

This represents the color of the powder which is left behind on drawing a piece of the solid bituminous material across the surface of unglazed porcelain. Hard bituminous materials only will yield to this test. The streak may be classified as white (where no streak is visible), yellowish, yellowish brown, brown, brownish black and black.

Specific Gravity

Hydrometer Method for Fluid Materials. Where speed is essential and great accuracy not required, the specific gravity of fluid bituminous materials may be determined with a hydrometer having its scale sub-divided to unity in the third place of decimals. (See also p. 1114.) Usually a series of hydrometers are used, ranging respectively from 0.800 to 0.900, 0.900 to 1.000, 1.000 to 1.080, 1.070 to 1.150, 1.150 to 1.230.

Most hydrometers are adapted to read at 60° F./60° F., or in other words, the instruments are calibrated for water at 60° F. taken as unity. The standard temperature for testing bituminous materials is 77° F., and they should accordingly be brought to this temperature when tested with the hydrometer. For correcting the reading to water at 77° F., it should be multiplied by 1.002, as follows:

$$\text{Sp.gr. at } 77° \text{ F.}/77° \text{ F.} = \text{Sp.gr. at } 77° \text{ F.}/60° \text{ F.} \times 1.002.$$

In running the test, the bituminous material is brought to 77° F., immediately poured into the hydrometer jar, and then the hydrometer slowly allowed to sink into it until it comes to a definite resting-point, whereupon it is raised slightly, and allowed to sink a second time. The reading is then noted. The hydrometer must not be pushed below the point at which it comes to rest until after the second reading has been taken, whereupon it should be pushed a slight distance below the end point to observe whether or not it will rise. If it fails to do so, it is evident that the bituminous material is too viscous to be tested by the hydrometer method, and some other method should be employed. Care should be taken that the hydrometer does not touch the sides or bottom of the cylinder when the reading is taken, also that the surface of the liquid is free from froth or bubbles.[1]

Westphal Balance Method. This is also adapted to testing fluid bituminous materials. The instrument as supplied by the manufacturer (see p. 1111) is provided with a cylinder of about 50 cc. capacity, calibrated for use at 60°/60° F. The test generally made at 77° F., is subject to the same correction as in the hydrometer method.

The Westphal balance may be adapted for as little as 8 cc. of the bituminous material, by using a special plummet, small enough to fit into a 10 cc. cylinder. The plummet may be made from a piece of glass tubing 7 mm. outside diameter, which is sealed at one end with a short platinum wire fused into the glass. Nine to ten grams of mercury are placed in the tube forming a column 35–40 mm. high. The tube is then cut off within 20 mm. of the top of the mercury column, and the open end sealed with a blow-pipe. This plummet should measure 55–60 mm. over all, and weigh from 10 to 12 g. If a represents the weight of the plummet in air, b its weight in water at a definite temperature, and c its weight in the bituminous material at the same temperature, then the specific gravity of the bituminous material at this temperature $= \dfrac{c-a}{b-a}$.[2]

[1] Bulletin No. 314, U. S. Dept. of Agr., Wash., D. C., Dec. 10, 1915; "Laboratory Manual of Bituminous Materials," by Prévost Hubbard, p. 30, N. Y., 1916; "Specific Gravity—its Determination for Tars, Oils and Pitches," by J. M. Weiss, J. Ind. Eng. Chem., **7**, 21, 1915.

[1] "Standard Methods of Sampling and Analysis of Creosote Oil" (Serial Designation: D 38–18), A. S. T. M. Standards Adopted in 1921, 806.

Pycnometer or Specific-Gravity Bottle Method. Several forms of glass bottles are used for this purpose, having a ground-glass stopper with a small vertical hole bored through, to enable it to be completely filled with the bituminous material. These are made in various sizes.

An improvised form which may be used to good advantage when a small quantity of liquid bituminous material is available, consists of a 1 cc. pipette, and a glass tube sealed at one end, the inside diameter of which is slightly larger than the outside diameter of the lower stem of the pipette. On using this instrument, the liquid is first brought to a definite temperature, then sucked to the upper mark of the pipette by means of a piece of rubber tubing temporarily attached to its upper stem. The outside is carefully wiped dry and the lower stem inserted in the glass tube which serves to retain any liquid which may drain from the pipette. A small piece of wire twisted about the pipette near the top is formed into a ring to hand it from the hook above a balance pan. The pipette is thus supported in a vertical position and weighed.[1]

If a represents the weight of the pipette with glass tube empty, b its weight filled with water at a definite temperature, and c its weight filled with the bituminous material at the same temperature, then the specific gravity may be calculated from the following formula:

$$(c-a) \div (b-a).$$

It is customary to determine the specific gravity of bituminous materials at 77°/77° F., although in the case of creosote oil it is often expressed at 100°/60° F. For converting the specific gravity of a substance found at a higher temperature to the standard temperature (lower), the following formula should be used:

Sp.gr. Substance at $t_1/t_1 = $ Sp.gr. Substance at $t_2/t_1 + k(t_2 - t_1)$,

in which $t_2 = $ the temperature at which the specific gravity of the substance was determined,

$t_1 = $ the temperature (lower) at which the specific gravity of the substance is to be calculated, and

$k = $ the coefficient of expansion, which is constant for the particular substance.

If perchance the specific gravity of the substance has been compared with that of water at a higher temperature, then to convert it to a lower temperature compared with water at the same temperature, the following formula should be used: [2]

Sp.gr. Substance at $t_1/t_1 = $ Sp.gr. Substance at $t_2/t_2 \times $ Sp.gr. Water at $t_2/t_1 + k(t_2 - t_1)$.

In both of the above formulae, the following values may be taken approximately for k, representing the coefficient of expansion per ° F.

Creosote oil from coal tar 0.00044
Residual oil 0.00040
Coal tar 0.00038
Coke-oven tar 0.00033
Semi-solid asphalt 0.00030
Semi-solid coal-tar pitch 0.00030

The pycnometer method may also be used for finding the specific gravity of hard and brittle bituminous substances, including hard asphalts of high fusing-point, asphaltites, asphaltic pyrobitumens, non-asphaltic pyrobitumens and pyrobituminous shales. Approximately 3.5 grams of the material ground to 60-mesh are carefully weighed and introduced into a 50-cc. pycnometer, with about 30 cc. of distilled water. A vertical condensing bulb is attached to the pycnometer with a small section of rubber tubing, the open end being connected with an aspirator to maintain a partial vacuum. The pycnometer is then boiled on a water bath to expel all the air from the sample. The inside of the condensing tube is then washed back into the pycnometer, which is cooled to the desired temperature, stoppered, filled to the mark with water at the same temperature and weighed. The specific gravity may then be calculated from the following formula:

$$(c-a) \div [(b-a) - (d-c)].$$

Where a represents the weight of the pycnometer empty, b its weight filled with water, c its weight containing the bituminous substance, and d its weight containing the bituminous substance also filled to the mark with water.

In the case of fusible semi-solid or solid bituminous materials, the dry pycnometer is filled half full with the melted substance, cooled to 77° F., then weighed, then filled with water at 77° F. to the mark and reweighed. The specific gravity is calculated by means of the foregoing formula.

[1] "Specific Gravity—Its Determination for Tars, Oils and Pitches," by J. M. Weiss, loc. cit.

[2] For the specific gravity of water at varying temperatures, see Bureau of Standards, Circular No. 19, p. 43, Mar. 30, 1916.

Viscosity

Engler Method. The method as described on p. 1114 is adapted for examining liquid to semi-liquid bituminous substances, which are generally tested at 77° F. (25° C.), 172° F. (50° C.), or 212° F. (100° C.) depending upon their consistency.

Float Test. This instrument is used largely for testing the viscosity or consistency of semi-solid bituminous materials. The range of the float test is limited, and it cannot be used with very fluid bituminous materials or with hard solids. It accordingly fills the gap between the Engler viscosimeter on one hand, and the needle penetrometer and consistometer on the other. The test is not affected by the presence of finely-divided mineral matter or free carbon.

The instrument is illustrated in Fig. 138. It consists of two parts, viz.: an aluminium saucer-shaped float and a conical brass collar weighing together exactly 50 g.

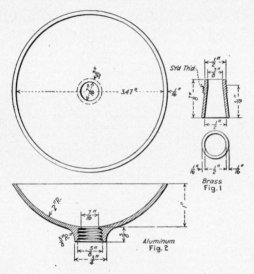

FIG. 138.—Float Tester.

The brass collar is filled with melted bituminous material upon placing it against a brass plate, the surface of which has been amalgamated by treatment with a dilute solution of mercuric chloride and then with mercury. After cooling, it is levelled, placed in water at 41° F. for 15–30 minutes along with the aluminium float, then screwed into the float and immediately floated with the brass collar downward on the surface of water warmed to the desired temperature. No standard temperature has been adopted for making this test, although 90° F. is recommended as most satisfactory in testing road binders, for which the instrument is intended. Very soft materials are tested at 32° F., and harder bituminous substances at 122° F. or 150° F.

As the heat is transmitted through the brass collar into the plug of bituminous material, the latter softens until it is forced upward and out of the collar by the weight of the instrument. The time elapsing between the placing of the float on the surface of the water, and when the water breaks through the plug is taken as a measure of the viscosity of the material under examination.[1]

[1] "Controlling the Consistency of Bituminous Binders," by C. N. Forrest, Eng. Rec., **59**, 584, 1909; J. Ind. Eng. Chem., **1**, 378, 1909; "Tentative Method of Float Test for Bituminous Road Materials" (Serial Designation: D 139–23T), Proc A. S. T. M., **23**, Part I, 756, 1923.

Hardness or Consistency

Needle Penetrometer. This was originally devised by H. C. Bowen in 1888.[1] This first crude instrument was further improved by A. W. Dow.[2] The Dow penetrometer as simplified in construction by Richardson and Forrest represents the type in use to-day,[3] both forms operating on the same principle and giving the same readings.

The Richardson-Forrest improved penetrometer is illustrated in Fig. 139. The base A may be levelled by the thumb screws B, and is attached to the standard C and also the platen D, which by means of a screw-shank raises or lowers the revolving disc E, on which is placed the sample of bituminous material to be tested. The standard C carries a bracket F adjustable as to elevation by a thumb-screw, also the bracket G, which on the back carries the clock-work H timing the duration of the test by half-second beats, and on the front the dial J divided into 360 degrees, with the hand K, marking the number of degrees, each of which represents one-tenth millimeter of penetration measured by rack on sliding gauge L, engaging in pinion on the shaft which actuates the hand K. The bevelled-edge mirror N adjustable through universal joints, serves to reflect light on the sample under test. The plunger O acts as a brake, which holds the needle bar, representing a weight of 50 g. together with the superincumbent weight in place, until pressed inward, which movement permits the needle and weight to act upon test-block without friction, and is easily operated by grasping the horns Q between two fingers and pressing the brake-head O with the thumb. M represents a weight of predetermined capacity, either 50 or 150 g. A form of penetrometer operated by an electrical timing device has also been constructed.[4] A miniature penetrometer for portable use is illustrated in Fig. 140.

Careful investigations have been made as to the diameter of the holder for the bituminous material;[5] the method of preparing the specimen;[6] the size and shape of the needle;[7] also other variable factors.[8] As a result of these, the following standard test has been adopted.[9]

[1] S. of M. Quarterly, **10**, 297, 1889; U. S. Pat. 494,974 of Apr. 4, 1893 to H. C. Bowen; "Report of the Operations of the Engineer Department of the District of Columbia," p. 106, for 1889–90; also article by Clifford Richardson in Eng. Record of Oct. 31, 1891.

[2] "Report of the Engineer Dept. of the District of Columbia, for year ending June 30, 1898," p. 127, "Report of the Inspector of Asphalt and Cement of the District of Columbia for the year ending June 30, 1901," p. 158, by A. W. Dow; "Testing of Bitumens for Paving Purposes," by A. W. Dow, Proc. Am. Soc. Testing Materials, **3**, 354, 1903; "Relation between Some Physical Properties of Bitumens and Oils," by A. W. Dow, Proc. Am. Soc. Testing Materials, **6**, 497, 1906.

[3] "The Development of the Penetrometer as Used in the Determination of the Consistency of Semi-Solid Bitumens," by Richardson and C. N. Forrest, Proc. Am. Soc. Testing Materials, **7**, 626, 1907; "A Further Development of the Penetrometer as Used in the Determination of the Consistency of Semi-Solid Bitumens," by C. N. Forrest, Proc. Am. Soc. Testing Materials, **9**, 600, 1909.

[4] U. S. Pat. 512,687 of Jan. 16, 1894 to A. W. Dow and T. R. Griffith; H. W. Mahr, J. Ind. Eng. Chem., **6**, 133, 1914; also U. S. Pat. 1,225,438 of May 8, 1917 to W. B. Howard.

[5] "Effect of Diameter of Bitumen Holder on the Penetration Test," by C. S. Reeve, Proc. Int. Assoc. Testing Materials, Sixth Congress, N. Y., XXV–3, 1912.

[6] Proc. Am. Soc. Testing Materials, **16**, Part I, 306, 1916: "Revised Standard Test for Penetration of Bituminous Materials," by L. W. Page, Chem. Eng. Manuf., **24**, 32, 1916.

[7] "A New Penetration Needle for Use in Testing Bituminous Materials," by C. S. Reeve and F. P. Pritchard, J. Agric. Research, **5**, 1121, 1916.

[8] "Effect of Controllable Variables on the Penetration Test for Asphalts and Asphalt Cements," by Prévost Hubbard and F. P. Pritchard, J. Agric. Research, **5**, 805, 1916.

[9] "Standard Method of Test for Penetration of Bituminous Materials" (Serial Designation: D 5–21), A. S. T. M. Standards Adopted in 1921, 728.

"Penetration is defined as the consistency of a bituminous material, expressed as the distance that a standard needle vertically penetrates a sample of the material under known conditions of loading, time and temperature. Where the conditions of test are not specifically mentioned, the load, time and temperature are understood to be 100 g., 5 seconds and 77° F. respectively, and the units of penetration to indicate hundredths of a centimeter.

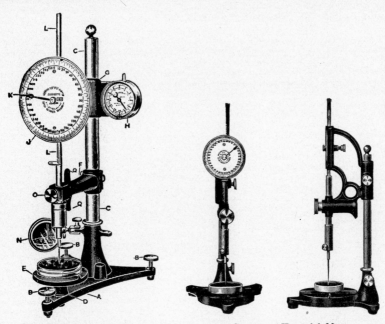

Courtesy of Howard & Morse.
Fig. 139.—Penetrometer.

Courtesy of Howard & Morse.
Fig. 140.—Miniature Penetrometer.

"The container for holding the material to be tested shall be a flat-bottom cylindrical dish, 55 mm. (2$\frac{3}{16}$ in.) in diameter and 35 mm. (1$\frac{3}{8}$ in.) deep. The needle for this test shall be a cylindrical steel rod 50.8 mm. (2 in.) long, having a diameter of 1.016 mm. (0.04 in.) and turned on one end to a sharp point having a taper of 6.35 mm. ($\frac{1}{4}$ in.). The water bath shall be maintained at a temperature not varying more than 0.2° F. from 77° F. The volume of water shall be not less than 10 litres, and the sample shall be immersed to a depth of not less than 10 cm. (4 in.) and shall be supported on a perforated shelf of not less than 5 cm. (2 in.) from the bottom of the bath. Any apparatus which will allow the needle to penetrate without appreciable friction and which is accurately calibrated to yield results in accordance with the definition of penetration, will be acceptable. The transfer-dish for container shall be a small dish or tray of such capacity as will insure complete immersion of the container during the test. It shall be provided with some means which will insure a firm bearing and prevent rocking of the container.

The sample shall be completely melted at the lowest possible temperature and stirred thoroughly until it is homogeneous and free from air bubbles. It shall then be poured into the sample container to a depth of not less than 15 mm. ($\frac{5}{8}$ in.). The sample shall be protected from dust and allowed to cool in an atmosphere not lower than 65° F. for 1 hour. It shall then be placed in the water bath along with the transfer dish and allowed to remain 1 hour.

"In making the test, the sample shall be placed in the transfer dish, filled with water from the water bath of sufficient depth to completely cover the container. The transfer dish containing the sample shall then be placed upon the stand of the penetration machine. The needle, loaded with specified weight, shall be adjusted to make contact with the surface of the sample. This may be accomplished by making contact of the actual needle-point with the image reflected by the surface of the sample from a properly placed source of light. Either the reading of the dial shall then be noted, or the needle brought to zero. The needle is then released for the specified period of time, after which the penetration machine is adjusted to measure the distance penetrated.

"At least three tests shall be made at points on the surface of the sample not less than 1 cm. ($\frac{3}{8}$ in.) from the side of the container, and not less than 1 cm. ($\frac{3}{8}$ in.) apart. After each test the sample and transfer dish shall be returned to the water bath and the needle shall be carefully wiped toward its point with a clean dry cloth to remove all adhering bituminous matter. The reported penetration shall be the average of at least three tests whose values shall not differ more than 4 points between maximum and minimum. When desirable to vary the temperature, time and weight, and to provide for uniform method of reporting results when such variations are made, the samples shall be melted and cooled in air as above directed. They shall then be immersed in water or brine, as the case may require, for 1 hour at the temperature desired. The following combinations are suggested:

32° F.; 200 g. weight; 60 seconds,
77° F.; 100 g. weight; 5 seconds,[1]
115° F.; 50 g. weight; 5 seconds."

Consistometer. This instrument is constructed according to scientific principles, and may accurately be duplicated at any time. It registers the degrees hardness on a scale ranging from 0 to 100, and is suitable for determining the hardness of substances as soft as vaseline (which will test 0.3 at 77° F.) to substances as hard as gilsonite (testing in the neighborhood of 100 at 77° F.). In all cases, the hardness or consistency is expressed as the cube root of the number of grams which must be applied to a circular flat surface 1 sq.cm. (100 sq.mm.) in area, to cause it to displace the substance at a speed of 1 cm. per minute. Readings for all bituminous substances and at all temperatures (whether 115, 77 or 32° F.) are expressed on a *single* scale. The harder the substance, the greater will be its hardness expressed numerically.

Four mushroom-shaped plungers are used, each having a round flat head with a reduced shank, so the perimeter of the penetrating surface forms a "knife" edge. This entirely eliminates the frictional adhesion of the bituminous substance to the sides of the plungers. The flat heads of the plungers are made in the following dimensions:

Plunger	Diameter in Mm.	Area in Sq. Mm.
No. 1	1.13	1
No. 10	3.57	10
No. 100	11.28	100
No. 1000	35.67	1000

The method of testing consists in forcing one of the plungers into the substance at a *uniform* speed of 1 cm. per minute. The force is automatically registered in grams or kilograms. For any plastic substance, the number of grams required to effect this displacement is directly proportional to the *volume* displaced. The volumes displaced per minute by the respective plungers are 0.01, 0.10, 1.00 and 10.0 cc. respectively. The relation between the plungers is therefore in the direct proportion of 1 : 10 : 100 : 1000.

[1] Inserted by author. Not included in the printed method published by the Am. Soc. Testing Materials.

Two interchangeable springs are supplied, one registering in grams on a scale ranging 0 to 1000 g., in 10 g. divisions, and the other for reading in kilograms on a scale ranging from 0 to 10 kgs., in 0.1 kg. divisions. In using plungers No. 1 and No. 10, the kilogram spring only should be employed. In using plunger No. 100 either the gram or the kilogram spring may be employed, depending upon the hardness of the material; in using plunger No. 1000, the gram spring *only* should be employed. The relations are expressed in the following table:

Plunger	Spring	Actual Reading	Converted to Grams per 100 Sq. Mm. Plunger	Cube Root Grams Applied 100 Sq. Mm. Plunger
1000 sq.mm........	G.	From 10 g. to 1000 g.	1 100	1.00 4.64
100 sq.mm........	G.	From 100 g. to 1000 g.	100 1,000	4.64 10.00
	Kg.	From 1.0 kg. to 10.0 kgs.	1,000 10,000	10.0 21.5
10 sq.mm... ..	Kg.	From 1.0 kg. to 10.0 kgs.	10,000 100,000	21.5 46.4
1 sq.mm..........	Kg.	From 1.0 kg. to 10.0 kgs.	100,000 1,000,000	46.4 100.0

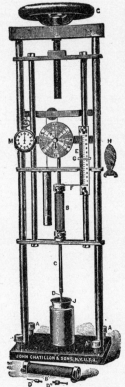

The consistometer is illustrated in Fig. 141. It is first levelled by the four screws A. The spring B is then attached, selecting the gram spring for soft substances, or the kilogram spring for hard substances. The steel shaft C is inserted and screwed firmly into place. The plunger D should then be screwed into the lower end of the shaft. Plunger No. 1 is used for hard and brittle substances, plunger No. 10 for moderately hard solid substances, plunger No. 100 for moderately soft semi-solid substances, and plunger No. 1000 for semi-liquid substances.

The scale E is graduated in grams on one side, and kilograms on the other, and is reversible. It should be inserted so that the graduations will correspond with the spring used, and adjusted so the indicator F will rest at the 0 division. The maximum indicator G is also brought to the 0 division using the small instrument H.

The bituminous substance is melted at the lowest possible emperature and poured into a small receptacle as described for the needle penetration method. The tin box J containing the bituminous substance is then supported underneath the machine in a vessel of water (not shown) maintained at the temperature at which the test is to be performed. The pressure is applied to the plunger by turning the hand-wheel O, and the speed of displacement controlled by following the pointer K, on the dial L, which should be caused to revolve at the same speed as the second hand of a chronometer M, conveniently suspended alongside. The numbers on the dial L correspond with those of the second hand on the chronometer. One revolution of the pointer K indicates that the plunger has moved downward exactly one centimeter.

At the termination of 60 seconds, after the pointer on the dial has made one revolution, the pressure on the plunger is relieved. The reading of the maximum indicator G on the scale E is then noted, and the corresponding degree of hardness ascertained by referring to the table supplied with the instrument.

FIG. 141—Consistometer.

When the plunger commences to displace the substance at the specified speed of 1 cm. per minute, a maximum reading is obtained which should remain constant throughout the entire displacement. The consistometer is simple to operate, gives closely concordant results, expresses the readings obtained at all temperatures on *one scale* and has a sufficiently great range to include all bituminous substances ordinarily encountered.[1]

Susceptibility Factor. This factor is a numerical expression representing the susceptibility of a bituminous substance to temperature changes. The more susceptible the material the higher will be its "susceptibility factor." It is calculated from the consistometer hardness and the K. and S. fusing-point in the following manner:

$$\text{Susceptibility Factor} = \frac{(\text{Hd at } 32^\circ \text{ F.}) - (\text{Hd at } 115^\circ \text{ F.})}{\text{Fusing-point, K. and S. Method}} \times 100$$

By means of the susceptibility factor, bituminous materials may be roughly divided into the following groups, viz.:

Susceptibility Factor under 40: Includes blown petroleum asphalts, fatty-acid pitches and fluxed asphaltites (having a factor between 8 and 40); also wurtzilite asphalts (having a factor between 30 and 40).

Susceptibility Factor between 40 *and* 60: Includes residual asphalts.

Susceptibility Factor over 60: Includes mineral waxes, pitches derived from tars, and asphaltites (of which the susceptibility factor varies from 75 to over 100).

Native asphalts have been excluded from the foregoing groups, since their susceptibility factors vary widely, ranging from 15 to greater than 100. The author has never examined a bituminous material having a susceptibility factor lower than 8.[2]

Ductility

This represents the capacity of the bituminous material for elongating or stretching.

There are two methods in use, depending upon the construction of the moulds, namely one devised by A. W. Dow, and one proposed by the author.

Dow Ductility Test. The Dow mould is constructed of four brass parts as illustrated in Fig. 142, and of the following dimensions: external length 9 cm., internal

Courtesy of Humboldt Mfg. Co.

Fig. 142.—Dow Ductility Mould.

length 7.5 cm., distance between the ends of clips 3.0 cm., extreme internal width of mould 3.0 cm., internal width at mouth of clips 2.0 cm., internal cross-section half-way between clips 1.0 cm., and thickness of briquette 1.0 cm.[3] The two centre pieces should

[1] "Improved Instruments for the Physical Testing of Bituminous Materials," by Herbert Abraham, Proc. Am. Soc. Testing Materials, **9**, 568, 1909; **11**, 676, 1911; U. S. Pat. 989,471 of Apr 11, 1911 to Herbert Abraham.

[2] "Improved Instruments for the Physical Testing of Bituminous Materials," by Herbert Abraham, Proc. Am. Soc. Testing Materials, **11**, 683, 1911.

[3] "The Testing of Bitumens for Paving Purposes," by A. W. Dow, Proc. Am. Soc. Testing Materials, **3**, 352, 1903; "Report of the Commissioners of the Dist. of Columbia, for the year ending June 30, 1904," p. 42; "Methods for Testing Asphalt," by A. W. Dow, Chem. Eng., **1**, 330, 1905; "Tests of Asphalts for Paving Purposes," by A. W. Dow and F. P. Smith, Munic. Eng., **40**, 437, 1911.

be well amalgamated to prevent the bituminous material from adhering, and the mould assembled on an amalgamated brass plate. The bituminous material is melted at the lowest possible temperature, poured in a steady stream into the center of the mould, and a slight excess added to allow for shrinkage on cooling. The mould is cooled in air and levelled off with a hot spatula. The center pieces are then removed, leaving the briquette of bituminous material held at either end by the clips, and carefully transferred to a vessel of water maintained within 1 degree of the required temperature for at least 1, but not longer than 2 hours. The clips should then be pulled apart under water maintained within 1 degree of the required temperature, at a uniform rate of speed of 5 cm. per minute. The line of pull should be horizontal or nearly so, and the separation effected without appreciable vibration. Three tests should be averaged.[1] It is custom-

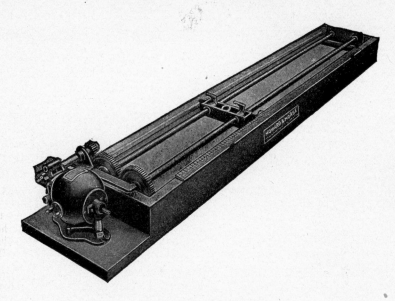

Courtesy of Howard & Morse.

Fig. 143.—Smith Ductility Machine.

ary to make this test at three temperatures, viz.: 115, 77 and 32° F. Various machines have been proposed for this purpose, including the one devised by Smith, illustrated in Fig. 143.[2]

[1] "Tentative Method of Test for Ductility of Bituminous Materials" (Serial Designation: D 113–22T), Proc. A. S. T. M., **22**, Part I, 807, 1922.

[2] "Machine for Testing the Ductility of Bituminous Paving Cements," by F. P. Smith, Proc. Am. Soc. Testing Materials, **9**, 594, 1909.

Abraham's Ductility Test. An improved mould designed by the author, is illustrated in Fig. 144 and shown in cross-section in Fig. 145. It consists of two cylindrical sections

FIG. 144.—Abraham's Ductility Mould.

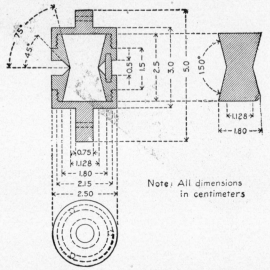

Note: All dimensions in centimeters

FIG. 145.—Cross-section Abraham's Mould.

constructed of hardened steel, resting together on circular knife-edges and maintained in that position by three guide pins. It is filled by unscrewing the upper cap and pouring in the melted bituminous substance, which on cooling forms a prismoid, whose altitude is 2.5 cm., the end-areas 1.8 cm. in diameter, with a minimum cross-section at the center of exactly 1.0 sq.cm. (1.28 cm. in diameter). The upper cap is screwed in place, the mould fastened in the tensometer and the two halves separated at the uniform speed of 5 cm. per minute. The elongation in cms. at the moment the material parts is a measure of its ductility.[1]

This mould has a number of advantages over the Dow type, including its adaptability to testing semi-liquid and semi-solid bituminous materials, no amalgamation is necessary, there is no danger of the material breaking in the mould upon being cooled to the proper temperature, the personal equation is eliminated in filling the mould with the assurance that the minimum cross-section will be *exactly* the proper size, and only a small quantity of the material is required in making the test.

[1] "Improved Instruments for the Physical Testing of Bituminous Materials," by Herbert Abraham, Proc. Am. Soc. Testing Materials, **10**, 444, 1910; **11**, 679, 1911.

HEAT TESTS

Fusing ("Softening") Point[1]

This constitutes one of the most valuable all-around tests. Several methods have been proposed for this purpose, viz.:

Kramer-Sarnow Method. This method is rapid, accurate, and adapts itself either to soft or hard bituminous materials, from residual oils up to grahamite. Its range is greater than that of any other fusing-point method.

It was first proposed by G. Kramer and C. Sarnow.[2] Various modifications have been suggested from time to time.[3] The author has made a careful study of this method, and recommends the following procedure:[4]

Substances Fusing below 194° F. This method consists in heating a plug of the bituminous substance 5 mm. long, in an open glass tube, 6–7 mm. internal diameter, and about 8 cm. long, the plug supporting 5 g. mercury, and the tube being immersed in a vessel of water, the level of which reaches approximately the center of the mercury column. In making the test, a thermometer is suspended in the liquid, so its bulb will be at the same level as the plug of bituminous material. The thermometer is supported in a separate glass tube of the same thickness and diameter as the other tube, but differing therefrom in having its lower end sealed, and containing sufficient mercury to surround the bulb. The water is heated at a uniform rate of 4° F. per minute, and the temperature at which the mercury drops through the plug of bituminous material recorded as its fusing temperature. The tube containing the bituminous substance may have a mark etched 5 mm. from the end, as a convenient guide for the quantity of bituminous material to be introduced. The plug of bituminous material may be introduced into the tube by inverting it and inserting from its lower end a well-fitting cork or wooden plug fastened to a stiff wire. The mercury is poured on same, and the plug raised or lowered until the meniscus of the mercury coincides with the mark etched on the tube. The bituminous material is then melted at a temperature slightly above its fusing-point and poured on top of the mercury, to completely fill the tube, which should be warmed slightly. When cool, the bituminous material is levelled off even with the end of the tube, whereupon the tube is inverted and the plug withdrawn. This is illustrated in Fig. 146.

The mercury is measured from a heavy-walled capillary tube of 1 mm. bore, terminating in a three-way cock, and calibrated to hold exactly 5 g. mercury at room temperature. The short limb of the tube is connected with a movable reservoir containing mercury, the height of which is adjusted so the mercury in the capillary tube exactly reaches the graduation.

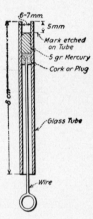

FIG. 146.—Method of Filling K. & S. Fusing-Point Tubes.

[1] The terms "fusing-point" and "softening point" have been used throughout the text in place of the phrase "melting-point," since the former are more expressive of the behavior of fusible bituminous substances under the influence of heat. They pass *gradually* from the solid to the liquid condition, the transition taking place slowly, owing to the heterogeneous character of the substances present. The phrase "melting-point" is more appropriately applied to chemical substances having a definite composition, which melt sharply, and within a narrow temperature range.

[2] Chem. Ind., **26**, 55, 1903.

[3] B. M. Margosches, Chem. Rev. Fett-Harz-Ind., **11**, 277, 1904; M. Wendriner, Z. angew. Chem., **18**, 622, 1905; E. Graefe, Chem. Zeit., **30**, 298, 1906; Bauert, Chem. Zeit., **29**, 382, 1905; Offermann, Petroleum, **6**, 2117, 1910; L. Barta, Petroleum, **7**, 158, 1911; V. Abeles, Chem. Zeit., **38**, 249, 1914.

[4] "Improved Instruments for the Physical Testing of Bituminous Materials," by Herbert Abraham, Proc. Am. Soc. Testing Materials, **9**, 575, 1909; **11**, 673, 1911.

The heating is conveniently effected by means of a resistance cell consisting of a beaker 75 mm. diameter by 100 mm. high, carrying 400 cc. water to which are added 4 drops of concentrated sulphuric acid.   The apparatus is assembled as shown in Fig. 147.   A *direct* current of 110 volts is used in conjunction with a rheostat provided with

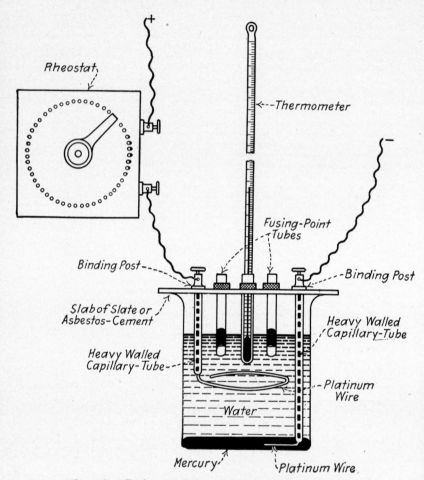

Fig. 147.   Resistance Cell for Fusing-point Determination.

25 to 35 notches, having a carrying capacity ranging from ½ up to 100 amperes (corresponding to a resistance of 220 down to 1.1 ohms).[1]

[1] Private communication from Mr. Dozier Finley, Emeryville, Cal.

A convenient device for controlling the temperature consists of a clock from which the hour hand has been removed, and the dial graduated in 240 divisions representing degrees Fahrenheit.   The rise in temperature is synchronized with the minute hand of the clock and controlled by the rheostat to increase *exactly* 4° F. *per minute*.   The initial temperature of the water should be at least 25° F. lower than the fusing-point of the material to be examined.   Six tests may be run simultaneously.

Substances Fusing above 194° *F.*   In this case the heating is performed by a direct flame, as illustrated in Fig. 148, the water being replaced with castor oil which may be

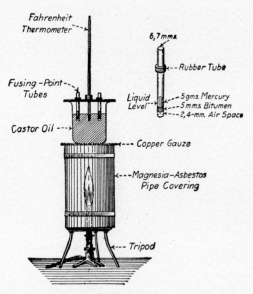

FIG. 148. — K. and S. Tester for High Fusing-Point Substances.

heated safely to about 600° F.   This method may be used for determining the fusing-point of asphaltites including grahamite.   A small quantity of the high fusing-point bituminous material is powdered and compressed in the lower end of the fusing-point tube, whereupon it is carefully heated above the flame of a burner, until the plug of bituminous material softens and fuses to the tube, which is evidenced by the color changing from a dull to a glossy black.   The tube is then stood upright against a block of wood, a snug-fitting glass rod inserted in the upper end, and pressed against the softened bituminous material to compact it into a solid mass 7 to 9 mm. long.   On cooling, the plug is then carefully scraped from the lower end of the tube until *exactly* 5 mm. remains, leaving an air space 2 to 4 mm. between the plug and the lower end of the tube.   Care should be taken when suspending the fusing-point tube in the heating bath to allow the free space below the plug to remain filled with air, otherwise oil will come in contact with, and prematurely soften the bituminous material.   The bath is heated at the uniform speed of 4° F. per minute.[1]

[1] "Improved Instruments for the Physical Testing of Bituminous Materials," Proc. Am. Soc. Testing Materials, **11**, 674, 1911.

Ball and Ring Method.[1]   This method has been adopted by the American Society for Testing Materials.   The apparatus is illustrated in Fig. 149 and consists of the following: " (*a*) A brass ring 15.875 mm. ($\frac{5}{8}$ in.) in inside diameter and 6.35 mm. ($\frac{1}{4}$ in.) deep; thickness of wall, 2.38 mm. ($\frac{3}{32}$ in.); permissible variation on inside diameter and thickness of ring, 0.25 mm. (0.01 in.).   This ring shall be attached in a convenient manner to a No. 15 B. & S. gage brass wire (diameter 1.79 mm. = 0.0703 in.).   (*b*) A steel ball 9.53 mm. ($\frac{3}{8}$ in.) in diameter weighing between 3.45 and 3.55 g.   (*c*) A glass vessel, capable of being heated, not less than 11 cm. (4.13 in.) in diameter by 14 cm. (5.51 in.) deep.[2]   (*d*) A thermometer which shall conform to the following specifications: Total length 370–400 mm., diameter 6.5–7.5 mm., bulb length not over 14 mm., bulb diameter 4.5–5.5 mm.   The scale shall be engraved upon the stem of the thermometer, shall be clear cut and distinct, and shall run from 32° to 176° F. in 1/10° F. divisions.   It shall commence not less than 7.5 cm. above the bottom of the bulb.   The thermometer shall be furnished with an expansion chamber at the top and have a ring for attaching tags.   It shall be made of a suitable quality of glass and be so annealed as not to change its readings under conditions of use.   It shall be correct to 0.5° F. as determined by comparison at full immersion with a similar thermometer calibrated at full immersion by the U. S. Bureau of Standards."

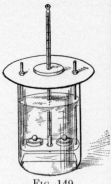

Fig. 149.

"The sample shall be melted and stirred thoroughly, avoiding incorporating air bubbles in the mass, and then poured into the ring so as to leave an excess on cooling. The ring, while being filled, should rest on a brass plate which has been amalgamated to prevent the bituminous material from adhering to it.   After cooling, the excess material shall be cut off cleanly with a slightly heated knife."

Substances Fusing below 194° *F.*   "Assemble the apparatus as shown in Fig. 149. Fill the glass vessel to a depth of substantially 8.25 cm. (3.25 in.) with freshly boiled, distilled water at 41° F.[3]   Place the ball in the center of the upper surface of the material

---

[1] "Standard Method of Test for Softening Point of Bituminous Materials other than Tar Products" (Serial Designation: D 36–21), A. S. T. M. Standards Adopted in 1921, 739.

[2] A 600-cc. beaker, Griffin low form, meets this requirement.

[3] The use of freshly boiled distilled water is essential, as otherwise air bubbles may form on the specimen and affect the accuracy of the results.

in the ring and suspend it in the water so that the lower surface of the filled ring is exactly 2.54 cm. (1 in.) above the bottom of the glass vessel[1] and its upper surface is 5.08 cm. (2 in.) below the surface of the water. Allow it to remain in the water for 15 minutes before applying heat. Suspend the thermometer so that the bottom of the bulb is level with the bottom of the ring and within 0.635 cm. (¼ in.) but not touching the ring. Apply the heat in such a manner that the temperature of the water is raised 9° F. each minute."[2]

"The temperature recorded by the thermometer at the instant the bituminous material touches the bottom of the glass vessel shall be reported as the softening point."

Substances Fusing above 194° F. "Use the same method as given above, except that glycerin shall be used instead of water."

The limit of accuracy of the test is ±1.0° F. The resistance cell described may be used to good advantage in the Ball and Ring method.

Tests made by the author indicate that the Ball and Ring fusing-points range 15 to 25° F. higher than those obtained by the K. and S. method. This relationship holds true regardless of whether the fusing-point of the material is low or high.

Cube Method.   This method is restricted to testing tar-pitches.[3]

For Pitches Fusing below 170° F. The following method has been proposed by the American Society for Testing Materials:[4]

"The apparatus is illustrated in Fig. 150 and shall consist of the following: (a) A mold suitable for forming a 12.7 mm. (½ in.) cube of pitch; (b) an L-shaped right-angled hook made of No. 12 B. & S. gage copper wire (diameter 2.05 mm. = 0.0808 in.) the foot of which shall be 2.54 cm. (1 in.) long; (c) a glass vessel, capable of being heated, not less than 8.5 cm. (3.34 in.) in diameter and measuring 10.5 cm. (4.13 in.) in depth from the bottom of the flare.[5] (d) a thermometer which shall conform to the following specifications: total length 370–400 mm., diameter 6.5–7.5 mm., bulb length not over 14 mm., bulb diameter 4.5–5.5 mm. The scale shall be engraved upon the stem of the thermometer, shall be clear cut and distinct, and shall run from 32 to 176° F. in 1/10° F. divisions. It shall commence not less than 7.5 cm. above the bottom of the bulb. The thermometer shall be furnished with an expansion chamber at the top and have a ring for attaching tags. It shall be made of a suitable quality of glass and be so annealed as not to change its readings under conditions of use. It shall be correct to 0.45° F. as determined by comparison at full immersion with a similar thermometer calibrated at full immersion by the U. S. Bureau of Standards."

[1] A sheet of paper placed on the bottom of the glass vessel and conveniently weighted will prevent the bituminous material from sticking to the glass vessel, thereby saving considerable time and trouble in cleaning.

[2] Rigid adherence to the prescribed rate of heating is absolutely essential to secure accuracy of results. The rate of rise of temperature shall be uniform and shall not be averaged over the period of the test. The maximum permissible variation for any minute period after the first three shall be ±0.9° F. All tests in which the rate of rise in temperature exceeds these limits shall be rejected.

[3] "Methods for Testing Coal Tar, and Refined Tars, Oils, and Pitches Derived Therefrom," by S. R. Church, J. Ind. Eng. Chem., **3**, 230, 1911; **5**, 195, 1913.

[4] "Standard Method of Test for Softening Point of Tar Products—Cube-in-Water Method" (Serial Designation: D 61–20), A. S. T. M. Standards Adopted in 1921, 743.

[5] A 600-cc. beaker, Griffin low form, meets this requirement.

"The pitch shall be formed into a 12.7 mm. ($\frac{1}{2}$ in.) cube, truly shaped and with sharp edges, either by melting and pouring, or softening and pressing into the mold. In all cases an excess of pitch shall be used and the surplus material shall be cut off cleanly with a slightly heated knife. The harder pitches specified can ordinarily be molded at room temperature, the softer pitches in water at about 40° F. If they are melted, they should first be thoroughly stirred, avoiding incorporating air bubbles in

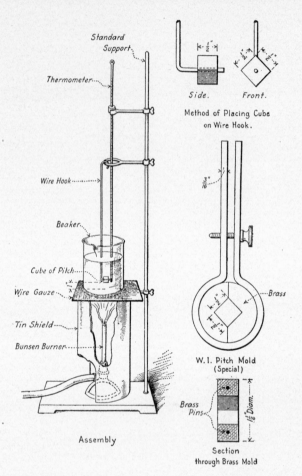

FIG. 150.—Cube-in-water Method for Low Fusing-point Substances.

the mass, and then poured into the mold so as to leave an excess on cooling. The mold should rest on a brass plate and the surface of the plate and the interior surfaces of the mold should be amalgamated to prevent the pitch from adhering to them."

"Assemble the apparatus as shown in Fig. 150. Fill the glass vessel with freshly boiled distilled water[1] to a depth of substantially 9.5 cm. (3.75 in.). With pitches having softening points below 109.4° F. the temperature of the water shall be 40° F., and with pitches having softening points between 109.4° and 170° F. the temperature of the water shall be 60° F. Place the cube of pitch on the wire as shown and suspend it in the water so that its lower edge is exactly 2.54 cm. (1 in.) above the bottom of the glass vessel[2] and its upper edge is 5.08 cm. (2 in.) below the surface of the water. Allow it to remain in the water for 15 minutes before applying heat. Suspend the thermometer so that the bottom of the bulb is level with the bottom edge of the cube of pitch and within 0.635 cm. ($\frac{1}{4}$ in.), but not touching the cube. Apply the heat in such a manner that the temperature of the water is raised 9° F. each minute.[3] The temperature recorded by the thermometer at the instant the pitch touches the bottom of the glass vessel shall be reported as the softening point."

"The limit of accuracy of the test is ±0.9° F."

For Pitches Fusing above 170° F. The heating is performed in an air bath in the apparatus illustrated in Fig. 151. The cube should be suspended in line with the

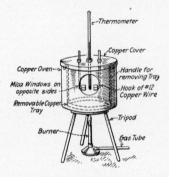

FIG. 151.—Cube-in-Air Method for High Fusing-point Substances.

observation windows, and the thermometer bulb brought to the same level. The temperature is raised 9° F. per minute, and recorded by the thermometer when the cube drops 1 in. To make the results obtained by this method correspond approximately with those obtained in water, 12° F. should be added to the observed fusing-point.

Investigations of the relationship between the Cube and the Ball and Ring methods indicate that the results vary considerably, depending largely upon the nature of the products tested and their fusing-points. No exact factors can be given.

[1] The use of freshly distilled water is essential, as otherwise air bubbles may form on the cube and retard its sinking.

[2] A sheet of paper placed on the bottom of the glass vessel and conveniently weighted will prevent the pitch from sticking to the glass vessel, thereby saving considerable time and trouble in cleaning.

[3] Rigid adherence to the prescribed rate of heating is absolutely essential in order to secure accuracy of results. The rate of rise of temperature shall be uniform and shall not be averaged over the period of the test. The maximum permissible variation for any minute period after the first three shall be ±0.9° F. All tests in which the rate of rise in temperature exceeds these limits shall be rejected.

Volatile Matter.

The following method of procedure has been adopted by the American Society for Testing Materials,[1] for determining the loss in weight (exclusive of water) of oil and asphaltic compounds when heated as described. The material under examination must therefore first be tested for water, and if water is found to be present, it must be removed by suitable methods of dehydration before the material is subjected to the loss on heating test; or another sample obtained which is free from water.

"The oven may be either circular or rectangular in form and may be heated by either gas or electricity. Its interior dimensions shall be as follows: height, not less than 40.64 cm. (16 in.); width and depth or diameter, at least 4.08 cm. (2 in.) greater than the diameter of the revolving shelf. It shall be well ventilated and shall be fitted with a window in the upper half of the door, so placed and of sufficient size to permit the accurate reading of the thermometer without opening the door. It shall also be provided with a perforated circular shelf preferably of approximately 24.8 cm. (9.75 in.) in diameter. (A recommended form of aluminium shelf is shown in Fig. 152.) This shelf shall be placed in the center of the oven and shall be suspended by a vertical shaft and provided with mechanical means for rotating it at the rate of 5 to 6 revolutions per minute. It shall be provided with recesses equidistant from the central shaft in which the tins containing the samples are to be placed."

"The thermometer shall be between 12.7 cm. (5 in.) and 15.24 cm. (6 in.) in length and the mercury bulb shall be from 10 mm. (0.39 in.) to 15 mm. (0.59 in.) in length. The scale shall be engraved on the stem, shall be clear cut and distinct, and shall run from 302° to 347° F. in $\frac{1}{2}$° F. divisions and shall commence substantially 3.81 cm. ($1\frac{1}{2}$ in.) above the top of the bulb. Every fifth degree shall be larger than the intermediate ones and shall be numbered . . . . It shall be made of a suitable quality of glass and be so annealed as to not change its readings under conditions of use. It shall be correct to 0.45° F. as determined by comparison at full immersion with a similar thermometer calibrated at full immersion by the U. S. Bureau of Standards."

"The container in which the sample is to be tested shall be of tin, cylindrical in shape, and shall have a flat bottom. Its inside dimensions shall be substantially as follows: diameter 55 mm. (2.17 in.); depth, 35 mm. (1.38 in.)[2]

"The sample as received shall be thoroughly stirred and agitated, warming if necessary, to insure a complete mixture before the portion for analysis is removed. Weigh 50 g. of the water-free material to be tested into a tared container of the form described. Bring the oven to a temperature of 325° F., and place the tin box containing the sample in one of the recesses of the revolving shelf. The thermometer shall be immersed for the depth of its bulb in a separate 50 g. sample of the material under test, placed in a similar container, and shall be conveniently suspended from the vertical shaft. This sample shall rest in one of the recesses upon the same shelf and revolve with the sample or samples under test. Then close the oven and rotate the shelf 5 to 6 revolutions per minute during the entire test. Maintain the temperature at 325° F. for 5 hours, then remove the sample from the oven, cool and weigh, and calculate the loss due to volatilization. During the 5-hour period the temperature shall not vary more than 2° F. All tests showing a greater variation in temperature shall be rejected.[3]

---

[1] "Standard Method of Test for Loss on Heating of Oil and Asphaltic Compounds" (Serial Designation: D 6–20), A. S. T. M. Standards Adopted in 1921, 731.

[2] A 3-oz. Gill style ointment box, deep pattern, fulfills these requirements.

[3] If additional periods of heating are desired, it is recommended that they be made in successive increments of 5 hours each.

"Up to 5 per cent loss in weight the results obtained may be considered as correct within 0.5. Above 5 per cent loss in weight the numerical limit of error increases 0.01 for every 0.5 per cent increase in loss by volatilization as follows:

Volatilization Loss, per cent	Numerical Correction	True Volatilization Loss, per cent
5.0	±0.50	4.50 to 5.50
5.5	±0.51	4.91 to 6.01
6.0	±0.52	5.48 to 6.52
10.0	±0.60	9.40 to 10.60
15.0	±0.70	14.30 to 15.70
25.0	±0.90	24.10 to 25.90
40.0	±1.20	38.80 to 41.20

"Under ordinary circumstances a number of samples having about the same degree of volatility may be tested at the same time. Samples varying greatly in volatility should be tested separately. Where extreme accuracy is required not more than one material should be tested at one time and duplicate samples of it should be placed simultaneously in the oven. Such duplicates shall check within the limits of accuracy given above. Results obtained on samples showing evidences of foaming during the test shall be rejected."

"When the penetration of the sample after heating is required, melt the residue at the lowest possible temperature and thoroughly mix by stirring, taking care to avoid incorporating air bubbles in the mass. Then bring it to the standard temperature and test as prescribed."

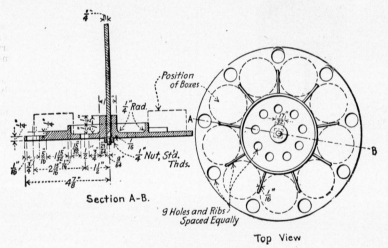

From A. S. T. M. Standards.

Fig. 152.—Shelf for Volatility Oven.

The oven ordinarily employed for determining the volatile matter, illustrated in Fig. 153, is composed of a cylindrical vessel with a hinged cover, surrounded by an insulated jacket, with an air-space in between acting as a flue to carry off the hot gases generated by the ring-burner underneath. The temperature may be conveniently regulated by a mercury thermostat.

Flash-point.

The flash-point procedure is used primarily for determining the adaptability of bituminous substances for certain definite usages, and serves as a criterion of the fire hazard.

A number of flash-point testers have been proposed, of which the following are most generally used:

Pensky-Martens Closed Tester. This apparatus has been adopted as standard by the Government of the United States, and foreign governments for testing high flash-point bituminous materials. The instrument is illustrated in Fig. 154, and consists

Courtesy of Wm. Boekel & Co.

Fig. 153.—Volatility Oven.

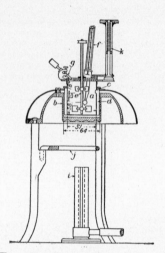

Fig. 154.—Pensky-Martens Closed
Flash-point Tester.

of an oil cup a, in a metal heating vessel b, surrounded with a flanged top to prevent loss of heat by radiation. An orifice c permits the overflow of the oil into the jacket d between the oil cup and the heating vessel. It is likewise provided with a mechanical stirring device e, the thermometer f, the test flame g, burner i, wire screen j, and spring k to work the slide under the test flame.

The approximate flash-point is ascertained by a preliminary test. The melted bituminous substance is poured into the Pensky-Martens tester, which should be perfectly level, taking care not to splash any on the sides of the cup, or to cause any froth on the surface. All bubbles should be pricked with a heated wire. The test flame is then regulated to correspond in size with the ivory bead on the cover (to burn 0.1 cu.ft. coal gas per hour). The burner i is lit, and the contents heated rapidly at first until the temperature reaches 50° F. below the expected flash-point, whereupon the rise in temperature should be controlled to increase exactly 5° F. per minute. At each degree the milled head k is turned and the flame g tilted into the cup for exactly one second. The test is continued until the flash-point occurs. Any slight flickering or spreading of the flame is ignored. The end point is evidenced by an unquestionable flash. The apparatus should be protected from draughts, and the sample stirred continuously during the test. If the thermometer is graduated to read for total immersion, the stem-correction should be applied. When this is done, it is suggested that "corr." be added to the reading, thus: "Flash 379° F. corr."

A simplified form of Pensky-Martens tester for approximately determining the flash-point, consists of a glass beaker or metal cup having the same dimensions, namely 5.0 cm. in diameter, and 5.5 cm. in depth, filled to within 1.8 cm. of its upper rim with the material to be tested. This is supported on a sand bath and the thermometer bulb immersed in the bituminous material without, however, touching the sides or bottom. The test flame is adjusted to a 3 mm. cross-section, and the test performed exactly as described for the Pensky-Martens tester.[1]

Cleveland Open Tester. This apparatus is described on p. 1120.

New York State or Elliot Closed Tester. The method of using this tester is described on p. 1109. For testing bituminous substances, the rise in temperature is carefully regulated to 10° F. per minute.

Fixed Carbon

The same procedure is followed as for testing coal, described on p. 1218 ("Volatile Combustible Matter"), also p. 1222.

Distillation Test

Flask Method of Distillation. If water is present, the bituminous material must first be dehydrated. This may be conveniently performed by distilling 500 cc. in an 800-cc. copper still, provided with a water-cooled condenser, the distillate being caught in a 200-cc. separatory funnel. When all the water is expelled, the distillate is allowed to settle, the water drawn off and the oils returned to the residue in the still after the contents have cooled below 212° F.

The apparatus as assembled is illustrated in Fig. 155. It consists of a standard 250-cc. Engler distilling flask.

The condenser tube shall have the following dimensions: adapter 70 mm.; length of straight tube 185 mm.; width of tube 12–15 mm.; width of adapter end of tube 20–25 mm.

A carefully standardized thermometer should be used. The cylinder used for collecting the distillate shall have a capacity of 25 cc. and be graduated in 0.1 cc. The burner should be provided with a tin shield, having a small hole for observing the flame. The thermometer bulb should be placed opposite the middle of the tubulature. Pour 100 cc. of the dehydrated bituminous material into the Engler flask and weigh. Then commence to distil at the rate of 1 cc. per minute, changing the receiver as the mercury column passes the following fractioning points, reporting the fractions by weight and by volume:

Start to 110° C.; 110–170° C.; 170–235° C.; 235–270° C.; 270–300° C.; and residue.

The residue is weighed after the distillation is completed and the flask cooled.[2]

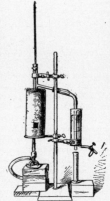

From A. S. T. M. Standards.

FIG. 155. — Flask Method of Distillation.

---

[1] "Flash Point of Oils," by I. C. Allen and A. S. Crossfield, Tech. Paper No. 49, Petroleum Technology 10, Dept. of Interior, Bureau of Mines, Wash., D. C., 1913.

[2] "Standard Method of Test for Distillation of Bituminous Materials Suitable for Road Treatment" (Serial Designation: D 20–18), A. S. T. M. Standards Adopted in 1921, 735.

Retort Method of Distillation.   This method is adapted principally for analyzing creosote oils suitable for impregnating timber.[1]   The distillation is performed in a glass retort, having a capacity of 250–290 cc. (measured by placing the retort with the bottom of the bulb and the end of the offtake in the same horizontal plane and pouring water into the bulb through the tubulature until it overflows through the offtake). The length of the offtake should be 25–30 cm., its internal diameter next to the bulb approximately 2.85 cm., and the diameter at the open end approximately 1.25 cm.   The diameter of the tubulature should be approximately 1.9 cm.

The condenser tube shall have the following dimensions: diameter of small end 12.5 mm. with a variation of 1.5 mm.; diameter of large end 28.5 mm. with a variation of 3.0 mm.; length 360 mm. with a variation of 4.0 mm.

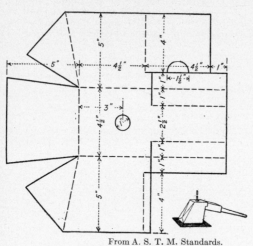

From A. S. T. M. Standards.

Fig. 156.—Asbestos Shield for Retort.

The asbestos shield for the retort shall have the form and dimensions illustrated in Fig. 156.   The receiver shall consist of Erlenmeyer flasks of 50–100 cc. capacity, and the thermometer shall be carefully standardized.

The apparatus is assembled as illustrated in Fig. 157.   Exactly 100 g. of dehydrated creosote oil are distilled at the rate of not less than 1, nor more than 2 drops per second, the distillate being collected and weighed in the receiver.   The condenser tube should be warmed whenever necessary to prevent the accumulation of solid distillate, and the receiver changed as the mercury passes the dividig temperatures of the following fractions: 210, 235, 270, 315 and 355° C. When the temperature registers 355° C., the flame shall be removed from the retort, and any oil which has condensed in the offtake drained into the 355° fraction.   The retort is cooled and reweighed to ascertain the

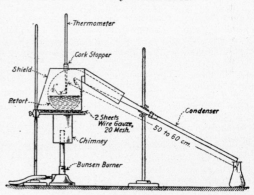

From A. S. T. M. Standards.

Fig. 157.—Retort Method of Distillation.

amount of residue, which is generally tested by the float test.   The various fractions should be reported by weight and also by volume, and their specific gravities calculated.

---

[1] "Standard Methods of Sampling and Analysis of Creosote Oil" (Serial Designation: D 38–18), A. S. T. M. Standards Adopted in 1921, 806.

SOLUBILITY TESTS
Solubility in Carbon Disulphide

With native asphalt containing over 10 per cent of mineral matter, it is advisable to separate the portion soluble in carbon disulphide for ascertaining its physical characteristics, fusing-point, and sometimes fixed carbon.

The tests generally employed for this purpose have been devised by the Am. Soc. Testing Materials[1] and are substantially as follows, deviating slightly in phraseology.

The bituminous material should first be freed from moisture. If the material is hard and brittle, it is ground and spread in a thin layer in an iron or nickel dish and kept in an oven at 125° C. for 1 hour, provided it is substantially free from volatile matter at this temperature. When it is not desirable to crush the rock or sand grains, a lump may be placed in the drying oven until it is thoroughly heated, when it may be crushed into a thin layer and dried as described. If volatile materials are present, it should be dehydrated by distillation at a low temperature, the water-free distillate being returned to the residue, and thoroughly incorporated with it.

Sufficient of the dehydrated material to insure the presence of 1–2 g. soluble in carbon disulphide is weighed into a 150-cc. tared Erlenmeyer flask, and 100 cc. of c.p. carbon disulphide poured into the flask in small portions, with continuous agitation until all the lumps disappear and nothing adheres to the bottom. The flask is then loosely corked and set aside. From this point on, one of two methods may be followed, depending on whether or not the bituminous material contains a substantial quantity of finely divided insoluble matter.

Procedure Used in the Presence of Substantial Quantities of Finely Divided Insoluble Matter. The flask is set aside to settle for 48 hours, and the solution decanted into a second tared flask, pouring off as much of the solvent as possible without disturbing the residue. The contents of the first flask are again treated with a quantity of carbon disulphide, shaken as before, and both the first and second flasks allowed to settle for another 48 hours. The liquids in both flasks are then carefully decanted upon a weighed Gooch crucible (measuring 4.0 cm. wide at the top, tapering to 3.2 cm. at the bottom, and 2.5 cm. deep), carrying freshly ignited long-fibered amphibole (asbestos) compacted in a layer not over $\frac{1}{8}$ in. No vacuum is to be used in filtering, and the temperature of the liquid kept between 65 and 77° F. The residue remaining on the filter is thoroughly washed with carbon disulphide until the filtrate becomes clear. The flasks are again shaken with fresh carbon disulphide, allowed to settle for 24 hours, or until it is seen that a good subsidation has taken place, and thereupon decanted through the filter. The residues remaining in both flasks are washed until the washings are practically colorless, all washings being passed through the Gooch crucible. The crucible and contents, likewise the two flasks, are heated for one-half hour at 220° F., cooled in a desiccator and weighed. The filtrate containing the soluble constituents is evaporated, the bituminous residue burned and ignited to a clean ash, whereupon a few drops of ammonium carbonate solution are added, the ash ignited at a low red heat and weighed. The weight of ash thus obtained is added to the residue in the two flasks and the crucible. The difference between the weight of the dehydrated material taken for analysis and the weight of the combined residues represents the proportion soluble in carbon disulphide.[2]

[1] "Standard Method of Test for Soluble Bitumen" (Serial Designation: D 4–11), A. S. T. M. Standards Adopted in 1921, 726; "Tentative Method of Test for the Determination of Bitumen" (Serial Designation: D 4–23T), Proc. A. S. T. M., **23**, Part 1, 751, 1923.

[2] For a discussion of the method, see "A Study of Certain Methods for Determining Total Soluble Bitumen in Paving Materials," by S. Avery and R. Corr, J. Am. Chem. Soc., **28**, 648, 1906; "The Proximate Composition and Physical Structure of Trinidad Asphalt, with Special Reference to the Behavior of Mixtures of Bitumen and Fine Mineral Matter," by Clifford Richardson, Proc. Am. Soc. Testing Materials, **6**, 509, 1906; "The Determination of Soluble Bitumen," by Hubbard and Reeve, Proc. Am. Soc. Testing Materials, **10**, 420, 1910; "The Bitumen Content of Coarse Bituminous Aggregates," by Prévost Hubbard, Proc. Int. Assoc. Testing Materials, XXV–2, 1912.

Procedure Followed with Materials Containing Little to No Finely Divided Insoluble Matter. This method is used for rapid work where the bituminous material does not contain insoluble matter which would clog the pores of the filter. Add 50 cc. of carbon disulphide and agitate the flask until all the lumps disappear and nothing adheres to the bottom. Then set the flask aside for 15 minutes, whereupon it is filtered through a weighed Gooch crucible. The liquid must be decanted with care, and the decantation stopped at the first sign of sediment coming over. The sides of the flask are washed with a small amount of fresh carbon disulphide, and the sediment caught on the filter, using a "policeman," if necessary, to remove all adhering material. Then wash residue on filter with carbon disulphide until the washings are colorless, and continue the suction until the odor of carbon disulphide is scarcely detectable. The outside of the crucible is cleaned by a cloth moistened with a small amount of the solvent. Heat the crucible for one half hour at 220° F., cool in a desiccator and weigh. The weight of residue in the crucible added to the residue obtained by igniting the carbon disulphide extract represents the insoluble matter. The portion soluble in carbon disulphide is calculated by difference.

The author finds that in the presence of large quantities of finely divided insoluble matter, the method may be materially shortened by adding a weighed quantity (about twice the weight of bituminous material) of freshly ignited, long-fibered amphibole to the bituminous substance in the first flask. On shaking with carbon disulphide, the asbestos serves to dilute the insoluble matter, preventing the latter from clogging the pores of the filter, and accordingly reducing the time of filtration. In many cases this procedure may be adopted to good advantage.

Carbenes

The expression "carbenes" has been generally applied to that portion of bituminous substances soluble in carbon disulphide but insoluble in carbon tetrachloride. This term was originally proposed by Clifford Richardson.[1] This test is of value in identifying bituminous substances, gauging their uniformity of supply, for purposes of factory control, and as a criterion of their quality. Certain hard native asphalts and asphaltites, particularly grahamite, normally contain a percentage of carbenes, whereas petroleum asphalts do not show carbenes unless they are overheated, or over-blown. If more than 0.5 per cent is present in petroleum asphalts, their quality is to be regarded as questionable. Carbenes are found in tars and pitches in varying amounts.[2]

This test[3] is carried out by following the same procedure as in determining the solubility in carbon disulphide, but replacing the latter with carbon tetrachloride. The carbon tetrachloride must be free from carbon disulphide, which may be insured by distilling it under a dephlegmator, discarding any distillate below 76° C. The solvent is then filtered through calcium chloride, and any free hydrochloric acid removed by blowing dry air through it.

[1] "Carbon Tetrachloride and its Use as a Solution for Differentiating Bitumens," by Clifford Richardson and C. N. Forrest, J. Soc. Chem. Ind., **24**, 310, 1905.

[2] "Some Relations of the Effect of Overheating to Certain Physical and Chemical Properties of Asphalts," by A. W. Hixson and H. E. Hands, J. Ind. Eng. Chem., **9**, 651, 1917; "The Value of the Carbene Requirement in Asphalt Specifications," by L. Kirschbraun, Munic. Eng., **35**, 349, 1909.

[3] "Tentative Method of Test for the Determination of Proportion of Bitumen Soluble in Carbon Tetrachloride" (Serial Designation: D 165–23T), Proc. A. S. T. M., **23**, Vol. I, 754, 1923.

The carbon tetrachloride is allowed to act on the bituminous substance overnight, care being taken to keep the vessel in a dark place to protect it from daylight or sunshine.[1] Richardson proposes blowing a gentle current of air through the solution *in the dark* for 1 hour[2] to coagulate the insoluble matter and assist in the filtration. The difference between the percentages soluble in carbon disulphide and carbon tetrachloride respectively, represents the per cent of "carbenes."

Solubility in 88° Petroleum Naphtha

The portion soluble in 88° naphtha has been termed "petrolenes" by some, and "malthenes" by others, whereas the non-mineral constituents insoluble in 88° naphtha are generally referred to as "asphaltenes."

It is important that the petroleum naphtha should be derived from petroleum composed entirely of open-chain hydrocarbons, and test exactly 88° Baumé, equivalent to a specific gravity of 0.638 at 60° F./60° F. At least 85 per cent by volume should distil between 95 and 150° F. The density and character of the naphtha is important, since heavy distillates, or products derived from petroleum containing unsaturated or cyclic hydrocarbons will exert a greater solvent action upon the bituminous substance.

This method is performed in the same manner as for determining the portion soluble in carbon disulphide, 88° petroleum naphtha being substituted for the latter. Hard bituminous substances should be powdered; liquid bituminous substances flowed in a thin layer over the bottom of the flask; and semi-solid to semi-liquid substances heated until fluid and distributed in a thin layer to present a greater surface to the solvent. It is advisable not to use a stirring rod, as this causes the bituminous substance to adhere to the inner surface of the flask and to the rod itself. The operation should take place at room temperature, and away from the direct rays of the sun. The introduction of a weighed portion of long-fibered asbestos to the solution will assist in its filtration.[3]

Solubility in Other Solvents.

Solvents other than those mentioned in the foregoing tests, including benzol, mixtures of benzol and toluol, acetone, etc., are occasionally used for identifying bituminous substances or to investigate their adaptability for a given use. The extraction may be carried out hot or cold, but in either event the method used should be clearly stated in reporting the results. If cold, follow the method described under the heading "Solubility in Carbon Bisulphide." If hot, follow the method described for determining "Free Carbon in Tars." Hard and brittle bituminous substances should be powdered. Medium and soft substances should be mixed with five times their weight of long-fibered amphibole (previously ignited) or ten times their weight of 20- to 30-mesh Ottawa silica, to prevent the material fusing together in a solid mass and retard the action of the solvent. Where the hot "extraction is used, the operation is continued for at least six hours, and until no further loss in weight is recorded, whereupon the contents of the filter cup are dried and weighed."

[1] "Studies on the Carbenes," by K. J. Mackenzie, J. Ind. Eng. Chem., **2**, 124, 1910; "On the Formation of Carbenes," by D. B. W. Alexander, J. Ind. Eng. Chem., **2**, 242 1910.

[2] "The Modern Asphalt Pavement," by Clifford Richardson, 2nd Edition, 546, 1908.

[3] "The Modern Asphalt Pavement," by Clifford Richardson, 2nd Edition, p. 543, 1908; "Laboratory Manual of Bituminous Materials," by Hubbard, 1st Edition, p. 90, 1916.

CHEMICAL TESTS

Water

Substances Distilling at Low Temperatures. This method is adapted to crude petroleum, tars, creosote oil and other fluid bituminous substances distilling at comparatively low temperatures.[1] The apparatus is set up as shown in Fig. 158. The

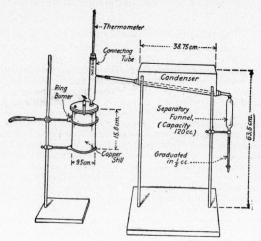

From A. S. T. A. Standards.

FIG. 158.—Still for Determining Water.

copper still is provided with a removable flanged top and yoke, which with a paper gasket will form an air-tight joint when clamped into place. The thermometer should be carefully standardized. The condenser consists of a copper trough carrying a straight-walled glass tube. The separatory funnel has a total capacity of 120 cc. with the outlet graduated in fifths of a cubic centimeter.

Pour 200–500 cc. of the bituminous material into the still and weigh. Clamp the top in place, using a paper gasket moistened with lubricating oil. Apply heat with the ring burner supported just above the level of the bituminous material at the beginning of the test, and then gradually lower it as the water distils over. Continue the distillation until the vapor temperature reaches 205° C. Collect the distillate in the separatory funnel, and let it stand until a clean separation of water takes place. Read off the volume of water, calculate its weight, and figure the per cent present in the crude bituminous material. Draw off the water, and return any light oil to the bituminous matter in the still. The dehydrated material should then be used for further tests.

[1] "Standard Methods of Sampling and Analysis of Creosote Oil" (Serial Designation: D 38–18), A. S. T. M. Standards Adopted in 1921, 806.

Substances Distilling at High Temperatures. This method is adapted to asphalts and other bituminous substances comparatively free from volatile constituents, and incapable of distilling without suffering decomposition.

Substances Fusing below 300° F. When it is desired to determine the percentage of moisture without using the residue for other purposes, a convenient method consists in weighing 100 g. into a distilling flask, adding 200 cc. of petroleum naphtha (of which 5% distils between 90° and 100° C., and 90% below 195° C.), or kerosene in the case of asphaltic products, or toluol in the case of tar products, and warming gently under a reflux condenser until the bituminous substance mixes with the solvent. Cool, add a quantity of dry pumice-stone to prevent bumping, and distil into a graduate until the liquid comes over clear. The distillate is then allowed to settle by gravity, and the volume of water read off directly; or else the water may be withdrawn with a pipette, and weighed. This method is said to be accurate to approximately 0.033 g. of water per 100 cc. of toluol or kerosene present in the distillate.[1]

Where the hydrated material is to be used for further examination, 25 g. are weighed into an Erlenmeyer flask, through which a current of dry illuminating gas is passed, and maintained at 105° C. for 1 hour. The vapors are led through a return condenser maintained at 50° C., and then into a weighed calcium chloride tube. When all the moisture is driven off, the calcium chloride tube is reweighed and the moisture calculated. If constituents are present, volatilizing below 50° C., the return condenser should be maintained at a corresponding lower temperature.

Substances not Fusing at 300° F. In this case the material is comminuted by powdering (to about 60 mesh) or shaving, and a weighed quantity spread in a thin layer on glass and maintained in an oven at 105° C. for 1 hour, or until the weight becomes constant. If the substance is oxidizable in air, it should be heated in an atmosphere of nitrogen or illuminating gas. Cool in a desiccator, reweigh and calculate the per cent moisture.

Oxygen in Non-Mineral Matter

There being no satisfactory direct method for determining oxygen, it is computed by subtracting the sum of the percentages of hydrogen (p. 120), carbon (p. 120), nitrogen (p. 340), sulphur (p. 1112), water and ash from 100 per cent. The result so obtained is affected by all the errors incurred in the other determinations, and especially by the change in weight of the ash-forming constituents on ignition. Iron pyrites will absorb oxygen from the air and change to ferric oxide, increasing the weight of ash, and thereby causing a negative error in the oxygen, equivalent to three-eighths of the pyritic sulphur. Any calcium carbonate present will tend to absorb sulphur combined with the bituminous constituents. On the other hand, there is always a loss on ignition of "water of composition" from the clayey and shaley constituents, also carbon dioxide from carbonates, etc., which tend to compensate for the absorption of oxygen.[2]

[1] "Methods for the Determination of Water in Petroleum and its Products," by I. C. Allen and W. A. Jacobs, Tech. Paper 25, Dept. of Interior, Bureau of Mines, Wash., D. C., 1912; "Tentative Method of Test for Water in Petroleum Products and Other Bituminous Materials" (Serial Designation: D 95–23T), Proc. A. S. T. M., **23**, Part I, 694, 1923.

[2] "Standard Methods of Laboratory Sampling and Analysis of Coal" (Serial Designation: D 22–21), A. S. T. M. Standards, 1921, 760.

Free Carbon in Tars

This represents an adaptation of the carbon disulphide method suitable for testing tars and pitches for the presence of non-mineral matter insoluble in hot toluol-benzol, which has been found the most satisfactory menstruum for this purpose.[1]

The apparatus used was devised by H. J. Cary-Curr and is illustrated in Fig. 159.

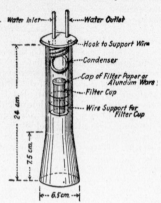

From A. S. T. A. Standards.

FIG. 159.—Cary-Curr Extraction Apparatus.

The filtering medium may consist either of a paper thimble or two thicknesses of Schleicher & Schuell's No. 575 hardened filter paper, 15 cm. in diameter, arranged in the shape of a cup by folding symmetrically around a stick 1 in. in diameter. It should be soaked in benzol to remove any grease, dried in an oven, desiccated and weighed.

Tars must be dehydrated before extracting, and pitches if sufficiently hard, ground to a fine powder. In testing materials containing more than 5 per cent of free carbon, 5 g. should be used, and 10 g. with smaller percentages. Weigh the prescribed amount in a 100-cc. beaker and digest with 50 cc. c.p. toluol on a steam bath with constant stirring for not exceeding 30 minutes. Place the prepared filter paper in a carbon filter-tube over a beaker or flask and decant the toluol extract through it. Wash with hot c.p. toluol until the filtrate is clear, using a "policeman" unaffected by toluol for detaching any free carbon adhering to the beaker. Finally wash the filter with hot c.p. benzol, and after draining, cover it with a cap of filter paper or alundum, and extract it in the Cary-Curr apparatus with c.p. benzol until the drippings become colorless. This will take at least 2 hours. The filter is then removed, the cap taken off, the paper dried in a steam oven, cooled in a desiccator and weighed. With pitches it is well to examine the free carbon for foreign matter, such as wood slivers, pieces of bagging, etc. If such foreign matter is present, the test should be rejected.

Solid Paraffines

The following method does not give absolute figures, since it merely discloses the paraffine hydrocarbons which are *solid* at room temperature, without taking the liquid paraffines into consideration; nevertheless the results are of value for purposes of comparison.[2] Weigh 50 g. of the material in a tared 6-oz. glass retort, and slowly distil

[1] "Free Carbon, Its Nature and Determination in Tar Products," by J. M. Weiss, J. Ind. Eng. Chem., **6**, 279, 1914; "Some Effects of Certain Solvents on Tars in the 'Free Carbon' Determination," by G. S. Monroe and H. J. Broderson, J. Ind. Eng. Chem., **9**, 1100, 1917; "Standard Methods of Sampling and Analysis of Creosote Oil" (Serial Designation: D 38–18), A. S. T. M. Standards Adopted in 1921, 806.

[2] "The Modern Asphalt Pavement," by Clifford Richardson, 2d Edition, 558, 1908; "Untersuchung der Kohlenwasserstofföle und Fette," by D. Holde, Berlin, 45, 1913; "Laboratory Manual of Bituminous Materials," by Prévost Hubbard, N. Y., 100, 1916.

until nothing but a residue of coke remains. The distillation should take in the neighborhood of 45 minutes from the time the first drop comes over. The distillate is caught in an Erlenmeyer flask, and weighed. Either 5 or 10 g. of the well mixed distillate, depending upon the quantity of solid paraffines present in the crude material, are transferred into a large test tube and dissolved in 25 cc. of absolute ethyl ether and 25 cc. of absolute ethyl alcohol. A similar mixture containing 25 cc. each of ether and alcohol is made up, and this together with the oil solution is cooled separately to exactly 0° F. for ½ hour in a mixture of ice and salt (to which if necessary calcium chloride may be added). The oil solution is then rapidly filtered through a weighed Gooch crucible, similarly maintained at 0° F. by a jacket of ice and salt, and washed with 50 cc. of the cooled ether-alcohol mixture. A simple and convenient apparatus consists of an inverted bottle 6 in. in diameter, having the bottom cut off, and attached to the same rubber stopper which supports the funnel holding the Gooch crucible. The space between the bottle, the crucible, and the supporting funnel is packed with the ice and salt mixture. The Gooch crucible is then removed, the outside wiped clean, placed on a tared glass and dried in an oven at 80° C. until the last traces of ether and alcohol are evaporated. The residue is weighed, and the percentage of solid paraffines calculated in the original 50 g. of substance taken for analysis.

Sulphonation Residue

The method of determining the sulphonation residue as proposed by Dean & Bateman,[1] consists in distilling sufficient of the material under examination by the flask method to obtain at least 10 cc. of distillate between 315 and 355° C. Exactly 10 cc. of this fraction are measured into a Babcock milk bottle, and 40 cc. of 37 normal sulphuric acid added, 10 cc. at a time. The bottle and its contents are shaken for 2 minutes after each addition, and when all the acid has been added, the bottle is kept at a constant temperature of 98–100° C. for one hour, during which it is shaken vigorously every 10 minutes. At the end of the hour, the bottle is removed, cooled, filled to the top of the graduations with ordinary sulphuric acid, and whirled for 5 minutes in a Babcock separator. The unsulphonated residue multiplied by 2 gives the per cent by volume directly (each graduation being equal to 1/200 of a cc.).

It is important that the acid should be of the proper strength. A mixture of fuming sulphuric acid and ordinary concentrated sulphuric acid should be prepared to contain exactly 80.07 per cent of SO_3, which constitutes 37 normal acid. If the sulphonation residue is dark in color, it should be treated with an excess of a 10 per cent sodium hydroxide solution, and if completely soluble in this reagent, the test is negative.

Unsaponifiable and Saponifiable Matters

Certain bituminous substances, such as montan wax, rosin pitch, and fatty-acid pitch are often composed largely of saponifiable constituents. Others, including pine tar, pine-tar pitch, hardwood tar, hardwood-tar pitch, peat tar, lignite tar, bone tar, bone-tar pitch and others forms of fatty-acid pitches contain smaller percentages. This test is also used for gauging the uniformity of supply, and in the case of fatty-acid pitches, as a criterion of the quality.

The following procedure has been devised by the author for specifically examining bituminous materials or admixtures of bituminous materials with animal or vegetable oils and fats, since the customary methods do not adapt themselves especially well, due to the formation of troublesome emulsions. The bituminous material is first freed from insoluble constituents, including any mineral matter, by boiling with carbon disulphide under a reflux condenser, cooling and filtering through a Gooch crucible.

[1] "The Analysis and Grading of Creosotes," Forest Service Circular 112, Wash., D. C.; "Modification of the Sulphonation Test for Creosote," Forest Service Circular 191, Wash., D. C.; "Methods for Testing Coal Tar and Refined Tars, Oils and Pitches Derived Therefrom," by S. R. Church, J. Ind. Eng. Chem., **3**, 233, 1911; **5**, 196, 1913; "Paraffin Bodies in Coal Tar Creosote and their Bearing on Specifications," by S. R. Church and J. M. Weiss, J. Ind. Eng. Chem., **6**, 396, 1914.

The insoluble constituents are dried at 100° C. and weighed. Sufficient of the bituminous substance should be taken to yield approximately 5.0 g. of extract. The benzol solution is evaporated or distilled to 50 cc. and 50 cc. of the saponifying liquid added from a pipette. This should consist of a 10 per cent solution of caustic potash, prepared by dissolving 100 g. of anhydrous potash in 500 cc. of 95 per cent ethyl alcohol, and diluting to a litre with 90 per cent benzol. The liquid is allowed to stand overnight to permit any carbonate to settle, and the clear solution decanted. After the saponifying agent is added, the mixture is boiled under a reflux condenser, for ½–1 hour, and the contents of the flask while still warm poured in a separatory funnel containing 150 cc. of boiling water and 25 cc. of a 10 per cent solution of potassium chloride. Add 250 cc. of benzol, agitate vigorously, and allow the funnel to rest quietly in a warm place until the solvent separates. If an emulsion forms which refuses to separate on standing, add 200 cc. more benzol and 100 cc. 95 per cent ethyl alcohol and stand in a warm place overnight. This will invariably effect a more or less complete separation of the solvent From this point on the method is illustrated by the following tabular outline:

Saponify as described:
Draw off the soap solution as completely as possible.
Decant the benzol layer, leaving the intermediate layer in the separatory funnel.

Aqueous Soap Solution. Exhaust with 200 cc. portions of benzol.		Benzol Layer.	Intermediate Layer.
Aqueous Soap Solution.	Combined Benzol Extracts.		
	Combine and exhaust with 100 cc. portions of 50% alcohol.		
	Benzol Solution.	Combined Alcoholic Extracts.	
		Combine and exhaust with benzol.	
		Combined Benzol Extracts.	Alcoholic Soap Solution.
	Combine, evaporate to a small bulk, complete the evaporation at 100° C., cool and weigh the *Unsaponifiable Constituents.*		

————— Combine —————

Transpose with dilute hydrochloric acid, warm and exhaust with benzol. Separate the aqueous solution containing the glycerol and mineral salts. Evaporate the combined benzol extracts to a small bulk, and then complete the evaporation of solvent at 100° C. Cool and weigh. Weight equals the *free acids derived from the saponifiable constituents.*

In the case of bituminous materials that are more or less completely saponifiable, the intermediate layer is apt to be absent. In this case the process will simplify itself considerably. The foregoing procedure will separate the unsaponifiable constituents in practically an ash-free state.

Diazo Reaction

This test is used for identifying bituminous substances carrying phenols, including wood tar and wood-tar pitch, oil-gas- and water-gas-tars and pitches, shale tar, peat- and lignite-tars and pitches, bone tar, bone-tar pitch and the various coal-tar pitches.

This reaction was devised by E. Graefe.[1] It is carried out by boiling 2 g. of the

[1] "Distinction between Lignite Pitch and other Pitches," Chem. Zeit., **30**, 298, 1906; Marcusson and Eickmann, Chem. Zeit., **32**, 965, 1908.

bituminous substance with 20 cc. N. aqueous caustic soda, for approximately 5 minutes. After cooling, the liquid is filtered.   If the filtrate is dark colored, it may be lightened by adding finely pulverized "salt."   It is then cooled in ice, and a few drops of freshly prepared diazobenzolchloride solution (prepared by treating anilin with hydrochloric acid and sodium nitrite) added.   If phenols are present a red coloration will result, sometimes accompanied by a reddish precipitate.

Assuming that the bituminous substance gives the diazo reaction, the question will often arise whether the product is a straight-distilled pitch, or an asphalt "cut-back" with a high boiling-point distillate containing phenolic bodies, derived from coal tar, lignite tar, etc.   Marcusson has worked out a method applicable under these circumstances,[1] which consists in dissolving 10 g. of the bituminous substance in 15 cc. of benzol, and pouring the solution into 200 cc. of 88° petroleum naphtha.   The resulting precipitate is washed with petroleum naphtha and dried.   It is then boiled for 15 minutes with N/2 alcoholic caustic potash under a reflux condenser to extract the phenols.   The liquid is cooled and filtered, the alcohol evaporated, and the residue dissolved in water.   Sodium chloride is added to clarify the liquid and remove any substances imparting a dark color, the solution is filtered and the filtrate treated for the diazo test described above.   If a straight distilled pitch containing phenols is present, a positive reaction will be obtained.   If the original substance gives the diazo test, but the residue treated in the above way does not, then the admixture of high boiling-point oils containing phenolic bodies with a substance free from phenols (e.g., asphalts, etc.) is established.   The presence of 10 per cent asphaltic substances may be detected.

Where bituminous substances contain calcium carbonate, the phenolic bodies present combine with the lime, forming insoluble calcium phenolate which yields but a faint diazo reaction.   However, on treating such substances with a solvent in the presence of hydrochloric acid, the calcium phenolate is decomposed, and the diazo reaction becomes much more delicate.

Anthraquinone Reaction

The anthraquinone reaction is used for detecting anthracene in tar products produced at high temperatures, including oil-gas-tar and pitch, water-gas-tar and pitch, and the various coal-tar pitches.

The tar or pitch is first subjected to distillation in accordance with the retort method, the offtake and condensing tube being kept warm to prevent the accumulation of any solid distillate.   The distillate passing over between 270 and 355° C. is caught separately and examined for anthracene in the following manner.   The fraction is heated until it is thoroughly fluid to secure a uniform sample, and 5 g. weighed out, while hot. After cooling, 10 cc. of absolute ethyl alcohol are added, the solids allowed to crystallize and the liquid decanted.   The solid substances containing the anthracene are dried on a water bath, transferred to a 500-cc. flask connected with a return condenser, 45 cc. of glacial acetic acid added, and the contents boiled for 2 hours.   The following mixture is then added drop by drop through a separatory funnel, viz.: 15 g. of anhydrous chromic acid dissolved in 10 cc. of glacial acetic acid, and 10 cc. of water.   The boiling is continued for another 2 hours, the flask cooled, and 400 cc. cold water added.   This treatment oxidizes the anthracene to anthraquinone, which on cooling separates as a solid mass.   This is filtered, washed with hot water, then with a hot 1 per cent solution of caustic soda and again with hot water.   The residue of anthraquinone is then dried and its weight multiplied by 0.856 to obtain the corresponding weight of anthracene. From 0.25 to 0.75 per cent of anthracene is found in coal tars, and a corresponding larger percentage in coal-tar pitches.

A color reaction for establishing the presence of anthracene consists in boiling the crystals of anthraquinone with zinc dust and caustic soda solution, whereupon an intense red colored solution is obtained, which on filtering becomes decolorized by air.

[1] Chem. Rev. Fett-und Harz-Ind., **18**, 47, 1911.

TABLE III.—SYNOPTICAL TABLE OF THE MOST IMPORTANT

	Fracture	Streak	Sp. gr. at 77° F. (Non-mineral Matter)	Consistency at 77° F.	Susceptibility Factor	Fusibility °F. (K. and S. Method)
Non-asphaltic petroleum.............	....	....	0.75–0.90	Liquid	......	<0
Mixed-base petroleum...............	....	....	0.80–0.95	Liquid	......	<0
Asphaltic petroleum.................	....	....	0.85–1.00	Liquid	......	<0
Ozokerite........................	Conc. to H	Wh. to Yel.	0.85–1.00	20–40	>80	140–200
Montan wax......................	Conch.	Yel.	0.90–1.00	>100	>100	170–200
Paraffine wax....................	Conc. to H	Wh.	0.85–0.95	15–80	>100	100–150
Native asphalts (contg. less than 10% mineral matter).................	Variable	Bn. to Bk.	0.95–1.12	0–>100	15–>100	60–325
Native asphalts (contg. greater than 10% mineral matter).............	Variable	Bn. to Bk.	0.95–1.15	5–>100	30–>100	60–350
Residual oils.....................	....	....	0.85–1.05	0–7	......	0–80
Blown petroleum asphalts...........	Variable	Bn. to Bk.	0.90–1.07	2–30	8–40	80–400
Residual asphalts..................	Conch.	Bk.	1.00–1.17	5–100	40–60	80–225
Sludge asphalts	Conch.	Bk.	1.05–1.20	5–100	40–60	80–225
Wurtzilite asphalt.................	Conch.	Bn. to Bk.	1.04–1.07	20–50	30–40	150–300
Gilsonite........................	Conch.	Bn.	1.05–1.10	90–120	>100	250–375
Glance pitch.....................	Conc. to H	Bk.	1.10–1.15	90–120	>100	250–350
Grahamite.......................	Conc. to H	Bk.	1.15–1.20	>150	>100	350–600
Elaterite........................	....	Bn.	0.90–1.05	Rubbery	......	Inf.
Wurtzilite.......................	Conc. to H	Bn.	1.05–1.07	>150	......	Inf.
Albertite........................	Conc. to H	Bn. to Bk.	1.07–1.10	>150	......	Inf.
Impsonite.......................	Hackly	Bk.	1.10–1.25	>150	......	Inf.
Asphaltic pyrobituminous shales.....	Conch.	Var.	1.50–1.75	>150	......	Inf.
Peat (dry).......................	Variable	Bn.	0.15–1.05	>150	......	Inf.
Lignite (dry).....................	Variable	Bn.	1.00–1.25	>150	......	Inf.
Bituminous coal..................	Hackly	Bn. to Bk.	1.20–1.40	>150	......	Inf.
Anthracite coal...................	Conc. to H	Bk.	1.30–1.60	>150	......	Inf.
Non-asphaltic pyrobituminous shales.	Conch.	Var.	1.30–1.75	>150	......	Inf.
Wax tailings.....................	....	Yel.	1.00–1.10	5–20	20–40	60–100
Oil-gas tar......................	....	....	0.95–1.10	0	......	<0–20
Oil-gas-tar pitch.................	Conch.	Bk.	1.15–1.30	10–100	>100	80–275
Water-gas tar....................	....	....	1.05–1.15	0	......	<0–10
Water-gas-tar pitch...............	Conch.	Bk.	1.10–1.20	10–100	>100	80–275
Pine tar........................	....	....	1.05–1.10	0	......	0–50
Pine-tar pitch....................	Conch.	Bn.	1.10–1.15	10–100	>100	100–200
Hardwood tar....................	....	....	1.10–1.20	0	......	0–20
Hardwood-tar pitch...............	Conch.	Bn. to Bk.	1.20–1.30	10–100	>100	100–200
Rosin pitch......................	Conch.	Yel. to Bn.	1.08–1.15	50–100	>100	120–200
Peat tar........................	....	....	0.90–1.05	0	......	40–60
Peat-tar pitch....................	Conch.	Bn. to Bk.	1.05–1.15	10–100	>100	100–250
Lignite tar......................	....	....	0.85–1.05	0	......	60–90
Lignite-tar pitch..................	Conch.	Bk.	1.05–1.20	10–100	>100	100–250
Shale tar.......................	....	....	0.85–0.95	0	......	60–90
Gas-works coal tar................	....	....	1.15–1.30	0	......	<0–25
Gas-works coal-tar pitch...........	Conch.	Bk.	1.15–1.40	10–100	>100	80–300
Coke-oven coal tar................	....	....	1.10–1.30	0	......	<0–25
Coke-oven coal-tar pitch...........	Conch.	Bk.	1.20–1.35	10–100	>100	80–300
Blast-furnace coal tar.............	....	....	1.15–1.30	0	......	<0–25
Blast-furnace coal-tar pitch.........	Conch.	Bk.	1.20–1.30	10–100	>100	80–300
Producer-gas coal tar.............	....	....	1.15–1.30	0	......	<0–25
Producer-gas coal-tar pitch..........	Conch.	Bk.	1.20–1.35	10–100	>100	80–300
Bone tar........................	....	....	0.95–1.05	0	......	<0–10
Bone-tar pitch....................	Conch.	Bk.	1.10–1.20	10–100	75–100	80–225
Fatty-acid pitch..................	Variable	Yel. to Bk.	0.90–1.10	0–40	8–40	35–225

Table III gives the limiting values of the tests ordinarily used for distinguishing the individual bituminous substances.

DISTINGUISHING CHARACTERISTICS OF BITUMINOUS SUBSTANCES

Fixed Carbon	Solubility in Carbon Disulphide	Non-mineral Matter Insoluble	Mineral Matter	Carbenes	Soluble in 88° Naphtha	Oxygen in Non-mineral Matter	Paraffine	Sulphonation Residue	Saponifiable Matter	Diazo Reaction	Anthraquinone Reaction
%	%	%	%	%	%	%	%	%	%		
½-2	98-100	0-½	0-2	0-½	98-100	0-2	10-25	90-100	0-2	No	No
2-5	98-100	0-1	0-2	0-1	95-100	0-3	½-10	85-95	0-2	No	No
5-10	98-100	0-1	0-2	0-1	90-100	0-5	0-Tr.	80-95	0-5	No	No
½-10	95-100	0-1	0-5	0-3	75-95	0-2	50-90	90-100	0-2	No	No
2-10	98-100	0-2	0-2	0-2	80-100	3-6	0-10	0-10	50-80	No	No
0-2	99-100	0-½	0-½	0	99-100	0-Tr.	95-100	95-100	0	No	No
1-25	60-98	0-40	0-10	0-5	25-95	0-2	0-5	90-100	0-2	No	No
5-25	Tr.-90	0-25	10-95	0-5	Tr.-85	0-2	0-5	90-100	0-2	No	No
2-10	98-100	0-½	0-½	0-1	80-99	0-3	0-15	90-100	Tr.-5	No	No
5-20	95-100	0-5	0-½	0-10	50-90	2-5	0-10	90-100	Tr.-2	No	No
5-40	85-100	0-15	0-1	0-30	25-85	0-2½	0-5	90-100	0-2	No	No
5-30	95-100	0-5	0-1	0-15	60-95	3-7	0-½	80-95	0-2	No	No
5-25	98-100	0-½	Tr.-2	0-2	50-80	0-2	0-Tr.	90-95	Tr.	No	No
10-20	98-100	0-1	Tr.-1	0-½	40-60	0-2	0-Tr.	85-95	Tr.	No	No
20-30	95-100	0-1	Tr.-5	0-1	20-50	0-2	0-Tr.	85-95	Tr.	No	No
30-55	45-100	0-5	Tr.-50	0-80	Tr.-50	0-2	0-Tr.	80-95	Tr.	No	No
2-5	10-20	70-90	Tr.-10	Tr.-2	5-10	1-5	0-Tr.	80-90	Tr.-15	No	No
5-25	5-10	80-95	Tr.-10	Tr.-2	Tr.-2	0-2	0-Tr.	90-98	Tr.	No	No
25-50	2-10	85-98	Tr.-10	Tr.-2	Tr.-2	0-3	0-Tr.	90-98	Tr.	No	No
50-85	1-6	90-99	Tr.-10	Tr.-2	Tr.-2	0-3	0-Tr.	90-98	Tr.	No	No
2-25*	Tr.-3	15-70	30-85	0-Tr.	0-Tr.	0-3	Tr.-3	90-98	Tr.	No	No
15-35	2-6	15-98	2-80	0-2	0-5	26-44	......	......	Tr.-15	No	No
25-50	2-15	65-98	2-25	0-1	5-10	15-28	......	......	Tr.-5	No	No
35-75	½-2	75-98	2-25	0-½	0-1	3-18	......	......	Tr.-1	No	No
60-90	0-½	75-98	2-25	0	0	1-5	......	......	0	No	No
20-45*	0-1	15-70	30-85	0	0-½	3-15	......	......	Tr.-2	No	No
2-8	98-100	0-2	0-Tr.	0-Tr.	95-100	0-2	Tr.-5	90-100	Tr.	No	Yes
10-25	98-100	0-2	0-1	0-2	50-85	1-2	0-5	20-40	Tr.	Yes	Yes
20-30	85-98	2-15	0-1	2-20	65-85	0-2	0-5	20-40	0-1	Yes	Yes
10-20	98-100	0-2	0-1	0-2	20-75	1-2	0-5	0-15	Tr.-2	Yes	Yes
25-40	85-98	2-15	0-1	2-15	50-80	0-2	0-5	0-15	0-1	Yes	Yes
5-15	98-100	0-2	0-1	0-2	65-95	5-10	0	Tr.-5	10-50	Yes	No
10-25	40-95	2-60	0-1	0-5	25-80	2-8	0	Tr.-3	10-40	Yes	No
5-20	95-100	0-5	0-1	0-2	50-90	2-10	0	Tr.-5	5-25	Yes	No
15-35	30-95	5-70	0-1	2-10	15-50	1-5	0	Tr.-5	5-25	Yes	No
10-20	98-100	0-2	0-1	0-5	90-100	5-10	0	Tr.-5	25-95	Yes	No
5-15	98-100	0-2	0-1	0-2	95-100	5-15	5-15	5-15	5-15	Yes	No
10-30	95-99	0-5	0-1	0-5	65-95	2-8	2-5	5-10	0-5	Yes	No
5-20	98-100	0-1	0-1	0-2	95-100	5-10	10-25	10-20	5-20	Yes	No
10-40	95-99	0-2	0-1	0-5	75-95	2-5	1-5	5-15	0-8	Yes	No
5-10	98-100	0-2	0-1	0-2	95-100	1-5	5-15	15-35	0-2	Yes	No
15-40	60-95	5-40	0-1	0-2	20-40	1-3	0	0-5	2-5	Yes	Yes
30-45	55-90	10-45	0-1	2-10	10-30	Tr.-2	0	0-5	Tr.-1	Yes	Yes
15-40	80-97	3-20	0-1	0-2	20-40	1-3	0	0-5	2-5	Yes	Yes
20-45	60-85	15-40	0-1	2-10	10-30	Tr.-2	0	0-5	Tr.-1	Yes	Yes
5-25	65-80	10-25	10-15	0-2	15-35	1-3	0	5-20	2-5	Yes	Yes
10-30	50-75	15-35	10-20	2-10	5-25	Tr.-2	0	5-20	Tr.-1	Yes	Yes
10-35	75-90	10-25	0-2	0-2	20-40	1-3	0	0-5	2-5	Yes	Yes
25-45	60-85	15-40	0-2	2-10	10-30	Tr.-2	0	0-5	Tr.-1	Yes	Yes
5-15	95-100	0-5	0-Tr.	0-2	95-100	2-8	0	0-5	5-40	Yes	No
15-25	85-95	1-15	0-Tr.	0-10	75-95	0-2	0	0-5	2-25	Yes	No
5-35	95-100	0-5	0-5	0-5	80-100	2-10	Tr.	0-5	5-98	No	No

* Calculated on mineral-free basis.

PART II

EXAMINATION OF BITUMINIZED MINERAL AGGREGATES

Products falling into this class include native and artificial mixtures of bituminous matter with mineral aggregates, viz.: bituminous macadam pavements, bituminous concrete pavements, sheet asphalt pavements, asphalt block pavements, asphalt mastic floorings, bituminous expansion joints (containing mineral matter but not felt), pipe-sealing compounds, moulding compositions and products used for electrical insulation.

PHYSICAL TESTS OF FINISHED PRODUCT

Tensile Strength. The following tentative test has been proposed for moulded insulating materials,[1] but may also be adapted to testing the surface course of sheet asphalt pavements, asphalt mastic floorings, expansion joints (not containing fabric), pipe-sealing compounds, etc. The specimen is cast under pressure to obtain the greatest possible density, in a hardened and ground steel mould of the dimensions shown in Fig. 160, then immersed in distilled water for 48 hours at 77° F., removed, wiped

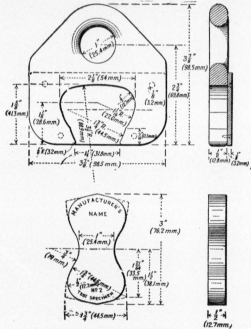

Make Steel Mold to these Dimensions. Limits ±0.002 (0.05mm)

From A. S. T. M. Tent. Standards.

Fig. 160.—Mould for Ascertaining the Tensile Strength of Bituminized Aggregates.

dry and pulled apart on any standard testing machine in air at 77° F., at a speed that will enable the beam to be well balanced. The results of the test shall be reported in the following order, viz.: the breaking load in kilograms or pounds; the thickness in centimeters or inches as measured by a micrometer at the point of fracture; the ultimate tensile strength in kilograms per square centimeter or in pounds per square inch as calculated from the actual area of the specimen at the point of fracture; the speed in

[1] "Standard Tests for Molded Insulating Materials" (Serial Designation: D 48-17 T), Proc. Am. Soc. Testing Materials, *20*. Part I, 776, 1920.

centimeters or inches per minute at which the jaws travel during the test. Three such tests should be averaged.

Compressive Strength. This test has likewise been proposed for moulded insulating materials,[1] and is adapted to all bituminized mineral aggregates in which the particles do not measure over ¼ in. in diameter. A 1-in. cube is moulded under pressure in a hardened steel mould to attain the greatest possible density, and immersed in distilled water at 77° F. for 48 hours. Wipe the surface dry and place sheets of lead $\frac{1}{16}$ in. thick both above and below the specimen to adjust irregularities. Any standard testing machine may be used, and the load shall be applied at such a rate of speed as will permit the beam to be kept well balanced. The results of the test shall be reported as follows, viz.: the dimensions of the specimen in millimeters or inches; the breaking load in kilograms or pounds at the first sign of failure; the average ultimate compressive strength in kilograms per square centimeter or pounds per square inch, calculated from the measured area of the specimen before the load is applied; the speed in centimeters or inches per minute at which the jaws travel during the test. Three such tests are averaged.

Impact Test. This test was originally devised by L. W. Page for testing the toughness of rock for road building,[2] having since been adapted by Richardson for testing bituminous aggregates.[3] The bituminous mixture is heated to the lowest possible temperature that will permit it being manipulated, and formed by compression into a cylinder 25 mm. high by 24–25 mm. in diameter, the ends of which shall be plane surfaces at right angles of its axis. The hot bituminous mixture is compressed in a hollow cylindrical steel mould, 24–25 mm. in diameter by 50 mm. long, having an accurately fitting steel plunger. The mould is loosely filled with the hot bituminous mixture and compressed with the plunger by sharp blows of a heavy hammer from the top and bottom respectively, until it is thoroughly compacted. The cylinder of bituminous material is then knocked from the mould and sawed off or ground down until it measures exactly 25 mm. high. The density of the specimen should be noted and reported. It shall be maintained in water at 77° F. for 48 hours, wiped dry, and tested in air at a temperature of 77° F. on any form of impact machine which will comply with the following essentials:

(*a*) A cast-iron anvil weighing not less than 50 kg. firmly fixed upon a solid foundation.

(*b*) A hammer weighing 2 kg. arranged to fall freely between suitable guides.

(*c*) A plunger of hardened steel weighing 1 kg. arranged to slide freely in a vertical direction in a sleeve, the lower end of the plunger being spherical, with a radius of exactly 1 cm.

(*d*) Means for raising the hammer and dropping it upon the plunger from any specified height from 1 to not less than 75 cm.

(*e*) Means for holding the cylindrical test-specimen securely on the anvil without rigid lateral support, and under the plunger in such a way that the centre of its upper surface shall, throughout the test, be tangent to the spherical end of the plunger at its lowest point.

The test shall consist of a 1 cm. fall of the hammer for the first blow; a 2 cm. fall for the second blow; and an increase of 1 cm. for each succeeding blow, until failure of the test specimen occurs. The number of blows required to shatter the test-piece is taken to represent the toughness, three such tests being averaged. Tests are performed at three temperatures, viz.: 32° F., 77° F. and 115° F.

Distortion under Heat. This test is applicable to bituminized mineral aggregates whose particles do not exceed ¼ in. in diameter. The material shall be compressed to the greatest possible density in a hardened steel mould, ground so its internal dimensions will measure ½ in. by ½ in. by 5 in.[4]

[1] "Tentative Tests for Molded Insulating Materials" (Serial Designation: D 48–17 T), Proc. Am. Soc. Testing Materials, *29*. Part I, 777, 1920.

[2] Bulletin No. 79, Bureau of Chem., U. S. Dept. of Agr., Wash., D. C.; Bulletin No. 44, Office of Public Roads, U. S. Dept. of Agr., Wash., D. C., June 10, 1912.

[3] "The Modern Asphalt Pavements," 2nd Edition, 1908, pp. 428 and 585.

[4] "Tentative Tests for Molded Insulating Materials" (Serial Designation: D 48–17 T), Proc. Am. Soc. Testing Materials, **17**, Part I, 703, 1918.

The apparatus used for this purpose is illustrated in Fig. 161. The specimen

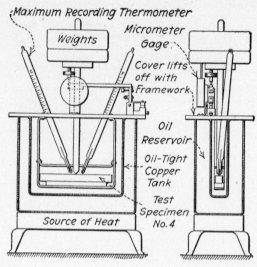

From A. S. T. M. Tent. Standards.

FIG. 161.—Apparatus for Recording Distortion of Bituminized Aggregates under Heat.

should rest on steel supports 100 mm. apart, and the load applied on top of the specimen vertically and midway between the supports, as in the transverse strength test. The machine shall be arranged to apply two different loads, viz.: 2.5 kg. and 5.0 kg. The specimen is placed in an air bath surrounded by an oil bath, the temperature of which is increased at a rate of exactly 1° F. per minute. The deflection of the specimen at its center between the supports is measured on a scale in millimeters or mils. The distortion point shall be considered the temperature at which the specimen has deflected 10 mils. The results of the test are reported as follows, viz.: the distortion point in degrees F.; the time required for the specimen to deflect 10 mils starting at 77° F.; two curves are plotted, showing the minutes horizontally, the deflection in mills shown vertically to the left and the temperature in degrees shown vertically to the right. One curve represents the deflection in mills at given time intervals and the other represents the temperature at given time intervals.

SEPARATION OF FINISHED PRODUCT INTO ITS COMPONENT PARTS

Separation of the Bituminous Matter and Mineral Aggregate

Bituminized aggregates are separated into their bituminous and mineral components for the combined purposes of ascertaining the percentage and nature of the mineral constituents, and for examining the physical and chemical characteristics of the bituminous binder, with the object of its identification or duplication. Two methods are used, including the hot extraction process devised by Forrest, and the centrifugal extraction method.

Forrest's Hot Extraction Method. The bituminous mixture should first be warmed until it may be broken apart without fracturing the mineral particles. The extraction is performed in an apparatus illustrated in Fig. 162, consisting of a cylindrical brass

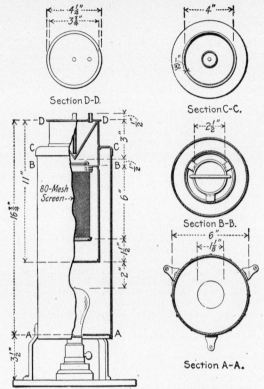

Section D-D.

Section C-C.

80-Mesh Screen→

Section B-B.

Section A-A.

From A. S. T. M. Proc.

FIG. 162.—Forrest's Hot-extraction Apparatus.

jacket surrounding an incandescent-light bulb to supply the necessary heat, and enclosing a brass vessel for holding the solvent, which in turn carries a cylindrical basket composed of 80 mesh-wire cloth for retaining the sample. Cold water is circulated through the inverted conical condenser, which also serves to cover the apparatus. Weigh out 500 g. of material if the mineral particles are coarser than $\frac{1}{2}$ in., or 300 g. if they are finer than $\frac{1}{2}$ in. Place it in the basket and cover with a pad of cotton or felt $\frac{1}{4}$–$\frac{1}{2}$ in. thick. Pour 175–200 cc. of carbon disulphide into the inner vessel, insert the cover and start the extraction by turning on the incandescent light. The extraction is usually completed in 3 hours' time, whereupon the apparatus is cooled, the basket containing the mineral aggregate removed, dried in an oven and weighed. Any fine mineral particles passing through the 80-mesh sieve constituting the basket are recovered by filtering the extract through a weighed asbestos Gooch filter, washed clean with carbon disulphide, dried and weighed. This method is used where the bituminous matter is to be separated in a pure state for further examination. An alternate method consists in measuring the extract in a glass graduate, thoroughly agitating it and pouring an aliquot portion into a tared crucible or dish, evaporating the solvent, burning the residue and igniting to ash. The fine mineral matter present in the entire extract may be calculated from the ash derived from the portion ignited. The total should be added to the coarser mineral aggregate previously separated, to arrive at the percentage present.[1]

[1] "Extractor for Bituminous Paving Mixtures," by C. N. Forrest, Proc. Am. Soc. Testing Materials, **13**, 1069, 1913; "Tentative Methods of Testing Bituminous Mastics, Grouts and Like Mixtures" (Serial Designation: D 147–23T), Proc. A. S. T. M., **23**, Part I, 805, 1923.

Centrifugal Method. The most efficient apparatus of this type was designed by C. S. Reeve,[1] as illustrated in Fig. 163. It consists of a 1/5 h.p. vertical motor a, capable of making 1100 revolutions per minute at 110 volts, with either direct or alternating current. Its shaft projects into a cylindrical copper vessel b, having a concave bottom and draining into the spout c. A circular brass plate d, $9\frac{1}{2}$ in. in diameter supports an inverted iron bowl e, $8\frac{1}{2}$ in. in diameter by $2\frac{5}{16}$ in. high, having a 2 in. circular hole at the top. A brass cup f is fastened to the inner side of the bowl, having a circle of $\frac{1}{8}$ in. holes for the admission of solvent, and terminating in a hollow axle which fits snugly through a hole in the center of the brass plate d. A felt ring g, $\frac{3}{4}$ in. wide and about 0.090 in. thick (cut from No. 80 roofing felt) is firmly pressed against the bowl by the milled nut h for which the hollow axle is suitably threaded. The axle in turn fits snugly over the shaft of the motor, to which it is secured by a slot and cross-pin.

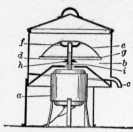

Fig. 163.—Centrifugal Extractor.

Weigh 300–500 g. of the bituminous mixture, broken up as previously described, into the bowl e, place the felt ring on the rim of the plate d, and bolt them together with the nut i. After assembling the apparatus, pour 150 cc. of carbon disulphide into the bowl through the small holes, place the cover over the copper box b, and slowly start the motor, gradually increasing its speed until the carbon disulphide extract flows in a thin stream from the spout c into an empty flask underneath. When the first charge has drained, the motor is stopped, fresh carbon disulphide added, and the operation repeated 4 to 6 times until the extract runs clear. The bowl is then removed, inverted, the nut unscrewed, and any carbon disulphide retained by the mineral matter allowed to evaporate spontaneously. The mineral matter is then dried and weighed. It is well to filter the extract through a Gooch crucible with an asbestos filter to recover any mineral matter which may have worked its way through the felt ring, adding same to the balance of the mineral matter.

Recovery of Extracted Bituminous Matter. From the weight of the extracted mineral matter, calculate the bituminous matter by difference, and evaporate the carbon disulphide extract to exactly this weight. This may be conveniently performed by distilling and condensing most of the carbon disulphide over an incandescent light or an electric stove. The concentrated solution is transferred to a tared dish, evaporated dry on a steam bath with constant stirring, which may be conveniently accomplished with a motor-driven agitator, and the last traces of solvent removed in an oven at 105° C. until the residue attains the calculated weight. Due allowance should be made for the fact that any non-mineral matter insoluble in carbon disulphide will be retained mechanically by the extracted mineral matter, which with asphaltic products is relatively unimportant, but will amount to a considerable item in the case of tar products.

Recovered Mineral Aggregate. The presence of any non-mineral matter insoluble in carbon disulphide will be revealed by the discoloration of the mineral particles. In this case, the weight of the latter should be corrected by igniting it until all carbonaceous matter is destroyed, and then reweighing.

Examination of Separated Bituminous Matter

This is subjected to the tests embodied in Part I.

[1] "Laboratory Manual of Bituminous Materials," 1st Edition, N. Y., 1916, p. 108.

Examination of Separated Mineral Matter

This will include any uncombined mineral matter as well as any colloidal mineral particles retained by an asbestos Gooch filter. It may be examined further as follows:

Granularmetric Analysis. The methods which follow have been standardized by the American Society for Testing Materials[1] for mineral aggregates used in connection with highways. The following three methods have been adopted:
For Sand or Other Fine Highway Material. The method consists of: (1) drying at not over 230° F. to a constant weight a sample weighing 50 g.; (2) passing the sample through each of the following mesh sieves.

Mesh Designation	Actual Mesh	Opening	Wire Diameter	Permissible Variations	
				Mesh	Diameter
10 . . . . {	3.9 cm.	2.00 mm.	0.56 mm.	±0.04	±0.05
	9.9 in.	0.079 in.	0.022 in.	±0.1	±0.002
20 . . . . {	8 cm.	0.85 mm.	0.40 mm.	±0.2	±0.015
	20.3 in.	0.0335 in.	0.0157 in.	±0.5	±0.0006
30 . . . . {	12 cm.	0.50 mm.	0.33 mm.	±0.4	±0.012
	30.5 in.	0.0197 in.	0.0130 in.	±1.0	±0.0005
40 . . . . {	16 cm.	0.36 mm.	0.26 mm.	±0.6	±0.010
	40.6 in.	0.0142 in.	0.0102 in.	±1.5	±0.0004
50 . . . . {	20 cm.	0.29 mm.	0.21 mm.	±0.8	±0.010
	50.8 in.	0.0114 in.	0.0083 in.	±2	±0.0004
80 . . . . {	31 cm.	0.17 mm.	0.15 mm.	±1	±0.008
	78.7 in.	0.0067 in.	0.0059 in.	±3	±0.0003
100 . . . . {	39 cm.	0.14 mm.	0.116 mm.	±1	±0.008
	99.1 in.	0.0055 in.	0.0046 in.	±3	±0.0003
200 . . . . {	79 cm.	0.074 mm.	0.053 mm.	±3	±0.005
	200.7 in.	0.0029 in.	0.0021 in.	±8	±0.0002

The order in which the sieves are to be used in the process of sifting is immaterial and shall be left optional; but in reporting results, the order in which the sieves have been used shall be stated; (3) determining the percentage by weight retained on each sieve, the sifting being continued until less than 1 per cent of the weight retained shall pass through the sieve during the last minute of sifting; and (4) recording the mechanical analysis in the following manner:

Passing 200-mesh sieve . . . . %
Passing 100-mesh sieve and retained on a 200-mesh sieve . . . %
Passing 80-mesh sieve and retained on a 100-mesh sieve . . . %
Passing 50-mesh sieve and retained on a 80-mesh sieve . . . %
. . . . %

    Total 100.00%

[1] "Standard Method of Mechanical Analysis of Sand or Other Fine Highway Material, Except for Fine Aggregates Used in Cement Concrete" (Serial Designation: D 7-18); "Standard Method of Mechanical Analysis of Broken Stone or Broken Slag, Except for Aggregates Used in Cement Concrete" (Serial Designation: D 18-16); "Standard Method of Mechanical Analysis of Mixtures of Sand or Other Fine Material with Broken Stone or Broken Slag, Except for Aggregates Used in Cement Concrete" (Serial Designation: D 19-16), A. S. T. M. Standards Adopted in 1921, 721, 723 and 724.

For Broken Stone or Broken Slag. The method shall consist of: (1) drying at not over 230° F. to a constant weight a sample weighing in pounds 6 times the diameter in inches of the largest holes required; (2) passing the sample through such of the following size screens having circular openings as are required or called for by the specifications, screens to be used in the order named: $3\frac{1}{2}$, 3, $2\frac{1}{2}$, 2, $1\frac{1}{2}$, $1\frac{1}{4}$, 1, $\frac{3}{4}$, $\frac{1}{2}$ and $\frac{1}{4}$ in.; (3) determining the percentage by weight retained on each screen; and (4) recording the mechanical analysis in the following manner:

Passing $\frac{1}{4}$-in. screen.. %
Passing $\frac{1}{2}$-in. screen and retained on a $\frac{1}{4}$-in. screen........ %
Passing $\frac{3}{4}$-in. screen and retained on a $\frac{1}{2}$-in. screen........ %
Passing 1-in. screen and retained on a $\frac{3}{4}$-in. screen........ %
.... %
  Total...100.00%

For Sand or Other Fine Material with Broken Stone or Broken Slag. The method shall consist of: (1) drying at not over 230° F. to a constant weight, a sample weighing in pounds 6 times the diameter in inches of the largest holes required; (2) separating the sample by the use of a screen having circular openings $\frac{1}{4}$ in. in diameter; (3) examining the portion retained on the screen in accordance with the method for broken stone or broken slag; (4) examining the portion passing the screen in accordance with the method for sand or other fine highway material; and (5) recording the mechanical analysis in the following manner:

Passing 200-mesh sieve............................... %
Passing 100-mesh sieve and retained on a 200-mesh sieve... %
Passing 80-mesh sieve and retained on a 100-mesh sieve... %
.... %
Passing 10-mesh sieve and retained on a 20-mesh sieve... %
Passing $\frac{1}{4}$-in. screen and retained on a 10-mesh sieve..... %
Passing $\frac{1}{2}$-in. screen and retained on a $\frac{1}{4}$-in. screen...... %
Passing $\frac{3}{4}$-in. screen and retained on a $\frac{1}{2}$-in. screen...... %
.... %
  Total...100.00%

Elutriation Test for Sand or Fine Filler. This test is adapted to fine mineral particles passing a 200-mesh sieve. Place 5 g. in a beaker about 120 mm. high, holding 600 cc., and fill almost to the top with distilled water at exactly 70° F. Agitate with compressed air until the mineral particles are brought into suspension, and in such a manner that no whirling results. Stop the blast and allow the liquid to stand exactly 20 seconds, whereupon the water above the sediment is immediately decanted through a 200-mesh sieve without, however, pouring off any of the sediment. The operations of agitation, sedimentation, and decantation are repeated with fresh water three times. The particles caught on the 200-mesh sieve are washed back into the sample remaining in the beaker, which is dried to constant weight and weighed. The difference represents the amount removed by elutriation, which should be expressed in percentage.[1]

Specific Gravity. Two methods are recommended, depending upon whether the particles are finer or coarser than 1 in. in diameter.

For Aggregates Whose Particles are Less than $\frac{1}{4}$ In. The Le Chatelier's flask is used for this purpose as described on p. 1199.

For Aggregates Composed of Fragments Larger than $\frac{1}{4}$ In. The Goldbeck apparatus[2]

[1] "Standard Forms for Specifications, Tests, Reports and Methods of Sampling for Road Materials," Bulletin No. 555, U. S. Dept. Agriculture, Wash., D. C., p. 32, Nov. 26, 1917; "Standard Method of Test for Quantity of Clay and Silt in Gravel for Highway Construction" (Serial Designation: D 74–21), A. S. T. M. Standards Adopted in 1921.

[2] "Standard Forms for Specifications, Tests, Reports and Methods of Sampling for Road Materials," Bull. No. 555, U. S. Dept. of Agriculture, Wash., D. C., p. 31, Nov. 26, 1917.

illustrated in Fig. 164 is used for this purpose; 1000 g. of aggregate are dried to constant

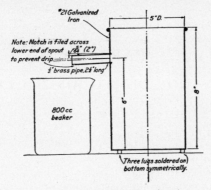

FIG. 164.—Goldbeck's Specific Gravity Apparatus.

weight, weighed to the nearest 0.5 g., and immersed in water for 24 hours. The pieces are then individually surface-dried with a towel, the sample reweighed and immediately introduced into the cylinder, which has previously been filled to overflowing with water at 77° F. The displaced water is caught in a tared beaker, and weighed. If the weight of the dry aggregate in air is a, and the weight of the displaced water b, then the apparent specific gravity is equal to a divided by b. The difference between the original weight of the specimen and its weight after 24 hours' immersion is used to determine the percentage of absorption. If c equals the weight of the water absorbed by the dry specimen in 24 hours, then the true specific gravity at 77° F. is equal to a divided by $(b-c)$.

Chemical Analysis. This may include a qualitative or a quantitative analysis, by any of the methods ordinarily used for this purpose. If a quantitative analysis is to be made, the reader is referred to other portions of this book, as well as to the following sources, viz.:

Mineral Constituents Naturally Present and Added Fillers. "Standard Methods of Ultimate Chemical Analysis of Refractory Materials" (Serial Designation: C 18–21), A. S. T. M. Standards Adopted in 1921, 628; "Standard Specifications and Tests for Portland Cement" (Serial Designation: C 9–21), A. S. T. M. Standards Adopted in 1921, 531.

Added White Pigments. "Standard Methods of Routine Analysis of White Pigments" (Serial Designation: D 34–17), A. S. T. M. Standards Adopted in 1921, 673.

Added Yellow, Red or Brown Pigments. "Standard Methods of Routine Analysis of Yellow, Orange, Red and Brown Pigments Containing Iron and Manganese" (Serial Designation: D 50–18), A. S. T. M. Standards Adopted in 1921, 689; "Tentative Methods of Routine Analysis of Yellow and Orange Pigments Containing Chromium Compounds, Blue Pigments and Chrome Green" (Serial Designation: D 126–22T), Proc. A. S. T. M., **22**, Part I, 754, 1922.

PART III

EXAMINATION OF BITUMINIZED FABRICS

This caption includes the following groups of products, viz.:

Q—Prepared roofings.
R—Composition shingles.
S—Deck and porch coverings.
T—Bituminized fabrics for constructing built-up roofs.
U—Bituminized fabrics for constructing waterproofing membranes.
V—Electrical insulating tape.
W—Waterproof papers for wrapping and packing.
X—Waterproof papers for insulating against heat or cold.
Y—Felt-base floor coverings (surfaced with linseed oil and pigment composition).
Z—Expansion joints for pavements.

These are constructed as shown in Table IV, where the index *a* indicates that asphaltic compositions have been used, and *t* signifies that coal tar (pitch) et al., have been used.

TABLE IV.

	Paper		Burlap		Duck		Light Cotton Fabric		Rag-Felt		Asbestos Felt		Burlap and Rag or Asbestos Felt		Paper and Light Cotton Fabric	
	a	t	a	t	a	t	a	t	a	t	a	t	a	t	a	t
Single Layered:																
Saturated only	WX	WX	U	U	...	...	...	...	TUY	TU	T	...	...	...	...	...
Coated only (one or two sides)	W	....	U	U	S	...	...	...	...	...	...	...	...	...	...	...
Saturated and Coated	X	....	U	U	QS	...	V	...	QR	....	Q	...	...	...	...	...
Laminated (Bituminated):																
Layers Saturated only	...	...	Z	...	...	...	...	...	Z	Q	QT	...	UZ	U	...	...
Layers Saturated and Coated	...	...	...	...	...	...	...	...	Q	...	Q	...	Q	...	...	...
Layers Unsaturated	W	W	...	...	...	...	...	...	...	...	...	...	...	...	W	W
One Layer Unsaturated and others saturated	W	W	...	...	...	...	...	...	...	...	...	...	...	...	W	W

PHYSICAL TESTS OF FINISHED PRODUCT

Weight. Carefully unpack the fabric, and where any dusting finish has been used be sure not to detach it. Make certain that the specimen is of rectangular form, and then weigh it with an accuracy of at least 0.25%. Then measure its length and breadth with an accuracy of at least 0.25%, and figure its area. Calculate its weight per unit area from the following formulae:

$$\text{Lbs. per sq. ft.} = \frac{\text{gms.}}{\text{sq. cms.}} \times 2.5 = \frac{\text{gms.}}{\text{sq. ins.}} \times 0.317,$$

$$\text{Ozs. per sq. yd.} = \frac{\text{gms.}}{\text{sq. cms.}} \times 295 = \frac{\text{gms.}}{\text{sq. ins.}} \times 45.71.$$

Pliability is tested by cutting lengthwise from the center of the roll a strip 1 in. wide, and commencing with the largest, successively bending it around various cylinders under water at temperatures of 77° and 32° F., respectively, recording the number of the cylinder on which the surface cracks. Five cylinders are used in the test, measuring $2\frac{1}{2}$, 2, $1\frac{1}{2}$, 1 and $\frac{1}{2}$ cm. in diameter, respectively. A convenient apparatus for this purpose is shown in Fig. 165. The fabric should be bent parallel to itself, through an arc of 180°, at a uniform speed, and in exactly 2 seconds time.

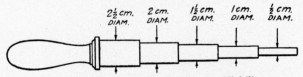

Fig. 165.—Mandrels for Testing the Pliability.

The pliability is expressed numerically from 1 to 10, as follows:

1 May be bent through an arc of 180° in one direction (*i.e.*, flat on itself) and then through an arc of 360° in the other direction (*i.e.*, flat on itself) without cracking the surface coatings.

2 May be bent in one direction through an arc of 180° (*i.e.*, flat on itself) without cracking the surface coatings, but will crack when bent through an arc of 360° in the other direction.

3 Surface cracks when bent through an arc of 180°.

4 Surface cracks on the $\frac{1}{2}$-cm. cylinder.

5 Surface cracks on the 1-cm. cylinder.

6 Surface cracks on the $1\frac{1}{2}$-cm. cylinder.

7 Surface cracks on the 2-cm. cylinder.

8 Surface cracks on the $2\frac{1}{2}$-cm. cylinder.

9 Both the surface and the interior of the sheet crack on the $2\frac{1}{2}$-cm. cylinder without, however, cracking *entirely* through the sheet.

10 The sheet cracks entirely through on the $2\frac{1}{2}$-cm. cylinder.

Thickness, in mils (thousandths of an inch) is determined with a micrometer caliper, having flat bearing surfaces about $\frac{1}{2}$ in. in diameter.

Strength is determined by subjecting a specimen cut in the direction of the length of the roll and of the dimensions shown in Fig. 166 to a tension which is increased at a uniform speed of 3 lbs. per second, the specimen being maintained at a uniform temperature of 77° F. during the test. A simple and effective instrument for finding the tensile strength is shown in Fig. 167. Ten such tests are averaged.

Resistance to Heat. A strip is cut exactly 12 in. ×12 in., care being taken not to disturb any of the detached mineral matter on the surface, and suspended in an oven from a thin wire fastened through holes in the upper edge of the strip. The piece should be allowed to hang freely and maintained at a temperature of 125° F. for 100 hrs. At the end of this time it is allowed to cool. The pliability, weight, thickness and strength are redetermined and the changes from the original figures expressed in percentages. Any change in the appearance of the surface should also be noted, *e. g.*, sliding of the mineral matter, absorption of the coating by the fabric, any yellowing of the surface, blistering, etc.

Resistance to Dampness. Accurately cut a strip of the bituminized fabric 18 in. × 18 in., and weigh. Remove the detached mineral particles from both sides of the sheet with a moderately stiff brush, and reweigh (area equals 2¼ sq. ft.). Suspend in a tight box containing sufficient water at the bottom to saturate the air with moisture. Cover tightly and allow the specimen to remain in the moist air for 100 hours at 77° F. As the moisture enters more readily through the cut edges of the sheet than through the surface itself, 6 in. should be trimmed from the edges at the termination of the test, leaving a strip measuring exactly 12 in. × 12 in., representing the central portion of the original specimen, and weighing 4/9 of the latter. Ascertain the weight, thickness and tensile strength of the 12 × 12 portion at the end of the test, and calculate any variation in percentage from the original figures. The increase in weight should be figured on the basis of the original material *including* the detached mineral matter.

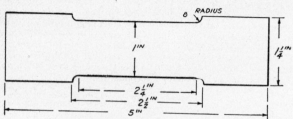

Fig. 166.—Tensile Strength Specimen.

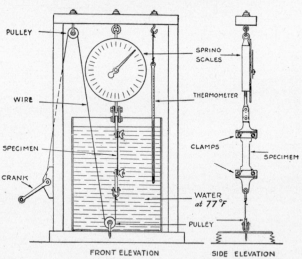

Fig. 167.—Instrument for Testing the Strength of Bituminized Fabrics.

Resistance to Water. This test is run exactly the same as the preceding, only in this case the specimen should be immersed entirely in water at 77° F. for 100 hours. An 18 in. × 18 in. sheet should be used in making the test, and trimmed to 12 in. × 12 in. before redetermining its weight, thickness or strength.

Resistance to Electrical Current. This test is applied to saturated and coated papers used for wrapping wires, cables and other insulative purposes, and consists in subjecting the paper at 77° F. to an alternating current of a frequency not over 65 cycles, the potential being increased at the rate of 125 volts per minute between flat disc terminals having bevelled edges, the areas of contact measuring exactly 1 sq. in. The terminals should be brought closely together, so that the paper will just slide between them, and the current increased until a breakdown occurs.

Special Tests for Adhesive Insulating Tape. (1) A strip protected from the direct rays of the sun, is hung indoors for 2 months. The diminution in tackiness is noted and is a measure of the extent to which it "dries out."

(2) The tensile strength is measured at 77° F. by separating a $\frac{3}{4}$ in. specimen at the rate of 20 in. per minute, the initial distance between the jaws of the testing machine being 12 in.

(3) The adhesion of the compound between the plies is measured by winding a strip 2 ft. long and $\frac{3}{4}$ in. wide upon a 1 in. mandrel under a tension of $7\frac{1}{2}$ lb. at the rate of 30 in. per minute, and then measuring the rate of separation per minute under a weight of 3 lb.

(4) A strip is first exposed to dry heat of 100° C. for 18 hours, cooled to room temperature, and then subjected to the test prescribed in (3), except that the weight applied to unwind the tape shall be 1 lb.

(5) The dielectric strength is recorded by winding the tape spirally with one third lap on a smooth copper rod, 1 in. in diameter, for a distance of 6 in. Two inches in the center are then covered with tin foil and bound down securely with tape, whereupon an alternating current of 1000 volts having a frequency of not over 65 cycles, is applied for 5 minutes between the metal rod and the tin foil, to observe whether a puncture occurs.

Resistance to Weather. For a detailed description of the procedure for conducting exposure tests on bituminized fabrics, and specifically composition roofings and shingles, the reader is referred to "Asphalts and Allied Substances" Second Edition published by D. Van Nostrand Co., New York, 1920, page 574 et seq.

SEPARATION OF FINISHED PRODUCT INTO ITS COMPONENT PARTS

Separation of Bituminous Matter, Mineral Matter and Fibrous Matter

SINGLE LAYERED FABRICS (SATURATED ONLY, OR COATED ONLY)

Moisture is determined by distilling a weighed quantity of the fabric, immersed in a bath of kerosene, in the apparatus illustrated under the heading "Water," Part I, and measuring the volume of water recovered in the distillate. From this, its weight is calculated in percentage based on the weight of fabric taken for analysis.

Treat another weighed specimen of the fabric, cut to a convenient size, in a Soxhlet extractor with carbon disulphide, and continue the extraction for several hours after the liquor syphons over colorless. Air-dry the extracted fabric, then heat it in a ventilated oven maintained at 110° C.; cool in a dessicator, and weigh as rapidly as possible. Repeat the drying until the weight of the fabric remains constant, as determined by two consecutive weighings taken not less than 10 minutes apart, showing a further loss of not more than 0.1%. This gives its weight in the "bone-dry" state. The total weight of moisture present in the original material figured against the weight of "bone-dry" fabric, will give the percentage of moisture extant in the original fabric exclusive of the bituminous constituents.

Fabrics treated with asphalt become readily desaturated upon extracting with carbon disulphide, whereas fabrics treated with coal-tar or coal-tar-pitch will retain much of the "free carbon" mechanically. Most of the free carbon may be removed, however, by vigorously agitating the desaturated fabric with carbon disulphide in a stoppered flask. One or more such treatments will remove the bulk of the "free carbon," which in turn may be recovered upon filtering the washings. [1]

The extracted fabric may be examined for ash, thickness and strength, also subjected to a microscopic examination to ascertain the fibres present, in accordance with the methods to be described.

Add any "free carbon," recovered as described above to the carbon disulphide extract, and evaporate the mixture, first on a steam bath, and then in an oven at 80° C., until the residue corresponds to the exact difference in weight between the original bituminized fabric and the combined weights of extracted "bone-dry" fabric plus the moisture present. The bituminous matter recovered in this manner may be examined as described later.

[1] "Tentative Methods of Testing Felted and Woven Fabrics Saturated with Bituminous Substances for Use in Waterproofing" (Serial Designation: D 146–23T), Proc. A. S. T. M., **23**, Part I, 796, 1923.

SINGLE LAYERED (SATURATED AND COATED) ALSO LAMINATED FABRICS

Since the fabrics and bituminous matter may be assembled in many different ways, the resultant products are too numerous to itemize. It is impractical, therefore, to give analytical methods applicable to each. The ones which follow have been devised specifically for examining prepared roofings and composition shingles.[1] These methods are typical ones, and with slight minor modifications and a little ingenuity, may be adapted to other forms of bituminized fabrics.

For all practical purposes, prepared roofings may be divided into the six types illustrated in Fig. 168.

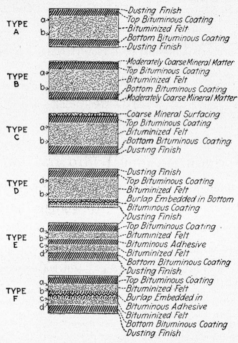

FIG. 168.—Types of Prepared Roofings.

Type A represents a layer of felt saturated and coated with bituminous matter. The surface coatings may be either finished plain or dusted with very fine mineral matter, and they may be either applied smooth and level or with a veined appearance.

Type B is similar to Type A, but surfaced on *both* sides with moderately coarse mineral matter embedded superficially in the coatings.

Type C is similar to Type A, but surfaced on *one* side with coarse mineral matter embedded in the coating.

Type D is composed of a layer of saturated felt and a layer of burlap or cotton duck cemented together and coated on top and bottom with bituminous matter. Its surface is finished similar to Type A.

Type E is composed of two layers of saturated felt cemented together and coated with bituminous matter, being finished on the surface similar to Type A.

Type F is composed of two layers of saturated felt, cemented together with a layer of burlap in between, and coated with bituminous matter. Its surface is finished as in Type A.

[1] "Analysis and Testing of Prepared Roofings," J. Ind. Eng. Chem., **9**, 1048, 1917

The mineral matter, bituminous matter and fibrous matter are distributed in the following manner:

MINERAL MATTER

1—Detached......... *Very Fine Mineral Matter* (e.g., finely ground talc, mica or silica) Types A, D, E and F (on top and bottom) also Type C (on bottom only).

2—Embedded in the top surface coating

Moderately Coarse Mineral Matter (e.g., sand, coarsely ground talc, and coarse mica flakes) Type B (on top and bottom).

3—Embedded in the bottom surface coating

Coarse Mineral Matter (e.g., crushed slate, crushed brick or tile, crushed feldspar or granite, small pebbles or gravel) Type C (on top only).

4—Admixed with the top surface coating (Types A, B, C, D, E and F)

5—Admixed with the bottom surface coating (Types A, B, C, D, E and F)

6—Admixed with the cementing layer (Types E and F)

May or may not be present. If present, consists of very fine mineral matter (e.g., clay, silica, limestone, shale, colored mineral oxides, etc.).

BITUMINOUS MATTER

1—Contained in the top surface coating (all types).
2—Contained in the bottom surface coating (all types).
3—Contained in the cementing layer (Types D and F).
4—Contained in the fabric, present in either one layer (Types A, B, C and D) or distributed in several layers (Types E and F).

FIBROUS MATTER

1—One or more layers of felt (all types).
2—Burlap or other fabric (Types E and F).

The separation of prepared roofing into its component parts is carried out as follows:

Weight Per 100 Sq. Ft. Carefully unpack the roll, taking care not to detach any of the mineral surfacing or dusting finish. Weigh the roofing after removing the wrapper, ends, nails and lap-cement packed in the core of the roll. Measure the length and breadth of the roll with a steel tape, recording the dimensions to $\frac{1}{16}$ in. Calculate the area in square feet.

Figure the weight of the finished roofing in lbs. per 100 sq. ft.................. (1)

Cut several strips *exactly* 3 in. wide *across* the sheet.

NOTE—With roofing 36 in. wide, these strips will measure exactly $\frac{3}{4}$ sq. ft., and with roofing 32 in. wide, they will measure $\frac{2}{3}$ sq. ft. Find the weight of each strip in grams.

Calculate the weight of the roofing in lbs. per 100 sq. ft....................... (2)

NOTE—With 36 in. roofing, wt. in lbs. per 100 sq. ft. $= 0.294 \times$ wt. 3 in. strip in grams.

With 32 in. roofing, wt. in lbs. per 100 sq. ft. $= 0.331 \times$ wt. 3 in. strip in grams.

CHECK—Result (1) should equal result (2).

Detached Mineral Matter. Remove the detached mineral particles from both sides of the 3-in. strips with a moderately stiff brush or cloth and reweigh in grams.

Calculate the weight detached mineral matter in lbs. per 100 sq. ft............. (3)

Dry Felt and Burlap; Total Embedded and Admixed Mineral Matter; Total Bituminous Matter. Extract one of the 3-in. strips in a Soxhlet extractor with benzol. Dry the extracted fabric together with any adhering mineral matter at 110° C. Cool in a desiccator and weigh the felt as rapidly as possible before it has an opportunity to absorb moisture from the air. Repeat the drying, until the weight is constant. Carefully brush off, weigh and set aside the adhering mineral matter.

Calculate the weight of each layer dry felt or burlap in lbs. per 100 sq. ft........ (4)

NOTE—Use the separated felt or burlap for examining its physical and chemical characteristics according to the methods to be described later.

Separate the mineral matter from the benzol extract by filtering or centrifuging; wash clean with successive portions of benzol, dry and weigh. Combine with the mineral matter brushed off the extracted felt.

Calculate the weight of the total embedded and admixed mineral matter in lbs. per 100 sq. ft. .... (5)

Screen through a set of standard sieves of different mesh.   A mere inspection of the particles retained by the various screens will enable one to distinguish the moderately coarse or coarse embedded mineral matter from any very fine admixed mineral matter present in Types B and C.

Calculate the weight of moderately coarse or coarse embedded mineral matter in
   lbs. per 100 sq. ft. for Types B and C; or calculate the combined weight of very
   fine embedded mineral matter and admixed mineral matter in lbs. per 100 sq. ft.
   for Types A, D, E and F . . . .   (6)

Calculate the total weight of bituminous matter in lbs. per 100 sq. ft., i.e. [1]
   $-[(3)+(4)+(5)]$ . . . .   (7)

Bituminous Saturation in the Felt.   Warm a strip about 2 in. wide cut lengthwise from the roll, and tear off the coatings as shown in Fig. 169, taking care that in so doing

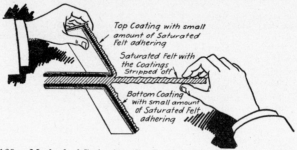

Fig. 169.—Method of Stripping the Coatings from the Saturated Felt.

as little as possible of the saturated felt is removed with the coatings, and, on the other hand, that *none* of the coatings or cementing layer remain adhering to the strip of saturated felt.   The small arrows to the left of the various types of roofing illustrated in Fig. 168 indicate approximately where the layers should be separated.   This can readily be accomplished with a little practice and dexterity.   Where the roofing is composed of one layer of felt, as in Types A, B, C and D, the zone between the arrows *a* and *b* should be separated.   Where the roofing is composed of two layers of felt, as in Types E and F, separate the zones between the arrows *a* and *b*, also *c* and *d*, respectively.   In this manner, about 25 g. of the saturated felt (free from the coating or cementing layers) are obtained from each layer.   Weigh and extract each portion separately in a Soxhlet with benzol.   Dry the extracted felt at 110° C. to constant weight, desiccate and weigh.   Calculate the weight of bituminous saturation by difference, and evaporate the benzol extract to exactly this weight.

Note—Use the residue of bituminous saturation recovered from each layer of felt
      for examining its physical and chemical characteristics, according to the
      methods described later.

Calculate the per cent of bituminous saturation carried by each layer of dry felt . .   (8)

Calculate the weight of bituminous saturation present in each layer of the felt in
   lbs. per 100 sq. ft. [i.e. $(8) \times (4)$] . . . .   (9)

Weights of Bituminous Matter in the Coatings and Cementing Layer.—In types A, B, C and D.   The combined weights of bituminous matter in the top and bottom coatings in lbs. per 100 sq. ft. may be calculated by subtracting (9) from (7).   To find the respective weights of bituminous matter in the top and bottom surface coatings, take a 3-in. strip cut across the sheet of roofing, from which the detached mineral matter has been removed, and split it lengthwise by tearing the felt midway between the points *a* and *b* (Fig. 168).   Weigh and extract each section separately in a Soxhlet.   Desiccate and weigh the dry felt in each section (and the burlap in Type D), also separate and weigh the total embedded and admixed mineral matter.   Calculate the weight of bituminous saturation present [i.e., weight of dry felt $\times$ (8)].   From the original weight of each section subtract the combined weights of dry felt, bituminous saturation, embedded and admixed mineral matter.   The difference represents the weight of bituminous matter in the surface coating carried by that particular section.

Calculate the weights of bituminous matter in the top and bottom coats, respectively, in lbs. per 100 sq. ft. . . . .   (10)

In Types E and F.   Take a 3-in. strip freed from the detached mineral matter as previously described, and split it into three sections, by tearing through the felt midway between the points a and b, also c and d, respectively (Fig. 168).   Weigh and extract each of the three sections separately in a Soxhlet.   Separate, and in each case weigh the dry felt (also the burlap in Type F) and the total mineral matter.   Following the method previously described:

Calculate weights of bituminous matter in the top and bottom coats respectively in lbs. per 100 sq. ft. . . . . (11)

Calculate weight of bituminous matter in the cementing layer in lbs. per 100 sq. ft.

Calculate weight of very fine mineral matter admixed with the cementing layer in lbs. per 100 sq. ft.

Very Fine Embedded Mineral Matter also Admixed Mineral Matter, in the Top and Bottom Coatings Respectively.   In types A, D, E and F.   Take another 3-in. strip from which the detached mineral matter has been brushed off, and remove the *outer* layer of the top and bottom coatings respectively, by means of moderately rough sand paper. Enough of the surface should be scraped to remove every vestige of the very fine embedded mineral matter, and at the same time care should be taken *not* to cut completely through the surface coatings into the saturated felt underneath.

In types A and D, split the scraped sheets lengthwise midway between the points a and b.   In types E and F, split the scraped sheets lengthwise midway respectively, between the points a and b, also c and d, discarding the central section. Extract the scraped outer sections separately with benzol as before, recovering and weighing:

The dry felt present in the respective scraped sections . . . . (12)

The admixed mineral matter present in the scraped sections . . . . (13)

The total bituminous matter present in the surface coating and saturating the felt in the respective scraped sections . . . . (14)

The dry burlap (in Type D).

Calculate the bituminous matter present in the felt in the respective scraped sections $[(8) \div 100 \times (12)]$ . . . . (15)

Hence the bituminous matter present in the surface coating remaining on the respective scraped sections $= (14) - (15)$ . . . . (16)

The proportion of very fine mineral matter admixed with the bituminous matter in each coating $= (13) \div (16)$ . . . . (17)

Total weight of very fine mineral matter *admixed* with the respective coatings in lbs. per 100 sq. ft. $= (17) \times (10)$ [in Types A and D] or $(17) \times (11)$ [in Types E and F] . . . . (18)

And weight of very fine mineral matter *embedded* in the surface of the respective coatings in lbs. per 100 sq. ft. $= (6) - (18)$.

Nature of the Bituminous Matter in the Coatings and Cementing Layer.   Brush off the detached mineral matter from a surface about 2 sq. ft. in area.   Then scrape off the outer portion of the surface coating with a sharp knife.   This is accomplished by holding the knife at right angles to the sheet of roofing resting on a firm, level surface, and rapidly drawing the blade sideways under moderate pressure.   Care should be taken to avoid scraping entirely through the surface coating.   This is important.   Weigh and then dissolve the scrapings in benzol.   Separate the mineral matter by filtering or centrifuging, and wash with successive portions of benzol.   Dry and weigh the mineral matter.   Calculate the weight of bituminous matter in the scrapings by difference, and evaporate the combined benzol extracts on the water bath to exactly this weight, completing the evaporation if necessary in an oven.   Both surface coatings should be treated separately in this manner.

In type D the bottom coating may readily be removed by cooling the specimen in an ice-chest and *rapidly* tearing off the burlap, which will carry most of the bottom coat with it.   This should be extracted, filtered and the extract evaporated to obtain the pure bituminous matter present.

In type F the central web of burlap may be torn out, and the bituminous matter contained in the cementing layer separated in the same manner.

In type E the bituminous matter may be separated from the cementing layer between the sheets of felt, by cooling in an ice-chest, rapidly tearing the specimen in two along the plane of the cementing layer, scraping and separating the bituminous matter as described for the surface coatings.

Use the separated bituminous matter for examining its physical and chemical characteristics.

30

Examination of Separated Fabric

Weight. This is ascertained as described under "Physical Tests of Finished Product." It is expressed arbitrarily by the trade in terms of the "number" as follows:

(a) In the case of paper, the "number" usually corresponds to the weight in pounds of a ream, consisting either of 500 sheets, for light papers, or 480 sheets, for heavy papers, each sheet measuring 24 in. by 36 in.   Other arbitrary methods are also sometimes used embodying a different number of sheets, or sheets of other sizes. The following formulae will be found useful in calculating the "number":

$$\text{"Number" } (500: 24{\times}36) = \frac{\text{gms.}}{\text{sq. cms.}} \times 6150 = \frac{\text{gms.}}{\text{sq. ins.}} \times 953,$$

$$\text{"Number" } (480: 24{\times}36) = \frac{\text{gms.}}{\text{sq. cms.}} \times 5903 = \frac{\text{gms.}}{\text{sq. ins.}} \times 914.$$

In stating the "number," the percentage of moisture present in the paper should also be given.

(b) In the case of felt, the "number" represents the weight in pounds of a ream consisting of 480 sheets, each measuring 12 in. × 12 in., the moisture content of which is arbitrarily set at 3.5%.   The following formula may be used:

$$\text{"Number" } (480: 12{\times}12) = \frac{\text{gms.}}{\text{sq. cms.}} \times 983 = \frac{\text{gms.}}{\text{sq. ins.}} \times 152.$$

(c) In the case of textile fabrics, the "number" represents the weight in ounces per lineal yard of a specified width, the moisture content being arbitrarily fixed at 6.5%.   With burlaps the width is 40 in., with "regular" ducks 29 in., etc.

Thickness. This is found as described under the heading "Physical Tests of Finished Product."

Strength. The strength is determined by one of the following methods:

(a) In the case of paper, the desiccated material is exposed for at least 2 hours in an atmosphere of 65% relative humidity, at 70° F.,[1] and while in this condition it is tested by means of a Mullen tester, increasing the tension at a *uniform* speed of 2 lb. per second until the specimen ruptures.

(b) In the case of felt, expose the desaturated fabric for 3 days to air at 77° F., completely saturated with moisture, and then find its tensile strength as in (a). The reason for this is because the strength of the dry felt is increased materially during the process of extracting with solvents, but it may again be brought to correspond closely with its original strength by treating as described.

(c) In the case of textile materials (e.g., cotton cloth, duck, burlap, etc.), it is customary to find the tensile strength when the desiccated fabric has assumed a moisture regain, established arbitrarily at 6.5% of its bone-dry weight.[2]   Two methods are used for finding the tensile strength.   One is known as the "Strip Test," in which a strip of the fabric, measuring 7 in. by 1½ in., ravelled to exactly 1 in. width, is clamped at each end by the jaws of the testing machine (measuring 1½ in. × 1½ in.), and strained to the point of rupture.   The initial distance between the jaws is 3 in. and their speed of separation 20 in. per minute.   The other method is known as the "Grab Test," in which the machine jaws, each of a definite area (i.e., 2 in. by 1 in.) are made to reach into the body of a rectangular piece of fabric 5 in. by 2 in., and clamped exactly 1 in. apart.   The jaws are separated at a speed of 12 in. per minute to the point of rupture.   In each method 5 tests are averaged separately for the warp and filling.

Thickness Factor. This is equal to the thickness in mils divided by the "number" of the fabric.

Strength Factor. This is equal to the strength in pounds divided by the "number" of the fabric.

Ash. The ash is determined by incineration and calculated in percentage.

---

[1] Mittheilungen a.d.K. Technischen Versuchsanstalten, **7** (1889), 2; **8** (1890), 8 to 19; "A Constant Temperature and Humidity Room for the Testing of Paper, Textiles, etc.," by F. P. Veitch and E. O. Reed, J. Ind. Eng. Chem., **10**, 1918, 38.
[2] "Standard General Methods of Testing Cotton Fabrics" (Serial Designation: D 39–20), A. S. T. M. Standard Methods Adopted in 1921, 834; also "Effect of Moisture on the Tensile Strength of Aircraft Fabrics," by G. H. Haven, ibid., page 380.

Fibres Present. The percentage composition of the fibres is determined micro-scopically by staining them with a solution of zinc-chlor-iodide (prepared by dissolving 4 g. of potassium iodide and 0.1 g. of iodine in 12 cc. of water, and then adding 20 g. of zinc chloride), and counting under a microscope having a magnification of about 100 diameters. The individual fibres are recognized by their characteristic shapes and the colors they are stained by the zinc-chlor-iodide solution. The percentages are ascertained by counting the fibres in a number of fields and finding their average. The following classes of fibres are reported:

Rag Fibres { Cotton fibres—stained wine-red
{ Wool fibres—unstained by the solution
{ Jute and manila fibres—stained a yellowish brown

Paper Fibres { Mechanical wood pulp—stained lemon-yellow
{ Chemical wood pulp (sulphite and soda)—stained grayish purple to
{ purple

The following solution has been suggested for distinguishing the different kinds of chemical wood pulp, including unbleached and bleached sulphite pulps.[1] The fibres are first moistened with a 5 per cent solution of ammonium molybdate and then with a solution of paranitroaniline (200 mg. dissolved in 80 cc. of distilled water, to which are added 20 mg. sulphuric acid, sp.gr. 1.767). This stains the fibres as follows:

Mechanical wood pulp . . . . bright reddish orange
Unbleached sulphite pulp . . . . faint dull orange to faint brownish
Bleached sulphite pulp and soda pulp . . . . . colorless.

Another reagent recently proposed for this purpose[2] is prepared by mixing equal volumes of N/10 ferric chloride and N/10 potassium ferricyanide solutions. The moist fibres are immersed for 15 minutes at a temperature of 35° C., removed and washed thoroughly with water. They are then immersed in a freshly prepared red stain com-posed of: benzopurpurin 4-B extra (Bayer & Co.) 0.4 g.; oxamine brilliant red BX (Badische Co.) 0.1 g.; and distilled water 100 cc. This is maintained at 45° C. for 5–6 minutes, the fibres thereupon removed, washed immediately with water, and examined under a microscope. Unbleached sulphite pulp, ground wood, jute, or any lignified fibres are stained a deep blue (the depth depending upon the lignin content); whereas bleached sulphite pulp, soda pulp, rags, wool or any thoroughly bleached fibres are stained a brilliant red.

Manila fibres may be differentiated from other rope fibres (*e.g.*, sisal, New Zealand, istle, Mauritius and maguez)[3] by immersion for 20 seconds in a solution of chloride of lime (containing about 5% of available chlorine) freshly acidulated with acetic acid (2 cc. of glacial acetic acid per 30 cc. chloride of lime solution); rinsing with water; then rinsing with 95% alcohol; and finally suspending the fibres over strong ammonia for 1 to 2 minutes. In 3 to 4 minutes thereafter, Manila fibres will turn brown, whereas the other rope fibres mentioned will assume a cherry red color.

Examination of Separated Bituminous Coatings, Saturating and Cementing Compounds

The bituminous compounds separated in their pure state as described above should be tested as outlined in Part I.

Examination of Separated Mineral Surfacing and Admixed Mineral Matter

The mineral ingredients separated in their pure state as described are examined as outlined in Part II, "Examination of Separated Mineral Matter."

[1] "Paper Reagent," by W. J. Schepp, Chemist Analyst, p. 20, September, 1917.
[2] "A Method to Distinguish between Bleached and Unbleached Sulphite Pulps," by C. G. Bright, J. Ind. Eng. Chem., **9**, 1044, 1917.
[3] "Distinguishing Manila from All Other Hard Rope Fibres," by C. E. Swett, J. Ind. Eng. Chem., **10**, 227, 1918.

PART IV

EXAMINATION OF BITUMINOUS=SOLVENT COMPOSITIONS (I.E., CEMENTS, PAINTS, VARNISHES, ETC.)

Bituminous paints, cements, varnishes, enamels and japans are all characterized by the presence of a volatile solvent with a bituminous base, combined in the form of "vehicle." Depending upon whether or not the bituminous paints and cements contain a pigment or filler, they may be divided into two general classes, viz.:

(1) Pigment or filler absent: incuuding bituminous varnishes and japans also certain bituminous paints and cements.

(2) Pigment or filler present: including bituminous enamels, also certain bituminous paints and cements.

The first class consists of a vehicle made up of a solvent and base. The second consists of a pigment or filler combined with a vehicle, the latter similarly being made up of a solvent and base. The bituminous base may be composed of bituminous matter, with or without the presence of animal and vegetable oils or fats, resins or metallic dryers. In making an analysis of the paint, cement, varnish, enamel or japan, the following components are separated and examined viz.: (1) solvent, (2) pigment or filler, (3) base.

PHYSICAL TESTS OF FINISHED PRODUCT

Specific Gravity. This may be ascertained by any of the methods described in Part I, care being taken to prevent evaporation of the solvent. The weight per gallon may be calculated from the specific gravity, by multiplying by 100 and dividing the product by 12.

Viscosity. The Engler Method may be used if the composition is sufficiently liquid, otherwise special instruments must be employed for the purpose.

Spreading Capacity. The paint or varnish should be spread on a clean metal surface by skilled workmen under actual working conditions, and the factors of light, temperature and moisture carefully noted. The area covered by one gallon under the conditions noted is an index of its spreading capacity.

Drying Properties. The time which elapses when the coating ceases to be tacky in the preceding test is an indication of the rate with which the composition dries.

Covering Power. A portion of the material is spread on a glass plate at the same rate as noted in the spreading capacity test, and when dry the opacity is recorded under conditions which may be duplicated readily.

Exposure Test. The composition is applied to the surface for which it is intended under carefully controlled working conditions and exposed to the direct action of the weather. The appearance of the surface is noted and recorded at periodic intervals until the coating no longer fulfils its protective action.

SEPARATION OF FINISHED PRODUCT INTO ITS COMPONENT PARTS

Solvent. *Rapid method used for determining the percentage of solvent present:*

The method devised by A. L. Brown is rapid and gives accurate results, but does not recover the solvent for further examination.[1] Deliver 3–4 cc. of the well-mixed material (cements as well as paints of a heavy body should first be thinned to fluid consistency with a weighed quantity of pure benzol) from a 10-cc. pipette into a weighed glass flask of 50 cc. capacity, as rapidly as possible. Stopper the flask immediately, weigh, and dilute to the mark with pure benzol. Deliver exactly 10 cc. of the well-mixed material from the pipette upon a weighed ground-glass plate, 10 by 15 cm. and 1.5–3.0 mm. thick, supported in a level position. The diluted material should be

---

[1] "Quantitative Determination of Body and Solvent in Varnish," by A. L. Brown, Proc. Am. Soc. Testing Materials, **14**, Part II, 467, 1914; "Determination of Volatile Thinner in Oil Varnish," by E. W. Boughton, Technologic Paper No. 76, Bureau of Standards, Wash. D. C., June 21, 1916.

flowed gradually on the plate, the object being to cover it entirely, without causing the solution to creep over the edges. It is recommended that 7 cc. be delivered first, and the remainder, a few drops at a time during the ensuing 2 minutes. The evaporation of the benzol will carry most of the solvent with it, and the film is so thin that the solvent will evaporate in $1\frac{1}{2}$-$2\frac{1}{2}$ hours, the plate being weighed every half hour to follow the course of evaporation. Should the material contain a drying oil, the plate must be placed in an atmosphere of illuminating gas after the first half hour, replacing it after each weighing. The solvent has entirely evaporated when a constant weight is obtained. From this calculate the percentage of solvent by weight. An idea of the drying qualities of the film may be gained by placing the glass in a free circulation of air after the solvent is eliminated, and weighing it every hour as the film oxidizes, until it no longer *increases* in weight. If the coating has a tendency to dry unevenly, a weighed quantity of 50-mesh sea sand, previously dried and ignited, may be sifted over the paint in a very thin layer, but so the paint will be visible between the grains of sand. This will insure a uniform evaporation of the solvent.

Method Used for Recovering the Solvent for Its Examination and Identification. Distil 100 g. paint in a 500-cc. flask, connected with a spray-trap and a vertical condenser and pass through it a current of dry steam, the flask being heated in an oil bath to 100° C. As the steam passes through, gradually raise the temperature of the bath to 130° C. Catch the distillate in a separatory funnel, continuing the distillation until the funnel contains 400 cc. of water. To prevent frothing and bumping, it is advantageous to weigh a small piece of broken glass or pumice-stone into the flask. Let the distillate stand until it separates into two layers, then draw off the water and determine the volume and weight of solvent recovered. Weigh out another 100 g. into a 250-cc. flask and distil without steam over an electric stove. Continue the distillation until the residue in the flask reaches a temperature of 200° C. This gives somewhat lower results than the first method, but the distillate should be tested for water soluble substances to correct the results obtained by the previous method. Turpentine dissolves to the extent of 0.3 g. for each 100 cc. of water condensed.[1]

Pigment and Filler. Dilute 100 g. of the well-mixed material with 500 cc. of benzol in an 800-cc. stoppered flask. Either centrifugate or let stand in a warm place until the pigment or filler has settled, then carefully decant the supernatant liquid into a clean flask of large capacity. The pigment or filler is shaken up with 250 cc. more benzol, allowed to stand in a warm place until it settles, and the supernatant liquid decanted into the second flask. Repeat the treatment with benzol until the vehicle has been completely extracted from the pigment. The combined extracts are allowed to stand quietly to recover any pigment that may have been carried over with the benzol, and then carefully decanted through a weighed Gooch crucible provided with an asbestos filter. The residues in the flask and on the Gooch crucible are washed with benzol as before, and combined with the balance of pigment or filler which is then dried at 110° C. and weighed. The pigment or filler thus extracted is used for a qualitative or quantitative analysis.[2]

Base. The combined extracts of the preceding test are distilled to a small bulk, transferred to a tared dish, and evaporated in an oven at 110° C. *exactly* to the calculated weight of the base, by subtracting the weights of solvent and pigment or filler from the original weight of material taken for examination. When oxidizable substances are present, the final evaporation should take place in an atmosphere of illuminating gas.

The base recovered in this manner will contain the bituminous material (with the exception of the "free carbon" which will be separated with the pigments), animal and vegetable oils or fats, resins and metallic bases and dryers. It should be tested by the methods described in Part I, to identify the materials used in its manufacture, or to aid in its duplication. It may be separated into its component parts as follows:

---

[1] "Some Technical Methods of Testing Miscellaneous Supplies," by P. H. Walker, Bulletin No. 109, Revised, Bureau of Chem., U. S. Dept. of Agri., Wash., D. C., Feb. 28, 1910; see also "Tentative Method of Test for Distillation of Gasoline, Naphtha, Kerosene, and Similar Petroleum Products" (Serial Designation: D 86–23T), Proc. A. S. T. M., **23**, Part I, 665, 1923.

[2] "Analysis of Paints and Painting Materials," by H. A. Gardner and J. A. Schaeffer, N. Y., 1911.

Method of Analyzing the Separated Base

Dissolve 50 g. in 150 cc. benzol. Add 10 cc. dil. nitric acid (1 : 1) and boil under a reflux condenser for ½ hour to decompose any metallic soaps (*i.e.*, driers, etc.). Add 150 cc. water, boil under reflux condenser, transfer to a separatory funnel, draw off the aqueous layer, boil with another 100 cc. water, and repeat if necessary until all the metals are removed.

Benzol Solution:
Distil to 100 cc., add 300 cc. of the saponifying liquid, boil under reflux condenser for 1 hour, and separate the unsaponifiable and saponifiable constituents as described.

Aqueous Extract:
Contains the metallic bases as nitrates. Examine qualitatively and then quantitatively for lead, manganese, cobalt, zinc, calcium, and magnesium.
(N.B.—The last three used for hardening rosin. The metallic dryers should *not* be found by ignition, since the lead will be reduced to metal by the organic matter, and volatilized.)

Unsaponifiable Matter:
If higher alcohols are present they may be extracted by boiling with twice the weight of acetic anhydride and filtering:

Hydrocarbons:
Contain the bituminous substances (*i.e.*, asphalt, coal-tar pitch, unsap. matter derived from fatty-acid pitch, etc.).
Examine by the methods included in Part I.

Higher Alcohols Etc.:
Contain cholesterol etc. derived from wool grease, also the unsaponifiable constituents originally present in resins (4 to 8%).
(See p. 1134.)

Saponifiable Matter:
Separate the fatty and resin acids as described on p. 1175.

Fatty Acids:
Include acids derived from vegetable and animal oils or fats, also from fatty-acid pitch.
(Note "A").

Resin Acids:
Include acids derived from rosin and the fossil resins.
(Note "B").

Aqueous Layer:
Determine percentage glycerol. Multiply this by 10 to estimate percent of vegetable or animal oils or fats (triglycerides) present in the original substance.
(Note "C").

Note "A"

The following means are used to distinguish between the fatty acids derived from oxidized vegetable or animal oils and fatty-acid pitch respectively:

	Fatty Acids Derived From Vegetable or Animal Oils	Fatty Acids Derived From Fatty-acid Pitch
Lactone Value	Less than 25	Greater than 25
K. and S. Fusing-point	Less than 80° F.	Greater than 80° F.
Hardness at 77° F.	Less than 5.0	Greater than 5.0
Color in Mass	Translucent yellow to brown	Opaque brown to black

Note "B"

Test qualitatively for rosin by the Liebermann-Storch reaction (p. 1139). Fossil resins may be distinguished from rosin by determining the saponification, acid and ester values of the mixed resin acids. The following figures have been reported on the resin acids separated as described:[1]

[1] "The Determination of Rosin in Varnishes," by A. H. Gill, J. Am. Chem. Soc., **28**, 1723, 1906; "Shellac Analysis," by E. F. Hicks, 8th Intern. Cong. of Applied Chem., **12**, 115, 1912.

	Saponification Value	Acid Value	Ester Value
Straight Rosin Varnish....................	182–185	160–162	22–24
Rosin ¼; Kauri ¾ Varnish.................	122–135	44–62	72–78
Rosin ½; Kauri ½ Varnish.................	143.5	88	55.5
Straight Kauri Varnish................·...	130	45	85
Untreated Rosin.........................	165–180	155–170	0–13
Untreated Kauri Gum....................	124	41	83

Other resins may be examined in a like manner, although unfortunately, figures are not at present available.

Note "C"

If this corresponds with the total saponifiable matter present, then fatty-acid pitch and resins are absent.

PART V

EXAMINATION OF BITUMINOUS EMULSIONS

These include bituminous emulsifying oils used for laying dust "dust palliatives," also bituminous emulsions used for waterproofing Portland-cement mortar and concrete. The following products are likely to be present, viz.: water, ammonia, various chemicals, bituminous matter, animal and vegetable oils or fats, other forms of non-bituminous organic matter and mineral matter.

Water is determined as described. Ammonia is liberated by rendering alkali with caustic potash and heating. If present, it is detected by its odor, and may be determined quantitatively by distilling into a standard solution of sulphuric acid and retitrating with alkali. The presence of chemicals may be detected by boiling with water, acidifying with hydrochloric acid and extracting the bituminous and fatty substances with benzol. The chemicals remain in the aqueous layer and may be determined by a qualitative or quantitative analysis. Bituminous matter is determined by saponifying the material and then extracting the unsaponifiable constituents as described. The non-bituminous organic matter and the chemicals are separated from the bituminous and fatty matters as previously described, and the non-bituminous organic matter in turn separated from the chemicals by suitable methods. Mineral matter is determined by incinerating a weighed quantity of the material and examining the ash as described.

Method of Proximate Valuation of Oil Shale

The following is the outline of the method used in the Colorado School of Mines.[1]

Two hundred and forty-one grams of shale (219.1 g. in case of rich ore) are placed in an iron retort (A, Fig. 169a), 20 cc. N.H$_2$SO$_4$ are placed in the tube (F) and the apparatus connected up as shown. After testing for leaks the shale is gradually heated, beginning with a low heat and increasing to the full heat of three Scimatico burners. The heating is continued until no more gas is evolved (3–5 hrs.). The oil is caught in the cylinder (B), the ammonia is caught in the acid of the tube (F) and determined as stated below. The gas is measured by the water displacement in the carboy (I).

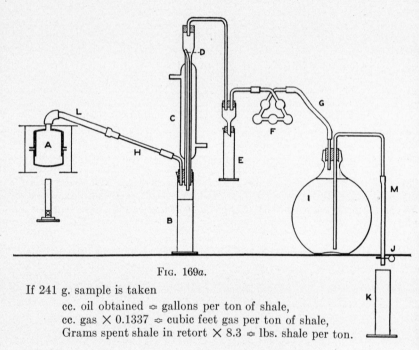

FIG. 169a.

If 241 g. sample is taken

cc. oil obtained $\backsimeq$ gallons per ton of shale,
cc. gas $\times$ 0.1337 $\backsimeq$ cubic feet gas per ton of shale,
Grams spent shale in retort $\times$ 8.3 $\backsimeq$ lbs. shale per ton.

Ammonia as Sulphate. The acid in (E) and the rinsings of (C), (D) and (E) are placed in a flask. CO$_2$ is expelled by boiling. The free acid is just neutralized with NaOH (litmus or cochineal ind.), 10 cc. neutral 40 per cent. formaldehyde added and the solution boiled 1 minute. The liberated H$_2$SO$_4$ is now titrated with N/5 NaOH.

$$6HCHO + 2(NH_4)_2SO_4 = (CH_2)_6N_4 + 2H_2SO_4 + 6H_2O,$$
1 cc. N/ 5NaOH $\backsimeq$ 0.10954 lb. (NH$_4$)$_2$SO$_4$ per ton shale.

[1] The Oil Shale Industry, by Victor C. Alderson, President of C. S. M., Golden, Col.

ANALYSIS OF IRON AND STEEL

STANDARD METHODS FOR THE ANALYSIS OF IRON AND STEEL

The analysis of steel may be considered under two general divisions: the analysis of ordinary or plain carbon steel and the analysis of alloy steels. In this chapter our attention is directed more specially to plain carbon steels, with a more or less cursory examination of alloy steels. The latter class will receive further attention in chapters dealing with principal constituents of such alloys.

The elements carbon, manganese, phosphorus and silicon are always included in the examination of ordinary or plain carbon steels, determinations of copper, nickel, chromium, arsenic, oxygen, hydrogen, nitrogen, etc., are less commonly required. The determinations of aluminum, chromium, molybdenum, nickel, tin, titanium, tungsten, vanadium, zinc, etc., are required in special alloy steels and these constituents are taken up in the chapters of their name.

In a steel works laboratory a large number of determinations are necessary for control of the metal shipped or used, so that the methods for examination must be rapid. It is no unusual practice for an analyst to make from 25 to 150 determinations per day, depending upon the constituent in demand.

The sampling of iron, steel and alloy steels or ferrous alloys as well as non-ferrous alloys is exceedingly important owing to the fact that segregation takes place in the metal causing an appreciable variation of composition in different portions of the bar or ingot. (Consult the paragraph " Metals " under " Preparation and Solution of the Sample " in the chapter on Copper.) Etching tests and microscopical examinations of the metal are necessary adjuncts to a chemical examination for a true interpretation of the condition of the material. A well-equipped laboratory should have facilities for conducting metallographical examinations and a chemist's training should include a knowledge of the subject.

In sampling pig iron, one pig is taken at random from each four ton lot, the surface cleansed from sand, etc., with a wire brush, the skin removed by an emery wheel to clean metal at the center upper surface and a drilling taken with a $\frac{1}{4}$-in. drill from the cleared center, passing through the pig. One drilling per pig is recommended by the A. S. T. M.

The quartered sample of coarse and fine material is sieved to separate coarse and fine, and portions taken for analysis in the ratio existing in the sample. For example, if the gross sample weighed 500 grams and the sieved samples weighed 400, 80 and 20 grams, on a 2-gram sample the ratios would be 1.6, 0.32 and 0.08 grams respectively.

The fines may be obtained by sieving through an 80- or if need be a 120-mesh sieve (80 or 120 meshes to linear inch).

Edited by W. W. Scott.

When nitric acid is used as a solvent the acid should be dilute, since strong nitric acid produces a passive condition of iron, the metal becoming inert to the acid.

Alloy steels, such as ferro-silicon, ferro-titanium, ferro-chromium, require fusion with a basic flux to effect decomposition. Fusion with sodium carbonate and magnesium oxide is generally effective, the fusion is now dissolved in hydrochloric acid, and the iron oxidized by adding nitric acid and applying heat.

The methods outlined in this portion of the text, under Iron and Steel, deal with the more common constituents—carbon, manganese, phosphorus, sulphur and silicon. Special alloy steels are taken up in the chapters throughout the book. Ferro-chromium, under Chromium, ferro-silicon under Silicon, ferro-titanium under Titanium, etc. Copper, nickel, cobalt, vanadium, etc., are taken up in the chapters on these elements. Determinations in a few of the more important alloy steels are given here.

STANDARD METHODS OF CHEMICAL ANALYSIS OF PLAIN CARBON STEEL

ADOPTED 1914; REVISED 1924 BY A. S. T. M.[1]

Determination of Carbon by the Direct=Combustion Method

The method of direct combustion of the metal in oxygen is recommended, the carbon dioxide obtained being absorbed in either (a) soda-asbestos with suitable purifying and protecting trains following the furnace, or (b) barium hydroxide solution, the precipitated barium carbonate filtered off, washed, dissolved in a measured excess of hydrochloric acid and the excess titrated against standard alkali. Owing to the diversity of apparatus by which correct results may be obtained in the determinations of carbon, the recommendations are intended more to indicate what is acceptable than to prescribe definitely what shall be used.

Apparatus and Reagents Common to Both Methods

Material for Lining Boats. Alundum, " RR Alundum, alkali-free, specially prepared for carbon determination," as supplied by dealers is suitable, and is recommended. The 90-mesh or finer grades are used. Low-silica chrome ore, properly sized and freed from materials causing a blank, may also be employed. No substance containing alkali or alkaline earth metals, or carbon as carbonates or in other form, should be used as a lining material. Quartz sand, owing to its liability to fuse or to slag with the oxides of iron, causing bubbles of gas to be enclosed, is objectionable. Aluminum oxide, made by calcining alum or otherwise, often contains sulphate not easily destroyed, or may contain objectionable substances of an alkaline nature.

Catalyzers. Suitable catalyzers are asbestos, copper oxide, platinized quartz or asbestos, or platinum gauze. One of these should be used in the forward part of the combustion apparatus, as well as in the preheater preceding the combustion tube (see below). Platinized materials sometimes give off volatile substances on heating, and whatever material is used should not be subject to this defect.

[1] By courtesy of American Society for Testing Materials.

Combustion Apparatus. Any apparatus heated by electricity or gas which will bring the sample to a temperature of 950° to 1100° C. may be used. Combustion tubes may be porcelain, glazed on one or both sides, quartz or platinum. Quartz is liable to devitrification when used continuously at temperatures above 1000° C., and may then become porous.

Boats or Other Containers of Samples Being Burned. These may be porcelain, quartz, alundum, clay, platinum, or nickel, and should always receive a lining of granular alundum or any other material found to be suitable for the purpose. Nickel boats should not be made of sheet nickel containing more than 0.3% of carbon. New boats should always be preheated in oxygen before use. In order to prevent spattering and attack of the tube, a platinum or nickel cover open at both ends and allowing free access of oxygen is desirable.

Purifying Train Before Combustion Apparatus. This consists of a tower filled with soda-asbestos, soda-lime or granular sodium hydroxide preceded by a preheater when necessary.

Oxygen. Oxygen of not less than 97% purity is recommended. Endeavor should be made to obtain oxygen which gives no blank, since the correction for or elimination of this is troublesome and uncertain. For the most accurate work, particularly with low-carbon products, such as ingot iron, etc., the blank should be completely eliminated by the use of a preheater before the furnace, with a carbon-dioxide absorbent interposed between furnace and preheater. The oxygen may be regulated either by means of a high pressure reducing valve or by means of a gasometer or gas holder.

Factors Influencing Rapid Combustion

Size of Particles of Sample. The finer the chips (short of dust, which causes low values on a hot boat) the better, except with samples which burn too vigorously (see under *Rate of Admitting Oxygen*). Particles too coarse to pass a 20-mesh sieve are not recommended, nor long curly drillings which will not pack closely. A $\frac{1}{2}$-in. flat drill may be used for taking the sample and the pressure and speed of the drill-press regulated to secure the desired result; or, better still, the sample may be obtained with a small milling machine suitable for sampling, or by a shaping machine. Oil, dust, and other foreign matter should be carefully excluded.

Manner of Distributing Sample in Boat. This is of considerable importance. With all samples, close packing in a small space is conducive to rapid combustion. In the case of samples which burn too vigorously, a satisfactory regulation may sometimes be attained by spreading the sample loosely over the lining in the boat.

Rate of Admitting Oxygen. The rate at which oxygen is admitted is also a factor in the velocity of combustion. Assuming the combustion apparatus to be heated to the temperature range above recommended (950° to 1100° C.), it is possible, if the material is closely packed and if oxygen is admitted at too rapid a rate, that the combustion may be so violent as to cause excessive spattering of fused oxides, and such fluidity of the molten slag that the boat or other container may be injured or destroyed; therefore a moderate rate of burning is to be sought. This is desirable also to insure the complete absorption of the carbon dioxide. The factors, temperature of combustion, apparatus, manner of distribution of sample, and rate of admission of oxygen, can be governed so as to burn successfully steels of a very wide range of compositions in either fine or coarse particles.

(a) Determination of Carbon (Carbon Dioxide Absorbed in Soda-Asbestos)

Special Apparatus

Purifying and Protecting Trains. This method requires a purifying train before and after the combustion furnace. The purifying train before the furnace may be the same as that specified under (b), namely, a calcium-chloride tower filled with soda-asbestos, soda-lime or granular sodium hydroxide placed before the furnace, or between the furnace and preheater, if the latter is necessary for the purpose of oxidizing organic matter in the oxygen. The purifying train after the furnace should be so designed that it will accomplish the following: (1) Remove impalpable oxide of iron which readily passes through loosely packed plugs of glass wool or asbestos or even solutions through which the oxygen is rapidly bubbled; (2) remove oxides of sulphur which are always formed; (3) dry the gases before entering the carbon-dioxide absorber; (4) dry the gases issuing from the absorber to the same extent as when they entered; and (5) protect the weighed carbon dioxide and water absorbents from outside effects.

Absorbing Bulbs. No special types are recommended although both Fleming and the Midvale (sometimes called Stetzer and Norton) bulbs have proven satisfactory. When filled, the tubes should not weigh over 200 g and they should always be weighed filled with oxygen and against a like counterpoise. Open bulbs such as the Midvale lose oxygen by diffusion. They should be filled with oxygen before weighing when not in continuous use, and the same time interval must be held between weighings.

Absorbents. The most desirable absorbent is soda-asbestos. The use of soda-lime is not recommended unless the reagent has been carefully tested and found to be satisfactory. Pulverized sodium hydroxide may be used.

General Arrangement of Apparatus. Fig. 169b presents a typical arrangement in works' laboratories. For work of the highest accuracy or with very low-carbon steels the issuing gases in this train would be bubbled through concentrated sulphuric acid saturated with chromic acid before passing through the phosphorus pentoxide tube, and the upper chamber of the Fleming bulb would be filled with phosphorus pentoxide.

Method

After having properly set up and tested the apparatus, moderately pack the desired weight of steel (in the form recommended above) on the bed material in the boat and introduce the boat into the combustion apparatus, which has already been heated to the proper temperature. Admit the gas after $\frac{1}{2}$ to 1 minute at such a rate that the gases leave the absorbents at the rate of 200 to 400 cc. per minute. The sample burns completely in one or two minutes, and all that is now necessary is to sweep all of the carbon dioxide into the absorption bulb. Regulate the rate of flow of the oxygen between 200 and 400 cc. per minute and continue the flow for from five to ten minutes. Withdraw the absorption tube while filled with oxygen, place by the balance, and finally weigh. Remove the boat from the tube and examine the fusion for evidences of incomplete combustion.

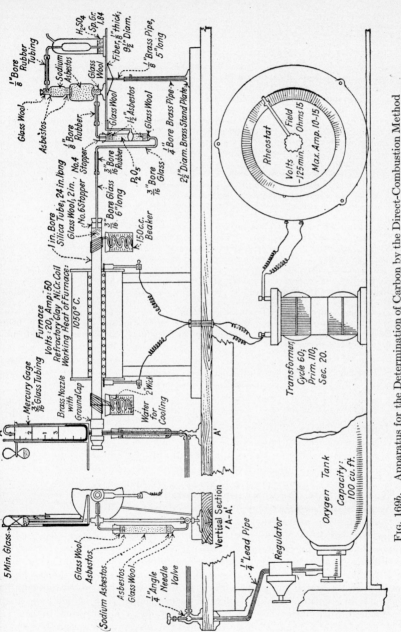

FIG. 169b.   Apparatus for the Determination of Carbon by the Direct-Combustion Method

Allowable Error. Percentages of carbon determined by the above method shoul(be accurate to ±[0.01+(0.02×the percentage of carbon found)].

NOTES

1. Oxides of sulphur may cause a positive error approximating 0.005 per cen carbon in combustions of factor weights of ordinary steels when no provision is mad(for their removal. Sulphur trioxide can be almost entirely removed by interposing some baffle which condenses it, such as asbestos, phosphorus pentoxide, or sulphuri(acid. Sulphur dioxide is not so easily removed; the most satisfactory medium is concentrated sulphuric acid saturated with chromic acid. If not removed, sulphur dioxide may cause positive errors approximating 0.001 per cent carbon.

2. The oxides of sulphur which are fixed and accumulate in the end of the combustion tube should be periodically removed by heating the end of the tube in the hot zone of the furnace.

3. In accurate work or when dealing with low-carbon steels it is desirable to include in the weighed system a dehydrating agent which will dry the escaping gas to the same degree as when it entered the system. The loss of water from a good grade of soda-asbestos may cause losses as high as 0.01 per cent carbon in ordinary combustions. In careful work it is also desirable to protect the weighed system from moisture and carbon dioxide by means of suitable end tubes.

4. Soda-asbestos is commercially known as "Ascarite" and directions for its preparation are to be found in the *Journal Industrial and Engineering Chemistry*, Vol. 8 pp. 1038–9 (1916). For the use of granular sodium hydroxide see the *Journal Industria(and Engineering Chemistry*, Vol. 13, p. 1052 (1921).

5. In some laboratories the absorbing bulbs are always kept in the balance case. In this case the balances are placed on the same table with the furnaces and each balance usually contains two absorbing bulbs which are connected by short lengths of rubber tubing to glass tubes extending out of the balance and connecting with a pair of furnaces.

6. The operator should occasionally test the apparatus and his technic by means of Bureau of Standards standard steels or steels which have been standardized in comparison with these.

(b) DETERMINATION OF CARBON (CARBON DIOXIDE ABSORBED IN BARIUM HYDROXIDE SOLUTION)

Special Apparatus

Purifying Train. This method eliminates the necessity of a purifying train following the furnace, inasmuch as no precautions are necessary to prevent access of water vapor or oxides of sulphur from the absorbing apparatus. All that is needed is the purifying train before the combustion apparatus as mentioned above.

The Train after the Combustion Apparatus. This consists merely of the Meyer tube for absorption of the carbon dioxide, protected by a soda-lime or soda-asbestos tube at the far end. Meyer tubes with 7 to 10 bulbs of 10 to 15-cc. capacity each, and large bulbs at the ends, having volumes equal to the combined capacity of the small bulbs, have been used and found satisfactory

Filtering Apparatus. In filtration for accurate work, care should be taken to protect the solution from access of extraneous carbon dioxide. This is accomplished in the apparatus shown in Fig. 169c. For work requiring less accuracy, the barium carbonate may be filtered off on a filter made by fitting a carbon funnel with a perforated porcelain disk and filtering by suction The precipitate is then washed with distilled water from which the carbon dioxide has been removed by boiling.

Reagents

Tenth-normal Hydrochloric Acid. This may be standardized by any of the accepted methods, or as follows: Measure out 20 cc. of the approximately 0.1 N acid (free from chlorides) with a pipette, and precipitate the silver chloride by an excess of silver-nitrate solution in a volume of 50 to 60 cc. After digesting at 70° to 80° C., until the supernatant liquid is clear, filter off the chloride on a tared Gooch filter and wash with water containing 2 cc. of HNO_3 (sp.gr. 1.42) per 100 cc. of water until free from silver nitrate. After drying to constant weight at 130° C., note the increase of weight over the original tare and from this weight, corresponding to the silver chloride, calculate the strength of the hydrochloric acid, after which adjust it to the strength prescribed. The standardization should be based upon several concordant determinations using varying amounts of acid.

$$1 \text{ cc. } 0.1 \text{ N HCl} = 0.0006 \text{ g. carbon.}$$

Methyl Orange. Dissolve 0.02 g. of methyl orange in 100 cc. of hot distilled water and filter.

Tenth-normal Sodium Hydroxide Solution. Standardize against the hydrochloric acid. Use methyl orange as the indicator. The sodium hydroxide solution should be stored in a large bottle from which it may be driven out by air pressure, protecting against carbon dioxide by soda-lime or soda-asbestos tubes.

Barium Hydroxide Solution. Filter a saturated solution and store in a large reservoir from which it is delivered by air pressure, protecting from carbon dioxide by a soda-lime or soda-asbestos tube. In each determination fill three or four small bulbs of the Meyer tube, and add CO_2-free water until the remaining small bulbs are filled.

Apparatus and Procedure for Filtration

The apparatus is shown to approximately one tenth size in Fig. 169c, which is self-explanatory. The stopcock is a three-way cock connected to the suction pipe. The rubber tubing connected to the Meyer tube should be of best-grade black rubber, and the lengths used should be so chosen as to permit of easy manipulation of the tube. The Meyer tube is connected or disconnected by the rubber stoppers which are left always attached to the rubber tubes. The carbon tube C is fitted with a perforated porcelain plate sliding easily.

The funnel is prepared for filtration by making on the porcelain disk a felt of asbestos about $\frac{1}{16}$ to $\frac{1}{8}$ in. in thickness, using amphibole (not serpentine) asbestos which has been carefully digested with strong hydrochloric acid for several hours and washed with water until it gives no acid reaction. On top of the asbestos pad is placed a layer of similarly treated quartz, mixed with asbestos, of the height shown. A mixture of quartz grains of various sizes (approximately 50% passing a 20-mesh sieve and 50% passing a 10-mesh and remaining on a 20-mesh sieve) is suitable. The mixture of quartz and asbestos may be obtained by filling the funnel from a beaker (directing against it a stream from a wash-bottle) while maintaining a gentle suction. In this way the asbestos is properly mixed with the quartz. A little experience and attention to these details will enable one to prepare the quartz-bed in a manner that will greatly expedite filtration. The stopper is now inserted in the funnel, the Meyer tube connected as shown and the liquid and precipitate sucked into the funnel.   Only a gentle suction should be used.   When necessary, P_3 is opened to admit air back of the column of liquid in the Meyer tube.   When

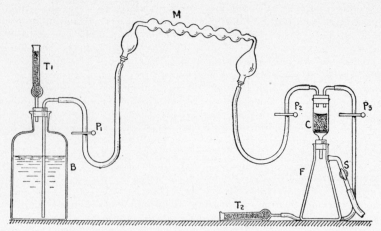

Fig. 169e.   Apparatus for Filtration in Determination of Carbon by the Direct-Combustion Method

the contents of the Meyer tube have been transferred, the large bulb nearest B is half filled with water by opening P_1; the stopcock S is operated during this and subsequent operations so as to maintain a gentle suction all the time. M is now manipulated so as to bring the wash water in contact with all parts of the interior, after which the water is sucked through C; P_2 is left open during this and subsequent washings.   After eight washings as directed, allowing the wash water to drain off thoroughly each time before adding more, M may be detached, the stopper removed from the funnel and the washings completed by filling C to the top with CO_2-free water, draining completely and repeating the operation once.   With care the washing may be done with 150 cc. of water.   Air is now admitted through the side opening of S, C is removed and the porcelain disk carrying the asbestos, quartz and barium carbonate is thrust, by means of a long glass rod, into a flask, removing any adhering particles from the sides of C, by a stream of water from a wash bottle. An excess of the standard acid is now added from a burette or pipette, using a portion to wash out M, and after the contents of the flask have been thoroughly agitated by shaking, the excess of acid is titrated against the standard alkali, using 3 drops of the methyl-orange indicator.

Notes

The operation of filtering can be carried out very rapidly after a little practice.

Glass wool should on no account be used as a substitute for the quartz, on account of the probability of errors arising from its attack by the alkali or acid.

It is well to wash out the rubber tubes connected to the Meyer tube with a little water each day before beginning work.

Method

After having properly set up and tested the apparatus, place 2 g. of steel (Note 1) in the form recommended above, in a moderately packed condition on the bed material and introduce the boat into the combustion apparatus, already heated to the proper temperature. After $\frac{1}{2}$ to 1 minute, admit oxygen somewhat more rapidly than it is consumed, as shown by the rate of bubbling in the Meyer tube (Note 2). A rate of 200 cc. per minute is satisfactory. The sample burns completely in 1 or 2 minutes, and all that is now necessary is to sweep all the carbon dioxide into the absorption apparatus. This is accomplished in 5 to 10 minutes by passing about 1 or 2 liters of oxygen. Detach the Meyer tube (Note 2) and filter and wash the barium carbonate, using the special filtering apparatus shown. After solution in a measured excess of standard hydrochloric acid (the Meyer tube being washed out with a portion of the acid, to remove adhering barium carbonate), titrate the excess of acid against alkali and from the data thus obtained calculate the percentage of carbon.

NOTES

1. When working with steels high in carbon (above 1 per cent), it is advisable not to use more than 1 g. in order that filtration may be sufficiently rapid.
2. As a precaution against error resulting from too rapid passage of the gases, it is well to attach a second barium-hydroxide tube to retain any carbon dioxide that may pass the first.
3. For the most accurate work the Meyer tubes should be washed with dilute acid before beginning work each day. After a determination is finished, the tube should be completely filled two or three times with tap water, then rinsed with distilled water, in order to remove the carbon dioxide liberated when dissolving the carbonate from the previous determination.
4. The flask containing the carbonate should be thoroughly agitated after adding the acid, since the carbonate sometimes dissolves rather slowly if this is not done; this is particularly the case if it has packed much during filtration.

Carbon in Alloy Steels

Nickel Steel. The procedure is the same as given for plain carbon steel.
Chrome Nickel Steel. The procedure does not differ from the one given.
Vanadium Steel. See method for plain carbon steel.
Chrome-Vanadium Steel. The procedure is the same as given.
Silicon-Manganese Steel. No special preliminary treatment is necessary.
Cast Iron and High Carbon Iron. Mix sample with twice its weight of ferric oxide and continue as recommended for plain carbon steel. The A. S. T. M. omit addition of ferric oxide. A one-gram sample of pig or cast iron is taken for analysis.

Determination of Combined Carbon, Colorimetric Method

Routine Work

Details of the procedure may be found in the chapter on carbon. A large number of determinations may be made by this rapid method, but in order to obtain reliable results the standard steel used should be of the same kind, of approximately the same composition, and in the same physical condition as the sample steel.

Reagent. *Dilute Nitric Acid*—1000 cc. HNO_3 (d. 1.42), 1200 cc. water.
Procedure. See page 128, Vol. I.

Determination of Manganese by the Bismuthate Method (Absence of Cobalt)

Solutions Required

Dilute Nitric Acid (1 : 3). Mix 500 cc. of HNO_3 (sp.gr. 1.42) and 1500 cc. of distilled water.

Dilute Nitric Acid (3 : 97). Mix 30 cc. of HNO_3 (sp.gr. 1.42) and 970 cc. of distilled water.

Ferrous Ammonium Sulphate Solution. Dissolve 12 g. of ferrous ammonium sulphate in a mixture of 950 cc. of distilled water and 50 cc. of H_2SO_4 (sp.gr. 1.84).

Standard Potassium Permanganate Solution. Dissolve 1 g. of $KMnO_4$ in 1000 cc. of distilled water. Allow it to stand for at least one week and then filter through purified asbestos. Standardize against the Bureau of Standards standard sodium oxalate as follows: In a 200-cc. beaker, dissolve 0.1 g. of sodium oxalate in 75 to 100 cc. of hot water (80° to 90° C.) and add 4 cc. of H_2SO_4 (1 : 1). Titrate at once with the permanganate solution, stirring the liquid vigorously and continuously. The permanganate must not be added more rapidly than 10 to 15 cc. per minute, and the last 0.5 to 1 cc. must be added dropwise, with particular care to allow each drop to be fully decolorized before the next is introduced. The excess of permanganate used to cause an end point color must be estimated by matching the color in another beaker containing the same bulk of acid and hot water. The temperature of the solution should not be below 60° C. by the time the end point is reached.

Standard Sodium Arsenite Solution. Dissolve 2 g. of sodium arsenite in distilled water, filter if necessary, and dilute to one liter. Standardize against a standard permanganate solution such as the above by titrating 10-cc. portions of the permanganate solution under the acidity and dilution conditions obtaining in the method. A clear green color free from brownish or purplish tints will be found a satisfactory and reproducible end point. The solution may also be standardized against Bureau of Standards standard plain carbon steels.

Method

In a 300-cc. Erlenmeyer flask dissolve 1 g. of steel in 50 cc. of dilute HNO_3 (1 : 3), and boil to expel the oxides of nitrogen. Cool, and add about 0.5 g. of sodium bismuthate and heat for a few minutes, or until the pink color has disappeared, with or without precipitation of manganese dioxide. Add small portions of ferrous sulphate (or any suitable reducing agent) in sufficient quantity to clear the solution, and boil to expel the oxides of nitrogen. Cool to 15° C., add an excess of sodium bismuthate and agitate for a few minutes. Add 50 cc. of dilute HNO_3 (3 : 97), filter through an alundum filter or asbestos pad, and wash with the same acid. Titrate by method (a) or (b) below.

(a) **Ferrous Sulphate-Permanganate Titration** (less than 0.05% chromium).

Add from a burette or pipette 10 to 50 cc. (depending on the amount of permanganic acid) of ferrous ammonium sulphate solution and then titrate with the standard $KMnO_4$ solution. In exactly the same manner carry through a blank determination using the same amounts of acid and bismuthate as was done with the regular sample. Finally add the exact volume of ferrous ammonium sulphate solution which was employed and titrate with the standard

KMnO₄ solution. The difference between the volumes required in the two titrations represents the manganese in the sample.

(b) **Arsenite Titration** (more than 0.05% chromium).

Titrate immediately with the standard sodium arsenite solution to the clear green color used as an end point in the standardization of the solution.

Allowable Error. Percentages of manganese determined by the above method should be accurate to $\pm[0.01+(0.02\times$the percentage of manganese found$)]$.

NOTES

In the method, the preliminary treatment with sodium bismuthate has been found by a number of investigators to be apparently unnecessary; however, the available data to confirm this position are not considered sufficient to warrant its omission.

In making the asbestos filter pad it is advisable to have a thin bed, and as much surface as possible. This insures rapid filtration, and the filter may be used until it becomes clogged with bismuthate.

The filtrate must be perfectly clear, since the least particle of bismuthate carried through the filter will vitiate the results.

This method can not be used in the presence of cobalt.

In the arsenite titration, permanganic acid does not react in accordance with the ratio $Mn_2O_7 : 2MnO$, but more nearly as indicated by the ratio $Mn_2O_7 : Mn_2O_3$. Consequently the theoretical titre of the arsenite can not be used and the manganese titre must be obtained by titration of material of known manganese content under the conditions that obtain in the method.

Determination of Manganese by the Persulphate Method (Routine and in the Presence of Cobalt)

Solutions Required

Dilute Nitric Acid (sp.gr. 1.20). Mix 380 cc. of HNO₃ (sp.gr. 1.42) and 620 cc. of distilled water.

Silver Nitrate (0.133%). Dissolve 1.33 g. of AgNO₃ in 1000 cc. of distilled water.

Ammonium Persulphate Solution (10%). Prepare as needed by dissolving 10 g. of the salt in 100 cc. of distilled water.

Sodium Chloride (0.2%). Dissolve 2 g. of NaCl in 1000 cc. of distilled water.

Standard Sodium Arsenite. Dissolve 0.8 g. of sodium arsenite in distilled water, filter if necessary; dilute to one liter and standardize against a standard steel or by means of 5 cc. of standard 0.03 N permanganate solution which has been reduced and then carried through the steps of the method described below.

Method

In a small Erlenmeyer flask or large test tube (8 by 1 in.) dissolve 0.1 to 0.3 g. of steel, depending on the manganese content of the sample, in 15 cc. of dilute HNO₃ (sp.gr. 1.20) with the aid of heat from a hot-plate or water-bath. The solution of carbon may be hastened by the addition of 1 cc. of the $(NH_4)_2S_2O_8$ solution (10%). When solution is complete and the liquid is clear, add 15 cc. of AgNO₃ solution (0.133%). If a tube is used, add 10 cc. of the $(NH_4)_2S_2O_8$ solution (10%) and heat in the water-bath until the color develops. If a flask is employed, bring the solution to boiling, add 10 cc. of the persulphate solution and then set aside in a warm place until the color develops. When the color has developed, cool the solution in running water, transfer to a 250-cc. beaker and dilute to a volume of 75 cc. Add 10 cc. of NaCl solution (0.2%) and titrate with the standard arsenite solution.

Notes

The persulphate oxidation requires careful attention; the solution must not be too acid and sufficient $AgNO_3$ must be present (about 15 times as much $AgNO_3$ as Mn). Consequently, in steels of high manganese content the amount of $AgNO_3$ and NaCl should be increased.

If it is desired, larger amounts of the sample can be used and correspondingly greater amounts of $AgNO_3$, NaCl and $(NH_4)_2S_2O_8$ (preferably in the form of stronger solutions).

Determination of Manganese—Modified Bismuthate Method

Reagents

Nitric Acid (1 : 3) and dilute acid for washing as previously given.
Sodium Arsenite-Standard Solution as given under plain carbon steel.

Procedure

A sample of 1 g. steel is dissolved in a 300-cc. Erlenmeyer flask in 50 cc. dilute nitric acid (1 : 3) and boiled to expel oxides of nitrogen. After cooling to 60°–70°, 0.5 g. sodium bismuthate is added, the solution heated to the disappearance of the pink color, with or without precipitation of MnO_2. The solution is cleared by addition of sulphurous acid or SO_2 or sodium sulphite, chromium being reduced at the same time. The solution is cooled in ice to 0° C. and excess of bismuthate added, and the mixture agitated. After standing for 30 seconds the solution is filtered rapidly, and the residue washed with ice cold 3% nitric acid. The filtrate is titrated immediately with standard sodium arsenite to the disappearance of the pink color.

Notes

The solution should be ice cold, 0° C., as any appreciable rise of temperature or the least particle of sodium bismuthate in the solution will vitiate results.

Manganese may be determined in chrome-nickel steel also by the Persulphate Method, using a chrome-nickel steel standard.

Vanadium Steel. Use Zinc-Oxide-Bismuthate Method given under chrome-nickel steel, or the Bismuthate Method under plain carbon steel.

Chrome-Vanadium Steel. Use methods for manganese under chrome-nickel steel.

Silico-Manganese Steel. Use methods for manganese under plain carbon steel.

Cast Iron. 1-gram sample is treated with 50 cc. of dilute nitric acid (1 : 3) and when all action has ceased the solution is filtered and the residue washed with 30 cc. more of the acid. The filtrate is now examined for manganese according to the procedures recommended for plain carbon steel.

Note

The carbide of white iron will prevent the quantitative conversion of manganese to permanganate by bismuthate according to the prescribed procedure, several treatments with sodium bismuthate may be necessary.

Ferro-Manganese and Manganese Alloys. See chapter on Manganese.

Determination of Phosphorus by the Molybdate= Magnesia Method

Solutions Required

Dilute Nitric Acid (sp.gr. 1.20). Mix 380 cc. of HNO_3 (sp.gr. 1.42) and 620 cc. of distilled water.

Dilute Nitric Acid (2 : 100). Mix 20 cc. of HNO_3 (sp.gr. 1.42) and 1000 cc. of distilled water.

Potassium Permanganate (2.5%). Dissolve 25 g. of $KMnO_4$ in 1000 cc. of distilled water.

Dilute Ammonium Hydroxide (1 : 2). Mix 300 cc. of NH_4OH (sp.gr. 0.90) and 600 cc. of distilled water.

Dilute Ammonium Hydroxide (1 : 19). Mix 100 cc. of NH_4OH (sp.gr. 0.90) and 1900 cc. of distilled water.

Ammonium Bisulphite (3%). Dissolve 30 g. of ammonium bisulphite in 1000 cc. of distilled water.

Ammonium Molybdate.

Solution No. 1. Place in a beaker 100 g. of 85 per cent molybdic acid, mix it thoroughly with 240 cc. of distilled water, add 140 cc. of NH_4OH (sp.gr. 0.90), filter, and add 60 cc. of HNO_3 (sp.gr. 1.42).

Solution No. 2. Mix 400 cc. of HNO_3 (sp.gr. 1.42) and 960 cc. of distilled water.

When the solutions are cold, add Solution No. 1 to Solution No. 2, stirring constantly; then add 0.1 g. of ammonium phosphate dissolved in 10 cc. of distilled water, and let stand at least 24 hours. Decant clear solution for use.

Magnesia Mixture. Dissolve 50 g. of $MgCl_2.6H_2O$ and 125 g. of NH_4Cl in 750 cc. of distilled water, and then add 150 cc. of NH_4OH (sp.gr. 0.90).

Method

In a 300-cc. Erlenmeyer flask dissolve 5 g. of steel in 75 cc. of dilute HNO_3 (sp.gr. 1.20). Heat to boiling; while boiling add about 12 cc. of the potassium permanganate solution, and continue boiling until manganese dioxide precipitates. Dissolve this precipitate by additions of ammonium bisulphite or ferrous sulphate solution, boil until clear and free from brown fumes and cool to 80° C. Add 100 cc. of the ammonium molybdate solution at room temperature, shake or agitate for 5 minutes, allow to settle, filter on a 9-cm. paper and wash the flask and precipitate at least three times with the dilute HNO_3 (2 : 100) to free from iron.

Dissolve the precipitate on the filter with dilute NH_4OH (1 : 2), letting the solution run into the original flask and avoiding the use of more than 10 to 20 cc. of the reagent. Pour a solution of 0.5 g. of citric acid in 15 cc. of water and 10 cc. of HCl (sp.gr. 1.19) through the filter in order to dissolve any ferric phosphate on the paper and render acid the ammoniacal solution of the phosphate. Transfer the solution to a 100-cc. beaker, add 10 cc. of the magnesia mixture and precipitate the phosphate by adding NH_4OH (sp.gr. 0.90) slowly and with constant stirring, until a crystalline precipitate is formed or the solution is alkaline. Finally add 10% by volume excess and set aside in a cool place for 2 to 6 hours. Filter, wash with dilute NH_4OH (1 : 19), ignite and weigh. Dissolve the precipitate of magnesium pyrophosphate in 5 cc. of dilute HNO_3 (5 : 6), and 20 cc. of distilled water, filter and wash with hot water.   Ignite and weigh.   The difference in weights represents pure magnesium pyrophosphate containing 27.87% of phosphorus.

Allowable Error.   Percentages of phosphorus determined by the above method should be accurate to ±[0.002 + (0.02 × the percentage of phosphorus found)].

NOTES

The ammonium molybdate solution should be kept in a cool place and should always be absolutely clear before using.

If arsenic is present in the steel, it will come down in part with the phosphomolybdate and contaminate the pyrophosphate.   In very accurate work, or when arsenic is present in appreciable amount, steps must be taken for its removal before precipitation with magnesia mixture.

Determination of Phosphorus by the Alkalimetric Method (Routine)

Solutions Required

Dilute Nitric Acid (sp.gr. 1.20).   See " Determination of Phosphorus by the Molybdate-Magnesia Method." [1]

Dilute Nitric Acid (2 : 100).   See " Determination of Phosphorus by the Molybdate-Magnesia Method.".[1]

Potassium Permanganate.   See " Determination of Phosphorus by the Molybdate-Magnesia Method." [1]

Ammonium Bisulphite.   See " Determination of Phosphorus by the Molybdate-Magnesia Method." [1]

Ammonium Molybdate.   See " Determination of Phosphorus by the Molybdate-Magnesia Method." [1]

Potassium Nitrate (1%).   Dissolve 10 g. of KNO_3 in 1000 cc. of distilled water.

Phenolphthalein Indicator.   Dissolve 0.2 g. of phenolpthalein in 50 cc. of 95% ethyl alcohol and 50 cc. of distilled water.

Standard Sodium Hydroxide.   Dissolve 6.5 g. of purified NaOH in 1000 cc. of distilled water, add a slight excess of 1% solution of $Ba(OH)_2$, let stand for 24 hours, decant the liquid, standardize it against a steel of known phosphorus content, as determined by the molybdate-magnesia method, and dilute so that 1 cc. will be equivalent to 0.01% of phosphorus on the basis of a 2-g. sample (see Notes).   Protect the solution from carbon dioxide with a soda-lime or soda-asbestos tube.

Standard Nitric Acid.   Mix 10 cc. of HNO_3 (sp.gr. 1.42) and 1000 cc. of distilled water.   Titrate the solution against the standard sodium hydroxide solution, using phenolphthalein as indicator, and make it equivalent to the sodium hydroxide solution by adding distilled water.

Method

In a 300-cc. Erlenmeyer flask dissolve 2 g. of steel in 50 cc. of dilute HNO_3 (sp.gr. 1.20).   Heat the solution to boiling and while boiling add about 6 cc. of the $KMnO_4$ solution and continue boiling until manganese dioxide precipitates.   Dissolve this precipitate by additions of ammonium bisulphite or ferrous sulphate solution, boil until clear and free from brown fumes, cool

See p. 1363.

to 80° C., add 50 cc. of the ammonium molybdate solution at room temperature, shake or agitate for 5 minutes, allow to settle and filter on a 9-cm. paper. Wash the flask and precipitate three times with dilute HNO_3 (2 : 100) to free it from iron, and continue the washing with the 1% potassium nitrate solution until the paper, precipitate and flask are free from acid.

Transfer the paper and precipitate to the flask, add 20 cc. of distilled water, 5 drops of phenolphthalein solution as indicator, and an excess of standard sodium hydroxide solution. Insert a rubber stopper and shake vigorously until solution of the precipitate is complete. Wash off the stopper with distilled water and determine the excess of sodium hydroxide solution by titrating with standard nitric acid solution. Each cubic centimeter of standard sodium hydroxide solution represents 0.01% of phosphorus.

NOTES

The ammonium molybdate solution should be kept in a cool place and should always be absolutely clear before using.

All distilled water used in titration should be freed from carbon dioxide by boiling or otherwise.

Appropriate Bureau of Standard Standard Steels are recommended for the standardization of the sodium hydroxide solution.

The composition of phosphomolybdate varies with changes in conditions such as acidity, temperature and concentration of the molybdate reagent; consequently care should be taken to keep conditions alike in standardization and in analysis. The ratio 23 molecules of sodium hydroxide to 1 atom of phosphorus represents the reaction very closely if the phosphomolybdate is precipitated at 35° to 45° C.

Phosphorus in Alloy Steels

Nickel Steel. Procedures are the same as in plain carbon steel.

Chrome-Nickel Steel. No modifications necessary.

Vanadium Steel. The procedure is similar to that for plain carbon steel with a slight modification.

Reagents

The same as those used in the plain carbon steel procedures, with an additional reagent—a saturated solution of ferrous sulphate, approximately 40 grams of ferrous sulphate dissolved in 100 cc. of water.

Procedure—Modified Molybdate-Magnesia Method

The sample is dissolved, permanganate added, and the manganese dioxide dissolved with ammonium bisulphite exactly as recommended for plain carbon steel. After expelling the brown fumes by boiling, the solution is cooled to 15°–20° C. and 5 cc. of the ferrous sulphate solution are added, and 2–3 drops of concentrated sulphurous acid, the addition of ammonium molybdate, precipitation of the phosphorus, first as yellow precipitate and then as ammonium magnesium phosphate, ignition and final estimation are the same as in plain carbon steel.

Procedure—Modified Alkalimetric Method

The procedure is the same as that for plain carbon steel with the exception just before addition of the 50 cc. of ammonium molybdate solution, the solution is cooled to 15°–20° C. and 5 cc. of saturated ferrous sulphate reagent and 2–3 drops of concentrated sulphurous acid are added.

Chrome-Vanadium Steel. Phosphorus is determined by the modified methods given for Vanadium Steel. The modification consisting of adding 5 cc. of a saturated solution of ferrous sulphate and 2–3 drops of a strong solution of sulphurous acid just before precipitation of the ammonium phospho-molybdate.

Silico-Manganese Steel. No modifications necessary. See plain carbon steel.

Cast Iron. One or more grams of the sample is dissolved in 50 cc. of dilute nitric acid. The solution is evaporated to dryness and baked at 200° C. for an hour. The residue is taken up with 15 cc. strong HCl and the evaporation repeated. The residue is again taken up with 15 cc. HCl and 20–30 cc. of water and the silica filtered off. The filtrate is evaporated to pasty consistency, near 15 cc. of strong HNO₃ added and the solution evaporated to dryness, the treatment is repeated and the residue taken up with 15 cc. of water and phosphorus now determined as usual. See methods in plain carbon steel.

Irons Containing Titanium. See procedure in chapter on Phosphorus.

For additional alloy steels consult chapter on Phosphorus. See also Reduction Method. (Phosphorus, Vol. I.)

Determination of Sulphur by the Oxidization Method

Solutions Required

Dilute Hydrochloric Acid (2 : 98). Mix 20 cc. of HCl (sp.gr. 1.19) and 980 cc. of distilled water.

Barium Chloride Solution (10%). Dissolve 100 g. of $BaCl_2.2H_2O$ in 1000 cc. of distilled water.

Barium Chloride—Hydrochloric Acid Washing Solution. Mix 10 cc. of the above solution, 10 cc. of HCl (sp.gr. 1.19) and 1000 cc. of distilled water.

Method

Dissolve 4.57 g. of the sample in 50 cc. of HNO₃ (sp.gr. 1.42) in a covered beaker or flask. In case solution is slow or difficult, HCl (sp.gr. 1.19) may be added dropwise at intervals. When solution is complete, add 0.5 g. of Na₂CO₃, evaporate to dryness and bake for 1 hour on the hot plate. Add 30 cc. of HCl (sp.gr. 1.19) and repeat the evaporation and baking. Add another 30 cc. of HCl (sp.gr. 1.19) and evaporate to syrupy consistency. Add 5 cc. of HCl (sp.gr. 1.19), 20 cc. of water, 5 g. of 20- to 30-mesh zinc (free from sulphur), and warm on the steam-bath until the iron is reduced to the ferrous state, and the evolution of hydrogen has nearly ceased. Filter by decantation on a small filter from the silica and undissolved zinc, wash with small portions of approximately 75 cc. of dilute HCl (2 : 98), warm to 60° to 70° C. and add 10 cc. of BaCl₂ solution (10%). Let stand for 18 to 24 hours, filter on a paper of close texture and discard the filtrate. Wash with hot BaCl₂-HCl washing solution until free from iron and then with hot water until free from chlorides. Reserve the paper and precipitate and evaporate the washings to dryness. Dissolve the slight residue in 50 cc. of hot dilute HCl (2 : 98), add 1 cc. of BaCl₂ solution (10%), and digest at 70° to 80° C.

for an hour or so, avoiding any undue evaporation. Filter on a small paper of close texture, wash with hot BaCl₂-HCl washing solution until free from iron and then with hot water until free from chlorides. Ignite both papers

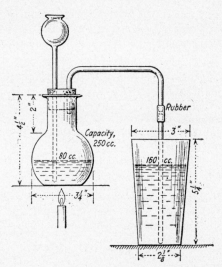

FIG. 169d. Apparatus for Determination of Sulphur by the Evolution Method

in a tared platinum crucible and treat with one drop of dilute H_2SO_4 (1 : 1) and 1 cc. of hydrofluoric acid. Evaporate to dryness, ignite and weigh. A blank should be carried through all steps of the determination and any $BaSO_4$ found deducted. The corrected weight of the ignited $BaSO_4$ multiplied by 3 represents the percentage of sulphur.

Allowable Error. Percentages of sulphur determined by the above method should be accurate to ±[0.002+(0.02×the percentage of sulphur found)].

NOTES

The precipitation of $BaSO_4$ must not be carried out in a solution containing more than 2 cc. of HCl (sp.gr. 1.19) per 100 cc.

The recovery of $BaSO_4$ which is obtained ordinarily represents approximately 0.001% of sulphur.

Precipitation of $BaSO_4$ in unreduced iron solutions of carefully regulated acidity gives low values of the order of 0.001 to 0.002% of sulphur.

Determination of Sulphur by the Evolution=Titration Method (Routine)

Apparatus

Fig. 169d shows a typical apparatus for this determination. A spray trap may be put in the outlet tube to prevent iron from passing over into the ammoniacal solution.

Solutions Required

Dilute Hydrochloric Acid (1 : 1). Mix 500 cc. of HCl (sp.gr. 1.19) and 500 cc. of distilled water.

Ammoniacal Cadmium Chloride. Dissolve 10 g. of cadmium chloride in 400 cc. of distilled water and add 600 cc. of NH_4OH (sp.gr. 0.90).

Ammoniacal Zinc Sulphate. Dissolve 20 g. of $ZnSO_4.7H_2O$ in 1080 cc. of water and add 920 cc. of ammonium hydroxide (sp.gr. 0.90).

Potassium Iodate. Dissolve 1.12 g. of KIO_3 and 12 g. of KI in 1000 cc. of distilled water. For general work the theoretical sulphur titre of this solution should be used; for specialized work on one kind of material, the solution may be standardized against like material. The theoretical titre is based on standard sodium oxalate and is obtained as follows: To 300 cc. of water in a 600-cc. flask, preferably glass stoppered, add 10 cc. of HCl (sp.gr. 1.19) and 1 g. of KI. Cool and add 25 cc. of 0.03 N $KMnO_4$ solution which has been standardized against sodium oxalate. Swirl gently, stopper, and let stand for five minutes. Titrate the liberated iodine with thiosulphate solution until the color fades. Then add 10 cc. of starch solution and continue the titration until the blue color is destroyed. Repeat the titration with the sole difference that 25 cc. of the iodate solution is substituted for the standard permanganate solution. Calculate the normality of the iodate solution, and dilute it if desired so that its normality is 0.0312 or 1 cc. is equivalent to 0.01% of sulphur on a 5-g. sample. For standardization against like material, 5-g. portions of the proper standard steel are carried through all steps of the method.

Starch Indicator. (1) To 1000 cc. of boiling distilled water add a cold suspension of 6 g. of starch in 100 cc. of water and boil vigorously for five minutes. Cool the solution, add 6 g. of $ZnCl_2$ dissolved in 50 cc. of cold water, thoroughly mix and set aside for 24 hours. Decant the clear supernatant liquid into a suitable container, add 3 g. of KI and mix thoroughly. (2) (Optional). Prepare an emulsion of 6 g. of soluble starch in 25 cc. of water, add a solution of 1 g. of NaOH in 10 cc. of water, and stir the solution until it gelatinizes. Dilute to 1000 cc., add 3 g. of KI, and mix thoroughly.

Method

Place 5 g. of steel in the flask and connect the latter as shown in Fig. 169d. Place 10 cc. of the ammoniacal cadmium chloride or zinc sulphate solution and 150 cc. of distilled water in the tumbler. Add 80 cc. of the dilute HCl (1 : 1) to the flask through the thistle tube, heat the flask with its contents gently until the solution of the steel is complete, then boil the solution for $\frac{1}{2}$ minute. Disconnect the delivery tube and remove the tumbler which contains all the sulphur as cadmium sulphide. Add 5 cc. of starch solution, then 40 cc. of dilute HCl (1 : 1) and titrate *immediately* with the potassium odate solution to a permanent blue color.

NOTES

This method succeeds best when the evolution of gas is rapid and the conditions are kept constant.

Some analysts prefer to add the dilute HCl at a temperature of 80° to 90° C. and to heat the flask on an electric heater instead of over gas. The use of concentrated HCl necessitates a condensing arrangement and does not offer any general advantages over the diluted acid. See chapter on Sulphur, Vol. I.

With most plain carbon steel, the results for sulphur which are obtained by the evolution method and the use of the theoretical sulphur titre check the gravimetric results within ±0.002%. Some steels dissolve too slowly and some, as, for example, certain steels containing high sulphur and carbon, do not yield all of their sulphur. In such cases the samples must be annealed as follows:

Transfer 5 g. of drillings to a 12.5-cm. filter paper, and wrap the sample securely in the paper so that at least three thicknesses of paper cover the steel. Place the package in a 25-cc. porcelain crucible, cover the crucible tightly so that no air can enter, and heat for 20 minutes at a bright red heat over a burner or preferably in a muffle. The filter paper should be charred but not burned. Cool and proceed as in the regular method.

Determination of Sulphur in Alloy Steels

Nickel Steel. Use methods in plain carbon steel.

Chrome-Nickel Steel. No modified methods necessary.

Vanadium Steel. The evolution method should not be used if the steel contains appreciable amounts of tungsten, or of copper or other metals precipitated by hydrogen sulphide from acid solution.

The annealing of the steel drillings is claimed to increase the refinement of the method.

In absence of interfering elements mentioned the methods used for plain carbon steel apply here.

Chrome-Vanadium Steel. See vanadium steel.

Silico-Manganese Steel. See vanadium steel.

Cast Iron and White Iron. The sulphur should be determined by the gravimetric method.

It is claimed that annealing the sample at 750°–850° in presence of yellow prussiate of potash prepares the material for the evolution method so that the results are reliable by this procedure.

Determination of Silicon by the Nitro=Sulphuric Method

Solutions Required

Nitro-Sulphuric Acid. Mix 1000 cc. of H_2SO_4 (sp.gr. 1.84), 1500 cc. of HNO_3 (sp.gr. 1.42) and 5500 cc. of distilled water.

Dilute Hydrochloric Acid (5 : 95). Mix 50 cc. of HCl (sp.gr. 1.19) and 950 cc. of distilled water.

Method

Add cautiously 80 cc. of the nitro-sulphuric acid to 4.676 g. of steel, in a platinum or porcelain dish of 300 cc. capacity, cover with a watch glass, heat until the steel is dissolved and evaporate slowly until copious fumes of sulphuric acid are evolved. Cool, add 125 cc. of distilled water and 5 cc. of HCl (sp.gr 1.19), heat with frequent stirring until all salts are dissolved and immediately filter on a 9-cm. paper. Wash the precipitate with cold dilute HCl (5 : 95) and hot water alternately to complete the removal of iron salts, and finally with hot water until free from acid. Transfer the filter to a platinum crucible burn off the paper carefully, finally igniting with the crucible covered over a blast lamp or in a muffle furnace at 1000° C. for at least 10 minutes; cool in a desiccator and weigh. Add sufficient dilute H_2SO_4 (1 : 1) to moisten the silica and then a small amount of hydrofluoric acid. Evapora to dryness, ignite and weigh. The difference in weights in milligrams divided by 100 equals the percentage of silicon.

Allowable Error. Percentages of silicon determined by the above method should be accurate to ±[0.005+(0.02×the percentage of silicon found)].

NOTE

A blank determination on all reagents used should be made and the results corrected accordingly.

Determination of Silicon by the Sulphuric Acid Method (Optional)

Solutions Required

Dilute Hydrochloric Acid (5 : 95). Mix 50 cc. of HCl (sp.gr. 1.19) and 950 cc. of distilled water.

Method

To 2.338 g. of steel, in a beaker of low form of 500 cc. capacity, add 60 cc. of distilled water, and then cautiously 15 cc. of H_2SO_4 (sp.gr. 1.84). Cover with a watch glass, heat until the steel is dissolved and evaporate until copious fumes of sulphuric acid are evolved. Cool, add 100 cc. of distilled water and heat with frequent stirring until the salts are in solution. Immediately filter on a 9-cm. paper, wash the precipitate with cold dilute HCl (5 : 95), until free from iron, and finally with hot water until free from acid. Ignite and weigh. Add sufficient dilute H_2SO_4 (1 : 1) to moisten the silica and then a small amount of hydrofluoric acid. Evaporate to dryness, ignite and weigh. The difference in weights in milligrams divided by 50 equals the percentage of silicon.

Allowable Error. Percentages of silicon determined by the above method should be accurate to ±[0.005+(0.02×the percentage of silicon found)].

NOTE

A blank determination on all reagents used should be made and the results corrected accordingly.

Determination of Copper

Solutions Required

Dilute Sulphuric Acid (1 : 5). Slowly stir 200 cc. of H_2SO_4 (sp.gr. 1.84) into 1000 cc. of distilled water.

Dilute Sulphuric Acid (2 : 98). Mix 20 cc. of H_2SO_4 (sp.gr. 1.84) and 80 cc. of distilled water.

Acidulated Hydrogen Sulphide Water. Saturate 500 cc. of the above solution with hydrogen sulphide.

Sodium Hydroxide (5%). Dissolve 50 g. of stick NaOH in 1000 cc. of distilled water and filter through asbestos if necessary.

Sodium Thiosulphate (50%). Dissolve 100 g. of $Na_2S_2O_3.5H_2O$ in 100 cc. of distilled water and filter if necessary.

Dilute Nitric Acid (1 : 1). Mix 500 cc. of HNO_3 (sp.gr. 1.42) and 500 cc. of distilled water.

Method

(a) Precipitation by Hydrogen Sulphide. Dissolve 10.00 g. of steel in 100 cc. of dilute H_2SO_4 (1 : 5), and when solution is complete, dilute to at least 500 cc. with water. Heat to boiling and saturate with H_2S. Digest a while, filter on paper or paper pulp and wash with acidulated hydrogen sulphide water. Ignite the residue and paper in a porcelain crucible and fuse with a small amount of alkali pyrosulphate. Dissolve the cooled melt in the crucible in 1 to 2 cc. of HCl (sp.gr. 1.19) and a few cc. of water, transfer to a 200-cc. beaker, dilute to 100 cc. and add NaOH (5%) solution in slight excess. Boil, digest, and filter, in order to separate such elements as vanadium, tungsten and molybdenum. Dissolve the precipitate in hot dilute HNO_3 (1 : 1), add cc. of H_2SO_4 (sp.gr. 1.84), evaporate to the appearance of fumes of sulphuric acid, cool, dilute to 40 cc., filter and add 10 cc. of NH_4OH (sp.gr. 0.90). Heat the feebly acid solution to boiling and saturate with H_2S. Digest a while, filter, wash thoroughly with acidulated hydrogen sulphide water, and proceed according to method 1 or 2 below.

(b) Precipitation by Thiosulphate. Transfer 5 g. of the sample to a 600-cc. beaker, add 100 cc. of H_2SO_4 (1 : 5), and heat until the sample is dissolved. Dilute to 300 cc., heat to boiling, add 15 cc. of thiosulphate solution (50%), and continue the boiling for five minutes or until the precipitate of copper sulphide has coagulated. Collect the precipitate upon an 11-cm. paper and wash *slightly* with dilute H_2SO_4 (2 : 98). Ignite the residue and paper in a porcelain crucible and fuse with a *small* amount of alkali pyrosulphate. Dissolve the cooled melt in the crucible in 1 to 2 cc. of HCl (sp.gr. 1.19) and a few cc. of water, transfer to a 200-cc. beaker, dilute to 100 cc. and add NaOH (5%) solution in slight excess. Boil, digest and filter in order to separate such elements as vanadium, tungsten and molybdenum. Dissolve the precipitate in hot dilute HNO_3 (1 : 1), carefully add 20 cc. of H_2SO_4 (sp. gr. 1.84), evaporate to the appearance of fumes of H_2SO_4, cool, dilute and filter. Dilute the solution to a volume of 300 cc. and precipitate the copper with thiosulphate as above. Filter, wash with dilute H_2SO_4 (2 : 98) until sodium salts have been removed and proceed according to method 1 or 2 below.

(1) *Electrolytic Method.* Dissolve the sulphides obtained as above in hot

dilute HNO_3 (1 : 1), and electrolyze after the addition of H_2SO_4 according to usual procedures.

(2) *Gravimetric Method.* Ignite the sulphides obtained as above and weigh as copper oxide. As this compound is somewhat hydroscopic, care must be observed to prevent the absorption of moisture.

Allowable Error. Percentages of copper determined by the above method should be accurate to $\pm[0.005+(0.02\times$the percentage of copper found)].

Determination of Copper (Routine)

Solutions Required

Potassium Ferrocyanide. Dissolve 10 g. of potassium ferrocyanide in 100 cc. of distilled water.

Standard Copper Nitrate. Dissolve 2 g. of purest electrolytic copper in 20 cc. of HNO_3 (1 : 1), and dilute to 1000 cc. with distilled water. Each cubic centimeter is equivalent to 0.02% of copper on the basis of a 10-g. sample.

Method

Proceed as in (*a*) Precipitation by Hydrogen Sulphide or (*b*) Precipitation by Thiosulphate, under "Determination of Copper," until the alkali pyrosulphate fusion has been made. Extract the cooled melt with hot water, filter, and complete the determination colorimetrically as follows:

Evaporate the filtrate to about 25 cc., make faintly ammoniacal, filter into a 100-cc. Nessler tube and wash with hot water.

(**a**) **If the solution is a strong blue,** to another 100-cc. Nessler tube add 50 cc of distilled water, 5 cc. of NH_4OH (sp.gr. 0.90) and from a burette the standard copper nitrate solution until the blue colors match.

(**b**) **If the solution is a faint blue,** to the filtrate in a Nessler tube add dilute H_2SO_4 (1 : 5) to faint acidity and then a few drops of the potassium ferrocyanide solution. To another 100-cc Nessler tube add 50 cc. of distilled water, a few drops of the potassium ferrocyanide solution, and from a burette the standard copper nitrate solution until the reddish brown colors match.

Determination of Nickel in Iron and Steel— Gravimetric Method

Dimethylglyoxime

Reagents

Hydrochloric Acid. Equal volumes of HCl (d. 1.2) and water.
Dimethylglyoxime. 1 g. salt per 100 cc. 95% alcohol.

Procedure

A sample of 1 gram of steel is dissolved in 20 cc. of dilute HCl and 2 cc HNO_3 to oxidize the iron. The solution is filtered and 6 g. tartaric acid added and then sufficient water to bring the volume of the filtrate and washings to 300 cc. The solution is made faintly ammoniacal (no iron should precipitate if sufficient tartaric acid is present) and then faintly acid with HCl and then heated to boiling. 20 cc. of the dimethylglyoxime reagent are added, the solu tion made faintly ammoniacal by adding ammonium hydroxide drop by drop, stirring vigorously. After settling an hour, the precipitate is filtered onto a weighed Gooch crucible, and washed with hot water. After drying at 110° to 120° C. to constant weight the nickel glyoxime is weighed. The precipitate contains 20.31% of nickel.

NOTE

The weight of steel taken is governed by the nickel content.

Determination of Nickel in Steel=Volumetric Glyoxime Method

Reagents

In addition to the above reagents, the following are required:
Silver Nitrate. 0.5 g. salt per liter.
Potassium Iodide. 20 g. salt per 100 cc.
Potassium Cyanide Standard Solution. 2.29 g. KCN per liter.
The solution is standardized against a steel of known nickel content as determined by the gravimetric method, the volumetric method following being then used with the reagent and standard steel. It is recommended to have the reagent of such strength that 1 cc. will be equivalent to 0.0005 g. Ni or 0.05% per gram sample of steel.

Procedure

The sample is dissolved and nickel precipitated and filtered onto a Gooch crucible exactly as has been described for the gravimetric determination above. The precipitate in the Gooch is now dissolved by adding drop by drop 10 to 20 cc. of hot, strong nitric acid and then washing with hot water 5 times, using suction. To the solution in a beaker are added 3 grams of ammonium persulphate and the sample boiled for 5 minutes is then cooled and made distinctly alkaline with ammonium hydroxide. 10 cc. of silver nitrate reagent and 10 cc. of potassium reagent are now added and the solution is titrated with standard potassium cyanide solution until a faint turbidity is obtained.

NOTE

As in case of the gravimetric method the amount of steel taken for analysis is governed by the nickel content.

Determination of Chromium in Steel—Volumetric and Colorimetric Methods

Reagents

Hydrochloric Acid. Equal volumes of HCl (d. 1.2) and water.
Sodium Carbonate. Saturated solution (60 g. salt per 100 cc. water).
Barium Carbonate. 10 g. of salt suspended in 100 cc. of water.
Sodium Chromate—Standard Solution. 2.6322 g. sodium chromate per liter of solution. 1 cc. contains 0.001 g. Cr equivalent to 0.02% per 5-gram sample of steel.
Potassium Permanganate-Standard Solution. 2 g. KMnO$_4$ per liter. Standardize against sodium oxalate. Na$_2$C$_2$O$_4$×0.2584=Cr. Dilute the solution so that 1 cc. is equivalent to 0.001 g. Cr.
Ferrous Sulphate. 25 g. ferrous ammonium sulphate, 900 cc. H$_2$O, 100 cc. H$_2$SO$_4$ (1 : 1).

Procedure

A sample of 5 g. of steel is dissolved in 50 cc. hydrochloric acid. When completely dissolved, sodium carbonate solution is added until the iron precipitate that forms dissolves with difficulty and the solution turns an amber or cherry red color, the free acid being nearly neutralized, the neutralization is completed by addition of barium carbonate in suspension, an excess of about one gram being added. After boiling for 10 to 15 minutes the precipitate is filtered rapidly and washed twice with hot water. The filter and residue is gently ignited in a platinum crucible and the residue fused with a mixture of 5 g. of sodium carbonate and 0.25 g. of potassium nitrate for 10 minutes. The fusion is dissolved in water, transferred to a beaker, 2 cc. of 3% hydrogen peroxide added, the solution boiled for a few minutes and then filtered, any residue being washed. The filtrate containing the chromium is examined by either of the following procedures.

(a) If the solution is a strong yellow color, add 10 cc. of dilute sulphuric acid (1 : 1) and then the ferrous sulphate solution in measured excess. After cooling, titrate the standard potassium permanganate solution. The number of cc. KMnO$_4$ required subtracted from the cc. KMnO$_4$ necessary for the total ferrous sulphate used (this can be determined by titrating an equivalent volume of ferrous sulphate by the permanganate solution) will give the volume of potassium permanganate equivalent to the chromium present in the material.

Note

All hydrogen peroxide added must be boiled out before acidifying, otherwise chromic acid will be reduced, vitiating results.

(b) If the solution is a light color, cool and transfer to a 100-cc. Nessler tube, and make to a volume of 100 cc. To another Nessler tube add about 50 cc. of water and then add sodium chromate solution until the depth of color looking through from top to bottom of the column of the standard matches the unknown.

Alloy Steels. Determination of Chromium, Vanadium and Tungsten. See chapters on the elements in question.

Determination of Hydrogen in Steel

The method is based upon the oxidation of hydrogen liberated from steel by heat in presence of a current of oxygen. The water formed is absorbed and weighed.

Procedure. Preliminary test. The apparatus is set up as shown in detail in Fig. 169e. The heat is turned on and the oxygen gas passed through the

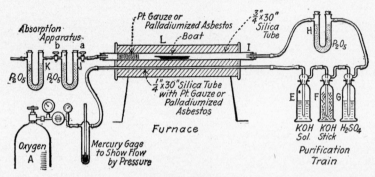

FIG. 169e.

silica tube I, heated to redness (850° C.) at the rate of 100 cc. per minute, this rate having been established by a preliminary test noting the rate of bubbling through the acid in G and the pressure in C with the desired volume per minute. The gas is purified by passing through D, E, F, G and H, any hydrogen present being decomposed in the preheated tube D. Proceed now as follows:

Allow the gas to pass through the system for 5 to 10 minutes, disconnect the tube J after turning off the cocks " a " and " b " in the order named. Place in the balance case for 5 minutes, then open and close " b " rapidly. The oxygen in J will be at atmospheric pressure and at the temperature in the balance. Now weigh. Replace the tube again in the train, open the cocks " a " and " b " and continue the flow of oxygen for another 10 minutes. If there is an increase in weight, repeat the test a third time, noting the increase of weight during a 30-minute run. This is the blank that must be deducted from the regular run. It should not exceed 1 milligram.

The Test. Place in a clay boat previously ignited in a current of oxygen, or in a platinum boat containing ignited alundum powder, 10 to 30 grams of steel in as large pieces as possible (hydrogen is liberated by drilling so that it is best to use the metal in strips or in a single piece). Insert the boat in the tube and quickly connect up the apparatus.

Turn on the oxygen at the rate of 100 cc. per minute and continue the flow for 30 minutes. Disconnect (after turning off cocks " a " and " b ") the absorption tube J. Place in balance case as before and equalize the pressure by opening the cock " b " for an instant. Weigh. The increase of weight, minus the blank, is due to the water formed. This weight multiplied by 0.111 gives the hydrogen of the sample.

NOTES

The blank is derived from the oxidation of the rubber connections, and this should be determined and deducted from the regular run.

It is not necessary to burn all the metal to oxide to eliminate the hydrogen. A 30-minute run is sufficient.

The P_2O_5 is placed in the tubes interspersed with glass wool, otherwise the tubes would pack, preventing the passage of the gas.

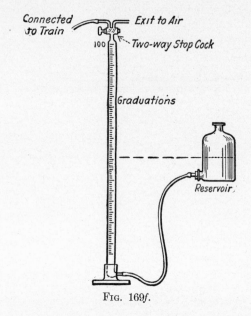

FIG. 169*f*.

Testing Gas Apparatus for Leaks. Connections between the parts of the gas apparatus, stopcocks, etc., should be tight to avoid intake or loss of gas, thus causing an error. The following simple method for testing for leaks is applicable to apparatus for the volumetric determination of gas as well as testing the tightness of combustion trains.

Procedure. Close one end of the train. To the other attach a Hempel gas burette with two-way stopcock and connected to a reservoir of water. Open the two-way cock to the air and raise the reservoir until half of the gas in the tube is expelled. Now turn the cock to open a passage to the combustion train (or gas apparatus). Have the level of the water in the reservoir and the burette the same and note the exact reading. Now raise the reservoir about 10 inches, the gas will be under pressure. Lower the reservoir to its former position, levelling the water. If the level in the Hempel tube has risen, an outward leak is indicated. See Fig. 169*f*.

Now lower the reservoir to the table and after a few minutes raise to the first position. After levelling the water as before, note whether the level has dropped in the Hempel. If so, the apparatus leaks under reduced pressure.

Determination of Nitrogen in Steel. See chapter on nitrogen, volume 1.

Determination of Oxygen in Steel

The properties of steel are affected by the presence of oxygen so that its determination is being recognized as an essential one in the analysis of this product.   It occurs in steel as occluded oxygen and as combined oxygen, i.e.,

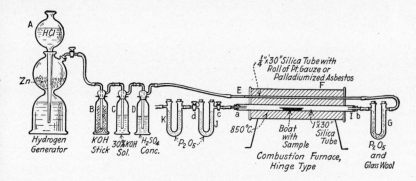

FIG. 170.   Apparatus for Determining Oxygen in Steel

oxides of iron, aluminum, manganese, silicon, titanium, etc.   The following method determines the occluded oxygen and the oxygen combined with iron, but does not determine that combined with manganese, aluminum and silicon, as these oxides are not reduced by hydrogen.

The method depends upon the combination of hydrogen with the oxygen of iron when the latter is heated in a current of hydrogen; the water formed is absorbed and weighed and the oxygen calculated.

The apparatus shown in Fig. 170 gives full details.   It is shown that hydrogen generated by the action of HCl on zinc is purified by passing through the wash bottles B, C, D, containing KOH and H_2SO_4, oxygen in the gas is removed by passing through a preheated tube containing platinum gauze or palladiumized asbestos, the water formed being absorbed in the P_2O_5 in G. The pure hydrogen now combines with the oxygen of the sample and the water formed is absorbed in P_2O_5 in the tube J.

Procedures.   *Preliminary.*   The apparatus is connected up as shown in Fig. 170 and hydrogen gas passed through for 5 to 10 minutes.   The P_2O_5 tube is now weighed as in regular test (see notes), the tube being disconnected from K, which is used as a guard to prevent moisture being absorbed by an accidental back suction of air.

The sample of 20 to 30 grams of the steel borings is placed in a nickel boat ($\frac{1}{2}'' \times \frac{1}{2}'' \times 6''$) and this inserted quickly through the opening at " a " into the combustion tube, the current of hydrogen flowing through the tube. The absorption tube J and its guard are connected up and the heat turned on. (All connections should be airtight.)   The temperature of bright-red heat (850° C.) is desired.   The hydrogen is passed at a rate of about 100 cc. per minute, the rate having been previously established by the speed of bubbles in D.   After 30 minutes the heat is turned off, the top of the hinged furnace lifted, and the tube raised and allowed to cool, hydrogen gas still passing. A blast of air assists the cooling.

The cocks " c " and " d " of J are turned off in the order named, the exit end of the guard K closed and the two connected placed in the balance for about 10 minutes. The exit end of the guard is now opened, the cock " d " quickly opened and shut, thus obtaining atmospheric pressure in the tube J without intake of air. The guard is now disconnected and J is weighed. The increase of weight due to absorbed water is multiplied by 0.889 to obtain the weight of occluded oxygen and the oxygen combined with iron.

NOTES

The tube J is weighed before and after the test filled with hydrogen under atmospheric pressure and at the same temperature, so that it is not necessary to aspirate air through the tube as is sometimes recommended. The preliminary run for obtaining the initial weight should be conducted under conditions the same as in the final test, the tubes J and K being closed, transferred to the balance and J finally weighed as stated at the end of the procedure, so that the conditions will be the same in regard to the inclosed hydrogen or the tube.

The P_2O_5 tubes are charged by packing alternate layers of P_2O_5 and glass wool, beginning and ending with the latter, otherwise the powder will pack and prevent the passage of gas.

The drilling of the samples should be done slowly to prevent heating, the drills being free of grease or oil. The samples should be taken from several sections of the ingot, whose surface has been cleaned by a cutting tool or by emery.

The apparatus should be tested for leaks as described in the notes on page 1368h.

Determination of Silicon, Aluminum, Titanium, Zirconium in Steel[1]

This method developed by Lundell and Knowles, Bureau of Standards, provides for the determination of silicon, aluminum, titanium and zirconium in one portion of steel in presence of one or more of the following: tungsten, chromium, uranium, cerium, manganese, phosphorus, vanadium, molybdenum, copper, nickel and cobalt.

Procedure. Dissolve five grams of the steel in 50 cc. of hydrochloric acid (sp.gr. 1.2) by gentle warming and the addition of 1 cc. portions of nitric acid from time to time to insure solution of the zirconium and titanium and also oxidation of the iron.

When solution is complete, evaporate to dryness, take up in 10 cc. of hydrochloric acid (sp.gr. 1.2), again evaporate to dryness, and finally bake at a gentle heat in order to decompose nitrates.

Cool, take up in 50 cc. of 1 : 1 hydrochloric acid, and filter when the iron is completely in solution. Wash the residue with cold 1 : 1 hydrochloric acid. Save the filtrate and washings.

Ignite the residue and paper in a platinum crucible, cool and weigh. Treat with 1 cc. of sulphuric acid (1 : 1) and sufficient hydrofluoric acid, fume off in the usual manner, ignite and weigh to obtain silica, and calculate silicon.

Fuse the slight residue left after the hydrofluoric acid treatment with a small amount of potassium pyrosulphate, dissolve in 10–20 cc. of 5% sulphuric acid and add the solution to the acid extract from the ether separation obtained as described below.

Evaporate the filtrate and washings from the silica determination to a syrupy consistency, take up in 40 cc. of hydrochloric acid (sp.gr. 1.1) and extract with ether in the usual manner. (The *ether* extract will contain most of the molybdenum, and this element may be qualitatively tested for in it. If molybdenum is present it is more conveniently determined in a separate portion of steel.) The acid extract will contain some iron, and all of the zirconium, titanium, aluminum, nickel, chromium, etc.

Gently boil off the ether in the acid extract, add the matter recovered from the silica, oxidize ferrous iron with a little nitric acid, dilute to 300 cc., cool and precipitate with 20% sodium hydroxide solution, adding 10 cc. in excess. Filter, and save the filtrate. Dissolve the precipitate in warm dilute 1 : 1 hydrochloric acid and reserve the solution for subsequent analysis.

(In precise work, it is advisable to treat as follows the filter used above: Ignite in platinum, fuse with sodium carbonate, digest with hot water, filter, wash, dissolve the residue in hot 1 : 1 hydrochloric acid and add to the main acid solution. This precaution makes certain the recovery of any zirconium held back on the filter as zirconium phosphate insoluble in acid.)

---

[1] Communicated to the editor by W. F. Hillebrand, U. S. Bureau of Standards, and published by his permission and the courtesy of the authors, G. E. F. Lundell and H. B. Knowles, Bureau of Standards.

Determination of Aluminum in the Absence of Chromium

Acidify the sodium hydroxide filtrate with hydrochloric acid, add a few drops of methyl red, boil, and make barely alkaline with ammonium hydroxide. After two minutes, filter and wash *thoroughly*, with warm 2% ammonium chloride solution. It is imperative that all sodium chloride be washed out of the filter paper. Ignite for aluminum oxide in the usual manner and calculate aluminum. (The sodium hydroxide reagent must be tested for substances precipitable by ammonia, and appropriate corrections must be made in the aluminum determination when these are present.)

Determination of Aluminum in the Presence of Chromium

Proceed as above until the sodium hydroxide filtrate is obtained. Then oxidize with a little bromine water, make just acid with 1 : 2 nitric acid, add ammonium hydroxide in slight excess, heat to boiling, filter, wash and ignite the aluminum hydroxide as directed above.

Determination of Zirconium and Titanium

Dilute the hydrochloric acid solution to 250 cc., neutralize with ammonium hydroxide so as to leave approximately 5% (by volume) of hydrochloric acid, add 2 grams of tartaric acid, and treat with hydrogen sulphide until the iron has been reduced. Filter if the sulphide group is indicated. Make the hydrogen sulphide solution ammoniacal and continue the addition of the gas for 5 minutes. Filter carefully and wash with dilute ammonium sulphide-ammonium chloride solution. Filter through a new filter if the presence of iron sulphide in the filtrate is indicated. Save the filtrate.

(The sulphide precipitate consists of ferrous sulphide, in addition to the greater part of any nickel, and manganese present in steel. It is preferable to determine these in separate portions of the steel.)

Acidify the ammonium sulphide filtrate with sulphuric acid, add 30 cc. in excess and dilute with water to 300 cc. Digest on the steam bath until sulphur and sulphides have coagulated, filter, wash with 100 cc. of 10% sulphuric acid and cool the filtrate in ice water.

Add slowly and with stirring an excess of a cold 6% water solution of cupferron. (The presence of an excess is shown by the appearance of a white cloud which disappears, instead of a permanent coagulated precipitate.) Immediately filter on paper, using a cone and very gentle suction, and wash thoroughly with cold 10% hydrochloric acid.

Carefully ignite in a tared platinum crucible, completing the ignition over a blast lamp or large Meker, cool and weigh the combined zirconium and titanium oxides.

Fuse with potassium pyrosulphate, dissolve in 50 cc. of 10% (by volume) sulphuric acid and determine titanium colorimetrically or volumetrically. Calculate titanium oxide and subtract the weight found from that of the combined oxides and calculate zirconium.

NOTES. 1. Phosphorus pentoxide contaminates the precipitate to so slight an extent that it can be disregarded.

2. Vanadium interferes no matter what its valency. The interference is not quantitative. If present in the steel, proceed as usual through the weighing of the cupferron precipitate. Then fuse thoroughly with sodium carbonate, cool, extract with water, filter, and determine the vanadium in the filtrate by adding sulphuric acid, reducing through a Jones' reductor into a solution of ferric phosphate acid and then titrating with standard permanganate. Ignite in the original crucible the matter insoluble in water, fuse with potassium pyrosulphate and proceed as directed for titanium.

3. Tungsten does not interfere since it is separated from zirconium and titanium by the sodium hydroxide treatment, and from aluminum by the ammonium hydroxide precipitation. If tungsten is present in large amount it may be found desirable to fuse the non-volatile residue from the silicon determination with sodium carbonate, extract with water, filter, dissolve the residue in hot 1 : 1 hydrochloric acid and add to the acid extract from the ether separation.

4. Uranium is partially carried down when present in the tetravalent condition, but not at all in the hexavalent state. If this element is suspected, boil out all hydrogen sulphide before the cupferron precipitation, oxidize with permanganate to a faint pink, cool and proceed with the cupferron precipitation.

5. Thorium and cerium interfere, but they are not thrown down quantitatively. In case these elements are suspected, the peroxidized solution used for the titanium determination must be quantitatively preserved and reduced with a little sulphurous acid. The solution is then treated with a few drops of a 0.2% alcoholic solution of methyl red, and made just alkaline with ammonium hydroxide. The precipitated zirconium hydroxide is then dissolved by warming with 5 cc. hydrochloric acid and the clear solution treated with 3 to 5 grams of oxalic acid. The solution is then diluted to 300 cc., allowed to stand over night, the precipitate filtered, washed with hot water, ignited, weighed, and the weight of the rare earth oxides subtracted from the original weight of the combined oxides.

6. Instead of the prescribed treatment for the removal of the bulk of the iron, Johnson's[1] method of fractional ammonium hydroxide precipitation may be used.

Other Methods for Determination of the Less Common Elements in Steel. See under the chapter dealing with the element in question. See Index.

Specifications for Steel

Carbon

Structural steel, for buildings, bridges, locomotives, ships, etc., the carbon may vary from 0.3 to 0.9 of a per cent and in some cases may be over 1%.

Manganese

This may vary from 0.2 to 1% and averages about 0.6%.

Phosphorus

This is generally kept below 0.05%.

Sulphur

The specifications generally limit this to a maximum of 0.05%.

Silicon

In silico-manganese steel from 1.5 to 2.1% is desired. For steel girders the silicon is kept below 0.2%.

Chromium, Vanadium

In chrome-vanadium steels, chromium runs between 0.80 to 1.10% while vanadium is about 0.15%.

[1] C. M. Johnson, Chem. and Met. Eng., **20**, 1919, p. 588.

Nickel

A minimum of 3.25% is fixed for nickel steel. For billets and slab forgings nickel may run as low as 1% and chromium 0.45% and vanadium 0.15%.

Full specifications for particular purposes may be found in reports of the American Society for Testing Materials, a number of which are given in the pages following.

Chemical Specifications for Steel and Alloy Steels, A. S. T. M.

ALLOY STEEL, BLOOMS, BILLETS AND SLABS FOR FORGINGS

Mn	0.50 –0.80	Ni	1.00–1.10 or over
P	0.04 –0.045	Cr	0.45–1.10 or over
S	0.045–0.05	V	0.15

AUTOMATIC SCREW STOCK, COLD DRAWN BESSEMER STEEL AND OPEN HEARTH

	Bessemer		Open Hearth
C	0.08 –0.16	C	0.15 –0.25
Mn	0.60 –0.80	Mn	0.60 –0.90
P	0.09 –0.13	P	0.06 maximum
S	0.075–0.15	S	0.075–0.15

AUTOMOBILE CARBON AND ALLOY STEEL

C	Mn	P	S
0.10–0.20	0.30–0.60	0.045 max.	0.05 max.
0.25–0.35	0.50–0.80	"	"
0.35–0.45	0.50–0.80	"	"
0.40–0.50	0.30–0.50	"	"
0.45–0.55	0.50–0.80	"	"

AUTOMOBILE NICKEL STEELS

C from 0.15 to 0.50
Mn from 0.3 to 0.8 depending on C content
P not over 0.04
S not over 0.045
Ni, 3.25 to 5.25

AUTOMOBILE NICKEL-CHROMIUM STEELS

C from 0.15 to 0.45%
Mn from 0.45 to 0.60
P not over 0.04
S not over 0.045
Ni, 1.52 to 3.75
Cr, 0.45 to 1.75

CHROMIUM–VANADIUM STEELS

C from 0.15 to 1.05
Mn from 0.2 to 0.8 depending on C content
P, 0.03 to 0.04
S, 0.03 to 0.04
Cr, 0.8 to 1.1
V, 0.15 to 0.18

AUTOMOBILE CHROMIUM-TUNGSTEN STEELS

C, 0.5 to 0.7%
Mn, 0.3 maximum
P, 0.035 maximum
S, 0.035 maximum
Cr, 0.5 to 4.0%
W, 1.50 to 15.0%

AUTOMOBILE SILICO-MANGANESE STEEL

C................	0.45 to 0.65	P and S...............	0.045 max.
Mn...............	0.60 to 0.90	Si....................	1.8 to 2.2%

AXLES, CARBON STEEL FOR CAR AND TENDER

	General	Cold Rolled
C..................................	0.35–0.55	0.4 maximum
Mn.................................	0.70 maximum	0.4–0.8
P..................................	0.05 max.	0.05 max.
S..................................	0.06 max.	0.05 max.

AXLES, SHAFTS AND OTHER FORGINGS FOR LOCOMOTIVES AND CARS

First...... 0.25–0.60	
Second.... 0.35–0.60 Mn.....0.4–0.7 P.....0.05 max. S.....0.05 max.	
Third...... 0.35–0.65	
Fourth..... 0.35–0.70	

Bessemer Steel		Open Hearth Steel	
C................	0.37–0.55	C................	0.50–0.75
Mn...............	0.80–1.10	Mn..............	0.60–0.90
P................	0.10 maximum	P...............	0.04 maximum
Si...............	0.20 max.	Si...............	0.20 max.

BILLET STEEL, CONCRETE REINFORCEMENT BAR

P, Bessemer........... 0.1 max.   P, Open Hearth.......... 0.05 max.

BLOOMS FOR LOCOMOTIVES AND CARS. WROUGHT IRON, ROLLED AND FORGED

	Class A	Class B
Mn.................................	0.07 maximum	0.15 maximum

BOILER AND FIREBOX STEEL FOR LOCOMOTIVES AND STATIONARY SERVICE

C..	0.25 maximum
Mn..	0.30–0.60
P...	Acid 0.05; Basic 0.04
S...	0.05–0.05

BOILER RIVET STEEL

Mn......... 0.3–0.5   P..........0.04 max.   S..........0.045 max.

BOILER TUBES FOR LOCOMOTIVES AND STATIONARY BOILERS LAP-WELDED AND SEAMLESS STEEL

C....................	0.08–0.18	P....................	0.04 max.
Mn....................	0.30–0.60	S....................	0.045 max.

CASTINGS

		Class A	Class B
C..		0.45 maximum	—
P { Acid..		0.07	0.06
{ Basic..		0.06	0.06
S..		—	0.06

FORGE WELDING STEEL PLATES

C.....................	0.15–0.20	P....................	0.06 max.
Mn....................	0.35–0.60	S....................	0.05 max.

GIRDER STEEL AND HIGH T STEEL RAILS

	Class A	Class B
C..	0.60–0.75	0.70–0.85
Mn...	0.60–0.90	0.60–0.90
P..	0.04 max.	0.04 max.
Si...	0.20 max.	0.20 max.

SCREW STOCK FOR AUTOMOBILES

	C	Mn	P	S
Bessemer..............	0.08–0.16	0.60–0.80	0.09–0.13	0.075–0.15
Open Hearth..........	0.15–0.25	0.6 –0.9	0.06 max.	0.075–0.15

SPRING-CARBON STEEL, AUTO AND VEHICLE

C....................	0.85–1.05	P....................	0.05 max.
Mn...................	0.25–0.50	S....................	0.05 max.

SPRING-CHROME-VANADIUM STEEL FOR AUTO AND RAILWAY

C....................	0.45–0.65	S.................	0.05 max.
Mn..................	0.50–0.90	Cr...............	0.80–1.10
P { Acid.............	0.05 max.	V...............	0.15 minimum
{ Basic.............	0.04 max.		

SPRING-CARBON STEEL BARS FOR RAILWAY SERVICE

C....................	0.90–1.15	P and S..............	0.05 max.
Mn..................	0.50 max.	Si...................	0.25–0.50

SPLICE BARS, HIGH CARBON STEEL

C.................... 0.45 max.   P.................... 0.04 max.

SPLICE BARS QUENCHED HIGH CARBON STEEL

C........ 0.6 max.   Mn........ 0.8 max.   P........ 0.04 max.

SPLICE BARS LOW CARBON STEEL

Bessemer, P............. 0.1 max.   Open Hearth, P....... 0.05 max.

SPLICE BARS MEDIUM CARBON STEEL

C.................... 0.3 max.   P.................... 0.04 max.

STRUCTURAL STEEL FOR BRIDGES, BUILDINGS, PLATES, LOCOMOTIVES, ETC.

	Bridges	Buildings	Plates
P.............................	0.04–0.06	0.06–0.10	0.06 max.
S.............................	0.05 max.	0.045 max.	0.05 max.
C...			0.15–0.22
Mn..			0.35–0.60

	Locomotives	Cars	Ships	Rivet
P...................	0.05 max.	0.04–0.06	0.04–0.06	0.04–0.06
S...................	0.06 max.	0.06 max.	0.06 max.	0.045 max.

Note in above P low for Basic and high for Acid.

STRUCTURAL NICKEL STEEL

	Structural	Rivet
C	0.45 max.	0.30 max.
Mn	0.70 max.	0.60 max.
P { Acid	0.05 max.	0.04 max.
P { Basic	0.04 max.	0.03 max.
S	0.05 max.	0.045 max.
Ni	not under 3.25	3.25 min.

TIRE STEEL

C	Class A, 0.5–0.7; Class B, 0.6–0.8; Class C, 0.7–0.85
Mn	0.75 max.
S and P	0.05 max.
Si	0.15–0.35

TRACK BOLTS, QUENCHED CARBON STEEL

C................ 0.30 minimum   P................ 0.04 maximum

TRACK BOLTS, ALLOY STEEL

P.. 0.035 maximum

WELDED AND SEAMLESS STEEL

P..not over 0.06

WHEELS, WROUGHT SOLID, CARBON STEEL FOR STEAM AND ELECTRIC RAILWAY SERVICE

	Acid	Basic
C	0.60–0.80	0.65–0.85
Mn	0.55–0.80	0.55–0.80
P	0.05 max.	0.05 max.
S	0.05 max.	0.05 max.
Si	0.15–0.35	0.10–0.30

ANALYSIS OF EXPLOSIVES[1]

The methods described in this chapter cover all of the more common types of explosives employed in the United States for both commercial and military purposes. Those of chief commercial importance are black powder, nitroglycerin dynamites, including "straight" dynamites, ammonia dynamites, gelatin dynamites, and low-freezing dynamites, "Permissible" coal mining explosives and nitrostarch blasting explosives. Military explosives include smokeless powder, guncotton, trinitrotoluene, picric acid, ammonium picrate, "Amatol," tetryl and tetranitroaniline. No sharp distinction can, however, be drawn between commercial and military explosives, as many are utilized for both purposes. Many tons of surplus TNT. have been used recently in commercial work; nitrostarch explosives found important application for military use during the war; mercury fulminate and other detonators and priming compositions are essential in every field of explosives.

The methods described have largely been used by the writer in practical explosives testing and analysis in connection with both Government and private work. Most of those applying to commercial explosives have been approved by the United States Bureau of Mines for use in its Explosives Chemical Laboratory.[2]

BLACK POWDER

The composition of black powder varies to some extent, depending chiefly on the purpose for which the explosive is to be used. Black blasting powder contains sodium nitrate, charcoal and sulphur; black gunpowder is quite similar except that potassium nitrate is generally substituted for the sodium nitrate; black fuse powder is similar to the latter, differing mainly in its granulation. The same general method of analysis is therefore applicable to all types of black powder.

Sampling. From 50 to 100 grams of the original sample is crushed in small portions in a porcelain mortar and completely passed through an 80-mesh sieve, care being taken to avoid undue exposure to the air. The separate powdered portions are promptly bottled and the entire sample is finally well mixed.

Moisture. The standard method of the Bureau of Mines is to desiccate a 2-gram sample on a 3-inch watch glass over sulphuric acid for three days, the loss of weight being moisture. It has been shown, however, that equally accurate results can be obtained by drying at 70° C. in a constant temperature oven to constant weight, for which 2–3 hours is usually sufficient. As much as 5 hours drying at 70° C. will not cause loss of sulphur. Drying at 100° C. gives results which are slightly high, due to loss of sulphur.

[1] Chapter by C. G. Storm. Published by permission of Chief of Ordnance, U. S. A.
[2] See Bureau of Mines Bulletin No. 51, "The Analysis of Black Powder and Dynamite," W. O. Snelling and C. G. Storm, 1913, and Bulletin No. 96, "The Analysis of Permissible Explosives," C. G. Storm, 1916.

Nitrates. About 10 grams of the finely ground sample in a Gooch crucible provided with an asbestos mat, is extracted with warm water by means of suction, the water being added in 15–20 cc. portions and each portion being allowed to stand in the crucible a short time before suction is applied. About 200 cc. of water is usually sufficient, but the last drops of filtrate should be tested by evaporation to ensure the absence of nitrates. A blue color on the addition of sulphuric acid containing a few crystals of diphenylamine will also indicate the presence of nitrates.

The water extract includes a small amount of water-soluble organic material from the charcoal in addition to the nitrate. It is made up to 250 cc. and an aliquot portion (50 cc.), evaporated to dryness on the steam bath, treated with a little nitric acid, again evaporated, heated to slight fusion and weighed.

If allowance for impurities in the nitrate is desired, a direct determination of nitrate may be made on a separate portion of the water extract by the Devarda method or by means of the nitrometer, but for all practical purposes the evaporation method is sufficient. The usual tests should be made to determine whether sodium nitrate or potassium nitrate is present.

The residue left in the crucible, consisting of sulphur and charcoal, is dried at about 70° C. to constant weight (for 5 hours or over night if more convenient), the loss of weight minus the moisture content being the water-soluble portion. This result serves as a check on the evaporation result.

Sulphur. The residue in the crucible is extracted in a Wiley extractor or other continuous extraction apparatus with carbon disulphide, until evaporation of a small portion of the solvent passing through the crucible shows absence of sulphur. The excess of carbon disulphide is then allowed to evaporate from the crucible in a warm place away from flame, and the residue finally dried to constant weight at 100° C. The loss of weight is considered as sulphur.

Charcoal. The dry residue in the crucible should consist only of charcoal.

Ash. The ash in the charcoal may be determined by ignition over a Bunsen burner until all of the carbon has been burned off, and weighing. This ash also contains, of course, any non-volatile matter that may have been present in the sulphur and nitrate.

Calculation of Results. Since a portion of the charcoal is always dissolved in the water extract, it is customary to express the content of charcoal by subtracting the sum of the following from 100%:

% Moisture (by desiccation or drying at 70° C.).

% Nitrate (by evaporation of water extract with HNO_3).

% Sulphur (by loss on extraction with CS_2).

NITROGLYCERIN DYNAMITES

" Straight " Dynamite

So-called "Straight" nitroglycerin dynamite has been manufactured to only a relatively small extent in this country during the past few years, owing to the high cost of glycerin. It has been largely replaced by the ammonia and low-freezing dynamites, in which a large part of the nitroglycerin is replaced by ammonium nitrate and nitrosubstitution compounds. Furthermore, developments in the manufacture of both ammonium nitrate and nitrocompounds during the war have rendered unlikely any great increase in the manufacture of straight dynamites. They are still largely used, however, where quick-acting blasting explosives of high strength are required, as in work in hard rock. They consist essentially of nitroglycerin absorbed in a "dope" composed of a combustible absorbent, usually wood pulp, and an oxidizing material (sodium nitrate), to which is added a small amount of an antacid (calcium carbonate, zinc oxide, etc.). The analysis is best carried out by successive extractions, usually with ether, water, and dilute hydrochloric acid.

Sampling. The wrappers are removed from a number of the cartridges, and from 3 to 5 cm. of the ends of the exposed roll of explosives rejected. The remainder is thoroughly mixed on a large sheet of paraffined paper or in a large porcelain dish, and an average sample selected and bottled—usually about one half pound. The importance of thorough mixing of the sample must not be overlooked, in view of the fact that there is frequently a decided tendency for the nitroglycerin to segregate due to insufficient or unsuitable absorbent, so that this liquid ingredient may not be uniformly distributed throughout the cartridge. Also if a carefully mixed sample has been allowed to stand for some days, especially in a warm place, segregation may occur in the bottle, so that it is advisable to again mix the sample before analysis.

Qualitative Examination. Although a qualitative analysis of a sample known to be straight nitroglycerin dynamite is usually unnecessary, the exact nature of the sample may be unknown, and a knowledge of the composition of some of the more complex types of dynamite is necessary before a quantitative analysis can be properly conducted.

About 25 grams of the sample is shaken with several successive portions of ether in a large stoppered test tube, the ether being decanted off through a filter paper and the residue finally washed on the filter. The ether solution is allowed to evaporate slowly on a steam bath and the filter paper spread out on a glass plate in an oven so that the residue may dry quickly. The evaporated ether extract may contain nitroglycerin, sulphur (especially in the lower grades of dynamite), rosin, vaseline, or paraffin oil (in ammonia dynamite), nitrotoluenes and other nitrocompounds (in low-freezing dynamites), etc.

Nitroglycerin is readily detected by shaking a drop of the liquid with one or two cc. of strong H_2SO_4 and about 1 cc. of mercury in a test tube, an evolution of brown fumes of nitric oxides being noted if nitroglycerin is present. Sulphur will appear as crystals in the evaporated extract, and may be identified by removing them, washing with acetic acid, and noting the odor of SO_2 on heating in a flame. Rosin, vaseline, oils, etc., appear as a greasy scum on the surface of the nitroglycerin or adhering to the walls of the beaker. These substances, like sulphur, are practically insoluble in acetic acid (70%), and may be separated from the nitroglycerin by means of this solvent. Trinitrotoluene will appear in the nitroglycerin as long yellowish needles, which may be removed, recrystallized from alcohol, and identified by their melting point (approx. 80° C.), or by the red color produced when the alcoholic solution is treated with a little caustic soda solution.

The residue insoluble in ether is replaced in the test tube and treated with water in a similar manner until all water-soluble material has been dissolved. The water solution is tested for sodium, potassium, barium, zinc, etc., and for nitrates, chlorides, etc., using the general methods of qualitative analysis.

The residue is again treated with cold dilute HCl, any effervescence being noted as indicating the presence of a carbonate, and the resulting solution tested for calcium, magnesium, zinc, etc., which may have been present as carbonates or oxides for the purpose of serving as antacids.

The residue insoluble in ether, water, and cold acid may contain wood pulp, starchy cereal products, sawdust, nitrocellulose, ground vegetable ivory (button waste), kieselguhr, ground nut shells, etc. It is most conveniently examined by means of a low-power microscope, whereby its constituents are usually readily determined. Starch is easily detected by heating a portion to boiling with dilute acid, cooling and adding a few drops of iodine solution (in KI), a blue coloration indicating starch.

Moisture. Moisture is best determined by desiccation over sulphuric acid, a sample of about 2 grams being spread evenly over the surface of a 3-inch watch glass and desiccated for 3 days. Continued desiccation causes a gradual loss of nitroglycerin, but the 3-day loss may be safely assumed to closely represent the actual moisture content. The time of the determination may be greatly shortened by the use of a vacuum desiccator, in which case 24 hours desiccation will give a close approximation to the true moisture content.

It must be remembered that in determining moisture in the presence of nitroglycerin, some volatilization of the latter is unavoidable, and that therefore the method followed must be an empirical one. An attempt to desiccate the sample to constant weight will show that there is undoubtedly a continual loss of nitroglycerin. This has been demonstrated[1] by a series of weighings of a sample exposed for a period of 459 days at a constant temperature of 33°–35° C. in an empty desiccator containing no desiccating agent. A gradual loss resulted during the entire period, totaling 17.52% of the original weight of the sample, the original moisture content of which was about 1%.

Extraction with Ether. Ether removes from dynamite not only the nitroglycerin, but, as has already been mentioned, sulphur, resins (present as a component or as a constituent of the wood pulp), oils (usually from cereal products present), etc. Nitrotoluenes, paraffin, vaseline, etc., are not normal constituents of straight dynamite and are considered under the type of explosive in which they are most likely to occur.

Reflux Condenser Method. From 6 to 10 grams of the sample is weighed in either a porcelain Gooch crucible with asbestos mat or a porous alundum filtering crucible of about 25 cc. capacity. The asbestos mat is best prepared as follows: A mixture of 1 liter of water and 5 grams of previously ignited and shredded short fibre asbestos free from hard lumps and very fine material is well shaken and about 10 cc. poured into the crucible. Suction is applied

[1] Storm, C. G., "The Analysis of Permissible Explosives," Bulletin No. 96, Bureau of Mines, pages 21–24, 1916.

and a smooth and perfect mat almost invariably results. The crucibles thus prepared are dried at 100° and are ready for use.

The sample in the extraction crucible is extracted with about 35 cc. of ether (U. S. P.) preferably in a continuous extraction apparatus (Wiley or similar type preferred), for about 45 minutes to 1 hour, water being continuously circulated through the condenser and the extraction tube heated on a water bath, or electric heater, the temperature of which is so regulated that the sample in the crucible will be kept covered with ether without overflowing.

Suction Method. If desired, the ether extraction may be carried out by suction, the Gooch crucible being held in a carbon tube passing through the stopper in a suction flask. About 100 cc. of ether in 6 to 8 portions is passed through the crucible, each portion being allowed to stand in the crucible for one minute before applying gentle suction. No more air than is necessary should be drawn through the sample in order to avoid condensation of moisture in the sample, which might dissolve a portion of the water-soluble salts. This method uses considerably more ether than the reflux condenser method and its chief advantage is that the apparatus required is more simple.

On completion of the extraction the crucible is at once placed in a drying oven, or the excess ether may be removed by suction before drying. If ammonium nitrate is present the drying should be conducted at 70° C. for 18 hours or overnight, but otherwise 5 hours at 100° C. is ample. The loss of weight represents all ether-soluble material plus the moisture in the original sample.

Evaporation of Ether Extract. The ether extract is washed out of the extraction tube or suction flask with a little ether into a tared evaporating dish or small beaker and the ether allowed to evaporate spontaneously in a warm place, or evaporated by means of the "bell jar evaporator."[1] The latter consists of a tubulated bell jar with openings at top and side, placed on a ground glass plate, a slow current of dry compressed air from two drying cylinders containing H_2SO_4 and soda lime respectively, entering the top opening through a glass tube, the lower end of which extends to about one half inch from the surface of the ether solution in the beaker, which is placed on the glass plate. The dry air current striking the surface of the solution with just enough force to cause a slight "dimple," causes rapid evaporation of the ether, and deposition of moisture in the beaker along with the evaporated residue is avoided. The low temperature produced by the rapid evaporation minimizes the loss of nitroglycerin by volatilization. From 5 to 6 hours is usually required for complete evaporation, which should be determined by check weighings. If the bell jar method is not used, the residue, after removal of the ether, must be desiccated over H_2SO_4 for at least 24 hours in order to remove moisture deposited during evaporation.

Nitroglycerin. Nitroglycerin is determined in the dried and weighed ether extract from which all ether has been removed as above described. This determination is best made by means of the du Pont modification of the 5-part Lunge nitrometer (see p. 354, Vol. I). The sample is dissolved in 5–10 cc. of pure sulphuric acid (specific gravity 1.84) and transferred to the generating bulb of the nitrometer, the beaker and cup of the nitrometer being washed with several further additions of acid until a total of 20–25 cc. has been used.

[1] Storm, C. G., "The Analysis of Permissible Explosives," Bulletin, 96, Bureau of Mines, page 35, 1916.

If the quantity of nitroglycerin present is too great, the sample, dissolved in sulphuric acid, is transferred to a burette and an aliquot part run into the nitrometer. The maximum amount of pure nitroglycerin used for the determination should not exceed 0.75 gram. The determination is carried out in the usual manner and the reading of the gas volume in the graduated reading tube divided by .1850 to find the weight of nitroglycerin in the sample used for the determination (pure nitroglycerin contains 18.50% N).

Sulphur, Resins, Oils, etc. It is always preferable to carry out the extraction with ether on duplicate samples, using one sample of the extract for the determination of nitroglycerin as above, and the other for determining sulphur, resins, oils, etc., that may also be contained in the ether extract.

The weighed extract is redissolved in a mixture of ether and alcohol, previously neutralized with standard alkali. The solution thus obtained is titrated with standard alcoholic potash solution using phenolphthalein indicator. 1 cc. of tenth normal alkali is equal to 0.034 grams of rosin (colophony).

A large excess of the alcoholic potash is now added and the mixture heated several hours or overnight on the steam bath to saponify the nitroglycerin. Shake with water and ether in a separatory funnel. The ether solution contains paraffin, vaseline, or mineral oils that may be present, and is evaporated and the residue weighed. The water solution is acidified with HCl, and Br added to oxidize any sulphur. Any separated rosin is filtered off and weighed as a check on the titration, and sulphur determined in the filtrate by precipitation as $BaSO_4$.

Sulphur may also be separated from nitroglycerin by means of acetic acid of approximately 70% strength, the nitroglycerin being quite soluble in acetic acid and the sulphur almost insoluble. The sulphur is filtered from the solution, washed slightly with alcohol to remove the acetic acid solution, dried and weighed.

If a considerable quantity of crystals of sulphur is found in the evaporated ether extract, it is possible that all of the sulphur has not been removed by the ether, and in this case an extraction is made with carbon disulphide, in exactly the same manner as the ether extraction. This extraction is made subsequent to the extraction with water, the sulphur being determined by loss of weight of the residue or by direct weight after evaporation of the carbon disulphide away from free flame.

Extraction with Water and Determination of Nitrates. The dried and weighed residue left in the crucible after extraction with ether, is extracted with water, using a suction flask fitted with a carbon filter tube in which the crucible is held by a short length of thin-walled rubber tubing. Cold water is used for this extraction, as hot water would gelatinize any starch present. A total of at least 200 cc. of water is passed through the sample, in at least 10 portions, each portion being allowed to stand in contact with the residue for a few minutes before being sucked into the flask. An evaporation test of a few drops of the filtrate will determine the completeness of the extraction. When the extraction is complete, the crucible with its insoluble residue is dried for 5 hours, or overnight, at 95°–100° C., and the loss of weight noted as total water-soluble material. This includes nitrates and other soluble salts that may be present, together with water extract from the wood pulp, flour or other absorbent. This soluble organic material may amount to as much as 2% of the total sample, when cereal products are present. Calcium, magnesium,

33

or zinc may also be present in solution, resulting from the action of acid decomposition products of the nitroglycerin on the carbonate or other antacid present. In routine analyses of ordinary dynamite, the loss of weight on extraction with water is usually considered as the alkaline nitrate (sodium or potassium), but where more exact results are desired an aliquot portion of the extract is evaporated to dryness with a little nitric acid to oxidize organic materials, and the residue weighed as alkaline nitrate. This weight may be corrected for inorganic impurities—chlorides, sulphates, iron, aluminum, calcium, etc.—determined separately by the usual methods.

Nitrates may be determined by means of the nitrometer, using an aliquot portion of water extract estimated to contain .6 to .8 gram of $NaNO_3$ or .8 to 1.0 gram of KNO_3. This is evaporated on the steam bath almost to dryness and transferred with as little water as possible, to the cup of the nitrometer. This solution is drawn into the generator and 30 to 40 cc. of 95–96% H_2SO_4 added slowly so as to avoid generating sufficient heat to crack the glass. The generator is then shaken for a total time of 8–10 minutes in order to be certain that the generation of gas is complete with the diluted acid. The gas is measured and the % of nitrate calculated as in the case of nitroglycerin.

Extraction with Acid. When starch is not present in the residue, a simple extraction of the residue insoluble in water is made with cold dilute HCl (1 : 10), 100 cc. being drawn through the sample in the crucible in small successive portions as described under "Extraction with Water." Several portions of water are then drawn through to wash out the acid, and the residue in the crucible dried for 5 hours at 95° to 100° C. The loss of weight is usually reported as antacid, but the base dissolved may be determined by the usual quantitative methods if desired. The acid-soluble materials generally present are calcium or magnesium carbonate or zinc oxide.

Determination of Starch. If starch is present in the residue insoluble in water, it is removed together with the antacid by boiling with dilute acid. The residue is moistened with water, scraped or washed out of the crucible into a 500 cc. beaker, the volume brought to about 250 cc. by the addition of water and 3 cc. of strong HCl, and the mixture boiled until a drop of the solution fails to give a blue color when treated on a spot plate with a drop of a solution of iodine in KI. This indicates that the starch has been completely hydrolyzed to dextrin. The mixture is then filtered through a fresh crucible, washed with water, dried and weighed, correction being made for the weight of the asbestos mat of the original crucible.

The antacid dissolved in the acid filtrate is determined as already described. The loss of weight by the boiling treatment, minus the antacid found, represents starch and other dissolved organic materials removed from cereal products or wood pulp. The insoluble residue includes the wood pulp and the crude fibre of the cereal products.

Because of the impracticability of exact separations it is customary to report all of the soluble organic material included in both water and acid extractions as "starch" or "starchy material," and the insoluble organic residue as "wood pulp and crude fibre," or the sum of these organic materials is often reported as "carbonaceous combustible material."

Insoluble Residue and Ash. The insoluble residue may contain wood pulp or sawdust, the crude fibre from various cereal products such as corn meal, wheat flour, middlings, bran, etc., ground nut shells, vegetable ivory meal, and more rarely inorganic material such as infusorial earth (kieselguhr), clay, etc. These can usually be identified by microscopic examination (see Bureau of Mines Bulletin 96, Page 74), and a determination of the ash will show whether inorganic materials are present. A high ash content may also indicate incomplete water or acid extractions.

Ammonia Dynamite

So-called ammonia dynamite is essentially "straight" dynamite in which a large part of the nitroglycerin is replaced by ammonium nitrate. The ammonium nitrate is frequently protected from moisture by a coating of vaseline or paraffin and is usually neutralized with zinc oxide. This type of dynamite generally contains less wood pulp than the corresponding grades of "straight" dynamite, and sulphur and cereal products, such as low grade flour, are usually present.

The determination of moisture and the various extractions are carried out as described for "straight" dynamite. An extraction with carbon disulphide is usually necessary to effect complete removal of the sulphur; this properly follows the extraction with water. The analysis of the ether extract may be conducted as already described. In drying the residue left in the crucible after extraction with ether, it is important that a temperature of approximately 70° C. be used, because in the presence of ZnO, the loss of ammonium nitrate is considerable at 100° C. Pure ammonium nitrate is not appreciably affected by even 24 hours heating at 100° C., but the presence of the ZnO causes decomposition at this temperature.

The water extract contains sodium nitrate and ammonium nitrate together with practically all of the zinc oxide present, the latter ingredient being dissolved with the ammonium nitrate, and a small amount of soluble organic material from the flour or other absorbent. It is analyzed as follows: An aliquot portion is evaporated to dryness in a platinum or silica dish on a steam bath, the ammonium nitrate volatilized by careful heating over a burner, a little nitric acid added to re-oxidize any nitrate that may have been reduced to nitrite, and the residue again dried on the steam bath. The zinc oxide is now in the form of zinc nitrate and may be separated from the sodium nitrate by either of the following methods:

1. The residue is dried at 110°–120° C. and weighed as $NaNO_3$ and $Zn(NO_3)_2$. It is then dissolved in water, the zinc precipitated with Na_2CO_3, filtered, ignited and weighed as ZnO, and the $NaNO_3$ taken by difference; the total $NaNO_3$ plus $Zn(NO_3)_2$ minus $(ZnO \times 2.33) = NaNO_3$.

2. The residue is gently heated over a burner until evolution of oxides of nitrogen from decomposition of the $Zn(NO_3)_2$ has ceased, and the remaining residue weighed as $NaNO_3$ and ZnO. It is then treated with water, the insoluble ZnO filtered on a Gooch crucible, ignited and weighed, the $NaNO_3$ being taken by difference.

Ammonium nitrate is determined in a separate portion of the water extract by the usual method of distillation and titration.

The sum of the amounts of NH_4NO_3, $NaNO_3$, and ZnO found will be somewhat less than the total water extract owing to the presence of water-soluble organic material from the carbonaceous absorbents.

Gelatin Dynamite

This is a form of nitroglycerin explosive in which the nitroglycerin, instead of being absorbed in porous materials such as wood pulp, is combined with nitrocellulose in the form of a gelatinous plastic mass. As little as 3.5% of suitable grade of nitrocellulose containing about 12% nitrogen will, when heated with nitroglycerin, at about 60° C., form a jelly-like non-fluid mass when cooled to ordinary temperature. "Blasting gelatin," used to a considerable extent where great explosive strength is required, is a stiff colloid composed of 90 to 93% nitroglycerin and 10 to 7% nitrocellulose.

All blasting explosives containing such colloids of nitroglycerin and nitrocellulose combined with an active "dope" or base, consisting of a nitrate and combustible material, are termed gelatin dynamites. This type of explosive is also known in some countries as "Gelignite."

Sampling. Owing to its pasty consistency the sample of gelatin dynamite must be prepared by cutting portions of a number of cartridges into thin bits with an aluminium or platinum spatula. The use of a steel spatula or knife for this purpose is not to be recommended for reasons of safety. An ample quantity of sample thus prepared is well mixed and bottled. Owing to its tendency to again form a solid mass upon standing, it should be analyzed as soon as possible after being prepared.

Analysis. The principal ingredients that may be found in the different types of gelatin dynamite are nitroglycerin; nitrocellulose; sulphur; rosin; sodium, potassium or ammonium nitrate; calcium or magnesium carbonate; wood pulp, cereal products and similar carbonaceous combustible materials. Low-freezing gelatins may also contain nitrotoluenes or other nitrosubstitution compounds.

Moisture is determined as described for "straight" dynamite, and the extraction with ether made in the usual manner except that ether free from alcohol (distilled over sodium) is used in order to prevent partial solution of the nitrocellulose. The latter is readily soluble in a mixture of ether and alcohol, and as ordinary U. S. P. ether contains about 4% of alcohol, there is a possibility that an appreciable part of the 0.5% to 2.0% of nitrocellulose present in the sample will be dissolved unless pure ether is used. The ether extract is evaporated and analyzed as already described and the water extraction made in the usual manner. If more than 1 or 2% of sulphur was present it will not have been completely removed by the ether, unless the extraction was continued for a sufficiently long time. In this event, it is necessary to make an additional extraction with carbon disulphide in the Wiley apparatus subsequent to extraction with water.

Nitrocellulose. After the extractions with ether, water, and CS_2 (if necessary) have been made, the nitrocellulose is determined, preferably by extraction with acetone, which is a better solvent for the purpose than a mixture of ether and alcohol. It is advisable to separate the dry residue from the crucible, leaving the asbestos mat intact if possible. The residue is transferred to a small beaker, covered with acetone and allowed to stand at least 3 or 4 hours with occasional stirring. It is then filtered through the original crucible, washed with acetone, dried and weighed, the loss of weight being regarded as nitrocellulose. To correct for small amounts of extract from the wood pulp or other carbonaceous material, the acetone solution may be evaporated to about 20–25 cc., and diluted gradually with a large volume (about 100 cc.) of hot water, which volatilizes the acetone, precipitating the nitrocellulose as a white flocculent mass, which is filtered, dried, and weighed.

The remainder of the analysis is conducted as for straight dynamite.

It will be found that the results of analysis of a gelatin dynamite do not agree with its trade markings. For example, the usual "40% strength" gelatin dynamite actually contains from 30 to 33% of nitroglycerin and about 1% of nitrocellulose. Weight for weight this explosive is considerably weaker than 40% straight dynamite, which contains 40% of nitroglycerin.

Low=Freezing Dynamite

Low-freezing dynamites vary from the dynamite types already discussed by containing an ingredient which reduces the freezing point of the nitroglycerin. This ingredient replaces a portion of the nitroglycerin which would be used in an equal grade of ordinary straight dynamite, ammonia dynamite, or gelatin dynamite. While straight nitroglycerin dynamite may freeze at temperatures as high as 8° C. (46° F.), some of the low-freezing dynamites freeze only at temperatures considerably below 0° C. Many of this type, however, cannot be relied upon to resist freezing at temperatures below the freezing point of water.

The additions made to nitroglycerin for this purpose include the nitrotoluenes, nitroxylenes, nitrohydrins, nitrosugar, and nitropolyglycerin (tetranitrodiglycern). Any of these substances present will be found in the ether extract together with, and in most cases dissolved in, the nitroglycerin.

Moisture. The determination of moisture is carried out as already described for "straight" nitroglycerin dynamite (p. 1375). Attention has been called to the fact that certain nitrosubstitution compounds, notably the mono- and dinitrotoluenes, are more or less volatile and would therefore be partly lost if the moisture is determined in a vacuum desiccator. The safest procedure is therefore to determine the moisture by desiccation for 3 days without vacuum. The difference between the total loss on extraction with ether and the direct weight of the ether extract, after evaporation of the ether in a bell-jar evaporator (p. 1376), should be equal to the moisture content of the sample. This figure will therefore serve as a check on the result obtained by desiccation.

Nitrotoluenes. Trinitrotoluene is not readily soluble in nitroglycerin and separates as crystals on evaporation of the ether from the ether extract, enabling it to be qualitatively separated and identified. It may be determined by difference, the nitroglycerin being determined by means of the nitrometer. Any dinitrotoluene present may also be determined in this manner together with the trinitrotoluene, but if mononitrotoluene is also present, the determination of the nitrogen of the nitroglycerin will be slightly in error by about 0.5530 gram of nitroglycerin for every gram of mononitrotoluene present.[1]

Mononitrotoluene is, however, seldom present except as an impurity in the so-called liquid di- and trinitrotoluenes used in low freezing dynamites, so that the determination of the nitroglycerin is usually fairly accurate and the nitrotoluenes may be calculated by difference.

[1] Storm, C. G., "The Effect of Nitrotoluenes on the Determination of Nitroglycerin by Means of the Nitrometer," Proc. 8th Int. Cong. Appl. Chem., Vol. 4, 1912, p. 117; also Bu. of Mines Bull. 41, p. 62, 1913.

The total nitrogen of the combined nitroglycerin and nitrosubstitution compound may also be determined, the nitrogen of the nitroglycerin deducted and the amount of nitrosubstitution compound calculated from the resulting difference, if the identity of the nitrosubstitution compound has been established. A suitable modification of the Kjeldahl method which has been found applicable to difficultly decomposable nitrocompounds is as follows:[1] This method is, of course, applicable to mixtures containing nitroglycerin.

Modified Kjeldahl Method for Nitrogen. About 0.5000 g. of the nitrocompound is weighed into a 500 cc. Kjeldahl flask, 30 cc. of 96% H_2SO_4 and 2 g. salicylic acid added and the sample dissolved by heating on a steam bath if necessary. Cool; add 2 g. zinc dust in small portions, with cooling and rotating the flask. Continue the shaking at 15 minute intervals for 2 hours and let stand overnight. Then heat over a small flame till fuming has ceased (about 2 hours), cool slightly and add 1 g. HgO. and boil $1-1\frac{1}{2}$ hours longer. Cool and add 7.5 g. K_2SO_4 and 10 cc. K_2SO_4 and boil $1\frac{1}{2}$ to 2 hours more. If the solution is not clear and almost colorless, add 1 g. more K_2SO_4 and boil longer. Cool and add 250 cc. H_2O to dissolve the cake formed, then add 25 cc. K_2S solution (80 g. per liter H_2O), 1 g. granulated Zn, and 85–90 cc. NaOH solution (750 g. per liter H_2O), and distill as usual in the Kjeldahl determination, collecting the NH_3 in standard H_2SO_4 solution. A blank determination without sample is advisable.

Separation of Nitrocompounds from Nitroglycerin. Hyde has devised a satisfactory method for actual separation of nitrosubstitution compounds from nitroglycerin, depending on the differences in solubility of these ingredients in carbon bisulphide and dilute acetic acid.[2] Nitroglycerin is only slightly soluble in CS_2, but readily soluble in dilute acetic acid, while most nitrocompounds are much more soluble in CS_2 and much less soluble in dilute acetic acid than nitroglycerin. CS_2 and acetic acid are only slightly miscible. Hence nitroglycerin and a nitrocompound may be partly separated by shaking the mixture with CS_2 and dilute acetic acid, allowing the two solvents to separate into two layers and drawing off one of the layers. The CS_2 layer will contain most of the nitrocompound and the acetic acid layer most of the nitroglycerin.

Hyde's method involves a continuous fractional extraction in a rather complicated apparatus consisting of 13 long narrow extraction tubes, connected with each other and with a condenser, reservoir and distilling flask so as to form a closed circulating system, the CS_2 continually passing in a train of fine drops through acetic acid in the series of extraction tubes, carrying with it the nitrocompound, the nitroglycerin tending to remain dissolved in the acetic acid. Practically a complete separation is finally obtained, the nitrocompound dissolved in the CS_2 collecting in the distilling flask at the end of the extraction train and the nitroglycerin remaining in solution in the acetic acid in the tubes. The CS_2 is evaporated and the nitrocompound weighed. Reference should be made to the original article by Hyde for details as to construction and operation of the apparatus.

[1] Cope, W. C., "Kjeldahl Modification for Determination of Nitrogen in Nitrosubstitution Compounds," J. Ind. and Eng. Chem., Vol. 8, p. 592, 1916.

[2] Hyde, A. L., "The Quantitative Separation of Nitrosubstitution Compounds from Nitroglycerin," J. Am. Chem., Soc., Vol. 35, p. 1173, 1913. (See also Bu. Mines Bulletin, 96, pp. 47–50, 1916.)

Nitrosugars. The nitrates of sugar, improperly called nitrosugar, are used to a considerable extent for lowering the freezing point of nitroglycerin. This substance is soluble in nitroglycerin, being prepared with the latter by nitrating a solution of cane-sugar in glycerin, and no method is known for its separation from nitroglycerin. Hoffman and Hawse[1] have reported on an optical method for the determination of nitrated sugar in nitroglycerin mixtures, based on the use of the polariscope. As an example of the application of the method, 10.65 g. of a nitrated mixture of glycerin and sugar was dissolved in 100 cc. alcohol and its angle of rotation found to be $a = 3.07°$. The specific rotatory power of sucrose octanitrate having been determined as $\alpha = 56.66$, the formula: C (concentration) $= a/2\alpha$ gives a result of 25.44% sucrose octanitrate in the sample.

The result of the optical method may be roughly checked by a determination of the total nitrogen of the combined nitroglycerin and nitrosugar, assuming the nitrogen content of the nitrosugar to be 15% (theoretical for sucrose octanitrate 15.95%), and that of nitroglycerin 18.50%.

Nitrochlorhydrins. Dinitromonochlorhydrin has been known for years as a partial substitute for nitroglycerin in explosives. It is a solvent for nitrocellulose in smokeless powders and has an appreciable effect in lowering the freezing point of nitroglycerin. During recent years it has come into use in this country as a substitute for nitrotoluenes in low freezing dynamites.

A mixture of dinitrochlorhydrin and nitroglycerin will have a lower nitrogen content than pure nitroglycerin, the dinitrochlorhydrin containing only 14.0% N, as compared with 18.50% N in nitroglycerin. The dinitrochlorhydrin may be readily identified and determined quantitatively by treating the mixture containing this substance and nitroglycerin with an excess of alcoholic solution of KOH, heating on the steam bath until saponification is complete, and determining the chlorine in the solution as chloride.

It must be noted that dinitrochlorhydrin is somewhat more volatile than nitroglycerin and therefore in evaporating the ether from the ether extract it is advisable to make use of the bell-jar evaporator (p. 1376) so as to minimize its loss during evaporation.

Nitropolyglycerin. Nitrated polymerized glycerin—usually a mixture of tetranitrodiglycerin and trinitroglycerin—is sometimes found in low-freezing explosives. This mixture will show a lower N-content than nitroglycerin, since pure tetranitrodiglycerin contains only 16.19 % N. The presence of the latter substance is indicated by low solubility in dilute acetic acid (60 volumes glacial acetic acid to 40 volumes water). One gram of nitroglycerin dissolves in about 10.5 cc. of this acid, while 1 gram of a mixture containing 82.25% tetranitrodiglycerin required 120 cc. of the acetic acid to completely dissolve it. In dissolving such a mixture, it will be found that a part of the mixture dissolves more readily than the remainder. If the more difficultly soluble portion is separated, dried in a desiccator and its nitrogen content determined in the nitrometer, it will be found to contain a much lower % N than the original mixture, approximating the figure for tetranitrodiglycerin, 16.19% (an actual trial gave 16.24% N).

If the presence of tetranitrodiglycerin is established by the above procedure and no other substances except nitroglycerin are present, the proportions of these two ingredients in the ether extract may be readily calculated from the N-content as found by the nitrometer.

[1] Hoffman, E. J. and Hawse, V. P., "The Nitration of Sucrose Octanitrate," J. Am. Chem. Soc., Vol. 41, pp. 235–247, 1919.

"PERMISSIBLE" EXPLOSIVES

"Permissible" explosives are coal mining explosives which have passed the prescribed tests of the Bureau of Mines and are recommended by the Bureau for use in gassy and dusty mines. Their important characteristic is a relatively low flame temperature, which is brought about by modifying the composition of the usual types of dynamites and other blasting explosives. The general methods of reducing the flame temperature of explosives[1] are summarized as follows:

(a) Addition of an excess of carbon,—forming less CO_2 and more CO in the gases of explosion.

(b) Addition of free water or of solids with water of crystallization.

(c) Addition of inert materials.

(d) Addition of volatile salts.

The analysis of explosives of this class is therefore generally more complicated than that of the ordinary types of blasting explosives because of the greater variety of ingredients used in manufacture. A partial list of substances which have been found in low-flame explosives manufactured in this country is shown below, arranged according to their solubility in the general scheme of analysis:

Soluble in Ether
Nitroglycerin
Nitropolyglycerin
Nitrotoluenes
Nitrosugars
Nitrochlorhydrins
Paraffin
Resins
Sulphur
Vaseline
Oils

Soluble in Water
Ammonium nitrate
"   chloride
"   sulphate
"   oxalate
"   perchlorate
Alum (cryst.)
Aluminum sulphate (cryst.)
Barium nitrate
Calcium sulphate (cryst.)
Gums
Magnesium sulphate (cryst.)
Potassium chlorate
"   nitrate
"   perchlorate
Sodium nitrate
"   chloride
"   bicarbonate
"   carbonate
Sugar
Zinc oxide

Soluble in Acids
Aluminum
Calcium carbonate
"   silicide
Ferric oxide
Magnesium carbonate
Zinc
Zinc oxide

Insoluble

Charcoal
Clay
Coal
Corn meal
Corncob meal
Kieselguhr
Nitrocellulose
Nitrostarch
Nitrated wood

Peanut shell meal
Powdered slate
Rice hulls
Sawdust
Turmeric
Vegetable ivory meal
Wheat flour
Wood pulp

[1] The thermochemical considerations involved are discussed in Bureau of Mines Bulletin No. 15, "Investigations of Explosives used in Coal Mines," 1912, and the details of analysis in Bureau of Mines Bulletin No. 96, "The Analysis of Permissible Explosives," C. G. Storm, 1916.

Qualitative Analysis. The qualitative examination of a "permissible" explosive is conducted in the same manner as has been described for dynamite (see page 1374), and, in view of the greater variety of constituents that may be present, is quite essential before a suitable scheme for quantitative separation can be chosen.

Tests for some of the more unusual substances not generally found in the ordinary types of blasting explosives, and not already discussed under "Low-freezing Explosives," are made as follows:

Test for Sugar. The presence of water-soluble organic substances is indicated by an appreciable charring of the residue obtained by evaporating a portion of the water extract to dryness and then heating gradually over a burner. A slight charring may result from water-soluble portions of cereal products, wood-pulp, etc., and may be disregarded. Sugar is identified by acidifying some of the water solution with a little dilute HCl, heating to boiling, neutralizing with KOH and then boiling with Fehling's solution. A precipitation of cuprous oxide indicates the presence of sugar.

Test for Gum Arabic. Gum arabic is precipitated by the addition of a solution of basic lead acetate to the water extract, a white, flocculent precipitate of indefinite composition resulting (see Determination of Gum Arabic, p. 1388).

Test for Nitrostarch. Nitrostarch is best identified by microscopic examination of the residue insoluble in water. It is easily distinguished from unnitrated starch by means of a solution of iodine in KI, which colors the starch granules dark blue but does not affect the granules of nitrostarch.

Test for Chlorides, Chlorates, and Perchlorates. These three substances present in a solution may be identified as follows: Acidify slightly with nitric acid, add excess of $AgNO_3$, heat to boiling, shake well, and filter off the silver chloride. To the filtrate add a few cc. of 40% solution of formaldehyde (formalin), and boil to reduce chlorates to chlorides. This reduction is best carried out by heating on the steam bath for about an hour. Any chloride thus formed is then separated by further precipitation with $AgNO_3$ and removed by filtration. The filtrate is then evaporated to dryness, the residue transferred to a crucible and fused with dry Na_2CO_3. The fused mass is treated with dilute HNO_3, when the presence of perchlorate will be indicated by an insoluble precipitate of AgCl.

Mechanical Separation of Solid Ingredients. It is frequently of advantage, especially in connection with the interpretation of the results of analysis of an explosive mixture containing a number of water-soluble salts, to determine the identity of one or more of the components of the mixture by means of screening or by a method of separation depending on variation in specific gravity of the components. Such methods are facilitated by the fact that the ingredients of blasting explosives are frequently not finely pulverized in the course of manufacture.

(a) *By Screening.* 25 to 50 grams of the sample is washed several times with ether to remove nitroglycerin and ingredients of an oily nature, the solid residue dried to remove adhering ether and then sifted through a set of sieves. An examination of the portions held by the 10- and 20-mesh screens will usually show the presence of coarse crystals which are large enough to be sorted out with the aid of forceps, submitted to qualitative tests and identified with certainty. A single crystal may sometimes be identified by dissolving it in a drop of water on a microscope slide, allowing the water to evaporate and examining the resulting crystals under the microscope. The writer has frequently identified three or four ingredients of an explosive in this manner.

(b) *By Specific Gravity Separations.* This method, applied to the analysis of explosives by Storm and Hyde,[1] depends on the separation of solids from a mixture by means of inert liquids of different specific gravities. A series of mixtures of chloroform (sp.gr. 1.49) and bromoform (sp.gr. 2.83) is prepared covering as wide a range of specific gravity as may seem desirable. Portions of the dried sample previously extracted with ether as in (a) are added to such liquid mixtures and the heavier salts, which settle to the bottom, separated from the lighter ones. For example a mixture of ammonium nitrate (sp.gr. 1.74) and sodium chloride (sp.gr. 2.17) is readily separated into its components in a liquid with a specific gravity of (*e.g.*), 1.90, so that the components can be tested separately and the analyst assured that the mixture is not composed of sodium nitrate and ammonium chloride,—which could not be ascertained by ordinary quantitative analysis. (For example, a mixture composed of 16.61% Na, 44.76% NO_3, 13.00% NH_4 and 25.63% Cl may contain either 61.37% $NaNO_3$ and 38.63% NH_4Cl, or 57.76% NH_4NO_3 and 42.24% $NaCl$, or varying proportions of all four ingredients.) The chloroform-bromoform mixtures are recovered by filtering and used repeatedly.

The specific gravities of some of the more common salts that may be found are as follows:

Ammonium alum (cryst.)	1.62
" chloride	1.52
" nitrate	1.74
" perchlorate	1.87
" sulphate	1.77
Barium nitrate	3.23
Calcium carbonate (ppt'd)	2.72
" sulphate (anhydrous)	2.97
" sulphate$+2H_2O$	2.32
Magnesium carbonate	3.04
" sulphate$+7H_2O$	1.68
Manganese dioxide	5.03
Potassium alum (cryst.)	1.75
" chlorate	2.33
" chloride	1.99
" nitrate	2.09
" perchlorate	2.52
" sulphate	2.66
Sodium chloride	2.17
" nitrate	2.26
" sulphate (anhydrous)	2.66
" sulphate$+10H_2O$	1.46

Moisture. The determination of moisture in all types of "permissible" explosives is carried out by the method described for nitroglycerin dynamites (page 1375). The influence of the slight volatility of nitroglycerin and of certain nitrosubstitution compounds on the results of this determination has been discussed (pp. 1375, 1381). A more serious factor in the case of many "permissible" explosives is the presence of salts containing water of crystallization. Most salts of this type (*e.g.*, $MgSO_4.7H_2O$) undergo a gradual loss of a large part of their combined water on desiccation over either H_2SO_4 or $CaCl_2$, thus rendering it impossible to differentiate between hygroscopic moisture and

[1] Storm, C. G., and Hyde, A. L., "Specific Gravity Separation Applied to the Analysis of Mining Explosives," Tech. Paper No. 78, Bureau of Mines, 1914.

combined water.   Attempts to remove the total water content by heating at a temperature high enough to drive off all of the water of crystallization are useless on account of the increased volatilization of nitroglycerin, ammonium nitrate, etc., at such temperatures.

In such cases it is necessary to determine all other constituents by direct methods and estimate moisture by difference, the salt to which the water of crystallization belongs being calculated as containing its full quota of water; or the crystallized salt may be calculated as anhydrous and the difference from 100% reported as "water of crystallization plus moisture."

Extraction with Ether.   The extraction with ether, the evaporation of the ether, and the analysis of the ether-soluble portion are conducted as already discussed for nitroglycerin dynamites (pp. 1375, 1376).

In drying the crucibles containing the residue insoluble in ether, a temperature of 100° C. may be used except when the residue contains ammonium nitrate or organic nitrates such as nitrocellulose, nitrostarch, or nitrated wood. When any of these substances are present, the residue should be dried to constant weight at 70° C.   Except when salts containing water of crystallization are present, the amount of ether-soluble material found is calculated by deducting the moisture determined by desiccation, from the difference between the weight of original sample and the weight of the dried residue insoluble in ether.   The procedure followed when water of crystallization is present is noted in the preceding paragraph.

Extraction with Water.   Water-soluble salts are extracted from the weighed residue insoluble in ether as already described, the residue left in the crucibles dried to constant weight at 95 to 100° C., cooled and weighed.   The water soluble salts in the solution are determined by the usual methods of inorganic analysis.

Nitrates.   In determining nitrates by the nitrometer method (see p. 354) it must be remembered that the presence of a considerable quantity of chlorides may interfere with the accuracy of the results.   Many of the "permissible" explosives contain sodium chloride in amounts varying from 1% to 10 or 15%. M. T. Sanders[1] has shown that if the sodium chloride is present in an amount exceeding 15–17% of the sodium nitrate, the result is not accurate within 0.1%. Smaller amounts of sodium chloride do not interfere, except to increase the amount of sludge formed in the nitrometer.

Nitrates may also be determined by the "nitron" method of Busch.[2]

Chlorates.   Chlorates may be determined by any of the methods described on page 152 (reduction with SO_2, $FeSO_4$, or Zn) or by the formaldehyde method.[3]   In the latter method a portion of the solution, containing about 0.5 g. of chlorate is diluted to 150 cc., 5–10 c. of 40% formaldehyde solution, 2 cc. dilute HNO_3 (1 : 3), and 50 cc. of approx. tenth normal silver nitrate added, the solution covered and heated on the steam bath for about 4 hours, when the precipitate of AgCl is filtered off, washed, dried and weighed.   This method is accurate to .05 to .10%.

[1] Sanders, M. T., "The Effect of Chlorides on the Nitrometer Determination of Nitrates," J. Ind. & Eng. Chem., 12, p. 169–170, 1919.

[2] See page 345, also, for further details, "The Analysis of Permissible Explosives," Bureau of Mines, Bulletin 96, pages 60–2.

[3] Storm, C. G., "The Analysis of Permissible Explosives," Bulletin 96, Bureau of Mines, pp. 63–4, 1916.

Perchlorates. The determination of perchlorates by reduction to chlorides on ignition with NH_4Cl in the presence of platinum is described on page 152. Perchlorates may also be determined by means of precipitation with "nitron" in exactly the same manner as for nitrates. The weight of nitron perchlorate $(C_{20}H_{16}N_4HClO_4)$ found, multiplied by 117.5 (mol. wt. of NH_4ClO_4) and divided by 412.5 (mol. wt. of nitronperchlorate) gives the weight of perchlorate found, expressed as NH_4ClO_4.

Gum Arabic. This substance, sometimes used as a binder in dry explosive mixtures—especially chlorate or perchlorate powders—is determined by precipitation with basic lead acetate solution, prepared by adding 150 g. of normal lead acetate and 50 g. lead oxide (PbO) to 500 cc. distilled water, heating almost to boiling, and filtering. This reagent is added to the solution containing the gum arabic until no further precipitation occurs; the mixture is allowed to stand for several hours, then filtered, washed with absolute alcohol, dried at 100° and weighed. The weight of precipitate multiplied by the factor 0.4971 (determined experimentally) gives the weight of gum arabic found. Chlorides or sulphates, if present, interfere with the determination and must be first removed.

Sugar. Sugar may be present as an ingredient in some "permissible" explosives, and is always found in small amounts in the water extract if cereal products such as corn meal or wheat middlings are present. A portion of the water extract is acidified with HCl (1 cc. conc. HCl to 100 cc. solution), heated just to boiling, cooled, nearly neutralized with Na_2CO_3, an excess of Fehling's solution added and the mixture heated until reduction is complete. The Cu_2O is filtered from the blue liquid, dried, ignited to constant weight, and weighed as CuO. This weight $\times 0.4308$ equals weight of cane sugar. The result is corrected for the result of a blank determination using distilled water instead of the water extract. By the use of this method after first extracting with ether, then with water, corn meal was found to contain 2.65% and wheat middlings 6.25–7.00% of sugar. Thus an explosive containing 25% wheat middlings would show as much as 1.75% of sugar in its water extract.

Extraction with Acid. As in the ordinary nitroglycerin dynamites, the substances removed from "permissible" explosives by acid extraction are chiefly substances added as antacids, including calcium carbonate, magnesium carbonate and zinc oxide. Other acid-soluble materials that may be present include metallic aluminum or zinc, ferric oxide, manganese dioxide, and calcium silicide. When starch is present, the residue from the water extraction is subjected to hydrolysis in boiling dilute HCl as already described (page 1378), and the acid-soluble inorganic components determined in the filtrate by the usual methods. An extraction with cold acid is made only when there is no starch present.

Extraction with Acetone: Nitrocellulose and Nitrostarch. If either nitrocellulose or nitrostarch is present, an extraction with acetone is made as described for gelatin dynamite (page 1380). It should be noted in connection with the preceding steps in the analysis that in order to avoid partial solution of these substances in ether, the ether used in the ether extraction should be alcohol-free (distilled from sodium), and also that all drying of residues containing these materials should preferably be conducted at 70° instead of 100°, in order to avoid partial decomposition. It is impracticable to separate nitrostarch from nitrocellulose but they are not likely to be found together in the same explosive. Small amounts of nitrocellulose are detected less readily than nitrostarch, which is easily identified by the microscope.

Insoluble Residue and Ash. The insoluble residue is usually carbonaceous combustible or absorbent material and is in most cases readily identified by means of a microscope (preferably binocular) with low power (25–50 diameters). The possible presence of any inorganic material which may have been overlooked in the analysis is detected by means of a determination of ash, the residue being ignited until all carbon is burned off and the mineral residue weighed. This is usually not over 0.2%. If higher than 0.5%, there is reason to suspect that some such material as kieselguhr or clay is present, or that the extractions with water or acid were not complete.

NITROSTARCH EXPLOSIVES

General Nature. Nitrostarch explosives have been for a number of years used to a very considerable extent in this country for commercial blasting purposes, chiefly for quarrying. During the war, explosives of this class were adopted by the United States for certain military purposes and proved satisfactory substitutes for trinitrotoluene as bursting charges for hand grenades, rifle grenades and trench mortar shell.

The commercial nitrostarch explosives may contain, in addition to the nitrostarch, any or all of the following components: oxidizing agents, as sodium or ammonium nitrates, combustible material, such as charcoal, flour, sulphur, etc., mineral oil, and antacids, such as calcium carbonate, or zinc oxide. Nitrostarch military explosives may consist of some such mixture as the above, or may be composed almost entirely of nitrostarch with the addition of relatively small amounts of oils and materials used for granulating. Some types of nitrostarch explosives proposed for military use contained water in amounts up to 10–15% combined with a mixture of nitrostarch and a soluble nitrate.

For commercial use, nitrostarch explosives are put up in cartridge form in paper wrappers, just as nitroglycerin explosives are prepared.

Moisture. Moisture is determined as in the case of nitroglycerin dynamites. 3 to 5 grams of the sample is desiccated over sulphuric acid for 2–3 days (2 days is usually sufficient to give constant weight), or for 24 hours in a vacuum desiccator with a vacuum of at least 700 mm. of mercury. Unlike nitroglycerin, nitrostarch does not volatilize and may be desiccated to constant weight. When heated to higher temperatures, e.g., 100° C., for any extended time, it undergoes, like all nitric esters, a gradual decomposition with loss of weight.

Extraction with Petroleum Ether: Oils, Sulphur, etc. The small amount of alcohol usually present in ordinary grades of ethyl ether, is sufficient to cause partial solution of the nitrostarch, if ethyl ether is used for removing oily ingredients, sulphur, etc., nitrostarch being readily soluble in mixtures of ether and alcohol. It is therefore advisable to use petroleum ether, which does not dissolve nitrostarch, for this extraction.

A sample of about 10 grams of the explosive, in a Gooch crucible with asbestos mat, is extracted with pure petroleum ether of about 0.65 specific gravity, the excess solvent removed by suction and the crucible with sample dried to constant weight at approximately 70° C. The % loss of weight, minus the moisture content, already determined, represents the percentage of ether-soluble material present. The petroleum ether is removed by evaporation, the residue of ether-soluble materials dried, weighed, and its components determined by the methods used for dynamites.

Extraction with Water: Nitrates, Gums, etc. The dried and weighed residue insoluble in petroleum ether is extracted with distilled water to remove the nitrates or other water-soluble materials. The insoluble residue left in the crucible is dried at a temperature of 80° C. (100° may cause some decomposition of the nitrostarch) for several hours, and weighed, the loss of weight being total water extract and serving as a check against the sum of the components separately determined.

Ammonium nitrate, if present, is determined in the water solution by the usual method of distillation of the NH_3 after adding an excess of alkali. Sodium nitrate is determined by evaporating the water extract, volatilizing ammonium salts, and weighing the residue after re-oxidizing with nitric acid if charring has indicated the presence of any water-soluble organic material (page 1378).

If the original explosive is granular in form, the presence of a binding or agglutinating material in the water extract may be suspected. Although numerous other substances may be used for the purpose, gum arabic is frequently employed as a binding agent in different types of dry explosives. A qualitative test for gum arabic has been mentioned on page 1385, and its quantitative determination may be conducted as described on page 1388, by precipitation with basic lead acetate solution.

Insoluble Residue: Nitrostarch, Charcoal, Cereal Products, etc. *Starch.* A microscopic examination of the weighed insoluble residue will usually serve to identify its components. Any un-nitrated starch or cereal products is readily distinguished from nitrostarch by treating with a drop of KI solution of iodine and examining under the microscope, when the un-nitrated starch granules will appear blue or black and the nitrated starch colorless or yellow. Charcoal is identified by its color.

Un-nitrated starch, if present in an amount greater than a trace, is determined by boiling with dilute H_2SO_4 or HCl until iodine solution no longer colors a drop of the liquid blue, then filtering and washing thoroughly. The residue is dried at 80° and weighed, the loss of weight representing starch.

Nitrostarch. Another portion of the insoluble residue (the analysis being conducted in duplicate), is extracted with acetone in a Wiley extractor or other continuous extraction apparatus, or by transferring the residue from the crucible to a small beaker, digesting in acetone with stirring, and filtering through the same crucible, washing with fresh acetone. This extraction dissolves all of the nitrostarch, leaving any charcoal or cereal products that may be present. The residue is dried at 100° and weighed, the loss of weight representing nitrostarch.

The nitrogen content of the nitrostarch may be determined, if desired, by precipitating the nitrostarch from the clear acetone solution by the addition of water and evaporation on a steam bath. A portion of the white, floury precipitate is then dried at 70°-80° C., weighed, and its nitrogen content determined in the nitrometer (see page 354 Vol. I).

Charcoal. If charcoal is present its weight may be taken direct, in the absence of cereal products or other substances. When the residue contains cereal products, the material left after hydrolysis of the starch and extraction of the nitrostarch will contain the crude fibre of the cereal together with charcoal or other insoluble ingredients. A separation of such components is usually impracticable.

Trinitrotoluene (TNT.)

Trinitrotoluene, commonly designated in this country by the abbreviation TNT., is also known in this and other countries by such names as triton, trotyl, tolite, trilite, trinol, tritolo, etc. The term trinitrotoluol, which is probably more commonly used than trinitrotoluene, is incorrect according to approved chemical nomenclature.

This explosive is of the greatest importance as a high explosive for military use, being adaptable as a bursting charge for high explosive shell, trench mortar shell, drop-bombs, grenades, etc., because of its powerful explosive properties, relative safety in manufacture, handling, etc., its stability, its lack of hygroscopicity, and absence of any tendency to form sensitive compounds with metals.

It is classified by the Ordnance Department, U. S. A., into three grades, according to purity—Grades I, II, and III, with solidification points of at least 80.0°, 79.5°, and 76° C., respectively. Other requirements—the same for all grades—are as follows: ash, not more than 0.1%; moisture, not more than 0.1%; insoluble, not more than 0.15%; acidity, not more than 0.01%.

Solidification Point. The determination of the solidification point or "setting point" of TNT. is the best single test for purity of this compound, and is preferably carried out as follows:

A sample of about 50 grams of TNT. is placed in a $1'' \times 6''$ test tube and melted by placing the tube in an oven at about 90° C. The tube is then inserted through a large cork stopper into a larger test tube about $1\frac{1}{2}'' \times 7''$, which, in turn, is lowered into a wide-mouth liter bottle, so that the rim of the large tube rests on the neck of the bottle. The inner test tube is provided with a cork stopper containing 3 openings—one for a standard thermometer graduated in $1/10°$ C., one for a short thermometer which is passed just through the stopper and is used for noting the average temperature of the exposed mercury column of the standard thermometer, and the third opening being a small v-shaped notch at the side of the stopper, through which passes a wire whose lower end is bent in a loop at right angles to the axis of the tube and which is used for stirring the molten sample of TNT.

The standard thermometer is so adjusted that its bulb is in the center of the molten mass, and the stirrer is operated vigorously, the thermometer being watched carefully as the temperature falls. The temperature will finally remain constant for an appreciable time and then rise slightly, owing to the heat of crystallization of the TNT. As this point is reached, readings should be taken about every 15 seconds until the maximum temperature of the rise is reached. This temperature will usually remain constant for several minutes while crystallization is proceeding. The maximum reading, corrected for the emergent stem of the thermometer, is taken as the solidification point of the sample.

Ash. About 5 grams of TNT. is moistened with sulphuric acid and burned in a tared crucible. The residue is again moistened with a few drops of nitric acid and sulphuric acid and again ignited and the resulting ash weighed.

Moisture. A sample of about 5 grams spread on a watch glass is desiccated over sulphuric acid to constant weight.

Insoluble. A sample of about 10 grams is treated with 150 cc. of 95% alcohol, heated to boiling, and filtered while hot through a tared Gooch crucible with asbestos mat. The insoluble residue is washed with hot alcohol, dried at 100° C. and weighed.

Acidity. A 10-gram sample is melted in a large test tube or a flask and shaken with 100 cc. of neutralized boiling water, cooled and the water decanted. A similar treatment is given using 50 cc. of boiling water, the two portions of water combined, cooled and titrated with tenth normal NaOH, using phenolphthalein indicator. The acidity is calculated as % H_2SO_4 in the original sample.

Nitrogen. Nitrogen is not usually determined in the inspection of TNT. but when necessary it may be determined by the Dumas combustion method or the modification of the Kjeldahl method described on page 1382.

Picric Acid

Ordnance Department, U. S. A., specifications for picric acid prescribe that it shall have a solidification point of not less than 120° C.; that it shall contain not more than the following amounts of impurities:

Moisture—0.2% for dry material.................22.0% for wet.
Sulphuric acid (free and combined)...............0.10%
Ash...0.2%
Insoluble in water...............................0.2%
Soluble lead.....................................0.0004%
Nitric acid (free)...............................none

Solidification Point. Dry the sample at a temperature not exceeding 50° C. Melt sufficient to give a 3-inch column in a 6-inch$\times\frac{3}{4}$-inch test tube immersed in a bath of glycerin heated to 130° C. When the sample is completely melted remove the tube from the bath and stir the sample with a standardized thermometer graduated in 0.10 degrees, until the picric acid solidifies. During solidification the temperature will remain constant for a short time and then undergo a slight rise. The highest temperature reached on this rise is recorded as the solidification point. The test may be more accurately carried out using the apparatus and method as described under trinitrotoluene (p. 1391).

Moisture. A weighed sample of about 10 grams is spread evenly on a tared watch glass and dried to constant weight (about 3–4 hours) at 70° C.

Sulphuric Acid. About 2 grams is weighed and dissolved in 50 cc. of distilled H_2O, acidified with HCl and heated to about boiling. Hot $BaCl_2$ solution is added with stirring and the mixture allowed to stand at least 1 hour on the steam bath. Filter hot on a tared Gooch crucible, wash with water, dry at 100° C. and weigh. Calculate $BaSO_4$ found as H_2SO_4 in original sample.

Ash. About 5 grams is weighed in a platinum crucible, moistened with sulphuric acid, burned carefully, and the residue ignited to burn off all carbon. The resulting ash is cooled and weighed.

Insoluble in Water. 10 grams of the sample is treated with 150 cc. boiling water, boiled for 10 minutes, filtered while hot through a tared Gooch crucible, washed well with hot water, and the insoluble residue on the filter dried at 100°, cooled, and weighed.

Soluble Lead. The presence of soluble lead in picric acid is highly objectionable, because lead picrate is an extremely sensitive explosive and its presence would greatly increase the dangers involved in handling and loading picric acid. A weighed sample of about 300 g. is digested in a 2-liter flask with 100 cc. of a hot saturated solution of barium hydroxide in 65% alcohol. 1400 cc. of 95% alcohol is then added and the digestion continued at a temperature below the boiling point (with reflux condenser), until everything except traces of insoluble matter is in solution. The picric acid is then allowed to crystallize on cooling, and the solution filtered off, decanting the clear liquid from the crystals until 500 cc. of filtrate is obtained. This 500 cc., representing 100 g. of picric acid, is treated with 5 drops HNO_3 and 10 cc. of 1% $HgCl_2$ solution, and H_2S passed through it for 15 minutes. Allow the precipitate to settle for 20 minutes, filter and wash with alcohol saturated with H_2S. Dry and ignite the precipitate, then dissolve the residue in 9 cc. of HNO_3 (sp.gr. 1.42) by warming, add warm water to bring the volume to 50 cc., and electrolize at 0.4 ampere and 2.5 volts, temperature 65° C., for 1 hour. Wash the electrode by replacing the beaker with another one containing distilled water without interrupting the current. Dry and weigh the previously tared anode. The weight of lead peroxide found $\times 0.8661$ gives the percentage of soluble lead found.

Nitric Acid. No coloration should result when a water solution of picric acid is treated with a solution of diphenylamine in sulphuric acid.

Ammonium Picrate

Ammonium picrate, also known in this country as "Explosive D," is of importance as a military explosive more on account of its insensitiveness to shock and friction, than because of its explosive strength, which is less than that of TNT. Its chief use is as a bursting charge in armor-piercing projectiles.

Military specifications require it to be prepared from picric acid of standard purity, to contain not less than 5.64% ammoniacal nitrogen, and not more than the following amounts of impurities:

Moisture	0.20%
Insoluble material	0.20%
Ash	0.20%
Free ammonia (NH_3)	0.004%

Moisture. A sample of about 10 grams spread on a tared watch glass is dried at 95° C. to constant weight (about 2 hours).

Insoluble Material. A 10-gram sample is boiled with 150 cc. of water for 10 minutes, filtered on a Gooch crucible, the residue washed with hot water, dried at 100° and weighed.

Ash. A sample of about 1 gram is saturated with melted paraffin and burned in a tared crucible, the residue ignited to burn off all carbon, and the ash weighed.

Free Ammonia. A sample of about 5 grams is ground in a porcelain mortar

34

with successive 50 cc. portions of water until the sample is entirely dissolved, each portion of the water being poured through a filter into a 500-cc. Erlenmeyer flask. Three to 5 drops of a saturated solution of sodium alizarin sulphonate in water are added as indicator and the solution titrated with N/10 acid.

Tetryl

Tetryl is the commercial term applied to the explosive trinitrophenyl-methylnitramine, also improperly called tetranitromethylaniline. Its chief use is as a " booster " charge in high explosive shell, where it serves to transmit the detonating wave from the detonator or fuze to the less sensitive bursting charge. Being in immediate contact with the fuze it must be of a high degree of purity, and is required by Ordnance Department specifications to have a melting point of at least 128.5° C. and to contain not more than the following amounts of impurities:

Moisture	0.10%
Surface acidity (as H_2SO_4)	0.01%
Occluded acidity (as H_2SO_4)	0.10%
Insoluble in benzene	0.40%

Melting Point. The sample to be used for this test is dried overnight in a vacuum desiccator and pulverized to pass a 100-mesh screen. A capillary melting-point tube is filled to about $\frac{1}{4}$ inch from the bottom and attached to the stem of a standard thermometer so that the sample is next to the center of the bulb. The bath is properly agitated and provision made for correcting for the emergent stem of the thermometer. The temperature of the bath is raised rapidly to 120° C., then at the rate of 1° in 5 minutes, the temperature at which the first meniscus appears across the capillary tube being noted as the melting point.

Moisture. A sample of about 5 grams is weighed in a wide shallow weighing bottle and dried over sulphuric acid in a desiccator for 48 hours, the sample being spread uniformly so that its depth is not over 0.5 cm. The loss of weight is regarded as moisture.

Surface Acidity. A 10-gram sample, finely powdered, is shaken for 5 minutes with 50 cc. of cold boiled distilled water, filtered, washed with 50 cc. more water, and the filtrate and washings titrated with N/20 NaOH solution using phenolphthalein indicator.

Occluded Acidity. The benzene filtrate from the determination of insoluble material is shaken with 100 cc. cold boiled distilled water in a separatory funnel, the water layer removed and the benzene solution given a second extraction with 50 cc. more water. The combined water extracts are titrated with N/20 NaOH solution, using phenolphthalein indicator.

Insoluble in Benzene. 5 grams of sample is dissolved in 75 cc. of benzene filtered through a tared Gooch crucible, and the residue washed with 25 cc. of acetone, dried to constant weight at 100° C. and weighed.

Mercury Fulminate

In commercial blasting caps and electric detonators mercury fulminate is generally found intimately mixed with potassium chlorate. It is, however, used without admixture in certain types of detonators, in the fuzes of high explosive shell and for other military purposes. It is usually purchased under specifications which provide that it shall be at least 98% pure, shall be free from acid, and contain not more than 2% insoluble matter, 1% free mercury, and 0.05% chlorine in the form of chlorides.

Preparation of Sample. Mercury fulminate being packed and handled in a thoroughly wet condition until dried just before use, it is generally necessary to dry the sample before testing. This may be done by exposing in a low temperature oven at not more than 50° C. until practically dry, then in a desiccator (not a vacuum desiccator) over sulphuric acid or calcium chloride until its weight is constant.

Mercury Fulminate Content. Exactly 0.3 g. is weighed into a wide-mouthed Erlenmeyer flask containing 250 cc. distilled water, and 30 cc. of a 20% solution of purest sodium thiosulphate is added quickly and the mixture shaken for exactly 1 minute. At once titrate with N/10 hydrochloric acid using 3 drops of methyl orange indicator, the titration to be commenced 1 minute after adding the sodium thiosulphate, and to occupy not more than 1 minute additional time.

The percentage of mercury fulminate is calculated from the volume of standard acid required, after deducting the volume of acid required for a blank determination. Four molecules of HCl are equivalent to 1 mol. of mercury fulminate, or 1 cc. N/10 HCl equals 0.00711565 g. mercury fulminate. The reaction is assumed to be as follows:

$$HgC_2N_2O_2 + 2Na_2S_2O_3 + 2H_2O = HgS_4O_6 + 4NaOH + C_2N_2.$$

Acidity. A 10-g. sample is extracted with 2 successive 25-cc. portions of boiled distilled water in a Gooch crucible, and 3 drops of methyl orange solution (1 g. per liter) added. No red tinge of color should be obtained.

Insoluble Matter. A 2-g. sample is dissolved in 20% $Na_2S_2O_3$ solution, filtered through a tared Gooch crucible and any insoluble washed several times with water and dried to constant weight at 60°–70° C.

Free Mercury. The residue of insoluble matter obtained as described above is treated with a solution of 3 g. KI and 6 g. $Na_2S_2O_3$ in 50 cc. H_2O by passing the solution through the Gooch crucible. Any organic mercury compounds are thus converted into mercuric iodide, which is soluble in $Na_2S_2O_3$ solution. The metallic mercury remains behind on the filter, and is washed with H_2O, dried 1 hour at 80°–90° C., and weighed.

Chlorides. A 5-g. sample of fulminate is extracted in a Gooch crucible with 2 successive 25 cc. portions of distilled water at 90°–100° C. Three drops of strong HNO_3 and 10 drops of 10% $AgNO_3$ solution are added to the filtrate. If a turbidity results, the AgCl should be determined gravimetrically or a fresh sample extracted and the filtrate titrated with a standard $AgNO_3$ solution.

Blasting Caps and Electric Detonators

Preparation of Sample. In the examination of blasting caps or detonators for either commercial or military use, the removal of the detonating composition from the copper or brass shell requires considerable precaution. Blasting caps are emptied by squeezing the cap gently in a pair of "gas forceps," the jaws of the forceps being passed through a small opening in a piece of heavy leather, rubber belting, or similar material, about 6″ square, which serves as a shield to protect the hand in case of the possible explosion of the cap in squeezing. After each squeeze, the loosened portion of the charge is shaken out on a piece of glazed paper, the cap turned slightly in the forceps and again squeezed· The pressure on the cap should be just sufficient to slightly dent it, and in shaking out the charge, the cap should not be tapped on the table or other surface. With these precautions there is little danger of an explosion.

Electric detonators[1] are opened by first cutting off the wires or "legs" close to the shell, then tearing off the uppef portion of the shell by means of pointed side-cutting pliers, the cap being held firmly in the fingers and a thin strip of the copper shell being torn off spirally by nipping the top edge of the shell with the forceps. This must be done with great care, especially as the portion of the shell containing the fulminate charge is approached. When the greater portion of the plug which holds the wires in place has been exposed, the plug and wires are gently pulled out, care being taken to avoid force and possible friction, and any adhering particles of the charge brushed off onto glazed paper. The charge is then removed from the lower part of the shell just as in the case of blasting caps.

The charge is removed separately from several of the caps or detonators and each weighed in order to determine the average weight of charge as well as variation of same.

"Reinforced" caps, or those which contain a small perforated inner copper capsule pressed on top of the charge, must be opened in the manner described for electric detonators, in order to remove the inner capsule. Detonators of this type usually contain a main charge of some nitro compound superimposed by a layer of mercury fulminate, mixture of fulminate and chlorate, or lead azide. Although a clean mechanical separation of the two layers is usually not possible, portions can be taken from each and identified by qualitative tests before proceeding with a quantitative examination.

Moisture. The moisture content of the composition is determined by desiccating to constant weight over sulphuric acid or calcium chloride.

---

[1] A safe apparatus for cutting open electric detonators is shown in Bureau of Mines Technical Paper No. 282, "Analysis of Detonating and Priming Mixtures." by C. A. Taylor and W. R. Rinkenbach, Plate I.

Analysis of Composition Containing Mercury Fulminate and Potassium Chlorate. About 2–3 grams of the well-mixed composition is weighed in a Gooch crucible provided with asbestos mat or disc of filter paper or silk, and first moistened with a few drops of alcohol, then extracted with 200–250 cc. of cold water in 15–20 cc. portions, using slight suction after each portion has remained in the crucible for a few minutes. The residue in the filter is dried to constant weight at 60°–70° C. (2–3 hours), and weighed.

The water extract contains the potassium chlorate and a portion of the mercury fulminate, which is slightly soluble in cold water. It is treated with 2 cc. of ammonium hydroxide and H_2S passed to completely precipitate the dissolved mercury fulminate as HgS. This black precipitate is filtered off, washed, dried and weighed. Its weight $\times 1.22$ gives the amount of mercury fulminate dissolved by the water. This weight added to the weight of the dried residue insoluble in water gives the total weight of mercury fulminate in the sample. The $KClO_3$ is found by subtracting the $\%$ of mercury fulminate $+\%$ moisture from 100%.

Analysis of Compositions Containing Nitrocompounds. Trinitrotoluene, tetryl or picric acid can be identified by melting point test, TNT. melting at about 79°–80° C., tetryl at about 128° C., and picric acid at about 120°–122° C. They may be extracted from the mixture by means of ethyl ether, in which mercury fulminate is only very slightly soluble, and the determination of $KClO_3$ and mercury fulminate then made as described in the preceding paragraph.

If the main charge is an organic nitrate such as nitrated vegetable ivory, nitrostarch, etc., such material will be left with the mercury fulminate in the insoluble residue after extraction with water. The mercury fulminate is then extracted by means of a hot 20% solution of sodium thiosulphate, leaving the organic nitrate in the Gooch crucible. These materials in the detonating composition can be readily identified by microscopic examination.

In detonators where TNT. or tetryl compose the main portion of the charge, a small amount of lead azide, with or without mercury fulminate may be used as a priming charge for the purpose of initiating the detonation of the nitrocompound. It should be identified in the top portion of the charge, next to the reinforcing cap, and will in all probability be present if mercury fulminate is not found. It is practically insoluble in water and in ether, and will be left in the insoluble residue. If present, fulminate is destroyed by treating the residue, in a flask, with 25 cc. of KOH solution. This converts the lead azide to potassium azide, KN_3. A slight excess of H_2SO_4 is added and the mixture distilled, the distillate, containing HN_3, being collected in water. Enough NaOH is added to the distillate to give an alkaline reaction with litmus, then a little $Pb(NO_3)_2$, when lead azide, PbN_6 will be regenerated as a white precipitate, which may be filtered off, washed with water, then with alcohol, dried in the air, and tested by striking a small portion with a hammer.

Primers

Variations in Composition. Many varieties of composition are used in primers for small arms ammunition, and for other military purposes. The composition must be ignited by the impact of the firing pin, and must give a flame of sufficient intensity and duration to ensure proper ignition of the propellant or of the detonator, depending on the purpose for which the primer is employed. As primers are used with various kinds and granulation of explosives, a priming composition suitable for one purpose is unsuited for another; hence there are many types of priming compositions, a few of which are indicated in the following table:

TYPES OF PRIMER COMPOSITIONS
APPROXIMATE COMPOSITION (PER CENT)

Ingredients	No. 1	No. 2	No. 3	No. 4	No. 5	No. 6	No. 7	No. 8	No. 9	No. 10
Mercury fulminate	31	25	11	..	..	..	..	..	..	28
Potassium chlorate	38	38	53	60	50	51	53	53	47	14
Sulphur	..	..	..	7	3	9	..	..	22	..
Powdered glass	..	..	..	..	..	12	..	..	..	35
Lead sulphocyanate	..	..	..	..	..	..	25	25	..	..
Copper sulphocyanate	..	..	..	3	..	..	..	..	..	..
Barium nitrate	..	6	..	..	..	..	..	..	..	..
TNT	..	..	..	..	..	..	5	..	..	..
Tetryl	..	..	..	..	..	..	..	3	..	..
Antimony sulphide	31	31	36	30	44	26	17	17	31	21
Lead oxide (PbO)	..	..	..	..	..	..	..	2	..	..
Shellac	..	..	..	..	..	2	..	..	..	2
Black powder (meal)	..	..	..	..	3	..	..	..	..	..

In addition to these ingredients most priming compositions are mixed with small amounts of some binding material dissolved in water or alcohol, such as gum arabic, gum tragacanth, glue, shellac, etc. These traces of binding materials are usually disregarded in the analysis of the compositions.

Preparation of Sample. If the caps contain anvils, these must first be carefully removed, as well as any covering of tin foil or paper. The primer composition is then carefully removed from a number of primers and weighed to determine the average charge. It is then carefully crushed, a little at a time, and the sample well mixed. If necessary, it may be removed from the caps by the aid of water or alcohol and the latter removed by evaporation before weighing.

Qualitative Examination. The following special tests may be made use of in connection with a qualitative analysis of the mixture:

A small amount is burned between two watch glasses, the formation of a mirror indicating mercury, antimony, copper or lead. The mercury mirror is readily volatile on gentle ignition.

Extract a portion of the mixture with ether, then with water, then with $Na_2S_2O_3$ solution, then with aqua regia, retaining each of these solutions.

TNT. or tetryl may be present in the ether solution and are identified by m.p. or color test, TNT. giving a deep red color with acetone and KOH. Sulphur is detected by burning a portion of the ether-soluble material and noting odor of SO_2.

The water extract is tested for $KClO_3$ by adding H_2SO_4, boiling, and noting odor of chlorine. A portion is treated with HCl and $FeCl_3$, a red color indicating thiocyanate. The usual $FeSO_4$ ring test is made for nitrates. A white precipitate with H_2SO_4 indicates Ba or Pb.

The aqua regia solution is diluted and tested with H_2S for antimony, lead, and copper. If the precipitate is not orange-red, lead or copper are indicated. Dissolve in HNO_3, neutralize with NH_4OH; a blue solution indicates copper, while lead is detected by the formation of a white precipitate with H_2SO_4.

Any material insoluble in aqua regia may be powdered glass or other abrasive material.

Quantitative Analysis. The method of analysis will depend entirely upon the ingredients indicated by qualitative tests. In general, a separation is best effected by successive extractions with ether, water, $Na_2S_2O_3$ solution (to remove fulminate), dilute or concentrated HCl, and aqua regia. The small amount of mercury fulminate present in the water extract may be determined by precipitation with H_2S or by adding 10–15 cc. of thiosulphate solution and a few drops of methyl orange and titrating with $N/10$ HCl or H_2SO_4 (see page 513 of Vol. I). Other materials in the water and acid solutions are determined by the usual analytical methods.

Nitrocellulose

General. The term nitrocellulose, or more correctly cellulose nitrate, applies to any nitration product of cellulose, ranging from products containing in the neighborhood of 10–11% N, which are used in the preparation of lacquers and other commercial products, to military guncotton with over 13% N. All of these products are undoubtedly mixtures of the various nitrates of cellulose, as indicated by the fact that there is always some material with low nitrogen content, soluble in ether-alcohol, in high nitrogen guncotton, and some insoluble material in the lower nitrated commercial products. It can usually be shown without great difficulty that any nitrated cotton is a mixture of various nitrates of cellulose.

The products of military importance are the insoluble guncotton of high N-content, and the so-called "pyro" or pyrocellulose, soluble in ether-alcohol and of about 12.60% N-content. In testing these products, the characteristics of most importance are content of nitrogen, solubility in ether-alcohol, and stability. Other determinations generally made are solubility in acetone and ash.

Preparation of Sample. If the sample contains a large excess of water, it is enclosed in a clean cloth and the excess water removed by means of a press or wringer. The pressed sample is then rubbed up in the cloth (not with the bare hand) until lumps are removed, then spread on clean paper trays in an air bath at about 35°–40° C. until "air-dry."

Samples for stability tests and nitrogen determination are treated as noted below, the air-dry sample being suitable for determining solubility and ash.

Nitrogen. About 1 to 1.05 g. of the air-dry sample is roughly weighed in a tared weighing bottle, dried at 95°–100° C. for $1\frac{1}{2}$ hours, cooled in a desiccator and accurately weighed. It is then transferred to the generating bulb of a nitrometer (Du Pont modification; see p. 354) using a total of 20 cc. of 95–96% c.p. H_2SO_4. The sample must be dissolved in the acid either in the weighing bottle or in the cup of the generator, before it is drawn into the generating bulb, and both the weighing bottle and the cup of the generator must be thoroughly washed out with the 20 cc. of H_2SO_4, so that none of the sample is lost. The determination in the nitrometer is completed in the usual manner (p. 354), the result being expressed as % N in the dried sample of nitrocellulose.

Solubility in Ether-Alcohol. (a) *Guncotton:* The amount of ether-alcohol soluble material in guncotton being usually not more than 10–12%, the determination may be made by evaporating a clear solution. Two grams of air-dry sample is placed in a clean dry cork-stoppered 250 cc. cylinder, 67 cc. of 95% ethyl alcohol added to thoroughly wet the guncotton, then 133 cc. of ethyl ether (U.S.P. grade, 96%), added and the mixture well shaken. If the mixture of 2 parts ether and 1 part alcohol be added at once to the sample, a gummy mass may result which dissolves with great difficulty, especially if the solubility is unusually high.

The cylinder is now allowed to stand at a constant temperature of usually 20° C. (15.5° C. is sometimes specified). The solubility of nitrocellulose *increases* as the temperature is *decreased*, hence a constant temperature of digestion is important. During the digestion, which requires at least 1 hour, the cylinder must be thoroughly shaken at 5-minute intervals. The cylinder is now allowed to stand for at least 4 hours, until the insoluble portion of the sample has completely settled and the supernatant liquid is perfectly clear.

50 cc. of the clear solution is now drawn off with a pipette, care being taken not to disturb the settled pulp, and evaporated in a weighed evaporating dish on a steam bath, avoiding loss from violent boiling of the ether. When 25–30% of the solution has been evaporated, 10 cc. of distilled water is added slowly and the evaporation continued to dryness. The effect of the water is to leave the residue in a white, brittle or powdery condition, rather than a tough film which would lose its solvent with difficulty.

The dish is finally placed in an oven at 95–100° C. for $\frac{1}{2}$ hour, cooled in a desiccator, and weighed. The weight of the residue, corrected for the residue in the 50 cc. of ether-alcohol and 10 cc. H_2O used, represents the soluble nitrocellulose in 0.5 g. of the guncotton.

(b) *Pyrocellulose:* The solubility of pyrocellulose may be determined in the manner described for guncotton, but owing to the much larger amount of soluble material present, the evaporation of the residue to constant weight without decomposition involves considerable difficulty. Sufficient water must be added to precipitate the soluble nitrocellulose from solution in a stringy or fibrous condition.

The determination is usually conducted by either the volumetric method or the filtration method.

In the volumetric method, one gram of the air-dry sample is covered with 100 cc. of 95% ethyl alcohol and allowed to stand at least 15 minutes with frequent stirring, 200 cc. of ethyl ether is then added with stirring and the agitation continued until solution is complete. The solution is now allowed to stand at least 4 hours with frequent stirring, during at least 1 hour of which time it is to be kept at a temperature of 15.5° C. It is then transferred to a "solubility tube" and allowed to stand for at least 16 hours, in order that the insoluble material may settle completely. The solubility tubes are glass tubes about 30.6 inches long×1.3 inches inside diameter, tapering at a point 6 inches from the bottom to a constricted portion about 3 inches long and about .375 inch inside diameter. This narrow bottom portion is graduated to read directly the percentage of insoluble material, the value of the graduations having been first ascertained by comparison with results obtained by the filtration method described below. The tubes are made of heavy glass and provided with vented ground glass stoppers. They hold 300 cc. when filled to about 8 inches below the top.

In the filtration method, the solution is prepared and settled in a solubility tube as described above, and the clear liquid removed as completely as possible by means of a narrow siphon tube of glass. Fresh alcohol and ether are then added as before, the tube shaken and allowed to stand again for 16 hours, when the process may be repeated several times, depending on the amount of insoluble material present. After the last decantation, the residue is washed from the tube to a beaker, using as small a quantity of ether-alcohol as possible, and the mixture filtered through a filtering tube consisting of a $1''×6''$ test tube with its lower end drawn out to a taper terminating in a hole about $\frac{1}{8}''$ diameter. In the lower end of this tube is a small plug of previously ignited asbestos. The filtration is facilitated if the greater part of the asbestos is mixed with the insoluble matter and solvent in the beaker, the mixture well stirred and quickly poured into the filtering tube on top of a small plug of asbestos. In this manner, the insoluble matter becomes mixed with the asbestos and the formation of a gelatinous, impenetrable mat in the tube is avoided. After filtering, the tube is washed with fresh ether-alcohol, dried at 40°–45° C. and finally for 1 hour at 100° C., then cooled in a desiccator and weighed. All combustible matter is then removed by careful ignition, and the tube again weighed, the loss of weight being the total insoluble material in the 1-gram sample.

Solubility in Acetone. A 1-gram sample of air-dry pyrocellulose is treated with about 200 cc. of acetone with frequent stirring until all gelatinous matter has dissolved. The solution is transferred to a solubility tube (described above), the volume made up to about 300 cc. with fresh acetone, well shaken, and allowed to settle for at least 16 hours. The graduations on the tube having been checked by gravimetric determinations, the percentage of residue insoluble in acetone may be read direct, or the filtration method described above may be applied.

Ash. One gram of air-dry sample is weighed in a tared crucible, moistened with 10–15 drops of concentrated nitric acid, and digested for 2–3 hours on a steam bath until converted to a gummy mass. The crucible is then heated carefully over a Bunsen burner until the mass is completely charred, then at a red heat until its weight is constant. The residue is the ash of the sample.

Stability Test: Heat test with Potassium Iodide Starch Paper. The "heat test" or KI test, as it is commonly designated, is the test most commonly employed for determining the stability or degree of purification of nitrocellulose, whether guncotton or pyrocellulose. This test, also referred to as the Abel test, depends on the action of oxides of nitrogen liberated by the nitrocellulose under the influence of heat, the gases in contact with the KI-starch paper liberating iodine which colors the starch.

The sample is dried with great care to avoid contamination, in a clean paper tray, at 35° to 43° C., until its moisture is reduced to the amount which will give the minimum heat test, usually 1.5 to 2%. The proper amount of moisture is determined as follows: During the progress of the drying, the sample on the tray is "rubbed up" from time to time, using a piece of clean tissue paper spread over the back of the hand. When the sample begins to adhere to the paper, due to static electricity, a sample of 1.3 g. is weighed into a standard test tube. These tubes are $5\frac{1}{2}$ inches long, not less than $\frac{1}{2}$ inch inside diameter and not more than $\frac{5}{8}''$ outside diameter, made of glass about 3/64 inch (1.2 mm.) thick. As soon as the first sample is weighed, the tray is replaced in the drying oven for 2–5 minutes, a second sample weighed, and this process repeated until a series of 5 samples have been taken, the last sample being completely dry. This series of samples, if properly taken, will cover the range of moisture content giving the minimum heat test. If the sample in the tray appears to have become too dry during the time the weighings are being made, it may be placed in a moist atmosphere for not more than 2 hours; the entire time of drying and making the test must not exceed 8 hours.

The tubes containing the samples are fitted with clean, fresh cork stoppers through which pass a piece of glass rod into the end of which is fused a small piece of platinum wire bent into a hook. The wire is heated in a flame to clean it, a piece of the standard KI starch test paper, $1'' \times \frac{3}{8}''$, attached, taking care that neither wire nor paper are touched with the fingers, and the paper moistened on its upper portion by touching it with a glass rod dipped in a solution of equal volumes of pure glycerin and water. The stoppers are then inserted in the tubes and the tubes placed in a constant temperature water bath, so that they are immersed to a depth of 2.25 inches. The time of placing in the bath and the time of the appearance of the first faint yellowish discoloration of the test paper are noted. The minimum test given by the 5 samples is taken as the result of the test. The discoloration appears at the lower edge of the moist portion of the paper. The temperature of the heat test bath is 65.5° C. (150° F.) for pyrocellulose, and usually 76.5° C. (170° F.) for guncotton. Pyro is usually required to stand a test of 35 minutes, and guncotton 10 minutes.

A standard test paper is absolutely essential, and is prepared as follows:[1]

The paper used in preparing the test paper is Schleicher and Schüll's filter paper 597. This is cut in strips about 6 by 24 inches, and after being washed by immersing each strip is distilled water for a short time is hung up to dry overnight. The cords on which the paper is hung are clean and the room is free from fumes. The washed and dried paper is dipped in a solution prepared as follows:

The best quality of potassium iodide obtainable is recrystallized three times from hot absolute alcohol, dried, and 1 gram dissolved in 8 ounces of distilled water. Cornstarch is well washed by decantation with distilled water, dried at a low temperature, 3 grams rubbed into a paste with a little cold water, and poured into 8 ounces of boiling water in a flask. After being boiled gently for 10 minutes, the starch solution is cooled and mixed with the potassium iodide solution in a glass trough.

[1] Storm, C. G., Proc. 7th Inter. Congress Appl. Chem., 1909; J. Ind. & Eng. Chem., vol. 1, 1909, page 802.

Each strip of filter paper is immersed in the above-mentioned mixture for about 10 seconds and is then hung over a clean cord to dry. The dipping is done in a dim light and the paper left overnight to dry in a perfectly dark room. Every precaution is taken to insure freedom from contamination in preparing the materials and from laboratory fumes that might cause decomposition. When dry the paper is cut into pieces about $\frac{3}{8}$ by 1 inch and is preserved in the dark in tight glass-stoppered bottles, the edges of the large strips being first trimmed off about one fourth inch to remove portions that are sometimes slightly discolored. When properly prepared the finished paper is perfectly white, any discoloration indicating decomposition due to contamination.

Stability Test at 135° C. In addition to the KI starch test, pyrocellulose is usually required to stand a test at 135° C., made as follows:

The sample is completely dried at 42° C., and 2.5 grams placed in each of 2 heavy glass tubes, 290 mm. long, 18 mm. outside diameter and 15 mm. inside diameter, closed with a cork stopper through which passes a hole 4 mm. in diameter. A strip of litmus paper or standard normal methyl violet paper, 70 mm. long and 20 mm. wide is placed in each tube, its lower edge 25 mm. above the sample, which is pressed down to occupy a depth of 2 inches, the walls of the tube being wiped clean with a roll of paper. The tubes are then heated in a constant temperature bath at 134° to 135° C., all but about 6–7 mm. of the tube being immersed in the bath. They are partially withdrawn for examination of the test papers every 5 minutes after the first 20 minutes of heating, and replaced at once. The time required for reddening of the litmus paper or for turning the methyl violet paper to a salmon pink color is noted as the time of the test. A minimum test of 30 minutes is required with the methyl violet paper, and heating is then continued for a total of 5 hours, during which time there should be no explosion.

The standard normal methyl violet paper is prepared as follows:

Preparation of Methyl Violet Test Paper. A solution is prepared containing the following ingredients: pure rosaniline acetate prepared from 0.2500 g. basic rosaniline, .1680 g. methyl violet (crystal violet), 4 cc. c.p. glycerin, 50 cc. water, and sufficient pure 95% ethyl alcohol to make up to 100 cc. This solution is placed in the angle of an inclined deep rectangular glass tray, and large sheets of Schleicher & Schüll filter paper (No. 597) cut in four strips are dipped in it. In dipping, the strip is held by one end and dipped to within $\frac{1}{4}''$ of this end, withdrawing it slowly up the side of the tray so as to remove surplus solution. The strip is then held horizontally and waved to and fro so as to prevent the solution from running and collecting in spots. As soon as the alcohol has evaporated the strip is suspended vertically to dry, and when dry is cut in strips 20×70 mm. These strips are bottled and kept for use in the 135° test.

SMOKELESS POWDER
Nitrocellulose Powders

At the present time the smokeless powder used by all nations is composed of either colloided nitrocellulose alone or a mixture of colloided nitrocellulose and nitroglycerin. All cannon powder used in this country is of the nitrocellulose type, small-arms powders being of both types. The form and size of the grains are of great variety, depending on the arm in which the propellant is to be employed.

Physical tests made in connection with the examination of smokeless powder include the compression test, determinations of average measurements of the grains, specific gravity, gravimetric density, number of grains per pound, and calculation of burning surface per pound.

Chemical tests include determinations of moisture and volatile solvent, diphenylamine used as stabilizer, ash, material insoluble in ether-alcohol and in acetone, and sometimes nitrogen content.

Stability tests include the 135° C. test, the 115° C. test, and the "Surveillance test."

Moisture and Volatiles. A sample of the powder weighing approximately 1 gram, in the form of thin shavings cut from at least 10 grains, or of whole grains if the powder is too small to cut conveniently, is placed in a clean, dried and weighed 250 cc. beaker, 50 cc. of redistilled 95% (by volume) alcohol, and 100 cc. redistilled ethyl ether added and the beaker allowed to stand under cover-jar with occasional stirring, until the powder is completely dissolved. This usually requires from 1 to 2 days. When all gelatinous particles of the powder have dissolved, the beaker is heated on the steam bath to evaporate part of the ether, before precipitation of the nitrocellulose with water. The amount of ether to be evaporated is important, since it largely determines the character of the nitrocellulose precipitate. The presence of too much ether causes a fine sandy precipitate; too little causes a gummy, gelatinous precipitate. A fine, flaky, or fibrous precipitate is desirable. The proper amount of evaporation can be best determined by practice; usually the solution may be evaporated to about $\frac{2}{3}$ its original volume before precipitating. When the proper volume is obtained, 50 cc. of water is added from a graduate, with continual stirring, in 5 cc. portions. If a thick gummy precipitate forms, add a little ether until it becomes flaky; then add the remainder of the 50 cc. of water. The heating is continued with stirring, until most of the ether has evaporated, and the beaker is then left on the bath until the precipitate is just dry. It is then placed in the 100° C. oven for 1 hour, cooled in a desiccator and weighed as rapidly as possible. To facilitate weighing the weights should be placed on the balance pan before the beaker is removed from the desiccator so that the exact weight can be adjusted quickly. If more than 10 seconds are consumed in this weighing, the error caused by absorption of moisture from the air is an appreciable one. In any event a check weighing should be made after an additional 30 minutes drying at 100° C.

The final weight of nitrocellulose precipitate subtracted from the weight of the original sample represents the weight of moisture and volatile solvent, and is calculated as per cent of the original sample. If the powder contains diphenylamine, this result is corrected by subtracting from it one fourth of the total diphenylamine content, it having been ascertained by actual trial that pproximately this proportion of the diphenylamine is volatilized during the vaporation.

Moisture. An approximation to the actual moisture content of the powder can be obtained by drying a sample of not less than 5 whole grains and ot less than 20 grams for 6 hours at 100° C., cooling in a desiccator and weighing, the loss of weight being regarded as equal to the hygroscopic moisture n the powder.

Diphenylamine. The content of diphenylamine used as a stabilizer in mokeless powder is most conveniently and rapidly determined by the "nitra-ion method" as follows:

5 grams of the powder in small grains or slices is treated with 30 cc. of oncentrated HNO_3 in a 250 cc. beaker, covered with a watch glass and heated n the steam bath until the powder has been completely decomposed. The olution is then cooled and added to 100 cc. of cold distilled H_2O in a second beaker, stirring vigorously, the first beaker being washed out completely into he second, using additional water. This mixture is now heated on the steam ath until the flocculent precipitate has settled and the liquid has a clear yellow olor. It is then cooled, filtered through a weighed Gooch crucible, the pre-ipitate dried at 100° C. and weighed. The weighed precipitate is now dis-olved by extracting with acetone, the crucible dried and weighed again, the oss of weight being the nitrodiphenylamine produced by action of the HNO_3 n the diphenylamine. This nitrodiphenylamine is a mixture of nitroproducts, nd the empirical factor 0.40576 has been determined for converting it to its quivalent in diphenylamine.

Ash. The ash is determined in the manner described for nitrocellulose p. 1401), the sample being in the form of slices or small grains, and the digestion vith HNO_3 continued until decomposition is practically complete, before leating over a flame.

Solubility in Ether-alcohol. One gram of the sample in slices or small grains is dissolved in 150 cc. of ether-alcohol (2 : 1) in the same manner as for the determination of moisture and volatiles, and transferred to a standard solubility tube (p. 1401), washing it in completely with fresh ether-alcohol so as to bring the total volume to 300 cc. The insoluble material is determined as in pyrocellulose (p. 1401).

Solubility in Acetone. This determination is made in the same manner as the solubility in ether-alcohol, described above.

Stability Test at 135° C. This test is made on duplicate samples in the same manner as described for pyrocellulose (p. 1403). The samples weigh 2.5 grams and are in as nearly whole grains as is consistent with this weight of sample, large grains being turned down on a lathe to fit the standard tubes. The samples are required to stand heating at 134°–135° C. for 5 hours without explosion and must not turn the normal methyl violet paper to salmon pink color in less than one hour.

Stability Test at 115° C. This test is also known as the Ordnance Depart-ment 115° test, or the Sy test. Five samples each consisting of not more than 10 grams and not less than 2 whole grains of the powder are weighed on watch glasses and heated at a temperature of 115° ± 0.5° C. for 8 hours daily for 6 days, the oven being brought each day to the proper temperature before the samples are inserted, the samples being allowed to stand at room conditions overnight. At the end of the sixth day's heating, the samples are cooled in a

desiccator and weighed.   The total loss of weight is regarded as an index c
the stability, and must not exceed a specified limit for each particular size c
grain.

"**Surveillance Test**" at 65.5° C.   Three samples of approximately 4
grams of powder in whole grains, or, in the case of very large grains, 5 whol
grains, are placed in 8-ounce wide-mouth glass stoppered bottles, the stopper
having been previously ground so as to fit tightly.   These bottles are the
heated in a constant temperature magazine at 65.5° ± 2° C.   They ar
observed several times daily and the time noted when visible fumes of oxides c
nitrogen appear in any bottle.   The number of days which powder is require
to stand this test depends on the web thickness of the grain, and varies fror
70 to 140 days.   The test is therefore not a laboratory test, but one whic
more nearly approaches service conditions.   It is of great value as an indicatio
of the possible "stability life" of the powder in service.

Nitrogen.   The determination of nitrogen in smokeless powder is no
usually necessary, in as much as the powder is usually made from nitrocellulos
of known nitrogen content, but when desired the determination is made a
follows:

An average sample of about 5 grams of the powder in slices or small grain
is dissolved in acetone (100 cc. to each 1 g. of sample).   When the sample i
dissolved, the solution is added drop by drop, preferably from a burette, t
200 cc. of hot water in a beaker, the beaker being immersed in boiling wate
so as to maintain its contents at about 90° C.   During this addition the ho
water is continually stirred with a glass rod, so that the precipitated nitro
cellulose forms stringy masses which wrap about the rod.   Small accumulation
of the precipitate are transferred frequently from the rod to another beaker c
hot water to prevent the formation of a colloided mass.   When 2 g. or mor
of the precipitate has been collected and the acetone has been volatilized b
the hot water, it is removed from the beaker and dried at 35°–40° C.   Abou
1 g. of this dry precipitate is placed in a tared weighing bottle, dried 1 hour a
100° C., weighed, and transferred to the cup of the nitrometer with sulphur
acid.   Part of the acid should be added to the precipitate in the weighing bott
before transferring to the nitrometer in order to avoid loss of the dry precipitat
in handling.   The determination of N is then completed as in the case c
nitrocellulose (page 1400).   If the powder contains diphenylamine, a correctio
is necessary for the amount of diphenylamine retained by the precipitate
nitrocellulose.   This has been found to be an added correction of 0.15% N i
the case of powders containing the usual amount of 0.4% diphenylamine
This correction compensates for the nitrogen which becomes combined wit
the diphenylamine, converting it to nitrodiphenylamines.

Instead of correcting for the effect of the diphenylamine, the latter ma
be removed from the precipitated nitrocellulose, after air-drying and befor
final drying at 100° C., by extraction with pure anhydrous ether.   Result
are quite accurate if the determination is conducted with proper precaution

Nitroglycerin Smokeless Powders

Powders of this type are composed mainly of nitrocellulose and nitro-glycerin and may contain other organic or inorganic substances, such as vaseline, nitro-substitution compounds, substituted ureas or other flame-reducing or surface-hardening agents, diphenylamine, metallic nitrates, carbonates, etc. The nitrocellulose may be either high-nitration guncotton insoluble in ether-alcohol, as in British cordite, or a low-nitration product soluble in nitroglycerin, as in ballistite, or may be a mixture of the two varieties.

The method of analysis usually employed consists of (1) an extraction of the nitroglycerin, nitrosubstitution compounds, vaseline, and other ether-soluble materials by means of anhydrous ether; (2) an extraction of the water-soluble materials; (3) determination of soluble and insoluble nitro-celluloses by separation with ether-alcohol (2 : 1).

The extraction with ether is usually made in a Soxhlet apparatus, using about 20 grams of the powder in slices or small grains, in a paper extraction thimble. About 4 hours is usually required for complete extraction. The ether extract is evaporated to dryness in a tared glass dish under a bell-jar evaporator (page 1376), and the ether-soluble residue weighed. To determine whether it contains other substances than nitroglycerin, it may be poured in small portions at a time into about 20 cc. of strong nitric acid (40° Be) heated on a steam bath. The oxidizing action of the nitric acid destroys the nitro-glycerin, and the mixture is then poured into 50–100 cc. of water. Any vaseline or similar substances separate, together with any nitrosubstitution compounds in their original condition or more completely nitrated, diphenylamine in the form of a nitroderivative, etc.

These materials may be separated with more or less completeness by fractional crystallization from ether or other solvent. The exact method to be followed depends on the nature of the materials present.

The residue insoluble in ether is dried and weighed, and then transferred to an Erlenmeyer flask and digested in warm water until any water-soluble materials present have been dissolved. The mixture is filtered, the residue washed with hot water, dried and weighed. The filtrate containing the water-soluble ingredients is examined by the usual analytical methods for inorganic ingredients.

The nitrocellulose insoluble in water is tested for nitrogen content, solubility in ether-alcohol and solubility in acetone, by the methods already described.

Typical Compositions of Commonly Used Explosives

Black Blasting Powder

Sodium nitrate.....................73
Charcoal..........................16
Sulphur..........................11 (Bu. of Mines, Bull. No. 80, p. 19.)

Black Military Powder

Potassium nitrate..................75
Charcoal..........................15
Sulphur..........................10

Typical Dynamite formulas—40% grades (Bu. Mines, Bull. No. 80, p. 21).

	Nitro-glycerin	Nitro-Substitution Com.	Ammo-nium Nitrate	Sodium Nitrate	Nitro-cellu-luse	Wood Pulp	Calcium Carbonate
40% straight Nitroglycerin Dynamite	40	......	......	44	......	15	1
"40%-strength" Ammonia Dynamite	22	......	20	42	......	15	1
"40%-strength" Gelatin Dynamite..	33	......	......	52	1	13	1
"40%-strength" Low-freezing Dynamite.......	30	10	......	44	......	15	1
"40%-strength" Low-freezing Ammonia Dynamite.............	17	4	20	45	......	13	1

Granulated Nitroglycerin Powder ("Judson Powder',

Nitroglycerin.................................... 5　　　　　10
Combustible material†............................35　　　　26
Sodium nitrate.............................. ....60　　　　64

Coal Mining Powders. (Permissible Type)

	I	II	III	IV	V	VI
Nitroglycerin...........................	25	15	10	......	......	10
TNT...................................	......	5	......	5	......	......
Ammonium nitrate......................	......	......	79	90	94	70
Sodium nitrate.........................	34	35	......	......	......	......
Sodium chloride........................	......	......	......	......	......	9
Wood pulp.............................	15	12	10	......	......	10
Flour.................................	25	17	......	5	......	......
Aluminum powder.......................	......	......	......	......	3	......
Charcoal..............................	......	......	......	......	3	......
Calcium carbonate.....................	1	1	......	......	......	1
Zinc oxide............................	......	......	1	......	......	......
Magnesium sulphate, cryst..............	......	15	......	......	......	......

* Sometimes contains also flour, cornmeal, sulphur, etc.
† Composed of sulphur, coal, and rosin.

WATER ANALYSIS

Probably at no other time has the importance of a water supply, either for domestic or industrial purposes, been so great, as in these early years of the twentieth century. The increasing realization of the effect of contaminating materials, both organic and inorganic, on a municipal or private drinking supply—and history's record of the devastating nature of epidemics due to water-borne disease organisms, have led to the careful investigation of water for its sanitary value and the development of materials and equipment to fight and eliminate such contamination, and have increased many hundreds of per cent the factor of safety to the public health. In like manner, and even to a greater extent, has the value of water for industrial uses been a matter for careful consideration. It is hard for the public to realize the immense quantities of water used for industrial purposes, not only for the development of steam and electric power, but also for purposes of manufacture.

From the standpoint of power development we are familiar with the heat losses and the increased operating expenses due to scale formation in the steam or locomotive boiler, and also to the continued rapid decrease in valuation of boiler property, or of power plant property, due to corrosion or rusting. Another element of trouble which is noticed not so much in stationary boiler practice as in locomotive boiler practice, is the element of foaming and priming of a water, which results in much more rapidly putting the steam raiser out of active service than either of the other types of trouble.

From the standpoint of plant deterioration due to rusting and corrosion one has only to look to the great mass of works on the corrosion of iron and steel which are largely results of the growing need for some information as to the cause and possible prevention of this particular phase of trouble.

In the world of industry the action of a hard water upon soap consumption has been known for centuries, and for a considerable period of time the value of a water was determined largely by the amount of soap that it would consume and render insoluble. This same hardness has a noticeable effect in the textile industry, in bleaching and dyeing, in the canning industry, especially when the water supply contains such substances in large quantities. In the photographic industry the presence of chlorides in water and certain alkalies is a source of considerable trouble, and in every case, before any intelligent effort can be made to overcome these troubles, a complete analysis of the water is necessary.

It shall be our purpose in the methods which follow to give, where it is possible, first a system of analysis whereby a complete analysis can be made, and to follow this up with optional methods which, individually, are equally as good as those occurring in the system of analysis, and in some cases more satisfactory where the laboratory has the required equipment, adding any special methods which may be found available.

Chapter by D. K. French.

SANITARY ANALYSIS

A sanitary analysis consists in the physical examination covering turbidity, color, odor and occasionally taste, the chemical analysis for total residue, loss on ignition and fixed solids, noting, where possible, the odor during ignition and also noting the appearance as regards color of the residue both before and after ignition, the determination of free and albuminoid ammonia, nitrogen as nitrite and nitrate, chlorine as chloride and oxygen consumed. Organic nitrogen is frequently determined upon polluted waters.

In sanitary analysis the principal determinations relate to the various forms and compounds in which nitrogen appears.

Organic Nitrogen. The initial form can be determined as such, or as is usually the case in all but highly polluted supplies, as albuminoid ammonia which gives a very close approximate. By decomposition the organic matter first gives nitrogen as free ammonia, then, by oxidation, nitrogen as nitrites, and finally the more stable form of nitrogen as nitrates is reached. Conversely the reactions are frequently reversed through the influence of bacteria and microscopic organisms.

Chlorine is determined and by its excess over the normal chlorine of a general district may indicate previous sewage contamination.

Oxygen Consumed, or " oxygen required," means the amount which carbonaceous organic compounds present consume in the presence of potassium permanganate and acid. From these figures additional evidence is obtained as to the sanitary character of a water, though many phases of interference can occur.

PHYSICAL TESTS

For the physical examination, standards for turbidity and color have been adopted.

Turbidity. Turbidity standards are based on parts per million of silica (SiO_2) suspended in water, and the adopted standard is that of the United States Geological Survey (A. P. H. A., p. 4). A water with a turbidity of 100 is one which has 100 p.p.m. of silica (SiO_2) in such a state of fineness that a bright platinum wire 1 mm. in diameter can just be seen when center of said wire is 100 mm. below the surface of the water and the observer is 1.2 meters above the wire. The observation must be in open air, not in sunlight, and in the middle of the day. Standards are prepared with precipitated fuller's earth (to pass 200-mesh sieve). One gram to one liter of distilled water makes a stock solution with 1000 turbidity. Standards for comparison are obtained by dilution.

The Illinois Water Supply Association outlines another method (Proc. I. W. S. A., 1914, pp. 49–51), whereby a suspension is prepared by shaking silica (SiO_2) or fuller's earth (ground to pass a 200-mesh sieve), settling for ten hours, and determining by evaporating and weighing the amount of silica (SiO_2) in a given portion. Standards are then prepared by dilution.

Color. All suspended matter should be removed by filtration. The standard designated as color 500 is obtained as follows:

1.246 grams potassium platinic chloride (PtCl$_4$2KCl)[1] containing 0.5 gram of platinum and 1 gram crystallized cobalt chloride (CoCl$_2$6H$_2$O) containing 0.25 gram cobalt (Co), are dissolved in water with 100 cc. hydrochloric acid and made to one liter with distilled water. This solution is diluted with distilled water for comparative purposes, but a water with a color greater than 70 should be diluted prior to comparison. The standards for observation should be in 100-cc. Nessler tubes with the mark 20–25 cm. above the bottom and should be viewed vertically downwards to a white reflective surface.

Standard glass disks are used by the United States Geological Survey [2] in place of the above standard.

Odor. Observations should be made both on cold and hot samples. Note should be made immediately on opening containers as some odors are very transient and rapidly disappear.

Cold. Shake sample violently in collecting bottle, same to be about half full. Remove glass stopper and smell at neck of bottle.

Hot. Use either open beaker, 400 cc., containing 150 cc. sample well covered and heated nearly to boiling, or sealed glass stoppered bottle or saponification flask, heating fifteen minutes just under boiling. Allow to cool slightly, remove stopper, shake and smell. Designate odor as aromatic, grassy, earthy, musty, fishy, putrid, disagreeable, peaty, sweetish, etc. The following table expressing intensity of odor is copied from the American Public Health Association Standard Methods, 1913, p. 12:

Numerical Value.	Term.	Approximate Definition.
0	None.	No odor perceptible.
1	Very Faint.	An odor that would not be detected ordinarily by the average consumer, but that could be detected in the laboratory by an experienced observer.
2	Faint.	An odor that the consumer might detect if his attention were called to it, but that would not attract attention otherwise.
3	Distinct.	An odor that would be detected readily and that might cause the water to be regarded with disfavor.
4	Decided.	An odor that would force itself upon the attention that might make the water unpalatable.
5	Very Strong.	An odor of such intensity that the water would be absolutely unfit to drink. A term to be used only in extreme cases.

Taste. May be made on hot and cold samples. A simple statement following largely the terms applied to odor in expressing results, brackish, astringent, salty, sweetish, etc.

[1] Care should be taken that this be the bright yellow platinic salt, and not contaminated with the reddish platinous salt.
[2] App. made by Builders' Iron Foundry, Providence, R. I.

CHEMICAL TESTS
Free Ammonia

Apparatus. The apparatus for this determination should be as far as possible free from joints or connections that are subject in any way to outside

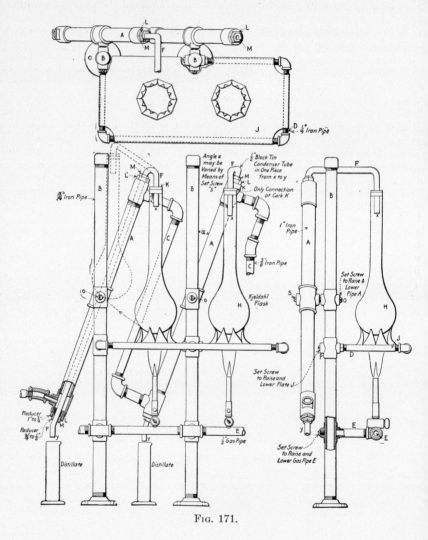

Fig. 171.

contamination or to decomposition. The apparatus is composed of a distillation flask and a condenser, with possibly a safety tube located somewhere near the flask to avoid the possible carrying over of impurities in connection with the steam.

Reagents. 1. *Ammonia-free Water.*

2. *Standard Ammonium Chloride Solution.* Dissolve 3.82 grams of ammonium chloride in 1 liter of distilled water. Dilute 10 cc. of this to 1 liter with ammonia-free water. 1 cc. = 0.00001 gram of nitrogen.

3. *Nessler's Solution.* Dissolve 50 grams of potassium iodide in the smallest possible quantity of cold water. Add a saturated solution of mercuric chloride until a faint show of excess is indicated. Add 400 cc. of 50% solution of potassium hydrate. After same has clarified by sedimentation, make up to 1 liter with water, allow to settle and decant.

Optional Method. Dissolve 61.75 grams of potassium iodide in 250 cc. of redistilled water, and add a cold solution of mercuric chloride which has been saturated by boiling with excess of salt. Pour in the mercury solution cautiously, and add an amount just sufficient to make the color a permanent bright red. With a little practice the exact depth of color can be easily duplicated. It will take a little over 400 cc. of the mercuric chloride solution to reach this end-point. Dissolve the red precipitate by adding exactly .75 gram of potassium iodide. Then add 150 grams of potassium hydrate dissolved in 250 cc. of water. Make up to 1 liter. Mix thoroughly and allow the precipitate formed to settle. Pour off the supernatant liquid. Mercuric chloride increases the sensitiveness and potassium iodide decreases it.

Operation. Clean apparatus thoroughly as follows:
Fill a flask, which for most satisfactory results should be an 800-cc. Kjeldahl flask, with 500 cc. of distilled water. Add a pinch of c.p. sodium carbonate and distill first of all with no running water in the condenser jacket until free steam blows through the apparatus. Then turn on condenser water and distill off approximately 250 cc., testing the last 50 cc. with Nessler's solution, and this portion should not show color in fifteen minutes' time. The flask is then emptied of the remaining water, 500 cc. of the water to be analyzed placed therein, and if acid, neutralized with c.p. sodium carbonate. A slight excess hurries the ammonia liberation but also tends to cause bumping. The distillation is then started, distilling 6 cc. to 10 cc. per minute, and three separate portions of 50 cc. each are caught in Nessler jars. After 150 cc. is distilled the flame should be removed. To each 50-cc. portion add 2 cc. Nessler's solution and after ten minutes' standing compare with standards from the standard ammonium chloride solution.

Albuminoid Ammonia

Reagent. 1. *Alkaline Potassium Permanganate.* Dissolve 200 grams of potassium hydrate and 8 grams c.p. potassium permanganate in 1250 cc. of water, boil down to 1 liter and bottle while still warm.

Operation. Add 50 cc. alkaline potassium permanganate solution and several pieces of washed and ignited pumice to the water remaining in the flask from the free ammonia determination and continue the distillation, taking off four or five separate portions of 50 cc. each in Nessler jars. Add 2 cc. Nessler's solution to each and after ten minutes standing compare color with standard as in the free ammonia determination.

Organic Nitrogen

While this determination is not usually made we give it for the sake of completeness.

The portion of sample from the free ammonia determination, or a new portion freed from free ammonia by distillation, is acidified with 5 cc. C.P. sulphuric acid (nitrogen-free) and digested in a hood until colorless and H_2SO_4 fumes are given off. A little ignited pumice will guard against bumping. Remove from flame, add potassium permanganate in small portions until a heavy greenish precipitate persists, cool, dilute with ammonia-free water, neutralize with 10% Na_2CO_3 solution (NH_3 free), distill into Nessler tubes and compare as in free and albuminoid ammonia.

Permanent standards [1] can be made using potassium platinic chloride, 2 grams dissolved in water, 100 cc. strong hydrochloric acid and made to 1 liter; and cobalt solution, 12 grams cobaltous chloride ($CoCl_2$ $6H_2O$) dissolved in distilled water, 100 cc. strong hydrochloric acid added and made to 1 liter. The following table represents the amounts used, to be made to 50 cc. with distilled water in Nessler tubes for comparison, the 150-cc. mark being 20–25 cm. above the bottom, but should be checked against Nesslerized standards and the Nessler solution modified, if necessary, until the standards agree. This is accomplished by varying the amounts of potassium iodide and mercuric chloride.

Equivalent Volume of Standard Ammonium Chloride, cc.	Platinum Solution, cc.	Cobalt Solution, cc.
0.0	1.2	0.0
0.1	1.8	0.0
0.2	2.8	0.0
0.4	4.7	0.1
0.7	5.9	0.2
1.0	7.7	0.5
1.4	9.9	1.1
1.7	11.4	1.7
2.0	12.7	2.2
2.5	15.0	3.3
3.0	17.3	4.5
3.5	19.0	5.7
4.0	19.7	7.1
4.5	19.9	8.7
5.0	20.0	10.4
6.0	20.0	15.0
7.0	20.0	22.0

Nitrogen as Nitrite

Reagent. 1. *Sulphanilic Acid.* Dissolve 8 grams of the acid in 1 liter of acetic acid, specific gravity 1.04. This is practically a saturated solution and keeps well.

2. *Naphthylamine Acetate.* Dissolve 5 grams of α-naphthylamine in 1 liter of acetic acid, specific gravity 1.04, and filter through absorbent cotton (previously washed).

NOTE. A slightly pink color resulting on standing does not materially interfere with the use of this solution.

3. *Sodium Nitrite Solution.* Dissolve 1.1 grams of silver nitrite in nitrite-free water. Precipitate the silver with sodium or potassium chloride solution and dilute

[1] Permanent Standards (Jackson, Tech. Quart., 1900, vol. 13, p. 320.)

to 1 liter. Dilute 100 cc. of this solution to 1 liter and then 10 cc. of this second solution to 1 liter with sterilized nitrite-free water, adding 1 cc. of chloroform and holding in a sterilized bottle. 1 cc. = 0.0001 milligram of nitrogen.

Operation. Take 100 cc. of the water after filtration and clarification, preferably with aluminum hydrate, to remove possible suspended iron and material which might interfere with color production. Add 2 cc. each of solutions No. 1 and No. 2. After ten minutes' standing compare with standards made up from the standard sodium nitrite solution (No. 3).

Permanent Standards

Cobalt Solution. Dissolve 24 grams of cobaltous chloride ($CoCl_2 \cdot 6H_2O$) in distilled water, add 100 cc. of strong hydrochloric acid and make up to one liter with distilled water.

Copper Solution. Dissolve 12 grams of dry cupric chloride ($CuCl_2 \cdot 2H_2O$) in distilled water, add 100 cc. of strong hydrochloric acid and make up to one liter with distilled water.

The standards are used in 100-cc. tubes with the mark 12–14 cm. above the bottom. The following table gives the proportions of each solution to be made up to 100 cc.:

cc. Cobalt Solution.	cc. Copper Solution.	p.p.m. Nitrite per 100 cc. of Water.
.0	.0	.000
1.1	1.1	.001
3.5	3.0	.003
6.0	5.0	.005
12.5	8.0	.010

The solutions to use for 100 cc. of water are the old ones, as follows: 1 cc. of hydrochloric acid (1 : 4), 2 cc. of sulphanilic acid (8 grams per liter), and finally 2 cc. of naphthylamine hydrochloride (8 grams per liter with 10 cc. of strong hydrochloric acid), and allow color to develop twenty minutes.

NOTE. Volume 28, page 742, J. Soc. Chem. Ind., calls attention to the possibility of a permanent standard composed of a solution of acid magenta (fuchsine–S, acid fuchsine according to Weigert). According to this article, 0.2 of a gram of this dye is dissolved in 50 cc. of 2/N HCl and made up to 2000 cc. with distilled water. Of this solution 200 cc. are mixed with 50 cc. of 2/N HCl and again diluted to 2000 cc. with distilled water. From this latter solution standard solutions can be prepared containing various quantities, these standards being made up to 200 cc. with distilled water after the addition of 5 cc. of 2/N HCl. Considerable work is being done on this, but the standards have not yet been accepted in this country. However, standards can be made by matching these solutions against standards prepared in the usual way and their permanence is much greater than such standards.

Nitrogen as Nitrate

Aluminum Reduction [1]

Reagents. 1. *Sodium or Potassium Hydrate Solution.* Dissolve 250 grams of the hydrate in 1250 cc. of distilled water, add several strips of aluminum foil and allow action to pass overnight. Boil down to 1 liter.

2. *Aluminum Foil.* Use strips of pure aluminum approximately 10 cm. long, 9 mm. wide, and $\frac{1}{3}$ mm. thick, same to weigh about $\frac{1}{2}$ gram.

Operation. 100 cc. of water is placed in a 300-cc. casserole. Add 2 cc. of the hydrate solution and boil down to about 20 cc. Pour the contents of the casserole into a test-tube about 6 cm. long and 3 cm. in diameter and of approximately 100-cc. capacity. Rinse the casserole several times with nitrogen-free water and add the rinse water to that already in the tube, thus making the contents of the tube approximately 75 cc. Add a strip of aluminum foil. Close the tube by means of a rubber stopper through which passes a Λ-shaped glass tube about 5 mm. in diameter. Make the short end of the tube flush with the lower side of the rubber stopper while the other end extends below the surface of distilled water contained in another test-tube. This apparatus serves as a trap through which the evolved hydrogen escapes freely. The amount of ammonia escaping into the trap is slight and may be neglected. Allow the action to proceed for a minimum period of four hours, or overnight. Pour contents of the tube into a distilling flask, dilute with 250 cc. of ammonia-free water, distill and collect in Nessler tubes and Nesslerize. When the nitrate content is high, collect the distillate in a 200-cc. flask and Nesslerize an aliquot portion. If the supernatant liquid in the reduction tube is clear and colorless, the solution may be diluted to a definite volume and an aliquot part Nesslerized without distillation.

NOTE. Where the nitrates are very high, from 50 parts per million up, take a smaller sample and dilute to 100 cc. before reduction.

[1] Univ. of Illinois Bull. Water Survey, Series 7, p. 14, 1909; Amer. Jour. Pub. Hygiene, **19**, 536, 1909.

Oxygen Consumed

Reagents. 1. *Standard Potassium Permanganate Solution.* Dissolve 0.4 gram C.P. salt in 1 liter of distilled water. 1 cc. is equivalent to 0.1 milligram available oxygen.

2. *Standard Ammonium Oxalate Solution.* Dissolve 0.888 gram C.P. ammonium oxalate in 1 liter of distilled water. 1 cc. is equivalent to 0.1 milligram of oxygen. The standard permanganate solution must be standardized against the ammonium oxalate solution.

3. *Dilute Sulphuric Acid 1–3.* Free from oxidizable matter by adding $KMnO_4$ until a faint pink color persists after several hours.

Operation. 100 cc. of water are measured into a 450-cc. Erlenmeyer flask, acidified with 5 cc. dilute sulphuric acid. Ten cc. of standard permanganate solution is run in from a burette and the flask is placed in a bath of boiling water, the level of which is above the level of the flask contents, for thirty minutes. Remove. Add 10 cc. of standard oxalic solution and then determine the excess with the standard permanganate solution. Deduct from the total permanganate solution used the 10 cc. of oxalic acid, and the remainder represents oxygen consumed. For particularly bad waters smaller quantities of the sample are taken and diluted to 100 cc., as it is undesirable at any time in the course of boiling that the pink color of permanganate be completely discharged.

Chlorine as Chlorides

Reagents. *Standard Salt Solution.* 16.48 grams fused C.P. sodium chloride are dissolved in 1 liter of distilled water. 100 cc. of this solution diluted to 1 liter gives a standard solution, each cc. of which contains .001 gram of chlorine.

Standard Silver Nitrate Solution. 4.8 grams dried silver nitrate crystals are dissolved in one liter of distilled water. Each cc. of this solution is equivalent to approximately .001 gram of chlorine, standardized against the Standard Salt Solution.

NOTE. N/50 solutions of both sodium chloride and silver nitrate can be used where it is inconvenient to make too many standard solutions, using the proper factors.

Potassium Chromate. Ten per cent solution neutral potassium chromate.

NOTE. A. P. H. A., page 43, recommends 5 per cent solution of neutral potassium chromate, adding after solution of the crystals in a few cc. of water, sufficient silver nitrate to produce a slight red precipitation. This is filtered off, and the filtrate made up to volume.

Operation. 100 cc. of the sample are titrated with silver nitrate solution, using 1 cc. of the potassium chromate as indicator to the first persistence of the silver chromate red. Subtract 0.2 cc. blank from the reading. A white porcelain dish or casserole is the preferable container, although a flint-glass beaker over a white porcelain plate may be used. Where a chlorine is high and more than 15 cc. of silver nitrate is used, a smaller sample (50 cc. or 25 cc.) should be taken and distilled water added to bring the volume up to approximately 100 cc. If the original water is noticeably colored, 25 to 30 by standard, it may be decolorized by adding precipitated aluminum hydrate, bringing to a boil and filtering. Titration must always be made in the cold, however.

NOTE. Precipitated aluminum hydrate is prepared by dissolving potash alum in water, precipitating by adding carefully ammonia and washing in a large jar with distilled water, by decantation, until free from chlorine, ammonia, and nitrites. An acid water should first be neutralized with sodium carbonate and a water containing free hydrates should be neutralized with sulphuric acid. Where specially accurate work is desired, observations may be made in a dark room with a yellow light. (A. P. H. A., page 44.) A yellow photographic glass may be used in daylight and at night the ordinary carbon filament electric light.

Total Solid Residue

Evaporate 50 cc. to dryness, in a platinum dish, at about 270° Fahr., and bake for at least 30 minutes at that temperature. An ordinary water-bath temperature will not remove water of crystallization from alkali sulphates or calcium sulphate. Where water is high in magnesium salts, as determined in mineral analysis, the water-bath temperature is more satisfactory, due to the readiness with which magnesium chloride and frequently magnesium carbonate will decompose to oxide. As a rule, however, a temperature from 240° to 270° meets most of the conditions.

Weight to tenths of milligram times   1168 = grs. per gal. total solids.
Weight to tenths of milligram times 20,000 = parts per million total solids.

Residues from acid waters should be ignited to a dull red heat after addition of a drop or so of sulphuric acid, to insure complete removal of the acid itself, which will not go off at the temperature stated. This will result in the decomposition of all iron compounds to the oxide form, and will fix all salts, lime, magnesium, sodium and potassium, in the sulphate form, and correction should be made for chlorides present, which would be converted into sulphate.

Waters high in magnesium salts should be evaporated at the first specified temperature, adding, however, a few cc. of 50 normal sodium carbonate solution to insure a slight excess of sodium carbonate, correcting for the weight of sodium carbonate added. Where the waters contain much organic matter after weighing, they may be very gently ignited at a very dull red heat until the carbon has been burned off. After cooling, the residue may be recarbonated with tested ammonia carbonate solution, and again dried in the usual way. The difference in weight after titrating for possible loss of chlorides, due to volatilization, gives a close approximation of the organic matter present. Similarly, waters high in magnesium chloride or nitrate compounds may be evaporated with a few drops excess of sulphuric acid, and ignited to a dull red heat, the residue being compared, where a complete analysis is made, with the sum of all bases calculated to the sulphate form. This is sometimes more convenient and satisfactory than the evaporation with excess sodium carbonate.

INTERPRETATION OF RESULTS

The interpretation of the results of a sanitary water analysis is largely a matter of experience, and it is impossible to lay down hard and fast rules covering this one matter. It is, however, possible to sum up the meanings of the various determinations made, as each determination has some bearing upon the sanitary condition.

In physical data the turbidity refers to insoluble matter in suspension. In many cases it is perfectly harmless, although less attractive, and frequently suggests contamination, which is as apt to be present as not. High turbidities, following rain storms or lake over-turnings, are usually accompanied by B. coli, the intestinal organism, in considerable quantity. The turbid waters of the West may cause stomach trouble until a person is accustomed to them. Color is due, usually, to an extract of vegetable or organic matter, or to iron salts, and in itself has no value save suggesting organic contamination. Highly colored water may have an astringent taste, and is not looked upon with favor by the consumer. It may cause corrosion in pipes and boilers.

Various organic matters are in no way determined in this analysis, the results obtained being simply indications of certain cycles in decomposition of nitrogenous material, as no decomposition can take place without some resulting nitrogen compound. Free ammonia represents the first stage in this decomposition, and represents the amount of organic matter present in a partially decomposed and decomposing state. Deep wells in glacial drift frequently also contain high ammonia, however, which would in no way suggest active contamination.

Albuminoid ammonia represents organic substances in an undecomposed state, which will, however, decompose under the proper conditions. The presence of nitrogen in such combination in large amount usually suggests the presence of pollution of a sewage character. However, its presence usually accompanies and varies in amount with the color and with the microscopic organisms.

The next stage in the cycle is nitrogen as nitrites, indicating that decomposition is actively progressing. Nitrite in surface water may indicate contamination when in considerable quantity, but in ground water is absolutely of no significance. (Proc. Am. W. W. Assoc., 1908, page 323.) Its presence is due to the action of certain types of bacteria either as a product of oxidation from free ammonia or as a product of reduction from nitrate. Ferrous compounds have also a bearing on such reduction.

The final state of decomposition is nitrogen as nitrate. This indicates the fact that at some time in the past organic matter has been present. Its presence indicates a purified water. In large amounts it may cause itching in sensitive persons. It is an important cause of corrosion in pipes and boilers.

The oxygen consumed represents the amount of oxygen required to oxidize organic matter already in the water. It has a bearing upon the organic matter, but there are many inorganic substances which also discharge the color of the permanganate solution, and the result should always be considered in the presence of the other determinations.

Chlorine as chlorides, if above the normal figure for any definite location, is a fairly good indication of sewage, as it is one of the most constant and principal constituents of sewage.

The total residue itself should not be too high, as an excess of inorganic materials would stamp the water unfit from an industrial point of view, and also from the standpoint of the individual, might make it unsatisfactory as a drinking supply, for daily consumption.

With reference to standards of purity, it is impossible to make absolute standards. We quote as a matter of interest a table published by the State of Illinois, giving their suggested limits of impurities for supplies in that State. (The remarks which follow are those of the State Geological Survey.)

	Lake Michigan.	Streams.	Springs and Shallow Wells.	Deep Drift Wells.	Deep Rock Wells.
Turbidity	None	10.	None	None	None
Color	None	.2*	None	None	None
Odor	None	None	Ncne	None	None
Residue on Evaporation	150.	300.	500.	500.	500.
Chlorine	4.5	6.	15.	15.	5.-100
Oxygen consumed	1.6	5.	2.	2.-5	2.-5
Nitrogen as:					
Free Ammonia	.01	.05	.02	.02-3	.02-3
Albuminoid Ammonia	.08	.15	.05	.20	.15
Nitrites	.000	.000	.000	.005	.000
Nitrates	.04	.5	2.00	.50	.5
Alkalinity	120.	200.	300.	300.	300.
Bacteria per cc	100.	500.	500.	100.	100.
Colon bacillus in one cc	Absent	Absent	Absent	Absent	Absent

*Modified Nessler or Natural Water Standard equal 26 p.p.m. platinum scale.

The formation of a reasonable and just opinion regarding the wholesomeness of a water requires that there be taken into consideration all the data of the analysis, together with the history of the water; the nature of the source; character of the soil and earth or rock strata, and the surroundings. The interpretation of results is a task for the expert. If possible a bacteriological examination should be made to supplement the sanitary analysis, as the latter is more useful in determining the source of pollution and indicating the stage of contamination.

Chlorine is the most permanent element shown in water analysis, as it is never removed from water by any changes or processes of purification. Salt deposits, however, in the soil must also be taken into consideration.

MINERAL ANALYSIS

Outline of Procedure

Evaporate 50 cc. of the sample of water to dryness and bake the residue at 270° F. in weighed platinum dish. Increased weight of dish represents *total solid residue.* (Can be used for SO_2 when sample is small.) Ignite for organic loss.

250 cc. Titrate with N/10 acid or alkali for *alkalinity or acidity.* (Can be re-used to make up volume of 500-cc. portion when water sample is small.) Methyl orange indicator.

100 cc. Titrate with N/10 $AgNO_3$ for *chlorine.*

100 cc. Acidify, boil, precipitate with $BaCl_2$, filter and weigh for *total sulphate.* (Use filtrate for Na and K when necessary.)

100 cc. Add 2 cc. 10% Na_2CO_3, evaporate to dryness, add phenolsulphonic acid, dilute, then excess of NH_4OH for *total nitrate.*

500 cc. Evaporate to dryness (with a few cc. concentrated HCl when very accurate SiO_2 figure is necessary) in No. 8 R. B. dish. Bake 30 minutes, cool, add boiling HCl (concentrated), dilute and filter.

Precipitate is SiO_2 and silicate impurities (also $BaSO_4$). Unless great accuracy is necessary, it should be weighed as such, otherwise SiO_2 can be removed by HF and correction made.	Filtrate. Add a few drops of HNO_3, concentrate to 50 cc., cool, add NH_4OH, boil and filter.		
	Precipitate (Fe,Al, Phos.) may be reported as such or as Fe and Al after Qual. test for phosphate has shown same to be absent. Otherwise both Fe and Phos should be determined and weight corrected.	Filtrate. Boil and add saturated Am. Oxalate drop by drop, boil and filter.	
		Prec. Ca as oxalate, dry, ignite and weigh as $CaCO_3$ or CaO.	Filtrate Mg (and Mn) add 50 cc. concentrated Sod. Phos. Solution, then 50 cc. NH_4OH, stir well 2 minutes, or more, let stand 4 hours, or more, filter and wash with 3% NH_4OH. Ignite and weigh (determine Mn separately and correct when necessary.

Note. For industrial purposes the original addition of HCl is not always necessary and correction for $BaSO_4$ Phos. Mn and separation of Fe and Al can be dispensed with unless there is cause to suspect one to be present in material amounts.

In the matter of mineral analysis of water, it is not so hard to obtain a complete analysis of the water, including the non-incrusting or "nearly always" soluble materials as well as the incrusting materials, as it is to make numberless individual or independent tests, in the hope of drawing conclusions from same. The scheme of analysis which follows is used exclusively in the writer's laboratories, and when carried out as given, makes it possible to complete analysis of a water, or a group of waters numbering up to ten, in the period of eight hours elapsed time, or twenty-four hours, assuming the work is arranged in such a way that the magnesia precipitates are allowed to stand overnight before filtration. On another page will be found a skeleton form for this complete analysis, and this skeleton will serve as a rough guide to the more extended discussion which will follow.

The complete analysis considers the quantitative determinations of silica, iron and aluminum, calcium, magnesium, sodium and potassium, as bases, and carbonate, hydrate, nitrate, sulphate, chloride, and phosphate, as radicals or acids, with suggested methods for manganese, ammonia, barium, and other materials which might possibly be present.

Prior to the starting of the analysis, the physical characteristics of the water should be noted, turbid waters should be filtered, the suspended matter analyzed separately when necessary, and the amount determined either by filtration and weighing of the separated material (alundum cones are very satisfactory), or by the difference between two residues, one of which represents the original water and one the filtered water. The mineral analysis should represent the filtered supply. This is due to the difficulty of getting uniform samples with suspended matter at different times.

Silica, Iron, Aluminum, Calcium, Magnesium

(Manganese, Phosphoric Acid)

NOTE. If from qualitative observations the water contains considerable mineral matter, smaller quantities varying from 100 to 250 cc. may be taken, or if the sample is apparently distilled or condensed and contains very little mineral matter, 1000 cc. should be taken, the object being to obtain a residue neither too large nor too small. 0.4 to 0.6 gram is a good quantity to work on.

Silica

Evaporate over free flame, then on $\frac{1}{4}$-in. asbestos board, to dryness, 500 cc. original water, using a No. 8 porcelain dish. Bake at 110–130° C. or on asbestos plate over flame for one-half hour. Moisten with 10 cc. concentrated HCl, add 50 cc. of water, boil fifteen to thirty seconds and filter. Wash with hot water.

NOTE. For great accuracy, evaporate twice to dryness as above, with the addition, prior to the sample going to dryness, of 10 cc. HCl, allow to bake as above, following from there on the usual procedure for filtration.

The precipitate retained on the filter paper represents the silica or siliceous matter, including possibly barium sulphate. Ignite and weigh.

NOTE. If the amount is over .01 gm. per liter, or 10 parts per million, moisten with a few drops of concentrated sulphuric acid and hydrofluoric acid, expel excess acids, and reweigh. This must be done in platinum. The loss represents silica, and should be recorded as such, and the residue represents bases, principally barium, combined with sulphuric acid. This will also catch possible calcium sulphate that might be left undissolved, due to short boiling, to low dilution, or conditions which would prevent its normal solubility in the original solution.

Iron and Aluminum (Gravimetric)

The filtrate contains iron, aluminum, calcium, magnesium, possibly manganese, and phosphate. Bring to a boil, add two or three drops conc. nitric acid and concentrate to about 25 cc. Remove from hot plate or flame, add ammonium hydroxide in slight excess, boil for one or two minutes, and filter.

The precipitate contains iron, aluminum, and possibly phosphates. Burn and weigh as oxides of iron and aluminum, plus phosphates, and test 50 cc. of the original water with treatment in the usual way to determine whether or not phosphates are present. Where this precipitate of iron and aluminum oxides is greater than 0.01 gm. per liter or 10 parts per million, or where the separation of the iron and aluminum is advisable, the precipitate should be fused with eight or ten times its weight of potassium bisulphate, redissolved in water, the iron reduced to the ferrous condition with zinc, and titrated with potassium permanganate, recording the difference in weight between the original precipitate and the iron determination as aluminum oxide.

$$Fe \times 1.43 = Fe_2O_3.$$

NOTE. Where much water is available and time is an object, an additional 500 cc. can be carried down to approximately 50 cc. with a few drops of nitric acid, the iron and aluminum precipitated as above mentioned with ammonia, and the precipitate before drying redissolved in acid, reduced and titrated with potassium permanganate. This portion can be started at the same time the original analysis is started, and will greatly simplify the determination and save time.

Total Iron (Colorimetric)

Reagents. *Iron Standard.* 0.7 gm. cryst. ferrous ammonium sulphate is dissolved in a small amount of distilled water, add 25 cc. dilute (1–5) sulphuric acid, warm slightly and oxidize completely with potassium permanganate, make up to 1000 cc. 1 cc. = 0.1 mg. Fe.

Potassium Sulphocyanide. 2 per cent solution.

Potassium Permanganate. 6.3 gms. per liter.

Operation. Instead of precipitating, or where *traces* of Fe are of importance, 100 cc. to 1000 cc. of the water may be carried to dryness with HCl and a few drops of Br, taken up with 5 cc. (1 : 1) HCl, diluted to 100 cc. in a Nessler tube, 10 cc. KCNS solution (20 gms. to a liter) added and the color compared with standards. The comparison should be made at once as the color fades.

NOTE. It is frequently as satisfactory to add the standard iron solution from a burette to a 100 cc. Nessler tube containing 5 cc. (1 : 1) hydrochloric acid (Fe free), 10 cc. potassium sulphocyanide solution (20 gms. to a liter) and sufficient distilled water until the color matches that of the sample.

(Ferrous Iron—Colorimetric)

(Frequently desirable in acid waters but rarely necessary.)

Reagents. *Iron Standard.* 0.7 gm. cryst. ferrous ammonium sulphate is dissolved in one liter of distilled water containing 10 cc. dilute H_2SO_4. (Not permanent. Should be made up as needed.) 1 cc. = 0.1 mg. Fe.

Potassium Ferricyanide Solution. (Prepare as needed.) 0.5 g. per 100 cc. distilled water.

Sulphuric Acid. 1 : 5.

NOTE. Prepare sample and standards at same time.

Operation. Place in 100 cc. Nessler jar 50 cc. of sample, 10 cc. dilute H_2SO_4 (1–5), filter, if necessary, to remove suspended matter, add 15 cc. potassium ferricyanide solution and make up to 100 cc. mark with distilled water. Compare with standards made as follows:

Place in 100 cc. Nessler jar 75 cc. distilled water, 10 cc. dilute H_2SO_4 (1–5) and 15 cc. potassium ferricyanide solution, and mix well. Add various amounts of iron standard from burette, mix and compare color. Determine ferric iron by deduction of ferrous iron from total iron.

Phosphates

Reagents. Ammonium Molybdate. 50 gms. c.p. neutral salt dissolved in 1 liter distilled water.

Nitric Acid (spec. grav. 1.07). Dilute about 1–5 with distilled water.

Standard Phosphate Solution. 0.5324 gm. c.p. cryst. Na_2HPO_4, $12H_2O$. Dissolve in distilled water, 100 cc. standard HNO_3 added. Dilute to 1 liter.

One cc. $= 0.0001$ gram P_2O_5.

Operation. Evaporate 50 cc. water to dryness in porcelain after addition of 3 cc. HNO_3 (spec. grav. 1.07). Bake two hours at 212° F. Take up with 50 cc. distilled water, add 4 cc. molybdate solution and 2 cc. HNO_3, and compare in Nessler tube with standards from phosphate solution made to 50 cc. and treated with same reagents. A tube 2.5 cm. by 24 cm. to 100-cc. mark of hard, white glass is most suitable.[1] Where waters are already colored the evaporation should be carried on with 3 cc. HNO_3 and 0.5 cc. (or more, if water is highly colored) of $KMnO_4$ solution, (1 gram per 1000 cc.), baking at 212° F. for the same time.[2] Where the phosphate is present in large enough quantities to precipitate the gravimetric methods may be used.

Calcium

The filtrate from iron, aluminum and phosphate precipitate contains calcium, magnesium, and possibly manganese. Concentrate to about 100 cc. Add to the hot ammoniacal solution a concentrated (saturated) solution of ammonium oxalate drop by drop, or add in small portions crystals of ammonium oxalate. Allow to boil two minutes, stirring, if necessary (on account of heavy precipitate and tendency to bump), remove, filter and wash. (Five complete washings are usually sufficient.)

NOTE. Where great accuracy is desired, the precipitate on the filter should be redissolved in a small amount of hot, dilute, hydrochloric acid and reprecipitated with ammonium oxalate.

The calcium oxalate upon the filter paper can now be burned and weighed either as calcium oxide or calcium carbonate.

[1] J. Am. Chem. Soc., **23**, 96, 1901.
[2] J. Ind. and Eng. Chem., **5**, 301–2, 1913.

NOTE. The burning of calcium oxalate to carbonate is not so difficult as it seems, as an intense heat is necessary to convert it to the oxide, and if the crucible is well watched and the flame gives just sufficient heat to carbonize and destroy the filter paper, there will be no chance whatever of any calcium oxide being formed, or any calcium oxalate being left. Where hypothetical combinations are used, it is very convenient to have the calcium as carbonate without calculation. Where burned to the complete oxide it is frequently necessary to use a blast lamp, as large precipitates require a high temperature to reduce completely to oxide form.

Optional (Volumetric)

Or it may be dissolved in 2% sulphuric acid and titrated with the standard solution of potassium permanganate. (N/50 $KMnO_4$ may be used.)

NOTE. Where the volumetric method is to be used, five complete washings are not, as a rule, sufficient, as the presence of traces of ammonia salts, while not interfering in any way with the gravimetric determination, are prone to have considerable influence upon the volumetric results, due to the possibility of traces of ammonium oxalate still being present.

$$\text{Fe Value} \times 0.895 = CaCO_3.$$
$$\text{Fe Value} \times 0.5016 = CaO.$$
$$\text{Fe Value} \times 0.3584 = Ca.$$

Magnesium

The filtrate contains magnesium (and possibly manganese). Acidify with HCl, concentrate, if necessary, to 150 cc., add 25 cc. saturated solution of ammonium sodium hydrogen phosphate (NH_4NaHPO_4, $4H_2O$, microcosmic salt), cool and make alkaline with ammonium hydrate. Allow to stand at least four hours, filter and wash with 3% solution of ammonium hydrate. Burn and weigh as $Mg_2P_2O_7$.

NOTE. Accurate results are also obtained with the use of sodium phosphate added direct to the filtrate from the calcium precipitate without previously acidifying with acid, with 25 cc. to 50 cc. of ammonium hydrate added to make strongly alkaline, after which the solution should be very thoroughly stirred (for at least two minutes), using a rubber-ended glass rod. Allow to stand at least four hours.

For very rapid work in either case, if the magnesium solution after the precipitation is cooled in ice-water, filtration can be frequently made in two hours' time.

For extremely accurate work the precipitate produced in either of the methods above should be redissolved in a little dilute HCl and the precipitation repeated.

Optional (Volumetric)

Reagent. *Sodium Arsenate,* 10% solution.

The filtrate from the calcium precipitate, or an original portion of 500 cc. from which iron, aluminum and calcium have been removed as above, is acidified. Concentrate to the point of crystallization, after which approximately one-third by volume of ammonium hydrate and 25 cc. sodium arsenate solution are added and the solution vigorously shaken for at least ten minutes, filtered, and the precipitate washed free from arsenic with distilled water to which has been added 3% C.P. ammonia water. Dissolve in 50 cc. dilute H_2SO_4 (1:3), transfer to precipitation flask, dilute to approximately 100 cc. and add 3.4 grams potassium iodide. Allow to stand five minutes and titrate with standard thiosulphate solution until the yellow color of the liberated iodine just disappears. Starch as an indicator is not satisfactory, nor necessary. This method is not so accurate as the gravimetric method, giving slightly high results, but is good for rapid work.[1]

[1] J. Am. Chem. Soc., **29**, 1464–7; ibid, **21**, 146.

Manganese

Where necessary, manganese should be determined separately in another portion of the water and corrections made. The Knorres Persulphate method is the most reliable for large amounts (10 milligrams Mn per liter); the Bismuthate method for smaller amounts.

Knorres, Persulphate Method (Volumetric)

Reagents. *Potassium Bisulphate* C. P.

Ammonium Persulphate Solution (60 grams per liter distilled water).

Hydrogen Peroxide Solution. Equivalent to N/10 $KMnO_4$. (Approx. 5.6 cc., 3% H_2O_2 diluted to 100 cc.)

Operation. Evaporate 5 liters or more to dryness, adding first 10 cc. concentrated H_2SO_4. Ignite after adding a few crystals of potassium bisulphate and take up in hot water. Transfer to 250-cc. Erlenmeyer flask with 5 cc. dilute (1 : 3) H_2SO_4, add 10 cc. ammonium persulphate solution, boil twenty minutes, cool, dissolve precipitate (manganese superoxide) in standard hydrogen peroxide solution. (If no ppt. forms no manganese is present.)

NOTES. When hydrogen peroxide solution is standardized against N/10 $KMnO_4$ 1 cc. will be equivalent to 2.754 milligram Mn.

An excess of 10–20 cc. H_2O_2 Sol. can be added and this excess titrated with N/10 $KMnO_4$.

Sodium Bismuthate Method (Colorimetric)[1]

Reagents. *Potassium Permanganate.* 0.288 gram $KMnO_4$ to 1000 cc. 1 cc. =0.1 milligram Mn.

Sodium Bismuthate (purest).

See method of preparation of reagent given on page 263.

Nitric Acid. (Spec. grav. 1.135) 3 parts concentrated HNO_3 to 1 part H_2O should be blown with air until free from oxides of nitrogen.

Sulphuric Acid. 25 cc. concentrated H_2SO_4 to 1000 cc. Add permanganate solution to a faint but noticeable color.

Operation. Evaporate 500 cc. in porcelain dish after adding 1 cc. dilute H_2SO_4 in excess to that necessary to neutralize all alkali. Ignite to remove free acid (organic matter and chlorine), cool and dissolve in 50 cc. HNO_3 (30 cc. concentrated HNO_3 to 1 liter), with heat if necessary. Cool again, add 0.5 gram sodium bismuthate and heat until pink color disappears, re-cool and add sodium bismuthate in excess, filter through asbestos in Gooch crucible (asbestos must be free from organic matter, thoroughly washed and ignited), or alundum crucible. Wash with nitrite-free distilled water containing 5% dilute HNO_3 (30 cc. concentrated HNO_3 per liter), into Nessler tube, make up to 100 cc. and match with color produced by necessary amount of standard $KMnO_4$ in 100 cc. H_2SO_4 reagent.

No. cc. standard $KMnO_4 \times 0.2$ =milligrams Mn per liter.

NOTE. The permanganate solution used for oxygen consumed (see Sanitary Method) contains 0.139 gram Mn per liter and may be used when necessary.

No. cc. $\times$ 0.278 =milligram Mn per liter.

' J. Am. Chem. Soc., **29**, 1074–78, 1907.

Sulphates

100 cc. of the water is slightly acidified with conc. HCl and 5 cc. 10 % NH₄Cl solution added, brought to a boil, and if turbid is filtered and washed four or five times with boiling water. The clear or original water is now brought to a boil and 10% barium chloride added drop by drop to the boiling solution in slight excess. Boil ten minutes, stirring from time to time, if the precipitate is heavy. Remove and *allow to cool* prior to filtering. The precipitate consists of barium sulphate. Wash free from chlorides, testing with AgNO₃. Dry, ignite and weigh.

$$BaSO_4 \times .411 = SO_4.$$
$$BaSO_4 \times .583 = CaSO_4.$$
$$\text{milligrams } BaSO_4 \times .338 = CaSO_4 \text{ grains per gallon.}$$

Benzidine Method (Optional)[1]

Reagents. *Benzidine Solution.* Triturate in a mortar with 5 cc. to 10 cc. water, 4 grams benzidine base. Transfer to liter flask, add 10 cc. HCl and make to volume. 1 cc. = .0013 gram SO₄.

Hydroxylamine Hydrochloride. 1% solution in water.

Operation. Add 10 cc. hydroxylamine hydrochloride to 250 cc. water, then add, at once stirring well, 100 cc. benzidine solution. Allow to stand fifteen to twenty minutes, decant through vacuum filter and wash with 10 cc. to 20 cc. distilled water (do not let filter run dry), return filter paper to beaker, cover with distilled water, bring to a boil and titrate with N/10 or N/50 NaOH, using phenolphthalein as indicator.

$$\text{One cc. } N/10 \text{ NaOH} = .0048 \text{ gram SO}_4.$$
$$\text{One cc. } N/50 \text{ NaOH} = .00096 \text{ gram SO}_4.$$

NOTE. An accurate method by the turbidimeter is given by Hale in the chapter on Coal, page 675.

N. B. Method by Muer, Jour. Ind. Eng. Chem., Vol. 3, Aug., 1911. When the sulphate is 25 p.p.m. or more, the determination may be made by the turbidimeter method direct on 100 cc. For less quantities, larger amounts of water are taken and evaporated.

Sodium, Potassium and Lithium

Sodium and Potassium

The filtrate contains sodium and potassium and lithium, and may be used for such unless the water is highly mineralized, in which case *a new portion, 100 cc. to 500 cc., should be taken.*

Evaporate to dryness, add saturated solution of barium hydrate in excess, filter, wash with hot water, add to the filtrate ammonium carbonate in excess and a few drops of ammonium oxalate, boil, filter, evaporate again to dryness and dry at a high temperature to expel excess of ammonia salts. Redissolve, add slight excess of ammonium carbonate again and continue until no further precipitate is formed on such addition. Evaporate to dryness in a weighed platinum dish, remove ammonium salts by high-temperature drying, and weigh the combined chlorides of sodium and potassium. Moisten with about 25 cc. of water and a few drops of HCl and add from 1 cc. to 5 cc. of 10% solution of platinic chloride

[1] Freidbaum and Nydegger, Z. Angew. Chem., 1907-9.

(1 cc. to each 25 milligrams to 30 milligrams total chlorides). Evaporate to dryness on water bath, take up and wash with 95% alcohol until filtrate is free from color. Dry, redissolve precipitate, washing through the filter paper in hot water. Evaporate again to dryness and weigh as K_2PtCl_6.

$$K_2PtCl_6 \times .161 = K.$$
$$K_2PtCl_6 \times .307 = KCl.$$

Deduct from combined weight of chlorides. Remaining $NaCl \times .394 = Na$.

NOTE. When separation is not necessary, the combined chlorides are calculated as sodium chloride and reported as sodium and potassium chlorides.

Lithium [1]

Use a large quantity of the sample. Obtain the combined chlorides of sodium, potassium and lithium. Transfer the combined chlorides to a small Erlenmeyer flask (50 or 100 cc. capacity) and evaporate the solution nearly, but not quite, to dryness. Add about 30 cc. of redistilled amyl alcohol. Connect the flask, the stopper of which carries a thermometer, with a condenser [2] and boil until the temperature rises approximately to the boiling point of amyl alcohol (130° C.), showing that all the water has been driven off. Cool slightly and add a drop of hydrochloric acid to convert small amounts of lithium hydroxide to lithium chloride. Connect with the condenser and continue the boiling to drive off again all water and until the temperature reaches the boiling point of amyl alcohol. The content of the flask at this time is usually 15 to 20 cc. Filter through a small paper or a Gooch crucible into a graduated cylinder and note exact quantity of filtrate, which determines the subsequent correction. Wash the precipitate with small quantities of dehydrated amyl alcohol. Evaporate the filtrate and washings in a platinum dish to dryness on the steam bath, dissolve the residue in water, and add a few drops of sulphuric acid. Evaporate on a steam bath and expel the excess of sulphuric acid by gentle heat over a flame. Repeat until carbonaceous matter is completely burned off. Cool and weigh the dish and contents. Dissolve in a small quantity of hot water, filter through a small filter, wash, and return filter to dish, ignite and weigh. The difference between the original weight of dish and contents and the weight of the dish and small amount of residue equals the weight of impure lithium sulphate. The purity of the lithium sulphate should be tested by adding small amounts of ammonium phosphate and ammonium hydroxide, which will precipitate any magnesium present with the lithium sulphate. Any precipitate appearing after standing over night should be collected on a small filter and weighed as magnesium pyrophosphate, calculated to sulphate, and subtracted from the weight of impure lithium sulphate. From this weight subtract 0.00113 gram for every 10 cc. of amyl alcohol filtrate exclusive of the amyl alcohol used in washing residue because of the slight solubility of solid mixed chlorides in amyl alcohol. Calculate lithium from the corrected weight of lithium sulphate. Dissolve the mixed chlorides from flask and filter with hot water, evaporate to dryness,

[1] See Standard Methods of Water Analysis. A. P. H. A. (1920), page 60.
[2] The amyl alcohol may be boiled off without the use of a condenser, but the vapors are very disagreeable.

ignite gently to remove amyl alcohol, filter and thoroughly wash; concentrate the filtrates and washings to 25 to 50 cc.

To the weight of potassium chloride add 0.00051 gram for every 10 cc. of amyl alcohol used in the extraction of the lithium chloride, which corrects for the solubility of the potassium chloride in amyl alcohol. Calculate to potassium.

The weight of sodium chloride is found by subtracting the combined weights of lithium chloride and potassium chloride (corrected) from the total weight of the three chlorides. Calculate sodium chloride to sodium.

Alkalinity

In ordinary cases titrate with N/10 or N/50 H_2SO_4, using methyl orange as indicator. Special cases will be considered later.

Reagents. Sulphuric acid, N/10. Methyl orange. Phenolphthalein.

Operation. 250 cc. of water in 400-cc. beaker or a casserole are titrated with N/10 H_2SO_4, using two to five drops of methyl orange indicator (or 50 cc. can be similarly titrated with N/50 H_2SO_4).

Calculate for 250-cc. sample.

No. cc.$\times 4 \times .005$ = gms. per liter $CaCO_3$.
No. cc.$\times 4 \times 58.4 \times .005$ = grs. per gallon $CaCO_3$.
Or $\times 1.168$ = grs. per gallon $CaCO_3$.

Distilled water, and neutral waters containing magnesium chloride and magnesium sulphate frequently give an alkaline reaction when used with methyl orange. In such cases from .2 to .8 cc. N/10 acid are required to discharge the alkaline color of the methyl orange. Such a procedure would suggest to the operator that the waters were alkaline. However, if such neutral waters are boiled with phenolphthalein as an indicator for twenty minutes and no pink color develops, the waters are not alkaline but neutral. The use of a blank of .2 cc. is of no value under such conditions and it appears to the writer as much the safest way when the titration is under 1 cc. of N/10 acid that the water be boiled with phenolphthalein in an effort to determine absolutely whether this water is alkaline, due to the presence of a carbonate as indicated by the methyl orange, or whether the alkalinity is entirely due to the hydrolyzing of the calcium or magnesium base present in the absence of alkali. When no pink color is produced the water should be pronounced neutral.

Phenolphthalein may also be used as indicator on another 250-cc. portion, using the above procedure. This titration in connection with the methyl orange titration makes possible a determination of the relation of carbonate, bicarbonate and caustic alkalinity.

The following is adapted from a table on page 39, Standard Methods of Water Analysis of the American Public Health Association, and is of value in showing the relation of the various titrations. Methyl orange has been used in place of erythrosine.

TABLE SHOWING RELATION BETWEEN ALKALINITY BY PHENOL-
PHTHALEIN AND THAT BY METHYL ORANGE IN PRESENCE OF
BICARBONATES, CARBONATES AND HYDRATES.

	Bicarbonates.	Carbonates.	Hydrates.
$P=O$	M	O	O
$P<\frac{1}{2}M$	M–2P	2P	O
$P=\frac{1}{2}M$	O	2P	O
$P>\frac{1}{2}M$	O	2(M–P)	2P–M
$P=M$	O	O	M

M = Methyl orange alkalinity.
P = Phenolphthalein alkalinity.

Acidity

For acidity use N/10 Na_2CO_3 and 250 cc. water.

Acidity due to	Indicator.	Hot or Cold.
Carbonic and sulphuric acids, also Fe and Al sulphates..........................	Phenolphthalein	Cold
Sulphuric acid, also Fe and Al sulphates......	Phenolphthalein	Boiling
Sulphuric acid alone....................... When desired, 20 cc. N/10 H_2SO_4 may be added. Boil fifteen to twenty minutes, cool and titrate, noting the excess of acidity over the original 20 cc.	Methyl orange	Cold

Hydrogen–Ion Concentration

It is frequently desirable to know, particularly in connection with waters for certain industrial uses and the filtration of supplies using alum as a coagulant, the actual reaction of the water in terms of the hydrogen-ion concentration in addition to the familiar titration with methyl orange which gives the total available alkalinity of the water and does not indicate the actual dissociation or pH value. The proper adjustment of the pH value along with treatment using alum as a coagulant is necessary for economical and efficient operation of this process.[1] In the use of water for steam making and for certain manufacturing processes the added data given by this determination is making possible more accurate adjustments and more advantageous selection of supplies and treatments.

The most accurate method for making these measurements is by means of the hydrogen electrode,[2] however, colorimetric methods have proved satisfactory for use with water. The following standard buffer solutions proposed by Clark and Lubs [3] together with their recommendations for the preparation

[1] J. Ind. Eng. Chem., 14 (1922), 1038; Chem. Met. Eng., May 3, 1922, Vol. 26, No. 18; J. Am. W. W. Ass'n, Vol. 11, No. 3, May, 1924.
[2] Clark, The Determination of Hydrogen Ions (Williams and Wilkins, 1920).
[3] Ibid.

and use of indicators make a convenient set of standards for this purpose, using 10 cc. of the standard buffer solution with five drops of the indicator compared with the sample used in the same proportions.

Indicator	pH Range	N/20 NaOH per Decigram
Methyl red	4.4–6.0	7.4
Brom thymol blue	6.0–7.4	3.2
Cresol red	7.2–8.8	5.3
Thymol blue	8.6–10.0	4.3

For the preparation of these solutions one decigram of the dry powder is ground in an agate mortar with the corresponding quantity of N/20 NaOH. When solution is complete, the thymol blue and brom thymol blue should be diluted to a 0.04% solution and the cresol red and methyl red to 0.02% solution.

Solutions

M/5 Acid Potassium Phthalate. Make up a solution of potassium hydroxide dissolving about 60 grams of a high grade sample in about 400 cc. of water. To this add 50 grams of resublimed anhydrid of orthophthalic acid. Test a cool portion of the solution with phenolphthalein. If the solution is still alkaline, add more phthalic anhydrid; if acid, more KOH. When roughly adjusted to a slight pink with phenolphthalein, add as much more phthalic anhydrid as the solution contains and heat until all is dissolved. Filter hot and allow to crystallize slowly. Recrystallize at least twice from distilled water. Dry at 110°–115° C. to constant weight. A M/5 solution contains 40.828 grams per liter.

M/5 Potassium Chloride. The salt should be crystallized three or four times and dried at 120° C. for two days. A M/5 solution contains 14.912 grams per liter.

M/5 Acid Potassium Phosphate. Recrystallize three times from distilled water, dry at 110°–115° C. A M/5 solution contains 27.232 grams per liter.

M/5 Boric Acid, M/5 Potassium Chloride. *M/5 Boric acid:* Recrystallize three times from distilled water, air dry in thin layers between filter paper and finally in a desiccator over $CaCl_2$ to constant weight. A M/5 solution contains 12.4048 grams per liter of boric acid and 14.912 grams of potassium chloride.

M/5 Sodium Hydroxide. Great care should be used in preparing this solution as free as possible from carbonate. It is preferable to use a factor rather than attempt exact adjustment. This solution should be kept in a paraffined bottle.

PHTHALATE—NaOH MIXTURES [1]

pH				
4.4	50 cc. M/5 KH Phthalate	7.50 cc. M/5 NaOH	Dilute to 200 cc.	
4.6	50 cc. "	12.15 cc. "	" " " "	
4.8	50 cc. "	17.70 cc. "	" " " "	
5.0	50 cc. "	23.85 cc. "	" " " "	
5.2	50 cc. "	29.95 cc. "	" " " "	
5.4	50 cc. "	35.45 cc. "	" " " "	
5.6	50 cc. "	39.85 cc. "	" " " "	
5.8	50 cc. "	43.00 cc. "	" " " "	
6.0	50 cc. "	45.45 cc. "	" " " "	

[1] Clark, The Determination of Hydrogen Ions (Williams and Wilkins, 1920).

KH$_2$PO$_4$—NaOH Mixtures

6.0	50 cc. M/5 KH$_2$PO$_4$	5.70 cc. M/5 NaOH	Dilute to 200 cc.
6.2	50 cc. "	8.60 cc. "	" " " "
6.4	50 cc. "	12.60 cc. "	" " " "
6.6	50 cc. "	17.80 cc. "	" " " "
6.8	50 cc. "	23.65 cc. "	" " " "
7.0	50 cc. "	29.63 cc. "	" " " "
7.2	50 cc. "	35.00 cc. "	" " " "
7.4	50 cc. "	39.50 cc. "	" " " "
7.6	50 cc. "	42.80 cc. "	" " " "
7.8	50 cc. "	45.20 cc. "	" " " "
8.0	50 cc. "	46.80 cc. "	" " " "

Boric Acid. KCl-NaOH Mixtures

7.8	50 cc. M/5 H$_3$BO$_3$, M/5 KCl	2.61 cc. M/5 NaOH	Dilute to 200 cc.
8.0	50 cc. " "	3.97 cc. "	" " " "
8.2	50 cc. " "	5.90 cc. "	" " " "
8.4	50 cc. " "	8.50 cc. "	" " " "
8.6	50 cc. ' "	12.00 cc. "	" " " "
8.8	50 cc. " "	16.30 cc. "	" " " "
9.0	50 cc. " "	21.30 cc. "	" " " "
9.2	50 cc. " "	26.70 cc. "	" " " "
9.4	50 cc. " "	32.00 cc. "	" " " "
9.6	50 cc. " "	36.85 cc. "	" " " "
9.8	50 cc. " "	40.80 cc. "	" " " "
10.0	50 cc. " "	43.90 cc. "	" " " "

The standard buffer solutions prepared as described above may be used as permanent standards. The methyl red series often deteriorates within a short time, but if the series is checked at frequent intervals, any change may be corrected. Standards using indicators other than methyl red have been used for four weeks before any change in color could be detected. In order to prevent the growth of mold, one drop of toluol may be added to each tube before sealing. If the tubes are corked, paraffined stoppers should be used and for accurate comparison tubes of equal diameter should be chosen.

Free Carbonic Acid [1]

Reagents. Either standard N/10 sodium carbonate or standard N/22 sodium carbonate. For the latter dissolve 2.41 grams of dry sodium carbonate in one liter of distilled water which has been boiled and cooled in a carbon dioxide free atmosphere. Hold both solutions in glass bottles protected by tubes filled with soda-lime.

One cc. N/10 Na$_2$CO$_3$ = 2.2 milligrams CO$_2$.
One cc. N/22 Na$_2$CO$_3$ = 1.0 milligram CO$_2$.

Operation. With N/10 sodium carbonate titrate 250 cc. of sample in 400-cc. beaker, using phenolphthalein as indicator. First faint but permanent pink denotes end-point.

Using 250 cc.

No. cc. N/10 Na$_2$CO$_3 \times 8.8$ = CO$_2$ parts per million.
No. cc. N/10 Na$_2$CO$_3 \times .513$ = CO$_2$ grains per gallon.

With N/22 sodium carbonate solution, use 100 cc. of sample, preferably in 100-cc. Nessler tube, titrate and rotate the tube until faint but permanent

[1] For criticisms of this method see Z. Nahr. Genussm., **24**, 429, also Chem. Abs., **5**, 1024; C.A., **6**, 3137; C.A., **7**, 38.

ink color 30 seconds without fading is produced, using phenolphthalein as indicator

Using 100 cc.

No. cc. $N/22$ $Na_2CO_3 \times 10 = CO_2$ parts per million.

No. cc. $N/22$ $Na_2CO_3 \times .583 = CO_2$ grains per gallon.

Chlorine

Titrate 100 cc. of water, using 1 cc. of 10% potassium chromate as an indicator, with $N/10$ $AgNO_3$ to first permanent indication of the red silver chromate. (Acid waters should be neutralized and sulphide waters boiled with a drop or so of nitric acid and then neutralized for reliable results.)

No. cc. $\times 3.42$ = grs. per gallon NaCl.

No. cc. $\times 58.46$ = parts per million NaCl.

No. cc. $\times 35.46$ = parts per million Cl.

NOTE. Where qualitative test shows chlorine to be high, smaller portions of the sample should be taken, either by certified pipette, or burette, and when the titration with $N/10$ $AgNO_3$ is less than .2 cc., $N/50$ or $N/100$ $AgNO_3$ should be used for accuracy.

Nitrates

(Also see Sanitary Analysis)

Phenolsulphonic Acid Method

Reagent. 1. *Phenolsulphonic Acid.* Dissolve 25 grams of pure white phenol in 150 cc. of pure concentrated sulphuric acid, add 75 cc. of fuming sulphuric acid (15% SO_3), stir well and heat for two hours at about 100°.[1]

2. *Ammonium Hydrate* 1-1.

3. *Sodium Carbonate.* 10% solution of anhydrous Na_2CO_3.

4. *Standard Nitrate Solution.* Dissolve 0.72 gram pure or C. P. potassium nitrate in 1 liter of distilled water. Evaporate carefully 10 cc. of this solution on water bath, moisten thoroughly with 2 cc. of solution No. 1 and dilute to 1 liter. 1 cc. of this = 0.001 milligram of nitrogen.

Determination. Carefully evaporate 100 cc. of water after the addition of 2 cc. of sodium carbonate solution. After this evaporate to dryness, cool and add 2 cc. phenolsulphonic acid (No. 1), mixing well with a glass rod. Dilute with 25 cc. of distilled water and add an excess of ammonium hydrate, making up to 100 cc. volume with distilled water.

The dilute solution is then compared with the standard solution.

NOTES. When the chlorides are over 100 parts per million in the original sample they should be removed with the addition of silver sulphate in the solid form and the water should be filtered prior to evaporation. It is for this reason that ammonium hydrate is used to develop the color instead of potassium hydrate, which is frequently recommended, as a slight excess of silver sulphate will result in a dirty precipitate when using potassium hydrate, whereas the use of ammonia has no effect. Furthermore, the filtration of a turbid nitrate solution does not result in a satisfactory color, as would be the case without filtration.

Permanent standards can be made by procedure given on page 539, or standards can be made using tripotassium nitrophenoldisulphonate. The following method is given in an article in J. Amer. Chem. Soc., Vol. 33, pp. 381-384:

[1] Jour. Amer. Chem. Soc., **33**, 382, 1911.

The theoretical amount of powdered potassium nitrate is added to the disulphonic acid regent in small pinches at a time (for each cc. of reagent 0.1076 gram KNO_3), stirring thoroughly after each addition. The product is then diluted, treated with dry barium carbonate to a deep yellow color, filtered and the precipitate washed with boiling water to remove the barium salt which is but slightly soluble in cold water. This extraction must be thorough. Filtrates and washings are united, the barium removed by the addition of potassium carbonate until alkaline, the solution filtered and the filtrate concentrated and crystallized. The solution may then be easily purified by crystallization. In preparing the standards, however, solutions made from known amounts of nitrate standards will match up with this recrystallized solution, and by means of proper dilutions the series of standards can be made. Standards made this way will last for many months, whereas standards made from the standard nitrate solution are apt to lose value in a month's period and should be made up very frequently.

Where nitrates are high, 85 to 90 parts per million, or 5 grains per gallon and over, colorimetric methods do not always give reliable results, and 500 cc. of the water should be first boiled with a slight excess of acid, then made alkaline with sodium or potassium hydroxide, reduced with 10 grams each of powdered Zn and Fe, or 10 grams powdered Al, and distilled into an excess of $N/10$ or $N/100$ HCl, as the case may be, and titrated back, using cochineal as indicator, and calculating the ammonia absorbed to NO_3 or $Ca(NO_3)_2$ as desired. (Where free ammonia or its compounds are present corrections must be made.)

A recent modification of this method depends upon the absorption of ammonia into a solution of boric acid (5 grams boric acid in 100 cc. of water). Due to the very weak acidity of the boric acid, it is possible to titrate the ammonia direct with standard acid, using methyl orange as an indicator, and this has the advantage of doing away with two standard solutions. The boric acid strength is based upon 5 grams of boric acid to 100 cc. of water to each .2 gram of ammonia absorbed. It is stated that even the cooled condenser is unnecessary, in this absorption.[1]

Ammonia and Its Compounds

Place 500 cc. or less in an 800-cc. Kjeldahl flask, make alkaline and distill into $N/10$, or weaker, HCl, titrate with cochineal or Nesslerize. (See Sanitary Analysis, page 536.)

Total Mineral Residue

Use a clean weighed platinum dish. Evaporate 50 cc. (certified pipette) to dryness at about 130° C. and bake for at least thirty minutes at that temperature. Ordinary water-bath temperature will not remove water of crystallization from Na_2SO_4 or $CaSO_4$. Weigh to the fourth decimal or .0001 gram.

Weight $\times 1168 =$ grains per gallon.

0.1 milligram $= 2$ parts per million.

[1] The Volumetric Determination of Ammonia. L. W. Winkler, Budapest. Z. angew. Chem., **26**, Aufsatzteil, 231–2.

Determination of Ammonia by the Boric Acid Method. L. W. Winkler, Z. angew. Chem., **27**, I, 630–2, 1914.

The Determination of Ammonia by the Boric Acid Method. E. Bernard, Z. angew. Chem., **27**, I, 664, 1914.

Residues of acid waters should be ignited to a dull red
acidity is low a drop or so of sulphuric acid should be added to
of all sodium and potassium salts as the sulphate. The ignitio
plete so that no free acid is left behind and to assure the decomp
compounds to the oxide form. In calculating, correction must
change in the iron salts and all other compounds converted to th
for comparison with the sulphated residue, and then the proper co
to give the theoretical residue on the original water.

Residues with much organic matter, after weighing, may be gently ignited until
the carbon has been burned off, cooled, recarbonated with tested $(NH_4)_2CO_3$ dried
and again weighed. The difference in weight after titrating for possible volatilized chlorides gives approximately the organic matter present.

Waters high in easily decomposed $MgCl_2$ or $Ca(NO_3)_2$ should be evaporated
with a few drops excess of H_2SO_4, or Na_2CO_3, and the residue compared with an
addition of all bases calculated to the sulphate form, or corrected for added carbonate.

NOTE. When acid is used, ignite to a dull red heat; when carbonate, evaporate
as in the case of the original residue.

Hydrogen Sulphide

Due to the fact that hydrogen sulphide is frequently very transient and often
oxidizes to sulphate in transit, it is advisable to collect this sample in a special
container at the point of sampling. Two or three bottles holding exactly 250 cc.
of water each, are used, each bottle containing 50 cc. N/100 iodine solution.
After filling, the bottle is sealed. The sample is titrated with standard N/100
sodium thiosulphate upon receipt at laboratory, at which time a blank is run,
using 50 cc. iodine solution made to mark with distilled water. The difference
between the titration of the sample and the blank represents hydrogen sulphide
present.

Iodine value $\times 0.1263 \times 4 =$ sulphur value grams per liter.

Oil

Frequently waters from condensing engine, or after passing heaters or oil
separators, still contain oil in small quantities. The following method has
been found most satisfactory:

Reagents. *Ferric Chloride Solution.* (10 grams of iron dissolved in 200
cc. HCl, oxidized with HNO_3 and made to one liter.)

Ammonia C.P.

Operation. Add to the water taken in a large beaker or flask 5 cc. of the
" ferric chloride " solution and heat nearly to boiling; then add ammonia in
excess, to precipitate the iron (which precipitate contains all the oil), and boil
for two minutes.

NOTE. If the oil exceeds 0.4 grain per gallon, use 500 cc., or less for the determination; if below 0.4 grain per gallon use 1 liter.

Allow to stand a few minutes and filter through a 15 cm. filter paper which has been previously extracted with ether, transferring the precipitate on to the paper with hot water, and washing three or four times with hot water. Then dry both filter and precipitate in the water oven at 100° C. and when dry, extract with ether in the soxhlet in the usual way, evaporate the ether extract and weigh the remaining oil.

Optional Method for Oil. Shake up the sample of water in a separatory funnel with 25 cc. ethyl ether or 25 cc. of benzol and separate the extract containing the oil. Three extractions, as directed above, will remove all oil from the water. The solvent is expelled by warming gently and the oil is weighed.

Dissolved Oxygen

Use the Winkler Method [1]

Reagents. No. 1. *Manganous Sulphate Solution.* 48 grams manganous sulphate dissolved in 100 cc. distilled water.

No. 2. *Iodide Solution.* 360 grams NaOH and 100 grams KI dissolved in 1 liter of distilled water.

No. 3. *Concentrated hydrochloric acid, or sulphuric acid sp.gr. 1.4 (dilute 1 : 1).*

No. 4. *Sodium Thiosulphate Solution.* N/100 solution is made as needed from the N/10 stock solution.

NOTE. Not permanent; should be frequently restandardized against N/100 potassium bichromate.

The addition of 5 cc. of chloroform plus 1.5 grams sodium or ammonium carbonate to each liter of solution on mixing will improve its keeping quality.

N/40 sodium thiosulphate containing 6.2 grams C.P. recrystallized salt per liter may be preferred to N/100 strength. 1 cc. of this solution is equivalent to 0.2 milligram oxygen by weight or 0.1395 cc. oxygen by volume, standard conditions.

5. *Starch Solution.* [2] The starch should first be made into a thin paste with cold water and about 200 times its weight of boiling water stirred in and boiled for a few minutes. A few drops of chloroform will assist in preserving this solution.

Collection of Sample. A small-necked, 250-cc. bottle should be used, etched or otherwise marked, with its exact volume previously determined. The collection should be so arranged to exclude outside air and result in several continuous changes of the contents before stoppering, care being taken to exclude air bubbles.

Operation. To sample as received add, in both cases by pipette, delivering below surface of water and away from the air, 2 cc. solution No. 1 (manganese sulphate) and No. 2 (NaOH,KI). Restopper and shake thoroughly. After precipitate has settled add 2 cc. HCl or H_2SO_4 and again mix by thorough shaking until precipitate has completely dissolved, transfer 100 cc. to flask, and titrate with solution No. 4 (sodium thiosulphate), using starch as indicator near end as the color approaches a faint yellow.

[1] Ber. deutsche Chem. Gesell., **21**, 2843, 1888. Also Z. Anal. Chem., **53**, 665–72, 1914; C.F.C.A., 8, 674, 1915.
[2] Hale gives the following method. "Rub 5 grams of potato starch with cold water to a thin paste together with 10 milligrams of mercuric iodide. Pour into one liter of boiling water and boil half an hour."

N = cc. N/100 thiosulphate solution.
V = capacity of bottle less 4 cc. (vol. sol. 1 and 2 added).
O = the amount of oxygen in parts per million in water saturated at the same temperature and pressure.

1) Oxygen in p.p.m. $= \dfrac{.0008N \times 1,000,000}{100} = .8N.$[1]

2) Oxygen in cc. per liter $= .7$ oxygen p.p.m.

3) Oxygen per cent saturation $= \dfrac{\text{Oxygen p.p.m. (observed temp. and pres.)}}{\text{Saturation oxygen p.p.m. (observed temp. and pres.)}}$.

METHODS FOR THE DETERMINATION OF SMALL AMOUNTS OF LEAD, ZINC, COPPER AND TIN

Very frequently a determination is desired of materials which are apt to be present in water due to the solvent action of such water upon pipes and containers. In most cases the estimates are made by colorimetric methods if the amounts present are exceedingly small. As these determinations are made only in rare cases it seems advisable to summarize, calling attention to the fact that all methods may be found in full in any of the editions of Standard Methods for Water Analysis gotten out by the American Public Health Association.

Where any or all of the metals, lead, zinc, copper and iron are apt to be present, a large quantity (1 to 4 liters), of the water is evaporated. The metals are separated as sulphides with ammonia and hydrogen sulphide. The precipitate after washing is dissolved in nitric acid and refiltered to remove suspended matter and then concentrated with H_2SO_4.

The lead is removed by taking up the concentrated solution with 50% alcohol (100 cc. to 150 cc.), filtering and dissolving the precipitate in ammonium acetate, after which the solution is made to volume and divided. One-half is saturated with hydrogen sulphide water to get an approximate idea of the amount of lead present. To the other half add two to three drops of acetic acid, then an excess of hydrogen sulphide water and compare the color with standards. This gives **lead.**

The alcohol is removed from the filtrate by evaporation and it is then treated with ammonia to remove possible iron. The filtrate from the iron precipitate is neutralized with H_2SO_4, then 2 cc. concentrated H_2SO_4 and 1 gram urea added. Copper is removed by electrolyzing (two hours with 0.5 ampere current). If the deposit is material it may be weighed as copper after washing with alcohol and drying. When the deposit is extremely small it should be dissolved in nitric acid, evaporated to dryness to remove acid taken up in water, after which potassium sulphide solution is added and the color compared with standards. This gives **copper.**

The solution from the above is nearly neutralized with ammonia. It is then concentrated and 2 grams potassium oxalate and 1.5 grams potassium sulphate are added and the zinc removed by electrolyzing. (Three hours with 0.3 ampere current.) This gives **zinc.**

[1] Correcting for displacement for 300-cc. bottle, .8N = .811N; for 275-cc. bottle, .8N = .812N.

No correction for displacement affects result .1 p.p.m. oxygen.

Twenty-five cc. variation in capacity of bottle affects result .01 p.p.m. oxygen.

The above formulæ are based upon N/100 thiosulphate, and titrating 100 cc. volume. N = cubic centimeters thiosulphate used.

Where copper only is desired it is frequently sufficiently satisfactory to co▮ centrate the water from 50 cc. to 75 cc., after which it is acidified with 2 to 5 c▮ concentrated H_2SO_4, depending upon whether the water is very alkaline wit▮ carbonate of lime, etc., and then the procedure for copper is followed.[1]

There is no satisfactory method for the quantitative determination of sma▮ quantities of tin. In the above-mentioned procedure, however, in case tin shoul▮ be present it would be removed with the ammonia precipitate for the removal c▮ iron and its presence may be avoided by dissolving the sulphides in the origina▮ precipitation in HNO_3, in which the tin would remain behind insoluble.

HARDNESS

Total Hardness

The most accurate method for total hardness is by calculation of the calciun▮ and magnesium determined gravimetrically as previously outlined, calculatin▮ the calcium as calcium carbonate and the magnesium to its calcium carbonat▮ equivalent in terms of parts per million.[2] However, where only the hardness i▮ desired, gravimetric methods are cumbersome and the following are accepted a▮ standard.

The standard method for the determination of total hardness, as well as tem▮ porary and permanent, depends upon the action of the lime and magnesia ir▮ solution upon soap, the soap added in a very dilute solution in alcohol. Tota▮ hardness represents the total soap acted upon by the water in its original state▮ permanent hardness represents the total soap acted upon by the water after th▮ water in question has been thoroughly boiled and separated from the suspende▮ matter, and temporary hardness represents the difference between the total hard▮ ness and the permanent hardness, and while it is supposed to represent combine▮ carbonates of lime and magnesia, and the permanent hardness is supposed t▮ represent lime and magnesia in other forms than carbonate, this is rarely so du▮ to the fact that a certain material amount of carbonate of lime and magnesia i▮ soluble in water, even in the absence of carbon dioxide gas. The reagents use▮ are *standard soap solution* and *standard calcium chloride solution,* the latte▮ being made under such conditions that 1 cc. of the solution is equivalent t▮ 0.2 milligram of calcium carbonate.

[1] Phelps, Jour. Amer. Chem. Soc., **28,** 369, 1906.
[2] C. Bahlmann, J. Ind. Eng. Chem., **6,** 209, 11.

Preparation of Solutions

0.2 gram pure calcium carbonate is dissolved in a small amount of dilute HCl, taking pains to avoid any loss due to effervescence or spattering. Evaporate the solution to dryness several times to remove excess acid. Dissolve in distilled water and make up to 1 liter.

Standard soap solution is obtained by dissolving approximately 100 grams dry castile soap in 1 liter 80% alcohol. This solution should stand several days. For standardizing, this solution should be diluted with alcohol (70% to 80%), until 6.4 cc. when added to 20 cc. of standard calcium solution will produce a permanent lather. Usually less than 100 cc. of the original soap solution will make 1 liter of standard solution.

For standardizing, use 250-cc. glass-stoppered bottle, add 20 cc. calcium solution with 30 cc. distilled water. The soap solution should be added from a burette, approximately .2 cc. at a time, after which the bottle is shaken vigorously until the lather formed remains unbroken for five minutes after shaking and after the bottle has been placed upon its side.

NOTE. Pure potassium oleate may be used in place of soap.[1]

Operation. Fifty cc. of the water in question are measured into a 250-cc. bottle, the soap solution added, approximately .2 cc. at a time, and in the same manner as described for the standardizing of said soap solution. The following table, copied from p. 33, Standard Methods of Water Analysis, A.P.H.A., 1913, may be used to obtain the total hardness from the results so noted:

TABLE OF HARDNESS SHOWING THE PARTS PER MILLION OF CALCIUM CARBONATE ($CaCO_3$) FOR EACH TENTH OF A CUBIC CENTIMETER OF SOAP SOLUTION WHEN 50 CC. OF THE SAMPLE ARE USED.

cc. of Soap Solution.	0.0 cc.	0.1 cc.	0.2 cc.	0.3 cc.	0.4 cc.	0.5 cc.	0.6 cc.	0.7 cc.	0.8 cc.	0.9 cc.
0.0	....	....	....	....	....	....	....	0.0	0.6	3.2
1.0	4.8	6.3	7.9	9.5	11.1	12.7	14.3	15.6	16.9	18.2
2.0	19.5	20.8	22.1	23.4	24.7	26.0	27.3	28.6	29.9	31.2
3.0	32.5	33.8	35.1	36.4	37.7	38.0	40.3	41.6	42.9	44.3
4.0	45.7	47.1	48.6	50.0	51.4	52.9	54.3	55.7	57.1	58.6
5.0	60.0	61.4	62.9	64.3	65.7	67.1	63.6	70.0	71.4	72.9
6.0	74.3	75.7	77.1	78.6	80.0	81.4	82.9	84.3	85.7	87.1
7.0	88.6	90.0	91.4	92.9	94.3	95.7	97.1	98.6	100.0	101.5

It is not desirable to use more than 7 cc. of soap solution for 50 cc. of the water, and when the figures are higher, the water should be diluted with distilled water. The reading in the table corresponding to the cc. of soap solution

[1] C. Blacher, Chem. Ztg., **36**, 541; J. Soc. Chem. Ind., **31**, 555, C. A., **7**, 1394; C. Blacher, P. Gruenberg, M. Kissa, Chem. Ztg., **37**, 56–8, C. A., **7**, 1938. L. W. Winkler, Z. Anal. Chem., **53**, 409–15, C. A., **8**, 2912.

used is then multiplied by the quotient $\dfrac{50 \text{ cc.}}{x \text{ cc.}}$; x cc. being equal to the amount of water taken. In making this determination there is frequently noted a false end-point sometimes known as the magnesium end-point. ₁To avoid error, it is advisable, after completing the titration, to read the burette, add 0.5 cc. more of the soap solution and shake well. If magnesium has been responsible for the false end-point, after such addition the lather will again disappear, and titration should be continued until a new and true end-point is reached. It is advisable to determine the strength of the soap solution from time to time, as it is very prone to change upon standing. Results should be recorded in terms of calcium carbonate, parts per million. There are various other means of reporting. The English degree frequently noted as Clark degree, represents grains calcium carbonate per Imperial gallon and should be multiplied by 14.3 to give parts per million. Conversely, the result obtained in parts per million divided by 14.3 will give Clark, or English degrees. French degrees represent parts per 100,000 calcium carbonate and should be multiplied by 10 to give parts per million. Conversely, division of the result obtained above by 10 will give French degrees. German degrees represent parts per 100,000 calcium oxide and should be multiplied by 17.8 to give parts per million calcium carbonate. The determination of hardness is not reliable on account of the varying action of calcium and magnesium salts, and should never be resorted to when possible to determine these bases direct.

NOTE. Dr. Hale claims that the soap method for hardness in skilled hands is accurate from 10 to 15 parts per million on waters as hard as 300 parts.

For *permanent hardness* the standard soap solution is used as above stated. The water, however, is boiled gently for one-half hour, allowed to cool, made to volume with boiled and cooled distilled water and filtered, after which the above method is used. The difference between total hardness and permanent hardness is supposed to represent temporary hardness. The *alkalinity* determination given on a previous page is a much more accurate method of determining temporary hardness, however, and is also much more easily carried out. When total hardness and alkalinity are determined, permanent hardness would be the difference between these two figures. For comparative use as against **total** and **permanent** hardness determined as such, the results would be much different, as the alkalinity determination of all the carbonates would give a permanent hardness representing absolutely non-carbonate hardness; whereas the determined permanent hardness would contain a material amount of combined carbonates of lime and magnesia. The American Public Health Association, Committee on Standard Method of Water Analysis, recommend that the determination of permanent hardness by the soap solution be discontinued in connection with softening process, as it is so unsatisfactory in general practice.

Magnesium Chloride

Frequently, when hypothetical combinations are used it is desired to check up these calculated combinations by some chemical method. Magnesium chloride is frequently produced in the course of hypothetical combinations and its presence is as frequently a source of much trouble in the determination of a mineral residue, owing to the ease with which it decomposes or carbonates. A method is suggested whereby a second 50 cc. portion similar to the total mineral residue is exactly neutralized with sufficient H_2SO_4, the amount to use being calculated from the total alkalinity obtained elsewhere. The solution is allowed to go to complete dryness, is baked at a temperature of 280° F. to 300° F., and after being cooled the chlorine is titrated. The difference between the chlorine thus determined and the total chlorine previously determined represents chlorine lost by volatilization as magnesium chloride. In the absence of organic matter this method is approximately accurate. Where organic matter or other reducing material is present, however, the results are not so satisfactory.

Calcium Sulphate

In a similar manner it is frequently desired to know whether or not a water would contain calcium sulphate, and a method of comparative satisfaction depends upon the evaporation of 250 cc. to 500 cc. of the original water to dryness. After cooling, 10 cc. of distilled water are added and the mineral matter loosened from the sides of the dish and partially dissolved. Ten cc. of 95% alcohol are then added and 100 cc. of 50% alcohol. After thorough stirring and solution this material is filtered, the precipitate washed with 50% alcohol and the filtrate made to volume, divided and tested for calcium and sulphates in the usual manner. The method is only approximate.

LIME AND SODA VALUE[1]

Two very simple methods have been devised for the rapid estimation of the amount of lime and soda-ash necessary for softening, when water treatment is considered from the outside softening-plant point of view.

Value for Lime

Reagents. *Saturated lime water* (strength to be known for each series of determinations). *N/10 hydrochloric acid.*

Process. Take 200 cc. of the water in question; add 50 cc. saturated lime-water solution in 250-cc. volumetric flask and heat to boiling. Allow to cool. Fill to the 250-cc. mark with water to replace that lost by evaporation; filter through a dry-folded filter and titrate 200 cc. of the filtrate with $N/10$ acid, using methyl orange as an indicator.

For calculation, let " a " equal number of cc. $N/10$ calcium oxide in 50 cc. the lime water, as determined: and let " b " equal the number cc. $N/10$ hydrochloric acid used in determination.

$(4a-5b) \times 3.51$ CaO will give milligrams of lime per liter required to soften the water tested.

Value for Soda

To the neutralized 200 cc. from above titration, add 20 cc. $N/10$ sodium carbonate. Heat to boiling. Transfer with CO_2 free distilled water into a 250-cc. flask to make up to mark with washings from the dish; mix thoroughly and filter, collecting 200 cc. of the filtrate in a beaker. Titrate with $N/10$ hydro-

[1] Drawe, Zeit. f. Angew. Chem., **23**, 52, 1910.

chloric acid for the excess alkali. Designate the number of cc. in this titration by " c."

Formula: $(20-b-\frac{5}{4}c)\times33.13\ Na_2CO_3$ = milligrams of soda per liter necessary to soften water in question.

NOTE. Both formulæ are based upon C. P. chemicals, and corrections must be made for the value of the commercial materials in use. These methods are valuable though for actual practice it is advisable to try out on a liter of water in question using the calculated amounts of lime and soda for experimental purposes.

METHODS OF REPORTING AND INTERPRETATION

The manner of reporting the results of a mineral analysis of any water calls for as much thought and uniformity as the methods of analysis themselves, and in this department there is much less uniformity than in the case of analytical methods. Undoubtedly, the ideal method of reporting is that which gives results in Ionic form (positive and negative radicals), in terms of parts per million or grains per gallon. The latter term is purely American and would have to be converted for comparison with results obtained in almost any foreign country. Parts per million, though newer and still unfamiliar to all but professional and scientific men, is gaining gradually a strong foothold, and the consideration of this terminology with the Ionic form of reporting will be considered prior to the discussion of hypothetical combination and grains per gallon.

Mr. Herman Stabler,[1] and R. B. Dole,[2] of the United States Geological Survey, have devised and simplified certain calculations and formulas, which greatly assist in the interpretation, comparison, and classification of waters for Industrial and Irrigation [3] purposes. Formulas with reference to dissolved solids will be the only ones discussed here. The following table gives reaction coefficients:

Positive Radicals.	Reaction Coefficients.	Negative Radicals.	Reaction Coefficients.
Ferrous Iron (Fe)	0.0358	Carbonate (CO₃)	0.0333
Aluminum (Al)	.1107	Bicarbonate (HCO₃)	.0164
Calcium (Ca)	.0499	Sulphate (SO₄)	.0208
Magnesium (Mg)	.0822	Chlorine (Cl)	.0282
Sodium (Na)	.0435	Nitrate (NO₃)	.0161
Potassium (K)	.0256		
Hydrogen (H)	.992		

Using the above table, the parts per million of each radical multiplied by its reacting coefficient will give its reacting value, and in the formulas which follow this will be indicated by " r " prefixed to the chemical symbol of the radical.

For checking the accuracy of the analysis, the sum of the positive reacting values should equal the sum of the negative reacting values, and the formula,

$$100\ \frac{r.\ Pos. - r\ Neg.}{r.\ Pos. + r\ Neg.} = E,$$ the percentage error of the analysis. The value of this error should never exceed 5 for waters of 100 p.p.m. or more dissolved solids, and should be 2 or less.

[1] Eng. News, **60**, 355, 1909.
[2] Water Supply Paper No. 274, p. 165, Water Supply Paper No. 254, J. Ind. and Eng. Chem., 6, (1914), No. 7, p. 710.
[3] U. S. G. S. W. S. Paper, 274, p. 177.

In ordinary analysis, silica, iron and aluminum are present in such small quantities that they may, for simplicity's sake, be ignored. The following formulas are given without comment, as full details can be found in Water Supply Paper No. 274.

Water Softening

For 1000 Gals. Water. Pounds lime (90% CaO) required
$$= 0.26(rFe + rAl + rMg + rH + rHCO_3 + .0454\, CO_2).$$

Pounds soda ash (95% Na_2CO_3) required
$$= 0.465(rFe + rAl + rCa + rMg + rH - rCO_3 - rHCO_3).$$

NOTE. Dr. Hale states the following. Instead of the extended formulæ of the Ionic system, I much prefer my simple formulæ.

(Alkalinity $\times .44 +$ free CO_2) $\times .0106$ = lbs. CaO per 1000 gals. feed water.
Also (Total hardness − total lime) $\times .0047$ = lbs. CaO per 1000 gals. feed water.
    or total magnesia as $CaCO_3$.
(Total hardness − alkalinity) $\times .009$ = lbs. Na_2CO_3 per 1000 gals. feed water.
    Expressed as $CaCO_3$.

Foaming and Priming

Foaming coefficient $F = 2.7\, Na.$
Taking into consideration the various boilers and the action of various waters in practice, the following approximate classification of waters for foaming conditions is of value:

Non-foaming, $F = 60$ or less.
Semi-foaming, $F = 60$–200.
Foaming, $F = 200$ or more.

Corrosion

For Acid Waters

Coefficient of corrosion $C = 1.008(rH + rAl + rFe + rMg - rCO_3 - rHCO_3).$

For Alkaline Waters

$$C = rMg - rHCO_3.$$

If C is positive, water will corrode.
If $C + .0503\, Ca$ is negative, water will not corrode on account of the mineral materials in the water.
If C is negative, but $C - .0503\, Ca$ is positive, the water may or may not corrode.

Scale

$$SiO_2 + 2.95\, Ca + 1.66\, Mg = \text{scale p.p.m.},$$

or

[1] $(.00833\, Sm + .00833\, Cm + .3\, rFe + .142\, rAl) + .168\, rMg + .492\, rCa$
$$= \text{scale lbs. per 1000 gallons.}$$

[1] Can be omitted or ignored unless suspended matter, silica, etc., are present in large quantities.

There are also formulas given in the above-mentioned Bulletin on soap cost, lime, soda, soda ash, cost hard scale (pounds per 1000 gallons) and a hardness coefficient of the scale formation.

Irrigating Waters

Alkali Coefficient

(a) When Na −.65 Cl is zero or negative.

$$\text{Alkali coefficient, } k = \frac{2040}{Cl}.$$

(b) When Na −.65 Cl is positive, but not greater than .48 SO$_4$,

$$\text{Alkali coefficient, } k = \frac{6620}{Na + 2.6\ Cl}.$$

(c) When Na −.65 Cl −.48 SO$_4$ is positive,

$$\text{Alkali coefficient, } k = \frac{662}{Na - .32\ Cl - .43\ SO_4}.$$

Classification on basis of alkali coefficient:

Alkali coefficient.	Class.	Remarks.
More than 18...	Good...	Have been used successfully for many years without special care to prevent alkali accumulation.
18 to 6.........	Fair....	Special care to prevent gradual alkali accumulation has generally been found necessary except on loose soils with free drainage.
5.9 to 1.2.......	Poor...	Care in selection of soils has been found to be imperative and artificial drainage has frequently been found necessary.
Less than 1.2...	Bad....	Practically valueless for irrigation.

Hypothetical Combinations

The use of hypothetical combinations in the reporting of a mineral water is frequently of value, in that it gives a more rapid way of placing in simpler terms the principal materials present in the water. It should never be assumed from the hypothetical combinations that the materials so reported are present in the water in that particular form, but it is assumed by most, that the form in which such materials are reported will represent the condition in which those materials will combine when the water is subjected to increased pressure and increased temperature. In other words, the hypothetical combinations most generally in use represent the way materials will appear when combined, due to the law of mass action under steam-boiler conditions.

For such purpose the method which takes care of the insoluble materials or materials leaving the water first is the most common method in use. This method combines as follows: Where the sum of the sulphate and carbonate radicals exceeds that of lime and magnesia as bases, the magnesia is first calculated to carbonate, the remaining carbonate is combined with lime, the remaining lime with sulphate and the remaining sulphate with sodium. This also takes care of the general condition where the carbonates alone are in excess of the combined carbonates of lime and magnesium, in which case the remaining carbonate naturally would be calculated to sodium and all the sulphate, as well as chloride, also, calculated to sodium. Where, however, the sum of the bases is greater than the sum of the carbonate and the sulphate radicals, two possible conditions or combinations exist. Where magnesium chloride is present in the water, the sum of the acids calculated to the soda radical should be greater than the total mineral residue. Partially decomposed magnesium chloride is indicated in this way, also the fact that magnesium chloride has a lower molecular weight than sodium chloride, which condition would be indicated in such a comparison. When this case exists, the sulphate is first calculated to calcium, the remaining calcium to carbonate, the remaining carbonate to magnesium, the remaining magnesium to chloride, the remaining chloride to sodium. Where the total mineral residue is greater than the sum of the acids and where nitrates are present, we then have nitrate of lime, which is assumed the commoner form than nitrate of magnesium, and the calculations are as follows: All the sulphate is calculated to lime, all the magnesium to carbonate, the remaining carbonate to lime, the remaining lime to nitrate, the remaining nitrate to sodium, and all the chlorides to sodium. In acid waters naturally the lime and magnesia, as well as the iron and aluminum, are calculated to the acid present in the greatest excess. These methods of calculation will give certain materials frequently found in scale formation and materials frequently supposed to cause certain characteristic troubles in either steam or domestic usage. It is possible in a purely qualitative way to judge or interpret the water on the basis of the lime and magnesium salts, for incrustation, and of the alkali salts for other troubles in boiler practice, also from the standpoint of irrigation, the various forms of the alkali salts as black and white alkali, without the necessity to use the formulas already considered.

Field Assay of Water

Mr. R. B. Dole has published in Water Supply Paper No. 151, of the U. S. Geological Survey, field methods for the assay of water in which tablets of known value are used for the determination of chlorides, carbonates, sulphates and iron. In this type of assay, a given amount of the water is taken and tablets are added to the water until certain definite reactions take place, when the number of tablets used is estimated and an approximate value obtained. The error in such work varies from 3 to 15 per cent, but the results of the test give valuable, if not accurate, information.

The author is indebted to Dr. F. E. Hale, Director of Laboratories Department of Water Supply, New York City, for a careful review of this chapter, and for valuable suggestions.

SANITARY ANALYSIS OF WATER

THE MICROSCOPICAL EXAMINATION OF WATER SUPPLY

Importance of the Determination

From the standpoint of palatability and of the aesthetic character of water supply there is no more important examination than the microscopical analysis. This examination discloses and measures the minute animal and plant life that is present in all surface waters and in some well waters.

Large amounts cause an unsightly turbidity and even relatively small quantities frequently cause complaint because of a scum produced when bath tubs are filled with hot water or of a stain left upon the sides of the white porcelain. The water of swimming pools, if unfiltered, may be unsightly. Industrial enterprises may be affected, for example the staining of clothes in laundries and interference with the manufacture of correct colors by dye manufacturers and with the dyeing of goods by the dyers. Photography may also be influenced.

The presence of certain types of microscopic organisms frequently serves to identify the source of a water, or indicate from what particular reservoir a supply may be drawn. In the case of New York City which serves to certain districts of Manhattan Borough water from the Croton supply, to other sections water from the Catskill supply and mixtures to others, the supply in any one section may be identified by the organisms as Catskill, Croton or a mixture. Again samples from cellars, excavations and conduits are frequently analyzed to determine whether the source is city water, sewage, or ground water. If microscopic organisms are present city water or sewage must be responsible and the chemical analysis and odor usually eliminate or indicate sewage. The contamination of a well supply by surface waters may be indicated by the presence of microscopic organisms.

The amounts of microscopic organisms bear a direct relationship to the various forms of nitrogen determined in the chemical analysis and frequently explain changes in these determinations.[1] As these growths increase free ammonia and nitrate decrease and albuminoid ammonia increases and as the growths decrease the reverse relationship holds.

The operation of filter plants, particularly the mechanical type, is much interfered with by heavy growths of microscopic organisms, the network of the latter interfering with the gelatinous formation of aluminum hydrate in mechanical filters and the bacterial jelly of slow sand filters, although certain types of the diatoms may assist in the latter case.

---

[1] "The Significance of Nitrogen in its Various Forms in Water Supply." F. E. Hale, Proc. Am. W. W. Assoc., 1908, pages 323–327.

Chapter contributed by F. E. Hale.

By far the most important reason for determining microscopic organisms is their connection with disagreeable, sometimes vile, tastes and odors in water supply. Those so-called littoral growths, which are attached to the banks or bottoms of reservoirs, and which attract the quickest attention are not concerned as a rule. The trouble is caused by minute floating forms, which manufacture essential oils or perfumes like those of flowers. Exceedingly minute amounts produce pleasant aromatic geranium or grassy odors which become fishy, oily, pungent or vile in larger amounts or upon decay of the plant growths. Particular species may frequently be identified by the odor by those who are trained.

Three groups of odors are distinguished:

Aromatic (geranium) caused by Diatomaceae.

Grassy caused by Cyanophyceae.

Fishy caused by Chlorophyceae and a few Protozoa.

The following table as given by Whipple in "The Microscopy of Drinking Water" contains those organisms which have been at one time or another in sufficient quantity in a water supply to produce characteristic odors.

Group	Organism	Natural Odor
Aromatic Odor.....	Diatomaceae:	
	Asterionella........	Aromatic-geranium-fishy.
	Cyclotella..........	Faintly aromatic.
	Diatoma...........	Faintly aromatic.
	Meridion..........	Aromatic.
	Tabellaria.........	Aromatic.
	Protozoa:	
	Cryptomonas.......	Candied violets.
	Mallomonas........	Aromatic-violets-fishy.
Grassy Odor.......	Cyanophyceae:	
	Anabaena.........	Grassy and moldy, green-corn, nasturtiums, etc.
	Rivularia..........	Grassy and moldy.
	Clathrocystis......	Sweet, grassy.
	Coelosphaerium.....	Sweet, grassy.
	Aphanizomenon....	Grassy.
Fishy Odor........	Chlorophyceae:	
	Volvox............	Fishy.
	Eudorina..........	Faintly fishy.
	Pandorina.........	Faintly fishy.
	Dictyosphaerium....	Faintly fishy, also nasturtium.
	Protozoa:	
	Uroglena..........	Fishy and oily.
	Synura............	Ripe Cucumber, bitter and spicy taste.
	Dinobryon.........	Fishy, like rockweed.
	Bursaria..........	Irish moss-salt marsh-fishy.
	Peridinium........	Fishy, like clam-shells.
	Glenodinium.......	Fishy.

In New York City's supply, despite the diversity of its sources, the only organisms which have given offense from odors have been *Asterionella, Tabellaria, Anabaena, Aphanizomenon* (with admixtures of *Clathrocystis, Microcystis,* and *Coelosphaerium*), *Uroglena, Synura, Dinobryon, Peridinium* and *Dictyosphaerium.*

Asterionella, when present in 500 to 1000 standard units per cubic centimeter, produces a slightly aromatic odor. At 1000 units, rarely less, the odor is distinctly similar to the odor of the geranium. The odor increases in intensity with increase in numbers until several thousand produce a fishy odor. The fishy odor is also produced when smaller quantities die.

Tabellaria, and similarly *Asterionella,* in very small amounts produces an earthy odor (also produced by large amounts of *Synedra*), passing through the aromatic, geranium and fishy stages with about the same relative quantities of organisms as *Asterionella.* At times the odor of *Tabellaria* has suggested illuminating gas, no other organisms being present. In the spring of 1919 extensive complaints of fishy taste in the Catskill supply were occasioned in New York City by only 700 units of *Tabellaria.* This was the result of intensification of odor by chlorination with liquid chlorine at Kensico reservoir. The odor was not noticeable in the water above the chlorination plant but appeared first just below the plant.

Anabaena and *Aphanizomenon,* when present in 500 to 1000 units, produce a faintly grassy odor like freshly-cut grass. With larger numbers the odor becomes pungent like nasturtium, or even onions. In large numbers, or when decaying, the odor is of vile, pigpen character. In the spring of 1918 from 500 to 800 units of *Aphanizomenon* in the Croton supply of New York City caused numerous complaints of an oily brown scum when bath tubs were filled with hot water. These complaints came chiefly from high class apartment houses.

Uroglena produces an oily fishy taste and odor, first noticeable in probably 500 to 1000 units. In larger quantities it is very disagreeable. The flavor is that of cod-liver oil. Chlorine has an influence on this organism also.

Synura has caused trouble in as small amount as 50 units. The odor is variously described as like cucumber, muskmellon, etc. It leaves a bitter after-taste. Chlorine intensifies the trouble.

Dictyosphaerium, about 700 units, under influence of chlorine has produced a grassy or pungent nasturtium odor.

Troublesome organisms occur chiefly in surface waters. Occasionally well waters containing iron or manganese cause trouble from growths of Crenothrix and associated forms which clog pipes and cause an unsightly turbid discolored water. Well strainers become clogged so as to prevent proper yield of water.

Microscopic organisms apparently do not affect the health. Possibly the taste and odor at times produce nausea or distaste for food. It would take 12,000 units of Asterionella per cubic centimeter to add a milligram of solid matter to a glass of water.

Sampling for Analysis

In sampling water for microscopical analysis precautions should be taken that the sample be representative and fresh. Water from a tap should be allowed to run to avoid heated stagnant water. Samples from a pond or reservoir should not contain surface scum nor littoral growths. Deep samples are best taken by the method usually employed for dissolved oxygen samples. A quart bottle is fastened by clamps to the side of a two-quart bottle in a water sampler. The bottles are fitted with two-hole rubber stoppers. Glass tubing is arranged as follows: A straight tube, projecting slightly above the stopper, extends to the bottom of the quart bottle. A bent tube is made flush with the underside of the same stopper and connected by a short piece of stiff rubber tubing to a bent glass tube extending through the stopper of the two-quart bottle to its bottom. A straight tube, flush with the underside of the stopper of the two-quart bottle, extends above the stopper from eight to ten inches in order to make a difference of head between the inlet and outlet tubes. The bottles are lowered quickly to the required depth by a marked and measured rope. Watch is kept for bubbles of air which rise to the surface of the water,

ometimes several feet away, until bubbling ceases, which takes two to four
ninutes.   Both bottles must be completely filled before raising, otherwise the
ample may be from some other depth than that desired.   The water enters
he small bottle first and, as it only takes one half minute to lower the apparatus
o the desired depth and at least two minutes for both bottles to fill, the
maller bottle is filled with the last water to enter which is from the desired
lepth.   If the large bottle were not completely filled, the bottles would be
illing while being drawn up and the water of the small bottle would represent
ome unknown depth.

Sedgwick=Rafter Method of Examination

Apparatus Required

\ microscope (not necessarily high priced).
Eyepieces—One inch (25 mm.) and one half inch (12 mm.).
)bjective—Two thirds inch (16 mm.) and one sixth inch (4 mm.).
)cular micrometer—Fitted to one-inch eyepiece.
    This is ruled with a square of such size that used with a one-inch eyepiece and
two-thirds inch objective the tube length of microscope may be adjusted so that
the area viewed on the stage will be one square millimeter.   The tube length is
adjusted by making the square in the eyepiece coincide with a stage micrometer.
The large square is usually divided into quarters, one quarter into 25 small squares
and one of the latter into 25 tiny squares; each of the last represents a unit of
measurement, 400 square microns (20 microns to the side).   A micron equals
.001 mm.
\ stage micrometer—graduated usually to tenths of a millimeter.
Sedgwick-Rafter Counting Cell—a thick slide to which is cemented a brass rim with
    internal dimensions of length 50 mm., width 20 mm., and depth 1 mm.   It has
    an area of 1,000 square millimeters and a capacity of 1 cubic centimeter.   Its
    depth only must be exact.   Several should be provided.
Thin cover glasses, 55 mm. by 25 mm., to use as covers for the cells.
)ne cubic centimeter pipettes (regular bacteria pipettes will do).
°ive cubic centimeter pipettes, volumetric.
\ small glass jar of distilled water—for rinsing cells and coverglasses.
Lintless cloth or handkerchiefs—for drying cells and coverglasses.
)ne-inch test tubes of heavy glass (bacteria dilution tubes).
°ive-eighths-inch test tubes of heavy glass (bacteria media tubes).
Sedgwick-Rafter funnels.   These are cylindrical, 2-inch diameter, sloping toward the
    bottom to a neck of ½-inch diameter.   The distance from top to slope is 9 inches,
    length of slope 3 inches, length to bottom 2½ inches.
\ small glass jar of distilled water—to furnish water for concentrates.
²erforated rubber stoppers—to fit one half inch tube of funnel.
Silk bolting cloth No. 15x.
Steel punch—to make ⅜″ diameter discs of bolting cloth for rubber stoppers.
White sand, 60 to 120 mesh, i.e., passing a sieve of 60 mesh to the inch and retained on
    120 mesh (Berkshire sand or ground quartz).
Support for battery of funnels.
\ small wooden mustard spoon—to measure sand.
Volumetric flasks, 200 cc. capacity.
Test-tube racks.
Record books designed for microscopic examinations.
    For field work, which is sometimes of importance due to destruction of organisms
in transit, a folding microscope and a metal sling filter are useful but not necessary.

Procedure.   The actual procedure of examination is simple.   Familiarity
with the various species is essential.   In the limited space of this chapter it is
mpossible to picture the thousands of forms that exist.   The best working
book, containing also plates, is "The Microscopy of Drinking Water" by
George C. Whipple.   References to other books showing plates will be found
at the end of the chapter.

Moisten the small end of rubber stopper with water so as to easily pick up a disc of silk bolting cloth from the table and insert tightly into the funnel Fill the mustard spoon with prepared sand and drop into funnel making one half inch layer. Pour in 200 cc. of the water to be examined from a flask an allow to filter, thus concentrating the organisms upon the sand. Do no allow the sand to stand until drained dry. Slight suction may be carefully applied to clogged filters. Remove funnel, hold in a slanting position and carefully remove stopper and insert the end of funnel into a one-inch test tube Wash sand and contents into the test tube by 5 cc. of distilled water, running the latter quickly around the sides of the funnel. Shake water and sand settle a few moments and decant liquid into the smaller ($\frac{5}{8}$ inch) test tube A rack of these concentrates may be prepared at one time for examination Rinse three or four Sedgwick-Rafter cells and coverglasses in distilled wate and carefully dry with lintless cloth. Place coverglasses slantingly across cell so as to leave air space at diagonally opposite ends. Run 1 cc. of concen trate into one corner of cell, air leaving at the opposite corner, and slide cover glass into position to close cell. Allow cells to stand at least five minutes before examining so that organisms will have an opportunity to settle completely as most of them will. This step is very important. While examination i being made of one cell, others will be settling. Thus at least three should b kept going in rotation when many samples are to be examined.

Examine under the microscope with one-inch ocular containing micromete and $\frac{2}{3}$-inch objective and proper tube length as previously determined. Esti mate the number of standard units of each organism present in an entire field within the large square of the eyepiece and note on record sheet. Area only is taken into account. Forms like *Asterionella, Diatoma, Synedra, Tabellaria* may be counted and multiplied by a factor to get the number of units—thus each arm of *Asterionella* may be estimated as equal to one half unit. Fila mentous forms like *Melosira, Anabaena, Aphanizomenon, Oscillaria* may be counted in lengths of five units (one-tenth of side of large square) and the total length divided by the number of filaments laid side by side that it would take to measure five units. The quotient multiplied by 25 gives the number of units in the field. *Synedra* in "fine-tooth-comb form," *Fragillaria, Uroglena, Synura* and bulky forms may be quickly compared with a 25-unit square and the number of units in the field estimated. The above method of estimating units is quicker than it reads and tends to eliminate largely the personal element from the count. After the bottom of the slide has been counted, focus should be changed to the top layer and Cyanophyceae, which float, estimated, that is *Anabaena, Aphanizomenon, Clathrocystis, Microcystis, Coelosphaerium,* etc.

Standard Methods of the American Public Health Association require 20 fields of the 1000 to be examined. In ordinary practice, however, a careful count of five representative fields is sufficient, choosing fields through the middle of the cell at each end, the center and half way between. After count ing, a search of the cell, particularly the edges, is made for missed forms, espe cially Crustacea which swim to the edges to get air and Protozoa like *Uroglena.* The latter are frequently rolling around in the body of the cell. *Anabaena, Uroglena* and *Dinobryon* commonly break up and disintegrate in the absence of air and must be recognized in such condition. The process of disintegration frequently may be witnessed under the microscope. Sometimes disintegration occurs in transit.

On the record sheet, the amounts of units of each organism are summed up or the number of fields examined and multiplied by a factor to find the total nits as referred to the original water. The latter amounts are summed to nd the total units of organisms per cubic centimeter.

If the quantities recommended in this chapter are used the factor is found s follows:

The ratio of total cell to counted fields is $\dfrac{1000}{5} = 200.$

The concentration is $\dfrac{200 \text{ cc.}}{5 \text{ cc.}} = 40.$

The final factor is then $\dfrac{200}{40} = 5.$

Fig. 172.—Collection Apparatus for Bacteriological Samples.

Large crustacea found only around the edges and not distributed through the cell should have their total units divided by the concentration rather than multiplied by the factor in referring the count to the original water.

In addition to the count an examination of the original sample in the bottle by naked eye is often useful in detecting such forms as *Uroglena, Cyclops,* etc., and in forming a general estimate of the amounts of organisms present.

Many errors may enter into the quantitative estimation of microscopic organisms. The sample bottle should be inverted to distribute the forms, as some float and others settle. Organisms may adhere to the sides of the funnel or to the sand. Others may pass through the sand and some may disintegrate. One of the greatest errors is caused by uneven distribution through the cell when organisms are not numerous. Whipple states that the total error does not usually exceed ten per cent. The author of this chapter believes this figure is too conservative and unavoidably so owing to the large personal element. However results are usually comparative at any one laboratory.

Tabular Outline Identification of Forms

Sample................. Date of Collection......... Number...............
Examined by............. Date of Examination...... Concentration...........

No. of Square	1	2	3	4	5	6	7	8	9	10	Total	Standard Units Per C. C.
DIATOMACEAE:												
Asterionella.................		1	2		1						4	20
Cyclotella..................												
Diatoma....................												
Fragilaria..................												
Melosira...................	3	5	4	10	2						24	120
Navicula...................												
Stephanodiscus.............	1	1	1	1	1						5	25
Synedra...................		20			5						25	125
Tabellaria.................					4						.4	20

List of Organisms

CHLOROPHYCEAE:
Closterium
Conferva
Eudorina
Pandorina
Pediastrum
Protococcus
Scenedesmus
Spirogyra
Staurastrum

CYANOPHYCEAE:
Anabaena
Aphanizomenon
Clathrocystis
Coelosphaerium
Microcystis
Oscillaria

SCHIZOMYCETES, ETC.:
Crenothrix
Mold Hyphae

PROTOZOA:
Ceratium
Dinobryon
Glenodinium
Mallomonas
Peridinium
Synura
Trachelomonas
Uroglena
Vorticella

ROTIFERA:
Anuraea
Polyarthra
Synchaeta

CRUSTACEA:
Bosmina
Cyclops
Daphnia

OTHER ORGANISMS:
Anguillula
Acarina

TOTAL ORGANISMS:
Amorphous Matter
Miscellaneous Bodies
Sponge Spicules

Amorphous matter comprises organic debris due largely to broken-down microscopic organisms and zoöglea.[1] It is usually of little importance but in connection with consumption of dissolved oxygen in reservoirs just below the thermocline and at the bottom it has been shown to have importance.[2]

[1] The estimation should not include mineral matter, silt, precipitated iron, etc., as indicated in the last edition of "Standard Methods of the American Public Health Association," since this can serve no apparently good purpose. Neither is such standard in agreement with Whipple.

[2] "Thermocline Studies at Kensico Reservoir," Hale and Dowd, Jour. Ind. Eng. Chem., Vol. 9, page 81.

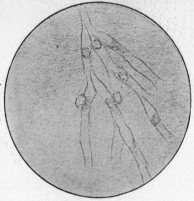

1. Dinobryon, magnification 250.

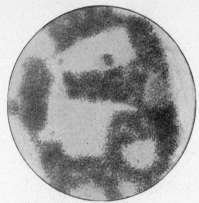

2. Clathrocystis, magnification 250.

3. Aphanizomenon, magnification 250.

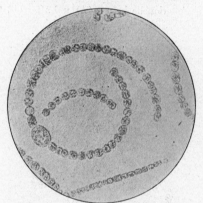

4. Anabæna, magnification 250.

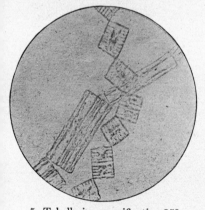

5. Tabellaria, magnification 250.
2, 3, 4. grassy to pig-pen odor.

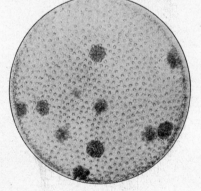

6. Volvox, magnification 100.
5. Aromatic geranium to fishy odor.

1, 6. Fishy odor.

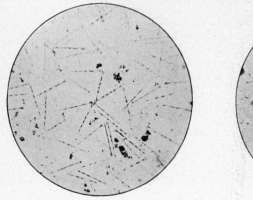
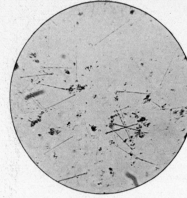

A   B

Asterionella before (A) and after (B) treatment with copper sulphate, 1/5 p.p.m. Note effect upon coloring matter. Magnification 150. Causes geranium to fishy odor.

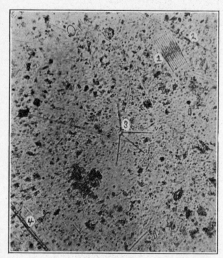
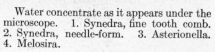

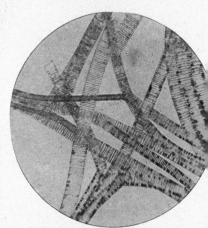

Fragilaria, magnification 150.

Water concentrate as it appears under the microscope. 1. Synedra, fine tooth comb. 2. Synedra, needle-form. 3. Asterionella. 4. Melosira.

Ulothrix, magnification 75.

Identification of Forms. On page 1448 is shown a section from a page of the record book used in New York City's Water Department Laboratories, showing the classification of organisms and the commoner forms found.

As the magnification used for counting is only 87 one must learn to identify the forms quickly at that magnification. Occasionally it is necessary to use the one-half-inch ocular to make certain the identification, the latter magnification being 146. Young forms frequently differ from mature forms and confusion arises. It may be helpful to mention certain distinguishing features for some of these commoner forms, avoiding so far as possible technical terms.

Asterionella (little star) in its usual form is readily recognized. Four to eight arms connected at one end, slightly larger than the other end, and radiating from the attached ends suggest its name. The arms are usually more slender near the center in girdle view. The coloring matter appears as regularly spaced dots or dashes strung along the arm in single row. There is another form of *Asterionella* in which the arms attach at either end in zig-zag manner with occasionally four arms arranged in star fashion. This form may be confused with "*Diatoma*" or "*Tabellaria*," but may be distinguished by the appearance of individual arms in valve view, *Diatoma* having cross striations and *Tabellaria* an oval outlined in a swollen center.

It may be mentioned that Diatoms have two valves fitting together like clams, oysters or scallops but different in that they overlap like the cover and bottom of a petri dish or a pill box. The valve view is that of the top of the box and girdle view that of the edge. (Different authors use different terms. The above is according to Whipple.)

Diatoma in girdle view has straight sides and square ends, joining at the corners to form zig-zag chains. The valve view is distinctive from *Asterionella* and from *Tabellaria*; it has cross striations.

Tabellaria usually has wider arms than *Asterionella* or *Diatoma* and two well-defined parallel marks or lines extending from each end nearly to the middle. In some forms these are missing. The arms join in zig-zag fashion with sometimes three or four in star shape. As mentioned before the valve view is distinctive, being swollen and marked with an oval at the center. There is also a distinctive short chubby form.

Synedra in common form looks like a fine-tooth comb, the needle-like individuals being attached side by side at the center forming a serrated edge. The edge distinguishes it from *Fragilaria* which also forms masses side by side but the ends of the latter are square with no appearance of teeth. Sometimes *Synedra* exists only in individual short needles and again in very long needles.

Meridion also joins side by side but being wider at one end than the other forms disc-like patterns. The valve view is also distinctive, like a base-ball club and striated cross-wise.

Gomphonema is also wedge-shaped like *Meridion* but does not join in masses and in valve view is shaped like a rolling pin. It has a pedicle which is frequently missing.

Many forms, once seen, are very readily distinguished, *Stauroneis* like an elongated diamond with a cross marked from corner to corner, *Pleurosigma*, with a double curve reminding one slightly of the letter "S," *Navicula*, shaped like a little boat, *Melosira*, with its cylindrical cells joined end to end to form filaments containing considerable coloring matter. *Cyclotella* appears usually as small perfect circles without contents whereas *Stephanodiscus* is a larger circle with coloring matter conspicuous and sometimes concentric marking visible on the circumference. On edge a view as of a pill box is often obtainable

The coloring matter of the *Diatoms* may appear from yellow to brown but often a mere black and white effect without much suggestion of color.

The Chlorophyceae (green growth) have green coloring matter. The common forms are readily distinguished and remembered from illustrations *Dictyosphaerium* and *Dimorphococcus* are similar small coccus-like forms joined by spider-like threads together, the former from a concave side, the latter from a convex side. *Pandorina* and *Eudorina* are coccus-like forms set in a jelly ball, the former with the coccus bodies grouped together closely at the center, the latter with them separated and spaced regularly near the surface *Volvox* is a large revolving jelly-like hollow ball with the surface dotted with coccus forms and similar to *Uroglena* of the Protozoa, but differs in containing several conspicuous larger green cells which are in reality young Volvoces.

The Cyanophyceae (blue growth) contain a blue-green coloring matter *Anabaena* appears like a string of beads. It differs from Nostoc in not having a gelatinous sheath, from *Sphaerozyga* in that its spores and heterocysts are not adjacent whereas in the latter a heterocyst is between two spores. The spores are larger than the vegetative cells. It differs from *Cylindrospermum* in that the latter has its heterocysts terminal with large spore adjacent, and the latter filament is sometimes tapering.

Aphanizomenon under high power has a beaded appearance and contains a very long oval spore which is scarce. Under the ordinary power *Aphanizomenon* appears like a pencil mark on drawing paper and frequently appears in attached masses of filaments.

Oscillaria is a pale blueish filament of even color without granulation, with rounded ends, straight sides (*i.e.*, no beaded appearance) and cross striations At times it may be seen to oscillate or wave back and forth (hence its name)

Of the Schizomycetes, *Crenothrix* is fairly common and occurs in well waters containing iron or manganese. It occurs as dark brown masses due to discoloration with iron or manganese. The latter may be dissolved by acid when the oblong cells become visible embedded in a gelatinous sheath, but not touching each other, and forming a filament. *Anthophysa* pedicles, a Protozoon, are sometimes mistaken for it but the latter is usually branched like a "Y" and has longitudinal striations.

The Protozoa are the lowest forms of animal life, unicellular in structure, though they may aggregate in colonies. Of *Dinobryon* frequently only the pencil-like outlines of the tiny cups or trumpet-like shells are visible (and difficulty seen), one set in another, to form branching aggregations. The spores of *Dinobryon* are sometimes mistaken for *Cyclotella*. *Glenodinium* and *Peridinium* are oval and each has a groove across the center. The former is smaller and has a smoother outline than the latter. *Synura* is a small moving yellowish ball of oval animalcules joined concentrically and closely packed. *Uroglena* is a large jelly-like hollow ball of minute animalcules, the latter embedded near the surface, similar in appearance to *Volvox*, as previously mentioned, but lacking the large green cells. It rolls around slowly in the center of the liquid of the cell. Broken pieces have the shape of a piece of a rubber ball. It is visible to the naked eye and recognizable in the bottle.

Rotifera, Crustacea, etc. (more complicated animal forms) are readily distinguished from their pictures in most instances. Many are visible to the aked eye. *Cyclops* may readily be recognized in the bottle by its shape and wift darting motion. It appears about the size of a pin head shaped somevhat like a tiny fish, but wider in proportion. *Bosmina* (little cow) and *Acariña* (little spider) each has a peculiar characteristic jerky motion.

Control of Microscopic Organisms

Troublesome microscopic growths are controlled as follows: Reservoirs are shut off from the service and bypassed until the forms die out under storage which may take three weeks to three months. Aeration by fountains vill disintegrate certain fragile forms like *Uroglena*, *Anabaena*, even *Asterionella*, nd assist in removing odors. It has lately been shown that *Crenothrix* may be controlled by chloramine or liquid chlorine (Montfort & Barnes). Liquid chlorine has also been recently employed by New York City to help control *Synura*, *Uroglena* and *Dinobryon*. But the method of widest application is hat of Moore & Kellerman, the application of copper sulphate in dosage ranging from .05 to 1.00 part per million by weight according to the particular species (or even varieties) of microscopic organisms present. The chemical has been usually applied by rowing around in boats dragging burlap bags, containing, usually, fifty pounds each, through the surface of the water, allowing wind, wave and diffusion to mix the treated water with the remainder.

New York City has demonstrated, very satisfactorily, that dry feed of the chemical by automatic accurate electrical apparatus to the water flowing in an aqueduct a short time before entering the reservoir is absolutely feasible and successful even at winter temperatures and with ice-covered reservoirs. The feed is by means of a slowly moving shutter fed from a hopper. The copper sulphate drops into a screen revolved by the water in a narrowed portion of the aqueduct. The metal parts of the apparatus should be made of copper to prevent corrosion. Dosage is similar to that used in the reservoirs by the boat method, and under such circumstances the killing dosage is known.

The effect of treatment of microscopic organisms by copper sulphate is shown by an immediate intensification of distinctive odors, by reduction of the number of organisms in the water through sedimentation, by the appearance of the organisms under the microscope—the coloring matter being knocked to pieces, so to speak. Sometimes there is an increase in the water bacteria which feed upon the decayed organisms. The Cyanophyceae may produce scum after treatment which is of varied colors, pale blue, yellow, red or brown.

Sometimes fish are killed by the treatment but this is more apt to occur from smothering due to clogging of the gills with dead organisms or reduction of oxygen by the dead organisms. It is only occasionally that fish are killed in quantities, even though larger doses are usually applied than shown in the following table calculated from data published by Moore & Kellerman:

Killing Dosage of Copper Sulphate for Fish

Fish	Parts per Million	Pounds per Million Gallons (Approximate)
Trout	0.14	1.2
Carp	0.33	2.8
Suckers	0.33	2.8
Catfish	0.40	3.5
Pickerel	0.40	3.5
Goldfish	0.50	4.2
Perch	0.67	5.5
Sunfish	1.33	11.1
Black Bass	2.00	16.6

38

Experience differs with waters of different composition and with tempera ture as to the right dosage to apply for each organism. It is believed that is a waste of copper sulphate to apply an insufficient quantity. When th correct quantity is applied the water is usually cleared within three to fou days. The following table is made up from data furnished by Moore & Keller man, Whipple, various other sources and personal experience. The latter ar starred.

Copper Sulphate Required for Treatment of Different Species

Organisms	Parts per Million	Pounds per Million Gallons
DIATOMACEAE:		
Asterionella	0.20*–0.12*	1.7–1.0
Fragilaria	0.25	2.1
Melosira	0.33	2.8
Navicula	0.07	0.6
Synedra	0.50*	4.2
Tabellaria	0.50*–0.12*	4.2–1.0
CHLOROPHYCEAE:		
Cladophora	0.50	4.2
Closterium	0.17	1.4
Coelastrum	0.33–0.05	2.8–0.4
Conferva	0.25	2.1
Desmidium	2.00	16.6
Draparnaldia	0.33	2.8
Eudorina	10.00	83.0
Hydrodictyon	0.10	0.8
Microspora	0.40	3.3
Palmella	2.00	16.6
Pandorina	10.00	83.0
Raphidium	1.00	8.3
Scenedesmus	1.00*	8.3
Spirogyra	0.12	1.0
Staurastrum	1.50	12.5
Ulothrix	0.20*	1.7
Volvox	0.25	2.1
Zygnema	0.50	4.2
CYANOPHYCEAE:		
Anabaena	0.12*	1.0
Aphanizomenon	0.50*–0.12*	4.2–1.0
Clathrocystis	0.12*–0.25*	1.0–2.1
Coelosphaerium	0.33–0.20*	2.8–1.7
Microcystis	0.20	1.7
Oscillaria	0.50*–0.20	4.2–1.7
PROTOZOA:		
Chlamydomonas	0.50	4.2
Cryptomonas	0.50	4.2
Dinobryon	0.33–0.25*	2.8–2.1
Euglena	0.50	4.2
Glenodinium	0.50*	4.2
Mallomonas	0.50	4.2
Peridinium	2.00–0.50*	16.6–4.2
Synura	0.25*–0.12*	2.1–1.0
Uroglena	0.10*–0.20*	0.8–1.6
SCHIZOMYCETES:		
Beggiatoa	5.00	41.5
Cladothrix	0.20	1.7
Crenothrix	0.33	2.8
FUNGUS:		
Leptomitus	0.40	**3.3**

NOTE. Range of dosage largely due to temperature.

The following illustration shows the corner of a bacteriological laboratory or the microscopical examination of water.

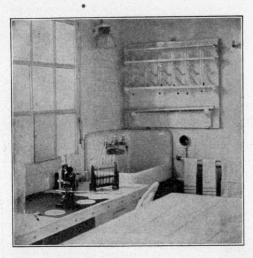

FIG. 173. Microscopical Apparatus, Catskill Laboratory Ashokan, N. Y.

REFERENCES

George C. Whipple, "The Microscopy of Drinking Water." Wiley & Sons.
Moore and Kellerman, "A Method of Destroying or Preventing the Growth of Algae, etc." Bulletin 64, Bureau of Plant Industry, U. S. Dept. of Agriculture.
Moore and Kellerman, "Copper as an Algicide and Disinfectant in Water Supplies." Bulletin 76, Bureau of Plant Industry, U. S. Dept. of Agriculture.
"The Use of Copper Sulphate and Metallic Copper for the Removal of Organisms and Bacteria from Drinking Water,—A Symposium," Vol. 19, No. 4, New England Water Works Association.
Monfort and Barnes, "Chloramine and Crenothrix." Journal of American Water Works Association, Vol. 6, page 196.
Amsbary, "Treatment of Water to Prevent the Growth of Crenothrix." Jour. Am. W. W. Assoc., Vol. 6, page 194.
Monfort, "Crenothrix Removal." Proc. Convention Indiana Sanitary Water Supply Assoc., April, 1919.
W. W. Brush, Engineering News-Record, Feb. 16, 1922.
Frank E. Hale, "Taste and Odor in New York City's Supplies," Jour. Am. W. W. Assoc., Vol. 10 (Sept., 1923), pp. 829–837.
Hudson and Gosse, "The Rotifera." Two volumes and supplement, Longman & Co.
W. Saville Kent, "A Manual of the Infusoria." Three volumes.
Wolle, "Fresh Water Algae of the United States." Two volumes.
Wolle, "Desmids of the United States." One volume.
Wolle, "Diatomaceae of North America." One volume.
Leidy, "Fresh Water Rhizopods of North America." U. S. Geological Survey of the Territories, Volume 12.
Ward and Whipple, "Fresh Water Biology." Wiley.
Griffith and Henfrey, "Micrographic Dictionary." London.

BACTERIOLOGICAL EXAMINATION OF WATER

The routine bacteriological examination is essentially simple. It consist of obtaining empirically the total number of bacteria under certain standar conditions and of testing for the intestinal group, *B. coli*. Usually only unde special conditions is search made for specific disease bacteria which may b carried by water supply, such as *Bacillus typhi, Bacillus paratyphi*—A and F *Spirillum cholerae, Bacillus dysenteriae*—various types, *Bacillus anthracis*, etc

Sampling

Samples must be taken in dry-sterilized bottles, with well-ground glas stoppers. Two ounce capacity is usually sufficient for routine tests. The bottles are preferably protected by covering the stoppers and necks with tinfoi and further protected by placing in a metal screw-top can (two inch by fou inch). It is frequently convenient to use quart bottles steam-sterilized a fifteen pounds pressure, and capped with tinfoil, when special samples are to be brought in by hand,—the same sample serving for the physical, micro scopical and chemical analyses after making the bacteriological examination Such samples transported in leather bags of proper size do not change tempera

FIG. 174. Sampling Apparatus for Deep Samples.

ture more than a few degrees in several hours on th hottest days though not protected by ice. For th two-ounce bottles special aluminum cases, holding small quantities of ice and fitting the bags, are ligh and convenient. For shipping, the small bottle may be packed in a copper-lined wooden box con taining a receptacle for the bottles and space for ic below. (See Fig. 172.)

In sampling care must be taken to take represen tative samples, avoiding contamination and avoiding stagnant water. Temperature is often a guide but i must be taken from the source or in a separate bottle with the thermometer bulb immersed in the water a few minutes before reading. Allow tap samples to run thoroughly, particularly in warm boiler rooms Handle sterilized bottles by the bottom and keep finger away from the necks. Handle stoppers with the tinfoi in place. Avoid splashing or over-running bottles In streams plunge bottle below the surface and sample by swinging hand up-stream with mouth of bottle pointed up-stream so as to avoid water washing over the hand into bottle. Similarly in a reservoir, swing the mouth of the bottle forward while filling. Do not rinse a sterilized bottle. These rather minute direc tions are given because in a long experience they have frequently been found necessary. Experts do not always take the samples though the value of their work depends upon the care with which the samples are taken. Men have even been caught reading thermometers after drawing them up twenty feet from the surface of a reservoir.

Chapter by Frank E. Hale.

Samples from a depth in a reservoir are best taken if possible from an effluent pipe when regular draft is from a depth. In other cases sterilized bottles may be lowered to the required depth and stoppers pulled out by means of special samplers. In many cases it has been found satisfactory to take them by the two-bottle method as used for dissolved oxygen and described under "Microscopic Examination of Water." In this case the quart bottle should be thoroughly cleaned, handled as little as possible, and the water poured into a bacteria bottle after drawing to the surface. The quart bottle is pretty thoroughly rinsed during the process of sampling.

Samples should be tested the same day they are collected, preferably within a few hours. Expressed and iced samples will probably give a fairly reliable index of *B. coli* content but cannot be relied on for total counts.

Apparatus and Materials Needed

Bacteria bottles—two-ounce glass-stoppered (well ground).
Metallic containers for above, screw-cap, two inch by four inch.
Tinfoil, five inch wide, in rolls for capping.
Bacteria certificates for sample data.
Containers for carrying samples—leather bags with aluminum ice cases to fit.
Containers for shipping samples—copper-lined ice chests.
Dry-sterilizer for bottles and pipettes, to operate at 170° C.
Autoclave to operate at 15 pounds steam pressure, sterilization of media.
1 cc. pipettes with two marks and also conveniently graduated to show 0.1 cc. above the
    upper 1 cc. mark.
10 cc. pipettes, preferably straight tube pipettes with graduation also for 5 cc. and 9 cc.
Pipette boxes for sterilized pipettes, $3\frac{1}{4}''$ square by $14''$ long.
Dilution test tubes, $1''$ diameter, medium weight.
Media test tubes, $\frac{5}{8}''$ diameter, heavy weight, not lipped.
Dilution flasks, Erlenmeyer, 16-ounce capacity, for sterilized water.
Flasks, $\frac{1}{2}$ liter, 1 liter, etc., for media preparation and bulk storage.
Test tube racks for dilution tubes.
Wire cages for media tubes, $4''$ by $5''$ by $5\frac{1}{2}''$ high.
Non-absorbent cotton for plugging tubes.
Footless Smith tubes for *B. coli* tests, or small test tubes inverted in large test tubes
    for same, capacity in either case four times the amount of water to be tested.
Metal racks for Smith tubes.
Agateware double boilers for making media.
Agateware kettles for making media.
Agateware funnels, 6 inch, for filtering media.
Cotton flannel for filtering media.
Large beakers for making media.
Earthenware pitchers for filling tubes with media.
Side-neck burettes for filling tubes with media (side neck connected to funnel of media).
Apparatus for keeping media warm while filtering.
Gas stoves for heating media.
Petri dishes, 10 cm. diameter and flat bottomed, with both glass covers (20° C. incuba-
    tion) and porous covers (37° C. incubation).
Agateware sauce pans for melting media in tubes before planting.
20° C. incubator with thermometer, automatic regulator and safety burner.
37° C. incubator with thermometer, automatic regulator and safety burner.
    (In many laboratories the incubators are now electrically operated.)
Burner for flaming tubes before planting.
Counting stand with engraved lines to assist in counting.
Engraver's lens for counting, B. & L. 146, magnification $2\frac{1}{2}$ diameters, $3\frac{1}{2}$ X.
Tallying register for counting.
Balance, similar to an apothecary's, for quick weighing.
Balance, analytical beam type, for accurate weighing.
Record books for bacteriological results.

Microscope with condenser and assortment of lenses: at least $\frac{1}{4}''$, $\frac{1}{2}''$ and $1''$ eyepiece and $\frac{2}{3}''$, $\frac{1}{6}''$ and $1/12''$ objectives. (Satisfactory hanging drops may be made with $\frac{1}{2}''$ eyepiece and $\frac{1}{6}''$ objective. The $1/12''$ is used only in oil immersion with condenser.)

Slides, plain and concaved (latter for hanging drops).

Cover slips, round or square.

Platinum needles with holders for transferring cultures.

Cleaning mixture for cleaning glassware.

Distilled water for preparation of all culture media and reagents.

Meat extract; Liebig's is Standard.

Peptone; Witte's is Standard (N. Y. City Water Department Laboratories have found Digestive Ferments Company's reliable and just as satisfactory if not better. Some laboratories have found Armour's and Fairchild's satisfactory).

Lactose and all other sugars the purest obtainable.

Agar. Frequently needs soaking in water and draining before use because of salt. Shall be dried $\frac{1}{2}$ hour at 105° C. before weighing.

Gelatine, of light color, containing not more than a trace of arsenic, copper, sulphides, free from preservatives, and of such a melting point that "standard nutrient gelatin" shall not melt below 25° C. Gelatin shall be dried $\frac{1}{2}$ hour at 105° C before weighing.

Litmus—reagent litmus of highest purity (not litmus cubes) or azolitmin (Kahlbaum's)

General chemicals—chemically pure so far as possible.

Preparation of Culture Media

Adjustment of Reaction. (a) Phenol Red Method for adjustment to a hydrogen-ion concentration of $pH+ = 6.8$–8.4. Withdraw 5 cc. of the medium

Fig. 175. Bacteriological Apparatus. Fermentation Tubes, Petri Dishes, Pipettes, Culture Media, etc.

dilute with 5 cc. of distilled water, and add 5 drops of a solution of phenol red (phenol sulphone phthalein). This solution is made by dissolving 0.04 grams of phenol red in 30 cc. of alcohol and diluting to 100 cc. with distilled water.

Titrate with a 1 : 10 dilution of a standard solution of NaOH (which need not be of known normality) until the phenol red shows a slight but distinct pink color. Calculate the amount of the standard NaOH solution which must be added to the medium to reach this reaction. After the addition check the reaction by adding 5 drops of phenol red to 5 cc. of the medium and 5 cc. of water.

(b) Titration with Brom Thymol Blue.   Range pH = 6.0–7.6.   Put 4 cc. of distilled water at 30° to 40° C. in a test tube.   Add 1 cc. of the medium to be tested and then ten drops of brom thymol blue (0.04 per cent solution in 5 per cent alcohol).   The resulting color should be either a yellowish green or vary to a deeper shade of grass green.

The reaction may be accurately determined by means of the buffered solutions of Sörensen or of Clark and Lubs.

The following simple procedure which has been found very satisfactory at Mt. Prospect Laboratory of the Department of Water Supply, New York City, should prove serviceable to smaller laboratories which cannot afford elaborate equipment.   Procure from the Pyro-Electric Instrument Company, Chemical Division, Trenton, N. J., " Sterile Universal Buffer Solution " M/10 concentration, also N/5 hydrochloric acid and N/5 sodium hydroxide, sterile and standardized by them.   Follow their chart in making standards, 20 cc. volume, making them pH 0.2 apart.   Procure brom thymol blue, powdered dye, from any of the firms supplying it for pH determinations.   The preparation of the dye solution is as follows according to Clark.   Rub up a decigram of the dye in 3.2 cc. of N/20 sodium hydroxide.   Dilute to 25 cc. with distilled water, making 0.4 per cent solution.   Dilute again for use to 0.04 per cent solution. Add 1 cc. of the last to 20 cc. volume in making up the standards and solutions to be tested.   Instead of using test tubes and a comparison block it has been found convenient and apparently as accurate and less strain on the eye to make up these standards and solutions to be tested in sterile 2-ounce glass-stoppered bottles such as are used for the regular bacteriological samples. (These bottles are blown seamless and may be procured from Whitall Tatum Co., New York City.)   The standards have been found to keep well for several months.   In testing bacteriological media, add to 16 cc. of warm distilled water 4 cc. of melted agar to which has been added 1 cc. of the dye in one of the above bottles.   In another bottle make another portion of diluted media without the dye.   In another bottle put 20 cc. of distilled water.   In comparing with the standards, arrange the bottles on a shelf at the height of the eye with a backing of diffused daylight.   Place the distilled water behind the bottle of diluted media containing dye and the bottle of diluted media without dye behind the dye standards.   Make up the media (plain agar) as near pH 7.0 as possible.   Results will be sufficiently accurate.

Sterilization.   All media and dilution water shall be sterilized in the autoclave at 15 lbs. (120° C.) for 15 minutes after the pressure reaches 15 lbs. All air must be forced out of the autoclave before the pressure is allowed to rise.   As soon as possible after sterilization the media shall be removed from the autoclave and cooled rapidly.   Rapid and immediate cooling of gelatin is imperative.

Media shall be sterilized in small containers, and these must not be closely packed together.   No part of the medium shall be more than 2.5 cm. from the outside surface of the glass.   All glassware shall be sterilized in the dry oven at 170° C. for at least $1\frac{1}{2}$ hours.

Nutrient Broth.   *To make one liter:*

1. Add 3 grams of beef extract and 5 grams of peptone to 1,000 cc. of distilled water.

2. Heat slowly on a steam bath to at least 65° C.

3. Make up lost weight and adjust the reaction to a faint pink with phenol red, or to the required tint with brom thymol blue.

4. Cool to 25° C. and filter through filter paper until clear.

5. Distribute in test-tubes, 10 cc. to each tube.

6. Sterilize in the autoclave at 15 lbs. (120° C.) for 15 minutes after the pressure reaches 15 lbs.

Sugar Broths: Sugar broths shall be prepared in the same general manner as nutrient broth with the addition of 0.5% of the required carbohydrate just before sterilization. The removal of muscle sugar is unnecessary as the beef extract and peptone are free from any fermentable carbohydrates. The reaction of sugar broths shall be a faint pink with phenol red or the required tint with brom thymol blue. Sterilization shall be in the autoclave at 15 pounds (120° C.) for 15 minutes after the pressure reaches 15 pounds, provided the total time of exposure to heat is not more than one-half hour; otherwise a 10 per cent solution of the required carbohydrate shall be made in distilled water and sterilized at 100° C. for $1\frac{1}{2}$ hours, and this solution shall be added to sterile nutrient broth in amount sufficient to make a 0.5 per cent solution of the carbohydrate and the mixture shall then be tubed and sterilized at 100° C. for 30 minutes, or it is permissible to add by means of a sterile pipette directly to a tube of sterile neutral broth enough of the carbohydrate to make the required 0.5 per cent. The tubes so made shall be incubated at 37° C. for 24 hours as a test for sterility.

Nutrient Gelatin. *To make one liter:*

1. Add 3 grams of beef extract and 5 grams of peptone to 1000 cc. of distilled water and add 100 grams of gelatin dried for one-half hour at 105° C. before weighing.

2. Heat slowly on a steam bath to 65° C. until all gelatin is dissolved.

3. Make up lost weight and adjust the reaction to a faint pink with phenol red, or to the required tint with brom thymol blue.

4. Filter through cloth and cotton until clear.

5. Distribute in test-tubes, 10 cc. to each tube, or in larger containers as desired.

6. Sterilize in the autoclave at 15 lbs. (120° C.) for 15 minutes after the pressure reaches 15 lbs.

Nutrient Agar. *To make one liter:*

1. Add 3 grams of beef extract, 5 grams of peptone and 12 grams of agar, dried for one-half hour at 105° C. before weighing, to 1000 cc. of distilled water. Boil over a water bath until all the agar is dissolved, and then make up the loss by evaporation.

2. Cool to 45° C. in a cold water bath, then warm to 65° C. in the same bath, without stirring.

3. Make up lost weight and adjust the reaction to a faint pink with phenol red, or to the required tint with brom thymol blue.

4. Filter through cloth and cotton until clear.

5. Distribute in test-tubes, 10 cc. to each tube, or in larger containers, as desired.

6. Sterilize in the autoclave at 15 lbs. (120° C.) for 15 minutes after the pressure reaches 15 lbs.

Litmus or Azolitmin Solution. The standard litmus solution shall be a 2 per cent aqueous solution of reagent litmus. Powder the litmus, add to the water and boil for five minutes. The solution usually needs no correction in reaction and may be at once distributed in flasks or test-tubes and sterilized as is culture media. It should give a distinctly blue plate when 1 cc. is added to 10 cc. of neutral culture medium in a Petri dish.

The standard azolitmin solution shall be a 1 per cent solution of Kahlbaum's azolitmin. Add the azolitmin powder to the water and boil for five minutes. The solution may need to be corrected in reaction by the addition of sodium hydrate solution so that it will be approximately neutral and will give a distinctly blue plate when 1 cc. is added to 10 cc. of neutral culture medium in a Petri dish. It may be distributed in flasks or test-tubes and sterilized as is culture media.

h. Eosin Methylene Blue Agar

1. To 1000 cc. distilled water add 10 grams of peptone, 2 grams of dipotassium phosphate (K_2HPO_4) and 15 grams of agar. Boil ingredients until dissolved and make up any loss due to evaporation with distilled water.

2. Place measured quantities (100 or 200 cc.) in flasks or bottles and sterilize in the autoclave at 15 pounds for 15 or 20 minutes.

3. Just prior to using, melt agar in streaming steam or on a water bath and add the following to each 100 cc. of agar:

> lactose, sterile 20% solution 5 cc.
> eosin, yellowish, 2% aqueous solution 2 cc.
> methylene blue, 0.5% aqueous solution 2 cc.

4. Pour medium into Petri dishes, allow to harden and inoculate by streaking on the surface.

Endo's Medium. *To make one liter*:

1. Add 5 grams of beef extract, 10 grams of peptone and 30 grams of agar dried for one-half hour at 105° C., before weighing, to 1,000 cc. of distilled water. Boil on a water bath until all the agar is dissolved and then make up the loss by evaporation.

2. Cool the mixture to 45° C. in a cold water-bath, then warm to 65° C. in the same bath without stirring.

3. Make up lost weight, titrate and adjust the reaction to a slightly higher alkalinity than is finally required.

4. Filter through cloth and cotton until clear.

5. Distribute 100 cc. or larger known quantities in flasks large enough to hold the other ingredients which are to be added later.

6. Sterilize in the autoclave at 15 lbs. (120° C.) for 15 minutes after the pressure reaches 15 lbs.

7. Prepare a 10 per cent solution of basic fuchsin in 95 per cent alcohol, allow to stand 20 hours, decant and filter the supernatant fluid. This is a stock solution.

8. When ready to make plates melt 100 cc. of agar in streaming steam or on a waterbath. Dissolve 1 gram of lactose in 15 cc. of distilled water, using heat if necessary. Dissolve 0.25 gram anhydrous sodium sulphite in 10 cc. of water. To the sulphite solution add 0.5 cc. of the fuchsin stock solution. Add the fuchsin-sulphite solution to the lactose solution and then add the resulting solution to the melted agar. The lactose used must be chemically pure and the sulphite solution must be made up fresh.

9. Pour plates and allow to harden thoroughly in the incubator before use.

(NOTE. The methods for nutrient broth, sugar broths, nutrient gelatin, nutrient agar, and litmus-lactose-agar are given above in that form because they are the present adopted standard methods of the American Public Health Association. It is the opinion of the author that the adoption of Liebig's beef extract for fresh beef infusion and the reduction of the peptone by one-half have too greatly weakened the media. Media made according to the 1912 edition standard methods are still in use in the Water Department Laboratories of New York City with the exception that hydrogen-ion concentration is determined colorimetrically to pH = 7.0 approximately.

Brilliant-Green Lactose Peptone Bile. The composition for approximately one liter is as follows:

Distilled water..	1,000 grams.
Oxgall (desiccated fresh entire bile).................	50 "
Peptone...	10 "
Lactose...	10 "
Brilliant Green.....................................	0.1 "

1. Heat 1 liter of distilled water in double boiler until water in outer vessel boils.

2. Add 50 grams of dried oxgall and 10 grams of peptone stirring until all ingredients are dissolved.

3. Continue boiling for one hour.

4. Remove from flame and add 10 grams of powdered lactose.

5. Filter through cotton flannel until clear.

6. To each liter of the filtrate add 10 cc. of a 1 per cent solution of brilliant-green.

7. Tube and sterilize in autoclave for 15 minutes at 15 lbs. pressure. Satisfactory results have been obtained with different brands and different samples of the dye obtained from a dozen sources.

Hesse Agar. The composition for approximately 1 liter is as follows:

Agar (dried)..	4.5 grams.
Peptone...	10. "
Beef extract, Liebig's..............................	5. "
Salt (sodium chloride)...............................	8.5 "
Distilled water.....................................	1,000. "

Dissolve 4.5 grams of dry agar in 500 cc. distilled water by heating over a free flame, making up loss in weight by evaporation. Into another vessel 500 cc. of distilled water is poured and to this is added 10 grams of peptone, 5 grams of Liebig's beef extract, and 8.5 grams of salt. This is heated until all is dissolved and the loss in weight by evaporation is made up by adding distilled water.

Add the two solutions together; boil 30 minutes; make up loss in weight with distilled water, filter through absorbent cotton held in the funnel by cotton flannel, passing the filtrate through several times until perfectly clear. Test the reaction; adjust, if necessary, to pH = 7.0, and tube, using 10 cc. in each tube. Sterilize for 15 minutes at 15 lbs. pressure in an autoclave. Cool with running tap water and store in an ice-chest, the air of which is saturated with moisture.

Russell Media. To ordinary extract agar adjusted neutral to litmus add 1 per cent of lactose and 0.1 per cent of glucose and sufficient litmus to give a good color. Tube and slant leaving a generous " butt " at bottom of tube for stab inoculation.

Examination of Water for Total Bacteria

The gelatine count is more particularly useful in connection with determining the efficiency of filter plants, since the counts are higher than the agar counts (averaging usually about ten times as high) and in examination of well waters by indication of surface contamination through the presence of liquifiers.

In plating with gelatine media it is usually necessary to use 0.1 cc., or less as well as 1 cc., in order to obtain the right amount of colonies on a plate. Standard methods require planting in duplicate.

Melt tubes of nutrient gelatine or nutrient agar in boiling water,—the latter needs thorough boiling for several minutes to entirely soften. Let cool until luke-warm, just barely warm to the touch. Shake the sample of water vigorously and introduce 1 cc. or less into the bottom of a petri-dish lifting the cover on one side but not removing from over the bottom. The quantity of water used should of course be accurately measured. Be careful not to contaminate the pipette by touching to anything other than the inside bottom of the petri-dish. Use glass-covered petri-dishes for incubation at 20° C. and porous covers for 37° C., in order to overcome spreaders at the higher temperature. Remove a tube of the media from the warm water, dry with a towel, remove the cotton plug, flame the open end of tube and pour into petri-dish. Carefully rotate dish to mix the media with the water and set on a level plate to harden. Agar hardens so quickly that it must be handled and mixed expeditiously. Incubate gelatine plates at 20° C. and agar plates at 37° C.

The gelatine plates are counted after 48 hours and the agar plates after 24 hours.

Each minute bacillus must grow where caught in the solid medium and after sufficient time forms a colony large enough to be seen with the naked eye. Many are however very tiny, so that a hand lens magnifying two and one-half diameters is used in counting. A tallying machine is used to keep count, one tally being made for every three colonies usually, to assist the speed of counting. For accuracy there should be 30 to 300 colonies on a plate, unless less than 30 grew from 1 cc. Fictitious accuracy should be avoided. The following table should be followed in recording results:

Number of bacteria per cc.

From	1 to	50 shall be recorded as found						
"	51 "	100	"	"	"	to the nearest		5
"	101 "	250	"	"	"	"	"	"	10
"	251 "	500	"	"	"	"	"	"	25
"	501 "	1,000	"	"	"	"	"	"	50
"	1,001 "	10,000	"	"	"	"	"	"	100
"	10,001 "	50,000	"	"	"	"	"	"	500
"	50,001 "	100,000	"	"	"	"	"	"	1,000
"	100,001 "	500,000	"	"	"	"	"	"	10,000
"	500,001 "	1,000,000	"	"	"	"	"	"	50,000
"	1,000,001 "	10,000,000	"	"	"	"	"	"	100,000

The counting stand is usually marked to facilitate counting, for example, by concentric circles and lines through the center forming sectors. With high numbers four opposite sectors may be counted, situated at right angles to each other, and multiplied by a factor.

Examination for B. coli

B. coli (bacillus of the colon) represents a group of bacteria inhabiting the large intestines of man and animals. Its presence in water supply signifie *possible* sewage contamination and the latter means *probable* typhoid, dysentery, etc., germs. In fact if a drinking water becomes contaminated by sewage an increase in typhoid fever is almost certain to follow. Animals do no spread typhoid though they may be a factor in paratyphoid. *B. coli* in water supply may be due to harmless sources and so of little significance.

The present Standard Methods define the *B. coli* group as including al non-spore-forming bacilli which ferment lactose with gas formation and grow aërobically on standard solid media.

The following new sub-classification is recommended in "Standard Methods c Water Analysis," 1920 to 1923, A. P. H. A.:

B. coli of fecal origin.....................
- Methyl red +
- Voges-Proskauer −
- Gelatin −
- Adonite −
- Indol, usually +
- Saccharose, usually −

B. aërogenes of fecal origin..........................
- Methyl red −
- Voges-Proskauer +
- Gelatin −
- Adonite +
- Indol, usually −
- Saccharose +

B. aërogenes, probably not of fecal origin...............
- Methyl red −
- Voges-Proskauer +
- Gelatin −
- Adonite −
- Indol, usually −
- Saccharose +

B. cloacae may or may not be of fecal origin.............
- Methyl red −
- Voges-Proskauer +
- Gelatin +
- Adonite +
- Indol, usually −
- Saccharose +

Procedure for the above identifications may be found in "Standard Methods o Water Analysis," 1923 edition, published by American Public Health Association.

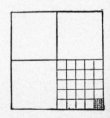

FIG. 176. Microscope for Bacteriological Examination.   FIG. 177. Ocular Micromete

Subclassification of B. coli[1]

B. coli Group. The general characteristics common to this group are:
Fermentation of dextrose and lactose with gas formation, short bacillus
with rounded ends, non-spore-forming, facultative anaërobe, gives positive test
with esculin, grows at 20° C. on gelatine and at 37° C. on agar, non-liquefying
in fourteen days on gelatine, gram-staining negative.

The group consists of four species:

> B. *communior* (Durham).
> B. *communis* (Escherich).
> B. *aërogenes* (Escherich).
> B. *acidilactici* (Hüeppe).

This group is differentiated as follows:

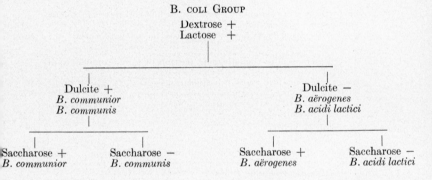

B. COLI GROUP
Dextrose +
Lactose +

| Dulcite +
B. *communior*
B. *communis* | Dulcite −
B. *aërogenes*
B. *acidi lactici* |

| Saccharose +
B. *communior* | Saccharose −
B. *communis* | Saccharose +
B. *aërogenes* | Saccharose −
B. *acidi lactici* |

The revised "Standard Methods" in testing for the *B. coli* group require
gas formation in lactose broth plus confirmation in accordance with the following procedure:

[1] Adopted by A. P. H. A., 1912, and recommended by the author.

Summary of Steps Involved in Making Presumptive, Partially Confirmed and Completed Tests for B. Coli

Steps In Procedure	Further Procedure Required

I. Inoculate lactose broth fermentation tubes; incubate 24 hrs. at 37° C.; observe gas-formation in each tube.

  1. Gas-formation, 10 per cent or more; constitutes positive presumptive test.

    (a) For other than smallest portion of any sample showing gas at this time, and for all portions, including smallest, of sewage and raw water this test is sufficient..................... None

    (b) For smallest gas-forming portion, except in examinations of sewage and raw water................................. III

  2. Gas-formation less than 10 per cent in 24 hrs.; inconclusive...... II

II. Incubate an additional 24 hours, making a total of 48 hours incubation; observe gas-formation.

  1. Gas-formation, any amount; constitutes doubtful test, which must always be carried further.................................. III

  2. No gas-formation in 48 hours; constitutes final negative test...... None

III. Make plate* from smallest gas-forming portion of sample under examination; incubate 18 to 24 hours; observe colonies.

  1. One or more colonies typical in appearance.

    (a) If only "partially confirmed" test is required............... None

    (b) If completed test is required, select two typical colonies for identification... V

  2. No typical colonies... IV

IV. Replace plate in incubator for an additional 18 to 24 hours; then, whether colonies appear typical or not, select at least two of those which most nearly resemble B. coli.............................. V

V. Transfer each colony fished to:

  1. Lactose broth fermentation tube; incubate not more than 48 hrs. at 37° C. Observe gas-formation.......................... None

  2. Agar slant; incubate 48 hours at 37° C.

    (a) If gas formed in lactose broth tube inoculated with corresponding culture...................................... VI

    (b) If no gas formed in corresponding lactose broth tube, test is completed and negative.............................. None

VI. Make stained cover-slip or slide preparation, and examine microscopically.

  1. If preparation shows non-spore-forming bacilli in apparently pure culture, demonstration of B. coli is completed................ None

  2. If preparation fails to show non-spore-forming bacilli or shows them mixed with spore-bearing forms or bacteria of other morphology. VII

VII. Replate, to obtain assuredly pure culture, select several colonies of bacilli and repeat steps V and VI.

* Endo- or Eosin Methylene Blue.

"Standard Methods" outlines the following procedure arranged by days:

Routine Procedure for Examination of Samples of Water

First Day:

1. Prepare dilutions as required.
2. Make two (2) gelatin plates from each dilution, and incubate at 20° C.
3. Make two (2) agar plates from each dilution, and incubate at 37° C.
4. Inoculate lactose broth fermentation tubes with appropriate amounts for B. coli tests, inoculating two (2) tubes with each amount.

NOTE. Where repeated tests are made of water from the same source, as is customary in the control of public supplies, it is not necessary to make duplicate plates or fermentation tubes in each dilution. It is sufficient, in such circumstances, to make duplicate plates only from the dilution which will most probably give from 30 to 300 colonies per plate.

Second Day:

1. Count the agar plates made on the first day.
2. Record the number of lactose broth fermentation tubes which show 10 per cent or more of gas.

NOTE. In case only the presumptive test for B. coli is required, fermentation tubes showing more than 10 per cent of gas at this time may be discarded.

Third Day:

1. Count gelatin plates made on first day.
2. Record the number of additional fermentation tubes which show 10 per cent or more of gas.
3. Make a eosin methylene blue or Endo's medium plate from the smallest portion of each sample showing gas. Incubate plate at 37° C.

NOTE. In case the smallest portion in which gas had been formed shows less than 10 per cent of gas, it is well to make a plate also from the next larger portion, so that, in case the smallest portion gives a negative end result it may still be possible to demonstrate B. coli in the next larger dilution.

Fourth Day:

1. Examine Endo's medium or eosin methylene blue plates. If typical colonies have developed, select two and transfer each to a lactose broth fermentation tube and an agar slant, both of which are to be incubated at 37° C.
2. If no typical B. coli colonies are found, incubate the plates another 24 hours.

Fifth Day:

1. Select at least two colonies, whether typical or not, from the Endo's medium or eosin methylene blue plates which have been incubated an additional 24 hours; transfer each to a lactose broth fermentation tube and an agar slant, and complete the test as for typical colonies.
2. Examine lactose broth fermentation tubes inoculated from plates on the previous day. Tubes in which gas has been formed may be discarded after the result has been recorded. Those in which no gas has formed should be incubated an additional 24 hours.

Sixth Day:

1. Examine lactose broth fermentation tubes reincubated the previous day
2. Examine microscopically agar slants corresponding to lactose fermentation tubes inoculated from plate colonies and showing gas-formation.

The above procedure is too troublesome for a laboratory handling large numbers of routine samples. The work is too great and the time too long for the value of the results. It was adopted because of the fact that *B. welchii,* a spore-forming group (though probably of fecal origin), also forms gas in lactose media. *B. welchii* is obligate anaërobic, gram positive, esculin negative, and a spore-former. It may easily be differentiated from *B. coli* by its appearance in a hanging drop. (Prepare hanging drop by placing a drop of salt solution, 0.85% sodium chloride, on a sterile coverglass and mix with a minute portion of the culture, taken direct from the fermentation tube. Invert this cover slip over a hollow slide, sealed by a ring of vaseline, and examine under the microscope.) It is a large, non-motile bacillus, occurring in chains particularly when grown in lactose bile media, as mentioned in the 1912 edition of "Standard Methods." Recently in a few instances aërobic spore-forming bacilli have been described which fermented lactose broth, but such instances are extremely rare, and they have not been found in lactose bile.

Since about one-third of the laboratories of the country are still using bile media, it seems fitting to include in this chapter a modification, " Brilliant-green lactose peptone bile " (see Preparation of Media), which *eliminates B. welchii* from the test. This modification, worked out by Muer & Harris, bacteriologists at Mt. Prospect Laboratory, Brooklyn, has been in use for several years in the New York City Water Department Laboratories with entire satisfaction. It makes the presumptive test for *B. coli* a practical certainty. Attention should be called to the fact, and emphasized, that since the 1912 standards were published lactose bile has been made more delicate by the use of only 5% bile and also in considering 10% or more of gas a positive test. Now the introduction of " brilliant-green " eliminates the *B. welchii* or spore-forming groups. Confirmation of *B. coli* has rarely failed in all cases tried. The only reason for making 10% of gas a lower limit is because of possible danger of inversion of a small amount of lactose to dextrose during sterilization. It is however very rarely that there is less than 10% of gas. The method has been investigated by a committee of the American Water Works Association.

In testing for *B. coli* 0.1 cc., 1 cc., and 10 cc. portions of water are introduced to the bottom of the bile tubes, or in polluted waters quantities varying by decimal multiples or fractions until a negative test is obtained. Sewage will usually show a positive test in 0.000001 cc. The plantings are made at the same time that the plates are prepared for total counts. The tubes are incubated at 37° C. for three days. Ten per cent of gas within three days is a positive test. Tubes showing no gas in two days are usually discarded.

Examination for B. Typhi, etc.

Direct test for *B. typhi* may be made from the bile tube or from larger quantities of water incubated in bottles of bile. The method of the 1912 edition of "Standard Methods" is still in use in the New York City Water Laboratories as a routine procedure. Dilutions from the bile tube media are mixed with 10 cc. melted Hesse agar (see Preparation of Media) in petri dishes with porous tops. The poured plates are hardened in the ice-box and then incubated 24 hours at 37° C. The colony is characteristic only when a few colonies are on a plate. They are large size, have a dense white nucleus, then translucent zone, then dense white seam. The colonies are perfectly round. They retain their appearance if placed in the ice-box, and as they develop further produce another translucent area and another seam, etc., giving the appearance of concentric rings. Other large colonies of other species usually become dense throughout. Forms most likely to interfere are *B. para-typhi*, *B. pyocyaneous*, *B. fluorescens liquefaciens*, and some very motile forms of *B. coli*.

From the edges of the colony direct tests should be made for *B. typhi* and *B. para-typhi* by specific agglutination tests.

Widal Test. To make the Widal test place a small portion of the culture in a drop of normal salt solution on a cover glass, and invert it over a rubber ring on a glass slide, using vaseline on the edges so as to prevent evaporation and consequent movement by currents in the drop.

If the bacteria are motile rods resembling *B. typhi* add a drop of equal size of highly diluted anti-typhoid serum (the latter diluted with physiological salt solution). If in the course of half an hour the bacteria cease their motions and agglutinate, the presence of *B. typhi* is practically established. In rare cases, some strains of *B. coli* and allied species may respond to the Widal test, but almost invariably in dilutions of 1–50 or less. The high-power dry lens is best for this work.

To determine the point of highest dilution at which agglutination takes place the Widal test is best made in tubes and examined macroscopically. Place a series of small test tubes in a rack and pour into each varying dilutions of anti-typhoid serum. To each tube add an equal amount of 24-hour broth culture of *B. typhi* and incubate at 37° C. for at least three hours. The highest point at which precipitation takes place is the highest point of agglutination.

Russell Media. As additional rapid means of differentiating between *B. typhi* and *B. para-typhi* A and B, needle stabs may be made into tubes of Russell media (see Preparation of Media) and incubated at 37° C. The reactions are based on the fact that the bacilli growing aërobically, that is on the slant, only utilize the carbohydrate when present in amounts over 0.1%, whereas, growing anaërobically stabbed in the butt, they must utilize the carbohydrates for their oxygen supply and therefore ferment the trace of glucose present. The indications of the Russell media reactions are as follows:

B. coli Group—Russell media—Slant, acid   (Glucose, acid and gas)
                         Butt, acid and gas (Lactose, acid and gas)

B. typhi Group   ⎫   ⎧ Slant unchanged (Glucose, acid only)
B. dysentery Group ⎬ Russell media ⎨ Butt, acid only   (Lactose, not
                         ⎭   ⎩   fermented)

B. paratyphi Group ⎫   ⎧ Slant unchanged (Glucose, acid and
                         ⎬ Russell media ⎨   gas)
B. enteritidis Group ⎭   ⎩ Butt, acid and gas (Lactose, not
                                                     fermented)

B. alkaligenes Group—Russell media—Slant unchanged (Glucose, not
                                                                 fermented)
                         Butt unchanged (Lactose, not
                                                              fermented)

In distinguishing between typhoid and dysentery (true or Shiga type)—typhoid bacilli are motile, dysentery non-motile, typhoid produces acid in mannite, dysentery does not.

There also exist three types of para-dysentery (non-motile): Type I (Park-Hiss), type II (Flexner) and type III (Strong). Para-dysentery are different from true dysentery in that they produce acid with mannite (the same as typhoid) but they all give positive indol, while dysentery and typhoid do not. Indol is sometimes doubtful with Flexner. The three para-dysentery groups are further distinguished among themselves by their reactions upon maltose and saccharose. The type I produces acid in neither, type II produces acid in maltose but not in saccharose, type III produces acid in saccharose but not in maltose. The usual final test for all these different types of typhoid and dysentery is the agglutination with specific serums. The sugar fermentation tests must be made upon freshly isolated cultures since after artificial cultivation Park-Hiss strains may ferment maltose and Flexner strains saccharose as demonstrated by Hiss and by Lentz.

The members of the typhoid, para-typhoid, dysentery and para-dysentery groups all form colorless colonies upon Endo media. This is frequently the starting point for isolation.

REFERENCES

"Standard Methods of Water Analysis." Am. Pub. Health Assoc., Editions 1905. 1912, 1917, 1920 and 1923. (Contain extensive bibliography.)
Park and Williams, "Pathogenic Microörganisms."
Prescott and Winslow, "Elements of Water Bacteriology."
Chester, "A Manual of Determinative Bacteriology."
Bergey's "Manual of Determinative Bacteriology."
"The Determination of Hydrogen Ions," Clark.

METHODS FOR THE DETERMINATION OF SOLUBILITY [1]

A quantitative determination of a solubility consists essentially of two operations; the preparation of the saturated solution and its subsequent analysis. In those cases where these steps are performed separately the method may, in general, be designated as the analytical and in those where they are combined, as the synthetic. In both cases, however, the consideration of first importance is the assurance that final equilibrium between solvent and solute has been reached. Since this point is that at which no further change occurs in the relation between the amount of the compound in solution and that remaining undissolved, the only criterion of saturation is the evidence that the concentration of the solution has not changed during a longer or shorter interval of time, during which those conditions which would tend to promote such a change have been allowed to operate.

Of the conditions which promote most effectively the attainment of equilibrium between a solute and a solvent, the provision for the intimate contact of the two is most important. In other words, only by the thorough mixing which agitation or effective stirring provides can the point of saturation be reached with certainty. In the case of the reciprocal solubility of liquids, the point of equilibrium is usually attained within a much shorter period than in the case of solids dissolved in liquids. In the latter case, the necessary disintegration of the solid, incident to its solution in the liquid, is a process which is restricted to the surface layers of the solid, and, therefore, unless a large area, such as a finely divided state provides, is available, and unless that portion of the solvent which has acted upon a given surface area is repeatedly replaced by fresh solvent, the process of solution will be greatly retarded. It is quite evident that, although a solution in contact with even very finely divided solid may promptly become saturated in the immediate vicinity of the solid without stirring, the distribution of the dissolved material to the remainder of the solvent would depend upon diffusion, and since the rate at which this proceeds would diminish as the concentration differences became equalized, the process would take place at a gradually diminishing rate. If the point of equilibrium is approached from supersaturation, the above remarks apply with equal effect, since only at the surface of the solid can the excess of salt leave the solution and, without other provision than diffusion for successively bringing the entire amount of the solution in contact with the solid, the deposition of the excess of dissolved material can occur only at a very slow rate. The importance of active and continuous agitation of the solid and solution, in effecting saturation, cannot, therefore, be too strongly emphasized. It may in fact be assumed that determinations of the solubility of solids, made without continuous agitation, are always open to the suspicion that the results do not represent the final equilibrium which such data are required to show.

[1] Reprinted from 2d Ed. of "Solubilities." Contributed by Atherton Seidell.

Since solubility is a function of temperature, the accurate control of the temperature in making a solubility determination is another one of the indispensable requisites of accuracy. In general, it may be stated therefore, that every procedure designed for preparing a saturated solution must include provision for the accurate control of the temperature and for active and continuous agitation or stirring of the solution. In the case of the solubility of gases, which will be considered in a separate section, provision for the control of the pressure must also be made.

It is obvious that since the solubilities of various compounds differ, and that of one compound is affected by the presence of another, the accurate determination of this constant for a particular molecular species presupposes that only this one substance is present in the pure solvent. That is, accuracy of results demand that only pure compounds be involved in a given determination, consequently, no effort should be spared to make it certain that the highest possible purity of both solute and solvent has been attained.

Apparatus for the Determination of the Solubility of Solids by the Analytical Method. The types of apparatus which have been developed for the preparation of saturated solutions of solids in liquids differ principally in respect to whether designed for multiple or single determinations at a given temperature. Examples of the first type are illustrated by Figs. 178 and 179.

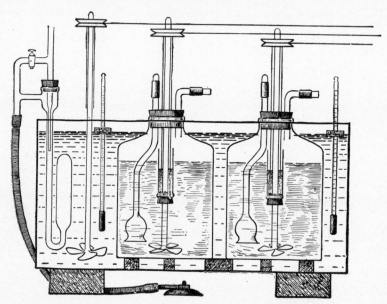

Fig. 178. Determination of Solubility of Solids.

It will be noted that in one case (Fig. 178) the bottles containing the solutions are stationary and the liquid in each and in the constant temperature bath is kept in motion by means of revolving stirrers. This form of apparatus was used by Moody and Leyson (1908) for the determination of the solubility

f lime in water and is particularly adapted for relatively slightly soluble com-
ounds for which rather large quantities of the saturated solution are needed
or accurate analysis.   There is also shown in the figure the provision for with-
rawing the saturated solution through a filter within the inverted thistle tube.
he stirrers in the bottles are fitted with mercury seals to prevent access of
ir containing carbon dioxide.   Other features of the apparatus will be readily
nderstood from the drawing.

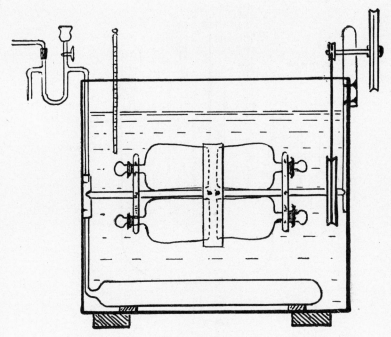

FIG. 179.   Noyes apparatus for determining the solubility of solids.

A more common type of apparatus, designed for the simultaneous saturation
of several solutions at the same temperature, is that illustrated by Fig. 179,
n which the bottles containing the solutions are slowly rotated in the constant
temperature bath.   The form shown is that described by Noyes (1892).
This type of apparatus has the advantage that the solid is, to a large extent,
kept in suspension in the liquid and, therefore, offers the most favorable opportunity for continuous and uniform contact with the solution.   Many examples
of this form of apparatus, differing principally in size and in the direction of
movement of the containers, are described in the literature.

Of the second type of apparatus, designed for a single determination at a
given temperature, many varieties have been developed for particular conditions.   Of these, the following examples have been selected as typical of this
class and, it is hoped, will illustrate most of their desirable features.   They
are, in general, adaptations of earlier designs and it is not intended that the

name given in connection with each is that of the investigator who deserve
the credit for originating the type.   The drawings will, for the most part, be
readily understood without detailed explanations.   The dimensions are no
stated, since they can usually be varied to suit the needs of almost any problem

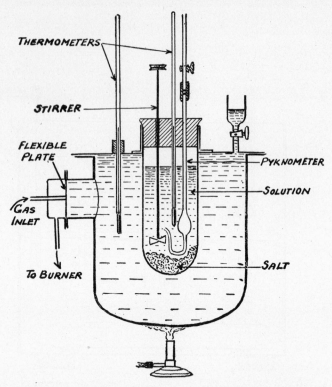

Fɪɢ. 180.   Berkeley's apparatus for determining solubility.

In Fig. 180 is shown the apparatus used by the Earl of Berkeley (1904) for
the very careful determinations of the solubility of inorganic salts in water.
The features of particular interest in connection with it are, that the water
bath itself is made to serve as the temperature regulating device, and the
apparatus for withdrawing and simultaneously filtering the saturated solution
is a combination of pipet and pycnometer.   This was provided with ground
glass caps for each end and the stem was accurately graduated.   It was, of
course, carefully standardized before use.   The flexible iron plate shown was
made of a disc from the receiver of a telephone.   The apparatus was used for
determinations at temperatures between 30° and 90° and the range of variations from the set temperature of the bath was, for 2–3 hour periods, within
about 0.2°.   For the inner vessel containing the salt, the range was about
0.05°.   At each temperature two determinations of density and solubility were
made;   one on the solution obtained by stirring a supersaturated solution in

contact with solid salt, and the other on the solution obtained by stirring an unsaturated solution in contact with an excess of salt.

In the case of determinations at the boiling point a special apparatus was required. Two forms, described by the Earl of Berkeley (1904), are shown in Figs. 181 and 182. The first was used for the less soluble salts and consisted of an

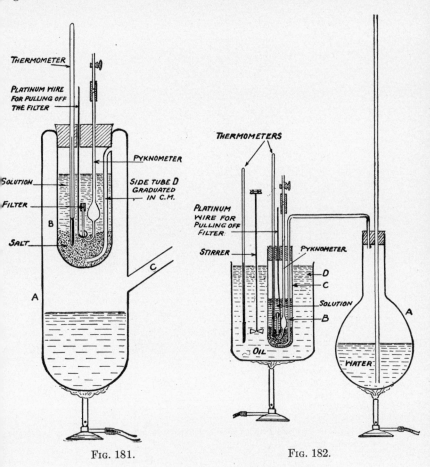

FIG. 181.   FIG. 182.

Berkeley's apparatus for determining solubility.

outer tube A containing water and an inner tube B containing salt and solution. By boiling the water vigorously and closing the side tube C, steam passing through the tube D stirred the solution thoroughly and the temperature rose to the boiling point of the saturated solution and remained constant when saturation was attained. The second form of apparatus (Fig. 182) was devised for use with extremely soluble alts. In these cases it was found that the larger quantity of steam required for thorough stirring dissolved so much salt that it was necessary to have a very large excess present. In this apparatus the steam was generated in a boiler A and conducted through the tube B to the bottom of the large test tube C containing the excess of salt and solution. The test tube was immersed in the oil bath D which was vigorously stirred and maintained at a temperature close to that of the boiling point of the saturated

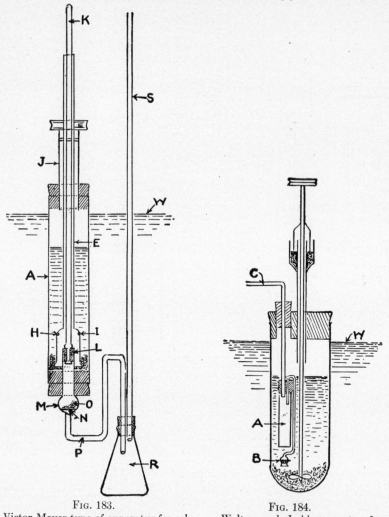

FIG. 183.
Victor Meyer type of apparatus for solubility determination.

FIG. 184.
Walton and Judd apparatus for solubilities.

solution. When the temperature of the oil bath was below the boiling point, salt dissolved; when above, salt was thrown out of solution. Considerable difficulty was experienced in filling the pycnometer with the saturated solution without introducing errors due to steam bubbles caused by the suction which was applied.

A comparatively simple form of the type of apparatus used by Victor Meyer in 1875 and modified by Reicher and van Deventer (1890) and by Goldschmidt (1895), is described by Hicks (1915) and shown in the accompanying Fig. 183. A glass cylinder A is closed at each end with large one-hole rubber stoppers. The mixture of salt and solution is contained in this cylinder and is stirred by the rotation of the tube E which is provided with an enlargement at its lower end in which there are two small holes at H and I. The stirrer rotates in the bearing formed by the hollow wooden cylinder J. The glass rod K carries a rubber stopper L which closes the filtering tube M, in which a platinum cone N supports an asbestos filter O. The siphon P connects the filtering tube with the flask R which is provided with an outlet through the small tube S. The apparatus is immersed in a constant temperature water bath W, to about the level shown. After stirring the mixture of salt and solution a sufficient length of time for attainment of saturation, the undissolved salt is allowed to settle and the rubber stopper is withdrawn from the filter tube by means of the glass rod K. Suction is applied through the tube S to hasten the filtering and the clear solution collected, at the temperature of the bath, in the previously weighed flask R.

A similar apparatus was used by Walton and Judd (1911), for determination of the solubility of lead nitrate in pyridine. This is shown in Fig. 184 and consists of a glass test tube fitted with a stirrer which turns in a mercury seal, thus preventing loss of solvent by evaporation or the admission of moisture from the air. To take a sample of the saturated solution, the weighing tube A was introduced into the larger tube through a hole in the stopper. After reaching the temperature of the bath the stirrer was stopped, the end of the small tube B, which was

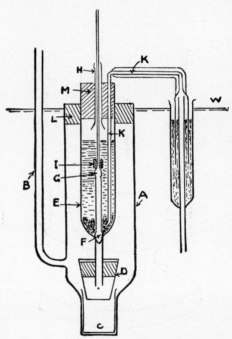

FIG. 185. Donnan and White apparatus for determining solubilities.

covered with a piece of closely-woven muslin, was dipped below the surface of the solution and the liquid drawn into A by applying suction at C. The tube A was then removed, weighed and the contents analyzed.

An apparatus which was used by Donnan and White (1911), for the determination of equilibrium in the system palmitic acid and sodium palmitate is shown in Fig. 185. The stirring in this case was accomplished by means of a current of dry air, free of carbon dioxide. The apparatus consists of two parts namely, an inner chamber E, where equilibrium was attained, and an outer case A, designed for isothermal filtration. The whole was immersed in a thermostat to the level W. A side tube B permitted connection with a filter pump. C is a weighing bottle to receive the filtered saturated solution and D a Gooch crucible provided with a paper filter. The cork, closing A, was covered with a plastic layer to render it airtight. The tube at the lower end of E was closed with a ground glass plug F, the stem of which was enlarged to a small bulb at G and then drawn out to pass easily through H, leaving an air

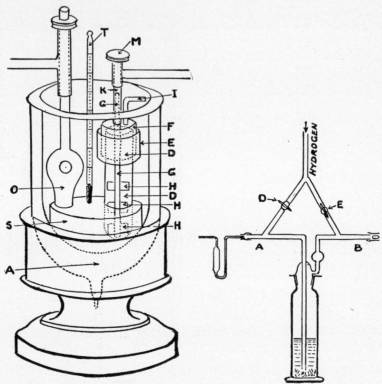

Fig. 186.   Cohen and Inouye apparatus   Fig. 187.   Bahr's apparatus for de.
            for solubilities.   termining solubilities.

free outlet around it. The small cork I was used to support the stopper when lifted to allow the contents of E to flow down for filtration. The dry air by which the mixture was stirred was drawn through K by applying suction at H. The preheating of this air was accomplished by drawing it through a thin spiral immersed in the thermostat. The connection between the equilibrium apparatus and preheater was made through a mercury seal, which permitted lifting the apparatus easily without damage to the fragile preheater permanently mounted in the bath. This apparatus provided for the recovery, separately, of he saturated solution and undissolved solid.   These authors also describe an improved electrically heated and controlled constant temperature bath.

Determinations at lower temperatures that can be constantly maintained with the aid of a water bath require special forms of apparatus which permit of temperature control under more or less restricted conditions.   An apparatus of this type, which was used by Cohen and Inouye (1910), for determination of the solubility of phosphorus in carbon disulfide, is shown in Fig. 186, and is intended for the range of temperature between $-10°$ and $+10°$.   The saturating vessel D consists of a glass cylinder to the upper end of which is cemented a steel collar E, containing a deep channel.   A mixture of litharge and glycerol was used as the cementing material for this purpose.   The inverted steel cover F fits into the channel of this collar and the seal of the joint is effected, in the usual way, by means of a layer of mercury.   The cover F is provided with a brass tube K, to which the pulley M is attached, and is also pierced by the tightly cemented-in glass tube I.   The glass rod G, containing on its lower end the three stirring wings $H\ H\ H$, is cemented into the brass tube K.   The saturating vessel is, for stability, tightly fastened in a hole in a block of lead, S, contained in the Dewar cylinder A.   An atmosphere of CO_2 in the saturating vessel is provided by introducing CO_2 under pressure through I and allowing the excess to escape through the mercury seal in E.   After charging the apparatus, I is closed with a rubber tube and plug and the stirrers $H\ H\ H$ set in motion.   A Witt stirrer, O, keeps the contents of the bath in rapid circulation.   Water is used in the bath for temperatures above $0°$, and alcohol for those below $0°$.   The regulation of the temperature is accomplished by addition of ice or solid CO_2 as found necessary and, therefore, requires very close attention on the part of the experimenter.

A novel and simple form of apparatus, which was used by Bahr (1911), for the determination of the solubility of thallium hydroxide at temperatures up to $40°$ is shown in Fig. 187.   As will be seen, this consists of a gas washing flask to the arms of which a Y tube provided with two stop-cocks is sealed. The inside walls of the apparatus were coated with hard paraffin and the required amounts of thallium hydroxide and water introduced.   It was then immersed in a water bath and the contents stirred by means of a current of hydrogen, which entered as shown and with A and E closed, passed through D and out at B.   When it was desired to remove a sample of the solution for analysis, B and D were closed and the liquid forced through A into the pycnometer by means of gas pressure entering through E.   For temperatures above $40°$, the form of apparatus shown in Fig. 188 was used.   In this case K represents a copper cylinder with double walls, of which the inner compartment G, contains concentrated salt solution which is stirred by a stream of air (not shown), and the outer compartment contains a layer of heating liquid H.   The glass tube L contains the mixture of thallium hydroxide and water which is stirred by means of a current of hydrogen (not shown).   When saturation is attained the tube A, of small bore and thick walls and provided with a small asbestos filter, is introduced and the saturated solution forced over into the receptacle B by pressure of hydrogen which enters at C. The heating liquid in B is the same as used in H. The following heating liquids with the boiling points shown were used: Allyl chloride, 46°; Ethylene chloride, 55°; Chloroform, 61°; Methyl alcohol, 66°; Benzene, 80°; Benzene-Toluene mixture, 91°; Water, 100°.

A somewhat more elaborate apparatus, in which the constant temperature is maintained by means of the vapor of a boiling liquid, is shown in Fig. 189.

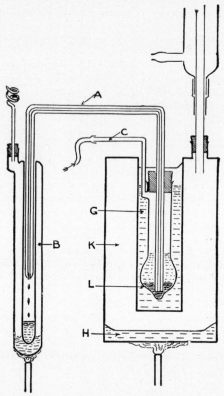

FIG. 188.

This apparatus was developed by Tyrer (1910) for the very accurate determination of the solubilities of anthraquinone, anthracene and phenanthraquinone in single and mixed organic solvents. The solvent with excess of the solute was placed in A and kept in constant agitation by means of the vertically acting stirrer shown. The tube A is surrounded by a bath of vapor which circulates through the cylinder B, condenses in C, and returns to the boiling flask M. When the solution is saturated it is allowed to settle, and the clear solution run out (by raising the tube D) into a small graduated flask E, which is maintained at the same temperature as the solution A. The temperature of the vapor bath is varied by changing the pressure under which the liquid in

he flask M is boiling. For this purpose, the manostat P is provided. The
emperature can, with care, be maintained constant to 0.01°. For this purpose
he apparatus must be airtight, the liquid in the boiling flask must not bump
which is entirely prevented by placing a layer of mercury in the flask) and a
ure boiling liquid must be used.

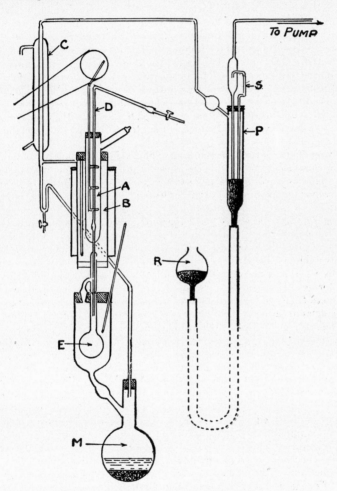

FIG. 189. Tyrer's apparatus for solubilities.

Although illustrations of special forms of apparatus designed for securing
quilibrium in solubility determinations could be extended far beyond the
umber given, it is believed that the principal features have been made clear
.nd it will no doubt be possible to adapt the devices here shown to many other
.ases for which accurate determinations of solubility may be desired.

Separation of Saturated Solution from Undissolved Solid. The next point after the establishment of equilibrium between the solvent and solution, is th matter of successfully separating the saturated solution from the undissolve solid, preparatory to its analysis. There are, undoubtedly, many cases where this is a very serious problem. This is especially so for extremely soluble com pounds, which yield viscous solutions as well as for those which do not readily settle out of the solution or cannot be removed by ordinary filtration. It is of course, necessary to maintain the mixture at the temperature at which satur ation was obtained until the complete separation of the solution and solid ha been effected. The operation should, therefore, as a general thing, be con ducted in the same bath used for preparing the saturated solution. Severa forms of apparatus designed for this purpose are shown in the diagrams given in the preceding pages. For solutions which can be readily separated from the undissolved solid, a graduated pipet to which a stem with a plug of filtering material can be attached and which is adapted to being easily weighed, is the most convenient.

Analysis of the Saturated Solution. The weight of a known volume of the perfectly clear solution, that is, its specific gravity, should always be deter mined. This weighed quantity of solution, or a known dilution of it, furnishes a very convenient sample for the determination of the amount of dissolve compound.

In regard to the analysis, the procedure must be selected entirely on the basis of the number and character of the constituents present. In cases of the solubility of single non-volatile compounds, in solvents which can be more o less easily removed by volatilization, the plan in most general use is the evap oration of a known amount of the solution to dryness and weighing the residue Special forms of apparatus to be used for this purpose have been proposed from time to time. These are, usually, vessels with tubular openings, arranged so that a current of dry air can be drawn over the surface of the heated sample

In the case of solubility determinations in which the saturated solution contains more than one dissolved compound, the application of the usual gravimetric or volumetric procedures will, of course, be necessary.

In certain cases, where the direct determination of the amount of the dis solved compound present in the solution would be very difficult or impossible, an indirect method can sometimes be used. For this purpose, a carefully weighed amount of the compound must be used, and, after the period of satur ation, the undissolved residue is filtered off under conditions which reduce losses to a minimum and, after drying to its original condition, it is weighed, and the amount which has been dissolved found by subtracting the weight of the undissolved residue from the quantity originally present.

Identification of the Solid Phase. The solubility of a compound, which is capable of existing in several forms, depends upon the particular form in which it is present in contact with the saturated solution. The question of the com position of the solid phase is, therefore, of considerable importance for the accurate determination of solubility. Although the identification of the solid phase presents little difficulty in the majority of cases, it sometimes happens that it can be made only by a more or less indirect method. The principal eason for this is that adhering solution can usually not be completely removed rom the solid phase and the analysis, consequently, does not give direct information of the required accuracy.

A method which has been used considerably for identifying the solid phase s that known as the *residue method* of Schreinemakers (1893). It is based on the principal that if an analysis is made of both the saturated solution and of a mixture of the saturated solution and the solid phase of unknown composition, the two points so obtained, when plotted on a coördinate system, ie on a line connecting the point representing the composition of the solid phase and the solubility curve of the system. Similar analyses of another saturated solution of the system and of its mixture with the solid phase, locate another such line. Since all lines so determined when extended, pass through the point representing the composition of the solid phase, their intersection ocates this point definitely.

Although the original description of this method by Schreinemakers was illustrated by an example drawn on the rectangular system of coördinates, it has been used much more extensively, in a practical way, in connection with the later developed equilateral triangular diagram. In this case, each apex of the triangle represents one of the three components of the system, each point on a leg, a mixture of two, and each point within the triangle a mixture of all three components. When a number of saturated solutions are analyzed, the results correspond to points on the solubility curve of the system. If now some of the solid phase with adhering solution is removed from each mixture and analyzed, it is evident that the results thus obtained, being for samples made up of both the saturated solution and the solid phase, give points which lie on ines connecting the two. The points on the curve for the pure saturated solutions being known, it is necessary only to connect them with the points for the corresponding mixtures of solid phase and saturated solution, and to prolong the lines to their common intersection. This will necessarily be at the point representing the composition of the pure solid phase.

In applying the residue method of Schreinemakers, if the intersecting lines which fix the point corresponding to the solid phase meet at a very narrow angle, definite information as to its composition may not be secured. For cases such as these, a procedure to which the name "*tell-tale*" method was given by Kenrick (1908) and which is described in detail by Cameron and Bell (1910), has been developed. This method consists in adding to the mixture a small amount of an entirely different compound which remains wholly in the solution. After equilibrium has been reached, a portion of the saturated solution and of the solid phase with adhering solution are analyzed, and the quantity of the added "tell-tale" compound in each determined. From the result, showing the concentration of the added compound in the saturated solution, and the amount of it found in the mixture of solid and solution, the quantity of solution in contact with the solid can be calculated. Since the composition of the solution is also known, the difference between the composition of the solid plus solution and of the amount of solution known to be present, is the composition of the pure solid.

Transition Temperatures can frequently be accurately determined by relatively simple means, and since such data are useful in establishing fixed points on solubility curves they are valuable adjuncts to directly determined solubility data.

Synthetic Method. The procedures which have, so far, been mentioned are all classed as analytical methods of solubility determination. In contradistinction to these is the equally useful reverse process, by which the solvent and solute are brought together in previously measured quantities and the temperature ascertained at which the solution is saturated. To this procedure the designation synthetic method of solubility determination has been applied. One of the earliest investigators to use this method extensively was Alexejeff (1886) and it is, therefore, frequently referred to as the Alexejeff synthetic method of solubility determination.

The synthetic method can, of course, be used both for the solubility of solids in liquids and for liquids in liquids, but it is in the latter case that it is of greatest service. Its points of superiority, particularly in the case of the reciprocal solubility of liquids, are that the upper limits of the determinations can be extended far beyond the boiling point temperature and are, in fact, limited only by the resistance of the glass to pressure or to the action of the liquid. Only small quantities of the solute and solvent are required for a determination. It is applicable to compounds for which quantitative methods of analysis are not available or are of a tedious character. The mixtures, being contained in sealed tubes, are not subject to the action of constituents of the air, nor are losses, due to volatilization, to be feared. Although, in the case of solids, difficulties incident to the supersaturation, resulting from failure of the crystals to separate on cooling, are encountered, with liquids the point of saturation is made instantly and strikingly evident by the beginning of opalescence or clouding which occurs, and errors due to supersaturation are rarely encountered. A sure criterion that supersaturation does not occur rests on the observation of the temperature at which the cloudy solution again clears. If this temperature coincides with the temperature of the beginning of opalescence, it is certain that supersaturation has not occurred. The observation of the temperature of saturation can be repeated as often as desired, and the accuracy of the determination is ordinarily limited only by the care taken in making it.

The limitations of the method, aside from the supersaturation which may occur in the case of solids, are principally those resulting from the low temperature coefficients of solubility possessed by certain compounds, and which usually occur in the vicinity of maxima or minima of solubility curves. Although a "critical clouding" occurs in the vicinity of the so-called critical solution point, this possesses a characteristic appearance which is easily distinguishable from the clouding observed at the saturation point, and errors of observation due to it are not to be apprehended. In fact, it has been pointed out that supersaturation disappears at the critical point, and the synthetic method is ordinarily very accurate in the vicinity of the critical solution temperature.

Since, by the synthetic method the results are necessarily obtained under different pressures, this question has been given consideration from the theoretical and the practical side. Although it is possible that extremely high pressures would exert an influence, the conclusion appears justified that under rdinary conditions, in which pressures of 10 atmospheres are not exceeded, o notable effect would be produced. The solubility curves obtained by this method do not show any abnormalities due to this cause.

In the case of the determination of the solubility of solids by the synthetic method, the operation consists in preparing a mixture of a carefully determined amount of the solvent and of the solid, and subjecting it to gradually increasing temperature and to constant agitation, while a continual observation of the changes taking place in the solid is made. When all but a few small crystals have dissolved, the change in temperature is regulated much more carefully and note is taken of the point at which the edges of these final crystals begin to change from sharp to rounded, or vice versa, or where the zes of the particles visibly increase or diminish. Care must, of course, be taken not to allow the last portions of the solid to dissolve; otherwise, on cooling, considerable supersaturation may occur before the solid begins to separate from solution. The method is, naturally, most serviceable where the change in solubility with temperature is considerable, and where convenient methods for the direct analysis of the solution are not available.

The procedure of a determination in the case of the reciprocal solubility of quids consists in introducing by means of capillary funnels weighed amounts f the two liquids into small glass tubes and sealing the ends. The amount f air space in the tubes should be kept low. Many convenient devices for eighing and introducing the liquids have been described. In the case of very olatile liquids it may be necessary to introduce them in thin walled bulbs, hich can be broken after the tube containing the mixture has been sealed. The tube is then placed in a large beaker of water, or higher boiling liquid if ecessary, and heat applied until the contents of the tube, on being shaken, ecome homogeneous. The temperature is then allowed to fall very slowly nd an observation made, while the tube is constantly agitated, of the temperature of first appearance of opalescence. This observation can be repeated as many times as desired and the temperatures of appearance and disappearance f the clouding, which usually differ by only a few tenths of a degree, can be scertained with certainty.

Since, by the synthetic method the data are for irregular intervals of temperature, in order to obtain results for a particular temperature it is necessary to plot the several determinations on coördinate paper and from the solubility curve so obtained, read the value for the temperature in question.

Freezing-point Method. A modification of the synthetic method, which is pplicable particularly to solutions which contain relatively large amounts of ne dissolved compound, is that which consists in a determination of the freezing-point of the mixture. This point is, in fact, the temperature at which the separating solid compound is in equilibrium with the solution.

The difference between the freezing-point determination and the observation of the point of growth or diminution of a crystal in a liquid is that, in the ormer, the establishment of equilibrium is recognized exclusively by the change of the thermometer. The solution is cooled gradually, during which he thermometer sinks slowly to a point below the freezing temperature. As oon as the first crystal appears, either spontaneously or by intentional introduction (seeding), the thermometer rises suddenly to the freezing-point and remains stationary for some time.

40

This method can, of course, be used in a large number of cases for the determination of solubility. Those portions of the solubility curves of salts in water for which ice is the solid phase, are practically always determined in this way and it may be said, in general, that for determinations made at low temperatures, the freezing-point method is to be selected whenever possible.

For the practical execution of the method the very well known apparatus of Beckmann is most convenient and satisfactory. The determinations must, of course, be made with all the refinements which have been developed for accurate freezing-point measurements.

The method has been used extensively for the discovery of addition compounds. Its use for this purpose is based upon the principle that if to a pure compound, A, a second, B, is added, the freezing-point of A is lowered; similarly the freezing-point of B is lowered by A, and the two descending curves thus obtained intersect at the eutectic. If, however, a compound, A_xB_y, is formed, this also acts as a pure substance and its freezing-point is lowered by either A or B. Hence the freezing-point lines do not meet at a single eutectic but exhibit in this case a maximum, the position of which indicates the composition of the compound.

Volume Change Method. Still another method, which is a modification of the synthetic, is that designed to indicate the reciprocal solubility of liquids by a determination of the volume changes which occur when two relatively sparingly miscible liquids are shaken together in a closed vessel. The apparatus consists usually of a cylindrical receptacle which is provided with a constricted graduated section either at one end or near the middle. Such volumes of liquids are chosen that the meniscus separating them lies in the constricted graduated tube. The determination consists in superimposing measured volumes of each liquid and noting the position of the meniscus before and after a period of shaking at constant temperature. From the increase or decrease of volume of the two layers, as estimated from the change in position of the meniscus, the reciprocal solubility of the two liquids is calculated. It is to be noted, however, that the solubility of liquids is in practically all cases reciprocal, and without an analysis of the two layers the true solubility can not usually be deduced.

Titration Method. A special case of the reciprocal solubility of liquids is that representing equilibrium in ternary systems yielding two liquid layers. Such equilibria are usually determined by relatively simple titration procedures, but for the interpretation and description of the results, special terms have been developed and these require more or less detailed explanation.

When a third liquid is added to a mixture of two others which are miscible to only a slight extent, the added liquid, if soluble in each of the others, will distribute itself between the two and an equilibrium will be reached. If the two layers are then analyzed and the results plotted on coördinate paper, two points, corresponding to the two layers, will be obtained. If more of the third liquid is added, equilibrium will again be established after a short period of shaking and the analysis of the two layers, to which the designation *conjugate* layers has been given, will fix two more points when plotted on the coördinate paper. The process may be repeated until a considerable number of points have been obtained. When this has been done, it will always be found that these points are the locus of a smooth curve, to which the designation *binodal* curve has been given. If the pairs of points corresponding to the conjugate

ayers are connected, the lines so obtained are defined as *tie lines*. Since it is
vident that with the continued addition of the third or *consolute* liquid, a
oint must finally be reached at which the resulting mixture will no longer
eparate into two conjugate layers, the tie lines successively determined as
bove described, will become shorter and shorter until finally the last one is
educed to the point corresponding to the homogeneous mixture of the three
omponents. To this is given the name *plait point*.

Although for the above example a ternary system made up of three liquids
as been taken, there are a large number of salts and other solid compounds
hich, when dissolved in mixtures of liquids of certain concentrations, cause
he latter to separate into conjugate liquid layers. These systems have aroused
auch interest from time to time and considerable data for them are given in
he literature.

Since it is usually difficult and frequently impossible to analyze directly a
omogeneous mixture of liquids, and thus determine the points on a binodal
urve, a simple titration method for this purpose has come into general use.
3y means of this a homogeneous mixture of known amounts of two of the
omponents is titrated with the third just to the point of initial separation of
he second layer, which is usually very sharply indicated by the appearance of
douding or opalescence. The procedure may also be reversed and the con-
olute liquid added just to the point of clearing of the cloudy mixture of the
ther two. By this plan the synthetically derived composition of one of the
wo conjugate layers and thus of one point on the binodal curve is known.
'he determination of the tie line and therefore, the identification of the cor-
esponding point on the curve for the conjugate liquid, requires an additional
xperiment for its location. Several procedures for this purpose have been
leveloped. They usually depend upon the determination of one or more
onstants of specially prepared pairs of conjugated liquids, such as their specific
ravities or refractive indices. In the case of mixtures of which one member
an be easily determined analytically, tie lines can be located by the quanti-
ative determination of this member in pairs of conjugated liquids.

In general, the titration method for the determination of the solubility of
iquids is applicable to many cases. The facts, that equilibrium is attained
o promptly in liquids and that the evidence of the appearance of a second
nsoluble layer is usually so striking, make it of great value. Refinements
aave been introduced such as the addition of liquid or solid dyes to the mix-
ure in order to facilitate the detection of the end point, and the development
of particular forms of apparatus for measuring and weighing the liquids.
The constituents of the mixtures are usually weighed but the volume relations
nd, therefore, the specific gravities can also be approximately estimated, by
ising graduated vessels for making the titrations, and measuring in them the
volumes of the final mixtures.

As a usual thing the temperature coefficients are not very great in the
ase of liquid mixtures and the very accurate control of the temperature is not
mperative. When such control is necessary, however, the use of a thermostat
loes not seriously complicate the determination.

Distribution Coefficients.   As mentioned above, when a third compoun[d] is added to a mixture of two liquids which are relatively immiscible, it wi[ll] dissolve to a certain extent in each and the composition of the two laye[rs] represent conjugate points on the binodal curve for the system.   The resul[ts] are, however, of interest from another point of view, namely that of the di[s]tribution of the compound between the two solvents.   This distribution coe[ffi]cient is, in many cases, of considerable interest in connection with analytic[al] methods based on shaking out procedures and also in connection with suc[h] problems as the molecular state of compounds in solution, their dissociatio[n] and other points of theoretical interest.   Distribution coefficients have, there[e]fore, been studied to a large extent and much data for them are availabl[e] In general, the determinations are made by relatively simple methods.   Th[e] amount of the compound present in a definite amount of each layer, after equ[i]librium has been established by adequate agitation, is determined in any ma[n]ner most convenient.   If the total amount of solute is known, and that foun[d] in one layer, the amount in the other can, of course, be calculated by differenc[e] The results are usually expressed on the volume basis, since it is the ratio [of] the amounts present in the same molecular state in equal volumes of the tw[o] layers which is a constant, independent of temperature and concentration.

It is evident that when the concentration at the saturation point is con[n]sidered, the amount of the compound which enters each layer depends upo[n] its solubility in the liquid, consequently the distribution coefficient is th[e] relation of the solubilities of the dissolved substance in the two solvent[s] Variations from this, aside from changes in molecular state, etc., in one or th[e] other solvent are due to such causes as the reciprocal solubility of the so-calle[d] immiscible solvents, which will, of course, be influenced by the presence of th[e] dissolved compound, especially at the higher concentrations.   Variations [of] the coefficient with temperature would result in cases where the solubiliti[es] of the compound in the two solvents do not change at the same rate wit[h] temperature.

Electrolytic Conductivity Method.   Of the physical properties which ca[n] be used for the determination of the concentration of a solution, such a[s] specific gravity, refractive index, etc., the electrolytic conductivity is of pa[r]ticular value in the case of those very sparingly soluble compounds which yiel[d] solutions too dilute to be analyzed by gravimetric or volumetric method[s] By its use the progress of the saturation can be followed without separating th[e] undissolved solid from the solution, or even removing the portion used for th[e] determination.   The special electrical equipment which is required, howeve[r] and the need for water of exceptional purity and of vessels of particular qual[i]ties, restrict its general use.

The method of calculating the concentration from the conductivity is base[d] on the assumption that at the very great dilutions involved, complete disso[s]ciation occurs.   Therefore, the limiting value to which the equivalent con[n]ductivity approaches at infinite dilution is, for practical purposes, attaine[d] and $\Lambda = \Lambda_\infty = l_a + l_k$, where l_a and l_k are the ionic conductivities of the anion[s] and kations.   These values are known for all the principally occurring ion[s] The observed specific conductivity κ is, however, connected with the equivalen[t] conductivity and the concentration η by the equation $\Lambda = \kappa/\eta$, in which η repre[e]sents the concentration in gram-equivalents per cubic centimeter.   Rearrange[e]ment and substitution give $\eta = \kappa/(l_a + l_k)$.   From this equation the solubilit[y] of the substance under investigation is calculated by substituting the measured specific conductivity of the solution and the known values of the ionic conductivities.

The Solubility of Gases in Liquids. When a gas and a liquid are intimately mixed by shaking, a definite amount of the gas will be dissolved by the liquid and, simultaneously, the vapor of the liquid will mix with the gas in the space above the liquid. The partial pressure of the liquid in the gas space is almost exactly the same as that of the pure liquid at the solution temperature, since the influence of the relatively slight amount of dissolved gas is insignificant in by far the most cases. The amount of gas which is dissolved depends both on the nature of the gas and of the liquid and is, furthermore, a function of the temperature, and pressure.

In regard to the influence of pressure, the absorption law of Henry holds for the most part, when the gas solubility is not too great. According to it, the amount of pure gas, which is taken up at constant temperature by a given amount of liquid is proportional to the pressure of the gas.

The temperature acts almost always in the sense that the solubility decreases as the temperature rises.

The solubilities of gases are usually expressed either in terms of the Bunsen "Absorption Coefficient" β,[1] or the Ostwald "Solubility Expression" l.[2]

The experimental methods for the determination of the solubility of gases vary according to the nature of the gas. For those which dissolve in relatively large amounts and can be analytically determined with accuracy, the saturated solution may be analyzed by ordinary quantitative methods. Thus, in the case of the solubility of sulfur dioxide in aqueous solutions of salts, the solutions were saturated by passing a stream of the gas through them at atmospheric pressure and, when equilibrium was attained, a measured portion of the solution was withdrawn, transferred to an excess of standardized iodine solution and the excess of the latter titrated with thiosulfate. A gravimetric procedure was used by Christoff (1905) for the determination of the solubility of carbon dioxide in aqueous salt solutions. In this case the solutions were weighed before and after the passage of the gas through them and the increase in weight, after applying necessary corrections, taken to represent the solubility at the temperature of the experiment and at atmospheric pressure. The absorption flasks were of special shape and the gas was previously passed through a series of U tubes, containing the same aqueous solution, in order to prevent loss of water from the experimental solution which, otherwise, would have occurred.

[1] $\beta =$ the **Bunsen Absorption Coefficient** which signifies the volume (v) of the gas (reduces to 0° and 760 mm.) taken up by unit volume (V) of the liquid when the pressure of the gas itself minus the vapor tension of the solvent is 760 mm.

$$\beta = \frac{v}{V\,(1 + 0.00367\,t)}.$$

[2] $l =$ the **Ostwald Solubility Expression** which represents the ratio of the volume (v) of gas absorbed at any pressure and temperature, to the volume (V) of the absorbing liquid, i.e. $l = \frac{v}{V}$. This expression differs from the Bunsen Absorption Coefficent, β, in that the volume (v) of the dissolved gas is not reduced to 0° and 760 mm. The solubility is therefore the volume of gas dissolved by unit volume of the solvent at the temperature of the experiment. The two expressions are related thus:

$$l = \beta\,(1 + 0.90367\,t), \qquad \beta = \frac{l}{(1 + 0.00367\,t)}.$$

In the great majority of cases, however, gas solubility is determined by
method based upon the measurement of the volume of the gas absorbed.   Th
apparatus consists essentially of an absorption flask for the liquid, connecte
by means of a tube of small bore to a graduated buret in which the gas i
measured above mercury, the level of which can be altered by raising or lowerin
a container connected with the buret by means of a rubber tube.   Many form
of this apparatus have been described and the disadvantages of the earlie
forms have gradually been remedied.   A relatively simple form of this appar

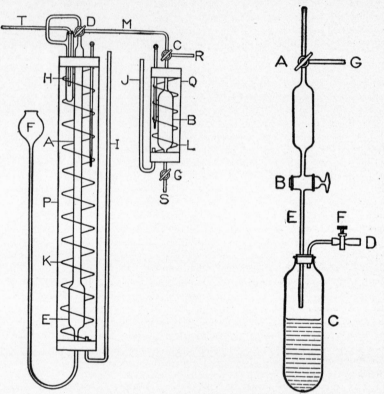

FIG. 190. McDaniel's apparatus for determining gas solubilities.   FIG. 191.

atus, but one which embodies the essential features required for accuracy, i
that described by McDaniel (1911) for the determination of the solubility o
methane, ethane and ethylene in a large number of organic solvents at variou
temperatures.

This apparatus is shown in Fig. 190.   *A* is an ordinary gas buret and *B* a
absorption pipet of the form first used by Ostwald.   "The buret and pipe
are connected by means of the glass capillary *M* sealed directly onto each, s
that the whole forms one solid piece of glass apparatus *without rubber or cemen
connections of any kind*; thus any possibility of leaks from these extremel
troublesome sources is entirely avoided.   The whole apparatus is clampe
solidly to a rigid support so that it can be taken up in the hands and shake

or the purpose of bringing the gas into intimate contact with the liquid.   The ipet and buret are each provided with a three-way stopcock, C and D.   These an be turned in such a way as to allow the gas to sweep out the air from the onnecting capillary.   By the same means the two vessels may also be connected directly with each other as well as separately with the outside air or ource of gas supply.   The pipet and buret are each provided with a water acket, P and Q.   The temperature of each is regulated by means of the lectrically heated coils K and L."   These coils are of manganin wire and are connected in series.   The rate of evolution of heat in the jackets was adjusted n the first place by varying the length of the manganin wire, until the temperaure was the same in each jacket.   Stirring was accomplished by blowing air hrough the tubes I and J.   The differences in temperature between the pipet and buret were never greater than $0.1°$.

In carrying out a determination by this method it is, of course, necessary hat the solvent be completely free of dissolved air or other gas.   This is perhaps the most important part of the determination and a special form of apparatus for the purpose is described by McDaniel (1911) and is shown in Fig. 191. "The liquid was boiled under diminished pressure in the flask C attached directly to the lower opening of the pipet by means of the rubber stopper as shown in the figure.   Connection with the air pump is made at D.   During the boiling the lower opening of the inlet tube E is above the surface of the liquid in C, the stopcock B being closed.   When the air has been completely expelled, the screw pinchcock F is closed while the air pump is still in operation.   The flask C is now raised until the lower end of E reaches nearly to the bottom of the flask.   The air pump is now connected at G and the cock H opened so as to make connection with the pipet. B is now opened and the inflow of air through D regulated by gradually opening F in such a manner that the liquid is very slowly forced up into the pipet.   In this manner the liquid never comes into contact with the air under full atmospheric pressure but only under greatly diminished pressure.   The absorption of air under these conditions can only be inappreciable, especially since the liquid in the flask remains perfectly quiet, and only the lower portion is used."

Having filled the pipet B, Fig. 190, with the air-free solvent as just described, "T is connected with the source of gas supply and the cocks C and D are turned in such a way as to allow the gas to sweep out the air from the capillary, M. The buret is then filled in the usual manner by lowering the leveling tube F, the cock D having been turned so as to connect T with E.   Care is taken to keep the entering gas under a slight pressure by keeping the mercury level in F slightly above that in A.   This prevents air from entering through any leaks in the train connecting the gas generator with the buret."   The gas must be completely saturated with the vapor of the solvent and this, with other than aqueous solvents, may require, in addition to drawing it through some of the solvent in H, that a thin layer be placed in the buret and time allowed for it to saturate the gas sample.

"After again allowing the current of gas to flow through the capillary M for a short time the buret and pipet are connected with each other by turning the three-way cocks D and C in the proper direction.   The determination of the amount of absorption is then made as follows: A portion of the gas is passed into the pipet by raising F and opening G, the displaced liquid being caught in a graduated cylinder.   The cock C is closed and the gas and liquid in the pipet brought into intimate contact with each other by shaking the whole apparatus. C is now opened to allow gas to enter from the buret to replace that absorbed. This process is repeated until, on opening C, there is no further decrease in the volume of gas in A. The volume absorbed is found by subtracting from the original volume of gas, the volume remaining in the buret plus the volume in the pipet. The volume of gas in the pipet is equal to the volume of liquid drawn off. The volume of liquid remaining is easily calculated from the known volume of the pipet. The absorption coefficient or 'solubility' is the ratio of the volume of gas absorbed, measured at the temperature of the experiment, to the volume of the saturated liquid. It may be reduced to the coefficient used by Bunsen by dividing by $(1+\alpha t)$."

In the case of the majority of investigators who have used this method, particularly for determinations at high or low temperatures, the absorption pipet has been kept at the temperature of the experiment and the gas measuring buret at room temperature, the two being connected by means of a flexible capillary which permits the absorption pipet to be independently shaken. This arrangement makes it necessary, in calculating the absorption coefficients, to apply the usual corrections for temperature and vapor pressure to the volume of gas in the buret. This is a complication which in some cases causes uncertainties in regard to the accuracy of the results as finally calculated.

An apparatus designed for determinations at very high pressures, using a Caillet compression tube, is described by Sander (1911–12). It was used for determination of the solubility of carbon dioxide in water, alcohols, and other organic solvents. The principle involved is that the pure gas is first compressed above mercury in a graduated tube and the volumes corresponding to given pressures noted. Similar readings are then taken for the same gas after a small accurately measured amount of solvent has been introduced into the graduated tube. The difference between the two volumes at the same temperature and pressure, reduced to 1 kg. per sq. cm. and 1 cc. of liquid, represents the solubility of the gas in the given solvent.

Finally, attention should be called to the method of determination of gas solubility based on the principle that, for volatile solutes which obey the laws of Dalton and Henry, the amount which is carried away by an inert gas when known volumes are bubbled through solutions of known strength of volatile solute, can be used to measure the comparative solubilities in solvents of different concentrations. An example of this method is the determination of the solubility of ammonia in aqueous salt solutions by Abegg and Riesenfeld (1902). The very ingenious apparatus consists of a generator for developing a stream of H_2+O_2 from aqueous NaOH, by means of an electric current measured with the aid of a copper voltmeter, and the volume of gas thus determined. This was passed through a spiral in the vessel containing the ammonia solution of known concentration. The mixed gases passing out of this were received in a third vessel containing 5 cc. of 0.01 n HCl. Electrodes were provided in this vessel and, by means of conductivity measurements, the point determined at which all of the HCl became saturated with NH_3. Since the volume of the H_2+O_2 required for this purpose was known, the partial pressure of the NH_3 in the mixture could be directly ascertained. Comparative determinations of the vapor pressure of the ammonia in water and a series of salt solutions made in this way were calculated to ammonia solubilities on the basis of the relation that, for two solutions of equal ammonia content, the ammonia pressure is reciprocally proportional to the solubility of the ammonia in them.

ACIDIMETRY AND ALKALIMETRY

The volumetric determination of a free acid or a free base may be accomplished with rapidity and accuracy by neutralization with a known quantity of standard base or alkali as the case may require. The point of neutralization or "end point" is accertained by means of certain compounds called indicators, which have a different color in acid solutions than in alkaline solutions, the point of transition from one color to the other occurs at the point of neutralization. This end point may also be recognized by the electrometric method by measuring the change of potential that occurs with the change of concentration of the hydrogen ions in the solution. This potential change is usually large and abrupt at the end point.[1]

Indicators. The change of color of indicators is attributed to a rearrangement of atoms in the molecule or to the fact that in certain cases the ions have a different color than the undissociated molecule.[2] In making acidimetric or alkalimetric titrations it must be remembered that the choice of indicators is important. In titrating phosphoric acid, for example, methyl orange and phenolphthalein indicate decidedly different end points. This difference in indicators is shown in the following table by Thompson.[3] The numerals refer to the number of atoms of hydrogen displaced by monatomic metals, such as sodium or potassium, when the indicator shows the neutral point.

Acids		Methyl Orange Cold	Phenolphthalein		Litmus	
Name	Formula		Cold	Hot	Cold	Hot
Sulphuric..........	H_2SO_4	2	2	2	2	2
Hydrochloric.........	HCl	1	1	1	1	1
Nitric..............	HNO_3	1	1	1	1	1
Thiosulphuric.......	....	2	2	2	2	2
Carbonic..........	H_2CO_3	0	1 dil.	0	....	0
Sulphurous.........	H_2SO_3	1	2	....	....	....
Hydrosulphuric.....	....	0	1 dil.	0	....	0
Phosphoric.........	H_3PO_4	1	2	....	....	....
Arsenic............	H_3AsO_4	1	2	....	....	....
Arsenious..........	H_3AsO_3	0	....	....	0	0
Nitrous............	HNO_2	indicator destroyed	1	....	1	....
Silicic.............	H_4SiO_4	0	....	....	0	0
Boric.............	H_3BO_3	0	....	....	....	....
Chromic...........	H_2CrO_4	1	2	2	....	....
Oxalic............	$H_2C_2O_4$	....	2	2	2	2
Acetic............	$HC_2H_3O_2$	....	1	....	1 nearly	....
Butyric...........	$HC_4H_7O_2$	....	1	....	1 nearly	....
Succinic..........	$H_2C_4H_4O_4$	....	2	....	2	....
Lactic............	$HC_3H_5O_3$	....	1	....	1	....
Tartaric..........	$H_2C_4H_4O_6$	....	2	....	2	....
Citric............	$H_3C_6H_5O_7$	....	3	....	....	....

[1] J. C. Hostetter and H. S. Roberts, J. Am. Chem. Soc., **41**, 1337 (1919).

[2] Theory of indicators—Scientific Foundations of Analytical Chemistry by McGowan Waddell, J. Phys. Chem., **2**, 171, 1898. Stieglitz, J. Am. Chem. Soc., **25**, 1112, 1903; Am. Chem. J., **42**, 115, 1909. Hewitt, Analyst, **33**, 85, 1908. Noyes, J. Am. Chem. Soc., **32**, 815, 1910. Thorpe Dictionary of Applied Chemistry, Vol. 1, 34–37.

[3] Volumetric Analysis, Sutton, Tenth Edition, page 44. R. T. Thomson, J.S.C., **1**, 12, 432.

Chapter by Wilfred W. Scott.

There are two general classes of indicators; (*a*) Those highly sensitive to weak acids. In this class we have phenolphthalein, turmeric, rosalic acid (*b*) Those insensitive to very weak acids, such as carbonic, hydrosulphuric boric acids. Among this list are methyl orange, methyl red, lacmoid, cochineal iodeosin. These indicators are specially sensitive to bases.

Methyl orange, methyl red, phenolphthalein, lacmoid and litmus are the most commonly used indicators for acidimetry and alkalimetry. The following table shows the best conditions for the use of each:

INDICATOR	CONDITION OF SOLUTION	GENERAL USE IN TITRATION
Methyl orange. acids = red alkalies = yellow.	Cold solution only.	Hydrates, carbonates, bicarbonates, sulphides, arsenites, silicates, borates of sodium potassium, ammonium, calcium, magnesium, barium, etc.
Methyl red. As above.	Cold solution only.	Especially adapted for titration of weak bases such as NH_4OH.
Phenolphthalein. acids = colorless alkalies = red.	Cold solutions.	Alkaline hydrates, the mineral acids organic acids, e.g., oxalic, citric, tartaric, acetic. The indicator very sensitive to acids and adapted to titration of weak acids —carbonic acid, etc.
	Hot solutions.	The indicator is sensitive in hot solutions to the above. It is generally used in hot solutions for titration of acids combined with comparatively weak bases.
Litmus. acids = red alkalies = blue.	Cold solutions.	Hydrates of Na, K, NH_3, Ca, Ba, etc. Silicates and arsenates of Na and K, HNO_3, H_2SO_4, HCl and $H_2C_2O_4$.
	Hot solutions.	In addition to above neutral and acid carbonates of K, Na, Mg; the sulphides and silicates of Na, K.
Lacmoid. In alcohol acids = red alkalies = blue.	Cold solutions.	The alkaline and alkaline earth hydrates, the arsenates, borates, mineral acids, many salts of metals which are acid to litmus and neutral to lacmoid, e.g., sulphates and chlorides of iron, copper and zinc, hence of value in determining free acids in their presence.
	Hot solutions.	In addition to the above, carbonates and bicarbonates of K, Na, Ca, Sr, Ba, etc.

In general, methyl orange, methyl red and lacmoid are especially sensitive to bases, but not so sensitive to acids and are not used for weak acids. Phenolphthalein is especially sensitive to acids and is of value in titrating weak acids. Litmus is commonly used as a test indicator (litmus paper) though with careful preparation, it is valuable for general acid and alkali titration.

The acid in the indicator must be weaker than the acid which it is required to determine by its means. Methyl-orange, for example, is a fairly strong acid, and is not sensitive to carbonic, hydrocyanic, boric, oleic acids; on the other hand, phenolphthalein, being an extremely weak acid, is decomposed by organic acids, H_2CO_3, etc., hence is of value in determination of these acids.

ULTIMATE STANDARDS

Sulphuric and hydrochloric acids are generally used as the ultimate standard acids. Benzoic acid and other acids are also used.

Sodium carbonate is the best of the alkali standards. This salt may be prepared in exceedingly pure form. It is generally used as the basic material or the volumetric standardization of the standard acid.

Preparation of Pure Sodium Carbonate

Bicarbonate of Soda made by the Ammonia-Soda process may be obtained in exceedingly pure form. The impurities that may be present are silica, ammonia, lime, arsenic, sodium chloride and sodium sulphate. With the exception of silica and lime the impurities may be readily removed by washing the bicarbonate of soda several times with cold water and decanting off the supernatant solution of each washing from the difficultly soluble bicarbonate. The washing is continued until the material is free from chlorine, as sodium chloride is the principal impurity, and its removal leaves an exceedingly pure product. The bicarbonate is dried between large filter papers in the hot air oven (100° C.).

Standard Sodium Carbonate is made from this pure sodium bicarbonate by heating at 290° C. to 300° C. in an electric oven. If a constant-temperature oven is not available a simple oven may be improvised by use of a sand bath and a large beaker or a sheet-iron cylinder covered at the upper end as shown in Fig. 192. A thermometer passing through this shield registers the temperature of the material, within a large platinum crucible. This crucible rests upon a triangle, so that the bicarbonate is entirely surrounded by an atmosphere of comparatively even temperature.

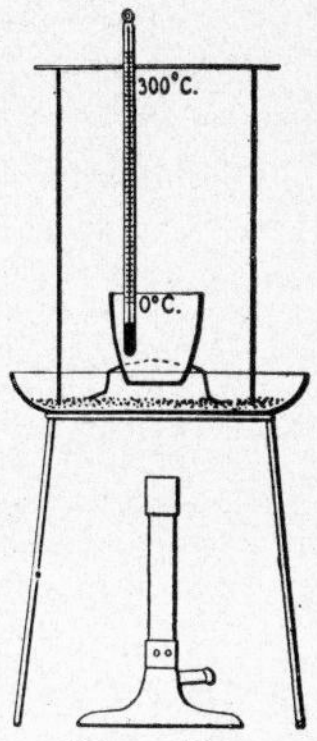

FIG. 192.

The sodium bicarbonate is converted to the carbonate. Constant weight will be obtained in about five or six hours. When the material no longer loses weight it is cooled in a desiccator and bottled for use, preferably in several small, glass-stoppered bottles. For exceedingly accurate work the material is analyzed and allowance made for the impurities that may still remain. The error caused by any such impurities is so small that for all practical purposes it may be neglected.

This purified sodium carbonate is the ultimate standard for acidimetric and alkalimetric volumetric analysis.

NOTE. The writer finds that much higher temperatures may be used for causing the transposition of bicarbonate to carbonate. Heating 100 grams $NaHCO_3$ to fusion point for a period of five hours produced less than 0.5% of oxide. Heating $NaHCO_3$ to fusion until constant weight is obtained (about $\frac{1}{2}$ hour) will give pure Na_2CO_3.

PREPARATION OF STANDARD ACID

Standard Sulphuric Acid

Fifty-two per cent sulphuric acid is in equilibrium with the average moistur present in the air of the laboratory; acid of this concentration is recommende for the standard stock solution.[1]

Pure 94 to 97% H_2SO_4 is diluted with sufficient water so that its gravity i about 1.4200 (42.7° Bé.). The acid is well mixed and poured into small clean an dry glass-stoppered sample bottles of about 200-cc. capacity. The bottles ar carefully sealed and placed aside for use as desired. To determine the exac strength of this standard acid a portion is standardized against the sodium car bonate, prepared according to directions given.

Method of Standardization. Procedure. A catch weight of about 10 gram of the acid is weighed out in a weighing bottle or 100-cc. beaker (10 cc. = approxi mately 13 grams) and placed aside for titration. The amount of sulphuric acid i the sample (weight of sample multiplied by per cent divided by 100) is neutralized by 1.0808 times its weight of sodium carbonate. As an excess of acid is necessary to drive out all the carbonic acid the following formula is used—(grams H SO −0.05) ×1.0808 = weight of Na_2CO_3 required.

The required amount of sodium carbonate is weighed and transferred to a 600-cc. Erlenmeyer flask and 100 cc. of water added. The acid is carefully poured into the flask and the rinsings of the weighing bottle or beaker added. The solu tion is boiled for 15 minutes to expel CO . A small filtering funnel inserted in the neck of the flask prevents loss during the boiling of the acid and carbonate mixture. The excess of acid is titrated with N/5 NaOH, using phenolphthalein indicator, the caustic being added drop by drop until a faint permanent pink color is obtained.

(The sulphuric equivalent to the NaOH added) + (weight of $Na_2CO_3 \times 0.9252$) = weight of pure H_2SO_4 present in the sample.

NOTES. CO_2-free water should be taken in all titrations with phenolphthalein. The indicator contains 1 gram of the compound per liter of 95% alcohol. One cc. of indicator of this strength is required for each titration.

Results should agree to within 0.05%.

The temperature of the acid should be observed at the time of standardization and this noted with results on the bottles containing the standard samples. The coefficient of expansion is .00016+ per degree F. risen in temperature or .000293 per degree C. per cc. of solution.

[1] Ninety-three thousand pounds of sulphuric acid, with an exposed surface of 1260 sq. ft. and depth of 10 in., had decreased in strength from 86 per cent to 52.12 per cent H_2SO_4, after standing in a lead pan, protected from the rain, for 42 days (Sept. 9th to Oct. 21st, 1916). Air was bubbled through a two-liter sample of this acid for seven consecutive days, when the solution was tested and found to contain 52.18 per cent H_2SO_4. The average temperature of the laboratory was 74° F., the average vapor of the air (7 tests) was 0.2223 gram H_2O per standard cubic foot. The average humidity for September and October was 68 per cent; the average temperature 62° F. The average humidity for the past 33 years was 72 per cent; average temperature 57° F.

Normal Sulphuric acid[1] contains 49.043 grams of H_2SO_4 per liter of solution. To make a liter of the normal acid the amount of the standard acid required is calculated by the formula $\dfrac{100 \times 49.043}{\text{per cent } H_2SO_4 \text{ in standard}} = $ grams standard acid necessary. The acid is weighed out in a small beaker, a slight excess being taken (0.1 gram). The acid is washed into a liter flask and made to volume. An aliquot portion is standardized against the standard sodium carbonate. The solution may now be adjusted to the exact strength required.

Example.[1] If 25 cc. of the acid is found to contain 1.25 grams H_2SO_4 we find the amount of dilution required as follows: 25 cc. of $N/1$ H_2SO_4 should contain 1.226075 grams, therefore $1.226075 : 25 :: 1.25 : x$, and $x = \dfrac{25 \times 1.25}{1.226075}$. Then x minus 25 = the amount of water required for 25 cc. Total dilution = dilution for 25 multiplied by the volume of acid remaining in the flask divided by 25 = cc. water required to make a normal acid solution.

Fifth normal and tenth normal acids[1] may be prepared by diluting the normal acid to five or ten volumes as the case requires.

Gravimetric Methods. Precipitation as BaSO₄. Sulphuric acid may be standardized by precipitating as $BaSO_4$ according to the procedure given for sulphur. $BaSO_4 \times 0.4202 = H_2SO_4$.

Determination as (NH₄)₂SO₄. To 10 cc. of the acid diluted to 50 cc. in a large platinum dish is added NH_4OH until the acid is neutralized and a faint odor of ammonia is perceptible. The solution is evaporated to dryness on the water bath and dried at 100° C. for half an hour. The residue is weighed as $(NH_4)_2SO_4$. $(NH_4)_2SO_4 \times 0.7422 = $ gram H_2SO_4.

Standard Hydrochloric Acid

This acid is occasionally preferred by chemists to sulphuric acid as a standard. At the constant boiling-point, with pressure of 760 mm., hydrochloric acid has a definite composition of 20.242% HCl. For every 10 mm. increase in pressure the percentage drops .024 and for every 10 mm. decrease in pressure the percentage rises .024% HCl. Advantage is taken of this fact in the preparation of standard hydrochloric acid. Strong, pure HCl is distilled, the first 25 or 30 cc. being rejected. The distillate is bottled in 200-cc. glass-stoppered bottles and sealed, a portion being reserved for standardization. The acid is best standardized against sodium carbonate, using the formula, Weight of HCl weighed for analysis minus 0.05) $\times 1.4533 = Na_2CO_3$ required. As in case of H_2SO_4 the Na_2CO_3 is weighed out, placed in an Erlenmeyer flask with the acid and boiled to expel CO_2. The excess of HCl is titrated with standard caustic. $N/5$ NaOH = 0.0072836 gram HCl per cc.

The exact weight of $Na_2CO_3 \times 0.6881 = $ HCl. To this add HCl obtained by NaOH titration = total HCl in the sample taken.

The exact amount of HCl being known, normal acid containing 36.468 grams HCl per liter may be made, and by diluting further, fifth normal and tenth normal acids obtained.

Gravimetric Determination of Hydrochloric Acid by Precipitation as AgCl.
Hydrochloric acid may be standardized by precipitation with silver nitrate
solution by the procedure for determination of chlorine. $AgCl \times 0.2544 = HCl$.
It is advisable to heat the sample, diluted to a convenient volume, and add the
hot silver nitrate in slight excess of that required by HCl, the amount of the
reagent being calculated, e.g., mol. wt. HCl : mol. wt. $AgNO_3$ :: Wt. HCl in
sample : x.

Benzoic Acid Standard

Benzoic acid may be obtained in exceedingly pure form by melting the resublimed acid in a covered platinum dish in a constant-temperature oven, at a temperature of 140° C. The acid is poured into test-tubes, cooled, and the sticks bottled
for use. The acid does not take up moisture to any appreciable extent, even
when exposed to the air for some time, so that it may be weighed without
danger of absorption of moisture.

Standard Caustic Solution

Standard normal sodium hydroxide is made by dissolving approximately 50
grams of NaOH sticks with 1 to 2 grams of $Ba(OH)_2$ in 200 to 300 cc. of water and
diluting to 1000 cc. The caustic is standardized against normal H_2SO_4, using
phenolphthalein indicator. The solution is adjusted to the exact strength
desired by addition of distilled water.

NOTE.—The addition of $Ba(OH)_2$ is made to precipitate the carbonate in the caustic,
as this would interfere with titrations in presence of phenolphthalein. As the presence
of barium would produce a cloudiness with H_2SO_4 it is advisable to add only an amount
sufficient to precipitate the carbonate.

To Make a Solution of Approximate Normality Strength without Weighing, from a Solution of Known Strength and Specific Gravity

Calculate the cc. of the reagent that contain the weight of the material
necessary per liter. Measure out this volume and dilute to 1000 cc.

Example. Required to make an approximate 0.1 N H_2SO_4 solution from
87% H_2SO_4 having a sp.gr. of 1.8.

A liter of normal solution contains 49.04 g. H_2SO_4, a 0.1 N 4.904 g. H_2SO_4.
1 cc. of the acid contains 1.8×0.87 g. H_2SO_4.

4.904 g. of H_2SO_4 is present in $\dfrac{4.904}{1.8 \times 0.87} = 3.13$ cc.

Dilute 3.13 cc. of the acid to 1000 cc.

STANDARD BURETTES

Burettes used for this work should be carefully checked for accuracy of delivery.

For accurate titration of acids or alkalies it is advisable to have a titration of 75 to 100 cc. Since the straight 100-cc. burette if graduated to twentieths of a cc. would be too long for convenient handling, the chamber burette is used. The chamber located in the upper portion of the apparatus holds 75 cc., the lower portion drawn out into a uniform-bore tube is graduated in twentieths of a cc. Each tenth of a cc. has a mark passing entirely around the tube so that there will be no error in reading, the eye being held so that the mark appears to be a straight line drawn across the tube. The burette is enclosed in a large tube filled with distilled water and carrying a thermometer. The burette is connected, by means of an arm at the base, with a reservoir of standard acid. The cut, Fig.193, shows the apparatus connected ready for use.

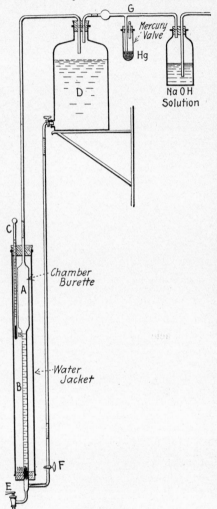

If vapor is lost from the standard reagents and this replaced by dry air, as in the common practice, the solution gradually changes in strength. A simple and ingenious device, designed by H. W. Herig (Gen. Chem. Co.), is shown at the top of Fig.193, which overcomes this difficulty. The air drawn into the reagent bottle is purified and saturated with moisture by passing it through sodium hydroxide. A mercury valve relieves the pressure if expansion of air in the reagent bottle occurs due to rise of temperature.

Note. The chamber burette shown in Fig.193 was designed at the Laurel Hill Laboratory, General Chemical Company.

Fig. 193.

Titration of Acids and Alkalies

In the acid titration the sample is conveniently titrated in a white porcelain casserole. This gives a white background that enables the analyst to see the end-point. The caustic is run into the acid, to within a few cc. of the end-point, rapidly and then cautiously to a faint change of color—faint pink with phenolphthalein or an orange-yellow with methyl-orange. Phenolphthalein is generally preferred to acid titrations. CO_2-free caustic and water should always be used.

ACIDS

METHODS OF WEIGHING ACIDS
Dilute Acids Non=Volatile under Ordinary Conditions

Dilute acids may be weighed directly in a beaker, weighing bottle or ordinary pipette (see directions given later) by measuring out the approximate amount desired. Since a burette reading from 75-cc. to 100-cc. should be used for this work it will be necessary to take such an amount of the acid as will require a titration between these extremes. This may be accomplished by taking the specific gravity of the acid and referring to the table for the approximate strength From this the volume necessary may readily be calculated.

Example. The case will be taken where a 75-cc. to 100-cc. burette is being used and the titration is to be made with normal caustic solution, the acid titrated is sulphuric acid. The capacity of the burette is $75 \times 0.049 = 3.675$ grams H_2SO_4 to $100 \times 0.049 = 4.9$ grams H_2SO_4. (For HCl the capacity would be 2.74 to 3.65 grams HCl and for HNO_3 it would be 4.73 to 6.3 grams HNO_3).

Suppose the sulphuric acid has a sp.gr. of 1.1600. From the table for H_2SO_4 we find that this acid is 22.25% H_2SO_4, then 1 cc. contains 1.16×22.25 divided by $100 = 0.2581$ gram H_2SO_4. Since the capacity of the burette is 3.675 to 4.9 grams H_2SO_4, we must weigh between $\dfrac{3.675}{.2225}$ to $\dfrac{4.9}{.2225}$ grams of the acid; to get this we should take $\dfrac{3.675}{.2581}$ to $\dfrac{4.9}{.2581}$ cc., that is to say, 14.5 to 18.5 cc. of the acid, which will weigh 16.8 grams to 21.5 grams.

Weighing Strong Acids, Fuming or Volatile under Ordinary Conditions

The acid must be confined during weighing and until it is mixed with water or standard caustic. The best forms of apparatus include the following:

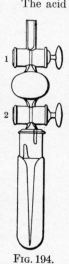

Lunge-Ray Pipette. The pipette is shown in Fig. 194. Two glass stop-cocks confine the acid in a bulb. The lower part of the pipette is protected by a ground-on test-tube. The dry pipette is weighed. Cock 2 is closed and 1 opened and a vacuum produced in the bulb by applying suction at the upper end of pipette and closing stop-cock 1 with suction still on. The sample may now be drawn into the pipette by immersing the lower end in the sample and opening the stop-cock 2, the vacuum producing the suction. The increased weight = acid drawn in. The pipette is emptied by running the acid under water.

Dely Weighing Tube.[1] This form of weighing tube has proven to be of exceptional value, to the busy works-chemist, in the analysis of oleum and mixed acids. Both speed and accuracy are gained by its use. The apparatus, shown in the cut on page 1499, consists of a long glass tube of small bore, wound in a spiral coil. Fig. 195

The sample of acid is drawn into the weighed coil by applying suction through a rubber tube attached to A and drawing in the required amount of acid, a mark, ascertained by a previous run being made to indicate the point to which the acid is drawn. The

Fig. 194.
Lunge-Ray
Pipette.

[1] J. G. Dely, Chemist, Gen. Chem. Co.

tip B is carefully wiped off with tissue paper and the tube and sample weighed. The weight of the tube deducted gives the weight of the sample.

The apparatus is now inclined so that the acid runs back into the crook at C to a point marked on the wall of the tube, in order to expel as much air as possible from this end. A rubber tube filled with water is attached to A, the other end of the rubber tube being connected to a bottle containing distilled water. A glass bead, such as is used in rubber-tipped burettes, fitting snugly in this tube, regulates the flow of water. The Dely tube is now inverted, the tip being immersed in 150 cc. to 200 cc. of distilled water in a 4-in. casserole—Fig. 195. By pressing gently on the bead, water is slowly admitted in the tube, forcing the acid before it. The acid and water are separated by a bubble of air. Before forcing out the last half-inch of acid, the tube connected to the water supply is disconnected and the weak acid from the casserole drawn back into the Dely tube for two or three inches, then again the acid is almost entirely expelled by water from the

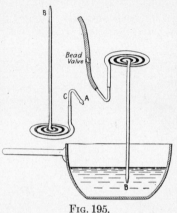

FIG. 195.

Dely Weighing Tube in Operation.

reservoir and the procedure repeated. This is to absorb the SO_3 gas that invariably is present in the bubble of air above mentioned, which would be lost if forced out directly by the water column. In order to facilitate this last step it is well to have a short rubber tube attached to the Dely tube, and a glass tip in the tube connected with the reservoir of water. The acid in the casserole, upon washing out the Dely tube, is titrated with standard caustic according to the procedure for titration of acids.

The tube is dried after washing with alcohol, followed by ether, by heating on an asbestos mat on a hot plate, dry air being aspirated through. ·

Snake Weighing Tube. The snake tube is a simple device that may be easily made by an amateur glass-blower. It is made out of a glass tube 8–10 ins. long, slightly thinner than a lead pencil. One end of the tube is drawn out to capillarity. The tube has a double bend, as shown in the illustration. It is so made that it rests on the double bend with the ends inclined upward to prevent the outflow of the acid. Fig. 196.

The tube is dried with alcohol, ether and air treatment, as in case of the Dely tube. After weighing the empty tube, acid is drawn into it by suction through an attached rubber tube. The capillary end that has dipped into the sample is wiped dry with tissue paper. The acid and tube are weighed and the acid estimated by difference.

The acid is run into 150 cc. of water in a casserole, the flow being regulated by the index finger pressed against the larger end of the tube. With careful regulation of the flow, practically no bumping occurs. With a small capillary opening it is not necessary to place the finger over the larger end of the tube as the acid flow will be slow. The tube should be kept in motion to prevent bumping from

FIG. 196.
Snake Tube.

41

overheating any one portion. Kicking back of the acid indicates that the capillary end of the tube is too large. When the contents of the tube have run out, the tube is rinsed by sucking up some acid from the casserole and allowing it to run out, repeating several times. Suction may be applied by means of a rubber bulb attached to the tube. The acid is now titrated with standard caustic, using phenolphthalein indicator.

Blay-Burkhard Graduated Weighing Burette. This apparatus, designed by V. L. Blay and W. E. Burkhard, General Chemical Company, is used for weighing acids or other liquids. The form for general use is shown in Fig. 197. The burette is graduated in half cc. divisions, from 0 to 20 cc. An apparatus half this size is used for oleum, where a 2-cc. sample is sufficient for a determination. For the purpose of running the sample under water a capillary tube (E, Fig. 197) with ground joint, is attached to the burette. This tube is placed in the solution during titration. The burette is provided with a glass vented stopper (A) on the top, and a glass cap for the tip, both having ground joints, to prevent escape of fumes from the sample.

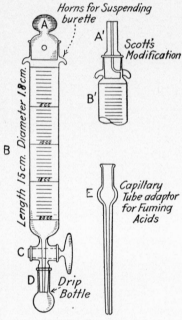

FIG. 197.—Blay-Burkhard Graduated Weighing Burette.

The Editor has modified the apparatus by replacing the fragile cap (A) by a tube stopper with capillary vent (see A', Fig. 197) The vent to the air is opened or closed by a slight turn of this stopper. By means of this tube acid may be drawn into the burette according to the Lunge-Ray pipette procedure. With these burettes a man can control his work very accurately and save a great amount of time, both in weighing and manipulation.

In the analysis of strong oleum, about 50 grams of neutral Glauber salt are placed in a casserole containing water, and the fuming acid allowed to flow under the undissolved salt. The violent reaction of the acid with water is thus avoided. The tube E, Fig. 197, should be made of fused silica.

The glass-bulb method is still used for analysis of strong oleum. The acid weighed in a sealed tube of known weight is mixed with water by breaking the bulb in a stoppered bottle containing water, the acid is cooled and titrated as usual.

ANALYSIS OF MURIATIC ACID

(Commercial Hydrochloric Acid)

Total Acidity and Hydrochloric Acid

The usual titration with standard caustic gives the total acidity, including, in addition to hydrochloric acid, nitric and sulphuric acids which may occur in the commercial product. The acidity due to these acids is deducted from the total acidity to find the actual HCl in the muriatic acid.

A catch weight, 10 to 15 grams of the acid, is weighed in a weighing bottle, or a large snake tube, or the Dely tube, as in case of oleum analysis, and the acid allowed to mix with water in a casserole; methyl-orange indicator is added and the acid titrated with standard normal caustic solution, the red color fading to a lemon-yellow. A fraction of a drop of the alkali will cause the change when the end-point has been reached.

$$\text{One cc. N/1 NaOH} = 0.03647 \text{ g. HCl.}$$

NOTE. Hydrochloric acid may be determined gravimetrically by precipitating the chloride with silver nitrate—$HCl + AgNO_3 = AgCl + HNO_3$, or by the volumetric methods for the determination of chlorine. See Chlorine.

Determination of Impurities in Commercial Hydrochloric Acid. Free Chlorine

Five cc. of the acid are diluted to 10 cc., about 5 cc. of fresh starch solution added and a few drops of 5% KI solution together with about 1 cc. of dilute H_2SO_4. A blue color indicates free chlorine. This color may be matched in a Nessler tube with a standard. It is possible to determine .0001% chlorine on a 5-cc. sample.

Nitric Acid or Nitrates in Hydrochloric Acid

About 5 cc. of the hydrochloric acid is cautiously added to 75 cc. of 95% H_2SO_4, the HCl being introduced under the surface of the sulphuric acid. The nitric acid may now be titrated with standard ferrous sulphate by the procedure for the direct determination of nitric acid and nitrates. (Method of Scott and Bowman.) The ferrous sulphate test for nitric is delicate. Traces of nitric acid produce a pink coloration; larger amounts a reddish brown to dark brown. The color is permanent when an excess of ferrous sulphate has been added. See page 1024.

Sulphuric Acid and Sulphates in Hydrochloric Acid

Free H_2SO_4. Fifty cc. of the sample is evaporated in a platinum dish (steam bath) to dryness or until the HCl has been expelled. A few drops of water are added and the material again taken to dryness (steam bath). The residue is taken up with water and titrated with N/10 NaOH, using methyl-orange indicator. One cc. = 0.0049043 gram H_2SO_4.

Total Sulphates. Fifty cc. of the muriatic acid is evaporated to about 5 to 10 cc. and then diluted to about 200 cc. and heated to boiling. Total SO_3 is now precipitated by adding $BaCl_2$ solution as in case of determination of total sulphur. The precipitated $BaSO_4$ includes the free H_2SO_4 and the combined SO_3. $BaSO_4 \times 0.4202 = H_2SO_4$.

Arsenic in Hydrochloric Acid

Commercial muriatic acid may contain arsenic. This is best determined by the Gutzeit Method given in detail under Arsenic. 10 cc. of sample is usually suffi cient for this determination. If much arsenic is present the distillation method may be followed, using a 25 to 50-cc. sample. The distillate is titrated with stand ard iodine according to procedure given for arsenic by the iodine titration page 43.

Barium Chloride in Hydrochloric Acid

Fifty cc. is evaporated to dryness and then over a low flame to expel SO_3. The residue is taken up with 1 cc. of 1 : 1 HCl and 50 cc. of water. 1 cc. H_2SO_4 i added and the precipitated $BaSO_4$ filtered off and weighed. If silica is presen in the sample its weight should be deducted. $BaSO_4 \times 0.8923 = BaCl_2$.

Total Solids and Silica

One hundred cc. of the HCl in a platinum dish is evaporated to dryness and the residue ignited and weighed. 5 cc. of HF is added with a few drops of H_2SO and the solution again evaporated and ignited. *The first weight = total solids The loss of weight in the second ignition = SiO_2.*

FIG. 198.—Hydrometer.

Determination of Specific Gravity

Control tests for strength of the common inorganic acids are generall made in the plant by means of the hydrometer. This instrument depends o the fact that when a solid floats in a liquid, the weight of the liquid displace is equal to the weight of the floating body. The hydrometer is a cylindrica instrument, generally with a spherical bulb, weighted with lead shot or mercury It has a narrow stem with graduations, which indicate the gravity. Th instrument floats vertically, after displacing its own weight of solution i which it is placed. The instruments are adapted for varying gravities extend ing over a range of ten to twenty divisions.

The Gravity tables given in the following pages have been developed with considerable care. By means of these one is able to obtain quickly and with fair degree of accuracy the strength of the acid or alkali of which the gravity is ascertained.

The following precautions should be observed in making hydrometer tests:

1. The hydrometer should be clean and dry, and at the temperature of the liquid, before immersing to make a reading.

2. The vessel in which the observation is made should be of clear glass of suitable size and shape, to allow the hydrometer to float freely (about $\frac{2}{3}$ inch greater in diameter than the hydrometer bulb) and of sufficient height to enable full reading of the hydrometer (*i.e.*, height greater than the length of the hydrometer).

3. The liquid should be thoroughly mixed by means of a stirrer reaching to the bottom of the vessel. There should be no air bubbles in the liquid or clinging to the sides of the vessel or the hydrometer.

4. The hydrometer is slowly immersed in the liquid, slightly beyond the point where it floats and is then allowed to float freely.

5. The reading is made with the line of vision horizontal to the plane and as near as possible to this. The point is taken where this surface line cuts the hydrometer scale.

7. The temperature of the liquid is taken before and after the reading and allowance made for variation of the temperature from standard conditions as indicated in the tables.

References. Cir. 16, 4th edition, Feb. 23, 1916, U. S. Bureau of Standards.
Sulphuric Acid Handbook by Thos. J. Sullivan, McGraw-Hill Book Co.
Thorpe Dictionary of Applied Chemistry, pp. 103–114. Longmans, Green and Co.

HYDROCHLORIC ACID

By W. C. Ferguson

Degrees Baumé.	Sp. Gr.	Degrees Twaddell.	Per Cent HCl.	Degrees Baumé.	Sp. Gr.	Degrees Twaddell.	Per Cent HCl.
1.00	1.0069	1.38	1.40	14.25	1.1090	21.80	21.68
2.00	1.0140	2.80	2.82	14.50	1.1111	22.22	22.09
3.00	1.0211	4.22	4.25	14.75	1.1132	22.64	22.50
4.00	1.0284	5.68	5.69	15.00	1.1154	23.08	22.92
5.00	1.0357	7.14	7.15	15.25	1.1176	23.52	23.33
5.25	1.0375	7.50	7.52	15.50	1.1197	23.94	23.75
5.50	1.0394	7.88	7.89	15.75	1.1219	24.38	24.16
5.75	1.0413	8.26	8.26	16.0	1.1240	24.80	24.57
6.00	1.0432	8.64	8.64	16.1	1.1248	24.96	24.73
6.25	1.0450	9.00	9.02	16.2	1.1256	25.12	24.90
6.50	1.0469	9.38	9.40	16.3	1.1265	25.30	25.06
6.75	1.0488	9.76	9.78	16.4	1.1274	25.48	25.23
7.00	1.0507	10.14	10.17	16.5	1.1283	25.66	25.39
7.25	1.0526	10.52	10.55	16.6	1.1292	25.84	25.56
7.50	1.0545	10.90	10.94	16.7	1.1301	26.02	25.72
7.75	1.0564	11.28	11.32	16.8	1.1310	26.20	25.89
8.00	1.0584	11.68	11.71	16.9	1.1319	26.38	26.05
8.25	1.0603	12.06	12.09	17.0	1.1328	26.56	26.22
8.50	1.0623	12.46	12.48	17.1	1.1336	26.72	26.39
8.75	1.0642	12.84	12.87	17.2	1.1345	26.90	26.56
9.00	1.0662	13.24	13.26	17.3	1.1354	27.08	26.73
9.25	1.0681	13.62	13.65	17.4	1.1363	27.26	26.90
9.50	1.0701	14.02	14.04	17.5	1.1372	27.44	27.07
9.75	1.0721	14.42	14.43	17.6	1.1381	27.62	27.24
10.00	1.0741	14.82	14.83	17.7	1.1390	27.80	27.41
10.25	1.0761	15.22	15.22	17.8	1.1399	27.98	27.58
10.50	1.0781	15.62	15.62	17.9	1.1408	28.16	27.75
10.75	1.0801	16.02	16.01	18.0	1.1417	28.34	27.92
11.00	1.0821	16.42	16.41	18.1	1.1426	28.52	28.09
11.25	1.0841	16.82	16.81	18.2	1.1435	28.70	28.26
11.50	1.0861	17.22	17.21	18.3	1.1444	28.88	28.44
11.75	1.0881	17.62	17.61	18.4	1.1453	29.06	28.61
12.00	1.0902	18.04	18.01	18.5	1.1462	29.24	28.78
12.25	1.0922	18.44	18.41	18.6	1.1471	29.42	28.95
12.50	1.0943	18.86	18.82	18.7	1.1480	29.60	29.13
12.75	1.0964	19.28	19.22	18.8	1.1489	29.78	29 30
13.00	1.0985	19.70	19.63	18.9	1.1498	29.96	29.48
13.25	1.1006	20.12	20.04	19.0	1.1508	30.16	29.65
13.50	1.1027	20.54	20.45	19.1	1.1517	30.34	29.83
13.75	1.1048	20.96	20.86	19.2	1.1526	30.52	30 00
14.00	1.1069	21.38	21.27	19.3	1.1535	30.70	30.18

HYDROCHLORIC ACID (Continued)

Degrees Baumé.	Sp. Gr.	Degrees Twaddell.	Per Cent HCl.	Degrees Baumé.	Sp. Gr.	Degrees Twaddell.	Per Cent HCl.
19.4	1.1544	30.88	30.35	22.5	1.1836	36.72	36.16
19.5	1.1554	31.08	30.53	22.6	1.1846	36.92	36.35
19.6	1.1563	31.26	30.71	22.7	1.1856	37.12	36.54
19.7	1.1572	31.44	30.90	22.8	1.1866	37.32	36.73
19.8	1.1581	31.62	31.08	22.9	1.1875	37.50	36.93
19.9	1.1590	31.80	31.27	23.0	1.1885	37.70	37.14
20.0	1.1600	32.00	31.45	23.1	1.1895	37.90	37.36
20.1	1.1609	32.18	31.64	23.2	1.1904	38.08	37.58
20.2	1.1619	32.38	31.82	23.3	1.1914	38.28	37.80
20.3	1.1628	32.56	32.01	23.4	1.1924	38.48	38.03
20.4	1.1637	32.74	32.19	23.5	1.1934	38.68	38.26
20.5	1.1647	32.94	32.38	23.6	1.1944	38.88	38.49
20.6	1.1656	33.12	32.56	23.7	1.1953	39.06	38.72
20.7	1.1666	33.32	32.75	23.8	1.1963	39.26	38.95
20.8	1.1675	33.50	32.93	23.9	1.1973	39.46	39.18
20.9	1.1684	33.68	33.12	24.0	1.1983	39.66	39.41
21.0	1.1694	33.88	33.31	24.1	1.1993	39.86	39.64
21.1	1.1703	34.06	33.50	24.2	1.2003	40.06	39.86
21.2	1.1713	34.26	33.69	24.3	1.2013	40.26	40.09
21.3	1.1722	34.44	33.88	24.4	1.2023	40.46	40.32
21.4	1.1732	34.64	34.07	24.5	1.2033	40.66	40.55
21.5	1.1741	34.82	34.26	24.6	1.2043	40.86	40.78
21.6	1.1751	35.02	34.45	24.7	1.2053	41.06	41.01
21.7	1.1760	35.20	34.64	24.8	1.2063	41.26	41.24
21.8	1.1770	35.40	34.83	24.9	1.2073	41.46	41.48
21.9	1.1779	35.58	35.02	25.0	1.2083	41.66	41.72
22.0	1.1789	35.78	35.21	25.1	1.2093	41.86	41.99
22.1	1.1798	35.96	35.40	25.2	1.2103	42.06	42.30
22.2	1.1808	36.16	35.59	25.3	1.2114	42.28	42.64
22.3	1.1817	36.34	35.78	25.4	1.2124	42.48	43.01
22.4	1.1827	36.54	35.97	25.5	1.2134	42.68	43.40

Sp. Gr. determinations were made at 60° F., compared with water at 60° F. From the Specific Gravities, the corresponding degrees Baumé were calculated by the following formula: Baumé = 145 − 145/Sp. Gr.

Atomic weights from F. W. Clarke's table of 1901. O = 16.

ALLOWANCE FOR TEMPERATURE:

10−15° Bé. − 1/40° Bé. or .0002 Sp. Gr. for 1° F.
15−22° Bé. − 1/30° Bé. or .0003 " " " 1° F.
22−25° Bé. − 1/28° Bé. or .00035 " " " 1° F.

AUTHORITY — W. C. FERGUSON.

This table has been approved and adopted as a Standard by the Manufacturing Chemists' Association of the United States.

W. H. BOWER,   JAS. L. MORGAN,
HENRY HOWARD,   ARTHUR WYMAN,
A. G. ROSENGARTEN,
Executive Committee.

New York, May 14, 1903.

HYDROCHLORIC ACID

Specific Gravity. $\frac{15°}{4°}$ in Vacuo.	Per Cent HCl by Weight.	1 Liter contains Grams HCl.	Specific Gravity $\frac{15°}{4°}$ in Vacuo.	Per Cent HCl by Weight.	1 Liter contains Grams HCl.	Specific Gravity $\frac{15°}{4°}$ in Vacuo.	Per Cent HCl by Weight.	1 Liter contains Grams HCl.
1.000	0.16	1.6	1.075	15.16	163	1.145	28.61	328
1.005	1.15	12	1.080	16.15	174	1.150	29.57	340
1.010	2.14	22	1.085	17.13	186	1.152	29.95	345
1.015	3.12	32	1.090	18.11	197	1.155	30.55	353
1.020	4.13	42	1.095	19.06	209	1.160	31.52	366
1.025	5.15	53	1.100	20.01	220	1.163	32.10	373
1.030	6.15	64	1.105	20.97	232	1.165	32.49	379
1.035	7.15	74	1.110	21.92	243	1.170	33.46	392
1.040	8.16	85	1.115	22.86	255	1.171	33.65	394
1.045	9.16	96	1.120	23.82	267	1.175	34.42	404
1.050	10.17	107	1.125	24.78	278	1.180	35.39	418
1.055	11.18	118	1.130	25.75	291	1.185	36.31	430
1.060	12.19	129	1.135	26.70	303	1.190	37.23	443
1.065	13.19	141	1.140	27.66	315	1.195	38.16	456
1.070	14.17	152	1.1425	28.14	322	1.200	39.11	469

COMPOSITION OF CONSTANT BOILING HYDROCHLORIC ACID*

Pressure mm. of Mercury.	Per Cent of HCl.	Grams constant boiling distillate for 1 mol. HCl.
770	20.218	180.390
760	20.242	180.170
750	20.266	179.960
740	20.290	179.745
730	20.314	179.530

Temperature of constant boiling hydrochloric acid is 108.54° at 763 mm. Specific gravity 1.09620^{25}.

* Hulett and Bonner, Jour. Am. Chem. Soc. xxxi, 390.

ANALYSIS OF HYDROFLUORIC ACID

The following constituents—hydrofluosilicic sulphuric and sulphurous acids—ommonly occurring with hydrofluoric acid, are determined in the analysis, long with the hydrofluoric acid, by titration. Generally the acid contains a light residue upon ignition. The titrations are made in presence of KNO_3, first ce cold, and then completed at 80° C. or more. The cold titration gives the hydrofluoric, sulphuric and sulphurous acids and one-third of the hydrofluosilicic cid and upon heating the titration gives the remaining two-thirds of the H_2SiF_6, he following reactions taking place. Titration cold, $H_2SiF_6 + 2KNO_3 = K_2SiF_6 + 2HNO_3 (= \frac{1}{3} H_2SiF_6)$. The liberated $2HNO_3$ requires $2NaOH$. Titration hot, $K_2SiF_4 + 4NaOH = 4NaF + 2KF + SiO_2 + 2H_2O (\frac{2}{3} H_2SiF_6)$.

The sulphuric acid is determined by titration with NaOH, upon expulsion of he accompanying more volatile acids. Sulphurous acid is determined by titration vith standard iodine.

Special Apparatus. Chamber burette graduated from 75 to 100 cc. in $\frac{1}{20}$ cc. s described under the determination of sulphuric acid, oleum, mixed acids, etc.

Platinum weighing tube. Length about 5 cm., diameter 1.4 cm. The tube itted with a platinum cap with a loop top to facilitate removal.

Brinton, Sarver and Stoppel found that the presence of silica in the NaOH auses an error in titration, hence it is necessary to determine the SiO_2 in he NaOH and apply corrective factor if SiO_2 is present. Keep reagent in eresin-lined bottles. If SiO_2 is present, the H_2SiF_6 will be too high and HF oo low. Calculate the SiO_2 in one cc. of the reagent and the total SiO_2 in he total titration (cold) may now be obtained. Multiply the total SiO_2 by .393 (factor H_2SiO_3 divided by SiO_2) and deduct result from H_2SiF_6 obtained or true H_2SiF_6. Multiply the total SiO_2 by 1.991 (6HF divided by SiO_2) nd add to the HF results for true HF content. Ref. Brinton, Sarver and Stoppel, Ind. Eng. Chem., **15**, 1880, Oct., 1923.

Details of Procedure. Total Acidity and Hydrofluosilicic Acid

A catch weight of the acid is taken by pouring the acid by means of the thief or directly from the paraffine bottle into the platinum weighing bottle, such a weight being taken as will require a titration of from 75 to 100 cc. of the normal austic solution. (This may be judged by a preliminary run if the approximate value is not known.)

About 10 cc. of a saturated solution of KNO_3 is poured into a large platinum lish (capacity about 125 cc.), and chipped ice added. About 50 cc. of N/1 NaOH olution is run in from a burette and three drops of the strong phenolphthalein dded. The platinum weighing bottle containing the sample is inverted beneath he surface of the caustic, the cover cautiously removed from the bottle by means of a heavy platinum wire, so as to allow the acid to mix very gradually with the tandard NaOH (rapid addition is apt to cause loss of acid by fumes). Standard N/1 NaOH is added from the burette until the first permanent pink color is btained. (The end-point will be uncertain and fading unless the solution is kept old—0° C.) The reading of the burette is noted—total $\dfrac{N/1 \text{ NaOH}}{\text{Wt. of sample}} = A$.

The dish is now placed on a hot plate and the solution warmed to about 0° C. and the titration completed with the N/1 NaOH solution to a permanent ink. Additional cc. required divided by weight of sample = B.

Sulphuric Acid in Hydrofluoric Acid

About 5 grams of the sample are weighed in the platinum capsule and trans ferred to a large platinum dish, the capsule being rinsed out into the dish with water. The solution is evaporated on the steam bath to small volume (the evaporation is assisted by passing a hot current of pure dry air over the sample see method on page 1529), a few drops of water are added and the evaporation repeated; no odor should be perceptible, all the hydrofluoric, hydrofluosilicic and sulphurous acids being expelled. The sulphuric acid is cooled, taken up with 100 cc. of CO_2-free water, three drops of strong phenolphthalein added and the acid titrated with N/1 NaOH solution in a 50-cc. burette. The cc. titration divided by the weight of the sample is noted as C. (See calculations at the close of the procedure.)

Sulphurous Acid in Hydrofluoric Acid

Ten grams of the sample are weighed in a tared platinum capsule with cover and washed into a large platinum dish with about 75 cc. of water. N/10 Iodine solution is added to a faint yellow. The end point is made more distinct by addi tion of a little starch solution near the end of the reaction.

One cc. of N/10 I $=0.0041$ g. H_2SO_3.   cc. N/10 I $\div$ wt. of sample $=$ D.

Calculation of Results.

Factors. $H_2SO_4 \times 0.4904 = H_2SiF_6$.

$H_2SO_4 \times 0.4080 = HF$.

One cc. N/10 I $=0.0041$ g. H_2SO_3.

Symbols.   A $=$ cc. NaOH for total acidity (cold) $\div$ wt. of sample.
B $=$ cc. of NaOH addition for H_2SiF_6 (hot) $\div$ wt. of sample.
C $=$ cc. NaOH for $H_2SO_4 \div$ wt. of sample.
D $=$ cc. N/10 iodine $\div$ wt. of sample.

Formulæ for Calculation. If E $=$ value of 1 cc. of the standard N/1 caustic in terms of H_2SO_4 then

$$\text{Per cent HF} = \left(A - \frac{B}{2} - C \right) \times E \times 0.408 \times 100 - 0.2D:$$

$$\text{Per cent } H_2SiF_6 = \frac{3}{2} B \times E \times 0.4904 \times 100;$$

$$\text{Per cent } H_2SO_4 = C \times E \times 100;$$

$$\text{Per cent } H_2SO_3 = D \times 0.0041 \times 100.$$

Residue. This is determined by evaporation of 15 to 20 grams of the acid in a platinum dish, and gentle ignition of the dry residue.

Notes and Precautions. Weighings should be made quickly in covered platinum weighing bottles.
See note under Special Reagents on previous page.
It is advisable to weigh out the sample for the sulphuric acid determination first and start the evaporation to facilitate more rapid results.
Iodine is preferred to permanganate for titration of H_2SO_3 as the latter also titrates organic matter that is apt to occur in the acid.

COMPLETE ANALYSIS OF NITRIC ACID

The acidity of nitric acid obtained by titration with standard caustic may be
ue not only to HNO_3 but to impurities H_2SO_4, HCl and lower oxides of nitrogen,
ence for extremely accurate analysis it is essential to look for these impurities
nd make allowances accordingly if they are found to be present.   Nitric acid may
e determined directly by titration with ferrous sulphate according to the pro-
edure given in detail, page 1512; this titration will include combined nitrates as
rell as the free acid, whereas the titration with caustic includes only free acids.
n addition to the above-mentioned impurities, commercial nitric acid frequently
ontains free chlorine, chlorides, chlorates, iodine, iodides, iodates, silica, and
uspended solids; the last is reported as insoluble residue.   In an analysis of
itric acid the impurities, which are known to be injurious to the art for which the
cid is used, are looked for and determined if present.

Determination of Total Acidity

As in case of mixed acids and, in fact, all accurate determinations of acids with
austic, such an amount of the sample should be taken as will require a titration
rithin the limits of the standard chamber burette—75 to 100 cc. For normal
austic this would require 4.726 to 6.3 grams of 100% HNO_3 or a fifth or tenth of
hi amount for N/5 or N/10 NaOH. From the specific gravity of the acid its
pproximate strength can be obtained by referring to the table for nitric acid and
alculating the volume and approximate weight required for analysis (see example
nder Methods of Weighing Acids—Dilute Acids—Non-Volatile under Ordinary
Conditions, page 1498).

The acid is weighed in a weighing bottle, or in the Dely tube or Blay-Burk-
ard pipette, if it is a fuming acid. The titration is made in a casserole, the acid
eing mixed with 150 to 200 cc. of CO_2 free water and titrated in presence of
henolphthalein indicator. (Methyl-orange is destroyed by nitrous acid.) The
otal acidity is expressed in terms of H_2SO_4 if other acids are present.

$$\text{c. } \frac{\text{N/1 NaOH} \times .049043 \times 100}{\text{Weight of the sample}} = \text{per cent } H_2SO_4 \text{ equivalent. } H_2SO_4 \times 1.285 = HNO_3.$$

$$\text{Direct calculation to } HNO_3 \frac{\text{cc. N/1 NaOH} \times 0.063018 \times 100}{\text{Weight of the sample}} = \text{per cent } HNO_3.$$

Determination of Sulphuric Acid in Nitric Acid

About 10 grams of the acid are evaporated to dryness on the steam bath. The
esidue is taken up with about 10 cc. of water and the evaporation repeated until
ree from nitric fumes, the residue finally diluted to 100 cc. and the sulphuric acid
itrated with N/5 NaOH, using phenolphthalein or methyl-orange indicator
iravimetrically the acid may be precipitated from a hot solution as $BaSO_4$ by
ddition of barium chloride reagent according to the method for determining
ulphur.

One cc. N/5 NaOH = 0.009809 gram H_2SO_4.

$BaSO_4 \times 0.4202 = H_2SO_4$. Per cent = 100 divided by weight of sample $\times H_2SO_4$
btained.

Determination of Hydrochloric Acid in Nitric Acid

A 5- to 50-gram sample is taken, that is to say, a sufficient amount of the aci so that a weighable amount of AgCl may be obtained. The sample is near neutralized with NH_4OH (it should be slightly acid with HNO_3) and a sligh excess of silver nitrate reagent added to the hot solution; the mixture is stirre thoroughly, then allowed to settle for one or two hours. The AgCl is filtere through a weighed Gooch crucible containing an asbestos mat, then washe dried and ignited at a low red heat. (See general method for the determination chlorine.)

Factors. $AgCl \times 0.2474 = Cl$. $AgCl \times 0.2544 = HCl$.

$AgCl \times 0.34212 =$ equivalent H_2SO_4.

Find the per cent HCl and the per cent equivalent H_2SO_4.

Lower Oxides.   Determined as Nitrous Acid

For practical purposes the lower oxides of nitrogen that may be present i nitric acid are calculated to N_2O_3 or HNO_2. If it is desired to report these as N_2O the conversion factor given below may be used. The lower oxides may be obtaine by titration with standard permanganate, other reducing agents being absen In presence of organic matter titration with standard iodine solution should b made. (See general procedure for determination of nitrous acid, etc.)

It makes but little difference whether the permanganate is added to the samp containing nitrite or the sample added to a measured amount of permanganat provided in the first method the titration be made as rapidly as possible to preven oxidation taking place due to dilution of the sample with water. The end-poin in the first procedure is quicker and sharper.

Potassium permanganate oxidizes nitrous acid to nitric according to th reaction $2KMnO_4 + 5HNO_2 + 3H_2SO_4 = K_2SO_4 + 2MnSO_4 + 5HNO_3 + 3H_2O$. There fore 1 cc. of $N/1$ $KMnO_4 = 0.02351$ gram HNO_2 or 0.019 gram N_2O_3.

Twenty-five cc. of the acid are diluted in a casserole to about 300 cc. with col water, and 25 cc. of dilute H_2SO_4, 1 : 4 added. The solution is titrated imme diately with $N/5$ $KMnO_4$, the reagent being added rapidly at first and finall drop by drop as the end-point is approached. The reaction near the end is ap to be slow, so that time must be allowed for complete oxidation. The titratio is completed when a pink color is obtained, that persists for three minutes.

cc. $N/5$ $KMnO_4 \times 0.004702 =$ gram HNO_2.

The result multiplied by $\dfrac{100}{\text{wt. sample}} =$ per cent.

$HNO_2 \times 1.0431 =$ equivalent H_2SO_4.

Nitric Acid

From the total acidity expressed as H_2SO_4 is subtracted the acidity due to HC and HNO_2 (lower oxides of nitrogen) expressed in terms of H_2SO_4. The remainde is due to nitric acid, in terms of sulphuric acid.

$H_2SO_4 \times 1.285 = HNO_3$.

Determination of Iodine in Nitric Acid

Fifty cc. of the acid in an Erlenmeyer flask is neutralized with caustic, the mixture being cooled in running water during the operation. The solution, poured into a separatory funnel, is made acid with dilute H_2SO_4 and a few drops of 1% solution of KNO_2 added, followed by about 25 cc. of CS_2 or CCl_4. The mixture is shaken to extract the free iodine and the CS_2 or CCl_4 drawn off and the extraction repeated by addition of KNO_2 and CS_2 or CCl_4 until all the iodine has been extracted. Iodine present as iodide is extracted by this method. To obtain the iodine from iodate, H_2S water is added and the extraction with addition of $NaNO_2$ and CS_2 repeated.

The combined extracts are washed in a separatory funnel until free of acid. The iodine is now titrated with standard sodium thiosulphate by adding 25 to 30 cc. of water together with 5 cc. of 1% sodium bicarbonate solution (10 grams $NaHCO_3$ per liter+1 cc. HCl).

$$\text{One cc. N/10 } Na_2S_2O_3 = 0.01269 \text{ gram I.}$$

Reactions.

$$2HI + 2KNO_2 + H_2SO_4 = K_2SO_4 + 2H_2O + I_2 + 2NO;$$

$$2Na_2S_2O_3 + I_2 = 2NaI + Na_2S_4O_6.$$

Determination of Free Chlorine in Nitric Acid

When a current of pure air is passed into nitric acid containing free chlorine the air blows out the chlorine. If air aspirated through a sample of nitric acid is passed through a solution of potassium iodide the free chlorine will displace the iodine. The liberated iodine may now be titrated with standard sodium thiosulphate and the equivalent chlorine calculated.

Total Non=Volatile Solids

These may be determined by evaporating a large sample of 100 to 200 cc. of the nitric acid to dryness. The residue is heated gently to expel the last traces of nitric acid and then washed into a platinum dish, again evaporated to dryness and ignited to a dull red heat. The residue is due to non-volatile solids.

FERROUS SULPHATE METHOD FOR THE DIRECT DETERMI NATION OF NITRIC ACID [1]

Although the test for nitric acid by ferrous sulphate in presence of strong su phuric acid has long been known, the reagent has not been used for an accurat quantitative method until F. C. Bowman and W. W. Scott, General Chemic: Company, developed the procedure herein given. Nitric acid may be determine quantitatively in arsenic acid by titration with ferrous sulphate containing fre sulphuric acid. The method is also applicable to the determination of nitric aci in phosphoric acid and in sulphuric acid, including oleums and mixed acid The reaction in phosphoric acid and arsenic acid goes further than it does i sulphuric acid. The following equations represent the reactions taking place:

Reaction in Arsenic or Phosphoric Acids:

$$6FeSO_4 + 2HNO_3 + 3H_2SO_4 = 3Fe_2(SO_4)_3 + 2NO + 4H_2O.$$

Reaction in Sulphuric Acid:

$$4FeSO_4 + 2HNO_3 + 2H_2SO_4 = 2Fe_2(SO_4)_3 + N_2O_3 + 3H_2O.$$

Oxidizing agents such as chlorates, iodates, bromates, etc., interfere, owing t their oxidizing action on ferrous sulphate, hence these should be absent from th sample or allowance made, if appreciable amounts are present. NaCl up t .002 gram does not interfere; larger amounts tend to lower results. KI and KB react in a similar manner to NaCl, 0.002 gram causing no interference. KNO present in amounts up to 50% of the HNO_3 does not interfere. The sampl should not contain over 25% water, nor should the temperature exceed 60° C during titration. 0.1 to 0.8 gram HNO_3 are accurately titrated, in sulphuric aci

Special Reagents Required. *Standard Ferrous Sulphate.*

A. Reagent to be Used in Titration of Nitric Acid in Sulphuric Acid Oleum, etc. 176.5 grams of $FeSO_4 \cdot 7H_2O$ are dissolved in about 400 cc. of water and 500 cc. of about 60% H_2SO_4 (1 vol. 66° Bé. acid per 1 vol. H_2O) are adde with constant stirring, and the solution (cooled if necessary) made up to 1000 cc 1 cc. will be equivalent to $0.02\pm$ gram HNO_3, the exact value being determined b standardization.

B. Reagent for Titration of Nitric in Phosphoric or Arsenic Acid. Fer rous sulphate to be used, should be made up as follows: 264.7 grams of $FeSO_4$ $7H_2O$ is dissolved in 500 cc. of water, 50 cc. of 66° Bé. H_2SO_4 (93.2%), added an the solution made up to 1000 cc. 1 cc. will be equal to approximately 0.02 gram HNO_3. The exact strength is ascertained by titrating a known amount of nitri acid in phosphoric or arsenic acid upon warming to 40° or 50° C.

Standard Nitric Acid. The acid should contain about 40 grams of HNO (100%) per liter of solution, e.g., 41 cc. of the desk reagent (sp.gr. 1.42) per lite will give the strength desired, the exact value being determined by titration of th acid against standard caustic.

Potassium Dichromate, N/2 $K_2Cr_2O_7$ Solution. The exact value in terms of iron should be known.

[1] The Jour. Ind. Eng. Chem., **7**, 766, 1915.

Standardization of Ferrous Sulphate Reagent

1. Titration against standard nitric acid.

A. *Reagent to be Used for Determination of Nitric in Sulphuric Acid.*
10 cc. of the standard $HNO_3 = 0.4 \pm$ g. (the exact amount having been ascertained), is run into 100 cc. of 66° Bé. (93.2%) H_2SO_4, free from oxidizing agents HNO_3, etc.) and the resulting mixture titrated with the standard $FeSO_4$ solution according to the directions given under the General Procedure for determining HNO_3 in H_2SO_4, page 1515.

Weight of HNO_3 taken divided by cc. of $FeSO_4$ minus 0.2 cc. [1] = grams HNO_3 cc. $FeSO_4$.

B. *Standardization of the Reagent Used in the Determination of Nitric in Arsenic and Phosphoric Acids.* 10 cc. of the standard $HNO_3 = 0.4 \pm$ gram (the exact amount having been ascertained) is run into 100 cc. of H_2AsO_4, or H_3PO_4, according to the product to be titrated, the mixture warmed and titrated according to directions given under Procedure for determination of HNO_3 in arsenic or phosphoric acid.

Weight of HNO_3 taken, divided by cc. $FeSO_4 =$ grams HNO_3 per cc. $FeSO_4$.

2. Standardizing Ferrous Sulphate with Standard Potassium Dichromate.

A. *Reagent to be Used in Determination of Nitric in Sulphuric Acid.*
25 cc. of $N/2$ $K_2Cr_2O_7$ (or 125 cc. $N/10$ $K_2Cr_2O_7$), are accurately measured out into a 250-cc. beaker and the solution titrated with the $FeSO_4$ reagent, until the first fraction of a drop of excess produces a blue color with potassium ferricyanide indicator on a spot plate. Usually between 19 to 20 cc. are required. The iron value of the dichromate multiplied by $0.5643 =$ gram HNO_3 for the total cc. of $FeSO_4$ required in the titration.

Calculation.

Since $N/2$ $K_2Cr_2O_7 = 0.024517$ gram salt, 1 gram $K_2Cr_2O_7 = 1.13882$ Fe, therefore 25 cc. $= 0.024517 \times 1.13882 \times 0.5643 \times 25 = 0.3939$ gram HNO_3 equivalent.

0.3939 divided by cc. $FeSO_4$ required in the titration = grams HNO_3 equivalent per cc.

B. *Reagent to be Used in Determination of HNO_3 in H_3AsO_4 or H_3PO_4.* 38 cc. of $K_2Cr_2O_7$ solution are titrated with $FeSO_4$ according to directions given in "A". The Fe value multiplied by $0.3762 =$ gram HNO_3.

Calculation. 38 cc. of $K_2Cr_2O_7 = 0.024517 \times 1.13882 \times 0.3762 \times 38 = 0.3991$ gram HNO_3 equivalent. 0.3991 divided by cc. $FeSO_4$ required in the titration = grams HNO_3 equivalent per c.c.

Factors.

$K_2Cr_2O_7$ to Fe $= 1.13882$, reciprocal $= 0.8781$.

2Fe to $HNO_3 = 0.5643$, recip. $= 1.7722$. 3Fe to $HNO_3 = 0.3762$, recip. $= 2.6582$.

HNO_3 to $2FeSO_4.7H_2O = 8.8235$ recip. $= 0.1133$.

HNO_3 to $3FeSO_4.7H_2O = 13.2348$, recip. $= 0.07556$.

$K_2Cr_2O_7$ to $HNO_3 = 0.6426$, recip. $= 1.5562$. (Titration of A reagent.)

$K_2Cr_2O_7$ to $HNO_3 = 0.4284$, recip. $= 2.3342$. (Titration of B reagent.)

---

[1] An excess of 0.2 cc. $FeSO_4$ is required to produce the desired color reaction in 100 cc. of pure H_2SO_4.

General Procedure. Determination of Nitric Acid in Sulphuric Acid

The procedure is applicable to the determination of nitric acid, free or combine as nitrate, sulphuric acid being used as the medium in which the titration is mad Although 0.1 to 0.8 gram HNO_3 may be accurately titrated, it is a general practic to have the nitric acid content of the sample taken for the titration about th same as the amount taken in standardization of the $FeSO_4$ reagent. A preliminar run on the original material is made, if the approximate nitric acid content is no known. Solids are dissolved in water and made to the desired volume, stron HNO_3 is diluted with water, in either case the dilution should be such that 10 cc of the solution will contain approximately 0.4 gram HNO_3. Mixed acids and oleur containing over 10% HNO_3 should be mixed with additional 66° Bé. (93+per cen H_2SO_4) and made to a definite volume, an aliquot part being taken for titration.

Evaluation of Nitric Acid or Nitrates

If the nitric acid is known to be free of other acids it may be titrated direct with caustic; combined nitrate cannot be titrated with caustic, but may be accu rately determined by the ferrous sulphate method. The approximate strengt of the HNO_3 or salt having been determined on 1 cc. or 1 gram sample (if the ma terial is a solid), the requisite amount is weighed and made to volume, 10 cc of which should contain not more than 0.8 gram or less than 0.1 gram HNO_3, pre erably about 0.4 gram.

Example. Suppose 1 cc. required a titration of 43.8 cc. $FeSO_4$, 10 cc. woul require a titration of 438 cc., whereas 20 cc. is desired. 438 divided by 20 = approx imately 22, e.g., the dilution should be to 22 volumes. 23 cc. of the solution dilute to 500 cc. will give a mixture of the desired strength. 23 cc. are accordingl weighed in a weighing bottle, the acid washed into a beaker transferred then t the graduated 500-cc. flask and made to volume. The preliminary run may b made in two or three minutes.

Titration. A 250-cc. beaker containing 100 cc. of strong, nitric free, H_2SO (93+%) is placed in a large casserole or deep porcelain dish containing cold water 10 cc. of the sample are measured out in an accurately marked pipette, graduate to contain exactly 10 cc. The solution is run under the surface of the sulphuri acid, the delivery tip of the pipette being kept in constant circular motion to pre vent too much local heating. Since the sides of the beaker are cooled, the tip o the pipette should be kept against the sides in the circular sweep during the de livery. By this procedure loss of nitric acid is reduced to the minimum.

The ferrous sulphate solution is now added from a burette in a fine stream unti the yellow color that first forms takes on a faint brownish tinge (dirty yellow) The pipette is now rinsed out by sucking up the mixture and draining it back into the beaker. The titration is now completed, adding the $FeSO_4$ cautiously drop by drop until the yellowish brown color again appears, a drop in excess producing an appreciable darkening of the solution. A larger excess produces a brownish red color. With small amounts of HNO_3 a pink color will be obtained, instead of the yellowish brown. The end-point once recognized is readily duplicated.

Calculation. The cc. titration minus the blank 0.2 cc. multiplied by the factor for $FeSO_4$ = weight of HNO_3. $HNO_3 \times 100 \div$ wt. = per cent.

Example. Suppose 10 cc. equivalent to 1/50 of a 42-g. sample weighed, requires 22 cc. $FeSO_4$ whose value = 0.02 g. HNO_3 per cc., then $(0.44 \times 100)/0.84$ = 52.4% HNO_3.

Determination of Nitric Acid in Oleum or in Mixed Acids. Ferrous Sulphate Method

The rapidity and accuracy of the method for determining HNO_3 in sulphuric ~id makes it valuable for determining nitric acid in oleums and mixed acids. itrated oleums may be weighed and titrated without diluting to definite)lume, mixed acids containing large percentages of nitric acid, however, re- ~ire dilution with H_2SO_4, as stated under General Procedure.

Procedure. The sample may be weighed in a Dely weighing tube (see analysis of leum and mixed acids), or in a standard pipette (5 cc. generally taken = 9.61 grams). ' the latter is used, the sample is sucked into the pipette, a rubber tube, with glass ~ad valve, being attached to the upper end, to which suction is applied without ~nger of drawing SO_3 fumes into the mouth. A little vaseline placed on the tip ' the pipette prevents loss of acid during the weighing. In routine analysis, here a large number of daily samples of oleum are analyzed, and the specific ~avity of the oleum does not vary appreciably, 5- to 10-cc. samples may be drawn ~t, by means of a pipette, and titrated without weighing, the weight being cal- ~lated from the gravity.

The acid is run under cold concentrated H_2SO_4 (93%), and titrated according) directions under General Procedure for Nitric acid. A blank of 0.2 cc.[1] having ~en deducted, cc. $FeSO_4 \times HNO_3$ factor for $FeSO_4 \times 100$ divided by wt. taken = per cent HNO_3.

Correction Factor. In making a number of runs with varying amounts of HNO_3, was found that small quantities of nitric acid required a proportional greater amount ' $FeSO_4$ than larger quantities of HNO_3. For example, 0.07392 gram HNO_3 required 9 cc. $FeSO_4$, four times the amount of HNO_3 required 15 cc. $FeSO_4$, in place of 15.6, ~.9 $\times$ 4) and six times 0.07392 gram HNO_3 required 22.5 cc. $FeSO_4$ in place of 23.4. It ~as observed that even traces of HNO_3 required a titration of over 0.2 cc. It is evi- ~nt that a deduction of 0.2 cc. makes the titrations multiples of the lowest, e.g., 3.7, ~.8 and 22.3. Again it was found that standardization of $FeSO_4$ with HNO_3 checked ~e dichromate factor when 0.2 cc. was deducted from the first series of titrations. This ~d to the conclusion that a constant blank of 0.2 cc. should be deducted from the ferrous ~lphate titrations of nitric acid in presence of 100 cc. of nitric free sulphuric acid, ~6° Bé.).

Comparison of results:

$FeSO_4$ value by HNO_3 corrected = 0.02067 gram.   Uncorrected = 0.02045 gram HNO_3.

$FeSO_4$ value by $K_2Cr_2O_7$ titration = 0.02083 gram HNO_3.

Accuracy of the Ferrous Sulphate Method. Results obtained by the ferrous sul- ~hate method agree closely with those obtained by the nitrometer. The following ~ata were obtained by Mr. B. S. Clark,[2] by the $FeSO_4$ method, on nitrated oleums. ~he figures below the first row are checks obtained on these samples by purchasers of ~e acid, the nitrometer method being used.

~SO₄ method.	2.40; 2.82; 3.23; 3.35; 3.52; 3.50; 3.48; 3.57; 3.53; 3.56.
~itrometer method.	2.35; 2.79; 3.26; 3.39; 3.57; 3.53; 3.50; 3.58; 3.57; 3.56.
)ifference.	0.05; 0.03; 0.03; 0.04; 0.05; 0.03; 0.02; 0.01; 0.04; 0.00.

[1] Back titrations of the excess of $FeSO_4$ may be made with standard $K_2Cr_2O_7$, using ~e ferricyanide spot test for ferrous iron.

Sp.gr. of twelve average samples of oleum had a difference of only 0.01.   5 cc. ~eighs 9.61 grams. This is found convenient for analysis.   10 cc. = 19.22 grams will ~ually give a titration of about 20+cc. on the usual nitrated oleum.

Determination of Nitric Acid in Arsenic and Phosphoric Acid by the Ferrous Sulphate Method

A direct procedure for the determination of nitric acid in arsenic acid phosphoric acid has been sought on account of the inaccuracy of the evaporation method, since it is difficult to completely expel HNO_3 from these acids. Ferrous sulphate, in presence of sulphuric acid, quantitatively titrates nitric in arsenic acid, the following reaction taking place:

$$6FeSO_4 + 2HNO_3 + 3H_2SO_4 + xH_3AsO_4 = 3Fe_2(SO_4)_3 + 2NO + 4H_2O + xH_3AsO_4.$$

The procedure is applicable to the determination of nitric acid in phosphoric acid, the end-point being sharper in this acid than in arsenic. The procedure gives very excellent results in either acid and is recommended for accuracy and rapidity.

Standardization of Ferrous Sulphate has already been given under special reagents. It must be remembered that the arsenic or phosphoric acid diluent should be free from nitric acid or the blank on 100 cc. be ascertained and deducted from titrations made in this diluent.

Procedure. The amount of the sample to be taken is governed by the nitric acid present as an impurity. This may be quickly determined by a preliminary run on a 10-cc. sample, the diluent being the same acid (HNO_3 free) as the acid titrated.

Example. Suppose 10 cc. require a titration of 4.5 cc. of $FeSO_4$, whereas titration of 20 cc. is desired, then $20 \times 10 \div 4.5 = 44.44$ cc. of the sample required

The required amount of the acid is measured out and weighed, if its sp.gr. not known. The acid is poured into a 4-in. casserole and diluted with 100 cc. of nitric free acid of the same kind as that being titrated. The mixture is gently warmed to 40 to 50° C. and titrated with standard ferrous sulphate reagent to permanent yellowish brown. Towards the end of the titration the acid will boil with each addition of the $FeSO_4$ and the characteristic reddish yellow fumes will be given off. (This does not occur in titrations of HNO_3 in H_2SO_4.)

When very small amounts of nitric acid are present it is often necessary to add a known amount of HNO_3 to start the reaction. The titration in excess of that required by the added HNO_3 is due to the nitric acid in the sample. Very small amounts of HNO_3 produce a pink color.

Calculation cc. $FeSO_4 \times HNO_3$ factor for $FeSO_4 \times 100$ divided by weight taken = per cent HNO_3.

Factors. Fe to $HNO_3 = 0.3762$. Reciprocal $= 2.6582$.

NOTE. In a 20-gram sample 1 cc. 0.02 reagent $= 0.1\%$ per cc.

DETERMINATION OF NITROUS ACID OR NITRITE PERMANGANATE METHOD

Principle. Potassium permanganate reacts with nitrous acid or a nitrite as follows:

$$5N_2O_3 + 4KMnO_4 + 6H_2SO_4 = 5N_2O_5 + 2K_2SO_4 + 4MnSO_4 + 6H_2O.$$
$$5HNO_2 + 2KMnO_4 + 3H_2SO_4 = 5HNO_3 + K_2SO_4 + 2MnSO_4 + 3H_2O.$$

Details of the general procedure for nitrites is given on page 358, Vol. I Nitrous acid in nitric acid may be determined as stated on page 1510. Lower oxides of nitrogen in mixed acids are determined as outlined on page 1530.

NITRIC ACID

By W. C. Ferguson

Degrees Baumé.	Sp. Gr. $\frac{60°}{60°}$ F.	Degrees Twaddell.	Per Cent HNO_3.	Degrees Baumé.	Sp. Gr. $\frac{60°}{60°}$ F.	Degrees Twaddell.	Per Cent HNO_3.
10 00	1.0741	14.82	12.86	21.25	1.1718	34 36	28.02
10.25	1.0761	15.22	13.18	21.50	1.1741	34.82	28.36
10.50	1.0781	15.62	13.49	21.75	1.1765	35.30	28.72
10.75	1.0801	16.02	13.81	22.00	1.1789	35.78	29.07
11.00	1.0821	16.42	14.13	22.25	1.1813	36 26	29.43
11.25	1.0841	16.82	14.44	22.50	1.1837	36.74	29 78
11.50	1.0861	17.22	14.76	22.75	1.1861	37.22	30.14
11.75	1.0881	17.62	15.07	23.00	1.1885	37.70	30.49
12.00	1.0902	18.04	15.41	23.25	1.1910	38.20	30.86
12.25	1.0922	18.44	15.72	23.50	1.1934	38.68	31.21
12.50	1.0943	18.86	16.05	23.75	1.1959	39.18	31.58
12.75	1.0964	19.28	16.39	24.00	1.1983	39.66	31.94
13.00	1.0985	19.70	16.72	24.25	1.2008	40.16	32.31
13.25	1.1006	20.12	17.05	24.50	1.2033	40.66	32.68
13.50	1.1027	20.54	17.38	24.75	1.2058	41.16	33 05
13.75	1.1048	20 96	17.71	25.00	1.2083	41.66	33.42
14.00	1.1069	21.38	18.04	25.25	1.2109	42.18	33.80
14.25	1.1090	21.80	18.37	25.50	1.2134	42 68	34.17
14.50	1.1111	22.22	18.70	25.75	1.2160	43.20	34.56
14.75	1.1132	22.64	19.02	26.00	1.2185	43.70	34.94
15.00	1.1154	23.08	19.36	26.25	1.2211	44.22	35.33
15.25	1.1176	23.52	19.70	26.50	1.2236	44.72	35.70
15.50	1.1197	23.94	20.02	26.75	1.2262	45.24	36 09
15.75	1.1219	24.38	20.36	27.00	1.2288	45.76	36.48
16.00	1.1240	24.80	20.69	27.25	1.2314	46.28	36 87
16.25	1.1262	25.24	21.03	27.50	1.2340	46.80	37 26
16.50	1.1284	25.68	21.36	27.75	1.2367	47.34	37.67
16.75	1.1306	26.12	21.70	28.00	1.2393	47.86	38.06
17.00	1.1328	26.56	22 04	28.25	1.2420	48.40	38 46
17.25	1.1350	27.00	22.38	28.50	1.2446	48.92	38.85
17.50	1.1373	27.46	22.74	28.75	1.2473	49.46	39.25
17.75	1.1395	27.90	23.08	29.00	1.2500	50.00	39 66
18.00	1.1417	28.34	23.42	29.25	1.2527	50.54	40.06
18.25	1.1440	28.80	23.77	29.50	1.2554	51.08	40.47
18.50	1.1462	29.24	24.11	29.75	1.2582	51.64	40.89
18.75	1.1485	29.70	24.47	30.00	1.2609	52.18	41 30
19.00	1.1508	30.16	24.82	30.25	1.2637	52.74	41 72
19.25	1.1531	30.62	25.18	30.50	1.2664	53.28	42 14
19.50	1.1554	31.08	25.53	30.75	1.2692	53.84	42 58
19.75	1.1577	31.54	25.88	31.00	1.2719	54.38	43 00
20.00	1.1600	32.00	26.24	31.25	1.2747	54.94	43.44
20.25	1.1624	32.48	26.61	31.50	1.2775	55.50	43 89
20.50	1.1647	32.94	26.96	31.75	1.2804	56.08	44 34
20.75	1.1671	33.42	27.33	32.00	1.2832	56.64	44.78
21.00	1.1694	33.88	27.67	32.25	1.2861	57.22	45.24

NITRIC ACID (Continued)

Degrees Baumé.	Sp. Gr. $\frac{60°}{60°}$ F.	Degrees Twaddell.	Per Cent HNO$_3$.	Degrees Baumé.	Sp. Gr. $\frac{60°}{60°}$ F.	Degrees Twaddell.	Per Cent HNO$_3$.
32.50	1.2889	57.78	45.68	40.75	1.3909	78.18	63.48
32.75	1.2918	58.36	46.14	41.00	1.3942	78.84	64.20
33.00	1.2946	58.92	46.58	41.25	1.3976	79.52	64.93
33.25	1.2975	59.50	47.04	41.50	1.4010	80.20	65.67
33.50	1.3004	60.08	47.49	41.75	1.4044	80.88	66.42
33.75	1.3034	60.68	47.95	42.00	1.4078	81.56	67.18
34.00	1.3063	61.26	48.42	42.25	1.4112	82.24	67.95
34.25	1.3093	61.86	48.90	42.50	1.4146	82.92	68.73
34.50	1.3122	62.44	49.35	42.75	1.4181	83.62	69.52
34.75	1.3152	63.04	49.83	43.00	1.4216	84.32	70.33
35.00	1.3182	63.64	50.32	43.25	1.4251	85.02	71.15
35.25	1.3212	64.24	50.81	43.50	1.4286	85.72	71.98
35.50	1.3242	64.84	51.30	43.75	1.4321	86.42	72.82
35.75	1.3273	65.46	51.80	44.00	1.4356	87.12	73.67
36.00	1.3303	66.06	52.30	44.25	1.4392	87.84	74.53
36.25	1.3334	66.68	52.81	44.50	1.4428	88.56	75.40
36.50	1.3364	67.28	53.32	44.75	1.4464	89.28	76.28
36.75	1.3395	67.90	53.84	45.00	1.4500	90.00	77.17
37.00	1.3426	68.52	54.36	45.25	1.4536	90.72	78.07
37.25	1.3457	69.14	54.89	45.50	1.4573	91.46	79.03
37.50	1.3488	69.76	55.43	45.75	1.4610	92.20	80.04
37.75	1.3520	70.40	55.97	46.00	1.4646	92.92	81.08
38.00	1.3551	71.02	56.52	46.25	1.4684	93.68	82.18
38.25	1.3583	71.66	57.08	46.50	1.4721	94.42	83.33
38.50	1.3615	72.30	57.65	46.75	1.4758	95.16	84.48
38.75	1.3647	72.94	58.23	47.00	1.4796	95.92	85.70
39.00	1.3679	73.58	58.82	47.25	1.4834	96.68	86.98
39.25	1.3712	74.24	59.43	47.50	1.4872	97.44	88.32
39.50	1.3744	74.88	60.06	47.75	1.4910	98.20	89.76
39.75	1.3777	75.54	60.71	48.00	1.4948	98.96	91.35
40.00	1.3810	76.20	61.38	48.25	1.4987	99.74	93.13
40.25	1.3843	76.86	62.07	48.50	1.5026	100.52	95.11
40.50	1.3876	77.52	62.77				

Specific Gravity determinations were made at 60° F., compared with water at 60° F. From the Specific Gravities, the corresponding degrees Baumé were calculated by the following formula :

$$\text{Baumé} = 145 - \frac{145}{\text{Sp. Gr.}}.$$

Baumé Hydrometers for use with this table must be graduated by the above formula, which formula should always be printed on the scale.
Atomic weights from F. W. Clarke's table of 1901. O = 16.

ALLOWANCE FOR TEMPERATURE :

At 10° — 20° Bé. — 1/30° Bé. or .00029 Sp. Gr. = 1° F.
    20° — 30° Bé. — 1/23° Bé. or .00044 "   " = 1° F.
    30° — 40° Bé. — 1/20° Bé. or .00060 "   " = 1° F.
    40° — 48.5° Bé. — 1/17° Bé. or .00084 "   " = 1° F.

AUTHORITY — W. C. FERGUSON.

This table has been approved and adopted as a Standard by the Manufacturing Chemists' Association of the United States.

W. H. BOWER,   JAS. L. MORGAN,
HENRY HOWARD,   ARTHUR WYMAN,
A. G. ROSENGARTEN,   *Executive Committee*

New York, May 14, 1903.

NITRIC ACID
LUNGE AND REY

Specific Gravity $\frac{15°}{4°}$ in vacuo	100 parts by weight contain		1 liter contains grams		Specific Gravity $\frac{15°}{4°}$ in vacuo	100 parts by weight contain		1 liter contains grams	
	% N_2O_5	% HNO_3	N_2O_5	HNO_3		% N_2O_5	% HNO_3	N_2O_5	HNO_3
1.000	0.08	0.10	1	1	1.195	27.10	31.62	324	378
1.005	0.85	1.00	8	10	1.200	27.74	32.36	333	388
1.010	1.62	1.90	16	19	1.205	28.36	33.09	342	399
1.015	2.39	2.80	24	28	1.210	28.99	33.82	351	409
1.020	3.17	3.70	33	38	1.215	29.61	34.55	360	420
1.025	3.94	4.60	40	47	1.220	30.24	35.28	369	430
1.030	4.71	5.50	49	57	1.225	30.88	36.03	378	441
1.035	5.47	6.38	57	66	1.230	31.53	36.78	387	452
1.040	6.22	7.26	64	75	1.235	32.17	37.53	397	463
1.045	6.97	8.13	73	85	1.240	32.82	38.29	407	475
1.050	7.71	8.99	81	94	1.245	33.47	39.05	417	486
1.055	8.43	9.84	89	104	1.250	34.13	39.82	427	498
1.060	9.15	10.68	97	113	1.255	34.78	40.58	437	509
1.065	9.87	11.51	105	123	1.260	35.44	41.34	447	521
1.070	10.57	12.33	113	132	1.265	36.09	42.10	457	533
1.075	11.27	13.15	121	141	1.270	36.75	42.87	467	544
1.080	11.96	13.95	129	151	1.275	37.41	43.64	477	556
1.085	12.64	14.74	137	160	1.280	38.07	44.41	487	568
1.090	13.31	15.53	145	169	1.285	38.73	45.18	498	581
1.095	13.99	16.32	153	179	1.290	39.39	45.95	508	593
1.100	14.67	17.11	161	188	1.295	40.05	46.72	519	605
1.105	15.34	17.89	170	198	1.300	40.71	47.49	529	617
1.110	16.00	18.67	177	207	1.305	41.37	48.26	540	630
1.115	16.67	19.45	186	217	1.310	42.06	49.07	551	643
1.120	17.34	20.23	195	227	1.315	42.76	49.89	562	656
1.125	18.00	21.00	202	236	1.320	43.47	50.71	573	669
1.130	18.66	21.77	211	246	1.325	44.17	51.53	585	683
1.135	19.32	22.54	219	256	1.330	44.89	52.37	597	697
1.140	19.98	23.31	228	266	1.3325	45.26	52.80	603	704
1.145	20.64	24.08	237	276	1.335	45.62	53.22	609	710
1.150	21.29	24.84	245	286	1.340	46.35	54.07	621	725
1.155	21.94	25.60	254	296	1.345	47.08	54.93	633	739
1.160	22.60	26.36	262	306	1.350	47.82	55.79	645	753
1.165	23.25	27.12	271	316	1.355	48.57	56.66	658	768
1.170	23.90	27.88	279	326	1.360	49.35	57.57	671	783
1.175	24.54	28.63	288	336	1.365	50.13	58.48	684	798
1.180	25.18	29.38	297	347	1.370	50.91	59.39	698	814
1.185	25.83	30.13	306	357	1.375	51.69	60.30	711	829
1.190	26.47	30.88	315	367	1.380	52.52	61.27	725	846

NITRIC ACID (Continued)

Specific Gravity 15°/4° in vacuo	100 parts by weight contain		1 liter contains grams		Specific Gravity 15°/4° in vacuo	100 parts by weight contain		1 liter contains grams	
	% N_2O_5	% HNO_3	N_2O_5	HNO_3		% N_2O_5	% HNO_3	N_2O_5	HNO_3
1.3833	53.08	61.92	735	857	1.495	78.52	91.60	1174	1369
1.385	53.35	62.24	739	862	1.500	80.65	94.09	1210	1411
1.390	54.20	63.23	753	879	1.501	81.09	94.60	1217	1420
1.395	55.07	64.25	768	896	1.502	81.50	95.08	1224	1428
1.400	55.97	65.30	783	914	1.503	81.91	95.55	1231	1436
1.405	56.92	66.40	800	933	1.504	82.29	96.00	1238	1444
1.410	57.86	67.50	816	952	1.505	82.63	96.39	1244	1451
1.415	58.83	68.63	832	971	1.506	82.94	96.76	1249	1457
1.420	59.83	69.80	849	991	1.507	83.26	97.13	1255	1464
1.425	60.84	70.98	867	1011	1.508	83.58	97.50	1260	1470
1.430	61.86	72.17	885	1032	1.509	83.87	97.84	1265	1476
1.435	62.91	73.39	903	1053	1.510	84.09	98.10	1270	1481
1.440	64.01	74.68	921	1075	1.511	84.28	98.32	1274	1486
1.445	65.13	75.98	941	1098	1.512	84.46	98.53	1277	1490
1.450	66.24	77.28	961	1121	1.513	84.63	98.73	1280	1494
1.455	67.38	78.60	981	1144	1.514	84.78	98.90	1283	1497
1.460	68.56	79.98	1001	1168	1.515	84.92	99.07	1287	1501
1.465	69.79	81.42	1023	1193	1.516	85.04	99.21	1289	1504
1.470	71.06	82.90	1045	1219	1.517	85.15	99.34	1292	1507
1.475	72.39	84.45	1068	1246	1.518	85.26	99.46	1294	1510
1.480	73.76	86.05	1092	1274	1.519	85.35	99.57	1296	1512
1.485	75.18	87.70	1116	1302	1.520	85.44	99.67	1299	1515
1.490	76.80	89.60	1144	1335					

VOLUMETRIC DETERMINATION OF PHOSPHORIC ACID AND ITS SALTS (METHOD OF SMITH)

In titrating free phosphoric acid it must be borne in mind that NaH_2PO_4 reacts acid to phenolphthalein and neutral to methyl orange, while Na_2HPO_4 is neutral to phenolphthalein and basic to methyl orange. The reactions are shown as follows:

$$H_3PO_4 + 2NaOH = 2H_2O + Na_2HPO_4 \text{ (neutral to P. acid to M.O.)}$$
$$H_3PO_4 = NaOH = NaH_2PO_4 = H_2O + NaH_2PO_4 \text{ (neutral to M.O. acid to P.)}$$

J. H. Smith outlines the following process for analysis of phosphoric acid free and combined:

Procedure. Take five or six grams of the material and dissolve in the minimum quantity of distilled water. Add two drops of phenolphthalein. If the solution is not colored pink by the indicator the absence of trisodium phosphate (Na_3PO_4) and sodium carbonate (Na_2CO_3) may be assumed. Heat to 55° C. and titrate with $N/1$ NaOH to the characteristic pink endpoint, being particularly careful to keep the temperature at 55° C. when near the endpoint. This precaution should be observed in all the titrations as the temperature governs the accuracy of the titrations (see paper by Smith).

Record this titration as "A" and the cc. NaOH required as (a).

The solution is now titrated back with $N/1$ HCl, using a few drops of methyl orange as indicator, to the pink endpoint.

Record this titration as "B" and the cc. acid required as (b).

Calculation of the Composition. If the solution contains only Na_2HPO_4 + NaH_2PO_4 or $NaH_2PO_4 + H_3PO_4$ or only one of these compounds we may assume the following:

If (a) is greater than (b)

$$(a) - (b) = \text{cc. equivalent of } N/1 \ H_3PO_4,$$
$$(b) = \text{cc. equivalent of } N/1 \ NaH_2PO_4.$$

If (b) is greater than (a)

$$(b) - (a) = Na_2HPO_4,$$
$$(a) = NaH_2PO_4.$$

If (a) = (b)

$$\text{Each titration} = NaH_2PO_4 \text{ present.}$$

If (a) = 2(b)

$$\text{Only } H_3PO_4 \text{ is present.}$$

To Ascertain the Presence of Other Salts. Add $N/1$ HCl (cc. HCl the same as cc. in titration B). Call this (b'). Boil for at least 15 minutes. By this procedure metaphosphoric acid or its salts is converted to the orthophosphate form, alkaline salts containing carbonates are destroyed and CO_2 evolved. Cool the solution to 55° C. and titrate back with $N/1$ NaOH first to "B" point in which (b'') cc. of alkali is used, and finally to third endpoint (C), where the phenolphthalein pink color is reached. The cc. $N/1$ NaOH required is recorded as (c).

In titrating back after boiling, the (b'') amount of alkali required to reach the methyl orange point where the pink coloration just appears should always be the same amount as the (b') excess of acid added for boiling (except in the case of polyphosphates being present—see paper). A slight loss of HCl during boiling may cause (b'') to be less than (b'). In any case it is preferable to consider the point reached after addition of the (b'') quantity of alkali as the identical point with B, so that (b') and (b'') are not used in the calculation, but simply employed as a comparative check on each other.

[1] J. H. Smith, Soc. Chem. Ind., **36**, 415 (1917).

If the "C" point coincides with the "A" point, *i.e.*, if $(c) = (b)$ metaphos-phoric acid and its salts as well as carbonates in the original substance are excluded.

If (c) is greater than (b) the presence of metaphosphates is indicated.

If (c) is less than (b) carbonates are evidently present.

With the aid of the three fixed points "A," "B," "C" and the amounts of acid or alkali required to reach them, *i.e.*, (a), (b) and (c) it is possible to calculate the percentages of practically all the phosphoric acids and their salts which may exist together in a compound, including the carbonates and the free alkali, which may be present with them.

Calculation of Constituents in a Mixture of Phosphates

If (a) is greater than (b)

$(a) - (b) = H_3PO_4$, $2(b) - (a) = NaH_2PO_4$, $(c) - (b) = NaPO_3$ (generally nil).

If (a) is greater than $2(b)$

Then $(a) - 2(b) =$ measure of metaphosphoric acid or the foreign acid present.

If (a) is less than (b)

(a) is the measure of NaH_2PO_4, $(b) - (a) = Na_2HPO_4$,

$(c) - (b) = NaPO_3$ (usually nil).

With alkaline salts "C." coincides with "A," *i.e.*, when no carbonate is present.

If (a) is less than (b) then

(a) is a measure of Na_3PO_4, $(b) - (a) = Na_2HPO_4$.

Where (c) is less than (b), *i.e.*, when carbonate is present.

If (a) is less than (b)

$(a) + (c) - (b) = Na_3PO_4$, $(b) - (a) = Na_2HPO_4$, $(b) - (c) = Na_2CO_3$.

Where no carbonate is present and (a) is greater than (b).

$(b) = Na_3PO_4$, $\frac{1}{2}(a-b) = Na_2O$.

Where carbonate is present and (a) is greater than (b)

$(b) - (c) = Na_2CO_3$, $(c) = Na_3PO_4$, $\frac{1}{2}(a-b) = Na_2O$.

In calculating the weight of constituents from the above formulae, since normal solutions are used in the titrations each cc. is equivalent to molecular weights divided by 1/1000. In case of Na_2CO_3 and Na_2O the absolute weights are 1/2000 of the respective molecular weights.

Formulæ	Mol. Wt.	1 cc. Equivalent of Titration	Formulæ	Mol. Wt.	1 cc. Equivalent of Titration
H_3PO_4....	98.14	0.09814 g.	$NaPO_3$....	80.05	0.08005
NaH_2PO_4.	120.05	0.12005	Na_2CO_3...	106.01	0.053905
Na_2HPO_4.	142.05	0.14205	Na_2O.....	62.00	0.031
Na_3PO_4...	164.04	0.16404			

With water of crystallization $NaH_2PO_4.H_2O = 138.07$, $NaH_2PO_4.2H_2O = 156.09$, $Na_2HPO_4.12H_2O = 358.24$, $Na_3PO_4.12H_2O = 380.23$, $Na_2CO_3.10H_2O = 286.17$, $Na_2CO_3.H_2O = 124.02$.

NOTES.—In presence of meta or pyro acids and their salts it is well to verify the results with qualitative tests. When pyro acid is present point "A" is obscured and lies much nearer "B," but the correct "A" point is "C" obtained after boiling with the excess acid.

In presence of metaphosphate it is advisable to repeat titrations employing N/1 H_2SO_4 and evaporating to near dryness to completely convert the meta to ortho compound.

Phosphates attack glass combining with the alkali present. The presence of NaCl obtained in the titrations counteracts this action.

PHOSPHORIC ACID AT 17.5°

Specific Gravity.	Per Cent. P_2O_5.	Per Cent. H_3PO_4.	Specific Gravity.	Per Cent. P_2O_5.	Per Cent. H_3PO_4.	Specific Gravity.	Per Cent. P_2O_5.	Per Cent. H_3PO_4.
1.809	68.0	93.67	1.462	46.0	63.37	1.208	24.0	33.06
1.800	67.5	92.99	1.455	45.5	62.68	1.203	23.5	32.37
1.792	67.0	92.30	1.448	45.0	61.99	1.198	23.0	31.68
1.783	66.5	91.61	1.441	44.5	61.30	1.193	22.5	30.99
1.775	66.0	90.92	1.435	44.0	60.61	1.188	22.0	30.31
1.766	65.5	90.23	1.428	43.5	59.92	1.183	21.5	29.62
1.758	65.0	89.54	1.422	43.0	59.23	1.178	21.0	28.93
1.750	64.5	88.85	1.415	42.5	58.55	1.174	20.5	28.24
1.741	64.0	88.16	1.409	42.0	57.86	1.169	20.0	27.55
1.733	63.5	87.48	1.402	41.5	57.17	1.164	19.5	26.86
1.725	63.0	86.79	1.396	41.0	56.48	1.159	19.0	26.17
1.717	62.5	86.10	1.389	40.5	55.79	1.155	18.5	25.48
1.709	62.0	85.41	1.383	40.0	55.10	1.150	18.0	24.80
1.701	61.5	84.72	1.377	39.5	54.41	1.145	17.5	24.11
1.693	61.0	84.03	1.371	39.0	53.72	1.140	17.0	23.42
1.685	60.5	83.34	1.365	38.5	53.04	1.135	16.5	22.73
1.677	60.0	82.65	1.359	38.0	52.35	1.130	16.0	22.04
1.669	59.5	81.97	1.354	37.5	51.66	1.126	15.5	21.35
1.661	59.0	81.28	1.348	37.0	50.97	1.122	15.0	20.66
1.653	58.5	80.59	1.342	36.5	50.28	1.118	14.5	19.97
1.645	58.0	79.90	1.336	36.0	49.59	1.113	14.0	·19.28
1.637	57.5	79.21	1.330	35.5	48.90	1.109	13.5	18.60
1.629	57.0	78.52	1.325	35.0	48.21	1.104	13.0	17.91
1.621	56.5	77.83	1.319	34.5	47.52	1.100	12.5	17.22
1.613	56.0	77.14	1.314	34.0	46.84	1.096	12.0	16.53
1.605	55.5	76.45	1.308	33.5	46.15	1.091	11.5	15.84
1.597	55.0	75.77	1.303	33.0	45.46	1.087	11.0	15.15
1.589	54.5	75.08	1.298	32.5	44.77	1.083	10.5	14.46
1.581	54.0	74.39	1.292	32.0	44.08	1.079	10.0	13.77
1.574	53.5	73.70	1.287	31.5	43.39	1.074	9.5	13.09
1.566	53.0	73.01	1.281	31.0	42.70	1.070	9.0	12.40
1.559	52.5	72.32	1.276	30.5	42.01	1.066	8.5	11.71
1.551	52.0	71.63	1.271	30.0	41.33	1.062	8.0	11.02
1.543	51.5	70.94	1.265	29.5	40.64	1.058	7.5	10.33
1.536	51.0	70.26	1.260	29.0	39.95	1.053	7.0	9.64
1.528	50.5	69.57	1.255	28.5	39.26	1.049	6.5	8.95
1.521	50.0	68.88	1.249	28.0	38.57	1.045	6.0	8.26
1.513	49.5	68.19	1.244	27.5	37.88	1.041	5.5	7.57
1.505	49.0	67.50	1.239	27.0	37.19	1.037	5.0	6.89
1.498	48.5	66.81	1.233	26.5	36.50	1.033	4.5	6.20
1.491	48.0	66.12	1.228	26.0	35.82	1.029	4.0	5.51
1.484	47.5	65.43	1.223	25.5	35.13	1.025	3.5	4.82
1.476	47.0	64.75	1.218	25.0	34.44	1.021	3.0	4.13
1.469	46.5	64.06	1.213	24.5	33.75	1.017	2.5	3.44

ANALYSIS OF SULPHURIC ACID

Sulphuric acid made by the contact process is exceedingly pure, the principal impurity being iron, which causes turbidity in strong acid. The acid made by this process is 99% strength. This is diluted to 66° Be (93.19% H_2SO_4) and is known as oil of vitriol. The acid is also commonly marketed as 60° Be acid (77.67% H_2SO_4) and 50° Be acid (62.18% H_2SO_4) obtained by further dilution of the stronger acid. 50° Be acid is also obtained by the chamber process; this acid is not as pure as that produced by the contact process. The impurities occurring in sulphuric acid are iron, lead, copper, zinc, antimony, selenium, arsenic, sulphur dioxide, hydrochloric acid, hydrofluoric acid, nitric acid.

Sulphuric acid up to 93% strength may be determined with a fair degree of accuracy by ascertaining its specific gravity by means of a hydrometer and referring to the tables on sulphuric acid.

Sulphuric acid readily absorbs SO_3 so that its acidity may be considerably over 100%. This acid, commonly known as oleum, fumes when exposed to the air due to its low vapor tension, the SO_3 combining with the moisture of the air with formation of H_2SO_4 mist.

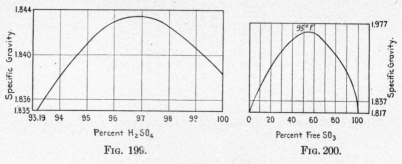

FIG. 199.　　　　　　　　　　　　FIG. 200.

Specific Gravity Charts—Sulphuric Acid.

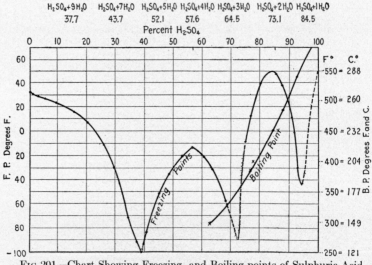

FIG. 201.—Chart Showing Freezing- and Boiling-points of Sulphuric Acid of Varying Concentration.

SULPHURIC ACID
Method of Analysis[1]

Procedure for Titration with Standard NaOH. Concentrated sulphuric acid absorbs moisture rapidly so that the weighing should be made quickly, the acid having been placed in a special closed receptacle as recommended on pages 1498 to 1500. Such an amount of acid is taken as will require a titration that can be read on the chamber burette used. For example if normal caustic is used and the chamber burette reads from 75 cc. to 100 cc. the acid should contain from 3.7 grams to 4.9 grams of H_2SO_4. The acid is added to CO_2 free distilled water, preferably in a porcelain casserole, 1 cc. of 1% phenolphthalein added and the titration made to a faint pink color with standard NaOH. It is advisable to titrate the acid using methyl orange if the presence of CO_2 is suspected in the water. Some chemists prefer the use of this indicator. It is a common practice to standardize the acidimetric and alkalimetric reagents in presence of methyl orange and phenolphthalein in separate titrations, recording factors for each.

The temperature of the titrating alkali should be noted and a correction of 0.032 cc. be made for each degree deviation from the temperature at which the reagent was standardized. For each 1° C. that the temperature is above that at standardization subtract this correction, and add this for each degree the temperature is below that at standardization.

(*cc.* titration $\times H_2SO_4$ value per cc. $\times 100$) ÷ wt. of sample = % H_2SO_4.

Determination of Impurities in Sulphuric Acid
Determination of Residue on Heating

50 to 100 grams of the acid are weighed into a platinum or silica dish and the acid evaporated (Hood) by heating gently over a direct flame. When no more fumes evolve, the dish is cooled and weighed. The increased weight of the dish is due to the residue, composed of substances not volatile at red heat and generally contains iron oxide. Chamber acid may have all of the substances occurring in sulphur ores present in this residue.

Determination of Lead

Minute Amounts. Determine by means of the colorimeter according to the procedure described on page 281, Vol. I.

High Lead Contamination. Larger amounts of lead sulphate may be determined gravimetrically. The lead may be extracted from the residue, obtained on evaporation of the acid and heating, by extracting with ammonium acetate according to the standard procedure, and lead precipitated from the extract made acid with acetic by addition of a small excess of $K_2Cr_2O_7$ solution. See method on page 274, Vol. I.

If preferred, lead may be determined as follows: 100 grams of the acid are diluted with an equal volume of distilled water and the solution stirred and cooled. Twice the volume of alcohol is added, the lead sulphate allowed to settle for two hours or more and the precipitate filtered on a Gooch crucible the residue washed with alcohol, dried and ignited at dull red heat and weighed as $PbSO_4$. If contamination of the lead sulphate is suspected, this residue may be extracted with ammonium acetate and lead precipitated from the extract as $PbCrO_4$ according to the regular procedure.

$$PbCrO_4 \times .641 = Pb. \qquad PbSO_4 \times .6331 = Pb.$$

[1] Certain details of procedure are published by courtesy of the General Chemical Company.

Determination of Iron

Traces of Iron. The colorimetric procedure is used, iron being determined by color comparison of the thiocyanate with standards. See procedure on page 258, Vol. I. Five grams of the acid are added to 10 cc. of water in a small beaker and the solution heated to dissolve any iron in suspension. The cooled acid is poured into a 100 cc. Nessler tube with rinsing of the beaker. A few drops of $N/10$ $KMnO_4$ are added in amount sufficient to obtain a faint pink color, then 10 cc. of a 10% solution of NH_4CNS and the solution made up to 100 cc. Comparison is now made as follows:

The standard is prepared by treating 5 cc. of iron-free sulphuric acid in exactly the same manner as the tested sample, in a separate Nessler tube. Standard iron solution is run in, stirring the solution with a glass plunger, until the color matches that of the sample. It is advisable to make the standard solution to contain 0.00005 g. Fe per 1 cc. Then each cc. will represent 0.001% Fe.

High Iron. If 0.02% of iron or over is present dilute 25 to 50 grams of the acid with distilled water. Add a few crystals of $KClO_3$ and boil. Cool and add a slight excess of NH_4OH. When the iron hydroxide has settled, filter and wash with hot water. Dissolve the precipitate with HCl (1 : 1) catching the solution in a casserole. Wash the iron out of the paper. Heat the combined filtrate to boiling and titrate with standard $SnCl_2$ solution. See page 257, Vol. I.

If antimony or arsenic are present the solution turns dark during the titration. If this occurs treat a fresh sample, diluted, with H_2S to remove As and Sb, and determine iron in the filtrate from the sulphides.

Determination of Arsenic

Traces of Arsenic. Amounts less than .00005%. Take 50 grams or more of the acid and distill off the arsenic as $AsCl_3$ according to the distillation method given on page 37. Determine arsenic in the distillate by the Gutzeit method. See page 46, Vol. I.

Amounts less than .005% may be determined directly by the Gutzeit method. When the arsenic is greater than 0.05% it may be determined by reducing the arsenic with tartaric acid and titrating with standard iodine solution, after neutralizing the acid with ammonia and adding sodium bicarbonate. 25–50 grams of the acid are taken and placed in a Kjeldahl flask and $\frac{1}{2}$ gram of tartaric acid added together with 2 grams of fused potassium bisulphate. The acid is heated over the direct flame until the color, first becoming dark, changes to a straw color. Fuming will cause loss of arsenic and should be avoided. The acid is washed into a beaker with 250 cc. of water, then neutralized with NH_4OH, and $NaHCO_3$ added. The titration with iodine is made in presence of starch. The end point is a blue color.

If antimony is present a separation of the arsenic must be made by distillation. 1 cc. $N/10$ $I = .003748$ g. As or .004948 g. As_2O_3. $As_2O_3 \times 1.11616 = As_2O_5$.

Determination of Antimony

The arsenic is first removed by distillation as $AsCl_3$ (page 37, Vol. I). The antimony is now distilled by adding 20 grams of zinc dissolved in 20 grams of concentrated HCl. The antimony in the distillate is determined by the modified Gutzeit method given in the chapter on Antimony, Vol. I, page 29.

Determination of Zinc

25 to 50 cc. of the acid are evaporated to dryness in a silica dish. The residue is treated with a strong solution of NH_4Cl and NH_4OH solution. After filtering off the ferric hydroxide, the filtrate containing the zinc is neutralized with H_2SO_4 and 10 cc. added in excess (sp. gr. $H_2SO_4 = 1.84$). Potassium ferrocyanide is now added in such amount that the solution will contain about 2.5 per cent. Compare the turbidity with standards.

With larger amounts of zinc the zinc is determined by titrating with standard potassium ferrocyanide. See chapter on Zinc, Vol. I.

The zinc may be determined gravimetrically on a 200-gram sample. The acid is fumed off until only 2–5 cc. remains in the dish. Water is added, the solution neutralized with ammonia, sufficient dilute H_2SO_4 added to make a 2.5 per cent free acid. Copper, lead, etc., are removed as sulphides by gassing with H_2S. Zinc is determined in the filtrate, after oxidation of the iron with bromine and removing it by adding NH_4OH and NH_4Cl. Zinc is precipitated as ZnS from the filtrate made acid (2% free acid) with formic acid, by H_2S. The washed sulphide is ignited and weighed as ZnO. $ZnO \times .8034 = Zn$.

Copper. This is determined colorimetrically. 25–50 cc. of the acid are evaporated to dryness, the residue taken up with 100 cc. of water 2 cc. HCl (sp.gr. 1.19) added and copper precipitated with H_2S. The washed precipitate is dissolved in HNO_3 and the solution made ammoniacal with ammonia. The color is now matched with standards containing known amounts of copper.

Determination of Selenium

Traces. 10 cc. of the acid diluted with an equal volume of water are placed in a test tube and 4 or 5 drops of 1% KI solution added. Heat to boiling to expel free iodine. The brick red color is compared with standards containing known amounts of selenium made up in the same way as the sample. If sufficient selenium is present this is thrown down as a brick red finely divided precipitate.

Standard selenium solution is prepared by dissolving .1 g. pure Se in 5 cc. HNO_3 and 10 cc. HCl. The solution is evaporated to dryness, then taken up with water and a little dilute H_2SO_4 and made up to 1000 cc. 1 cc. = .0001 g. Se.

Larger Amounts. 500 grams of the acid is diluted by pouring into a liter of water, 100 cc. strong HCl added and the solution saturated with SO_2. The selenium is allowed to settle 15 to 20 hours, then filtered through a fine fibre filter. The precipitate is dissolved by placing the filter and precipitate in sulphuric acid nitric acid mixture 5 cc. $H_2SO_4 + 50$ cc. HNO_3. The solution is evaporated to fumes, adding more HNO_3 if the solution is dark, and again evaporated to expel HNO_3. After diluting with water and filtering, the filtrate is made up to about 100 cc. and gassed boiling hot with H_2S. The precipitated selenium is settled, filtered into a Gooch, washed with water, then alcohol and ether and dried with a current of warm air to constant weight.

Sulphur Dioxide Determination in Sulphuric Acid. 1–10 cc. of N/10 iodine solution are run into 200 cc. of water, starch solution is added and the acid to be tested is allowed to flow from a burette into this reagent, until the blue color disappears.

$$1 \text{ cc. } N/10 \text{ iodine} = .0032 \text{ g. } SO_2.$$

SULPHURIC ACID

Hydrochloric Acid Determination in Sulphuric Acid. 50 to 100 cc. of the acid is diluted to about 200 cc. by running the acid into chlorine-free water 10 cc. of 1% silver nitrate solution is added and the turbidity compared against a standard made by adding standard sodium chloride solution from a burette into a solution containing an equal amount of sulphuric acid (free from chloride) diluted with water and containing silver nitrate as in case of the sample When the turbidity is the same as the sample the number of cc. of NaCl solution are noted. The turbidity is best seen by placing the two solutions side by side on a black paper. Standard chloride solution contains .16 g. NaCl per liter. 1 cc. = .0001 g. HCl.

If considerable hydrochloric acid is present it may be determined by Volhard's method given on page 149, Vol. I. The sample of acid is diluted to about 20% strength. A measured excess of N/10 $AgNO_3$ added and the excess titrated with N/10 NH_4CNS solution in presence of ferric ammonium alum.

$$1 \text{ cc. } N/10 \text{ } AgNO_3 = .003647 \text{ g. HCl.}$$

Determination of Nitric Acid

Traces. In absence of selenium traces of HNO_3 may be determined colorimetrically. To 100 cc. of the acid $\frac{1}{2}$ cc. saturated solution of $FeSO_4$ is added. Comparison is made in a Nessler tube with a standard by adding to 100 cc. H_2SO_4, $\frac{1}{2}$ cc. $FeSO_4$ solution and running in standard HNO_3 until the color matches, the solution being stirred with a plunger during the addition. Standard HNO_3 solution should contain .0001 g. HNO_3 per cc.

Larger Amounts. See method on page 1024.

Determination of Fluorine. This is determined by the etch test described in Vol. I, page 224. The acid should not contain over 10% H_2O. Strengthen with oleum if necessary.

THE ANALYSES OF OLEUM OR FUMING SULPHURIC ACID AND OF MIXED ACID

The analyses of fuming sulphuric acid and mixed acid are placed under one general scheme as the procedure for oleum is included in that of mixed acid. The term oleum is given to strong sulphuric acid containing free SO_3, the combined

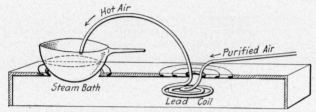

FIG. 202.—Method for Rapid Evaporation of Liquids.

water in the product decreasing (along with sulphuric acid) with the increase of free SO_3 or sulphuric anhydride.   Mixed acid is the technical name for the mixture of strong sulphuric acid and nitric acid or of oleum and nitric anhydride, the product being commonly used in nitrating glycerine, cotton and other materials. The analysis includes the determinations of H_2SO_4, HNO_3, N_2O_5, N_2O_3 and in the case of oleum, the determination of SO_3.   In the presence of the latter, HNO_3 is assumed to lose its combined water according to the reaction:

$$2HNO_3 + SO_3 = H_2SO_4 + N_2O_5$$

In absence of nitric acid SO_2 may be present.   It is assumed that if HNO_3 is present the SO_2 is oxidized to SO_3 with formation of H_2SO_4 and the anhydrides SO_3 and N_2O_3 according to the reaction.

$$N_2O_5 + H_2O + 2SO_2 = N_2O_3 + SO_3 + H_2SO_4$$

Some chemists prefer to express the reaction:

$$2HNO_3 + SO_2 = H_2SO_4 + N_2O_4.$$

The analysis is carried out by three titrations—(a) determination of total acidity, (b) determination of sulphuric acid including SO_3 free in case of oleum, (c) determination of lower oxides.

For economy of time the following order should be observed: The sample for the determination of sulphuric acid and free SO_3 (oleum) should be weighed, diluted with water according to the detailed procedure and placed on the steam bath for evaporation. During the evaporation the titration for total acidity of the sample and the titration for the lower oxides are made and finally that of oleum on the evaporated sample.

Special Reagents.

Normal Sodium Hydroxide. One cc. $= 0.04904$ gram H_2SO_4.

Tenth Normal Potassium Permanganate. 3.16 grams $KMnO_4$ per liter. Standardized against $N/10$ solution of Sorensen's Sodium Oxalate. (See Preparation of Standard Reagents.) One cc. $= 0.0019$ gram N_2O_3, or 0.002351 gram HNO_2.

Procedure. Total Acids

The sample is accurately weighed by one of the procedures recommended for strong acids. The Dely or Blay-Burkhard tubes are best for this purpose. Such a weight being taken as will require a titration between 75 and 100 cc., e.g., containing an equivalent of 3.6 5 grams to 4. grams H_2SO_4. The acid is now run under cold CO_2 free water according to directions on pages 1011 and 1012, and the acid titrated with $N/1$ solution of NaOH.

One cc. NaOH $= 0.04904$ g. H_2SO_4. Calculate to per cent $\dfrac{\text{cc. NaOH} \times .04904 \times 100}{\text{Weight of Acid Taken}}$.

Lower Oxides

Ten cc. of the sample, weighed in a pipette with capillary delivery tip, are cautiously run into about 400 cc. of cold water, keeping the delivery tip well under the water and in rapid motion to prevent overheating through local action. The mixture is titrated with $N/10$ $KMnO_4$ until a pink tint is obtained that does not fade in three minutes.

1 cc. $N/10$ $KMnO_4 = 0.0019$ g. N_2O_3.   (N_2O_3 to N_2O_4 factor $= 2.42$.)

1 cc. $N/10$ $KMnO_4 = 0.0046$ g. N_2O_4.

1 cc. $N/10$ $KMnO_4 = 0.00235$ g. HNO_2.   Equivalent $H_2SO_4 = 0.0049043$ g. per cc.

1 cc. $N/10$ $KMnO_4 = 0.0032035$ g. SO_2.

1 cc. $N/10$ $KMnO_4 = 0.0041043$ g. H_2SO_3.

NOTE. With exactly $N/10$ $KMnO_4$ on a 19-gram sample 1 cc. $= 0.01\%$ N_2O_3.

Sulphuric Acid and Free SO_3

The sample is weighed in a Dely tube and run under cold water, as in case of total acids, using in this case about 45 to 50 cc. of water in a 4-in. casserole. The solution is evaporated on the steam bath to expel the volatile acids, lower oxides and nitric. The evaporation is hastened by blowing a current of hot, dry, pure air over the sample, see Fig. 202. Instead of a casserole, a shallow glass cell, 3 inches in diameter and $1\frac{1}{2}$ inches deep may be used. The air current in is case is unnecessary. About 5 cc. of water are added and this again evaporated off. The acid thus obtained is $H_2SO_4+SO_3$.

The acid is taken up with water and titrated with standard caustic, using CO_2 ee water and phenolphthalein indicator.

One cc. N/1 NaOH $=0.004904$ gram H_2SO_4.

Nitric Acid

This may be obtained from the above determinations according to calculations llowing. It may be obtained by direct titration with standard ferrous sulphate, y running a weighed amount of mixed acid into 100 cc. of cold sulphuric acid and trating to a yellowish red tint. For the detailed procedure see Nitric Acid, age 515.

Calculation of Results.

A. Nitric Acid and SO_2 being Absent.

The total acidity is calculated to SO_3. Reference is made to the table for leum from which the per cent H_2SO_4 and free SO_3 are obtained.

Example. Suppose the total acidity in terms of SO_3 was found to be 84.2. he acid contains 86% H_2SO_4 and 14% free SO_3.

B. Nitric Acid Absent, SO_2 is Present in the Mixture.

Total SO_3. From total acidity as SO_3 subtract $SO_2\times1.25$ (i.e., equivalent O_3).

Combined water. $100-(total\ SO_3+SO_2)=H_2O$.
Combined SO_3. $H_2O\times4.4445=SO_3$ equivalent or combined SO_3.
Free SO_3. Total SO_3-combined $SO_3=$free SO_3.
Sulphuric acid. Combined SO_3+H_2O.
Example. If SO_2 was found to be 2% and the total acidity in terms of SO_4 $=83.5\%$

$$Total\ SO_3=83.5-(2\times1.25)=81\%.$$

$$Water=100-(81+2)=17\%. \qquad Report$$

Combined $SO_3=17\times4.4445=75.56\%.$ $\qquad$ Sulphuric acid $=92.56\%.$

Free $SO_3=81-75.56=5.44\%.$ $\qquad$ Free $SO_3=5.44.$

Sulphuric acid $=75.56+17=92.56\%.$ $\qquad$ $SO_2=2.00.$ Total 100.

C. Nitric Acid Present and SO_2 Absent.

Nitric acid in presence of free SO_3 is assumed to be the anhydride N_2O_5.

N_2O_5. From the total acidity is subtracted the acidity after evaporation, both being calculated to equivalent SO_3. The difference multiplied by $1.349=$per cent N_2O_5.

H_2O. Total SO_3 (after evaporation)$+N_2O_5$ subtracted from $100=H_2O$.
Combined SO_3. $H_2O\times4.4445=SO_3$ equivalent to H_2O.
Free SO_3. Combined SO_3 subtracted from total $SO_3=$free SO_3.
Sulphuric acid. Combined $SO_3+H_2O=H_2SO_4$.

Example. If total acidity$=84\%$ in terms of SO_3 and the total SO_3 (after evaporation)$=82\%$, then the difference $2\times1.349=2.698\%$ N_2O_5.

43

Water $= 100 - (82 + 2.698) = 15.302\%$.

Combined $SO_3 = 15.302 \times 4.4445 = 68.01\%$.

Free $SO_3 = 82 - 68.01 = 13.99\%$.

$H_2SO_4 = 68.01 + 15.302 = 83.312\%$.

Report

$H_2SO_4 = 83.312\%$.

Free $SO_3 = 13.980\%$.

$N_2O_5 = 2.698\%$.

Total 100.

D. N_2O_5 Required to be Reported as HNO_3, 96%.[1]

HNO_3, $96\% = SO_3$ equivalent (acid expelled by evaporation)$\times 1.64$. 10 $-$per cent HNO_3 $(96\%) = $ Oleum.   Total SO_3 in oleum $= \dfrac{100 \times \text{total } SO_3}{\text{per cent oleum}}$.

Reference to the oleum table will give the per cent free SO_3 in the oleum.

Example. Suppose total acidity in terms of $SO_3 = 84\%$ and the SO_3 after evaporation $= 82\%$, then HNO_3, $96\% = $ the difference $= 2 \times 1.64 = 3.28\%$ HNO (96%).

Oleum $= 100 - 3.28 = 96.72\%$.

Total SO_3 in oleum $= 100 \times 82$ divided by $96.72 = 84.78$.

From the oleum table 84.78 gives 17.10% free SO_3.

Report

Nitric acid, $96\% = 3.28\%$

Oleum $\qquad = 96.72\%$

Free $SO_3 \qquad = 17.10\%$

Total $SO_3 \qquad = 84.78\%$

The nitric acid and oleum make a total of 100.

[1] This is the usual strength of the commercial concentrated acid.

Formulæ for Diluting or Strengthening Solutions.

To dilute a solution with water:

$$(a)\ \frac{DZ}{A}=X;\qquad Y=Z-X;\qquad \text{or}\qquad (b)\ \frac{A-DX}{D}=Y.$$

To dilute a strong with a weaker liquid:

$$(a)\ \frac{A-DZ}{A-B}=Y;\qquad X-Z=Y;\qquad \text{or}\qquad (b)\ \frac{A-DX}{D-B}=Y.$$

To strengthen a weak with a stronger liquid:

$$(a)\ \frac{D-AZ}{C-A}=X;\qquad Y=Z-X;\qquad \text{or}\qquad (b)\ \frac{D-AY}{C-D}=X.$$

A = actual concentration of the solution that is to be corrected;
B = concentration of the diluting solution;
C = concentration of the strengthening solution;
D = desired concentration;
X = amount of the stronger solution to be added, taken or prepared;
Y = amount of weaker solution to be added or taken;
Z = amount of solution desired or given.

All data are in terms of weight of the constituents.

Dilution of Solutions

If a = per cent of solution desired, b = specific gravity of solution to be diluted and c its percentage then

Volume or ratio of the strong solution is d

$$\frac{a}{b \times \frac{1}{100}\, c} = d.$$

Volume or ratio of water required

$$100 - \frac{a}{c \div 100} \text{ or } 100 - b \times d.$$

Example. To make 75% sulphuric acid from 87% solution having a specific gravity of 1.8.

Substituting in above formula $\dfrac{75}{1.8 \times 0.87}$ = cc. or liters or cubic feet, etc.

of acid to be taken, i.e. ratio is 47.9 and $100 - \dfrac{75}{0.87}$ = cc. or liters or cubic feet of water required for dilution, i.e. ratio is 13.79.

47.9 cc. of the strong acid diluted with 13.79 cc. of water will make the acid 75% strength.

It is evident that the ratio being known large volumes of solution may be made so that the procedure is applicable for factory use.

SULPHURIC ACID

By W. C. Ferguson and H. P. Talbot

Degrees Baumé.	Specific Gravity $\frac{60°}{60°}$ F.	Degrees Twaddell.	Per Cent H_2SO_4.	Weight of 1 Cu. Ft. in Lbs. Av.	Per Cent O. V.*	Pounds O. V. in 1 Cubic Foot.
0	1.0000	0.0	0.00	62.37	0.00	0.00
1	1.0069	1.4	1.02	62.80	1.09	0.68
2	1.0140	2.8	2.08	63.24	2.23	1.41
3	1.0211	4.2	3.13	63.69	3.36	2.14
4	1.0284	5.7	4.21	64.14	4.52	2.90
5	1.0357	7.1	5.28	64.60	5.67	3.66
6	1.0432	8.6	6.37	65.06	6.84	4.45
7	1.0507	10.1	7.45	65.53	7.99	5.24
8	1.0584	11.7	8.55	66.01	9.17	6.06
9	1.0662	13.2	9.66	66.50	10.37	6.89
10	1.0741	14.8	10.77	66.99	11.56	7.74
11	1.0821	16.4	11.89	67.49	12.76	8.61
12	1.0902	18.0	13.01	68.00	13.96	9.49
13	1.0985	19.7	14.13	68.51	15.16	10.39
14	1.1069	21.4	15.25	69.04	16.36	11.30
15	1.1154	23.1	16.38	69.57	17.58	12.23
16	1.1240	24.8	17.53	70.10	18.81	13.19
17	1.1328	26.6	18.71	70.65	20.08	14.18
18	1.1417	28.3	19.89	71.21	21.34	15.20
19	1.1508	30.2	21.07	71.78	22.61	16.23
20	1.1600	32.0	22.25	72.35	23.87	17.27
21	1.1694	33.9	23.43	72.94	25.14	18.34
22	1.1789	35.8	24.61	73.53	26.41	19.42
23	1.1885	37.7	25.81	74.13	27.69	20.53
24	1.1983	39.7	27.03	74.74	29.00	21.68

Sp. Gr. determinations were made at 60° F., compared with water at 60° F. From the Sp. Grs., the corresponding degrees Baumé were calculated by the following formula: Baumé = 145 − 145/Sp. Gr.

Baumé Hydrometers for use with this table must be graduated by the above formula, which formula should always be printed on the scale.

* 66° Baumé = Sp. Gr. 1.8354 = Oil of Vitriol (O. V.).

1 cu. ft. water at 60° F. weighs 62.37 lbs. av.

Atomic weights from F. W. Clarke's table of 1901. O = **16**.

H_2SO_4 = 100 per cent.

	% H_2SO_4		% O. V.		%60°
O. V.	= 93.19	=	100.00	=	119.98
60°	= 77.67	=	83.35	=	100.00
50°	= 62.18	=	66.72	=	80.06

SULPHURIC ACID (Continued)

APPROXIMATE BOILING POINTS

Degrees Baumé.	* Freezing (Melting) Point. F.
0	32.0
1	31.2
2	30.5
3	29.8
4	28.9
5	28.1
6	27.2
7	26.3
8	25.1
9	24.0
10	22.8
11	21.5
12	20 0
13	18.3
14	16.6
15	14.7
16	12.6
17	10.2
18	7.7
19	4.8
20	+ 1.6
21	− 1.8
22	− 6.0
23	−11
24	−16

APPROXIMATE BOILING POINTS

50° B,	295° F.
60° "	386° "
61° "	400° "
62° "	415° "
63° "	432° "
64° "	451° "
65° "	485° "
66° "	538° "

FIXED POINTS

Specific Gravity.	Per Cent H₂SO₄.	Specific Gravity.	Per Cent H₂SO₄.
1.0000	.00	1.5281	62.34
1.0048	.71	1.5440	63.79
1.0347	5.14	1.5748	66.51
1.0649	9.48	1.6272	71.00
1.0992	14.22	1.6679	74.46
1.1353	19.04	1.7044	77.54
1.1736	23.94	1.7258	79.40
1.2105	28.55	1.7472	81.32
1.2513	33.49	1.7700	83.47
1.2951	38.64	1.7959	86.36
1.3441	44.15	1.8117	88.53
1.3947	49.52	1.8194	89.75
1.4307	53.17	1.8275	91.32
1.4667	56.68	1.8354	93.19
1.4822	58.14		

Acids stronger than 66° Bé. should have their percentage compositions determined by chemical analysis.

* Calculated from Pickering's results, Jour. of Lon. Ch. Soc., vol. 57, p. 363.

AUTHORITIES — W. C. FERGUSON; H. P. TALBOT.

This table has been approved and adopted as a standard by the Manufacturing Chemists' Association of the United States.

W. H. BOWER,
HENRY HOWARD,
JAS. L. MORGAN,
ARTHUR WYMAN,
A. G. ROSENGARTEN,

New York, June 23, 1904.   *Executive Committee.*

SULPHURIC ACID (Continued)

Degrees Baumé.	Specific Gravity $\frac{60°}{60°}$ F.	Degrees Twaddell.	Per Cent H_2SO_4.	Weight of 1 Cu. Ft. in Lbs. Av.	Per Cent O. V.	Pounds O. V. in 1 Cubic Foot.
25	1.2083	41.7	28.28	75.36	30.34	22.87
26	1.2185	43.7	29.53	76.00	31.69	24.08
27	1.2288	45.8	30.79	76.64	33.04	25.32
28	1.2393	47.9	32.05	77.30	34.39	26.58
29	1.2500	50.0	33.33	77.96	35.76	27.88
30	1.2609	52.2	34.63	78.64	37.16	29.22
31	1.2719	54.4	35.93	79.33	38.55	30.58
32	1.2832	56.6	37.26	80.03	39.98	32.00
33	1.2946	58.9	38.58	80.74	41.40	33.42
34	1.3063	61.3	39.92	81.47	42.83	34.90
35	1.3182	63.6	41.27	82.22	44.28	36.41
36	1.3303	66.1	42.63	82.97	45.74	37.95
37	1.3426	68.5	43.99	83.74	47.20	39.53
38	1.3551	71.0	45.35	84.52	48.66	41.13
39	1.3679	73.6	46.72	85.32	50.13	42.77
40	1.3810	76.2	48.10	86.13	51.61	44.45
41	1.3942	78.8	49.47	86.96	53.08	46.16
42	1.4078	81.6	50.87	87.80	54.58	47.92
43	1.4216	84.3	52.26	88.67	56.07	49.72
44	1.4356	87.1	53.66	89.54	57.58	51.56
45	1.4500	90.0	55.07	90.44	59.09	53.44
46	1.4646	92.9	56.48	91.35	60.60	55.36
47	1.4796	95.9	57.90	92.28	62.13	57.33
48	1.4948	99.0	59.32	93.23	63.65	59.34
49	1.5104	102.1	60.75	94.20	65.18	61.40
50	1.5263	105.3	62.18	95.20	66.72	63.52
51	1.5426	108.5	63.66	96.21	68.31	65.72
52	1.5591	111.8	65.13	97.24	69.89	67.96
53	1.5761	115.2	66.63	98.30	71.50	70.28
54	1.5934	118.7	68.13	99.38	73.11	72.66
55	1.6111	122.2	69.65	100.48	74.74	75.10
56	1.6292	125.8	71.17	101.61	76.37	77.60
57	1.6477	129.5	72.75	102.77	78.07	80.23
58	1.6667	133.3	74.36	103.95	79.79	82.95
59	1.6860	137.2	75.99	105.16	81.54	85.75

SULPHURIC ACID (Continued)

Degrees Baumé.	* Freezing (Melting) Point. °F.				
25	−23	ALLOWANCE FOR TEMPERATURE			
26	−30	At 10° Bé. .029° Bé. or .00023 Sp. Gr. = 1° F.			
27	−39	" 20° " .036° " .00034 " = 1° "			
28	−49	" 30° " .035° " .00039 " = 1° "			
29	−61	" 40° " .031° " .00041 " = 1° "			
		" 50° " .028° " .00045 " = 1° "			
30	−74	" 60° " .026° " .00053 " = 1° "			
31	−82	" 63° " .026° " .00057 " = 1° "			
32	−96	" 66° " .0235° " .00054 " = 1° "			
33	−97				
34	−91				
35	−81				
36	−70	Per Cent 60° Baumé.	Pounds 60° Baumé in 1 Cubic Foot.	Per Cent 50° Baumé.	Pounds 50° Baumé in 1 Cubic Foot.
37	−60				
38	−53				
39	−47				
40	−41	61.93	53.34	77.36	66.63
41	−35	63.69	55.39	79.56	69.19
42	−31	65.50	57.50	81.81	71.83
43	−27	67.28	59.66	84.05	74.53
44	−23	69.09	61.86	86.30	77.27
45	−20	70.90	64.12	88.56	80.10
46	−14	72.72	66.43	90.83	82.98
47	−15	74.55	68.79	93.12	85.93
48	−18	76.37	71.20	95.40	88.94
49	−22	78.22	73.68	97.70	92.03
50	−27	80.06	76.21	100.00	95.20
51	−33	81.96	78.85	102.38	98.50
52	−39	83.86	81.54	104.74	101.85
53	−49	85.79	84.33	107.15	105.33
54	−59	87.72	87.17	109.57	108.89
55	.. ⎫	89.67	90.10	112.01	112.55
56	.. ⎪ Below 40	91.63	93.11	114.46	116.30
57	.. ⎬	93.67	96.26	117.00	120.24
58	.. ⎪	95.74	99.52	119.59	124.31
59	− 7 ⎭	97.84	102.89	122.21	128.52

SULPHURIC ACID (Continued)

Degrees Baumé.	Specific Gravity 60° F. / 60°	Degrees Twaddell.	Per Cent H₂SO₄.	Weight of 1 Cu. Ft. in Lbs. Av.	Per Cent O. V.	Pounds O. V in 1 Cubic Foo
60	1.7059	141.2	77.67	106.40	83.35	88.68
61	1.7262	145.2	79.43	107.66	85.23	91.76
62	1.7470	149.4	81.30	108.96	87.24	95.06
63	1.7683	153.7	83.34	110.29	89.43	98.63
64	1.7901	158.0	85.66	111.65	91.92	102.63
64¼	1.7957	159.1	86.33	112.00	92.64	103.75
64½	1.8012	160.2	87.04	112.34	93.40	104.93
64¾	1.8068	161.4	87.81	112.69	94.23	106.19
65	1.8125	162.5	88.65	113.05	95.13	107.54
65¼	1.8182	163.6	89.55	113.40	96.10	108.97
65½	1.8239	164.8	90.60	113.76	97.22	110.60
65¾	1.8297	165.9	91.80	114.12	98.51	112.42
66	1.8354	167.1	93.19	114.47	100.00	114.47

Degrees Baumé.	Freezing (Melting) Point.	Per Cent 60° Baumé.	Pounds 60° Baumé in Cubic Foot.	Per Cent 50° Baumé.	Pounds 50° Baumé in Cubic Foot.
60	+12.6	100.00	106.40	124.91	132.91
61	27.3	102.27	110.10	127.74	137.52
62	39.1	104.67	114.05	130.75	142.47
63	46.1	107.30	118.34	134.03	147.82
64	46.4	110.29	123.14	137.76	153.81
64¼	43.6	111.15	124.49	138.84	155.50
64½	41.1	112.06	125.89	139.98	157.25
64¾	37.9	113.05	127.40	141.22	159.14
65	33.1	114.14	129.03	142.57	161.17
65¼	24.6	115.30	130.75	144.02	163.32
65½	13.4	116.65	132.70	145.71	165.76
65¾	− 1	118.19	134.88	147.63	168.48
66	−29	119.98	137.34	149.87	171.56

XI.—SULPHURIC ACID TABLE
94–100% H₂SO₄
By H. B. Bishop

Bé.	Sp. Gr. at 60° F.	Per Cent. H₂SO₄	Wt. 1 Cu. Ft.	Allowance for Temperature.
66	1.8354	93.19	114.47	At 94% .00054 sp.gr. = 1° F.
66.12	1.8381	94.00	114.64	" 96 .0053 " = 1° F.
66.23	1.8407	95.00	114.80	" 97.5 .00052 " = 1° F.
66.31	1.8427	96.00	114.93	" 100 .00052 " = 1° F.
66.36	1.8437	97.00	114.99	
66.36	1.8439	97.50	114.99	
66.36	1.8437	98.00	114.99	
66.30	1.8424	99.00	114.91	
66.16	1.8391	100.00	114.70	

FUMING SULPHURIC ACID EQUIVALENTS

Total SO₃	Equivalent H₂SO₄	Per Cent H₂SO₄	Per Cent Free SO₃	Total SO₃	Equivalent H₂SO₄	Per Cent H₂SO₄	Per Cent Free SO₃
81.63	100.00	100	0	90.82	111.25	50	50
81.82	100.23	99	1	91.00	111.48	49	51
82.00	100.45	98	2	91.18	111.70	48	52
82.18	100.67	97	3	91.37	111.93	47	53
82.37	100.90	96	4	91.55	112.15	46	54
82.55	101.13	95	5	91.73	112.37	45	55
82.73	101.35	94	6	91.92	112.60	44	56
82.92	101.58	93	7	92.10	112.82	43	57
83.10	101.80	92	8	92.29	113.05	42	58
83.29	102.03	91	9	92.47	113.28	41	59
83.47	102.25	90	11	92.65	113.50	40	60
83.65	102.47	89	11	92.84	113.73	39	61
83.84	102.70	88	12	93.02	113.95	38	62
84.02	102.92	87	13	93.20	114.17	37	63
84.20	103.15	86	14	93.39	114.40	36	64
84.39	103.38	85	15	93.57	114.62	35	65
84.57	103.60	84	16	93.76	114.85	34	66
84.75	103.82	83	17	93.94	115.08	33	67
84.94	104.05	82	18	94.12	115.30	32	68
85.12	104.27	81	19	94.31	115.53	31	69
85.31	104.50	80	20	94.49	115.75	30	70
85.49	104.73	79	21	94.67	115.97	29	71
85.67	104.95	78	22	94.86	116.20	28	72
85.86	105.18	77	23	95.04	116.42	27	73
86.04	105.40	76	24	95.22	116.65	26	74
86.22	105.62	75	25	95.41	116.88	25	75
86.41	105.85	74	26	95.59	117.10	24	76
86.59	106.07	73	27	95.78	117.33	23	77
86.78	106.30	72	28	95.96	117.55	22	78
86.96	106.53	71	29	96.14	117.77	21	79
87.14	106.75	70	30	96.33	118.00	20	80
87.33	106.98	69	31	96.51	118.22	19	81
87.51	107.20	68	32	96.69	118.45	18	82
87.69	107.42	67	33	96.88	118.68	17	83
87.88	107.65	66	34	97.06	118.90	16	84
88.06	107.87	65	35	97.25	119.13	15	85
88.24	108.10	64	36	97.43	119.35	14	86
88.43	108.33	63	37	97.61	119.57	13	87
88.61	108.55	62	38	97.80	119.80	12	88
88.80	108.78	61	39	97.98	120.03	11	89
88.98	109.00	60	40	98.16	120.25	10	90
89.16	109.22	59	41	98.35	120.48	9	91
89.35	109.45	58	42	98.53	120.70	8	92
89.53	109.67	57	43	98.71	120.92	7	93
89.71	109.90	56	44	98.90	121.15	6	94
89.90	110.13	55	45	99.08	121.37	5	95
90.08	110.35	54	46	99.27	121.60	4	96
90.27	110.58	53	47	99.45	121.83	3	97
90.45	110.80	52	48	99.63	122.05	2	98
90.63	111.02	51	49	99.82	122.28	1	99
				100.00	122.50	0	100

Compiled from the table by H. B. Bishop, Van Nostrand's Chemical Annual, 1913.

METHOD OF ANALYSIS OF CHLOROSULPHONIC ACID

Chlorosulphonic acid, $SO_3 \cdot HCl$, decomposes to H_2SO_4 and HCl on addition of water, the reaction being violent. Considerable care must be exercised to prevent loss of acid during dilution with water for examination of the product. The following method of analysis has been found satisfactory:

Total Acidity. Three to four grams of the chlorosulphonic acid are weighed in a Déli tube or small glass bulb. About 25 cc. of distilled (neutral) water and about 10 cc. less NaOH (normal strength) than is necessary to neutralize the sample (i.e., $\dfrac{\text{weight sample}}{0.04001} - 10 = \text{cc.}$ NaOH to be taken) are placed in a heavy wall glass bottle (250–300 cc. capacity). If the sample is weighed in a Déli tube it is run into the NaOH solution according to the procedure described on page 506. If the bulb is used, the bottle, with the sample inserted, is stoppered, wrapped in a towel and shaken vigorously until the bulb breaks and the acid mixes with the water and NaOH. The excess of acid is now titrated with N. NaOH, using phenolphthalein or methyl red indicator. The total acidity is calculated to SO_3 and recorded as per cent SO_3.

Titration of Chloride. The NaCl formed is titrated with $N/3$ $AgNO_3$ solution, using K_2CrO_4 indicator. The cc. of the reagent are calculated to the equivalent HCl. Since NaOH is apt to contain NaCl, the blank is subtracted to obtain the true HCl equivalent in the sample. The per cent HCl is calculated.

The Composition of the Acid is now determined as follows:

(a) Total acid as per cent $SO_3 = a$.

(b) HCl obtained by titration of the neutralized solution (made faintly acid) with $N/3$ $AgNO_3$ (the HCl blank for the NaOH used in (a) having been subtracted) $= b$. The HCl is converted to its equivalent SO_3 by multiplying by $1.0978 = b'$.

(c) SO_3 (combided and free). The SO_3 equivalent of HCl obtained in b is subtracted from the total acidity as SO_3 of (a) is $a - b' = SO_3$ total.

(d) $100 - (\text{per cent } SO_3 + \text{per cent } HCl) = \text{per cent } H_2O$ in sample. This is combined with a portion of the SO_3 as H_2SO_4. Calculate to per cent H_2SO_4 by multiplying by 5.4444. Allowance must be made for impurities if present.[1]

(e) The SO_3 combined with H_2O is subtracted from the total SO_3 of (c). The result is the SO_3 of the chlorosulphonic acid and free SO_3 (if any).

By inspection it is possible to ascertain whether the product contains free SO_3 or free HCl since $SO_3 \cdot HCl$ are in the proportion 31.29 per cent HCl and 68.71 per cent SO_3, i.e., HCl : SO_3 :: 1 : 2.2.

If SO_3 is in excess. The HCl is calculated to $SO_3 \cdot HCl$ by multiplying by 3.1956, the result is the *per cent chlorosulphonic acid* in the sample.

Free SO_3 is obtained by subtracting per cent $SO_3 \cdot HCl$ + per cent H_2SO_4 from 100.

If HCl is in excess. The per cent SO_3 obtained in (e) is multiplied by 1.4555; the result is the *per cent chlorosulphonic acid*.

FreeHCl is obtained by subtracting per cent $SO_3 \cdot HCl$ + per cent H_2SO_4 from 100.

Results are reported as per cent $SO_3 \cdot HCl$, H_2SO_4, free SO_3 or free HCl.

Factors:

$HCl \times 1.0978 = SO_3$, $HCl \times 3.1956 = SO_3 \cdot HCl$ and $HCl \times 2.1959 = SO_3$ in SO_3HCl.

$SO_3 \times 0.8998 = HCl$, $SO_3 \times 1.4555 = SO_3 \cdot HCl$ and $SO_3 \times 0.4554 = HCl$ in SO_3HCl.

$H_2O \times 5.4444 = H_2SO_4$, $H_2SO_4 \times 0.1837 = H_2O$, $H_2SO_4 \times 0.7436 = HCl$.

$NaCl \times 0.6238 = HCl$, $SO_3 \cdot HCl = 31.29$ per cent HCl and 68.71 per cent SO_3.

---

[1] $(100 - \text{impurities non-titratable}) - (\%SO_3 + \%HCl) = \%H_2O$.

OLUMETRIC ESTIMATION OF FREE ACID IN PRESENCE OF IRON SALTS

The red precipitate formed when solutions containing iron are titrated with austic makes it difficult to detect the end-point of neutralization; the method suggested by C. A. Ahlum[1] takes advantage of the white compound formed by precipitating the iron as a phosphate and the fact that monosodium phosphate is neutral to methyl-orange indicator.

Reactions

$$Fe_2(SO_4)_3 + 2NaH_2PO_4 + x \text{ free acid} = 2FePO_4 + Na_2SO_4 + x \text{ free acid} + 2H_2SO_4,$$

r $2FeCl_3 + 2NaH_2PO_4 + x$ free acid $= 2FePO_4 + 2NaCl + x$ free acid $+ 4HCl$.

The acid equivalent to ferric iron is deducted from the total acid found, the xcess acid being due to the free acid in the solution.

Procedure. To the solution containing the iron and free acid is added an excess f C.P. solution of monosodium phosphate (neutral to methyl-orange), and then few drops of the indicator. The acidity of the solution is now determined by titration with standard caustic in the usual way, the solution being cold. From his titration the total free and combined acid are calculated.

Iron is now determined in a separate portion by titration with stannous chloride r dichromate.

Calculation.

A) $Fe_2O_3 \times 1.2285 = g. H_2SO_4$ (combined). $Fe_2O_3 \times 0.9135 = g. HCl$ (combined).

B)   One cc. N/5 NaOH $= .00981$ gram H_2SO_4 or $.00729$ gram HCl.

Total acid (B) minus combined acid (A) $= free acid$.

[1] C. A. Ahlum, The Analyst, **31**, 168, 1906.

ORGANIC ACIDS

Titrations of organic acids are made preferably with phenolphthalein. Methyl orange cannot be used. The water used for diluting the organic acid must be free of carbon dioxide.

ANALYSIS OF FORMIC ACID

Formic acid occurs in solutions of varying strength, *i.e.*, 30, 50, 75, 90% etc. The impurities that are frequently present are sulphuric and hydrochloric acid. If formic acid alone is present it may be determined by direct titration 1 cc. N/10 NaOH = 0.004602 gram formic acid. In presence of other acid the following method is recommended.

Procedure. About 10 grams of the sample weighed in a tared bottle (Blay-Burkhard form is convenient) is run into about 200 cc. of distilled water in a graduated flask of 500 cc. capacity and made to volume. 50 cc. of the diluted sample pipetted into an Erlenmeyer flask is made alkaline with Na_2CO solution. After warming a measured excess of N/10 $KMnO_4$ is added. Formic acid is oxidized to $H_2O + CO_2$ and a precipitate of MnO_2 is thrown down. 10 cc. of dilute H_2SO_4 are added and a measured volume of N/10 oxalic acid added until all of the precipitate has dissolved and the permanganate color has disappeared. The excess of oxalic acid is now titrated with N/10 permanganate reagent. From this the cc. $KMnO_4$ required by the formic acid is obtained.

$$1 \text{ cc. } N/10 \text{ } KMnO_4 = 0.002301 \text{ gram formic acid}$$

The equivalent cc. values of the $KMnO_4$ and $H_2C_2C_4$ should be obtained by titration.

Sulphuric Acid. This is conveniently determined on about 20 gram sample diluted to 200 cc. by precipitation with $BaCl_2$ according to the standard procedure.

$$BaSO_4 \times 0.4202 = H_2SO_4$$

Hydrochloric Acid. This may be determined on a 20 gram sample by precipitation with $AgNO_3$ in presence of 5 cc. conc. HNO_3, the sample having been diluted to about 200 cc.

$$AgCl \times 0.2545 = HCl$$

ANALYSIS OF ACETIC ANHYDRIDE—ACIDITY METHOD

Acetic anhydride $\begin{matrix} CH_3CO \\ CH_3CO \end{matrix}\!\!>\!\!O$ is a volatile, colorless liquid, possessing a characteristic sharp penetrating odor. The vapor is very irritating to the nose and eyes. The pure anhydride boils at 137° C. Mixed with water strong acetic anhydride settles out into a distinct layer very similar to carbon disulphide. It hydrolyzes slowly forming a solution of acetic acid. When below 0% in strength (the diluting liquid being acetic acid) the product mixes readily with water at ordinary temperatures (20° C.). Distinct separation from water takes place when the strength of the anhydride is over 55%, the product being added to the water dropwise. The separation becomes more decided with increase of the percentage of anhydride.

The analysis consists in titrating the acetic acid formed by the hydrolysis of the anhydride. Since the product is volatile it is weighed in stoppered bottles. Low results are obtained if sufficient time is not allowed for complete hydrolysis.

Procedure. A sample of approximately 5 to 5.5 grams is weighed in a bottle 6 to 8 cc. in capacity. A small 2-dram apothecaries' bottle with No. 00 rubber stopper is satisfactory. The stopper is fitted loosely and the bottle containing the sample is immersed in 100 cc. of normal NaOH and 300 cc. of distilled water in a 500 cc. "salt mouth" bottle with rubber stopper. The bottle is closed tightly and shaken to free the small rubber stopper from the weighing bottle, and permit the sample to mix with the reagent. After hydrolyzing for at least one hour the sample is titrated with N/5 H_2SO_4 to determine the excess of N/1 NaOH, using phenolphthalein indicator.

Calculation.

$$\frac{cc.\ NaOH \times 0.06003}{wt.\ sample} \times 100 = \%CH_3COOH$$

$$(\%\ CH_3COOH - 100) \times 5.665 = \%\ (CH_3CO)_2O.$$

Example. If the sample titrated 101% CH_3COOH then

$$(101 - 100) \times 5.665 = 5.665\%\ (CH_3CO)_2O.$$

NOTES. 100 per cent. $(CH_3CO)_2O = 117.65\%\ CH_3COOH.$

$$Per\ cent.\ Anhydride = \frac{A - 100}{117.65 - 100} \times 100$$

$$= (A - 100)5.665.$$

$$A = \%CH_3COOH\ by\ titration.$$

$$H_2SO_4 \times 1.2241 = CH_3COOH.$$

DETERMINATION OF ACETIC ANHYDRIDE— ANILINE METHOD

Procedure. The analysis should be carried out in duplicate runs, each portion being determined as follows: Two cc. of anhydride are run from burette into a tared 5 cc. weighing bottle and carefully weighed, the bottle being stoppered. The sample in now placed in an Erlenmeyer flask containing 50 cc. N NaOH and 50 cc. distilled water, the stopper of the bottle being loosened so that the anhydride mixes with the alkali. After forty minutes with occasional shaking of the flask to assist the mixing, the residual NaOH is titrated with N H_2SO_4, in presence of phenolphthalein indicator, 2 or 3 cc. of acid added in excess. After standing fifteen minutes longer the excess acid is titrated back with N/10 NaOH. From the amount of N NaOH required by the anhydride calculate the amount of N NaOH required by 100 grams of the sample. Record this as "A."

Twenty cc. of recently redistilled, perfectly dry aniline are run into a 5 cc. tared weighing bottle and 2 cc. of the anhydride added from a burette. The sample is added slowly, swirling the aniline to get an equal distribution. When the mixture has cooled to room temperature the weight of the anhydride is determined (the aniline and bottle having previously been weighed). After an hour the mixture is transferred to a 500 cc. volumetric flask and the solution diluted to mark with neutral alcohol and distilled water (1 : 1). Fifty cc. of this solution are titrated with N/10 NaOH. From the number of cc. required calculate the cc. N NaOH corresponding to the residual acetic acid from 100 grams of the sample. Record this as "B."

Then A–B corresponds to one half the anhydride in 100 grams of the sample. This value multiplied by 0.10207 = per cent acetic anhydride.

0.10207 = molecular weight of acetic anhydride divided by 1000

Correction for Mineral Acids if Present. In weighed portions (10 grams) determine hydrochloric acid by precipitation with $AgNO_3$ and sulphuric acid by precipitation with $BaCl_2$ in the usual way, the samples having hydrolyzed in 100 cc. portions of water. From the percentages of mineral acids present calculate to cc. normal equivalents and deduct from the titrations above, or calculate the anhydride equivalent and make deduction.

1 cc. N H_2SO_4 = .04904 g. 1 cc. N HCl = .03647 g. 1 cc. N CH_3COOH
= .06003 g. $CH_3COOH \times 0.85 = (CH_3CO)_2O$
$H_2SO_4 \times 1.0404 = (CH_3CO)_2O$, $HCl \times 1.3889 = (CH_3CO)_2O$

ANALYSIS OF ACETIC ACID

The acidity of acetic acid may be determined by titration with standard caustic, using phenolphthalein as indicator.

About 4 to 5 grams of glacial acetic acid or a corresponding amount of dilute acid are taken for analysis, being weighed out in a weighing bottle or other suitable container used for strong and weak acids. The acid is mixed with about 250 cc. of water and titrated in the presence of phenolphthalein indicator with normal caustic.

One cc. N/1 NaOH = 0.06003 gram CH_3COOH.

Impurities in Acetic Acid

The more important impurities that are looked for in commercial acetic acid are formic acid, furfurol, acetone, sulphuric acid, sulphurous acid, hydrochloric acid, metals.

In the examination of the acid the physical appearance—turbidity and color are noted.

Formic Acid in Acetic

Qualitative. Ten cc. of the acid (glacial diluted 1 : 10) are heated with 1 gram of sodium acetate and 5 cc. of 5 per cent mercuric chloride solution. A turbidity indicates formic acid.

Quantitative. Five grams of glacial acetic acid or corresponding quantity of dilute acid are treated with 5 grams of sodium acetate and 40 cc. of mercuric chloride solution (5 per cent) and 30 cc. of water added. The mixture is heated for two hours in a flask with a return condenser, the flask being surrounded by steam. The precipitated mercurous chloride, HgCl, is filtered off, dried and weighed.

Weight of HgCl × 0.0977 = formic acid equivalent.

Furfurol in Acetic Acid

Qualitative. Aniline dissolved in pure glacial acetic acid (5 cc. aniline in 2 cc. glacial acetic acid) and added to 100 cc. of the sample will produce a red color in presence of furfurol.

Quantitative. The test may be made quantitative by comparing the color produced with standard solutions containing known amounts of furfurol. One gram of redistilled furfurol is dissolved in 100 cc. of 95 per cent alcohol. 1 cc. of this solution is diluted to 100 cc. with 95 per cent alcohol. 1 cc. = 0.0001 gram of the reagent.

Test for furfurol in vinegar. Fifty cc. of the vinegar is neutralized with sodium hydroxide, and 15 to 20 cc. are distilled. Two cc. of colorless aniline and 15 cc. of hydrochloric acid (1:12) added. The mixture is warmed to about 15° C. for a few minutes and the color compared with standards prepared in the same way.

Gravimetric Method with Phloroglucid

Place a quantity of the material, chosen so that the weight of phloroglucid obtained shall not exceed 0.300 gram, in a flask, together with 100 cc. of 12 per cent hydrochloric acid (specific gravity, 1.06), and several pieces of recently heated pumice stone. Place the flask on a wire gauze, connect with a condenser and heat, rather gently at first, and so regulate as to distill over 30 cc. in about ten minutes, the distillate passing through a small filter paper. Replace the 30 cc. driven over by a like quantity of the dilute acid added by means of a separatory funnel in such a manner as to wash down the particles adhering to the sides of the flask, and continue the process until the distillate amounts to 360 cc. To the completed distillate gradually add a quantity of phloroglucol (purified if necessary) dissolved in 12 per cent hydrochloric acid and thoroughly stir the resulting mixture. The amount of phloroglucol used should be about double that of the furfural expected. The solution first turns yellow, then green, and very soon an amorphous greenish precipitate appears, which grows rapidly darker, till it finally becomes almost black. Make the solution up to 400 cc. with 12 per cent hydrochloric acid, and allow to stand overnight.

Filter the amorphous black precipitate into a tared Gooch crucible through an asbestos felt, wash carefully with 150 cc. of water in such a way that the water is not entirely removed from the crucible until the very last, then dry for four hours at the temperature of boiling water, cool and weigh, in a weighing bottle, the increase in weight being reckoned as phloroglucid. To calculate the furfural, pentose, or pentosan from the phloroglucid, use the following formulas given by Kröber:

(a) For weight of phloroglucid " a " under 0.03 gram.

$$\text{Furfural} = (a+0.0052) \times 0.5170.$$
$$\text{Pentoses} = (a+0.0052) \times 1.0170.$$
$$\text{Pentosans} = (a+0.0052) \times 0.8949.$$

(b) For weight of phloroglucid " a " over 0.300 gram.

$$\text{Furfural} = (a+0.0052) \times 0.5180.$$
$$\text{Pentoses} = (a+0.0052) \times 1.0026.$$
$$\text{Pentosans} = (a+0.0052) \times 0.8824.$$

For weight of phloroglucid " a " from 0.03 to 0.300 gram use Kröber's table or the following formulas:

$$\text{Furfural} = (a+0.0052) \times 0.5185.$$
$$\text{Pentoses} = (a+0.0052) \times 1.0075.$$
$$\text{Pentosans} = (a+0.0052) \times 0.8866.$$

The phloroglucol is purified by recrystallization from hydrochloric acid. For details of the procedure see Bulletin 107, U. S. Dept. of Agriculture, Bureau of Chemistry. (1912, page 54.)

Acetone in Acetic Acid

Fifteen grams of glacial acetic acid, or a corresponding amount of weak acid, is treated with 70 cc. potassium hydroxide (10 per cent solution), or sufficient caustic o make the solution slightly alkaline. The solution is cooled and 25 cc. N/5 iodine solution added and sufficient hydrochloric acid to make the mixture faintly acid. The excess of iodine is titrated with N/5 sodium thiosulphate, using starch indicator. The total iodine solution taken minus the equivalent cc. of thiosulphate = the iodine combined with the acetone, then the weight of iodine in grams multiplied by 0.07612 = grams acetone in the sample.

Sulphuric Acid in Acetic Acid

This is best determined by the turbidity test. About 5 cc. of the sample are taken and 1 drop of hydrochloric acid and half a cc. of 10 per cent barium chloride. The turbidity is now compared with a standard pure acetic acid solution containing a known quantity of $BaSO_4$, the standard being added to a comparison cylinder until the turbidity is the same as that of the sample, which has been diluted to a convenient volume in a Nessler tube or similar comparison cylinder. The apparatus used in determining small amounts of titanium, lead, etc., is suitable for this test. In this case the glowing wire or filament of an incandescent light is viewed through the solutions, the brightness of the wire acting as a guide in matching the solutions.

Sulphurous Acid in Acetic Acid

This is best detected by placing in a small flask about 20 cc. of the sample, adding 5 cc. of strong hydrochloric acid and about 3 grams of zinc and covering with a filter paper saturated with lead acetate. The blackening of the paper indicates SO_2 in the sample (e.g., reduced to H_2S by the hydrogen generated by the zinc).

The sulphurous acid is best titrated with N/10 iodine solution, using starch indicator. 1 cc. $N/10\ I_2 = .0032$ gr. SO_2.

Hydrochloric Acid in Acetic Acid

Determined by the turbidity test as in case of sulphuric acid, silver nitrate solution being used to precipitate AgCl, and nitric acid substituted for hydrochloric acid.

Metals in Acetic Acid

Total Solids. Ten to 100 grams of the acid is evaporated to dryness in a platinum dish. The residue contains the non-volatile solids.

ACETATES

Two to 5 grams of the material is placed in a Kjeldahl flask connected by means of a condenser to a receiving flask containing half normal caustic. About 20 cc. of 85 per cent phosphoric acid are added and about 150 cc. of water. Gentle heat is applied and gradually increased. About 100 cc. of the solution is distilled into the caustic. Additional hot water is added to the residue in the Kjeldahl flask and the distillation continued. This is repeated until about 800 cc. of solution has been distilled over. The CO_2 is boiled out of the distillate, a reflux condenser being used to prevent loss of the acetic acid. If the solution is alkaline, a known

44

amount of acid is added and the CO_2 boiled out. The excess acid is now titrate
and the amount of acetic acid in the distillate calculated.

One cc. N/2 NaOH = 0.030015 gram CH_3COOH.

$CH_3COOH \times 1.3169 = Ca(CH_3CO_2)_2$, or $\times 1.3663 = CH_2COONa$.

Acetates of the Alkalies and Alkaline Earths. In absence of other organi
acids, nitrates, etc., a quick method is suggested by Sutton (Vol. Analy., X. Ed
p. 91). The salts are converted into carbonates by ignition and the residu
titrated with normal acid.

One cc. N/1 acid = 0.06003 gram CH_3COOH.

ACETIC ACID AT 15°

OUDEMANS

Specific Gravity.	Per Cent $H_2C_2H_3O_2$.	Specific Gravity.	Per Cent $H_2C_2H_3O_2$.	Specific Gravity.	Per Cent $H_2C_2H_3O_2$.	Specific Gravity.	Per Cent $H_2C_2H_3O_2$.
0.9992	0	1.0363	26	1.0623	51	1 0747	76
1.0007	1	1.0375	27	1 0631	52	1.0748	77
1.0022	2	1.0388	28	1 0638	53	1.0748	78
1.0037	3	1.0400	29	1 0646	54	1.0748	79
1.0052	4	1.0412	30	1.0653	55	1 0748	80
1.0067	5	1.0424	31	1.0660	56	1.0747	81
1.0083	6	1.0436	32	1.0666	57	1.0746	82
1.0098	7	1 0447	33	1.0673	58	1 0744	83
1.0113	8	1.0459	34	1.0679	59	1 0742	84
1.0127	9	1 0470	35	1 0685	60	1.0739	85
1.0142	10	1 0481	36	1.0691	61	1.0736	86
1.0157	11	1 0492	37	1.0697	62	1.0731	87
1.0171	12	1.0502	38	1.0702	63	1 0726	88
1.0185	13	1.0513	39	1.0707	64	1.0720	89
1.0200	14	1.0523	40	1.0712	65	1 0713	90
1.0214	15	1.0533	41	1.0717	66	1 0705	91
1.0228	16	1.0543	42	1.0721	67	1 0696	92
1.0242	17	1.0552	43	1.0725	68	1.0686	93
1.0256	18	1.0562	44	1.0729	69	1.0674	94
1.0270	19	1.0571	45	1.0733	70	1.0660	95
1.0284	20	1.0580	46	1.0737	71	1.0644	96
1.0298	21	1.0589	47	1.0740	72	1.0625	97
1.0311	22	1.0598	48	1.0742	73	1 0604	98
1.0324	23	1.0607	49	1.0744	74	1.0580	99
1.0337	24	1.0615	50	1.0746	75	1 0553	100
1.0350	25						

CARBONIC ACID
Free Carbonic Acid in Aqueous Solution
The method is based on the reaction
$$H_2CO_3 + Ba(OH)_2 = BaCO_3 + 2H_2O.$$
Procedure. An excess of standard barium hydroxide solution is added to the water containing the carbonic acid. Barium carbonate is precipitated as shown, in the reaction above. The excess of $Ba(OH)_2$ is now titrated with standard hydrochloric acid, using phenolphthalein indicator.
1 cc. N/10 Ba (OH)$_2$ or 1 cc. N/10 HCl is equivalent to 0.0022 g. CO_2.

Carbonic Acid Present as Bicarbonate
Reaction. $NaHCO_3 + HCl = NaCl + H_2O + CO_2.$
Procedure. The solution is titrated with standard HCl, using methyl orange indicator.
1 cc. N/10 HCl = 0.0044 g. CO_2.

Carbonic Acid Present as Carbonate
Reaction. $Na_2CO_3 + 2HCl = 2NaCl + H_2O + CO_2.$
Procedure. The solution is titrated with standard HCl, using methyl orange indicator. Carbonates of barium, strontium, calcium and magnesium are titrated with an excess of hydrochloric acid and this excess determined with standard alkali.
1 cc. N/10 HCl = 0.0022 g. CO_2.

CITRIC ACID
The free acid may be titrated with sodium hydroxide, using phenolphthalein indicator. One cc. N/1 alkali = 0.07 gram crystallized citric acid.

VOLUMETRIC DETERMINATION OF OXALIC ACID
Permanganate Method
About 3 grams of the oxalic acid or its salt are dissolved in 200 cc. of CO_2 free water and 50 cc. 2N sulphuric acid added. The solution is heated to about 70° C. and titrated with standard, normal solution of potassium permanganate, to a faint pink, persisting for three minutes.
1 cc. N/KMnO$_4$ = 0.04501 g. $H_2C_2O_4$ or 0.06302 g. $H_2C_2O_4.2H_2O$.
The acid may also be titrated with standard caustic solution. Titration is made in a hot solution, using phenolphthalein indicator.

DETERMINATION OF PHENOL (CARBOLIC ACID)
Bromine reacts with an aqueous solution of phenol decomposing it to the water insoluble tribromophenol and forming hydrobromic acid as shown in the reaction
$$C_6H_5OH + 3Br_2 = C_6H_2Br_3(OH) + 3HBr.$$
The excess of bromine is determined by adding potassium iodide solution and determining the liberated iodine by titration with standard thiosulphate. The method is applicable only to pure preparations of carbolic acid.

Reagent. Standard Bromine. A solution of free bromine in water cann be kept. The reagent may be prepared, however, by adding a definite amou of bromate to a bromide solution, which on acidification, will liberate a defini amount of bromine according to the reaction $KBrO_3 + 5KBr + 6HCl = 3B + 6KCl + 3H_2O$. The acid is added only to the portions of the reagent use for the tests. In preparing a N/10 solution 2.784 grams of pure dry potassiu bromate and 10 grams of potassium bromide are dissolved in a little water a diluted to 1000 cc.

Procedure. 0.5 gram of phenol is dissolved in a little water and diluted 1000 cc. To 100 cc. of this, equivalent to 0.05 g. of sample are added (in stoppered bottle) 50 cc. of the bromate solution and the mixture shake 5 cc. of strong HCl are now added, the solution again shaken and after minutes 2 grams of potassium iodide are added. The liberated iodine titrated in presence of starch solution with N/10 thiosulphate.

$$1 \text{ cc. N/10 } Na_2S_2O_3 = 0.001567 \text{ g. } C_6H_5OH.$$

TARTARIC ACID

Tartaric acid, cream of tartar, Rochelle salt, tartar emetic, normal pota sium tartrate, iron tartrate and other salts of tartaric acid are obtained fro the residues of wine manufacture. The raw materials consist of lees, tartar calcium tartrate. Tartaric acid is present in these residues in the form potassium hydrogen tartrate (bitartrate of potassium) or as normal calciu tartrate. In the examination of the raw material for its evaluation tot tartaric acid and that present as bitartrate are determined.

Estimation of Acid Potassium Tartrate—Oulman's Method

Procedure. 3.76 grams of the powdered tartar is placed in a liter flas 750 cc. of water added, the solution heated to boiling and boiled for 4 to minutes. Prolonged boiling is avoided, as changes may occur which wou cause error in results. The flask is filled to the mark and allowed to coc After readjusting to exactly one liter the solution is filtered through a dry filt and 500 cc. of this evaporated to dryness on the water-bath in a porcela casserole. 5 cc. of water is added to moisten this residue and 100 cc. of 95 pe cent alcohol added on cooling. After standing half an hour the alcohol decanted through a dry filter, allowed to drain and any potassium bitartra on the filter is washed back into the dish with hot water. The solution made up to about 100 cc. and titrated hot with N/5 KOH. A correction 0.2 cc. is added for the loss of bitartrate in the alcohol.

Estimation of Total Tartaric Acid.   Goldenberg Method, 1907

Procedure.   Six grams of the sample containing more than 45 per cent of
.rtaric acid or 12 grams if it contains less than 45 per cent are added to 18 cc.
hydrochloric acid (sp.gr. 1.1) and the mixture stirred 10 minutes.   This is
»w transferred to a 200 cc. measuring flask and distilled water added to the
.ark.   The well mixed solution is now filtered through a dry filter into a beaker.
)0 cc. is pipetted out and added to 10 cc. of a solution of potassium carbonate
ntaining 66 grams of the anhydrous salt per 100 cc. in a 300 cc. beaker.
he breaker is covered by a clock glass and the solution boiled gently for
venty minutes; the calcium carbonate precipitates in a crystalline form
.ring this heating.   The solution is transferred to a 200 cc. measuring flask,
.ade up to mark after cooling, and filtered through a dry filter.

100 cc. of the filtrate is evaporated in a porcelain casserole (or pyrex beaker)
1 the water bath until the volume is about 15 cc.   To the hot solution 3.5 cc.
' glacial acetic acid are added gradually with constant stirring and the mixture
.irred for 5 minutes more after the addition.   After standing 10 minutes
)0 cc. of 95 per cent alcohol are added and the mixture again stirred 5 minutes.
'pon settling 10 minutes the precipitated bitartrate is filtered off, suction being
pplied.   The precipitate is washed with alcohol until free of acid.   (Test
0 cc.   This should require the same titration with N/5 alkali with phenol-
hthalein indicator as 30 cc. of the alcohol used in the washing.)   The pre-
ipitate on the filter is washed into a porcelain dish with 200 cc. of hot water
.nd titrated hot with N/5 potassium or sodium hydroxide, using litmus paper
.s indicator.

The alkali is standardized against pure potassium hydrogen tartrate.

Corrections.   Deduct 0.3 per cent for material containing less than 45 per
ent tartaric acid, 0.3 per cent for raw material containing 45–60 per cent and
.2 per cent for material containing 60–70 per cent.   No correction is made
.or better grades of material.

Impurities in Tartaric Acid

Iron and Alumina (alum.).   These are determined in the ash of the ignited
.roduct, the ash being dissolved in hydrochloric acid. P_2O_5 may also be
.etermined in this ash.

Arsenic.   This may be determined by the Gutzeit Method.   (See chapter
.n Arsenic in Volume I.)

Lead.   This is determined by the colorimetric procedure given on page 281,
.ol. I.

Free Sulphuric Acid in Tartaric Acid Liquors.   The solution 10 cc. or more
.s treated with ten times its volume of alcohol, and after settling overnight
.he mixture is filtered.   Sulphuric acid is determined in the alcohol filtrate in
.he usual way.

ALKALIES
ANALYSIS OF SODIUM HYDROXIDE

Commercial caustic soda, purchased in blocks packed in iron drums, shou be sampled with care. The hydroxide sets first on the outside, so that t impurities segregate towards the core of the block. In order to get a repr sentative sample different sections of the block should be tapped. The materi takes up moisture and carbon dioxide from the air, so that the surface of t sample should be removed before weighing. The weighing and dissolving the sample should be done as rapidly as possible.

Procedure

Ten grams of the hydroxide are dissolved in water and the solution ma up to exactly 500 cc. Aliquots of this solution are taken for the followi determinations.

Total Alkali. Fifty cc. of the caustic solution, equivalent to 1 gram of t solid, are titrated with N/H_2SO_4 in presence of methyl orange indicator, unt the faint pink end-point is obtained.

1 cc. $N/H_2SO_4 = .031$ grams of Na_2O (total alkali actual).

NOTE. In the New York and Liverpool test N/H_2SO_4 value is .032 g. NaOH per c

Sodium Hydroxide. Fifty cc. of the sample is treated with 100 cc. of 10 $BaCl_2$ solution and the NaOH then titrated with N/H_2SO_4 in presence phenolphthalein indicator.

1 cc. $N/H_2SO_4 = .04$ gram NaOH.

Sodium Carbonate. Multiply the difference between the total alkali titr tion and the titration for NaOH by .053 the result is grams Na_2CO_3.

Alternative Methods. Sodium Hydroxide and Sodium Carbonate. Ca bon dioxide is readily picked up by NaOH so that it is invariably present caustic soda forming sodium carbonate. The carbonate and hydrate may determined in the same solution as follows.

Fifty cc. of the sample equivalent to one gram of the solid, are titrated wit normal H_2SO_4, in presence of phenolphthalein, until the pink color just di appears. This occurs when all of the sodium hydroxide is neutralized and th carbonate has been converted to bicarbonate. This titration may be recorde as cc. A.

Methyl orange is now added and the titration continued until the yello color changes to pink. This titration is recorded as cc. B.

Then $NaOH = (A - B) \times 0.04$ and $Na_2CO_3 = 2B \times 0.053$.

Determination of Impurities

Sodium Chloride. This may be determined on 25 to 50 cc. (0.5–1 gram) the above solution by Volhard's method described in Vol. I, page 149, or th method for NaCl in soda ash, page 1064, this volume.

1 cc. $N/20$ $AgNO_3 = 0.002923$ gram NaCl.

Sodium Sulphate. Fifty cc. of the solution equivalent to 1 gram of th solid are acidified with hydrochloric acid (H_2SO_4 free) and the sulphate pr cipitated from a boiling solution by addition of 10% $BaCl_2$ solution accordin to the standard procedure.

$BaSO_4 \times 0.6086 = Na_2SO_4$.

The following determinations are seldom required.

Sodium Silicate. 10 grams of the sample are dissolved in about 100 cc. of water and the solution acidified with hydrochloric acid. After evaporation to dryness the residue is taken up with water. Silica remains insoluble and is filtered off, washed, ignited and weighed. $SiO_2 \times 2.0282 = Na_2SiO_3$.

Sodium Aluminate. The water extract from silica contains the alumina as soluble chloride. $Al(OH)_3$ may be precipitated with ammonia according to the standard procedure, then filtered off, washed, ignited and weighed as Al_2O_3. $Al_2O_3 \times 1.6067 = Na_2Al_2O_4$.

Insoluble Matter. 100 grams of the material is dissolved in a liter of water, phenolphthalein indicator is added and the solution almost neutralized with hydrochloric acid, the solution should be slightly alkaline. The sample is filtered and the residue of sand, Fe_2O_3, etc., weighed as insoluble matter. Caustic solutions attack filter paper so that it is advisable to partly neutralize the free alkali before filtration.

Water. 5 to 10 grams of the hydroxide are placed in a small Erlenmeyer flask, whose weight is known, a funnel is placed in the neck of the flask to prevent loss of the material and to prevent its absorbing carbon dioxide from the air. After placing in a sand bath the material is kept at about 150° C. for about four hours. It is now allowed to cool, the funnel remaining in the flask, and the loss of weight determined.

Determination of Strength of Caustic Liquors by the Hydrometer

The specific gravity of the liquor is taken by the hydrometer exactly as in case of acids. The strength of the liquor is ascertained by reference to the table on Sodium Hydroxide, page 1558.

POTASSIUM HYDROXIDE

Analysis of potassium hydroxide is similar to that of sodium hydroxide. The following molecular weights will be of use in the calculations:

$$KOH = 56.11; \qquad K_2CO_3 = 138.21; \qquad KCl = 74.56; \qquad K_2Al_2O_4 = 196.4;$$
$$K_2SiO_3 = 154.5.$$

Volumetric Determination of Carbonate in Sodium Bicarbonate [1]

$NaHCO_3$ in presence of $BaCl_2$ gives insoluble $BaCO_3$ and $NaCl$, neither subject to hydrolysis nor acting of phenolphthalein.

The $NaHCO_3$ to be analyzed is added to a solution of $NaOH$ of known strength and $BaCl_2$ is added to the Na_2CO_3 formed. By determining the free $NaOH$, that which is combined with $NaHCO_3$ can be calculated and the equivalent $NaHCO_3$ thus determined.

[1] Ref. J. C. Chiarino, C. A., **18**, 1799 (June 20, 1924).

ANALYSIS OF SODIUM CARBONATE
Soda Ash

Sodium carbonate, Na_2CO_3 (soda ash), and two forms with water of crystallization crystal carbonate, $Na_2CO_3.H_2O$ and soda crystals or washing soda, $Na_2CO_3.1OH_2O$, are commonly known. In the analysis of soda ash the customary demand is for total alkali, sodium carbonate, sodium bicarbonate and sodium chloride. In a complete analysis, including the insoluble residue, iron, Fe_2O_3, sodium sulphate, sodium thio-sulphate, sodium sulphite, sodium sulphide, sodium silicate, sodium hydroxide, alumina, and water may be required.

Procedure

Total Alkali, Na_2O. Five grams of the soda ash are dissolved in 50 cc. of distilled water, preferably in an Erlenmeyer flask, with a funnel, the stem extending in the neck of the flask. 95 cc. of normal sulphuric acid are added and the solution boiled gently to expel the CO_2, the funnel prevents loss during boiling. After cooling, methyl orange indicator is added and the titration completed. The end point is a faint pink color.

$$1 \text{ cc. } N/H_2SO_4 = .031 \text{ gram } Na_2O.$$

Note. "New York and Liverpool test" the value of 1 cc. $N.H_2SO_4 = .032$ g. Na_2O.

Sodium Bicarbonate, $NaHCO_3$. Five grams of the soda ash are dissolved in 100 cc. of water and the solution titrated with normal sodium hydroxide until a drop of the solution on a spot plate produces an immediate dark color with a drop of silver nitrate.

$$1 \text{ cc. } N/NaOH = .084 \text{ gram } NaHCO_3.$$

Sodium Carbonate. Deduct the cc. titration of NaOH for $NaHCO_3$ from the cc. H_2SO_4 titration for Na_2O, the difference in cc. multiplied by .053 = gram Na_2CO_3.

Sodium Chloride. Two grams of the ash by the Solvay process or 5 grams by the Leblanc process are dissolved in 50 to 100 cc. of distilled water and 5 cc. of colorless HNO_3 (sp.gr., 1.42) added. 2 cc. of ferric ammonium sulphate are used as indicator, followed by a few drops of N/20 KCNS solution, the exact amount of this being noted. The chloride is now titrated with N/20 $AgNO_3$ solution until the color is just destroyed, then 1 cc. in excess is added. The precipitate is filtered off and washed. The filtrate and washings are now titrated with N/20 KCNS to a permanent pink color.

The total cc. KCNS is deducted from the cc. $AgNO_3$ added and the difference multiplied by 0.002923 gram NaCl.

Note. See Volhard's method for chloride in Vol. I, page 149.

In addition to the above determinations the following may be desired:

Insoluble Matter. Fifty grams of the soda ash are dissolved in about 500 cc. of water the insoluble matter allowed to settle, the clear solution decanted through a double filter, which has been weighed, and finally the residue washed onto the filter. The residue and filters are dried at 100° C. and weighed.

Weight minus tare of filters multiplied by 100 = per cent insoluble matter.

[1] *Ferric ammonium sulphate* 6 per cent solution made by dissolving the salt in 50 parts of water to 6 parts of salt and adding an equal volume of colorless nitric acid.

[2] N/20 silver nitrate contains 8.495 g. $AgNO_3$ per liter. Standardize against pure NaCl.

[3] N/20 potassium thiocyanate, KCNS, contains 4.86 grams of the salt per liter. The solution should be standardized against the silver nitrate solution.

Iron, Alumina, Lime and Magnesia. These are determined in the insoluble residue by dissolving out by means of dilute hydrochloric acid. The residue consists of *sand* and *carbonacious matter*. Iron and alumina are precipitated out together by addition of ammonia according to the standard procedure, and determined as oxides, Fe_2O_3 and Al_2O_3. Iron may be determined in this residue by dissolving in HCl and titrating with stannous chloride according to the procedure given in Vol. I, page 373. Alumina is obtained by difference. Lime and magnesia will be found in the filtrates from iron and alumina precipitates. Calcium is thrown out as an oxalate and magnesium as a phosphate and determined as usual.

Sodium Sulphate. Dissolve 5 to 10 grams in dilute HCl and add $BaCl_2$. The precipitate $BaSO_4$ is washed and ignited as usual.

$$BaSO_4 \times 0.6086 = gram\ Na_2SO_4.$$

Sodium Sulphite. 5 grams are dissolved in water and the solution acidified with acetic acid. Starch solution is added and the sulphite titrated with N/10 iodine until the blue color appears.

$$1\ cc.\ N/10\ I = 0.006303\ gram\ Na_2SO_3.$$

Sodium Silicate. Ten grams of the soda ash are treated with an excess of HCl and the solution evaporated to dryness, the silica dehydrated at 110° C. After leaching with water the insoluble SiO_2 is determined by filtering off and igniting by the standard procedure.

$$SiO_2 \times 2.0282 = Na_2SiO_3.$$

Sodium Sulphide. This may be estimated by titration with an ammoniacal solution of silver nitrate (13.81 g. silver per liter = 1 cc. = .005 g. Na_2S). Add the reagent until no further precipitation occurs of Ag_2S. To get a good end point the solution is filtered just before this point is reached and the titration completed. See also chapter on Sulphur, Volume I.

Loss on Ignition. The sample 10 grams is ignited at a temperature slightly below 300° C. The loss is due largely to water and organic matter.

MODIFIED SODAS

Causticized Ash

The determination of total alkali, sodium hydroxide and sodium carbonate are generally required. 20 grams of the sample are dissolved in water and the solution made to one liter. Aliquot portions of this solution are taken for analysis.

Total Alkali. The determination is similar to that described for soda ash on page 1064 the test being made on 50 cc. of the solution equivalent to 1 gram of sample. It is advisable to add a slight excess of N/H_2SO_4 and titrate back with N/NaOH using methyl orange indicator. The end point is a faint pink.

$$1\ cc.\ N/H_2SO_4 = 0.031\ gram\ Na_2O.$$

Sodium Hydroxide. Fifty cc. of the sample equivalent to 1 gram of the solid is taken. The analysis is the same as that described for determining NaOH in caustic soda on page 1552.

Sodium Carbonate. The difference between the acid titration for total alkali and that for sodium hydroxide is multiplied by 0.053 = gram Na_2CO_3.

Washing Soda (Neutral Soda)

The determination of total alkali, sodium carbonate, sodium bicarbonate, and sodium chloride are generally required. The method of analysis is the same as has been described under soda ash. See page 1554.

ESTIMATION OF THE CARBONATES AND HYDRATES OF POTASSIUM AND SODIUM WHEN TOGETHER IN SOLUTION

Procedure. A measured volume of the solution is titrated, using phenolphtha lein as indicator. The acid used is equivalent to all of the hydrate and half the carbonate; methyl orange is now added and the titration completed; the additional amount of the acid used is equivalent to half the carbonate, therefore the amount of acid required for the carbonates and for the hydrates can be calculated from these figures.

The fully neutralized solution is evaporated to dryness and the residue weighed. The result is the weight of the mixed sulphates, due to the carbonates and hydrates of potassium and soda in the solution.

Calculate the total acid required to its equivalent of potassium sulphate, sub tract from this result the weight of the mixed sulphates, and the difference is due to the sodium sulphate in the mixed sulphates, owing to the difference in the molecu lar weights of potassium sulphate and sodium sulphate. The whole of the acid used has been calculated to potassium sulphate, and as the acid was neutralized by carbonates and hydrates, it is evident the proportion of total sulphate, due to the carbonates and hydrates, is equivalent to the amount of the acid used for each respectively; therefore the proportion of the above obtained difference due to the carbonates and the hydrates respectively is also proportional to the amount of acid used for each.

Example. A solution of the mixed carbonates and hydrates of potassium and sodium required:

(40 cc. NaOH : 40 cc. KOH) 80 cc. of acid to neutralize the hydrates.

(10 cc. Na_2CO_3 : 10 cc. K_2CO_3) 20 cc. of acid to neutralize the carbonates.

100 cc. total acid required to neutralize the solution.

Total acid 100 cc. calculated to K_2SO_4	=0.87 gram
Total neutralized solution evaporated to dryness ($K_2SO_4+Na_2SO_4$)	=0.79 gram
Difference due to Na_2SO_4 in weighed sulphates	=0.08 gram

($K_2SO_4-Na_2SO_4$) : Na_2SO_4 : : Diff :
  32 : 142 : : 0.08 : 0.355 Na_2SO_4 present in the mixed sul phates.

And the mixed sulphates 0.79 gram $-0.355 =0.435$ K_2SO_4 present in the mixed sulphates.

Therefore the mixed sulphates consist of Na_2SO_4 0.355 gram, K_2SO_4 0.435 gram

The proportion of the acid used for the hydrates is 80/100 and for the car bonates is 20/100.

Therefore the proportion of the difference (0.08) due to Na_2SO_4 from the hydrate NaOH is $0.08\times80/100 =0.064$. For the carbonates $=0.08\times20/100 =0.016$.

By the above ratios 32 : 142 : : 0.064 : 0.284 Na_2SO_4 from NaOH $=40$ cc N/10 acid. 32 : 142 : : 0.016 : 0.071 Na_2SO_4 from Na_2CO $=10$ cc. acid.

[1] W. A. Bradbury and F. Owen. C. N., **107**, 2778, 85 (Feb. 21, 1913).

80 cc. acid used for the hydrates = 0.696 K_2SO_4.

0.284 Na_2SO_4 from the NaOH = 0.348 K_2SO_4.

Difference = K_2SO_4 from KOH = 0.348 = 40 cc. N/10 acid.

20 cc. acid used for the carbonates = 0.174.

0.071 Na_2SO_4 from the Na_2CO_3 = 0.087.

Difference = K_2SO_4 from K_2CO_3 = 0.087 = 10 cc. acid.

The figures correspond with the quantities taken.

80 cc. of acid to neutralize the hydrates.

20 cc. of acid to neutralize the carbonates.

$$Na_2SO_4 = 0.355 \left\{ \begin{array}{l} NaOH \quad 0.284 = 40 \text{ cc. acid} \\ Na_2CO_3 \; 0.071 = 10 \text{ cc. acid} \end{array} \right\} 80 \text{ cc. acid.}$$

$$K_2SO_4 = 0.435 \left\{ \begin{array}{l} KOH \quad 0.348 = 40 \text{ cc. acid} \\ K_2CO_3 \quad 0.087 = 10 \text{ cc. acid} \end{array} \right\} 20 \text{ cc. acid}$$

Totals   0.790   0.790(a)100

Calculate these sulphates to the corresponding hydrates and carbonates.

DETERMINATION OF SODIUM BICARBONATE AND SODIUM CARBONATE IN PRESENCE OF ONE ANOTHER

Five grams of the sample are dissolved in CO_2-free water, and the solution made up to exactly 250 cc. in a measuring flask. Aliquot portions of 25 cc., equivalent to 0.5 gram, are taken for analysis. The sample taken is titrated with N/5 hydrochloric acid in presence of phenolphthalein indicator (2–3 drops). The cc. titration recorded as "A," represents one half of the sodium carbonate present. Methyl orange indicator is now added (2–3 drops) and the titration with the acid continued until the solution turns faintly pink. The remaining carbonate and all of the bicarbonate are now titrated. The cc. titration are recorded as B.

2A × 0.0106 = Na_2CO_3 and B−A × 0.0168 = $NaHCO_3$.

The author desires to acknowledge his indebtedness to Dr. W. B. Hicks, Chief of the Analytical Department, The Solvay Process Company, for his review of the section on Alkalies.

SODIUM HYDROXIDE SOLUTION AT 15°
Lunge

Specific Gravity.	Degrees Baumé.	Degrees Twaddell.	Per Cent Na$_2$O.	Per Cent NaOH.	1 Liter contains Grams	
					Na$_2$O.	NaOH.
1.007	1.0	1.4	0.47	0.61	4	6
1.014	2.0	2.8	0.93	1.20	9	12
1.022	3.1	4.4	1.55	2.00	16	21
1.029	4.1	5.8	2.10	2.70	22	28
1.036	5.1	7.2	2.60	3.35	27	35
1.045	6.2	9.0	3.10	4.00	32	42
1.052	7.2	10.4	3.60	4.64	38	49
1.060	8.2	12.0	4.10	5.29	43	56
1.067	9.1	13.4	4.55	5.87	49	63
1.075	10.1	15.0	5.08	6.55	55	70
1.083	11.1	16.6	5.67	7.31	61	79
1.091	12.1	18.2	6.20	8.00	68	87
1.100	13.2	20.0	6.73	8.68	74	95
1.108	14.1	21.6	7.30	9.42	81	104
1.116	15.1	23.2	7.80	10.06	87	112
1.125	16.1	25.0	8.50	10.97	96	123
1.134	17.1	26.8	9.18	11.84	104	134
1.142	18.0	28.4	9.80	12.64	112	144
1.152	19.1	30.4	10.50	13.55	121	156
1.162	20.2	32.4	11.14	14.37	129	167
1.171	21.2	34.2	11.73	15.13	137	177
1.180	22.1	36.0	12.33	15.91	146	183
1.190	23.1	38.0	13.00	16.77	155	200
1.200	24.2	40.0	13.70	17.67	164	212
1.210	25.2	42.0	14.40	18.58	174	225
1.220	26.1	44.0	15.18	19.58	185	239
1.231	27.2	46.2	15.96	20.59	196	253
1.241	28.2	48.2	16.76	21.42	208	266
1.252	29.2	50.4	17.55	22.64	220	283
1.263	30.2	52.6	18.35	23.67	232	299
1.274	31.2	54.8	19.23	24.81	245	316
1.285	32.2	57.0	20.00	25.80	257	332
1.297	33.2	59.4	20.80	26.83	270	348
1.308	34.1	61.6	21.55	27.80	282	364
1.320	35.2	64.0	22.35	28.83	295	381
1.332	36.1	66.4	23.20	29.93	309	399
1.345	37.2	69.0	24.20	31.22	326	420
1.357	38.1	71.4	25.17	32.47	342	441
1.370	39.2	74.0	26.12	33.69	359	462
1.383	40.2	76.6	27.10	34.96	375	483
1.397	41.2	79.4	28.10	36.25	392	506
1.410	42.2	82.0	29.05	37.47	410	528
1.424	43.2	84.8	30.08	38.80	428	553
1.438	44.2	87.6	31.00	39.99	446	575
1.453	45.2	90.6	32.10	41.41	466	602
1.468	46.2	93.6	33.20	42.83	487	629
1.483	47.2	96.6	34.40	44.38	510	658
1.498	48.2	99.6	35.70	46.15	535	691
1.514	49.2	102.8	36.90	47.60	559	721
1.530	50.2	106.0	38.00	49.02	581	750

AQUA AMMONIA
According to W. C. Ferguson

Degrees Baumé.	Sp. Gr. $\frac{60°}{60°}$ F.	Per Cent NH_3.	Degrees Baumé.	Sp. Gr. $\frac{60°}{60°}$ F.	Per Cent NH_3.	Degrees Baumé.	Sp. Gr. $\frac{60°}{60°}$ F.	Per Cent NH_3.
10.00	1.0000	.00	16.50	.9556	11.18	23.00	.9150	23.52
10.25	.9982	.40	16.75	.9540	11.64	23.25	.9135	24.01
10.50	.9964	.80	17.00	.9524	12.10	23.50	.9121	24.50
10.75	.9947	1.21	17.25	.9508	12.56	23.75	.9106	24.99
11.00	.9929	1.62	17.50	.9492	13.02	24.00	.9091	25.48
11.25	.9912	2.04	17.75	.9475	13.49	24.25	.9076	25.97
11.50	.9894	2.46	18.00	.9459	13.96	24.50	.9061	26.46
11.75	.9876	2.88	18.25	.9444	14.43	24.75	.9047	26.95
12.00	.9859	3.30	18.50	.9428	14.90	25.00	.9032	27.44
12.25	.9842	3.73	18.75	.9412	15.37	25.25	.9018	27.93
12.50	.9825	4.16	19.00	.9396	15.84	25.50	.9003	28.42
12.75	.9807	4.59	19.25	.9380	16.32	25.75	.8989	28.91
13.00	.9790	5.02	19.50	.9365	16.80	26.00	.8974	29.40
13.25	.9773	5.45	19.75	.9349	17.28	26.25	.8960	29.89
13.50	.9756	5.88	20.00	.9333	17.76	26.50	.8946	30.38
13.75	.9739	6.31	20.25	.9318	18.24	26.75	.8931	30.87
14.00	.9722	6.74	20.50	.9302	18.72	27.00	.8917	31.36
14.25	.9705	7.17	20.75	.9287	19.20	27.25	.8903	31.85
14.50	.9689	7.61	21.00	.9272	19.68	27.50	.8889	32.34
14.75	.9672	8.05	21.25	.9256	20.16	27.75	.8875	32.83
15.00	.9655	8.49	21.50	.9241	20.64	28.00	.8861	33.32
15.25	.9639	8.93	21.75	.9226	21.12	28.25	.8847	33.81
15.50	.9622	9.38	22.00	.9211	21.60	28.50	.8833	34.30
15.75	.9605	9.83	22.25	.9195	22.08	28.75	.8819	34.79
16.00	.9589	10.28	22.50	.9180	22.56	29.00	.8805	35.28
16.25	.9573	10.73	22.75	.9165	23.04			

ALLOWANCE FOR TEMPERATURE

The coefficient of expansion for ammonia solutions, varying with the temperature, correction must be applied according to the following table:

Degrees Baumé.	Corrections to be Added for Each Degree Below 60° F.		Corrections to be Subtracted for Each Degree Above 60° F.			
	40° F.	50° F.	70° F.	80° F.	90° F.	100° F.
14° Bé	.015° Bé	.017° Bé	.020° Bé	.022° Bé	.024° Bé	.026° Bé
16°	.021 "	.023 "	.026 "	.028 "	.030 "	.032 "
18°	.027 "	.029 "	.031 "	.033 "	035 "	.037 "
20°	.033 "	.036 "	.037 "	.038 "	.040 "	.042 "
22°	.039 "	.042 "	.043 "	.045 "	.047 "	
26°	.053 "	.057 "	.057 "	.059 "		

ANALYSIS OF AQUA AMMONIA

Details for the complete analysis of crude ammoniacal liquor will be found in Volume I on pages 344–345.

The per cent ammonia in a solution free from other substances may be determined with a fair degree of accuracy by determining the specific gravity of the solution by means of the hydrometer. Since the specific gravity of aqua ammonia is less than 1, hydrometers graduated for measuring liquids lighter than water are used. The formula for 1 degree Baume = (140/sp.gr.) −130. Reference is made to the table on Aqua Ammonia.

Provided no other basic constituent is present, free ammonia in solution is best determined by direct titration with an acid in presence of methyl orange or methyl red as indicator.

Procedure. About 10 grams of the solution in a weighing bottle with glass stopper is introduced into an 800-cc. Erlenmeyer flask containing about 200 cc. of water and sufficient $\frac{1}{2}$ normal sulphuric acid to combine with the ammonia and about 10 cc. in excess. The flask is stoppered and warmed gently. This forces out the stopper in the weighing bottle, the ammonia combining with the acid. Upon thorough mixing, the solution is cooled, and the excess of acid is titrated with half normal caustic.

$$\text{One cc. } \tfrac{1}{2} \text{ N. } H_2SO_4 = 0.0085 \text{ gram } NH_3.$$

Factor. $H_2SO_4 \times 0.3473 = NH_3$.

NOTE. The aqua ammonia exposed to the air will lose ammonia, hence the sample should be kept stoppered. This loss of ammonia is quite appreciable in strong ammoniacal solutions.

The Effect of Hydrogen Ion Concentration on Chemical Indicators [1]

When an acidic or basic substance is dissolved in water, it ionizes, the former always producing hydrogen ions, the latter hydroxyl ions. E.g., $HCl \rightarrow H^+ + Cl^-$,

$$NaOH \rightarrow Na^+ + OH^-.$$

The strength of an acid or base depends entirely on the extent to which it is ionized, that is, on the concentration of hydrogen or hydroxyl ions it produces.

Water itself is slightly ionized: $H_2O \rightarrow H^+ + OH^-$, so that an acid solution always contains a small concentration of hydroxyl ions, and an alkaline solution hydrogen ions.

A neutral solution is best defined as a solution in which the concentration of hydrogen equals the concentration of hydroxyl ions. If the hydrogen ions are in excess, the solution is acid; if the hydroxyl, it is basic.

The product of the concentrations (in normality) of hydrogen and hydroxyl ions is constant and equal to approximately 10^{-14} at 25° C. Hence in pure water, where the concentrations are assumed equal, $C_{H+} = 10^{-7}$ and $C_{OH-} = 10^{-7}$. In other words water is a 0.0000001 normal solution of H^+ and OH^-, containing 0.0000001 g. hydrogen ion and 0.0000017 g. hydroxyl ion per liter at 25° C.

The common abbreviation for expressing the acidity of a solution is pH, which is the negative of the power to which 10 must be raised to give the hydrogen ion concentration.

$$\text{E.g., when } C_{H+} = 10^{-7}, pH = 7,$$
$$\text{``} \quad C_{H+} = 10^{-5.5}, pH = 5.5.$$

From the preceding two paragraphs it can be seen that when pH is less than 7 (e.g., when pH = 5 or $C_{H+} = 10^{-5}$) the solution is acid; when pH is greater, it is basic.

Indicators used in acidimetric or alkalimetric titrations are compounds which in solution change color with changing acidity. At any given acidity or alkalinity they have definite colors; that is, their color is a function of the hydrogen ion concentration.

The useful indicators have a marked color change at some point in their range, and this point is taken as the end-point in a titration. This change occurs with some on the acid side of true neutral (that is, where pH is less than 7), as for example with methyl orange and methyl red; with others it occurs on the alkaline side (where pH is greater than 7), as for example with phenolphthalein. This characteristic of an indicator together with the sharpness of its color change determines its suitability for a given titration.

In making an acidimetric or alkalimetric titration the end-point is not usually the true neutral point, but the point at which an amount of acid (or base) equivalent to the amount of base (or acid) to be determined has been added. In the case of a weak base and a strong acid (NH_4OH and HCl, for example) the solution will be slightly acid at this point, and an indicator will be required whose most marked color change takes place on the acid side (e.g., methyl red); conversely with a weak acid and a strong base (e.g., H_2CO_3 and $NaOH$) an indicator must be used whose most marked color change is on the alkaline side (e.g., phenolphthalein). In other words, the solution of hydroxyl ions produced by a very small excess of ammonia is not concentrated enough to change the color of phenolphthalein but can change that of methyl red. Conversely for the hydrogen ion solution produced by carbonic acid.

[1] By Marston Lovell Hamlin, Ph.D.   Lefax, Sep., 1921.

Titrations with two indicators of solutions of substances of different acidity, lil H_3PO_4 and Na_2PO_4, or NaOH and Na_2CO_3, are explained on this principle (see Lefa Data Sheet 6-216, page 2).

With the two indicators methyl red and phenolphthalein available practically a the ordinary titrations liable to come up in ordinary work may be made. Solutio should be standardized with the indicator with which they are to be used; NaO solutions to be used with phenolphthalein should be substantially free of carbonate (These may be made up as follows: Dissolve NaOH in water in the ratio 125 g. : 150 c. and let stand until the upper part is clear, two weeks or more; nearly all of the Na_2CO and other impurities will be precipitated and settle, and the clear solution may l pipetted off for making up standard solutions, which must be protected from absorbin CO_2 from the air by soda-lime tubes).

Indicators have another important use besides their use in titrations. They may h directly used in many cases for the determination of the acidity or basicity, that is, th hydrogen ion concentration, of solutions.

The conditions under which they may be so used are: The solution to be teste must be clear enough and free enough of color to allow its color after addition of th indicator to be compared with standards; its hydrogen ion concentration must be withi the range covered by the indicators available (usually pH between 1.2 and 10); i must be free from substances that destroy, precipitate or otherwise interfere with th normal behavior of the indicator; the temperature must not be too hgih, say below 50° C

The method consists in adding a definite amount of indicator solution (e.g., 0.3 c.c. to a definite amount of the solution to be tested (e.g., 10 c.c.), and comparing the resultin color with standards containing the same amount of indicator per 10 c.c. The standard are buffer solutions, several series of which have been worked out and tested by differen workers. A set covering the range pH 1.2 to pH 10 can be made from KCl, HC KH-phthalate ($KHC_2O_4.C_6H_4$), NaOH, KH_2PO_4, and H_3BO_3. In making up th solutions pure dry salts, carbonate-free NaOH and ammonia-free HCl must be used i boiled distilled water. The quantitative composition is given in the following tabl (Clark)

TABLE I

Standard Buffer Solutions

pH	c.c. 0.2 M KCl	c.c. 0.2 M HCl	Dilute to	pH	c.c. 0.2 M KH-phthalate	c.c. 0.2 M HCl	Dilute to
1.2	50	64.5	200 c.c.	2.2	50	46.70	200 c.c.
1.4	"	41.5	"	2.4	"	39.60	"
1.6	"	26.3	"	2.6	"	32.95	"
1.8	"	16.6	"	2.8	"	26.42	"
2.0	"	10.6	"	3.0	"	20.32	"
2.2	"	6.7	"	3.2	"	14.70	"
				3.4	"	9.90	"
				3.6	"	5.97	"
				3.8	"	2.63	"

pH	c.c. 0.2 M KH-phthalate	c.c. 0.2 M NaOH	Dilute to	pH	c.c. 0.2 M KH_2PO_4	c.c. 0.2 M NaOH	Dilute to
4.0	50	0.40	200 c.c.	5.8	50	3.72	200 c.c.
4.2	"	3.70	"	6.0	"	5.70	"
4.4	"	7.50	"	6.2	"	8.60	"
4.6	"	12.15	"	6.4	"	12.60	"
4.8	"	17.70	"	6.6	"	17.80	"
5.0	"	23.85	"	6.8	"	23.65	"
5.2	"	29.95	"	7.0	"	29.63	"
5.4	"	35.45	"	7.2	"	35.00	"
5.6	"	39.85	"	7.4	"	39.50	"
5.8	"	43.00	"	7.6	"	42.80	"
6.0	"	45.45	"	7.8	"	45.20	"
6.2	"	47.00	"	8.0	"	46.80	"

pH	c.c. soln. containing 0.2 M H_3BO_3 and 0.2 M KCl	c.c. 0.2 M NaOH	Dilute to
7.8	50	2.61	200 c.c.
8.0	"	3.97	"
8.2	"	5.90	"
8.4	"	8.50	"
8.6	"	12.00	"
8.8	"	16.30	"
9.0	"	21.30	"
9.2	"	26.70	"
9.4	"	32.00	"
9.6	"	36.85	"
9.8	"	40.80	"
10.0	"	43.90	"

TABLE II

INDICATORS AND THEIR COLOR CHANGES

pH	Thymol blue (acid range)	Brom-phenol blue	Methyl red	Brom-cresol purple	Brom-thymol blue	Phenol red	Cresol red	Thymol blue
1.0	red							
1.5	dull red							
2.0	orange							
2.5	yellow-orange							
3.0	yellow	green-yellow						
3.5	....	yellow-gray						
4.0	....	lavender-gray						
4.5	....	lavender	deep rose					
5.0	....	....	pink					
5.5	....	....	buff	tan				
6.0	....	....	yellow	violet-gray	yellow			
6.5	....	....	....	lavender	yellow-green	pale-buff		
7.0	....	....	....	violet	green	pink-buff	pale-yellow	
7.5	....	....	....	....	blue	pink	pink-buff	
8.0	....	....	....	....	....	deep-rose	pale-magenta	very pale olive
8.5	....	....	....	....	....	....	magenta	olive-gray
9.0	....	....	....	....	....	....	deep-magenta	blue-gray
9.5	....	....	....	....	....	....	....	blue
10.0	....	....	....	....	....	....	....	deep-blue

NOTE: The materials used should be dried as follows: KCl at 120° C. for 2 days; cid potassium phthalate at 110°–115° to constant weight; dihydrogen potassium hosphate, the same; boric acid at room temperature. constancy of weight being tested n thin layers kept in a desiccator over $CaCl_2$.

45

Of course the mere naming of colors, as in Table II, can only give a relative and approximate idea of the changes undergone by each indicator, but it may be useful in choosing indicators for special purposes and in rough work.

The strengths of the indicator solutions and the amounts to add to 10 c.c. of the solution to be tested to get the colors of Table II are shown in Table III. To make up the solutions grind 0.1 g. of the dye (the free acid) with the indicated amounts of 0.05 N NaOH in a mortar, and dilute to 25 c.c. This gives a concentrated 0.4% stock solution to be diluted to the indicated strength for use (Clark).

TABLE III

INDICATOR SOLUTIONS

For 0.1 g. of	Of 0.05 N NaOH Use.	Dilute to	Of this Use.
Thymol blue................	4.3 c.c.	0.04%	1 c.c. or 0.5 c.c.*
Bromphenol blue............	3.0	0.04	0.5
Methyl red.................	7.4	0.02	0.3
Bromcresol purple...........	3.7	0.04	0.5
Bromthymol blue............	3.2	0.04	0.5
Phenol red.................	5.7	0.02	0.5
Cresol red.................	5.3	0.02	0.5

* 1 c.c. for acid range.

Methyl red may also, and perhaps more conveniently, be prepared by dissolving 0.1 g. in 300 c.c. neutral alcohol and diluting to 500 c.c. with distilled water. Phenolphthalein is used in a 0.02% solution in neutral 95% alcohol.

A more extended but less detailed list of indicators is given in Table IV.

TABLE IV

INDICATORS AND THEIR RANGES

Indicator.	Color.	pH.	Reference
Mauveine..........	Yellow......................	−0.3	Salm
	Green.......................	0.0	
	Blue green..................	+1.0	
	Blue........................	2.0	
Methyl violet.......	Gold yellow to green...........	−0.3 to 0	Salm
	Green to green blue...........	0 to +1	
	Green blue to blue...........	1 to 2	
	Blue to violet.................	2 to 3	
Tropaeolin 00.......	Red to yellow................	1.4 to 2.6	Sorensen
Congo red..........	Blue to scarlet................	3 to 5	Prideaux
Methyl orange	Red to orange................	3.1 to 4.4	Sorensen
Litmus.............	Red to blue...................	4.5 to 8.3	"
Cochineal...........	Brown rose to lilac............	4.8 to 6.2	"
Alizarine...........	Brown yellow to pale lilac.......	5.5 to 6.8	"
Rosolic acid........	Brown to red.................	6.9 to 8.0	"
Tropaeolin 000......	Yellow to orange..............	7.6 to 8.9	"
Phenolphthalein......	Colorless to deep rose...........	8.3 to 10	"
Tropaeolin 0........	Yellow green to orange..........	11.1 to 12.7	"

The best article on the quantitative theory of indicators is A. A. Noyes, J. Am. Chem. Soc., **32** (1910), 815. The theory and methods of determining hydrogen ions are given in Clark's book, "Determination of Hydrogen Ions," Williams and Wilkins 1920. See also Sorensen's articles in the Biochemische Zeitschrift.

Buffer solutions, indicators, etc., may be obtained from the La Motte Chemical Products Co., Baltimore, Md.

RUBBER

Rubber is obtained from the latex of certain plants belonging to the Natural Orders, *phorbiaceæ, Apocynaceæ, Urticaceæ*. The latex is a " milky " juice showing Brown-movement; an emulsoid of rubber in a watery serum, and it is associated with ny other substances (resins, sugars, protein). The chief rubber-bearing plants are *vea brasiliensis* (Pará), *Castilloa, Ficus* and the *Landolphias*. In *Parthenium argenta-n* (Guayule) the rubber occurs solid in the parenchyma.

The *function* of the rubber in the plant is unknown. The resins are considered degradation products. The protein acts as a protective colloid preventing the coales-ce of the globules in the latex, and coagulation consists in destroying this protection. agulation is brought about by heat, or chemical reagents, or both.

The *essential constituent* of rubber is a hydrocarbon (caoutchouc). It is a poly-ne, or polymerized terpene, $(C_{10}H_{16})n$. The physical differences of the various bers are due to variation in chemical aggregation or the value of n, i.e., the degree of lymerization: also the amount and nature of the associated foreign matter. Harries' rk on the ozonides of rubber shows the hydrocarbon to be an unsaturated body with o ethylene linkages. By bubbling ozone through a solution of rubber in chloroform. ozonide $-C_{10}H_{16}O_6$ (soluble in $CHCl_3$) is formed.

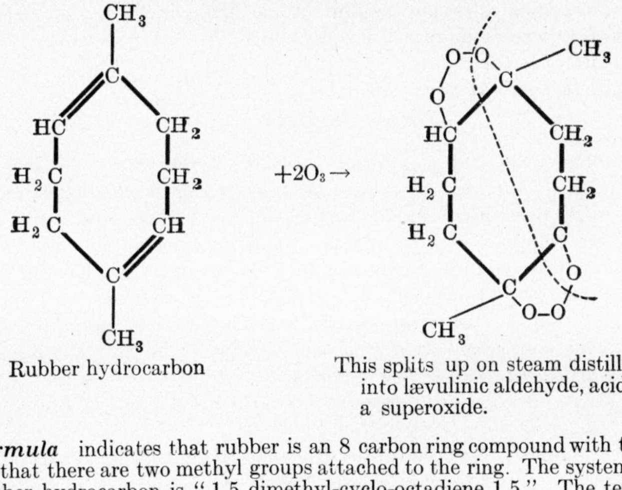

$+2O_3 \rightarrow$

Rubber hydrocarbon

This splits up on steam distillation into lævulinic aldehyde, acid, and a superoxide.

The *formula* indicates that rubber is an 8 carbon ring compound with two double nds and that there are two methyl groups attached to the ring. The systematic name the rubber hydrocarbon is " 1.5 dimethyl-cyclo-octadiene 1.5." The term " octa-ne " signifies an 8 C ring with two ethylene linkages. The 1.5 at the end states the sition of the bonds in the ring whilst the 1.5 at the beginning of the expression refers nilarly to the methyl groups. The compounds of the rubber hydrocarbon are addition oducts (except the nitrosite), $C_{10}H_{16}O$, $C_{10}H_{16}S_2$, $C_{10}H_{16}Br_4$, etc.

Rubber is a *colloid,* and is not, strictly speaking, soluble: it forms pseudo-solutions vellings). A colloid is represented by suspended particles which, by carriyng like - or −) electrical charges, repel one another continuously, and thus refuse to settle

Chapter by L. E. Salas.

by gravity. The addition of an electrolyte neutralizing the electric charges causes t
particles to coalesce (coagulation), whereupon they settle out. A colloidal soluti
appears as a united mass of particles which, on greater dilution, decrease in size, disa
pearing to form a " sol," apparently limpid, although the beam of light employed in t
ultramicroscope discovers solid particles. The first effect of the " solvent " is to sw
the polyprene, forming a network or sponge. When the whole of the rubber is " swoller
diffusion of the solvent takes place.

The principal *rubber solvents* are carbon disulphide, turpentine, petroleum, be
zene and its homologues, carbon tetrachloride and chloroform.

EXAMINATION OF RAW RUBBER

The following information concerning a consignment of rubber might
required:

1. Origin, botanical source, method of collection, method of coagulatio
despatch and packing.

2. The gross weight of shipment at the time of despatch, gross weight at t
time of sampling, average tare, condition of the packages at unloading in doc

3. The method of sampling is an important point to be decided betwe
buyer and seller. Storage plays an important part as regards ship consig
ments of rubber, for rubber stored in ships' holds near the engine room wou
be much drier than that in the bottom of either the bow or stern holds.

4. The washing loss, the content of washed dried rubber, and its appearanc
color and strength after removal from the vacuum pans.

5. The percentage nitrogen content of the dried rubber, the percentage
acetone extract, percentage of ash.

6. Quantity of rubber (pure).

7. Results of trial vulcanizations.

Raw Rubber

Raw Rubber (wild and plantation) appears on the market as sheets, block
slabs or scraps. Each kind of rubber possesses a characteristic odor due to t
contained resin, decaying protein matter, or the material used in coagulatio
The vegetable refuse, earthy impurities, moisture and soluble matter (organ
acids, carbohydrates, tannins) may together constitute more than 50 per cent
the whole, which the process of washing and drying removes (residual moistu
about 0.5 per cent). Plantation rubber is more carefully prepared and arriv
clean, and being comparatively dry (as sheet, crêpe, or blocks) requires little or i
washing. Purified raw rubber has a density of 0.91–0.97. It is highly elastic b
loses its elasticity at 0° C. or if heated above 60° C. It melts at 100° C. to a bla
liquid.

Technical analysis of crude rubber (for factory control and valuation) consis
in the estimation of washing loss, true rubber, resin and ash. The **sampling**
crude rubber is difficult because the packages differ greatly. If the bales are ve
heterogeneous the whole consignment should be washed and dried, as hand sampl
are quite unsatisfactory. The washing loss should be ascertained by weighi
the whole shipment (or at least one-quarter of it) in batches of about 1 cwt., su
tracting the tare, washing the rubber (preferably in presence of representatives
buyer and seller), weighing the vacuum-dried rubber after removal from the va
uum driers, and calculating the percentage of loss in each drier and taking t
average. Determine " total insoluble " in hot pyridine.

Laboratory samples should not be less than 20 lbs. One sample should l ken from each case, unless the packages are many and are much alike, when every ird or fifth package may be sampled. In this case, wash and dry samples from e first half of the range and compare with results from the other half. If these sults are within 1 per cent, take the mean. By using a long-bladed knife or othless saw a wedge-shaped sample, having its apex at the center, may be cut, in the case of a prismatic block the best sample may be obtained by cutting out a arter. A slice through the center is obviously " against the seller." It is some-nes found that the rubber contains so little moisture or is so tacky that cutting very troublesome. In this case the knife must be wetted and the superfluous ater removed afterward, otherwise serious error will be caused if the small mples be taken.

Tackiness. Tacky rubbers always show a low state of colloidal aggregation com-red with sound rubbers of the same species—their viscosity is also low. As they ve the same figure on bromination, the tackiness is not due to oxidation or chemical ange, but may be a physical degradation due to sunlight, heat, bacteria and enzymes, sence of moisture or presence of excessive moisture. Guayule is very susceptible, pending on its preparation and overheating during stowage in transit. The use of tiseptics in the wash water does not prevent tackiness, but Spence says that bacteria ay be responsible for producing a condition in rubber favorable to tackiness. Morton s isolated an enzyme which will produce tackiness even in fine hard Pará. The chem-ls used in coagulation may cause the condition—Spence considers sulphuric acid is imical, also other mineral acids. Organic acids give hard and brittle rubbers. In y case strong coagulants produce the best rubbers. Antiseptics are advisable d cleanliness essential; overheating in drying rooms and ships is to be guarded ainst, and sunlight is to be avoided.

Commercial evaluation does not depend on chemical analysis alone. Physical sts and vulcanization trials (open and press cure, time and temperature and mixing riation) must be considered. Valuable information may be acquired by curing th 10 per cent sulphur, at 45 lbs. steam pressure, and withdrawing samples at rtain intervals of time. The object of analysis is to assist the manufacturer in ctory control and improvement of the manufactured articles, and to serve as a ide to the value and adaptability of the raw material.

Besides ordinary equipment, the *factory laboratory* should be provided with a nall washing mill and vacuum drying oven, a mixing mill, centrifuge, Soxhlet extractors tted as usual) preferably with ground-glass joints. Talc baths are better than water ths (absence of steam). Cork connections should not be used for acetone extractions. small muffle furnace, a crucible furnace and a small tube furnace will be useful. An -to-date rubber laboratory should contain a small experimental press, a small vulcan-ng pan and a tensile-strength testing machine.

Analysis of Crude Rubber

Chief Determinations. Moisture, resin (acetone extract), insoluble, nitrogen, sh, rubber, traces of coagulant.

Moisture. Place 10 grams of rubber (cut into the smallest pieces possible with a air of scissors) into a flat porcelain dish and dry the material in a vacuum oven r two hours at 50° C. (apply vacuum gradually). Estimation may be made in n ordinary air oven heated at 80° C. for three hours or until weight is constant, · r the moisture may be determined by difference (after extraction with acetone).)riginal weight of rubber −(extract+residue) =moisture. Determination of mois-ure by desiccation *in vacuo* in presence of conc. H_2SO_4 is a refinement for research urposes.

Resin (acetone extract). Two 3–5 gram samples from the washed and dried

rubber are cut up or rolled into a very thin strip. If tacky and liable to coale
interleave the material with muslin or filter paper. Charge the thimble a
extract for six hours with 60 cc. acetone (freshly distilled over anhydrous K_2C
using the fraction 56°–57° C.). Distill the solvent and heat the residue at 1(
until the weight is constant. The flask should be inclined in order to exped
removal of the solvent. Increase in weight of the tared flask = acetone extra
Dry *in vacuo* to attain constant weight.

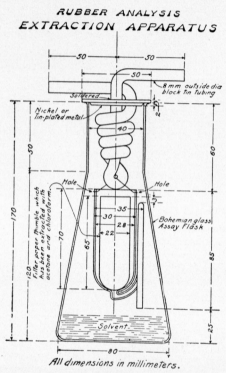

RUBBER ANALYSIS
EXTRACTION APPARATUS

All dimensions in millimeters.

FIG. 203.

The percentage of resin is generally characteristic of the brand. Pará (1.3 per cent
Congo (4–6 per cent), Kassai (4.5 per cent), Borneo (10 per cent), Ceylon Plant
tion (3.2 per cent), Guayule varies (average 18 per cent), Pontianak (85 per cent
The extractor used should enable the material to be continually surrounded by aceto
vapor at the boiling point of the solvent. The character of the residue is impo
tant, as, technically, rubber containing hard resin is preferred (resin up to 8 per ce
is not objectionable if it is hard). Part of the acetone extract is saponifiable (KO
value) and part contains unsaturated bodies. Iodine value of rubber-resins—Born
(30.6) Pará (118), Kassai (107), Guayule (94). All rubbers except Pará contain optical
active resins. This fact has been proposed as a means of detecting rubber other tha
Pará in a mixture. The optical activity is always dextro-rotatory, and the mo
optically active the less saponifiable is the resin. Congo and Guayule $[\alpha]_D = 12$, Jel
tong $[\alpha]_D = 50.9$.

Ash Heat 5 grams of the sample in a flat porcelain dish on an asbestos car
from which a small hole has been cut. Fuse gently. Increase heat to redness

the muffle. The ash of washed "plantation" ranges from 0.1–1.5 per cent. If white or pale yellow. and infusible—silica, lime, and magnesia are indicated. If highly ferruginous the ash is of a brick-red color.

Having determined the moisture, resin, ash and dirt, the *rubber may be calculated by difference.*

Resins containing rubber from Borneo, Sumatra and Malay (Jelutong, Pontianak, Dead Borneo), are used in vulcanized and unvulcanized rubber compositions, also in cements and chewing gum. These rubber-bearing resins should be examined for moisture (a 50 grams sample is heated *in vacuo* at 95° C.), dirt, resin (rubber by difference). The resins are hard and crystalline. Resin is determined by extracting a 2-gram strip rolled in filter paper, or as particles loose in the thimble. After extracting for two hours the shrunken mass should be again cut up and re-extracted.

Insoluble. Take 1 gram original or washed, dry rubber (if sticky), or use the residue from the acetone extraction if the rubber is firm.

(a) Weigh out 25 grams of washed, dried rubber and mix on the rolls. To 2 grams of this in a flask add 10 cc. toluene and heat for two hours under a reflux-condenser upon a talc bath. Allow to settle and filter, or better, centrifuge for one half-hour. Pour off the supernatant liquid, add more toluene and whirl again. The compact insoluble is received on a tared ashless filter. Weigh residue (1), incinerate and weigh (2), difference = organic insoluble. (Caspari.)

(b) Heat 1 gram of the finely divided sample in a large test tube with 10 cc. of phenetol for five hours. Allow to settle, filter, rinse on to a tared dish—dry and weigh. (Beadle and Stevens, I. R. Journal, 1912, p. 193.)

(c) Warm 2 grams of rubber with 15 cc. petroleum (B. P. 200° C.) in a small flask for one half-hour; dilute with 100 cc. benzene. Filter or centrifuge as in (a). (Caspari.)

Protein. (Total Nitrogen). Place 2 grams of the washed, dried rubber in a Kjeldahl flask with 30 cc. conc. H_2SO_4 (or 20 cc. conc. $H_2SO_4 + 10$ cc. fuming H_2SO_4) and one small drop (0.2 gram) of Hg. Loosely stopper the flask and heat over a naked flame, increasing heat gradually to vigorous boiling until the liquid is light straw-colored, and transparent (two or three small crystals of $KMnO_4$ added towards the end will assist). Cool and dilute with water cautiously. Rinse into a 500 cc. flask, and add a solution of 2 grams sodium sulphide in 20 cc. water. Add 80 cc. NaOH solution (1.35) together with 0.5 gram Zn in small pieces. Connect for distillation and distill off the NH_3 into a flask containing 20 cc. N/5 H_2SO_4. Titrate the excess of N/5 H_2SO_4 with N/5 NaOH (using Methyl Orange as indicator). Calculate N, and multiply by 6.25 to obtain the weight of protein in the washed and dried rubber. N.B. Unwashed rubber contains substances rich in N. (See pp. 338 and 350.)

Wilfarth's modification of the Kjeldahl process is also recommended for the total nitrogen in rubber. It consists in digesting 1 gram of rubber with 30 cc. of conc. H_2SO_4, 7 grams K_2SO_4, and 1 gram anhydrous copper sulphate, for four hours and then proceeding as usual.

Rubber. For technical purposes it is sufficient to subtract the sum of the percentages of washing loss (moisture and dirt) ash, organic insoluble, and nitrogenous matter from 100 to obtain the percentage of rubber-hydrocarbon.

(a) Spence's Method. Take 1.5 gram acetone-extracted and vacuum-dried rubber. Add 100 cc. cold benzene. After swelling, make up to 200 cc.; mix and filter through a tared funnel plugged with glass wool. Cover with a watch glass. Take 100 cc. of the filtrate in a tared flask, distill solvent, dry and weigh. Residue = pure soluble rubber. Calculate the percentage on the original weight. The remainder is diluted and filtered, washed with benzene and then with alcohol. Dry the residue at 65° C. and weigh. Residue = insoluble rubber + insoluble impurities.

(b) **Precipitation Method.** Weigh out 3 grams of material and swell in 10 cc. toluene, make up to 100 cc. with toluene, allow to settle (or use centrifuge). Into 100 cc. warm alcohol (95 per cent), transfer by means of a pipette 50 cc. of the supernatant liquid, stirring meanwhile. Remove the clot by means of a glass rod to another dish and redissolve in 100 cc. toluene. Reprecipitate in alcohol. Squeeze out the alcohol and transfer the clot to a tared watch-glass. Dry to constant weight (preferably *in vacuo*). Calculate percentage of rubber. If the rubber contains much resin use the acetone-extracted material.

(c) **As Tetrabromide:** (**Budde's Method,** Spence and Galletly modification). The value of this method is lessened by the fact that proteins and resins absorb bromine.

Dissolve 3 cc. Br and 0.5 g. I in 500 cc. CCl_4. Weigh out 0.2 gram of original rubber material. Extract with acetone. Place the residue in a wide-mouthed bottle, cover it with 50 cc. CCl_4 and allow it to swell overnight. Add 50 cc. of the Br-I solution and allow reaction to continue six hours with the occasional shaking. Add 50 cc. alcohol with stirring, and wash the pptd. tetrabromide by decantation, with alcohol. Drain the ppt. and allow it to swell in CS_2 (50 cc.). Reprecipitate the tetrabromide ($C_{10}H_{16}Br_4$) by adding 50 cc. petroleum ether, wash with alcohol and dry below 60° C. Transfer ppt. to a porcelain crucible. Mix it with 4 grams of a mixture of Na_2CO_3 and KNO_3 (2 : 1). Gradually heat to redness. Dissolve the residue in distilled water, acidify with HNO_3 and boil. Cool. Add excess of N/10 $AgNO_3$ and titrate excess of $AgNO_3$ with N/10 AmCNS sol., using Fe alum as indicator. Calculate Br. Br $\times$ 0.42 = rubber hydrocarbon.

(d) **Nitrosite Method** (**Alexander**). Dissolve 1 gram of rubber (preferably acetone-extracted) in benzene contained in a weighed beaker. Pass nitrous fumes (from conc. $HNO_3 + As_2O_3$ in small lumps, or starch) through a drying tower containing P_2O_5, and thence into the benzene-rubber solution for one hour, by means of a wide tube. Settle and decant the liquid through a weighed Gooch, and wash with benzene. Add 50 cc. fresh benzene, again pass the gas, and allow the beaker to stand overnight. Decant through Gooch, wash with benzene and with absolute ether. The beaker, tube and crucible are placed in the desiccator for one half-hour to remove ether. Dry in air oven at 80° C. Dissolve the nitrosite in acetone, and again dry and weigh the beaker and tube. The difference = rubber nitrosite. R. N. $\times$ 0.47 = rubber hydrocarbon.

Note. For works-control, the ash, resin and washing loss must be determined upon every lot. The efficiency of the drying ovens must be tested after each operation—samples of the dried rubber being taken from several drying-pans and the moisture determined. The residual moisture should be less than 0.5 per cent. The soluble albuminoids are determined from the difference of N content of the unwashed and that of the washed rubber, the remainder being insoluble protein. (Caspari).

FILLERS (Organic)

A rubber article may contain only 50 per cent rubber and sometimes much less. The **non-rubber portion** consists of a wide variety of substances, organic or inorganic. The **organic** fillers are generally substances of an oily, waxy or resinous nature. The **inorganic** fillers are finely-divided dry powders.

Vulcanization consists in the preparation of a dough containing essentially rubber, fillers and sulphur, and heating it at 125° C. to 175° C. for one to three hours, and the compounding materials are added (1) to impart desired effects (hardness, softness, pliability, strength, insulatory properties, resistance to chemical action), or (2) to give desired color, weighting or lightening the manufactured article, (3) cheapening, (4) modifying the vulcanization.

The **organic** diluents in common use are " Factice," reclaimed rubber and rubber waste, pitches (M. R. and coal-tar pitch), waxes, oils, petroleum residues, resins, dextrin, and cellulose. Factice, reclaim, waste and bitumen, cheapen the product. Waxes and oils are added for specific effect.

Factice is obtained by the interaction of glyceride-oils (linseed, cotton, maize, castor and rape) with sulphur chloride, S_2Cl_2 at 80° C. to 100° C., forming *white substitute;* or with sulphur alone at 160° C. to 180° C. yielding *brown substitute.* The product is a stiff jelly, insoluble in rubber solvents but swelling in them to form " gels." Factice is saponified by alcoholic alkali yielding glycerine and alkali soaps (both soluble in water). Factice is a complex mixture of factice proper, unvulcanized fatty oil, free sulphur and added impurities, such as paraffin wax, heavy petroleum, resin and bitumen.

For **analysis of factice** take samples from different parts of the consignment and thoroughly mix them upon the rolls.

Moisture. Dry 3 grams at 60° C. until constant in weight.

Acetone Extract. Weigh 2 grams into an extraction thimble, plug with cotton wool and extract with acetone. Dry the extract at 100° C. and weigh. The extract consists of unvulcanized oil, unsaponifiable matter and free sulphur. On cooling, paraffin wax, if present, will crystallize out and mineral oil will show fluorescence.

Total Sulphur. Add 2–3 grams of factice in small portions to 20 cc. conc. HNO_3 contained in a porcelain dish. Allow reaction to continue in the cold for fifteen minutes. Gradually heat upon a water bath until the contents of the dish is reduced to a syrup. Add 5 cc. fuming HNO_3 and evaporate again. Fuse the residue with KOH and a little KNO_3. Cool and dissolve in water. Precipitate the sulphur as $BaSO_4$. Calculate S.

Sulphur in the Fatty Acids. Saponify 10 grams of factice with alc. KOH. Decompose the soap produced with HCl. Collect the fatty acids, dry and weigh. Or after decomposing the soap with acid (HCl) warm upon a steam bath. Add 5 grams of pure, hard paraffin wax (correctly weighed) and allow it to melt with the fatty acids. Cool in a cold water-bath. Remove the cake and weigh after drying on blotting paper. Take an aliquot part of the fatty acids and determine the sulphur by a potash fusion (as above). Free $S = $ total $S - S$ in factice acids.

Saponifiable Matter. Take two 2 gram portions of the mixed factice and extract with acetone as before. Add 50 cc. N. alc. KOH. Evaporate the alcohol and take up the residue with water. Transfer to a separatory funnel and shake out twice with ether. Evaporate the ether extract, and weigh. Total acetone extract $-$ (free sulphur + unsaponifiable) $=$ *unvulcanized oil.* The residue insoluble in acetone $=$ factice proper.

Take 1 gram of the " residue from acetone " and make a nitrate fusion, or use the potash peroxide method. Gently heat in an iron basin with 10 grams of stick

KOH and add 10 cc. 95 per cent alcohol. Add 1 cc. water, heat and stir. Cool, and dissolve in water. Divide into two equal portions:

(a) Determine *sulphur* by adding excess of HCl, and BaCl$_2$ solution.

(b) Determine *chlorine* by adding excess of HNO$_3$ and AgNO$_3$ solution.

Acidity. Stir 5 grams of factice with 20 cc. alcohol. Total acidity is determined by titrating with N/10 NaOH, using phenolphthalein as indicator. Free sulphuric acid is sometimes present. Shake 5 grams of factice with hot water. Cool and filter, add HCl and precipitate with BaCl$_2$. Express each acidity in terms of oleic acid. Total acidity (as oleic) −sulphuric acid (as oleic)=free fatty acid (as oleic), (in absence of neutral sulphates).

Ash. Incinerate two grams in the usual manner. Examine qualitatively.

Assay deliveries for acetone extract, free sulphur and unsaponifiable. Experimental mixings and vulcanization will determine the effect in manufacture.

Bitumen and Pitch

Asphaltum is used in cable coverings to remove microporosity, and to increase insulation. Mineral rubber (M. R.) is a cheapening diluent and can be added in large proportions.

Analysis. *Asphaltene.* Soak 1 gram of the bitumen in 50 cc. cold petroleum ether for six hours. Crush with a glass rod and shake until disintegrated. Settle, filter, and wash the residue with petrol. The residue is known as the "asphaltene fraction." Dry and weigh. (a) Dissolve in benzene. Residue= mineral matter+carbon. Dry and weigh, (b) $A - B$=asphaltene. The solution in petrol, "petrolene" fraction, is brown and greasy, and may contain solid paraffin. If it is fluorescent and carbon is found in the residue, coal-tar pitch is indicated. (Caspari.)

Softening Point of Bitumen and Pitches. (Barta's modification of Kramer's and Sarnow's method.) Several pieces of glass tubing (6 mm. bore) are cut and ground true at both ends so as to be exactly 5 cm. long. Fill with melted and well-stirred bitumen. Cool and shave off surplus bitumen. Connect the tube by means of rubber to a similar but longer empty tube. Pour into the empty tube 5 grams of mercury. Fit the tubes into a test tube and heat in a bath of molten paraffin. Apply heat, increasing the temperature at the rate of 2° C. per minute. Note the temperature at which the Hg drops through. The softening point is generally 30° C. to 35° C. (Chem. Ind., 1903, p. 55.)

Carbon in Coal-tar Pitch. Dissolve 1 gram of pitch in 100 cc. hot benzene and allow to settle. Pour the supernatant liquid through a tared Gooch. Boil the residue again with 100 cc. benzene and filter: wash, dry and weigh.

Ceresine is soluble in hot acetone, but very slightly soluble in alcohol o cooling. Determine the M. P.; and acidity by N/100 NaOH; 20 grams shoul not require more than 1 cc. Beeswax (used in ebonite), camphor, glycerin an resin should be looked for. All coloring matter used in the rubber industr should be examined for acidity. Pigments containing copper and chromiu (examine ash) should be rejected. Paraffin wax and ceresine are used reduce microporosity.

Rubber Waste and Reclaim

Reclaim is prepared by grinding waste and treating it with water at high temperatu in presence of acid or caustic alkali. Although reclaimed rubber contains its origin combined sulphur it can be revulcanized. Regenerated rubber appears as a stiff doug and has not the resilience or strength of new material.

The following **determination**; should be carried out. Specific gravity, acetone extract, quantity of factice, quantity of factice in reclaim, etc.

Dry the " residue from acetone " and boil it in a small flask for three hours (under reflux) with 50 cc. of N/5 alcoholic KOH and pour off. Evaporate alcohol, boil with water, acidify and shake out with ether. Evaporate ethereal solution. Dry and weigh the residue (fatty acids). Multiply the weight of fatty acids by 1.1 to obtain the weight of *factice proper*.

100 — (percentage of extract+percentage of factice+percentage of ash) = percentage of rubber.

Reclaim should be examined for gritty matter and copper.

Compounding Materials (Fillers and Modifiers)

The **most important** powders are: Litharge and white lead, zinc oxide, zinc sulphide, barytes, lithopone, antimony-sulphide (a rubber factory usually now employs two types, one containing 15/17% of free sulphur, the other practically free from sulphur), vermilion, ferric oxide, lime, chalk, magnesia, magnesium carbonate, kieselguhr, ultramarine, clay, mica, glass-powder, pumice and carbon-black. Consignments of these should be examined on arrival and checked with the sample. They must contain no injurious adulterants. (See present volume under separate heads for detection of impurities.)

All these materials should be in fine powdered form. Pass the powders through a sieve and examine for fragments of wood and metal. The most satisfactory sieves are Nos. 30, 60, and 90 mesh. In employing sieves of these grades the possibility of small hard foreign particles likely to cause such defects as blowholes in mechanical goods, football bladders, aircushions, etc., is avoided. Determine **moisture** by drying 10 grams on Petri dish for two hours at 60° C. *Free mineral acid* (where likely) is determined by boiling 5 grams of the material with distilled water, filtering and titrating with N/50 NaOH. Calculate to H_2SO_4. This should be less than 0.1 per cent. Test for copper by NH_4OH.

Rapid Method for the Determination of Inorganic Fillers (Mineral Matter, etc.) in Rubber Mixings. Weigh out 1 gram of the sample. Extract with acetone and dry the residue at 50°-60° C. Heat it with 25 cc. petroleum B. P., 230°-260° C. in a 100 cc. Erlenmeyer flask in a paraffin-wax bath until the rubber has gone into solution. Fill the flask with benzene and allow it to stand for 24 hours to settle. Filter through a Gooch crucible which has been prepared by forming in it (over the usual two thicknesses of filter paper) a filter bed of kieselguhr of about half the depth of the crucible. Filtration is complete in 2 hours, a perfectly clear filtrate being obtained in one operation. The same filter can be employed again after removing the surface to a depth of two millimeters.

The **litharge** used should be completely soluble in HNO_3 without effervescence. Objectionable impurities—PbO_2 (black flakes left in HNO_3 solution) and copper. (See page 1184.)

Red Lead is used as an accelerator and may contain $CaCO_3$ and Fe_2O_3. (See page 634.)

Test **Magnesia** for water of hydration, Ca and silica. Test for Mn and Cu. (See page 1292.)

Barytes should be pure white. Test for SiO_2 and Fe. (See page 60.)

Determination of Barium as Sulphate and Carbonate in Vulcanizing

Rubber. J. B. Tuttle (J. I. & E. Ch., 1916). The total Barium is determined as sulphate. To determine the $BaCO_3$ weigh out into a porcelain boat 1 gram of rubber and place it in a glass tube and ignite in a current of CO_2. The finely ground residue is treated with 10 grams Am_2CO_3, 15 cc. strong ammonia and 50 cc. water. Boil 15 minutes to convert the Pb to carbonate. Filter off the insoluble $BaSO_4$ and carbonates of Pb, Ba, Ca and Zn and wash the ppte. to remove the soluble sulphates. Add 10 cc. glacial acetic acid and sufficient water to bring total volume to 100 cc. Heat to boiling. Filter. The Pb is removed as sulphide and the Barium is determined as carbonate. The Ba as sulphate is determined by difference.

Ultramarine may be present to disguise a yellow tint. (For analysis see page 1183.) **Whiting** ($CaCO_3$) should be free from SiO_2, Fe and Mn. (See page 105.)

Silica must be white; determine moisture, ignition loss and bases. (Remainder = Silica.) (See page 1187.)

Dry 1 gram at 110° C. ignite, add HF and three drops of conc. H_2SO_4. Evaporate and ignite to oxides. (Loss = SiO_2.)

Talc is hydrated magnesium silicate. Test sample between finger and thumb for grit. Analysis should approximate to: Ignition loss 6 per cent, silica 60 per cent, Al_2O_3 9 per cent, MgO 25 per cent. (See page 293.) For the manufacture of white goods all white pigments or fillers should be white and also remain white when treated with sulphuretted hydrogen. Other grades can of course be used in low-grade white or dark colored mechanical goods.

Asbestos. Determine water of hydration, SiO_2, Fe and Mg.
Rubber pigments may be tested by experimental mixing and vulcanization.

Zinc Oxide is completely soluble in 10 per cent acetic acid, without effervescence. Fe, Cu and Pb should be absent.

Lithopone is obtained by mixing BaS and $ZnSO_4$ in molecular proportions and should therefore consist of an intimate mixture of $BaSO_4$ (70.5 per cent) and 29.5 per cent ZnS. Determine soluble barium salts, soluble zinc salts, barium carbonate, moisture, acidity, insoluble, and total sulphide. (See page 1186.)

Antimony in Rubber Goods.[1] Three grams of the finely rasped rubber are treated in a Kjeldahl flask with 40 to 45 cc. of strong sulphuric acid. A small quantity of mercury or mercury salt is added, together with a small piece of paraffine wax. The mixture is heated until the rubber is dissolved and the black liquid begins to clear. Two to 4 grams of potassium sulphate are then added and the heating continued until a colorless or pale yellow liquid is obtained. After cooling, 1 to 2 grams of potassium metabisulphite are added and an excess of tartaric acid. The liquid is diluted sufficiently to prevent the charring of the tartaric acid and boiled until the odor of sulphurous acid has disappeared. A few cc. of dilute hydrochloric acid are added, the liquid diluted to 200 cc., filtered through a dry filter, and 195 cc. titrated either with iodine or with potassium bromate (the latter in acid solution), as described under the volumetric procedures, 21, 25.

Zinc sulphide is liable to contain ZnO as impurity. (Page 597.)

Determination of Zinc Sulphide. Take average sample and dry 5 grams for moisture; weigh 0.2 gram into a stoppered bottle, and shake with 50 cc. N/10 iodine solution. Add 5 cc. conc. HCl and allow bottle to stand two hours with occasional shaking. Titrate excess of iodine with sodium thiosulphate. One gram I = 0.384 gram. ZnS. (See also page 605.)

[1] The original procedure may be found in Chem. News, Vol. XXI, p. 124.

Antimony Sulphides. Crimson Sb_2S_3 (prepared by boiling $SbCl_3$ and $Na_2S_2O_3$). Orange (by boiling powdered stibnite with polysulphides and precipitating the sulphantimonate with mineral acids). Plastered antimony contains 30–50 per cent $CaSO_4$. Antimony sulphide is tested for free sulphur, Sb, $CaSO_4$ and sulphide-sulphur. Free sulphur: Extract 2 grams with CS_2 (freshly distilled); drying extract at 60° C. Expel solvent from residue in thimble and dissolve $\frac{1}{2}$ gram in conc. HCl, boil, add 2 grams tartaric acid and 150 cc. distilled water. Filter and weigh siliceous residue. Pass H_2S and determine Sb gravimetrically or volumetrically. (See page 21.)

Approximate rapid methods:

(1) Heat in porcelain crucible 1 gram with HNO_3 (1.4) and ignite. Residue $= SbO_2 + CaSO_4$.

(2) Mix 1 gram with 2 grams pure AmCl in a porcelain crucible, ignite ($SbCl_3$ is volatilized). Residue $= CaSO_4 + $ Silica. Total S by ignition with HNO_3, etc.

Rouge.—Determine Fe by boiling 0.5 gram with 500 cc. HCl (1.20). Add AmOH. Filter, ignite and weigh. Add HF and H_2SO_4. Ignite and weigh (loss $=$ silica). Divide the filtrate into two equal parts and determine Ca and SO_4. (See page 247.)

Vermilion should contain no free sulphur, ash, soluble Hg salts nor aniline dyes. (See page 1192.)

Lampblack. Test for grease by extracting 2 grams with acetone. Ignite 2 grams for ash or shake 2 grams with acetone in 100 cc. flask, make up to 101 cc. Add 1 drop dil. HCl, allow to settle and pipette 50 cc. into a tared flask. (See page 1196.)

In **bone-black** determine amorphous carbon, calcium phosphate and calcium carbonate. Carbon is determined by dissolving out the mineral matter with HCl. Ignite residue and deduct ash.

Magnesium Compounds. French chalk (silicate of Mg). Determine moisture, ignition loss, magnesium carbonate and oxide. Find sp. gr. and degree of fineness by flotation method. Determine CO_2 in Schroetter apparatus. (See page 124.)

Lime is used as a hastener of vulcanization. Determine CaO in presence of carbonate by dissolving out with a solution of cane sugar. Estimate SiO_2, carbonate, Mn, and Cu.

Zinc Compounds generally are tested for $ZnSO_4$, Pb, Fe. Estimate Zn by Ferrocyanide method. (See page 603.)

" **Flowers of Sulphur** " is obtained by sublimation. It contains **moisture** and free H_2SO_4 (determine by shaking 10 grams with 20 cc. alcohol neutral to Phenolphthalein: Filter and titrate with N/10 NaOH). Maximum acidity allowable $= 0.2$ per cent. There should be no residue on ignition. (See page 519.)

Sulphur chloride distills between 130° and 140° C. Maximum residue $= 5$ per cent and consists of sulphur. Determination of Cl and S (**Weber's Method**). Weigh 5 grams S_2Cl_2 into a 100-cc. flask, shake with benzene 100 cc. Pipette 10 cc. into 25 cc. N. alcoholic KOH. Digest on water bath for one hour. Distill solvent and dry at 100° C. Add 100 cc. hot water and two drops of HNO_3. Add 10 cc. of 10 per cent $CuSO_4$ solution, filter and determine Cl by Gay-Lussac or Völhard method. Chemically pure S_2Cl_2 contains 52.5 per cent Cl. (See also page 149.)

Examination of Solvents

Solvent naphtha is the xylene fraction of coal-tar spirit and 95 per cent of it distills between 125° C. and 150° C. **90 per cent benzene** is so called because 90 per cent of it distills below 100° C. Similarly with **50 per cent benzol.** CS_2 **as an impurity in naphtha** is estimated thus: Add 1 cc. phenylhydrazine to 100 cc. naphtha—allow it to stand one day. The crystalline deposit (the phenylhydrazine salt of phenyl-thiocarbazidic acid) is filtered off and weighed. Multiply by 0.26 for CS_2. CS_2 (B. P. 46° C; sp. gr. = 1.27) should not have an offensive odor. The distillation residue should be less than 1.5 per cent. Detection and determination as above. (Caspari.) Pyridine, or its homologues, and naphthalene are likely to occur in naphtha.

CCl_4 (B. P. 77° C., sp.gr. 1.63) should leave no residue on distillation.

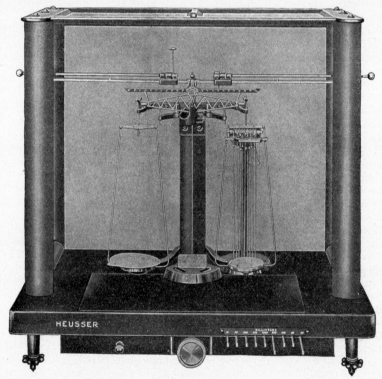

Fig. 203a. Analytical Balance. (By courtesy of The Mine and Smelter Supply Company.)

Vulcanized Rubber

The properties of manufactured rubber vary with the contents and vulcanization process. Oxygen or air causes the rubber to be hard and brittle especially in the case of low grades. Free H_2SO_4 and traces of copper increase the tendency to oxidation. Light also favors the change and sunlight increases the acetone extract (degradation of rubber to resins). Soft rubber is stable towards dilute acids and alkalis. Rubbers containing CaO, MgO, ZnO are affected by acids. Strong H_2SO_4 chars rubber and HNO_3 oxidizes it.

Specific Gravity of Rubber. Introduce into a pyknometer 5 grams of the rubber, cut into small pieces (not ground). Take care that no air bubbles are included. Calculate sp. gr. (water at $15°$ C.$=1$).

The most important physical properties of vulcanized rubber are stability to change of temperature, impermeability to water and gases, electric insulation. Well-vulcanized rubber absorbs very little water at ordinary pressure but gutta-percha is preferred for deep-sea cables under high pressure. Permeability to gases (N = 1000, standard) CO 1113, air 1149, CH_4 2148, O 2556, H 5500, CO_2 13,580. From these figures it is seen that diffusion is supplementsd by another action—adsorption (Ditmar). Paraffin lessens the permeability. Rubber is inferior to gold-beater's skin for balloons. In presence of oxygen, ultra violet light has a less effect upon vulcanized rubber than on the crude substance. A chrome-yellow ultra-violet light screen is used for balloons.

Vulcanization was introduced by Goodyear, 1839, who secured no patent until 1844. Thos. Hancock, in 1843, patented a process in England; Parkes in 1846. The use of molds in curing was introduced by Hancock in 1846. Hollow goods were first made by Goodyear in 1848 and ebonite in 1851.

Chief Methods of Vulcanization.—1. Heating with sulphur, with or without sulphur carriers, such as lead compounds, either in hot air by means of steam and pressure.

2. Cold cure, by means of sulphur chloride dissolved in CS_2. Cold-cured goods contain chlorine as well as sulphur. The change from rubber hydrocarbon to ebonite is *probably* represented by the following formulæ.

The amount of combined sulphur depends upon the amount of sulphur introduced, the temperature, and time of vulcanization.

$$\text{The } \textit{coefficient of vulcanization} = \frac{\text{sulphur of vulcanization}}{\text{rubber substance}}$$

Wo. Ostwald is of opinion that the process is adsorption, giving a whole series of sulphur-additions, the members of which have not yet been isolated.

Analysis of Vulcanized Rubber. (Manufactured goods)

Sample and its Preparation. *Sampling for analysis.* If the material is hard
ebonite raspings and shavings are well mixed or the ebonite is broken up by slowly
grinding in a small coffee-grinder. Soft rubbers should not be worked on the mill
as they heat up (increase in acetone extract). They may be broken up by passing
through a household mincing machine. A good sample is obtained by selecting
representative portions and cutting these with scissors into the smallest possible
particles. The *object of analysis* is the detection or control of constituents
and may comprise the following *determinations:* Moisture, ash, acetone extract
free sulphur, total sulphur, alcoholic potash extract.

Acetone extraction removes free-sulphur resins, oils, waxes, the acetone
soluble portion of mineral rubbers and substitutes. Soft rubber requires a
least eight hours and ebonite two days for extraction. The process may b
hastened by digesting with acetone at 100° C. in a sealed bottle.

Make two extractions on 2-gram samples and treat as in the case of crude
rubber. If the acetone extract is fluorescent, the presence of coal-tar pitc
and mineral oil is indicated. A yellow-colored extract indicates bitumer
On cooling, crystals of sulphur or paraffin wax may appear.

Unite the two extracts and add 50 cc. alc. KOH (almost colorless). Boil under
reflux for two hours. Distill the alcohol. Heat the residue with 10 cc. distilled
water, cool somewhat and add ether (20 cc.). Shake until waxes, etc., are in solu
tion and transfer the whole to a separator; wash out the flask with ether and warm
water. Shake and allow the contents to separate. Draw off the aqueous solution
into another separatory funnel, leaving the flocculent portion in the first separator
Add pure ether to the second funnel and unite ether layer with ethereal layer in
first funnel. Filter the ethereal portion (through small plug of cotton wool) into a
weighed flask. Evaporate the solvent, dry at 100° C. and weigh the unsaponifiable
matter in the acetone extract. (Reserve this residue for estimation of hydrocarbons,—paraffin.) The unsaponifiable residue from the alcoholic KOH may contain hydrocarbons and unsaponifiable resins. The resins, and part of the hydrocarbons are soluble in alcohol and may be thus estimated:

Add 3 cc. conc. H_2SO_4, cover, and heat for four hours at 110° C. in an air oven
Cool, and add 30 cc. petrol. Boil under reflux for one hour. Pour off the petrol
portion carefully into a separator, wash it with 15 per cent KOH to which an equal
volume of alcohol has been added. Draw off the petrol solution and evaporate it
in a tared flask. The increase in the weight of the flask = hydrocarbon (paraffin
wax or mineral oil). The aqueous portion in the separatory funnels contains the
free sulphur and the saponifiable part of the acetone extract (as potassium salts).

The estimation of the free and combined sulphur can now be more conveniently carried out by a method described in the India Rubber Journal
March 6, 1920, page 4, details of which are as follows:

Five grammes finely cut rubber is put into a 500-cc. Ernlenmeyer flask
(Pyrex glass, heavy type), 10 grs. " zinc oxide-nitric acid " solution is added
and the flask whirled rapidly to thoroughly moisten the sample. The zinc
oxide-nitric acid solution is prepared by adding 200 grs. chemically pure ZnO
to one liter chemically pure HNO_3.

If convenient the mixture may be allowed to stand over night at this point.
By so doing the sample becomes partially decomposed which permits the
addition of nitric acid with no danger of ignition of the sample.

Joint Rubber Insulation Committee Method

Outline

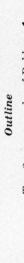
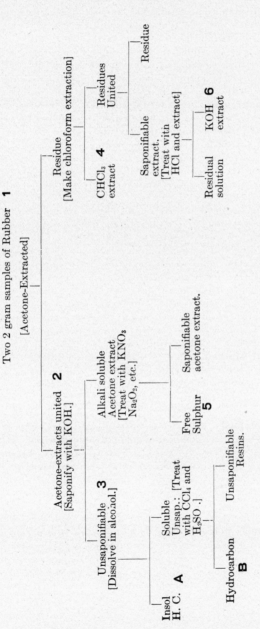

Two 2 gram samples of Rubber **1**
[Acetone-Extracted]

Residue
[Make chloroform extraction]

Acetone-extracts united **2**
[Saponify with KOH.]

CHCl₃ **4**
extract

Residues
United

Residue

Saponifiable
extract.
[Treat witn
HCl and extract]

Unsaponifiable **3**
[Dissolve in alcohol.]

Alkali soluble
Acetone extract
[Treat with KNO₃
Na₂O₂, etc.]

Saponifiable
acetone extract.

Residual
solution

KOH **6**
extract

Soluble
Unsap.: [Treat
with CCl₄ and
H₂SO₄.]

Free
Sulphur
5

Unsaponifiable
Resins.

Insol
H. C. **A**

Hydrocarbon
B

[Total waxy Hydrocarbons A+B. Weigh substances ringed, others by difference.]

(See Jour. Ind. & Eng. Chem., Jan., 1914.)

46

15 cc. nitric acid is then added all at once and the flask is whirled rapidl to keep the sample immersed in the solution in order to avoid ignition by to rapid oxidation. When solution of the rubber is complete, 5 cc. of saturate bromine water is added and the mixture evaporated to a foaming syrup.

For the determination of total sulphur in unvulcanized mixture use 3 cc of bromine water in place of the above quantity.

If particles of organic matter remain at the end of the evaporation, a few cc. HNO₃ (fuming) are added to the syrup and evaporated as before.

The flask is then cooled and a few crystals of KClO₃ are added to assis in the oxidation of the sulphur and the decomposition of any nitrates. Th mixture is then evaporated to dryness over an Argand burner and the content of the flask finally baked until all the nitrates are decomposed and no mor nitrogen peroxide fumes can be detected. Care should be used at this poin to ensure uniform penetration of the heat throughout the contents of the flask and to remove the flask as soon as the baking is complete.

When the baking is complete the flask is cooled and the residue taken u with 50 cc. 1 : 6 HCl and heated until solution is complete. If litharge wer present, lead salts not otherwise removed will be eliminated in the final washin with boiling water.

The solution is then filtered up to 300 cc. and precipitated with BaCl₂ Filter, wash with boiling water, dry, ignite in the usual manner and weigh.

Evaporate the aqueous liquid to small bulk, transfer it to a nickel dish add 2 grams KNO₃ and evaporate to dryness upon an asbestos card from whic a convenient central hole is cut; heat to quiet fusion. Dissolve the melt i hot water, and transfer it to a porcelain dish. Acidify with HCl, evaporat to dryness and dehydrate in an air oven (150° C. for one hour). Add 2 cc conc. HCl, take up with water, filter and wash. Bulk should be 200 cc Boil and add slowly from a pipette a slight excess of BaCl₂ 10 per cent solution Treat the BaSO₄ in the usual manner. Calculate sulphur.

The **free sulphur** may be estimated directly upon the acetone extract.

Thiocyanate Method.[1] To the acetone extract add 25 cc. 95% alcohol an a lump (1 gram) of KCN. Boil under reflux for half an hour. Remove excess o cyanide and boil off alcohol. The sulphur now exists as KCNS. Dilute and ad

1 cc. HNO₃ and a little Fe alum. Titrate with N/10 AgNO₃. $S = \dfrac{Ag}{0.297}$

Oxidation Method. Heat acetone extract with 5 cc. conc. HNO₃ and a little powdered KClO₃. Cover and heat on a hot plate for six hours. Dilute with weak HCl, filter and precipitate with BaCl₂. Test the original substance or the residue from the acetone extract with CS₂,—a brown solution indicates bitumen or pitch. The acetone has removed part of the bitumen. If bitumen is indicated air-dry the residue, plug the thimble and extract with CS₂ for six to ten hours. (Note Vulcanized rubber is insoluble in CS₂). Distill the solvents, and weigh the extract.

The Residue from Acetone. (*Chloroform Extraction*) Extract with chloroform (60 cc.) for four hours. Distill the solvent and weigh the extract, which will contain that part of the bitumen (brown color) that was insoluble in acetone. Any uncured rubber present will be dissolved out by chloroform, although even a properly cured compound will yield a little extract to chloroform.

[1] Davis and Foucar, J. S. C. I., 1912, p. 100.

Alcoholic KOH Extraction. The residue from the chloroform extraction
nsists of rubber, factice and mineral charge. It is now boiled (in a flask fitted
th a ground-in reflux condenser), with 50 cc. alc. KOH for four hours. Pass
e solution through a filter, wash with absolute alcohol and subsequently with
ot water. Evaporate the solution to a pasty condition to expel the alcohol.
ake up with hot water and transfer the liquid to a separator. Acidify with
lute HCl, make up to 100 cc. with water, and allow the liquid to cool. Add
) cc. ether and shake. Draw off aqueous solution and treat it with ether again.
nite the ether solutions in a separator and wash with water until the ether solu-
on is acid free. Filter ethereal solution into a tared flask, washing the filter
ith ether. Allow the ether to evaporate gently. Dry the residue at 95° C.
nd weigh.

The residue in the flask consists of the free fatty acids of "factice." Mul-
ply by 1.2 if Cl was found in the alc. KOH extract, or by 1.3 if Cl was absent.

The material left in the flask in which the saponification with alc. KOH
ook place consists of rubber-hydrocarbon, combined sulphur and mineral
marge and possibly organic fillers such as cellulose, cork dust, etc.

The **coefficient of vulcanization** involves three determinations:

1. Total combined sulphur.
2. "Inorganic" sulphur.
3. Rubber hydrocarbon.

The **total combined sulphur** is determined in the residue from the alc. KOH
xtraction.

Henrique's Method. Weigh out 1 gram of the material into a large porcelain
rucible. Add 15 cc. HNO_3. Cover and gradually heat until evaporated. Add
lowly 5 grams $Na_2CO_3 + KNO_3$ (2 : 1). Heat until action starts, withdraw flame
nd cover the crucible. Heat to fusion and pour the melt into a beaker of water.
lixiviate, filter and estimate S as $BaSO_4$. Reserve the residue for the determina-
ion of Pb, Zn, Ba, Mg. (See pages 55, 271, 291.)

$$\text{The coefficient of vulcanization} = \frac{\text{S combined with rubber}}{\text{Rubber present}}.$$ When no sulphur

s present in the organic or mineral fillers the estimation is simple. The combined
ulphur corresponds to the sulphur of vulcanization and equals "total sulphur—
ree sulphur." If substitutes are present, estimate the sulphur of vulcanization
on the dried sample after the alcoholic NaOH treatment and calculate the result
on the original amount of rubber.

If mineral matter containing sulphur be present:

1. Estimate the combined sulphur and sulphur in the mineral matter after
removal of rubber by kerosene. Difference = combined sulphur of vulcanization.
2. Separate rubber from the mineral by solution in xylene (under pressure).
Isolate the rubber from the solvent by distillation in steam. Then estimate
he sulphur of vulcanization directly on the rubber. See J. S. C. I., 1911.

The **isolation of the solid compounding materials** is effected by means of petro-
eum. Take 2 grams of original, or equivalent amount of acetone-extracted material.
Soak overnight in 10 cc. petroleum (B. P. 200° C.). Heat under reflux. Rinse
the contents into a tube and centrifuge for half an hour. Pour off supernatant
iquid and repeat with more petroleum. Weigh the residue, which consists of
inorganic matter, starch, carbon, etc.

Cellulose and cork are frequent constituents to-day in rubber flooring, etc.,
and an article in the India Rubber Journal of March 27, 1920, gives methods
in detail for their estimation.

Mineral Matter.—Incineration may produce change in the mineral constituents. $MgCO_3$ would lose CO_2: some Sb and Hg compounds being reduced b
carbonaceous matter would volatilize even at low temperature, and sulphide
would gain in weight on oxidation to oxide or sulphate. Therefore ashing will giv
only approximate results. Incinerations should be slowly carried out at a low re
heat. The vapors should not inflame. Take 1 to 5 grams according to sp. gr. c
rubber and heat in a flat porcelain dish. Transfer the char to a muffle and bur
off the carbon.

Solvent Method. Take the acetone-extracted material. Two grams are finel
divided and covered in a 50 cc. conical flask with 10 cc. kerosene (B. P. = 200° C.)
Soak overnight. Reflux on sand bath with frequent shaking for two hours. Coo
and settle. Transfer to centrifuge tube and whirl. Pour off liquid (or siphon)
Add fresh petroleum and centrifuge again; and weigh residue.

Total Sulphur. Weigh into a conical beaker 1 gram rubber and add 15 cc
fuming HNO_3, cooling under tap if necessary. Warm on a water-bath, transfe
to a porcelain basin and evaporate twice with fuming HNO_3 to a syrup. Mix wit
5 grams of fusion-mixture and fuse. Lixiviate and filter (if Pb or Ba is present)
Acidify with HCl and evaporate. Add 5 cc. HCl and dissolve in water. Filte
and add $BaCl_2$. Proceed as on page 341.

Stevens' Method for the determination of total sulphur in vulcanized rubbe
(Analyst 1918, 43) is as follows: Half a gram of the sample is digested with 20
cc. HNO_3 (1.42) and 0.5 gram $KClO_3$ is added. Boil for three hours under reflux
condenser. Evaporate dry in a porcelain basin with the addition of 3 grams o
magnesium nitrate. Heat residue cautiously over a naked flame. (The magnesium salt moderates the combustion.) Any unburnt carbon is destroyed by
digestion with HNO_3 and $KClO_3$. The excess of acid is expelled. Add 10 cc
strong HCl and cover the dish with a clock-glass. Gently heat until the red
fumes cease to be evolved. Dilute liquid, filter, make up to 300 cc. Heat to
boiling point and precipitate $BaSO_4$ with 5 cc. $BaCl_2$ sol. (10%). Allow to stand
overnight and filter.

Note on Total Sulphur:

The Carius method is the most reliable, but it requires special apparatus. The
rapid method of Kaye and Sharpe is carried out as follows: 0.25–0.5 gram of the
finely divided sample is intimately mixed with 5 parts by weight of pure zinc oxide and
four parts of KNO_3 in a porcelain crucible and a thin layer of ZnO replaced on the
surface. Cover the crucible and heat it gently until the reaction commences, when the
flame is removed for a time. Subsequently heat with the full flame for five minutes
Cool. Dissolve the contents of the crucible in dilute HCl and precipitate the sulphu
as $BaSO_4$.

Chlorine. Heat 3 grams of the finely divided rubber with fusion mixture and
fuse. Lixiviate, and acidify with HNO_3. Precipitate with $AgNO_3$. This may be
run on the alcoholic NaOH extract when substitutes are present. Evaporate the
extract to dryness and proceed as above.

Estimation of the Rubber. (*Hübener's Method*). 0.2 gram finely divided
rubber is extracted with acetone. Boil with a little water until wet in a conical
beaker. Close the beaker with a stemless funnel, and allow to cool. Add more
water: then 5 to 10 cc. bromine. Gradually heat to boiling, and break up the
precipitate with the round end of a test-tube. Wash and transfer precipitate to
the beaker and again treat with Br. Filter, wash free from bromine (test with
$AgNO_3$). Transfer the precipitate (with filter) to the beaker. Add 20 cc. conc.
HNO_3 and 20 cc. N/10 $AgNO_3$. Boil down with HNO_3 until only AgBr remains.

Dilute and titrate cold with AmCNS, using iron-alum indicator.   We know the amount of bromine from the tetrabromide by the amount of Ag consumed by it (=20 cc. minus the Ag found by titration).   We also know the amount of S in the precipitate.   Assuming that the sulphur is attached at the double bonds and that the bonds unsatisfied by sulphur are satisfied by Br, then

Each atom of S corresponds to $\frac{1}{2}$ mol $C_{10}H_{16}$, giving $C_{10}H_{16}S_2$.
$\qquad$ 32 $\qquad\qquad\qquad\qquad$ 136 $\quad$ .... $\quad$ .... $\qquad$ .... $\quad$ ....

Each atom Br corresponds to $\frac{1}{4}$ mol $C_{10}H_{16}$, giving $C_{10}H_{16}Br_4$.
$\qquad$ 80 $\qquad\qquad\qquad\qquad$ 136 $\quad$ .... $\quad$ .... $\qquad$ .... $\quad$ ....

Therefore
Rubber present corresponds to

$$\left(S\times\frac{136}{2}\times\frac{1}{32}\right)+\left(Br\times\frac{136}{4}\times\frac{1}{\text{c0}}\right),$$

0.2 gram of the original rubber is treated in the same way except that the filtrate is preserved, and the tetrabromide is discarded.   The filtrate contains the free sulphur.   The difference between this and the total sulphur = the sulphur in tetrabromide.

Analysis of Rubber Solutions.   These consist of a 5 to 10 per cent solution of rubber in benzene or petroleum, carbon disulphide, carbon tetrachloride or mixtures of these solvents.   Take 50 grams of rubber-solution and distill with steam. Separate the turbid liquid from the clear and re-distill.   Determine the *sp gr. of the solvent*.   Take 20 grams of rubber solution and spread it out on a Petri dish, cover and weigh.   Evaporate, draw off film and dry to constant weight.   The *dry residue* is analyzed by the usual methods.   Calculate percentage of solvent.

Ebonite.   The acetone extraction should continue for twenty-four hours. Mineral matter is determined by incineration, Sb, Hg, and carbon being separately determined.   Casein sometimes occurs as a filler and would be indicated by high nitrogen content (Kjeldahl), Factor=6.7.   (Caspari.)

Estimation of **Carbon in rubber goods.**   Comminute 2 grams, evaporate twice with 20 cc. HNO_3 in a porcelain basin.   Rinse into a beaker and boil with 350 cc. water.   Filter through a tared paper and wash with hot water.   Rinse contents into another beaker and boil with excess AmOH (dilute).   Add 0.25 gram NH_4Cl. Remove fatty matter by ether.   Settle and pour the clear liquid through the original filter.   Boil residue with AmOH and AmCl and filter again.   Boil the residue with dilute HCl (100 cc.) and filter through the original paper.   Wash, dry and weigh (=$BaSO_4$+$CaSO_4$+carbon).   Incinerate and weigh.   Difference = carbon.

Determination of Antimony and Mercury in Rubber Goods.   Heat 2 grams rubber with 20 cc. conc. H_2SO_4 in a Kjeldahl flask.   Boil for three hours.   Cool, add 1 gram $KMnO_4$ crystals gradually.   Boil for ten minutes.   Cool and take up with 300 cc. water.   Boil and filter.   Precipitate the Sb and Hg by H_2S and determine in the usual way if present alone.   If together, collect the mixed sulphides on a tared filter; wash and rinse into a beaker.   Warm with Na_2S solution. Filter and wash.   Reprecipitate the Sb by HCl and determine as on page 251. The sulphide residue contains the Hg.   Boil with HCl (1 : 1).   Filter and pass H_2S.   Collect the precipitate and add it to the HgS undissolved by the Na_2S solution.   Wash with very dilute HCl, remove the water by alcohol, CS_2, dry and weigh.   (Or use method on page 310.)

Analysis of Mechanical Goods

Acetone Extract. Place 2 grams material in a paper thimble and extract with acetone for eight hours. Transfer the extract to a tared flask. Drive off the solvent and dry the flask at 90° C. *in vacuo.* (Acetone extract uncorrected.)

Free Sulphur. Add to the flask containing the acetone extract (uncorrected) 60 cc. distilled water and 3 cc. Br. Heat until colorless. Filter, and cover with a watch glass. Heat to boiling on a steam bath. Add 10 cc. of 10 per cent $BaCl_2$ solution, and allow to stand several hours. Filter and treat the $BaSO_4$ as usual.

Total Sulphur. 0.5 gram rubber is weighed into a porcelain crucible (100 cc.). Add 20 cc. nitric acid and bromine solution. Cover with a watch glass and allow the whole to stand for one hour. Heat gently, rinse the cover with distilled water and evaporate to dryness. Add 5 grams fusion-mixture together with 4 cc. distilled water. Digest for five minutes. Dry in a steam bath or upon a hot plate; fuse. Cool the crucible and place it in a large beaker. Cover it with water and digest. Filter the liquid and make up (with washings) to 500 cc. Add excess of HCl and heat. Precipitate with $BaCl_2$, etc.

Rosenstein's Method. Weigh exactly 0.5 gram of the ground sample into a 300 cc. Erlenmeyer flask. Add 15 cc. saturated solution of arsenic acid, 10 cc. fuming HNO_3 and 3 cc. saturated Br water. Cover with a watch glass and boil until the sample is completely oxidized and a clear solution is obtained. Evaporate the liquid to a syrup. Add a few crystals of $KClO_3$ to ensure complete oxidation, and to expel nitrogen oxides. Evaporate to dryness. Cool and take up with 50 cc. 10 per cent HCl. Heat until dissolved, filter and dilute to 300 cc. with distilled water. Precipitate with $BaCl_2$ in the usual way.

Ash. One gram comminuted rubber is wrapped in filter paper and extracted with acetone for four hours. Transfer the rubber and filter to a porcelain crucible and ignite it at low temperature. Cool and weigh.

Sulphur in Ash. Add a few drops of HNO_3 to the ash. Stir and expel excess of acid by heating on a water bath. Add 5 grams fusion mixture. After fusion treat the melt as usual. Barytes is calculated from the content of barium in the ash.

1. Subtract the free sulphur from the acetone extract, uncorrected.

2. Subtract the sulphur in the ash from the total ash to obtain " ash (sulphur free)."

3. Subtract from the total sulphur the percentage of sulphur as barytes (total sulphur corrected). Add the sulphur so deducted to the ash, reporting the ash as " ash corrected."

4. Subtract from 100 the sum of acetone extract corrected, total sulphur, ash (sulphur free), and call the remainder " rubber by difference."

Sulphide Sulphur. *Stevens' Method.* The vulcanized rubber is first swollen in a suitable solvent in which the aqueous acid is partly soluble. By this means the PbS and ZnS are decomposed. The solvent used is methylated ether. The liberated H_2S is estimated and calculated to percentage of sulphide sulphur, by absorption in lead acetate solution.

Twenty cc. conc. HCl and 30 cc. methylated ether are placed in a Voigt's flask. Expel the air by a current of CO_2. Connect the flask to an absorption apparatus containing lead acetate solution. Introduce a weighed quantity of the rubber into the flask. The rubber swells gradually and after fifteen minutes the ether together with the evolved H_2S is driven over into the absorption apparatus by a gentle heat. Boil the mixture for ten minutes. Collect the PbS, wash and titrate with iodine. The residue in the flask is extracted again with HCl and the sulphate is determined as $BaSO_4$.

Alternative Scheme for Rubber Analysis:

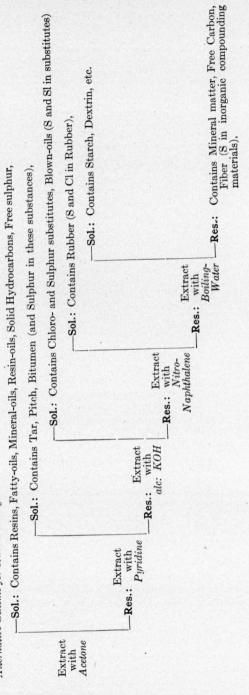

Extract with *Acetone*

— **Sol.:** Contains Resins, Fatty-oils, Mineral-oils, Resin-oils, Solid Hydrocarbons, Free sulphur,

— **Res.:** Extract with *Pyridine*

  — **Sol.:** Contains Tar, Pitch, Bitumen (and Sulphur in these substances),

  — **Res.:** Extract with *alc: KOH*

    — **Sol.:** Contains Chloro- and Sulphur substitutes, Blown-oils (S and Sl in substitutes)

    — **Res.:** Extract with *Nitro-Naphthalene*

      — **Sol.:** Contains Rubber (S and Cl in Rubber),

      — **Res.:** Extract with *Boiling-Water*

        — **Sol.:** Contains Starch, Dextrin, etc.

        — **Res.:** Contains Mineral matter, Free Carbon, Fiber (S in inorganic compounding materials).

GUTTAPERCHA AND BALATA

Guttapercha is obtained from the latex of certain plants belonging to the natural order Sapotaceæ, growing wild in the Malay Peninsula, Sumatra and Borneo. Balata is obtained from Venezuela and Guiana. The hydrocarbon present in guttapercha and balata is similar to that of rubber, but a larger proportion of resin is associated with the former. When cold the gutta hydrocarbon is hard and tough like leather, yet pliable, whilst elasticity is almost entirely absent. On warming guttapercha and balata they soften and become plastic. Guttapercha is used chiefly for cable coverings, surgical and chemical utensils, whilst balata is used chiefly for belting. Although guttapercha and balata can be vulcanized their value is not thereby increased. Therefore the material is used after it is merely washed and dried. No compounding materials are added, but the material is sometimes deresinated in order to produce harder mouldings.

Sampling. The only satisfactory way to arrive at a washing loss of a parcel of guttapercha is to wait until the whole of the consignment has passed through the washing mills and drying ovens and then to calculate the shrinkage from the yield of the washed and dried material. The shrinkage ranges from 25 per cent to 50 per cent.

Analysis. Determinations required: Moisture, resin, dirt, gutta hydrocarbon.

Moisture. Weigh out 3 to 5 grams of the material reduced to small particles, and dry it on a flat dish *in vacuo* at 90° C. for six hours, or heat the guttapercha in a current of dry CO_2.

Resin. Extract 2 grams of the finely divided sample with acetone, as in the case of rubber, for twelve hours. Evaporate the solvent and dry the residue to constant weight at 110° C.

Acetone is the most trustworthy solvent for the extraction of balata and guttapercha. Ether dissolves a part of the gutta or balata, and so gives high results, whilst with alcohol the gutta becomes plastic on account of the higher boiling point of the solvent, and the extraction is, therefore, incomplete.

Gutta: Rapid Method. Boil 1 gram sample with 20 cc. redistilled toluene. Heat to 100° C. on a water bath until dissolved. Pour the solution into 50 cc. 95 per cent alcohol. Allow the contents of the vessel to stand for a few hours. Warm and agitate to clear the liquid. Remove the clot, redissolve in toluene and reprecipitate by alcohol. Dry *in vacuo* and weigh.

Dirt (generally less than 0.5 per cent) and mineral matter are determined by incineration.

The *residue* may be examined for ZnO, lithopone, antimony sulphide and carbon.

The **examination of Balata** is conducted similarly.

Works of Reference on Rubber: recommended, and to which acknowledgments are due:

Rubber: P. Schridrowitz, Ph.D., F.C.S.
The Chemistry of the Rubber Industry: H. E. Potts, M.Sc.
Indiarubber Laboratory Practice: W. A. Caspari, B.Sc., Ph.D., F.I.C.
Indiarubber and Gutta Percha: Seeligmann, Torrilhon and Falconnet.
Rubber: (Recent research on its chemistry.) Dubose and Luttringer.
The Chemistry of Indiarubber: C. O. Weber.
Indiarubber: H. L. Terry, F.I.C.
Methods of Analysis of Raw-rubber: Spence. Quarterly Jour., vol. II, page 91.
Caoutchouc and Guttapercha: Tassilly. 1911.
Die Analyse des Kautschuks, etc.: Ditmar.

STANDARD METHODS FOR THE ANALYSIS OF RUBBER GOODS [1]

Reasons for the Analysis

Acetone Extract. If the acetone extraction is made on a vulcanized compound, the acetone removes the rubber resins, the free sulphur, any mineral oils or waxes, and part of any bituminous substances or vulcanized oils that may have been used. The percentage of free sulphur is determined and deducted from the total extract. The corrected figure thus obtained will at times give valuable information regarding the quality of the rubber present. For the best grades of Hevea rubber, this corrected extract should not exceed 4% of the rubber present. A higher extract may indicate the presence of inferior or reclaimed rubbers.

Chloroform Extract. The chloroform extraction removes a portion of the bituminous substances and serves as an indication of their presence.

Alcoholic-Alkali Extract. The purpose of the alcoholic-alkali extraction is to detect the presence of rubber substitutes.

Free Sulphur. The free sulphur is defined as that which is removed during the acetone extraction.

Total Sulphur. This represents the sulphur that occurs in the compound either free or chemically combined.

Ash. The ash is the residue left after ignition, and consists principally of the nonvolatile mineral fillers, together with their reaction products with sulphur.

Sulphur in Ash. The sulphur in ash consists of the sulphur from the mineral fillers, and also part of the sulphur that was with the rubber, but which during ignition enters into combination with one or another of the mineral fillers.

Special Determinations. Special methods are given for the analysis of compounds that contain glue, carbon, antimony, and waxy hydrocarbons.

Rubber. Up to the present time no simple method has been devised for the direct determination of the amount of rubber present in a vulcanized

[1] Approved by the Supervisory Committee on Standard Methods of Analysis, American Chemical Society, March 1, 1924.

[2] Personnel of Committee: S. Collier, *chairman*, H. E. Simmons, W. B. Weigand, A. H. Smith, E. W. Oldham, H. B. Pushee, A. H. Flower, F. J. Dugan, W. W. Evans.

[3] C. R. Boggs, *chairman*, J. M. Bierer, H. J. Force, W. W. Evans, C. B. Martin, M. C. McDonnell, J. B.Young, E. H. Grafton, A. H. Nuckolls, C. W. Walker, P. L. Wormeley, C. G. Miller, Leon A. Smith, W. H. DelMar, G. d'Eustachio, P. J. Freeman, W. S. Clark.

compound. Therefore, an indirect method is proposed which will give satis factory results in all cases known to-day, except where there are found to b present decomposable fillers, such as carbonates, cellulose, and high percent ages of mineral rubbers. As practically all insulating compounds contai some of these ingredients, the said compounds when specified shall be analyze in accordance with Joint Rubber Insulation Committee's method, as given i Paragraph 34.

When carbonates, talc, and asbestine are present, more accurate result are obtained by the use of the Joint Rubber Insulation Committee's method given in Paragraph 34.

If high percentages of mineral rubber are used, no accurate method i known. If cellulose is present, the best results are obtained by the metho given in Paragraph 35.

Preparation of Sample

1. Before preparing a sample for analysis, the analyst shall, by inspection assure himself that it has not been contaminated. The sample shall be pre pared by taking pieces from various parts of the original sample and separatin them from foreign matter.

2. The pieces shall be ground to the required fineness on a rubber mill o cut with scissors so as to pass a No. 14 sieve.

3. Hard rubber should be prepared by rasping with a coarse file, cleanin with a magnet, and passing through a No. 14 sieve.

4. Crude, reclaimed, or unvulcanized rubber shall be sheeted out very thi on an experimental mill, and shall be rolled in holland or other cotton clot to prevent the sample from sticking. If no mill is available, the sample sha be cut as fine as possible with scissors.

5. Samples of rubberized cloth shall be prepared by cutting into piece 1.5 cm. square and then mixing well.

6. Cements: Cements shall be evaporated to dryness and the residu analyzed as an unvulcanized sample. A separate sample shall be steam distilled if examination of the solvent is desired.

Reagents

7. The acetone shall be chemically pure and shall be freshly redistille over anhydrous sodium carbonate, using the 56° to 57° C. fraction

8. The alcoholic-alkali solution shall be of normal strength. It shall b made by dissolving the required amount of alkali (either potassium or sodiun hydroxide) in the smallest quantity of hot, distilled water and adding this t specially purified alcohol, which shall be prepared as follows:

Dissolve 1.5 g. of silver nitrate in 3 cc. of water, and add it to 1000 cc. o alcohol. Dissolve 3 g. of alkali in the smallest amount of hot water, cool add it to the alcoholic-silver nitrate solution, and shake thoroughly. Allov the solution to stand for at least 24 hrs., filter, and distil. (Alcohol denature with 10% by volume of methanol may be used in place of ethyl alcohol.)

9. The nitric acid-bromine reagent shall be prepared by adding a consider able excess of bromine to concentrated nitric acid and shaking thoroughly It can be used immediately.

10. The zinc oxide-nitric acid solution is made by adding 200 g. of zin oxide to 1000 cc. of concentrated nitric acid.

11. Barium chloride solution shall be made by dissolving 100 g. of crystal-ized barium chloride in 1 liter of distilled water and adding 2 to 3 drops of oncentrated hydrochloric acid. If there is any insoluble matter or cloudiness, he solution shall be heated over night on the steam bath and filtered. Care hould be taken not to add more acid than the amount specified.

12. Standard 0.1 N potassium permanganate solution shall be made as ollows:

Dissolve approximately 3.1 g. of potassium permanganate in 1 liter of vater, and when it is dissolved filter through an ignited asbestos pad. Weigh ut 0.25 g. of pure metallic antimony and transfer to a 600-cc. Erlenmeyer lask. Add 12 to 15 cc. of concentrated sulphuric acid, 10 to 12 g. of potassium sulphate, and heat until all the antimony is dissolved. Dilute to 250 cc. vith water, add 20 cc. of concentrated hydrochloric acid, cool to 10° to 15° C., and titrate with permanganate solution until a faint pink color is obtained.

$$1 \text{ cc. of } 0.1 \text{ N KMnO}_4 = \frac{\text{Wt. of metallic antimony}}{\text{Cc. of permanganate}} = \text{wt. of antimony.}$$

13. Starch-iodate paper shall be prepared by impregnating filter paper with a solution obtained by heating 2 g. of starch with 100 cc. of water and, after solution, adding 0.2 g. of potassium iodate dissolved in 5 cc. of water.

14. A Gooch crucible shall be prepared in the following manner:

Cut amphibole asbestos fine with shears, digest with 10% caustic soda solution, wash with water, and then digest with concentrated hydrochloric acid for a few hours on the steam bath. After it has been washed compara-tively free from acid by decantation, shake up the asbestos with water and use the resulting mixture in preparing the pads. The Gooch crucibles should be ignited, and are then ready for use.

15. The purity of all material shall be checked and determined by blank analyses.

Methods of Analysis

16. **Specific Gravity.** This shall be determined by the use of a pycnometer, using alcohol in place of water to eliminate the errors due to air bubbles.

$A =$ Wt. of pycnometer filled with alcohol,
$B =$ Wt. of pycnometer filled with sample and alcohol,
$C =$ Wt. of sample.

$$\text{Sp.gr.} = \frac{C}{C-(B-A)} \times \text{Sp.gr. of alcohol.}$$

17. **Acetone Extract.** The extracting apparatus used here and for other extractions shall be of the type similar to that shown on page 1566. (See also Industrial and Engineering Chemistry, **9** (1917), 314.) The flask shall be heated so that the period of filling an empty siphon cup with acetone and completely emptying it will be between 2.5 and 3.5 min.

Place 2 g. of rubber in a thimble made by folding a filter paper so that it will fit in the extraction cup, which is suspended in a weighed extraction flask. Extract the sample continuously for 8 hrs., unless the solution in the thimble is still colored at the end of that time, when the extraction shall proceed for a further period of 4 hrs. or longer. For hard rubber the extraction period shall be a minimum of 72 hrs. Carefully note all characteristics of the acetone extract, both when hot and cold. Distil off the acetone on the steam bath at as low a temperature as possible. Loss of extract by bumping can be avoided by means of a gentle current of air or by slightly inclining the flask.

Care must be taken to avoid allowing the flasks to stand on the steam bath after the solvent has been removed, because appreciable quantities of free sulphur may be lost by so doing. Dry the extraction flask and contents in an air bath for 1 hr. at 70° C., cool, and weigh. Call the residue " Acetone Extract, Uncorrected."

$$\text{Percentage of acetone extract, uncorrected} = \frac{\text{Wt. of extract}}{\text{Wt. of sample}} \times 100.$$

Save the rubber sample and keep for future determination.

18. **Chloroform Extract.** The rubber sample (Paragraph 17), without removing the acetone from it, is suspended in a second weighed extraction flask and extracted for 4 hrs. with chloroform. Care should be taken that any small particles of rubber, which are often carried down into the extract, are filtered off. Evaporate off the solvent and dry the residue to constant weight— usually 1 hr. at 70° C.—cool, and weigh. The color of the chloroform solution should be recorded. Reserve the rubber for extraction with alcoholic-alkali.

$$\text{Percentage of chloroform extract} = \frac{\text{Wt. of extract}}{\text{Wt. of sample}} \times 100.$$

19. **Alcoholic-Alkali Extract.** Dry the rubber from the chloroform extraction at about 70° C. to remove the chloroform, transfer to a 200-cc. Erlenmeyer flask, add 50 cc. of alcoholic-alkali solution, and heat under a reflux condenser for 4 hrs. Filter into a 250-cc. beaker, wash with two portions of 25 cc. each of boiling alcohol, then with three 25-cc. portions of boiling water, and evaporate the filtrate to dryness. Use about 75 cc. of distilled water to transfer the residue to a separatory funnel. Acidify the solution with 10 per cent hydrochloric acid, testing with Congo red paper. Extract with four 25-cc. portions of ether, unless the fourth portion is colored, when the extraction must be continued until no further quantity can be removed. Unite the ether fractions and wash thoroughly with distilled water until free from acid (two washings are generally sufficient). Filter the ether solution through a plug of absorbent cotton into a weighed flask, wash with ether, evaporate, dry to constant weight at 70° C., cool, and weigh.

$$\text{Percentage of alcoholic-alkali extract} = \frac{\text{Wt. of extract}}{\text{Wt. of sample}} \times 100.$$

20. **Free Sulphur.** Add to the flask containing the acetone extract, uncorrected (Paragraph 17), 50 to 60 cc. of distilled water and 2 to 3 cc. of bromine, and cover with a watch glass. (If the acetone extract indicated a large amount of free sulphur, the amount of bromine used may be increased.) Allow the flask to stand 0.5 hr. on the side of the steam bath, then heat cautiously over the direct steam bath until the solution is practically colorless, filter into a 250-cc. beaker, and dilute to about 175 cc. with distilled water. Precipitate with barium chloride and determine in the usual manner, taking the proper precautions to prevent the reduction of the barium sulphate during the ignition.

$$\text{Percentage of free sulphur} = \frac{\text{Wt. of } BaSO_4 \times 0.1373}{\text{Wt. of sample}} \times 100.$$

21. Total Sulphur. Place 0.5 g. of rubber in a porcelain crucible of about 75 cc. capacity, add 15 cc. of the nitric acid-bromine mixture, cover the crucible with a watch glass, and let it stand for 1 hr. in the cold. Heat for an hour on the steam bath, remove the cover, rinse it with a little distilled water, and evaporate to dryness. Add 3 cc. of nitric acid, cover, warm a short time on the steam bath, then let it cool. Carefully add in small portions, by means of a glass spatula, 5 g. of sodium carbonate (weighed to 0.5 g.). The watch glass is to be raised only high enough to permit the introduction of the spatula. The carbonate is allowed to slide down the side of the crucible and is not dropped directly into the acid. Rinse the watch glass with 2 or 3 cc. of hot

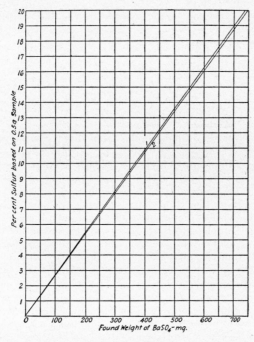

FIG. 203b.

distilled water and stir the mixture thoroughly with a glass rod. Digest for a few minutes, spread the mixture halfway up the side of the crucible to facilitate drying, and dry on a steam bath. Fuse the mixture by heating over a sulphur-free gasoline flame.

Place the crucible in an inclined position on a wire triangle and start the ignition over a low flame. The tendency for the rubber to burn too briskly is controlled by judicious use of the stirring rod with which the burning portion is scraped away from the rest. When part of the mass is burned white, a fresh portion is worked into it, and so on until all of the organic matter is destroyed. It is necessary to hold the edge of the crucible with tongs. Toward the last half of the operation the flame should be increased somewhat, but it

is never necessary to heat the crucible to redness.   With care a crucible can
be used for at least ten or twelve fusions.

After a fusion, allow the crucible to cool, place it in a 400-cc. beaker, add
sufficient distilled water to cover the crucible (about 125 cc. are required),
and digest on the steam bath for 2 hrs., with occasional stirring.   If the filtration cannot be made in the same day, do not add the water, but allow the fusion
to stand over night.

Filter the solution into a covered 400-cc. beaker containing 5 cc. of concentrated hydrochloric acid, and wash the residue thoroughly with hot water.
(A qualitative test for barium sulphate can be made on the residue.)   Now
complete the acidification of the filtrate and washings in the cold and add
2 cc. of concentrated hydrochloric acid in excess.   Cover the beaker and
heat the solution on the steam bath.   The total volume of the solution should
not exceed 300 cc.   The solution must be acid to Congo paper in order to insure
the complete destruction of the carbonates.   Precipitate with barium chloride
and determine the sulphur in the usual manner.

$$\text{Percentage of total sulphur }[1] = \frac{\text{Wt. of BaSO}_4 \times 0.1373}{\text{Wt. of sample}} \times 100.$$

22. Alternative Method.   When this method is used, the total sulphur
determined represents the sulphur exclusive of that as barytes, if used in the
compound.

Place a 0.5-g. sample in a 500-cc. Erlenmeyer destruction flask (Pyrex
glass).   Add 10 cc. of zinc oxide-nitric acid solution and whirl the flask rapidly
to moisten the sample thoroughly.   If convenient, the mixture may be allowed
to stand over night at this point.   By so doing the sample becomes partly
decomposed; this permits the addition of fuming nitric acid with no danger
of ignition of the sample.   Add 15 cc. of fuming nitric acid and whirl the
flask rapidly to keep the sample immersed to avoid ignition by too rapid
oxidation.   With some samples it will be found necessary to cool the flask
under a stream of tap water.

When the solution of the rubber is complete, add 5 cc. of saturated water
solution of bromine, and slowly evaporate the mixture to a foamy sirup.
(For the determination of total sulphur in unvulcanized mixtures use 3 cc.
of bromine in place of bromine water.)

If particles of organic matter remain at the end of the evaporation, add a
few cc. of fuming nitric acid, and reëvaporate as before.   Cool, and add a few
crystals of potassium chlorate to assist in the oxidation of the sulphur and
the decomposition of any nitrates.

Place the flask on asbestos gauze and evaporate the mixture to dryness
over a Tirrill burner.   Then bake the mixture at the highest temperature of
the burner until all nitrates are decomposed and no more nitrogen peroxide
fumes can be detected.   (Care should be taken to insure uniform penetration
of the heat throughout the contents of the flask and to remove the flask as
soon as the " baking " is complete.)   When the baking is complete, cool the
flask, add 50 cc. of (1 : 6) hydrochloric acid, and heat until solution is complete.
(In case the original mixture contains barium salts, they will be precipitated
at this point.   If litharge is present in the mixture, lead salts, not otherwise

[1] To correct the sulphur for occlusion use Graph 1, line marked 2.

emoved, will be eliminated in the final washing with boiling water.) Filter he solution, dilute to 300 cc., precipitate with barium chloride, and determine he sulphur in the usual manner.

$$\text{Percentage of total sulphur }^1 = \frac{\text{Wt. of BaSO}_4 \times 0.1373}{\text{Wt. of sample}} \times 100.$$

23. **Ash.** Wrap a 1-g. sample in a filter paper, extract with acetone for 4 rs., and transfer to a weighed, approximately 50-cc. porcelain crucible. Ash the sample in a muffle furnace by heating at the following rate:

Time, min.	0	5	10	15	70	75	80	85	145
Temp., ° C.	0	100	200	300	300	400	500	550	550

Remove crucible from the furnace, cool, and weigh.

If no furnace is available, distil off the rubber over a very small flame, not llowing it to catch fire, and ignite gently until burned clean, cool, and weigh.

$$\text{Percentage of ash} = \frac{\text{Wt. of ash}}{\text{Wt. of sample}} \times 100.$$

24. **Sulphur in Ash.** Add 3 cc. of nitric acid-bromine mixture to the ash 'Paragraph 23), cover with a watch glass and heat for 1 hr., remove the cover, inse it with a little distilled water, and evaporate to dryness. Complete the letermination of sulphur as described under Paragraph 21.

$$\text{Percentage of sulphur in ash }^1 = \frac{\text{Wt. of BaSO}_4 \times 0.1373}{\text{Wt. of sample}} \times 100.$$

Save the insoluble residue after filtering the solution of the fusion mixture in water for testing according to Paragraph 25.

25. **Barium Sulphate.** The barium sulphate is calculated from the barium in the ash, which is determined as follows: Filter off the insoluble matter after the fusion and extraction in Paragraph 24, wash back into the original beaker with hot water, dissolve the residue in the beaker and any traces on the filter paper with hydrochloric acid, and heat the solution on the steam bath. Filter through the same filter as before and wash thoroughly with hot water. Nearly neutralize the solution with ammonium hydroxide, leaving it slightly acid. Saturate the solution with hydrogen sulphide in the cold, and when the lead sulphide has settled, filter into a 400-cc. beaker and wash thoroughly. The total volume should be not over 200 cc. Precipitate with 10 per cent sulphuric acid and determine the barium in the usual manner. Barium sulphate determined above is assumed to have been added as such. Obviously, if barium carbonate is used, it must be determined in order that an undue correction shall not be made.

$$\text{Percentage of sulphur as barium sulphate} = \frac{\text{Wt. of BaSO}_4 \times 0.1373}{\text{Wt. of sample}} \times 100.$$

26. **Total Antimony.** When a qualitative test indicates that antimony is present, place a 0.5-g. sample, and transfer in a Kjeldahl flask, add 25 cc. of concentrated sulphuric acid and 10 to 12 g. of potassium sulphate, place a funnel in the neck of the flask, and heat until the solution becomes colorless. Cool and wash the funnel, dilute the solution to 100 cc. with water, and transfer

[1] To correct the sulphur for occlusion use Graph 1, line marked 1.

to a 400-cc. beaker, dilute to 250 cc. with hot water, and precipitate the anti
mony with hydrogen sulphide. Filter and transfer the precipitate to a Kjeldah
flask, add 15 cc. of concentrated sulphuric acid, 10 to 12 g. of potassium sul
phate, and heat as described above until the solution is colorless. Wash th
funnel, dilute the solution to 100 cc. with water, add 1 to 2 g. of sodium sulphite
and boil until all the sulphur dioxide is driven out. This is shown when n
blue color is obtained with starch iodate paper. Add 20 cc. of concentrate
hydrochloric acid, dilute to 250 to 275 cc. with water, cool to 10° to 15° C.
and titrate with standard 0.1 N permanganate solution until a faint pin
color is obtained. If iron is found to be absent, it is not necessary to precipi
tate the antimony with hydrogen sulphide, and the second heating in a Kjeldah
flask can be eliminated.

$$\text{Percentage of antimony} = \frac{\text{Sb (Paragraph 12)} \times \text{cc. of permanganate}}{\text{Wt. of sample}} \times 100.$$

27. Antimony in the Ash. This is determined in the ash of a 1-g. sample
Transfer the ash to a 600-cc. Erlenmeyer flask, add 12 to 15 cc. of concentrate
sulphuric acid and 10 to 12 g. of potassium sulphate, and boil until solutio
is complete. It may be necessary to warm part of the sulphuric acid in th
crucible to transfer any adhering particles to the flask. Rinse with th
remaining portion of acid. Then complete the determination as described i
Paragraph 26.

Percentage of antimony as Sb_2O_4 in ash

$$= \frac{\text{Sb (Paragraph 12)} \times \text{cc. of permanganate} \times 1.26}{\text{Wt. of sample}} \times 100$$

28. Free Carbon. Extract a 0.5-g. sample for 8 hrs. with a mixture o
chloroform and acetone in a volume ratio of 2 : 1. Transfer the sample to
250-cc. beaker and heat on the steam bath until it no longer smells of chloro
form. Add a few cc. of concentrated nitric acid and allow to stand in th
cold for about 10 min. Add 50 cc. more of hot concentrated nitric acid
taking care to wash down the sides of the beaker, and heat on the steam
bath for at least 1 hr. At the end of this time there should be no more bubble
or foam on the surface. Pour the liquid while hot into the crucible, taking
care to keep as much as possible of the insoluble material in the beaker. Filte
slowly with gentle suction and wash well by decantation with hot concentrate
nitric acid. (Caution: Empty the filter flask.) Wash with acetone and
mixture of equal parts of acetone and chloroform until the filtrate is colorless
Digest the insoluble material, which has been carefully retained in the beaker
for 30 min. on the steam bath with 35 cc. of 25% sodium hydroxide solution
This treatment with alkali can be omitted if silicates are absent. Dilute t
60 cc. with hot distilled water and heat on the steam bath. Filter the solutio
of alkali and wash well with hot 15 per cent sodium hydroxide solution.

Next wash the residue four times with hot concentrated hydrochloric acid
Neutralize the last washing with ammonia and test for the presence of lea
with sodium chromate solution. If none is present, finally wash with warm
5% hydrochloric acid. Remove the crucible from the funnel, taking care tha
the outside is perfectly clean, dry it in an air bath for 1.5 hrs. at 110° C., cool
weigh, burn off the carbon at a dull red heat, and reweigh. The differenc

n weight represents approximately 105 per cent of the carbon originally present in the form of lamp-black or gas black.

Percentage of free carbon

$$= \frac{\text{Wt. of crucible with carbon} - \text{wt. of crucible after ignition}}{1.05 \times \text{wt. of sample}} \times 100.$$

29. Detection of Glue. Extract a 2-g. sample for about 6 hrs. with acetone. Then heat for 2 hrs. on the steam bath, with sufficient water to cover it, cool, filter, and pour slowly into a 1 per cent solution of tannic acid. If a permanent cloudiness, however slight, appears, glue is present.

30. Nitrogen Calculated as Glue. When glue is found to be present, a correction must be made for the natural protein in the rubber. The average amount of nitrogen is 0.4 per cent. (See Paragraph 40 for calculations.)

Extract a 2-g. sample for 8 hrs. with acetone. Remove the solvent from the sample, and transfer the latter from the filter paper to a 750-cc. Kjeldahl flask. Add 25 to 30 cc. of concentrated sulphuric acid and 10 to 12 g. of sodium sulphate. Place the flask on the Kjeldahl digesting apparatus. Heat gently until the first vigorous frothing ceases, then raise the heat gradually until the liquid boils. Continue the boiling until the solution becomes clear. Allow the flask to cool, dilute carefully with 150 cc. of water, and allow to cool. Add 100 cc. of 50% sodium hydroxide solution, pouring it carefully down the side of the flask so that it does not mix immediately with the acid solution. Add about 1 g. of granulated zinc to prevent bumping and a piece of paraffin the size of a pea to diminish frothing. Connect the flask quickly with a condenser, the delivery tube of which dips into a 500-cc. Erlenmeyer flask, containing 50 cc. of 0.1 N sulphuric acid diluted to about 100 cc. Carefully swirl the flask to mix the contents and start to heat gently, increase the flame as the danger of foaming over diminishes, and, finally, boil briskly until about one-half of the liquid has passed over into the receiver. Add methyl red solution and titrate the excess acid by means of 0.1 N sodium hydroxide solution. A blank determination should be made.

Percentage of nitrogen as glue

$$= \frac{100(\text{cc. } H_2SO_4 \times \text{normality} - \text{cc. NaOH} \times \text{normality}) (0.014) (6.5)}{\text{Wt. of sample}}$$

$$= (\text{cc. } H_2SO_4 \times \text{normality} - \text{cc. NaOH} \times \text{normality}) \times 4.55.[1]$$

31. Unsaponifiable Matter. If this determination is made, the free sulphur shall be determined on a separate 2-g. sample.

Add to the acetone extract obtained from two 2-g. samples (Paragraph 17) 50 cc. of N alcoholic-alkali solution, heat on the steam bath under a reflux condenser for 2 hrs., remove the condenser, and evaporate to dryness. Transfer to a separatory funnel, using about 100 cc. of water, add 25 cc. of ether, and shake. Allow the two layers to separate thoroughly, then draw off the water layer. Continue the extraction of the water layer with fresh portions of ether until no more unsaponifiable matter is removed, unite the ethereal layers, and wash with distilled water. Transfer the ether to a tared flask, distil off the ether, dry to constant weight at 70° C., cool, and weigh.

47   [1] Simplified formula when a 2-g. sample is used.

$$\text{Percentage of unsaponifiable matter} = \frac{\text{Wt. of extract}}{\text{Wt. of sample}} \times 100.$$

32. Hydrocarbons A. To the unsaponifiable matter (Paragraph 31) add 50 cc. of absolute alcohol, and heat on the steam bath for 0.5 hr. Let the flask stand in a mixture of ice and salt for 1 hr. Filter off the separated waxy hydrocarbons on filter paper by applying a gentle suction. Wash with alcohol (95% will do), which has been cooled in an ice-salt mixture. The funnel should be surrounded by a freezing mixture.

Dissolve the precipitate from the filter paper with hot chloroform, and catch the solution in a weighed 100- to 150-cc. beaker. Wash the flask with hot chloroform, which is added to the same beaker, in order to include any undissolved waxy matter adhering to the walls of the flask. Evaporate off the solvent, dry to constant weight at 70° C., cool, and weigh.

$$\text{Percentage of hydrocarbons A} = \frac{\text{Wt. of extract}}{\text{Wt. of sample}} \times 100.$$

33. Hydrocarbons B. Evaporate the alcohol from the flask containing the alcohol-soluble unsaponifiable material, add 25 cc. of carbon tetrachloride and transfer to a separatory funnel. Shake with concentrated sulphuric acid, drain off the discolored acid, and repeat with fresh portions of acid until there is no longer any discoloration. After drawing off all the acid, wash the carbon tetrachloride solution with repeated portions of water until all traces of acid are removed. Transfer the carbon tetrachloride solution to a weighed flask, evaporate off the solvent, and dry to constant weight at 70° C., cool and weigh.

$$\text{Percentage of hydrocarbons B} = \frac{\text{Wt. of extract}}{\text{Wt. of sample}} \times 100.$$

34. Rubber Hydrocarbons by Joint Rubber Insulation Committee's Method. Add to the flask containing the rubber residue from the alcoholic-alkali extraction sufficient water to make the total 125 cc., and then add 25 cc. of concentrated hydrochloric acid. Heat for 1 hr. at 97° to 100° C. Decant the supernatant liquid through a hardened filter paper on a Büchner funnel, 7 cm. in diameter, using suction. Wash the residue with 25 cc. of hot water and decant. (While a Büchner funnel is recommended, it is permissible to use an 11-cm. hardened filter paper with platinum cone in a 60-degree funnel.) Perform this entire treatment with water and hydrochloric acid three times. The rubber at this stage should be white and practically free from black specks of undissolved fillers; if it is not, continue the acid treatment until the black specks disappear. (If carbon is present, all the particles of rubber will be grayish, bluish, or black, depending on the form and quantity of carbon used. Black specks in light particles of rubber usually indicate the presence of lead sulphide, which must be removed to prevent the formation of lead sulphate on igniting the residue *C*.) Add 150 cc. of hot water to the flask and let stand on a steam bath or hot plate for half an hour and decant through the filter paper, repeating until the washings are free from chlorides. Transfer all the rubber in the flask to the filter paper and dry as much as possible by suction. Wash the rubber with 50 cc. of 95% alcohol, using suction. Transfer the entire residue to a weighing bottle.

ry at 95° to 100° C. for an hour, cool in a vacuum desiccator under reduced ressure, and weigh. Dry for 30 min., cool, and weigh, repeating this process ntil either constant weight is reached or the weight starts to increase. Let is weight be represented by C. Determine the ash, E, in a portion, D, of is residue, C, and sulphur, H, in the remaining portion, G. Also, determine ie sulphur, F, in the ash, E. Perform the ash determination as described nder Paragraph 23, and the sulphur determination as described under Paragraph 21. Calculations:

$$\text{Percentage of rubber hydrocarbons} = 100\,\frac{C}{2}\left(1 - \frac{H}{G} - \frac{E-F}{D}\right).$$

35. Cellulose. Treat 0.5 g. sample of rubber with 25 cc. of freshly distilled resol (b. p. 198° C.) on the electric hot plate for 4 hrs. at 165° C. Allow to ool and add 200 cc. of petroleum ether very slowly and with constant agitation. fter the solution has settled completely, filter through a Gooch crucible and ash three times with petroleum ether. Wash very thoroughly with boiling enzene and finally with acetone. Treat the contents of the flask with hot 0% hydrochloric acid, and transfer the entire contents to the Gooch crucible ith the aid of a " policeman." Continue to treat with hot 10% hydrochloric cid until the pad has been washed at least ten times. Wash the pad free rom chlorides with boiling water, and run small portions of acetone through until the filtrate is colorless. Treat with a mixture of equal parts of acetone nd carbon disulphide in the same manner. Wash with alcohol and dry for hr. and 30 min. at 105° C. Remove the pad from the crucible with help f a pair of sharp-pointed tweezers, using the underneath portion of the pad s a swab to clean the sides of the crucible, and place all of this material in a ared weighing bottle. Replace in the drying oven for about 10 min., cool, nd weigh.

Veight of weighing bottle, pad, insoluble fillers, and cellulose
− weight of weighing bottle
= weight of pad, insoluble fillers, and cellulose.

Transfer the contents of the weighing bottle to a 50-cc. beaker and pour ver it 15 cc. of acetic anhydride and 0.5 cc. of concentrated sulphuric acid, nd allow to digest for at least 1 hr. on the steam bath. After the mixture as cooled thoroughly, dilute with 25 cc. of 90% acetic acid and filter through a veighed Gooch crucible. To guard against traces of the material being carried hrough, this filtration, as well as the ones to follow, must be very slow and only entle suction can be used. Wash with hot 90% acetic acid until the filtrate omes through absolutely colorless, and then wash about four times more. Wash vith acetone about five times. After having taken care that all of the material as been washed out of the beaker in which the acetylation took place, remove he crucible from the funnel, clean the outside thoroughly and dry for 2 hrs. t 150° C. Cool and weigh. Original weight of crucible+weight of pad, illers and cellulose − weight of crucible after acetylation = cellulose.

$$\text{Percentage of cellulose} = \frac{\text{Cellulose}}{\text{Wt. of sample}} \times 100.$$

36. Barium Carbonate. Barytes was determined by the calculation to arytes of all barium found in the sample. Obviously, if barium carbonate is present, it must be determined in order that an undue correction shall not be made. The determination is as follows: A 1-g. sample, in a porcelain boat, is placed in a combustion tube through which passes a current of carbon dioxide. The sample is ashed in the tube. After ignition and cooling in the atmosphere of carbon dioxide, the boat is removed, the residue finely ground in an agate mortar, transferred to a 250-cc. beaker, and treated with 5 to 10 g of ammonium carbonate, 15 to 20 cc. of strong ammonia water, and about 50 cc. of distilled water. The mixture is boiled for 20 min., filtered, and the precipitate thoroughly washed to remove all soluble sulphates. The residue on the filter paper is washed back into the original beaker and about 10 cc of glacial acetic acid with sufficient water to make the total volume about 100 cc. are added. This is heated to boiling and filtered through the same paper as before. Hydrogen sulphide is passed into the filtrate to precipitate the lead, and the solution is subsequently treated as in the determination of barytes. The final weight of barium sulphate obtained is calculated to barium carbonate.

Percentage of sulphur required to convert barium present as carbonate to

$$\text{sulphate} = \frac{\text{Wt. of } BaSO_4 \times 0.1373}{\text{Wt. of sample}} \times 100$$

Calculations

37. Percentage of organic acetone extract = percentage of acetone extract (uncorrected) − percentage of free sulphur.

38. Percentage of acetone extract (corrected) = percentage of organic acetone extract − percentage of waxy hydrocarbons.

39. Percentage of waxy hydrocarbons = percentage of hydrocarbons A + percentage of hydrocarbons B.

40. Calculations for glue: Multiply the percentage of rubber as compounded (Paragraph 46) by 0.004 and 6.5 and call this value A. Subtract A from the percentage of glue (Paragraph 30) and call this value B. Substitute B for glue in Paragraph 45 in calculating the percentage of rubber hydrocarbons and then complete the calculations.

41. Percentage of sulphur as antimony trisulphide = percentage of total antimony $\times \dfrac{S_3}{Sb_2}$ = percentage of total antimony $\times 0.400$.

42. Percentage of total antimony as trisulphide = percentage of total antimony $\times \dfrac{Sb_2S_3}{Sb_2}$ = percentage of total antimony $\times 1.400$.

43. Percentage of total sulphur corrected = percentage of total sulphur − percentage of sulphur as barium sulphate − percentage of sulphur as antimony trisulphide. When barium carbonate is found, the percentage of sulphur necessary to convert it to sulphate must be added to the total sulphur (corrected).

44. Percentage of ash (corrected) = percentage of ash − percentage of sulphur in ash (+ percentage of sulphur as barium sulphate) − percentage of antimony in ash, calculated to Sb_2O_4.

45. Percentage of rubber hydrocarbon = 100 − the sum of the following percentages, except when it is determined by the J. R. I. C. method as in Paragraph 34.

Organic acetone extract	Ash, corrected
Chloroform extract	Carbon
Alcoholic-alkali extract	Glue
Total sulphur corrected	Total antimony as trisulphide

46. Rubber as Compounded. Percentage of rubber hydrocarbon plus 5 per cent of its weight is taken as "rubber as compounded," except when the sum of the percentages of the acetone extract (corrected), chloroform extract, and alcoholic-alkali extract is less than the figure represented by the arbitrary per cent, as in many high-grade compounds. Percentage of rubber as compounded is then: Percentage of rubber hydrocarbon plus the sum of the percentages of the organic acetone extract, the chloroform extract, and the alcoholic-alkali extract.

47. Rubber by Volume. Percentage of rubber by volume =
percentage of rubber as compounded (Paragraph 40) $\times$

$$\frac{\text{sp.gr. of compound}}{0.94 \text{ (taken as the average sp.gr. of crude rubber)}}.$$

48. Ratio of organic acetone extract =

$$\frac{\text{Percentage of organic acetone extract}}{\text{Percentage of rubber as compounded}} \times 100.$$

49. Ratio of sulphur to rubber =

$$\frac{\text{Percentage of total sulphur, corrected}}{\text{Percentage of rubber as compounded}} \times 100.$$

Statement of Results

Per cent	Per cent
Organic acetone extract	Sulphur as barium sulphate
Waxy hydrocarbons	Total antimony
Chloroform extract	Sulphur as antimony trisulphide
Alcoholic-alkali extract	Carbon
Free sulphur	Glue
Total sulphur corrected	Rubber hydrocarbon
Ash corrected	Rubber as compounded
Cellulose	Rubber by volume

Ratio of acetone extract to rubber as compounded
Ratio of sulphur to rubber as compounded
Specific gravity

Determination of Rubber and Inorganic Materials in Soft Rubber Goods—Solution Method [1]

The general method consists in the removal of the rubber in the compoun by solution, quantitative separation of the inorganic materials by filtration, an their partial analysis.

Method

1. Weigh two portions (*a* and *b*) of 0.5 gram of the finely ground sampl Extract each with a mixture of 32 parts by volume of acetone and 68 parts c chloroform for a minimum of 8 hours. If the liquid in the extraction bucket still colored at the end of this time, continue the extraction. Remove th samples and put each into a 150-cc. lipped assay flask, add 20 to 25 cc. of th mixed oils (75% No. 32 and 25% No. 34 mineral oils, percentages by volume)

Cover with a watch glass, and heat in an air bath at a temperature of 150° t 155° C. until solution appears complete, about 3 hours, the oil appearing clea Remove the flasks from the air bath and cool to about 110° C. and add 1 to 15 cc. benzene in a small stream, mixing thoroughly; allow to cool an then dilute with sufficient petroleum ether to fill the flask to within 2 cm. of th top; mix thoroughly, cover the flasks to prevent evaporation, and allow th mixture to stand over night.

2. **Treatment of Portion a.** Prepare a Gooch crucible with finely divide asbestos that has been treated alternately with strong caustic soda and concen trated hydrochloric acid and then washed well with water. Ignite the crucible cool and weigh, record weight as " *c*." Filter the mixture by decantatio through the crucible, using suction; wash well with petroleum ether, followe by warm acetone, and by a warm mixture of equal volumes of acetone an chloroform if the filtrate is dark. Finally, wash with hot alcohol. A portio of the pigments will remain in the flask. Dry the crucible and flask with thei contents for 1 hour at a temperature of 105° to 110° C. Cool and weigh Designate the weight of the flask and its adhering residue " *d* " and the crucibl and its contents " *e*."

3. Remove the acid-soluble materials from the flask and crucible as follows Add to the flask and crucible a few cc. of boiling alcohol; allow to digest fo 2 to 3 minutes and then wash two or three times with boiling water; let th flask cool, add 10 cc. of concentrated hydrochloric acid, rotate the flask to brin the acid in contact with the pigments. Pour the acid from the flask into th crucible, and allow to stand until effervescence ceases. Carbonates are liabl to cause loss by foaming; it is advisable to add the acid cautiously, sucking th first few drops through the pad, and then adding the remainder of the acid from the flask. When the gas ceases to evolve, draw the acid through the pad by

[1] By R. T. Mease and N. P. Hanna, Ind. Eng. Chem., **17**, 161, Feb. 1925. Issue by the Bureau of Standards, Washington, D. C.

[2] Properties of oils:

	No. 32	No. 34
Viscosity at 20° C. (Saybolt)	56 sec.	52 sec.
Viscosity at 37.8° C. (Saybolt)	45 sec.	43 sec.
Flash point	132.2° C.	129.4° C.
Fire point	176.7° C.	157.2° C.
Specific gravity	0.8530	0.8405
Acidity	0.01%	0.04%
Sulphur	0.13%	0.10%

pplying suction, and wash with 20 cc. of additional acid, added in small
portions to the flask and decanting through the crucible, then wash well with
hot water and transfer as much as possible of the residue in the flask to the
crucible. If antimony is present, the filtrate and washings are saved for its
estimation as described in (4). The flask and crucible are again dried for an
hour at 105° to 110° C. and cooled and weighed. The weight of the flask is designated as "f" and the crucible and residue as "h." Burn the organic residue
from the asbestos pad by ignition in a furnace at 700° C., cool and weigh,
designate weight as "k." If barytes is present, determine as shown under 5.

4. **Antimony Trisulphide.** Determine the antimony and express the sulphur
present as antimony trisulphide. Designate the percentage as "s."

5. **Barytes.** The contents of the crucible from 3 is fused in a porcelain
crucible with a mixture of equal parts of sodium carbonate and nitrate. The
cooled fusion then extracted with water and the carbonate residue dissolved in
hydrochloric acid, filtered from the asbestos and barium precipitated as sulphate
and determined as usual. The percentage of sulphur present as barytes is
designated as "m."

6. **Treatment of Portion b for Sulphur in Compounding Materials.** Treat
portion b as described under 2, but omit the weighing of the crucible. After the
pigments have been dried, transfer the asbestos pad and pigments into the flask.
The last traces of pigments can be removed from the sides of the crucible with
wads of absorbent cotton moistened with a little warm water. Add to the
flask about 10 cc. of bromine water, rotating the flask to moisten the contents.
Add 20 cc. of concentrated nitric acid saturated with bromine. Allow to stand
cold for 15 minutes and then heat on the steam bath for 1 hour. Transfer the
solution to a large crucible or porcelain dish and evaporate to dryness. (A
small beaker will do.) Sulphur is now determined in the residue as usual by
precipitation as barium sulphate and the percentage designated as "n."

The percentage of total inorganic materials corrected equals

$$100 \frac{(e + d + k) - (c + f + h)}{0.5} + (m + s) - n.$$

To determine the rubber hydrocarbon subtract from 100 the sum of the
percentages of acetone, chloroform, alcoholic alkali extracts, free carbon, glue,
total sulphur corrected, and total inorganic materials corrected.

References on Rubber Analysis

Total sulphur—Waters and Tuttle, B.S. Tech. Paper, No. 174.
    Collier, Levin and Mease, J.I.E.C., **15**, 953, 1923.
    Kratz, Flower, and Coolidge, India Rubber World, **6**, 356, 1920.
Total antimony—Collier, Levin, and Scherrer, Rubber Age and Tire News, **8**, 3, 104–
    105, 1920.
Free carbon—Smith and Epstein, B.S. Tech. Paper, No. 136.
Rubber hydrocarbons by joint committee—Report of Joint Rubber Committee, April,
    1917.
Cellulose—Epstein and Moore, B.S. Tech Paper, No. 154.
Barium Carbonate—Tuttle, B.S. Tech. Paper, No. 64.

STANDARD METHODS FOR THE SAMPLING AND ANALYSIS OF COMMERCIAL SOAPS AND SOAP PRODUCTS[1]

APPLICABILITY OF THE METHODS

It is admitted that the methods of sampling may not in all cases yield samples that are truly representative of the whole lot, but any method that would do so would be so cumbersome and expensive as to defeat its own purpose. The methods given do not favor either buyer or seller, and are believed to be as accurate as the economic considerations warrant, and if mutually agreed upon should be satisfactory to all interested parties.

The methods of test differ somewhat in form, and in some cases in substance, from those given in the previous report, because the committee has attempted to cover methods that would be of importance in commercial transactions rather than methods that would be mainly of theoretical interest and only applicable in special cases. As presented, the methods of sampling and testing can be directly applied to commercial transactions, and it may be of interest to state that the methods prescribed in the specifications for various soap products recommended as U. S. Government Standards by the Federal Specifications Board are essentially the same as these.

A. Sampling

The seller shall have the option of being represented at the time of sampling and when he so requests shall be furnished with a duplicate sample.

I. Cake Soaps, Flake and Powdered Soap Products when Packed in Cans and Cartons. One cake (can or carton) shall be taken at random from not less than 1 per cent of the vendors' shipping containers, provided such containers contain not less than 50 lbs. In the case of smaller containers, a cake (can or carton) shall be taken at random from each lot of containers totaling not more than 5000 lbs. The total sample shall in all cases consist of not less than three cakes (cans or cartons) taken at random from separate containers. With very large lots where the sample drawn as above will amount to more than 20 lbs., the percentage of packages sampled shall be reduced so that the amount drawn shall not exceed 20 lbs.

Wrap the individual cakes (cans or cartons) tightly in paraffined paper at once and seal by rubbing the edges with a heated iron. The inspector shall accurately weigh each wrapped cake (can or carton), record its weight and the date of weighing on the wrapper, place the wrapped cakes (cans or cartons)

[1] Approved by the Supervisory Committee on Standard Methods of Analysis, American Chemical Society, July 29, 1922.

Personnel of Committee: Archibald Campbell, *Chairman*, The Globe Soap Co., Cincinnati, Ohio; C. P. Long, The Globe Soap Co., Cincinnati, Ohio; Percy H. Walker, Bureau of Standards, Washington, D. C.; J. R. Powell, Armour Soap Wks., Chicago, Ill.; R. E. Divine, Armour Soap Wks., Chicago, Ill.

Chapter submitted by Archibald Campbell.

in an airtight container which would be nearly filled, and seal, mark, and send to the laboratory for test.   Samples should be kept cool until tested.

II. Flake and Powdered Soap Products when in Bulk.   A grab sample of not less than $\frac{1}{2}$ lb. shall be taken at random from not less than 1 per cent of the vendors' shipping containers, provided such containers contain not less than 100 lbs.   In case of smaller containers, a grab sample of not less than $\frac{1}{2}$ lb. shall be taken at random from each lot of containers totaling not more than 10,000 lbs.   The total sample in all cases shall be from separate containers.   With very large lots where the sample drawn as above will amount to more than 20 lbs., the percentage of packages sampled shall be reduced so that the amount drawn shall not exceed 20 lbs.   The inspector shall rapidly mix the sample, place in an airtight container, which shall be filled, and seal, mark, accurately weigh, record its weight and date of weighing on the package, and send to the laboratory for test.   Samples should be kept cool until tested.

III. Liquid Soap.   A sample of not less than $\frac{1}{2}$ pt. shall be taken at random from not less than 1 per cent of the vendors' shipping containers, provided such containers contain not less than 10 gal. each.   In case of smaller containers, a sample of not less than $\frac{1}{2}$ pt. shall be taken at random from each lot of containers totaling not more than 1000 gal.   The total sample shall in all cases consist of not less than three portions of $\frac{1}{2}$ pt. each taken at random from separate containers.   Before drawing the sample from the container selected, the contents of the container shall be thoroughly agitated.   The inspector shall thoroughly mix the samples drawn, place in clean, dry cans or bottles, which shall be completely filled and securely stoppered with clean corks or caps, seal, mark, and send to the laboratory for test.

IV. Paste Soap Products.   (1) *When packed in cans or cartons of 5 lbs. or less.*   One can or carton shall be taken at random from not less than 1 per cent of the vendors' shipping containers, provided such containers contain not less than 50 lbs.   In case of smaller containers, a can or carton shall be taken at random from each lot of containers totaling not more than 5000 lbs.   The total sample shall in all cases consist of not less than 3 cans or cartons taken at random from separate containers.   With very large lots where the sample drawn as above will amount to more than 20 lbs., the percentage of packages sampled shall be reduced so that the amount drawn shall not exceed 20 lbs.   Wrap, seal, mark, and send to laboratory for test.

(2) *When packed in bulk.*   Take a trial sample at random of not less than $\frac{1}{2}$ lb. from not less than 1 per cent of the vendors' shipping containers, provided such containers contain not less than 50 lbs.   In case of smaller containers a trial sample shall be taken at random from each lot of containers totaling not more than 5000 lbs.   The total sample shall in all cases consist of not less than 3 half-pound portions taken at random from separate containers.   With very large lots where the sample drawn as above will amount to more than 10 lbs., the percentage of packages sampled shall be reduced so that the amount drawn shall not exceed 10 lbs.   The inspector shall promptly place the combined sample in a clean, dry, air- and watertight container, which shall be filled, and seal, mark, and send to the laboratory for test.

B. Preparation of Samples

I. Cake Soap. In case of samples that can be easily disintegrated and mixed, run the entire sample through a suitable chopper. When the sample is large, each cake may be quartered and one quarter of each cake run through the chopper. With samples that cannot be handled as above, select a cake of average weight, quarter it by cutting it at right angles in the center and shave equally from all freshly cut surfaces sufficient soap for analysis. Mix and weigh out all portions for analysis promptly. Preserve the remainder in an airtight container in a cool place.

II. Powdered and Chip Soaps. Rapidly disintegrate and mix the sample; if desired, quarter down to about 1 lb. and weigh out all portions for analysis at once. Unused portions of the sample for analysis shall be preserved in an airtight container in a cool place.

III. Liquid Soap. No preparation of the sample, other than thorough mixing, is necessary unless it is received during very cold weather, when it should be allowed to stand at least 1 hr. after it has warmed up to room temperature (20° to 30° C.) before it is noted whether it forms a satisfactory lather.

IV. Paste Soap Products. Mix thoroughly by kneading and quarter down to about 1 lb. Weigh out all portions for analysis promptly and preserve remainder in an airtight container in a cool place.

C. Methods of Analysis

When a determination shows nonconformity with the specifications, a duplicate shall be run.

I. Matter Volatile at 105° C. Weigh 5 g. of the sample in a porcelain or glass dish about 6 to 7 cm. in diameter and 4 cm. deep, dry to constant weight in an inert atmosphere at a temperature not exceeding 105° C.

II. Total Matter Insoluble in Alcohol. Free Alkali or Free Acid. (1) *Matter insoluble in alcohol.* Digest hot a 10-g. sample with 200 cc. of freshly boiled ethyl alcohol neutral to phenolphthalein (94% or higher). Filter through a counterpoised filter paper neutral to phenolphthalein, or a weighed Gooch crucible with suction, protecting the solution during the operation from carbon dioxide and other acid fumes. Wash the residue on the paper, or in the crucible, with hot neutral alcohol until free from soap. Dry the filter paper, or crucible, and residue at 100° to 105° C. for 3 hrs., cool, and weigh the total matter insoluble in alcohol.[1]

(2) *Free alkali or free acid.* Titrate the filtrate from the above, using phenolphthalein as indicator, with standard acid or alkali solution, and calculate the alkalinity to sodium hydroxide (or potassium hydroxide), or acidity to oleic acid.

[1] The matter insoluble in alcohol will contain most of the alkaline salts, such as carbonates, borates, silicates, phosphates and sulphates, as well as starch, and may be used for the approximate determination of these constituents. These salts are not entirely insoluble in alcohol, so for accurate determinations separate portions of the soap should be used.

For determination of carbonates see C-XI; phosphates, C-XII; sulphates, C-XIII, silicates, C-XX; borax, C-IX; starch, C-XIV (4).

(3) *Matter insoluble in water.* Proceed as in the determination of matter insoluble in alcohol. After filtering and thoroughly washing the residue, extract it with water at 60° C., and wash the filter thoroughly. (When the matter insoluble in water is all inorganic, boiling water may be used for the extraction and washing.) Dry the filter and residue at 100° to 105° C. for hrs., cool, and weigh matter insoluble in water. The nature of this matter may be determined by further examination.

(4) *Total alkalinity of matter insoluble in alcohol.* (*Alkaline salts.*) Titrate f filtrate from the determination of matter insoluble in water with standard acid, using methyl orange as indicator. Calculate the alkalinity to sodium oxide (Na_2O), and, if desired, to any other basis agreed upon by the parties interested.

III. Combined Alkali. Total Anhydrous Soap. Dissolve 5 to 10 g. of the sample, depending upon the anhydrous soap content, in 100 cc. of water in a 250-cc. Erlenmeyer flask. When solution is complete, add dilute sulphuric acid in slight excess, insert a small funnel in the neck of the flask, and heat the flask at a temperature not exceeding 60° C. until the fatty acids separate as a clear layer. Transfer to separatory funnel, draw off the acid layer into a second separatory funnel and shake the acid aqueous liquid with two 20-cc. portions of ethyl ether. Dissolve the fatty acids in the ether used for washing the aqueous liquid and shake with 10-cc. portions of water until they are no longer acid to methyl orange. Unite the water portions used for washing and shake with 20 cc. of ether. Wash this ether until the wash water is neutral to methyl orange. Save the acid water for chloride determination. Unite the ether solutions (if necessary, filter, washing the paper with ether) in a suitable weighed vessel, add 100 cc. of neutral alcohol free from carbon dioxide, add phenolphthalein and titrate to exact neutrality with standard sodium hydroxide solution. Evaporate off the alcohol, dry to constant weight as in the determination of matter volatile at 105° C. and calculate the percentage of soda soap. This soap naturally includes any mineral oil and neutral fat, which, if determined separately, must be deducted from the result to obtain the true soap. Calculate the combined sodium oxide (Na_2O) and deduct from the weight of soda soap to give the anhydrides. If the original soap was potash soap, proper calculation must be made to reduce to potassium oxide (K_2O), or the titration made directly with standard potassium hydroxide solution. In case the soap shows an excess of free acid, proper corrections must be made in calculating the combined alkali in the original soap.[1] (See determination of rosin.) With soaps containing a large amount of soluble silicates and soap products containing a high percentage of finely divided material insoluble in water, the foregoing procedure cannot be applied as given. In such cases the filtrate obtained in the determination of total matter insoluble in alcohol can be used after neutralizing any free acid or alkali. Evaporate off the alcohol on a steam bath, take up in water and proceed as above.

With soap products containing a high percentage of matter insoluble in alcohol where approximate results will suffice, such as may be the case with cleansers, soap powders, scouring compounds, pastes, etc., and where agreed upon by the parties interested, the alcoholic solution, obtained after filtering off and washing the matter insoluble in alcohol, may be evaporated directly

[1] A blank test should be made on the sodium or potassium hydroxide solution for neutral salts and the proper corrections made if necessary.

in a weighed vessel, dried at 105° C. to constant weight, and the result reported as soap.

IV. Chloride. Neutralize with chlorine-free alkali the acid water obtained in paragraph C-III. Titrate with standard silver nitrate solution, using potassium chromate as indicator, and calculate the result to sodium chloride or potassium chloride as the character of the soap indicates.

In case the total anhydrous soap is not to be determined, it will be more convenient to use the following method. Dissolve 5 g. of the sample in 300 cc. of water, boiling if necessary to effect solution. Add an excess of neutral chlorine-free magnesium nitrate solution (about 25 cc. of a 20% $Mg(NO_3)_2.6H_2O$ solution). Without cooling or filtering, titrate with standard silver nitrate solution, using potassium chromate as indicator. See Vol. 1, page 150.

V. Unsaponified and Unsaponifiable Matter. Weigh 5 g. of the soap into a beaker and dissolve in about 100 cc. of 50% alcohol on the steam bath. If the sample has been found to contain free fatty acid, add just enough aqueous alkali to neutralize this. Evaporate off the bulk of the alcohol, take up with about 200 cc. of hot water and transfer to a separatory funnel of about 500 cc. capacity, designated as No. 1. When cool, rinse out the beaker with about 50 cc. of ether and add it to the soap solution. Shake thoroughly for one minute. By the addition of small amounts of alcohol (5-cc. portions and the total not to exceed 25 cc.), a clear and rapid separation of the aqueous and ether layers is effected. After adding each alcohol portion the separatory funnel is not shaken but merely given a whirling movement. Draw off the aqueous portion into another separatory funnel, designated as No. 2. Wash the ether solution with 10-cc. portions of water until this water is no longer alkaline to phenolphthalein. Add all these washings to Funnel No. 2 and extract this solution with 20-cc. portions of ether until the ether is absolutely colorless (3 or 4 extractions should be sufficient). Combine these ether extracts in a third separatory funnel (No. 3) and wash with 10-cc. portions of water until the water is no longer alkaline to phenolphthalein. Now add the ether in Funnel 3 to that in Funnel 1, a small amount of ether being used to rinse out Funnel 3. Wash the ether solution with 20 cc. of 10% hydrochloric acid solution and then successively with 20-cc. portions of water until the water is no longer acid to methyl orange. Filter the ether solution through a dry filter paper into a weighed beaker or flask. Evaporate or distil off the ether on the steam bath, dry as under the determination of matter volatile at 105° C. and weigh the residue, then heat with alcohol and, when cool, neutralize with standard alkali, using phenolphthalein. Deduct any appreciable amount of fatty acid found by this titration from the weight of the residue. This residue consists of the unsaponifiable matter and any neutral fat that may have been present in the soap. In case it is desired to separate these, thoroughly saponify the residue with alcoholic alkali and repeat the foregoing procedure. The residue obtained is unsaponifiable matter only.

VI. Rosin. *Wolff's method.*[1] Dissolve 5 g. of the sample in 100 to 200 cc. of hot water, add a slight excess of dilute sulphuric acid, heat until the fatty acids collect in a clear layer, cool to room temperature, extract with a small portion of ether, draw off the water layer and wash the ether solution with water until free from mineral acid. Transfer to a 200-cc. Erlenmeyer flask, evaporate off the ether and dry 1 hr. at 105° C., cool and dissolve in 20 cc.

[1] Chem.-Ztg., **38** (1917), 369, 382, 430; C. A., **8** (1914), 2495.

f absolute alcohol. Then add 10 cc. of a solution of one volume of concen-
rated sulphuric acid (sp.gr. 1.84) and 4 volumes of absolute alcohol, and
oil on the steam bath for 4 min. under a reflux condenser. Remove from
team bath, add to the liquid about 5 times its volume of 7 to 10% sodium
hloride solution, and extract with ether. Shake out the aqueous portion 2
r 3 times with ether. Unite the ether solutions and wash with sodium
hloride solution until the washings are neutral to methyl orange. Add 30 cc.
eutral alcohol, and titrate the rosin acids with standard sodium hydroxide
olution, using phenolphthalein as indicator. Calculate to rosin or rosin soap,
s desired (1 cc. normal alkali=0.346 g. rosin or 0.377 g. rosin soda soap).
f the true fatty acid soap is desired, subtract the rosin soap from the total
nhydrous soap obtained under C-III.

VII. Titer Test. (1) *Preparation of total fatty matter (fatty and rosin acids
nd unsaponified matter).* Dissolve about 50 g. of soap in 500 cc. of hot water,
dd 100 cc. of 30% sulphuric acid, heat until the fatty matter collects in a
lear layer, siphon off the acid layer and wash the fatty matter free from
ulphuric acid with hot water. Decant the fatty matter into a dry beaker,
ilter, using a hot-water funnel, or placing both funnel and receiving beaker
n a water-jacketed oven, and dry for 20 min. at the temperature of boiling
vater.

When other determinations are to be made on the total fatty matter, and
olatile and readily oxidizable fatty acids are present, the following method
hould be used: Dissolve about 50 g. of the soap in 300 cc. of hot water,
ransfer to a separatory funnel, add 150 cc. of approximately 2 N sulphuric
cid, cool somewhat, add 120 cc. of ether, shake, draw off the acid layer, and
vash the ether layer free from acid with a strong salt (NaCl) solution. Then
lraw off the aqueous layer as completely as possible, transfer the ether layer
o a flask (it is not necessary to transfer quantitatively), add 20 to 30 g. of
nhydrous sodium sulphate, stopper the flask, shake, and let stand at a tem-
erature below 25° C. until the ethereal liquid becomes perfectly clear, showing
hat all water has been taken up by the sodium sulphate. Filter through a
lry paper into another Erlenmeyer flask, and completely evaporate off the
ther by passing through the flask a current of dry air and heating the flask
o a temperature not above 50° C.

(2) *Determination*: [1] (a) *Thermometer.* The thermometer shall be a stand-
rd titer thermometer graduated at zero and in tenth degrees from 10° to
5° C., and certified by the U. S. Bureau of Standards.

(b) *Procedure.* Transfer the fatty acids prepared as under VII (1), when
:ooled somewhat, to a titer tube 25 mm. by 100 mm. placed in a 16-oz. salt-
nouth bottle of clear glass 70 mm. by 150 mm., fitted with a cork that is
erforated so as to hold the tube rigidly when in position. Suspend the titer
hermometer so that it can be used as a stirrer and stir the fatty acids slowly
about 100 r.p.m.) until the mercury remains stationary for 30 sec. Allow
he thermometer to hang quietly with the bulb in the center of the tube and
eport the highest point to which the mercury rises as the titer of the fatty
cids. The titer should be made in a room at about 20° C. for all fats having
titer above 30° C. and at 10° C. below the titer for all other fats.

[1] "Methods of Analysis of Assoc. Official Agr. Chem.," 1920, 242. Fat Analysis
Committee Method, The Cotton Oil Press, **11** (1919), 1163.

VIII. Acid Number of Fatty Acids. (1) *Preparation of fatty acids.* Follow procedure given under C-VII.

(2) *Determination.* In a 250-cc. Erlenmeyer flask dissolve 2 g. of the fatty acids, accurately weighed, in 20 to 30 cc. of neutral 95% ethyl alcohol. Titrate with standard alkali, using phenolphthalein as indicator. Calculate the acid number (mg. of KOH per g. of fatty acids).

IX. Borax Determination.[1] Weigh 10 g. of the soap (or 5 g. if more than 5% of borax is present) into a platinum dish and add 2.15 g. of fusion mixture (consisting of 200 g. sodium carbonate, 15 g. silica in fine powder). To this mixture add 15 cc. of alcohol, mix with the aid of a glass rod and, after washing the rod with a little alcohol, evaporate the mass to dryness on the water bath. Ignite until the combustible material is destroyed, cover the dish with a piece of platinum foil and fuse. Completely disintegrate the fusion by boiling with water and transfer the solution to a 250-cc. round bottom flask. Acidify with 20 cc. of dilute hydrochloric acid (1 : 1), heat nearly to boiling, and add a moderate excess of dry precipitated calcium carbonate. Connect with a reflux condenser and boil vigorously for 10 min. Filter out the precipitate through a folded filter, washing several times with hot water, but keeping the total volume of liquid below 100 cc.

Return the filtrate to the flask, add a pinch of calcium carbonate and again boil under a reflux condenser. Remove the flame and connect the top of the condenser with a water pump. Apply the suction until the boiling has nearly ceased. Cool to ordinary temperature, add 50 cc. of neutral glycerol and titrate the solution with 0.1 N sodium hydroxide, free from carbonate, using phenolphthalein as indicator. After the end-point is reached add 10 cc. more of glycerol and again titrate. Repeat this process until the addition of glycerol causes no further action on the end-point. The number of cubic centimeters required multiplied by 0.00955 will give the equivalent of borax ($Na_2B_4O_7.10H_2O$) present in the solution.

X. Determination of Silica Present as Alkaline Silicates. When the material contains no mineral matter that is insoluble in water, ignite a sample of the soap containing not to exceed 0.2 g. of silica in a platinum dish at a low temperature. When charred, extract the soluble salts with water, return the paper and charred residue to the dish and complete the ignition. Unite the residue in the dish and the water extract, carefully acidify with hydrochloric acid, finally adding the equivalent of from 5 to 10 cc. strong hydrochloric acid in excess. The dish or casserole containing the solution should be covered with a watch glass while adding acid so as to avoid loss by spray.

When the material contains mineral matter insoluble in water, or a determination of highest accuracy is not necessary, take a portion of the solution after titrating the matter insoluble in alcohol C-II (4) containing not more than 0.2 g. silica and add 5 to 10 cc. strong hydrochloric acid.

Evaporate the acidified solution (washing off and removing the cover glass if used) to dryness on steam bath or hot plate at a temperature not exceeding 200° C. Cool, moisten with concentrated hydrochloric acid, let stand 5 to 10 min., breaking up all lumps with a stirring rod. Add about 25 cc. of hot water. Heat a few minutes and filter through a small ashless paper. Wash thoroughly with hot water.

[1] Poetschke, Ibid., **5** (1913), 645.

Evaporate the filtrate to dryness and repeat the above treatment, filtering a second paper. Carefully ignite the two papers and contents in a weighed atinum crucible, first at a low temperature until the paper is consumed, at finally heating to constant weight over the blast lamp; cool in a desiccator fore weighing. If extreme accuracy is desired, moisten the contents of e crucible with water, add 10 cc. hydrofluoric acid and 4 drops of strong lphuric acid, evaporate to dryness over a low flame, ignite at the temperature the blast lamp for about 2 min., cool in a desiccator and weigh. The differce between this weight and the previous weight is the weight of the silica iO_2).[1]

To calculate sodium silicate ($Na_2Si_4O_9$) multiply weight of SiO_2 by 1.26.

XI. Determination of Carbon Dioxide (Carbonates). For most determiations the dry matter insoluble in alcohol as obtained in C-II (1) will be suitable r this determination. In some cases it might be desired to run the test rectly on an original sample of the soap. This should always be done when e highest accuracy is required. Any reliable absorption method for deterining carbon dioxide may be used.[2]

The following is a method which has proved satisfactory:

A 250-cc. Erlenmeyer flask is placed on a gauze over a burner. The flask equipped with a 2-hole rubber stopper, through one opening of which is a)-in. reflux condenser and through the other a thistle tube equipped at the ter end with a 3-way stopcock. The lower end of the thistle tube is drawn a small point, which is placed very close to the bottom of the flask. To e straightaway end of the stopcock is attached a small funnel for the introuction of acid to the flask. The other opening of the stopcock is attached) receive air from a purifying train consisting of a wash bottle containing ncentrated sulphuric acid and a second at the outer end of the train containing 50% solution of potassium hydroxide. The top of the reflux condenser is ttached first to a drying wash bottle containing concentrated sulphuric acid, nd then to a weighed absorbing train consisting of a suitable potash bulb narged with 50% potassium hydroxide, and a second containing concentrated lphuric acid. This train is attached to a protective U-tube containing lcium chloride. The U-tube is attached to an aspirator.

Procedure. Set up the apparatus, leaving out the weighed train, and spirate with a slow stream of the dry carbon-dioxide-free air until the appaitus is freed from carbon dioxide. Insert the train and continue the aspiration or $\frac{1}{2}$ hr. Check the weight of the train to determine if the air is passing hrough too fast, or if the system is free from carbon dioxide. The system ust be free from leaks. Weigh out 1 or 2 g. of the sample into the Erlenmeyer ask, cover with 20 cc. freshly boiled distilled water, close the apparatus with he train in place. Add 20 cc. dilute hydrochloric acid (1 : 1) through the innel very slowly, with no heat being applied to the flask. The rate of dding acid should be carefully controlled so that the gas does not pass through he train too rapidly. As soon as the acid is added, start aspiration gently. Vhen the absorption begins to stop the gas flow, start heating gently and ntinue until the contents of the flask have boiled 15 to 20 min. Stop heating

---

[1] "The Analysis of Silicate and Carbonate Rocks," by W. F. Hillebrand, U. S. Geol. urvey, Bull. 700, 102.

[2] "Methods of Analysis of Assoc. Official Agr. Chem.," 1920, 277, Bur. Chem., ull. 107, 169. See also chapter on Carbon, Vol. 1, S.M.C.A., Scott.

and continue aspirating until the flask has cooled down.   Remove the tra
and weigh.   Calculate increase of weight as carbon dioxide.   Carbon dioxi
multiplied by 2.41 equals sodium carbonate.

XII. Determination of Phosphates.   If a qualitative test has shown t
presence of phosphates and their determination is desired, the matter insolub
in alcohol C-II (1) or the ash from the incineration of an original sample c
be used.   An original sample should always be used when the highest accura
is desired.

1. *Reagents: (a) Molybdate solution.*   Dissolve 100 g. of molybdic acid
dilute ammonium hydroxide [144 cc. of ammonium hydroxide (sp.gr. 0.9
and 271 cc. of water]; pour this solution slowly and with constant stirri
into dilute nitric acid [489 cc. of nitric acid (sp.gr. 1.42) and 1148 cc. of wate
Keep the mixture in a warm place for several days or until a portion heate
to 40° C. deposits no yellow precipitate of ammonium phosphomolybdat
Decant the solution from any sediment and preserve in glass-stoppered vessel

(b) *Ammonium nitrate solution.*   Dissolve 200 g. of commercial ammoniu
nitrate, phosphate-free, in water, and dilute to 2 liters.

(c) *Magnesia mixture.*   Dissolve 110 g. of crystallized magnesium chlorid
($MgCl_2.6H_2O$) in water, add 280 g. of ammonium chloride, 261 cc. of ammoniu
hydroxide (sp.gr. 0.90), and dilute to 2 liters.

(d) *Dilute ammonium hydroxide for washing.*   Dilute 100 cc. of ammoniu
hydroxide (sp.gr. 0.90) to 1 liter.

2. *Determination.*   Weigh out a 2-g. sample of the alcohol-insoluble or asl
and proceed as in C-X for removal of silica, saving the filtrate.   Make up t
250 cc., concentrating if necessary.   Take an aliquot corresponding to 0.50
or 1 g., neutralize with ammonium hydroxide, and clear with a few drops
nitric acid.   Add about 15 g. of dry ammonium nitrate or a solution containi
that amount.   To the hot solution add 70 cc. of the molybdate solution f
every decigram of phosphoric acid (P_2O_5) present.   Digest at about 65° C. f
an hour, and determine if the phosphoric acid has been completely precipitate
by the addition of more molybdate solution to the clear supernatant liqui
Filter and wash with cold water or, preferably, ammonium nitrate solutior
Dissolve the precipitate on the filter with ammonium hydroxide and hot wate
and wash into a beaker to a bulk of not more than 100 cc.   Nearly neutraliz
with hydrochloric acid, cool, and from a buret add slowly (about 1 drop pe
sec.), stirring vigorously, 15 cc. of magnesia mixture for each decigram
phosphoric acid (P_2O_5) present.   After 15 min. add 12 cc. of ammoniu
hydroxide (sp.gr. 0.90).   Let stand till the supernatant liquid is clear (2 hrs
is usually enough), filter, wash with the dilute ammonium hydroxide until th
washings are nearly free from chlorides, ignite to whiteness or to a grayis
white, weigh, and calculate to phosphoric acid (P_2O_5), or alkaline phosphat
known to be present.   See chapter on Phosphorus, Vol. 1.

XIII. Determination of Sulphates.   For most determinations the matte
insoluble in alcohol obtained under C-II may suffice.   If a determination o
the highest accuracy is desired, ignite a 10-g. sample of the soap and use th
ash from the ignition.   Digest with 100 cc. of water, cover with a watch glass
and neutralize carefully with hydrochloric acid.   When neutralized, add 5 cc
excess of hydrochloric acid, filter, and wash the residue thoroughly.   Mak

[3] "Methods of Analysis of Assoc. Official Agr. Chem.," 1920, 1

up the filtrate to 250 cc. in a beaker, and boil.   To the boiling solution add 15 to 20 cc. 10% barium chloride solution slowly drop by drop from a pipet. Continue boiling until the precipitate is well formed, or digest on a steam bath over night.   Set aside over night or for a few hours, filter through a prepared Gooch crucible, ignite gently, and weigh as barium sulphate.   Calculate to sodium sulphate, or the alkaline sulphate known to be present.

XIV. Determination of Glycerol, Sugar, and Starch.   (1) *Determination of glycerol in the absence of sugar.*

SOLUTIONS REQUIRED

Potassium Dichromate, 74.552 g. per liter
Sodium Thiosulfate, 0.1 N
Potassium Iodide, 10 per cent

Dissolve an accurately weighed sample of the soap[1] equivalent to not more than 3.0 g. of glycerol in 200 cc. of hot water in a 600-cc. beaker.   Decompose with 25 cc. sulphuric acid (1 : 4).   If alcohol is present, volatilize it by boiling it for 20 to 30 min.   Cool, remove, and rinse the cake of fatty acids, transfer the acid water and rinsings to a 500-cc. graduated flask, add about 0.25 g. silver sulphate to precipitate traces of chlorides and soluble fatty acids.   Make up to volume and mix contents thoroughly.

Transfer a filtered, accurately measured 50-cc. aliquot of the above to a 400-cc. beaker, to this add 75 cc. accurately measured potassium dichromate solution, followed by 25 cc. of sulphuric acid (sp.gr. 1.84).   Cover with a watch glass, and oxidize by heating in a steam bath for 3 hrs.   Conduct a blank in like manner but using 100 cc. of water, 25 cc. of sulphuric acid (sp.gr. 1.84), and 25 cc. accurately measured potassium dichromate.

Cool and make up the solution to 1000 cc. in graduated flasks.   The excess of potassium dichromate is determined by taking 50 cc. aliquot of the above, adding 50 cc. of water, 20 cc. of 10% potassium iodide solution, and titrating the liberated iodine with 0.1 N thiosulphate, using starch solution as indicator.

Calculate the percentage of glycerol (1 cc. of the potassium dichromate solution equals 0.0100 g. of glycerol).

(2) *Determination of sugar.*[2]   Dissolve 10 g. of the soap in 200 cc. of hot water in a 600-cc. beaker.   Decompose with 25 cc. of sulphuric acid (1 : 4), boil gently for 20 min. to invert the cane sugar completely.   Cool, remove, and rinse the cake of fatty acids.   Extract the acid liquid with 25 cc. of ether. Transfer the acid liquid to a 500-cc. graduated flask, make up to volume and mix thoroughly.   Determine invert sugar in 50 cc. of this solution by the Munson-Walker Method.[3]   To calculate sugar (sucrose), multiply the amount of invert sugar found by 0.95.

(3) *Determination of g ycerol in the presence of sugars.*[4]   Proceed as above under (1), taking a sample so that the sum of the glycerol and sugar is not

---

[1] If starch is present, it will be necessary to remove the matter insoluble in water as described under this determination [C-II (1) and (3)].   Combine the alcohol and water solutions, evaporate off the alcohol, and proceed.

[2] If starch is present, see footnotes 13 and 18, and determination of starch XIV (4).

[3] J. Am. Chem. Soc., **28** (1906), 663; Bur. Chem., Bull. 107; "Methods of Analysis of Assoc. Official Agr. Chem.," 1920, 78.

[4] Hoyt and Pemberton, The Cotton Oil Press, **14** (1922), 54; Correction, **14** (1922), 40.

more than 3.0 g.[1]   The solution must be boiled in all cases at least 20 min. to insure complete inversion of cane sugar.   Determine the amount of potassium dichromate solution required to oxidize both the sugar and glycerol. Determine also the sugar by the method given in (2).

Calculate the percentage of glycerol after deducting the amount of potassium dichromate required by the sugar.

1 cc. potassium dichromate equals 0.0100 g. glycerol.

1 cc. potassium dichromate equals 0.01142 g. invert sugar.

(4) *Determination of starch.*[2]   Separate the matter insoluble in water as under C-II (3), using a sample of soap that will give not more than 3 g. of starch.   Transfer the insoluble matter, without drying, to a beaker and heat for $2\frac{1}{2}$ hrs. with 200 cc. of water and 20 cc. of hydrochloric acid (sp.gr. 1.125) in a flask provided with a reflux condenser.   Cool, and nearly neutralize with sodium hydroxide.   Complete the volume to 250 cc., filter, and determine the reducing sugars by the gravimetric method as given under method for the determination of sugar.

Calculate the amount of dextrose (*d*-glucose) equivalent to the cuprous oxide obtained.   This multiplied by 0.90 equals the amount of starch.

XV. Volatile Hydrocarbon.   Weigh not less than 250 g. of the sample into a flask of about 5-liter capacity, which is so placed on a gauze that it can be heated.   Add 2 to 3 liters of distilled water.   Place a 2-holed rubber stopper in the flask, through one hole of which is inserted a copper or brass tube extending into the flask and terminating in a small circular ring of the tubing, bent so that the ring is in a horizontal position.   Numerous small holes are drilled in the upper side of this ring and the end of the tube is sealed.   This ring should be near the bottom of the flask.

Through the other hole of the stopper is inserted a glass tube provided with a trap of suitable form, the upper end of which is bent so as to be connected with a plain Liebig condenser.   The end of the condenser tube is bent so as to extend into a buret graduated to 0.1 cc.

Introduce steam (free from oil) into the flask through the brass tube and collect the distillate in the buret.   When the buret becomes full, draw off the water by opening the stopcock.   The foam which forms in the flask may be controlled by momentarily shutting off the steam and by regulating heat applied to the flask.[3]

Read from time to time the amount of hydrocarbon distillate which collects on the top of the water in the buret, and when there is no further increase in this distillate the operation is finished.   Allow the buret to stand over night, tightly stoppered, and then, after reading the amount of distillate, draw off the water as carefully as possible.   Determine the specific gravity of the distillate, and calculate the weight and percentage in the original sample.

[1] See footnote 13, if starch is present.

[2] "Methods of Analysis of Assoc. Official Agr. Chem.," 1920, 95; Bur. Chem., Bull. 107, 53.

[3] Some find it an advantage to add 200 to 300 g. calcium chloride to the flask containing the soap solution, to prevent foaming.

SLAG ANALYSIS [1]

The slags made in metallurgical operations consist of complex mixtures and solid solutions of silicates, oxides, aluminates, fluorides and many other compounds. In the molten condition some of these components are probably in igneous solution in each other, their exact composition and the nature of their association depending upon the state of equilibrium at the time the slags were produced. The composition of slags is important both because of its influence upon furnace operations and because of its effects upon the character of the metallic products. For these reasons it is necessary to make frequent slag analyses in all metallurgical plants.

In iron blast-furnace slags the principal constituents are silica, alumina, lime and magnesia, with small amounts of iron oxide, manganese oxide, calcium sulphide and phosphoric acid. Titanium oxide is also frequently present. In modern blast-furnace practice, which involves the use of high lime slags, in order to keep sulphur out of the iron, the percentage of lime and sulphur in the slags is closely watched. In open-hearth furnace slags the amount of phosphorus may be high enough to warrant the sale of the slag as fertilizer.

Lead blast-furnace slags consist mainly of silica, iron oxide, manganese oxide, lime, alumina and zinc oxide, with small percentages of magnesia, barium oxide, lead, copper and sulphur. Of these the most important to the metallurgist are silica, iron oxide, lime, zinc oxide and lead, and determinations of them must be made at least once a day. The other components are determined less frequently. In some of the Mexican lead-smelting plants calcium fluoride occurs in the blast-furnace slags. The lime combined as fluoride is determined separately, as it is not available for the saturation of silica.

Copper slags are made up mainly of silica, iron oxide, lime and alumina. The manganese oxide and the zinc oxide are usually less than in lead slags. The silica and alumina, however, are generally higher. This is especially true in the case of reverberatory slags, in which a greater viscosity can be permitted. The percentage of copper is quite important as it measures the chief source of loss of that metal. The percentage of copper in the slag is usually about one hundredth of that in the matte. The amount of lime in copper slags varies a great deal more than it does in lead slags, as it is of less importance in influencing the metallurgical results. In converter slags the copper may amount to several per cent, and the slag then becomes an important by-product.

Composition of Slags

Blast-Furnace Slags. $SiO_2 = 35$ to 45%; $FeO = 0.2$ to 0.5%; $CaO = 32$ to 46%; $Al_2O_3 = 14$ to 17%; $MgO = 1.0$ to 1.5%; $MnO_2 = $ trace to 0.1%; $S = 1.5$ to 2.0%; $P_2O_5 = 0.01$ to 0.96%.

Lead Blast-Furnace Slags. $SiO_2 = 36.7\%$; $FeO = 29.5\%$; $CaO = 20.9\%$; $Al_2O_3 = 3.16\%$; $MgO = 1.69\%$; $MnO = 0.91\%$; $S = 0.75\%$; $BaO = 0.54\%$; $ZnO = 4.19\%$; $Pb = 1.38\%$; $Cu = 0.10\%$; $Au = 0.001\%$; $Ag = 0.70\%$.
Average of one year's analyses on representative samples.

Copper Blast-Furnace Slags. $SiO_2 = 23$ to 49%; $Fe(MnO) = 2.5$ to 57%; $Ca(MgO) = 2.5$ to 25%; $Al_2O_3 = 1.5$ to 18%; $ZnO = $ nil to 23%; $Cu = 0.15$ to 1.1%; $S = $ nil to 1.5%.

Edited by Wilfred W. Scott.

Decomposition of the Sample and Analysis

General Reverberatory Slag. Usually 0.5 gram of the finely ground slag is taken for a determination, a larger amount when the constituents sought are present in very small amount. The material placed in a platinum crucible is fused with 5 to 6 grams of Na_2CO_3 at red heat (muffle furnace, if possible) for 10 minutes. The mass is cooled on the side of the crucible, and the fusion dissolved in a casserole by adding an excess of HCl, followed by a few cc. of HNO_3. The solution is evaporated to dryness and the residue baked. The mass is taken up with dilute HCl. Silica remains as a residue and is filtered off and determined. The metals are determined in the filtrate.

Chilled Blast Furnace Slag. The sudden chilling of the molten slag by dropping into water causes a physical change in the material which enables a decomposition by means of acids without resort to fusion, as given above.

About 0.5 gram of the finely ground chilled slag in a small casserole is moistened with water and about 3 cc. of concentrated HCl added. All lumps are broken up by stirring with a glass rod until a smooth jelly results. A few drops of HNO_3 are added to oxidize the iron and the jelly is worked up around the sides of the casserole in an even layer to the height of about $\frac{1}{2}$ inch. (This permits rapid dehydration of the silica and reduces loss by " spitting.") The acids are expelled by evaporation and the residue gently baked. (If the temperature is too high, some alumina will combine with the silica and give high results for SiO_2.) After cooling, about 20 cc. of concentrated HCl are added and the mixture boiled for a few minutes, then diluted with an equal volume of hot water and filtered hot. SiO_2 remains as a residue, the metals are in solution.

Silica. The residue obtained from the decomposition is washed with hot water until free from chlorides, the washings being added to the main filtrate. The residue and filter are ignited, then cooled and weighed as SiO_2.

NOTE. Should barium be present, as is the case with many lead slags, nitric acid is omitted in the decomposition, as this would cause contamination of the silica with barium sulphate. If nitric acid is used, it is advisable to obtain the silica by difference, by first weighing the residue. This is placed in a weighed platinum dish, then treated with hydrofluoric acid and a few drops of sulphuric acid. The solution is evaporated, all the acids and the silica being expelled (as silicon fluoride). Any remaining residue is weighed and subtracted from the first weight obtained. The loss represents the SiO_2.

Copper slags carrying 40 to 45% of SiO_2 are more troublesome than those with 35 to 37% of SiO_2 in regard to alumina uniting with the silica during dehydration.

Lime. (In presence of iron oxide and alumina) Ammonia is added to the filtrate from silica and then oxalic acid little by little until the precipitated iron and aluminum hydroxides just dissolve. The solution is again made ammoniacal and oxalic acid again added to dissolve iron. The solution should appear a light apple-green color. It is now boiled for a few minutes and the precipitated calcium filtered off and washed with hot water until free from oxalic acid, six or seven times being generally sufficient.

The filter containing the calcium oxalate is dropped in a beaker, 150 cc. of hot water added together with 15 cc. of (1 : 1) H_2SO_4 and the oxalic acid titrated with standard potassium permanganate.

$$1 \text{ cc. of } 0.1 \text{ N } KMnO_4 = 0.0028 \text{ gram of CaO.}$$

The Fe value of $KMnO_4$ multiplied by $0.5 = $ CaO value.

NOTES. If preferred, iron and aluminum may be precipitated as hydroxides, and filtered off, calcium being determined in the filtrate. It is advisable to redissolve the precipitate to recover any occluded lime and again precipitate the hydroxides with ammonia, the filtrate being combined with the main filtrate.

In place of titrating the oxalate of lime, it may be ignited and the residue weighed directly as CaO.

If oxalic acid is added in the form of a fine powder instead of a solution, the calcium precipitates in a much more granular form and requires less boiling before filtering.

Iron. (In presence of silica) Half a gram or more of the finely ground chilled slag in a beaker is treated with 50 cc. of boiling water, the particles stirred up and kept in suspension and about 25 cc. of concentrated HCl added. The solution is boiled until clear. (If coke dust is present it will still be evident, but may be neglected.) Stannous chloride solution is added, drop by drop, until the iron is reduced (solution becomes colorless) and 2–3 drops excess added. The solution is cooled by placing the beaker in cold water. Mercuric chloride, $HgCl_2$, solution is added to precipitate the excess of stannous chloride.

The iron is determined by titration with standard potassium dichromate, using ferricyanide indicator on a spot plate. See subject in the chapter on Iron. Report as FeO.

1 cc. of 0.1 N $K_2Cr_2O_7 = 0.00558$ g. of Fe, 0.00719 g. of FeO,

$Fe \times 1.2865 = FeO$.

NOTE. The iron may be precipitated as hydroxide, then dissolved in dilute H_2SO_4, the solution reduced by boiling with test lead or reduced in cold solution with zinc and the solution titrated with standard potassium permanganate. This method is frequently preferred where previous fusion to decompose the ore has been required. Lime may be determined in the filtrate from iron.

Determination of Other Constituents in Slags

Alumina. *Phosphate Method.* The filtrate from the silica determination is diluted to about 400 cc. with cold water and 30 cc. of 10% ammonium phosphate added. Dilute ammonia water is added until a slight permanent precipitate forms.

1.5 cc. of concentrated HCl is added and 40 cc. of 20% solution of Na_2S_2O and the mixture boiled for about two or three minutes. 15 cc. of 20% ammonium acetate and 6 cc. of strong acetic acid are added and the boiling continued for about 15 minutes.

The precipitate is allowed to settle for 15–20 minutes, the clear solution decanted through a filter and finally the aluminum phosphate filtered and washed. (The presence of the acetate makes the compound more granular. 10 washings with hot water are sufficient.

The precipitate is dried, ignited and weighed as $AlPO_4$.

The precipitate contains 41.85% Al_2O_3.

NOTE. The slag may be decomposed by treating 0.5 gram in a platinum dish with 5 cc. HNO_3, 6 cc. of HF and about 2 cc. of (1 : 1) H_2SO_4. The sample is taken to strong fumes of SO_3, then cooled and 10 cc. of HCl added and the mixture boiled. Alumina and iron may now be precipitated as hydroxides, and filtered off and washed. After dissolving in HCl precipitate $AlPO_4$ as in the method above.

Manganese. Half a gram of the slag is placed in a beaker and about 50 cc. of water added, the solution stirred until the material is in suspension and about 15 cc. of HCl added, followed by 5 cc. of HNO_3, and the solution boiled until most of the chlorine has been expelled.

Hot water is added to make up to a volume of about 100 cc. The iron is now precipitated by adding ZnO emulsion until the acid is neutralized and an excess of ZnO forms on the bottom of the beaker.

The solution is boiled for a few minutes and the manganese titrated while the solution is still hot (in presence of the precipitate) with standard potassium permanganate.

The end-point is best seen by allowing the precipitate to settle slightly and observing the clear upper stratum of the liquid.

$$\text{1 cc. of 0.1 N } KMnO_4 = 0.00165 \text{ g. of Mn.}$$

The lime value of the $KMnO_4 \times 0.588 = Mn.$

NOTE. In place of the method given above consult the chapter on Manganese for the volumetric oxalic acid method.

Zinc. To 0.5 gram (1 gram if zinc is low) of the sample in a casserole is added 3 cc. of water, 5 cc. of HCl and 2 cc. of HNO_3. When the SiO_2 is completely gelatinized, about 4 grams of NH_4Cl is stirred in.

The sample is dehydrated only until the residue crumbles easily as baking is liable to volatilize some zinc as chloride. About 30 cc. of hot water are added and the solution brought to boiling, filtered and the residue washed with hot water.

To the filtrate ammonium persulphate and bromine are added, the amount being governed by the manganese present, *i.e.*, 0.03 g. of ammonium persulphate and 10 cc. bromine for every 0.01 g. of Mn in solution. Ammonia is added in slight excess, the solution boiled about 2 minutes, filtered, and the residue, MnO_2, etc., washed. (It is advisable to redissolve the precipitate in a little dilute HCl and again precipitate with persulphate and bromine, adding the filtrate to the main filtrate.)

The solution is just neutralized with HCl and 5 cc. excess added, followed by 2 grams of test lead. The solution is boiled about 15 minutes.

About 8–10 cc. of HCl are added, the solution heated to about 60° C. and the potassium ferrocyanide added. When the titration is almost completed, the bluish-white color of the precipitate changes to nearly pure white.

If the ferrocyanide is made up by adding 21.63 grams of potassium ferrocyanide per liter of solution, 1 cc. will equal very nearly 0.005 gram of Zn. Consult chapter on Zinc.

In place of the above method the rapid method given in the chapter on Zinc may be followed.

Magnesia. 0.5 gram or more of the finely ground chilled slag, placed in a casserole, is moistened with water, 5 cc. of HCl and a few drops of HNO_3 added. The acids after reacting with the slag are evaporated off and the silica dehydrated. The residue is taken up with 15 cc. of HCl and about 30 cc. of water, and boiled.

Silica is filtered off and washed.

The filtrate is made slightly alkaline with ammonia, 8 cc. of $(NH_4)_2S$ and 1 gram of $(NH_4)_2CO_3$ added and the solution boiled for a few minutes, the precipitate then filtered off and washed several times with water containing a little $(NH_4)_2S$.

The filtrate is made slightly acid with HCl and boiled down to about 50 cc. The precipitated sulphur is filtered off and the filter washed. If the solution is cloudy, it is cleared by adding bromine water and boiling.

Ammonia is now added and a small amount of ammonium oxalate to remove any CaO still remaining; after boiling, the oxalate of calcium (" lime ") is filtered off and washed.

Magnesia is now precipitated in the filtrate by addition of Na_2HPO_4 or another alkali phosphate, and the magnesium ammonium phosphate filtered off, washed with 2% ammonium nitrate solution, ignited and weighed as $Mg_2P_2O_7$. Consult the chapter on Magnesium.

$$Mg_2P_2O_7 \times 0.3621 = MgO.$$

Copper. *Colorimetric Method with Ammonia.* The percentage of copper normally present in blast furnace slags should not exceed 0.3%. Converter slags may contain as much as 2.5% copper. The colorimetric method is especially adapted for this determination owing to its simplicity and speed.

Slags which have been " chilled " are *readily* decomposed by HCl. Stirring constantly during the acid action and diluting as soon as decomposition is complete prevents the separation of gelatinous silica and hastens the solution of copper.

Procedure. *Color Standards.* 0.2 gram of pure copper foil is dissolved in 20 cc. of 1 : 1 HNO_3 in a covered beaker, warming gently. After evaporating down to about 10 cc., the solution diluted to 50 cc. is transferred to a graduated liter flask, 200 cc. of ammonium hydroxide added and the solution diluted to 1000 cc.

5, 10, 20, 30, 40, 50, 60, 70, 80, 90 and 100 cc. portions are taken and placed in 100-cc. Nessler colorimetric tubes. (In place of the tubes clear

white glass bottles of about 150 cc. capacity may be used.) The volume of
each solution is diluted to 100 cc. with 1 : 5 ammonium hydroxide.

If a colorimeter is available, a standard is taken that corresponds to that
of the sample as prepared according to directions below and comparisons made
by viewing the solutions through the depth of solutions adjusted to give the
same intensity of color.

Preparation of the Sample. Two grams of the finely crushed sample
(100-mesh) is treated in a beaker with 10 cc. of water to thoroughly moisten
the powder, 10 cc. of strong HCl are added and the mixture stirred, warming
gently until the undissolved residue becomes flocculent, remaining in suspension.

About 90 cc. of H_2S water are added or the same volume of water and H_2S
gas passed in until the solution is saturated. The solution is warmed gently
until the copper sulphide coagulates. The precipitate is filtered through a
small filter (Witt filter is O.K.) and washed with H_2S water.

The sulphide is now dissolved in 5 cc. strong HNO_3 (in the beaker in which
the CuS was precipitated), 30 cc. 1 : 5 NH_4OH solution are added, the solution
filtered through a second filter, and this washed with 1 : 5 ammonia reagent.

The copper solution is transferred to a Nessler tube (bottle or colorimeter
tube as the case may require) and comparison made with a standard, the
solution being made up to 100 cc. with 1 : 5 NH_4OH.

Electrolytic and Iodide Method for Copper

For extreme accuracy the electrolytic or iodide methods are recommended. Details of these methods may be found in the chapter on Copper. See also the chapter on Fire Assay Methods by I. A. Palmer.

Lead. The determination of lead is frequently required in slags. Slags high in silica are apt to contain lead in appreciable quantities, probably combined as silicate. The decomposition of the slag by treatment with HF as given in the footnote on page 691 is recommended.

The determination of lead in slag does not differ materially from its determination in ores. Reference is made to the chapter on Lead for its estimation.

Other Constituents. The determination of barium, titanium, sulphur, phosphorus, chromium, cobalt, nickel, alkalies, etc., is occasionally necessary. The procedures for these determinations may be found in the chapters dealing with the elements in question.[1]

[1] The introduction to this section "Slag Analysis" was written by Prof. I. A. Palmer, Department of Metallurgy, Colorado School of Mines.

A number of the procedures appearing in this chapter on slag analysis are standard methods used at the Washoe Smelter of the Anaconda Copper Mining Company and are procedures originally suggested by Professor H. W. Thomson, Department of Mining, The University of British Columbia.

METHODS FOR ANALYSIS OF COAL AND COKE

Such tremendous value attaches in boiler-room economy to the character of the fuel that the purchase of coal upon the results of laboratory analysis has grown in importance. Specifications have been drawn with such exact requirements that fairness to the coal contractor requires that only exact methods of analysis be employed.

SAMPLING

In order that the laboratory sample shall be representative of the delivery, great care must be taken, however; the personal element should be eliminated as far as possible. When possible, coal should be delivered by chutes and a shovelful taken at regular intervals throughout the delivery. If delivered in wagons a portion should be taken from each wagon load. Boat loads are best sampled while being loaded or unloaded. If a pile of coal must be sampled, portions should be taken from all sides, top and bottom. The gross sample should preferably be 200 pounds for deliveries up to 100 tons and one-tenth of 1% of the amount delivered for quantities over 100 tons. Larger sizes should be crushed to at least pea size (about $\frac{3}{4}$ in.) and preferably under. The gross sample should be thoroughly mixed with a shovel, piled up, and quartered. Opposite quarters should then be mixed, piled up, and quartered again and this continued until a sample of about 5 pounds is obtained.[2] This sample should then be forwarded to the laboratory in a sealed moisture-tight container. The most satisfactory container is one made of galvanized iron, to prevent rusting, cylindrical in shape with screw cap flush with the sides. A convenient size is 6 ins. in diameter by 8 ins. height. Such a can is readily cleaned and sealed. Sealing is conveniently made by pasting a strip of paper around the can over the joint, or by means of wax and an impression seal.

PREPARATION OF SAMPLE FOR ANALYSIS

The laboratory sample should first receive a number which should follow the sample through all phases of preparation in order to avoid confusion. The whole sample, when received at the laboratory, should be crushed to 4-mesh size or less. The Chipmunk Jaw Crusher is rapid and easily cleaned, as one jaw is removable. If too wet to crush, causing clogging of the crusher, the whole sample should be dried on the steam bath, the moisture so lost determined and added to the analytical moisture later determined on the pulverized sample. Shallow agateware pans large enough to take the complete sample are convenient and should set in large holes on the steam bath, so that the body of

---

[1] Chapter by Frank E. Hale. Director of Laboratories, Dept. Water Supply, Gas and Electricity, New York City.
[2] The U. S. Bureau of Mines uses a 3-pound sample and New York City a 7-pound sample.

the pan is exposed to the steam and drying is hastened. A few hours only is necessary. The U. S. Bureau of Mines dries in a special oven with a current of dried air at 30–35° C., but this occasions a delay of twelve to ninety-six hours. The crushed sample should be mixed and quartered, preferably by hand. This is best and most rapidly done in the old-fashioned way by raising alternately the corners of a large piece of oilcloth or rubber sheet. The pile may be quickly quartered by two V-shaped pieces of galvanized iron to cut and pull away opposite quarters. The remaining quarters should be again mixed and quartered in the same way and the process continued until a 100-gram representative

Fig. 204.—Illustrates Method of Quartering Coal, Ball Mill for Pulverizing, and Suction Ventilator.

portion is obtained. The discarded quarters should be returned to the can to be retained in case a second analysis is desired. Such check analysis should always be made upon a freshly quartered and pulverized sample of the remaining portions of the original gross laboratory sample.

The 100-gram sample should then be pulverized in an Abbé Ball Mill for three-quarters of an hour. The jar should be nearly full to produce the most rapid pulverization, that is, contain the full charge of pebbles, about 10 pounds for the 9-in. jar. The speed of revolution should be 60 per minute. Natural flint pebbles are least abraded and produce no appreciable effect upon the ash. The ball mill has two distinct advantages. It conserves the moisture of the coal and it pulverizes so fine that the coal will usually all pass a 60-mesh screen and a large part the 100-mesh screen. This greater fineness prevents incomplete combustion of anthracite coal in the bomb determination to be described later. The pebbles and coal should then be dumped on a covered ash-sifter resting on the oilcloth or rubber sheet, shaken quickly and pebbles and sifter brushed clean. The sample should then be passed through the 60-mesh screen and brushed at once into a moisture-tight container. Any material retained on the 60-mesh screen, which occasionally happens, should be quickly pulverized in a small steel mortar. One-half pint, glass-covered lightning jars are convenient for containers.

As the dust in coal sampling is so fine as to penetrate through the clothing to the skin, it is wise to use an aspirator to protect the lungs and also use a suction ventilator to keep the air fresh and clean. The suction should connect with small hoods over the crusher and over the quartering table.

METHODS OF ANALYSIS

Moisture. Moisture may be accurately determined on a 10-gram sample heated for one hour at 105° C. Close checks will be obtained and weighing is rapid, as the weight need only be taken to the nearest milligram. Glass evaporating dishes of $2\frac{3}{4}$-in. diameter are convenient for this determination. The Beans electric thermo-regulator for gas has been found very satisfactory for oven regulation, as the oven may be heated rapidly and will quickly come to adjustment.

Most laboratories employ a 1-gram sample, however, and later use the residue for ash determination. The Bureau of Mines uses a special drying oven and a specially prepared sample for moisture. The 4-mesh sample is crushed in a roll or coffee-mill crusher to 20-mesh, and bottled quickly without sieving.

Ash. The ash represents the mineral matter in coal after ignition. No attempt is made in common practice to calculate the original form of the constituents. It is best determined upon a separate portion of coal, and preferably in silica crucibles, as the wear on platinum is considerable. Heating should be slow and careful at first, to avoid loss from volatile matter and to avoid the effect of coking. Later the contents should be stirred with a platinum wire to facilitate combustion, not neglecting to tap the wire free from ash. The silica crucibles should rest on silica or nichrome triangles. Some laboratories employ a muffle furnace and others an electric furnace.

The residue from moisture may be used for ash determination, but the residue from volatile combustible matter should not be so used, as there is danger of mechanical loss of ash in the rapid heating, and the accuracy of the ash-figure is far more important than the volatile combustible matter.

A 1-gram sample is used for the ash determination.

Volatile Combustible Matter. This determination is entirely empirical and should be performed under strictly standard conditions. The determination is made upon a 1-gram sample heated for seven minutes, timed by a stop-watch, in a platinum crucible of 25-30 cc. capacity, and with tight-fitting cover. The crucible and cover should be kept brightly polished. A special apparatus should be arranged. Construct a cylinder of asbestos or galvanized iron to protect flame and crucible. Connect an adjustable Méker burner (Scimatco type is preferable) with a U-tube to measure gas pressure. Arrange a platinum wire from triangle to support the bottom of crucible always at same distance from the burner.

Calibrate the apparatus by adjusting the burner and pressure so that the crucible is entirely surrounded by the flame and the temperature is about 950° C. This may be determined by an optical or other pyrometer, but most conveniently by the fusing-point of potassium chromate. Note the gas pressure required and in the analyses set the gas at this pressure. In this way close checks may conveniently be obtained when the right conditions have been determined.

The loss in weight minus the moisture is the volatile combustible matter.

A 10–20-cc. crucible has recently been advocated to reduce the effect of oxidation by oxygen in the crucible. Several different schemes have been advocated in order to obtain uniform results. An electric furnace is used by some. Any method is empirical, as the determination does not represent any

Fig. 205.—V. C. M. Apparatus

very definite constituent of the coal. Originally intended as a measure of coking ability the V.C.M is now mainly a means of discriminating between different kinds of coal and as a means of keeping within the smoke ordinances.

Volatile Sulphur. The total sulphur in a coal is of little importance. If desired, it may be determined by the well-known Eschka method. The volatile sulphur is of great importance both in its bearing upon fusibility by indicating the presence of pyrites in the coal and in its relation to corrosion by the formation of sulphurous acid.

Volatile sulphur is determined in the bomb washings after a calorific determination. These washings are filtered if necessary and titrated for acidity for one of the corrections in the calorific calculation. The sulphur is then determined most rapidly and conveniently by a Jackson Candle Turbidimeter.

"The titrated solution is made up to 200 cc. The amount of acidity found is used as a guide in selecting the aliquot for the sulphur determination. In

TURBIDIMETRIC SULPHUR TABLE

For use with Jackson's candle turbidimeter

Sulphur and SO$_3$ contained in 100 cc. precipitated

Depth. Cm.	S. Mg.	SO$_3$. Mg.	Depth. Cm.	S. Mg.	SO$_3$. Mg.	Depth. Cm.	S. Mg.	SO$_3$. Mg.
1.0	20.0	50.0	5.0	3.66	9.15	9.0	2.30	5.75
1.1	18.0	45.0	5.1	3.60	9.00	9.1	2.28	5.70
1.2	16.5	41.3	5.2	3.54	8.85	9.2	2.26	5.65
1.3	15.0	37.5	5.3	3.49	8.73	9.3	2.25	5.63
1.4	13.5	33.8	5.4	3.43	8.58	9.4	2.23	5.58
1.5	12.5	31.3	5.5	3.38	8.45	9.5	2.21	5.53
1.6	11.2	28.0	5.6	3.33	8.33	9.6	2.19	5.48
1.7	10.0	25.0	5.7	3.28	8.20	9.7	2.18	5.45
1.8	9.5	23.8	5.8	3.24	8.10	9.8	2.16	5.40
1.9	9.0	22.5	5.9	3.20	8.00	9.9	2.15	5.38
2.0	8.5	21.3	6.0	3.15	7.88	10.0	2.13	5.33
2.1	8.0	20.0	6.1	3.11	7.78	10.1	2.11	5.28
2.2	7.6	19.0	6.2	3.07	7.68	10.2	2.10	5.25
2.3	7.3	18.3	6.3	3.03	7.58	10.3	2.09	5.23
2.4	7.0	17.5	6.4	2.99	7.48	10.4	2.07	5.18
2.5	6.7	16.8	6.5	2.95	7.38	10.5	2.06	5.15
2.6	6.5	16.3	6.6	2.92	7.30	10.6	2.04	5.10
2.7	6.3	15.8	6.7	2.88	7.20	10.7	2.03	5.08
2.8	6.1	15.3	6.8	2.85	7.13	10.8	2.02	5.05
2.9	5.9	14.8	6.9	2.82	7.05	10.9	2.01	5.03
3.0	5.7	14.3	7.0	2.79	6.98	11.0	2.00	5.00
3.1	5.5	13.8	7.1	2.76	6.90	11.1	1.98	4.95
3.2	5.4	13.5	7.2	2.73	6.83	11.2	1.97	4.93
3.3	5.2	13.0	7.3	2.70	6.75	11.3	1.95	4.88
3.4	5.1	12.8	7.4	2.67	6.68	11.4	1.94	4.85
3.5	5.0	12.5	7.5	2.64	6.60	11.5	1.93	4.83
3.6	4.85	12.25	7.6	2.61	6.53	11.6	1.92	4.80
3.7	4.75	12.00	7.7	2.59	6.48	11.7	1.91	4.78
3.8	4.63	11.75	7.8	2.56	6.40	11.8	1.90	4.75
3.9	4.52	11.50	7.9	2.54	6.35	11.9	1.89	4.73
4.0	4.43	11.25	8.0	2.51	6.28	12.0	1.88	4.70
4.1	4.33	11.00	8.1	2.49	6.23	12.1	1.87	4.68
4.2	4.24	10.75	8.2	2.47	6.18	12.2	1.86	4.65
4.3	4.16	10.50	8.3	2.44	6.10	12.3	1.85	4.63
4.4	4.08	10.25	8.4	2.42	6.05	12.4	1.84	4.60
4.5	4.00	10.00	8.5	2.40	6.00	12.5	1.83	4.58
4.6	3.93	9.83	8.6	2.38	5.95	12.6	1.82	4.55
4.7	3.86	9.65	8.7	2.36	5.90	12.7	1.81	4.53
4.8	3.79	9.48	8.8	2.34	5.85	12.8	1.80	4.50
4.9	3.72	9.30	8.9	2.32	5.80	12.9	1.79	4.48

TURBIDIMETRIC SULPHUR TABLE.—*Continued*

Depth. Cm.	S. Mg.	SO₃. Mg.	Depth. Cm.	S. Mg.	SO₃. Mg.	Depth. Cm.	S. Mg.	SO₃. Mg.
13.0	1.78	4.45	17.1	1.49	3.73	21.1	1.24	3.10
13.1	1.77	4.43	17.2	1.49	3.73	21.2	1.23	3.08
13.2	1.76	4.40	17.3	1.48	3.70	21.3	1.23	3.08
13.3	1.75	4.38	17.4	1.47	3.68	21.4	1.22	3.05
13.4	1.74	4.35	17.5	1.47	3.68	21.5	1.21	3.03
13.5	1.73	4.33	17.6	1.46	3.65	21.6	1.21	3.03
13.6	1.73	4.33	17.7	1.45	3.63	21.7	1.20	3.00
13.7	1.72	4.30	17.8	1.44	3.60	21.8	1.20	3.00
13.8	1.71	4.28	17.9	1.44	3.60	21.9	1.19	2.98
13.9	1.70	4.25	18.0	1.43	3.58	22.0	1.18	2.95
14.0	1.70	4.25	18.1	1.43	3.58	22.1	1.18	2.95
14.1	1.69	4.23	18.2	1.42	3.55	22.2	1.17	2.93
14.2	1.68	4.20	18.3	1.41	3.53	22.3	1.16	2.90
14.3	1.67	4.18	18.4	1.41	3.53	22.4	1.16	2.90
14.4	1.66	4.15	18.5	1.40	3.50	22.5	1.15	2.88
14.5	1.66	4.15	18.6	1.40	3.50	22.6	1.15	2.88
14.6	1.65	4.13	18.7	1.39	3.48	22.7	1.14	2.85
14.7	1.64	4.10	18.8	1.38	3.45	22.8	1.13	2.83
14.8	1.63	4.08	18.9	1.38	3.45	22.9	1.13	2.83
14.9	1.62	4.05	19.0	1.37	3.43	23.0	1.12	2.80
15.0	1.62	4.05	19.1	1.37	3.43	23.1	1.11	2.78
15.1	1.61	4.03	19.2	1.36	3.40	23.2	1.11	2.78
15.2	1.60	4.00	19.3	1.35	3.38	23.3	1.10	2.75
15.3	1.60	4.00	19.4	1.35	3.38	23.4	1.09	2.73
15.4	1.59	3.98	19.5	1.34	3.35	23.5	1.08	2.70
15.5	1.59	3.98	19.6	1.34	3.35	23.6	1.08	2.70
15.6	1.58	3.95	19.7	1.33	3.33	23.7	1.07	2.68
15.7	1.57	3.93	19.8	1.32	3.30	23.8	1.06	2.65
15.8	1.57	3.93	19.9	1.32	3.30	23.9	1.05	2.63
15.9	1.56	3.90	20.0	1.31	3.28	24.0	1.05	2.63
16.0	1.56	3.90	20.1	1.30	3.25	24.1	1.04	2.60
16.1	1.55	3.88	20.2	1.30	3.25	24.2	1.03	2.58
16.2	1.54	3.85	20.3	1.29	3.23	24.3	1.03	2.58
16.3	1.54	3.85	20.4	1.28	3.20	24.4	1.02	2.55
16.4	1.53	3.83	20.5	1.28	3.20	24.5	1.02	2.55
16.5	1.53	3.83	20.6	1.27	3.18	24.6	1.01	2.53
16.6	1.52	3.80	20.7	1.26	3.15	24.7	1.01	2.53
16.7	1.52	3.80	20.8	1.26	3.15	24.8	1.00	2.50
16.8	1.51	3.78	20.9	1.25	3.13	24.9	1.00	2.50
16.9	1.50	3.75	21.0	1.25	3.13	25.0	1.00	2.50
17.0	1.50	3.75						

the case of anthracite coals, the amount taken is one-fourth to one-half; in the case of soft coals from one-fourth to one-tenth of the whole."

"The aliquot of the solution to be tested is measured into the turbidimeter tube, diluted to near the 100-cc. mark, shaken, then acidified with 1 cc. of 1 : hydrochloric acid, made up to the mark, and mixed well by shaking. A barium chloride tablet [1] weighing 1 gram and compressed without the use of a binder is then dropped in and the tube closed by means of a clean rubber stopper. The tube is then tilted up and down, causing the tablet to roll back and forth through the solution by gravity.

When the precipitation appears to be complete, the remainder of the tablet may be dissolved by rapidly rotating the tube; but violent shaking should be avoided, since it would have a tendency to cause aggregation of the precipitate. The turbid liquid is then transferred to a beaker, the candle lighted, a small quantity of the liquid poured into the glass tube to prevent overheating and cracking, and the tube put in place. More of the liquid is then poured in, allowing it to run down the side of the tube, rapidly at first, until the image of the flame becomes dim, then more slowly, waiting a moment after each addition until the liquid in the tube is quiet, and continuing thus until the image of the flame just disappears. The depth of the liquid in centimeters is noted. The mixture is then returned to the beaker, poured back and forth from beaker to tube two or three times, and read again as before.

"The precipitated solution is read at least twice, and the readings usually check exactly, unless they fall in the upper part of the tube, where they may differ by a centimeter without materially altering the results. In this case readings may be averaged. The amount of sulphur corresponding to the depth of liquid in the tube is found in the table, and multiplied by the proper factor, depending on the aliquot of the original solution taken.

"All dilutions must be made before precipitation, for otherwise the results will not be concordant for different dilutions." The average time required is ten minutes or less. The method carried out as described is accurate to about 0.05% sulphur.

[1] These tablets are prepared on order by the Fraser Tablet Co., of Brooklyn, N. Y., Formula No. 188,663.

On standing for some time, some of the tablets become coated with a thin layer of effloresced salt. This should be removed by gently rubbing between the fingers before using the tablet. It is not advisable to keep the tablets in a moist atmosphere to prevent this efflorescence, as they become extremely hard and difficult to dissolve.

Procedure for Hot Precipitation Method [1]

Dilute an aliquot portion of the solution to be tested to 100 cc. and add
cc. of 1 : 1 HCl.   Heat to 80° C., add 0.5 gram powdered $BaCl_2$ and mix
y rotating for one minute.   Cool to 25° C. at once and let stand for 5 minutes.
our down the side of the turbidimeter tube and take readings when image
the light just disappears.

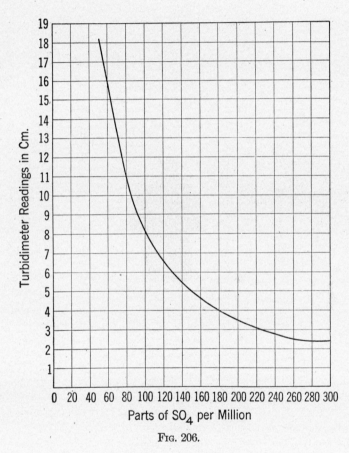

Fig. 206.

[1] Contributed by Prof. A. H. Gill.

Fixed Carbon. Fixed carbon is found by adding the moisture, ash, an volatile matter together, and subtracting from 100%.

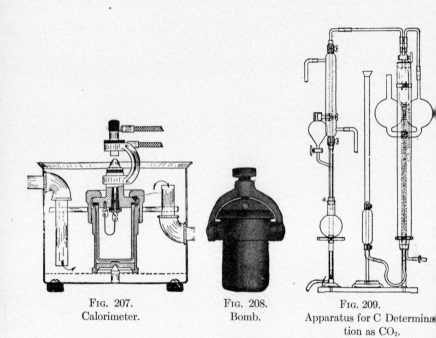

FIG. 207.
Calorimeter.

FIG. 208.
Bomb.

FIG. 209.
Apparatus for C Determina tion as CO_2.

Calorific Value. Heat value is expressed as "small calorie (cal.)," th amount of heat required to raise the temperature of 1 gram of water 1° C. "large calorie (Cal.)," the amount of heat required to raise the temperatur of 1 kilogram of water 1° C., and "British thermal unit (B.t.u.)," the amoun of heat required to raise the temperature of 1 pound of water 1° F., at or nea 39.1° F. Small calories per gram of coal multiplied by 1.8 equal B.t.u. pe pound of coal.

It is preferable to express results as B.t.u. per pound of dry coal, instead of coal as received, since comparison between different samples of coal and the results of different analysts and laboratories are facilitated. The othe determinations except moisture are also better expressed on the dry basis.

As a check upon accuracy of work and to catch errors, results of B.t.u. uld also be calculated to B.t.u. per pound of combustible, that is, divide the .u. dry basis by (100% minus the per cent of ash). For the same run of l, this value changes but little, usually within 200 B.t.u.

The calorific determination should be made by means of a bomb calorimeter. platinum-lined Atwater type is convenient. The Emerson is more commonly used in this country.

Unfortunately the Atwater bomb is no longer manufactured, although it is used by laboratories possessing it. The Emerson bomb calorimeter is an ellent type available in the American market.

One gram of the 60-mesh sample of coal prepared for analysis is weighed o a nickel capsule (28 mm. top width, 23 mm. bottom width, and 12 mm.

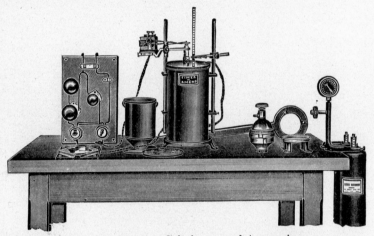

Fig. 210. Emerson Calorimeter and Accessories.

pth) in the bottom of which has been placed an ignited disc of asbestos paper. e latter prevents incomplete combustion of anthracite coal by preventing illing of the coal after combustion starts. In weighing large numbers of mples a piece of tared platinum foil is convenient and the coal transferred th a camel's-hair brush into the nickel capsule. The capsule is supported on platinum ring suspended by a platinum wire from the head of the bomb. piece of iron fuse wire, No. 34 B. & S. gauge, and weighing 10 milligrams, attached at one end to the wire supporting the tray and at the other end to other platinum wire extending downward from the head, but insulated from . Attachment of the fuse wire is made by winding around the platinum ires several times. The center of the fuse wire should dip into the coal ightly. A convenient method of obtaining pieces of fuse wire of uniform eight is to wind around a flat piece of board or cardboard and cut the loops.

The shell of the bomb is rinsed with water and sufficient moisture, one-h
cc., is thus left to take up the acids formed by combustion. The head is n
joined gas tight to the shell of the bomb by the collar. Lead gaskets ren
these joints tight. Oxygen gas is slowly introduced, so as not to blow
coal out of the pan, until about 21 atmospheres pressure is recorded in
bomb. The needle valve is then closed just tight enough to prevent leaka
the valve on oxygen tank closed and the bomb disconnected. Twenty atm
pheres pressure should remain in the bomb for the combustion, an amou

Fig. 211.—Illustrates Method of Connecting Two Oxygen Cylinders for Filling Bom
when Pressure in One is below Twenty Atmospheres.

sufficient for complete combustion of the coal and an amount containing su
ficient nitrogen together with the nitrogen in the air trapped in the bomb
cause the sulphur to burn to sulphuric acid completely, unless the sulphur
unusually high.

The bucket is filled with enough distilled water, about 3° C. below the roo
temperature, to make the water equivalent of the calorimeter some round nu
ber, i.e., 2000 g. with Atwater, 2900 g. with Mahler, or 2350 g. with Emerso
The water is best weighed on a balance, capable of delicacy with such heav
weights, and the amount of water should be sufficient to cover the bomb. Th
bomb is placed in its support and placed in the water in the bucket. The latte
is set in the calorimeter, the stirrer added so as not to touch bomb or bucket

ers applied and thermometer placed in the water and adjusted so that it be read during the combustion. The thermometers should be special and ndardized by the Bureau of Standards. The Fuess type of Beckmann is ellent.

Connect the poles of six dry cells to the stem and insulated post of the bomb. nnection should be made with a button for firing the coal. It is also con- ient to have a small electric lamp connected with the button to indicate t the batteries are in condition, before a run is started.

The calorific determination should be made in a room protected from lden changes of temperature and from draughts. If a current of air strikes e thermometer during a determination, the results will be untrustworthy. echanical stirring is preferable and should be at a moderate rate. The stirrer started and after a couple of minutes or so, when conditions have become iform, the thermometer is read by means of a telescope and readings taken ery one-half minute for six readings. Interpolate to the 0.001° C. A clock iking every half minute is convenient. After the sixth reading, fire the coal pressing the button connected with the batteries and take approximate idings of the thermometer every half minute, reading to the 0.001° C. as soon the rise is slow enough to do so. After the maximum temperature has been iched, take six more readings at half-minute intervals.

Remove the bomb from the bucket and allow the gas to escape slowly. Dis- nnect the head and rinse out the bomb thoroughly. Titrate the washings th N/10 sodium carbonate, using methyl orange as indicator. Determine the lphur, after titration, with the turbidimeter as under Volatile Sulphur.

Calculation of B.T.U. The table on page 1226 is an example of an actual termination, showing corrections as applied.

Corrections must be applied to the thermometer in accordance with the rtificate furnished for each thermometer by the Bureau of Standards, includ- g the correction for temperature of setting of Beckmann thermometers and nergent stem correction for others.

The thermometer should also be fitted with a vibrator to overcome meniscus ror. This is conveniently done by arranging a small electric vibrator so at the hammer hits the rubber-covered metal clamp supporting the ther- ometer. The vibrator should, of course, be connected to a push-button and y batteries.

Correction must also be made for changes of temperature due to radiation. simple formula which yields results within 0.002° C. as compared with the ore elaborate formulæ is the following:

$$\frac{x(a+b)}{2} + yb = \text{radiation correction.}$$

=average preliminary period change per half minute;

=average final period change per half minute;

=number of half-minute intervals of combustion period during which the rise of temperature (expressed to the nearest 0.01°) was greater than 10% of the total rise. This is readily seen by inspection;

=remaining number of half-minute intervals of combustion period.

The algebraic signs must be observed in the formula.

The end of the combustion period is taken as the first reading after maximum temperature. The reason for this rests in the fact that the ꜟ maximum rarely occurs at a half-minute interval reading, as shown by a dr during the first period after the maximum temperature read, of less than

NO. 1 BUCKWHEAT COAL

Thermometer used (T_5), zero set at 20.4° C.
Room Temperature 22.5° C. Atwater bomb.

Acid found equal 7.2 cc. N/10 $Na_2CO_3 \times 1.45$ cal.	= 10.4 calories
Volatile sulphur (aliquot $\frac{1}{2}$) 8.6 cm. = .0048 gram $\times$ 13 cal.	= 6.2 calories
Iron wire (10 milligrams)	= 16.0 calories
	32.6 calories

Thermometer readings,
Half minute intervals

Preliminary period
{
0.979
0.980
0.981
0.983
0.984
0.986
}

Average rise in temperature:
$$\frac{.007}{5} = .0014$$

Combustion period
{
1.600
3.270
4.050
———
4.225
4.267
4.278
4.279
4.278
}

Final period
{
4.273
4.270
4.268
4.264
4.260
}

Average fall in temperature:
$$\frac{.018}{5} = .0036$$

Corrected temperature, end of combustion period.........	4.?
Corrected temperature, end of preliminary period.........	0.?
Apparent rise in temperature corrected for thermometer calibration..........	3.?
Thermometer correction for setting and room temperature.........	+0.?
Apparent rise in temperature, corrected for thermometer setting.........	3.?

Radiation correction:
$$3\left(\frac{(-.0014)+(+.0036)}{2}\right)+5(+.0036) \qquad +0.?$$

Corrected rise in temperature.........	3.?
Water equivalent (grams).........	2000
Calories (2000×3.334).........	6668.?
Correction for acidity, sulphur trioxide and iron.........	32.?
Actual calories, coal as received.........	6635.4
Calories (dry basis) $6635.4 \div .9522$ (100% −moisture).........	6968.?
B.t.u. per lb. of coal (dry basis) (6968.5×1.8).........	12,543
B.t.u. per lb. of combustible (dry basis) $12543 \div .842$(100%−ash).........	14,897

B.T.U...........	12,543	
V.C.M...........	7.7	%
Ash...........	15.8	
Vol. sulphur......	0.48	
Moisture........	4.78	

average final change. Correcting for an extra combustion interval counterac this error.

The nitrogen in the coal and in the air of the bomb forms nitric acid. T does not occur when coal is burned in the furnace, hence the bomb determ nation is too high by the amount of heat thus produced. The calorific value nitrogen burning to nitric acid is 230 calories per gram of nitric acid. Ea ubic centimeter of N/10 sodium carbonate used in the titration represents .45 calories.

Furthermore, sulphur in the furnace burns to the dioxide and in the bomb to the trioxide. This excess heat in the bomb must be corrected for as well as the fact that all of the above acidity is not nitric, but is partly sulphuric acid. This correction is conveniently made by adding to the acidity correction made as if it were all nitric acid) 13 calories for each 0.01 gram of sulphur. This represents the excess which the oxidation correction is over its expression as the formation of nitric acid as obtained from the titration.

The correction for the iron fuse wire is 16 calories for each 10 milligrams.

All other corrections are met by standardization under conditions similar to those under which the calorimeter is to be used. Such errors arise from loss of heat by evaporation of water while stirring (probably covered by the radiation correction), gain in heat due to combustible gases in the oxygen, changes in specific heat of water at various temperatures, changes in the gases present after combustion, and changes of pressure of the gases in the bomb. The last three errors are too small to take into account. The oxygen error has disappeared since the introduction of the purer gas manufactured by the Linde Air Products Company.

Inspection of the bomb contents should always be made to insure that there are no sooty deposits or coal thrown from the capsule. Some coals require to be compressed into pellets to prevent the above.

The procedure outlined above, using half-minute intervals, saves considerable time (nearly one-half) over the usual procedure and produces very accurate results.

Standardization of the Calorimeter. While there are several ways of determining the water equivalent of the calorimeter, that is, the heat capacity of the apparatus expressed as though it were all water, only one method should be used by commercial laboratories, and that is to burn in the calorimeter a known weight of pure substance, the calorific value of which has been determined by the Bureau of Standards, Washington, D. C. Of those furnished, benzoic acid is preferable, as it readily ignites and burns completely. If cane sugar should be used, a few milligrams of benzoic acid are necessary to assist ignition and correction must be made for its heating value. Cane sugar does not always burn completely.

Procure standardized benzoic acid from the Bureau of Standards. Compress into pellets by means of pellet press sufficient benzoic acid to produce approximately as many calories as are given by the coal, that is, about 7000 calories. One gram of benzoic acid produces 6320 calories. Determine in the calorimeter the temperature rise produced by the benzoic acid with the precautions used in a regular coal analysis, correcting for thermometer and radiation errors. Multiply the grams of benzoic acid taken by 6320 calories, add the calories produced by formation of nitric acid as obtained from the titration and add the calories produced by the iron fuse wire. Divide this sum by the corrected rise in temperature. The quotient is the water-equivalent of the calorimeter. The amount of water added to the bucket is then changed so as to make the total calorimeter equivalent a round number, such as 2000 for the Atwater or 2900 for the Mahler, or 2350 for the Emerson. The water should entirely immerse the bomb and avoid spattering by the stirrer. Then restandardize with the new quantity of water. The conditions of combustion should be as closely as possible like those prevailing during regular coal analysis.

DETERMINATION OF FUSIBILITY OF COAL ASH

This determination has become of increasing importance in recent year especially in relation to mechanical stokers and gas manufacture. The com position of the ash, not its amount, is the determining factor. Alumina the most refractory constituent and its fusing-point, 2000° C., is lowered propo

FIG. 212.—Hoskins Electric Furnace, Optical Pyrometer in Position, Also (X) Method of Supporting Cone in Graphite Block.

tionately to the amounts of silica, alkalies, and iron present. In many coals the amounts of all but the latter do not lower the fusing-point sufficiently to cause trouble, that is, below 1400° C. The amount of iron becomes then of supreme importance, as the last straw that breaks the camel's back. This is popularly shown in the classification of coals as red ash and white ash. The condition of the iron is of great importance also, as in the ferric condition it has but slight effect, but in ferrous condition it lowers the fusion-point greatly. The influence of sulphur upon fusing-point probably depends upon the accompanying presence of iron as pyrites. In the coal bed in the presence of burning carbon the ferric oxide may be reduced to ferrous oxide or not, according to the care of the fire and the amount of oxygen supplied. This explains discrepancies occurring between the facts of clinkering of the coal on the grates and the fusing-point as determined in a laboratory furnace. The fusing-point varies in different types of furnaces for the same reasons. It seems safest to choose such furnaces in laboratory tests as give reducing atmospheres and hence lower fusing-point, indicating the possible danger.

A convenient furnace, for high temperatures especially, is the Hoskins Electric Furnace. The heat is generated by passing a heavy alternating current of low voltage through a series of carbon plates. Temperature is regulated by compression of these plates. This furnace uses a 60-cycle alternating current, 220 volts, about 40 amperes. The current is transformed by an air-cooled transformer to a current of 10 volts. The maximum temperature produced by the furnace is about 2000° C.

The coal is burned to ash at as low a temperature as possible in clay dishes. The ash is moistened with water and moulded into the shape of a Seger cone ($\frac{1}{2}$ in. by $2\frac{1}{2}$ ins.) by pressing into a mould conveniently made of lead. A piece of thin paper, moistened, is laid in the mould to facilitate removal of the cone. Some coals may require 10% dextrin paste as a binder, but it is usually unnecessary. The use of smaller cones has recently been advocated. The cones may be set in triangular holes in a Dixon graphite block and placed in the furnace so that the cone is horizontal. This position gives as concordant results as the vertical position, if not closer. The fusing-point is taken when the cone droops into a vertical position. The temperature must not rise too rapidly when near the fusing-point, about 5° C. per minute. The temperature is conveniently read by a fixed-focus total-radiation pyrometer or an optical pyrometer of the Wanner type. Reducing atmospheres preclude the use of metallic couples at high temperatures.

NOTE. The methods in this chapter are based upon those in use at the Mt. Prospect Laboratory, of the Department of Water Supply, Gas and Electricity, New York City. The method for fusibility was obtained originally from the Laboratory of the Consolidated Gas Company, New York City.

Conversion of Percentages of Constituents in a Substance from One Moisture Basis to Another, or from Dry to Wet Basis or Vice Versa [1]

The moisture content of a sample may vary in the original from that of the material analyzed. For example, in the analysis of coal the finely ground sample contains less moisture than the original lumps so that it is necessary to recalculate results to get the actual quantities present in the material as received. The results obtained bear the same ratio to the actual content as the total solids in the sample analyzed bear to the total solids in the original sample. For example, if the original lump contained 15% of moisture and the finely ground sample contained 10%, the ratio of total solids of the analyzed to the original material would be 90 : 85, hence all results multiplied by 85/90 would give the true percentages existing in the original material.

Rule. Multiply all percentages by the factor obtained by dividing the per cent total solids in the material to which the conversion is desired by the total solids in the material analyzed.

Examples. *A.* The moisture in the original sample was found to be 15%, the moisture in the powdered sample analyzed was 10%, the ash in the latter was found to be 5%, what was the ash in the original sample? The total solids are 85 and 90 respectively. $85 \div 90 = .947$ and $5 \times .947 = 4.75\%$ ash in the original sample.

B. In case the examination was made of a dry material which originally contained 15% moisture, the factor would be $85 \div 100 = .85$ so that 5% ash in the dry sample would be $5 \times .85 = 4.25\%$ in the original.

C. Should it be desired to figure from the wet basis to the dry basis, in case the sample analyzed contained 15% of moisture and the ash was 5%, then on the dry basis this would be $(100 \div 85)5 = 5.88\%$.

---

[1] In our work we always calculated B. T. U., V. C. M., ash and volatile sulphur to the dry basis, expressing only moisture on the wet basis. Only by so doing can one make a fair comparison between different coals as to quality. It is of no advantage to calculate these values to the weight of coal as delivered, since frequently coal is wet down before delivery, drains and loses a large amount of moisture before burning. Correction for moisture as delivered was made in the payments where it existed over a certain amount which is the reason for calculating moisture to the wet basis, i.e., coal as delivered.—F. E. Hall.

REFERENCES

General

E. E. Somermeier, "Coal, Its Composition, Analysis, Utilization and Valuation." McGraw-Hill Book Company.

Von Jüptner, "Heat, Energy and Fuels." McGraw-Hill Book Company, 1908.

A. Humboldt Sexton, "Fuel and Refractory Materials." Van Nostrand & Co. 1910.

Reports of Coal Analysis Committee, American Society for Testing Materials and American Chemical Society. Jour. Ind. Eng. Chem., Vol. **5**, 1913, p. 517. Proc. Am. Soc. Testing Materials, Vol. **14**, Report Committee E4. Proc. Am. Soc. Testing Materials, June, 1915, convention.

Bulletin No. 41, Bureau of Mines, pp. 74–91.

Technical Paper, No. 8, Bureau of Mines. "Methods of Analyzing Coal and Coke."

Fieldner, Jour. Ind. Eng. Chem., Vol. **5**, Apr., 1913, p. 270. "Accuracy and Limitations of Coal Analysis."

Bulletin No. 332, U. S. Geological Survey. "Report of the Fuel Testing Plant at St. Louis, Mo."

[1] Method by W. W. Scott.

Sampling

Technical Paper No. 1, Bureau of Mines. "The Sampling of Coal in the Mine."
Technical Paper No. 76, Bureau of Mines. "Notes on the Sampling and Analysis of Coal."

Moisture

Bulletin No. 28, Bureau of Mines, 1911, 51 pp.

Volatile Combustible Matter

Bulletin No. 1, Bureau of Mines. "The Volatile Matter of Coal."
Fieldner and Hall, Proc. 8th Int. Cong. App. Chem., Vol. 10, 1912, p. 139. "The Influence of Temperature on the Determination of Volatile Matter in Coal."
Fieldner and Davis, Jour. Ind. Eng. Chem., Vol. 2, July, 1910, p. 304. "Some Variations in the Official Method for the Determination of Volatile Matter in Coal."
A. G. Stillwell. The Chemist Analyst, No. 13, April, 1915, p. 9. "Note on Coal Analysis."

Volatile Sulphur

H. F. Muer, Jour. Ind. Eng. Chem., Vol. 3, August, 1911. "The Determination of Sulphur in Coal by Means of Jackson's Candle Turbidimeter." See also S. H. Register, under " Calorimetry."

Calorimetry

Bulletin No. 124, Bureau of Animal Industry. "Methods and Standards in Bomb Calorimetry."
Circular No. 11, Bureau of Standards. "Standardization of Bomb Calorimeters."
S. H. Register, Jour. Ind. Eng. Chem., Vol. 6, October, 1914, p. 812. "Oxidation of Sulphur Compounds of Coal, and of Nitrogen in the Bomb Calorimeter, and the Correction to be Applied in Determining the Heating Value of Coal."

Melting-point of Ashes

E. G. Bailey, Power, Vol. 34, No. 22, p. 802. "The Fusing Temperature of Coal Ash."
E. J. Constan, Z. Ver. Gas und Wasser Oesterr. (Jour. Gas Lighting, 124, 572.) "Melting-point of Coal Ashes."
Palmenberg, Jour. Ind. Eng. Chem., Vol. 6, 1914, p. 277. "Relation of Composition of Ash in Coal to its Fusing-point."
Burgwin, Jour. Ind. Eng. Chem., Vol. 6, 1914, August, p. 694. "Relation of Composition of Ash in Coal to its Fusing-point."
Fieldner and Hall, Jour. Ind. Eng. Chem., Vol. 7, June, 1915, p. 474: and May, p. 399; and Sept., p. 742. "Fusibility of Coal Ash in Various Atmospheres," Vol. 7, Oct. 1915, p. 829. " A New Method and Furnace for the Determination of the Softening Temperature of Coal Ash under Fuel Bed Conditions."
F. C. Hubley, Engineers' Club of Philadelphia, Proc., January, 1915, pp. 35–83. "Bituminous Coal; Predetermination of Their Clinkering Actions by Laboratory Tests."

Miscellaneous

Technical Paper No. 5, Bureau of Mines. "Constituents of Coal Soluble in Phenol."
Technical Paper No. 16, Bureau of Mines. " Deterioration and Spontaneous Heating of Coal in Storage."
Bulletin No. 382, U. S. Geological Survey. "Effect of Oxygen in Coal."
Technical Paper No. 2, Bureau of Mines. "Escape of Gas from Coal."
Technical Paper No. 65, Bureau of Mines. "Study of the Oxidation of Coal."
H. C. Porter, Jour. Ind. Eng. Chem., Vol. 7, March, 1915, p. 239. "The New Knowledge of Coal and Its Practical Application."
Bulletins Nos. 471J and 531M, U. S. Geological Survey. "Miscellaneous Analyses of Coal Samples from Various Fields of the United States."
Bulletin No. 54, Bureau of Mines. "Publications on Fuel Technology."

METHODS FOR ANALYSIS OF FUELS
Sodium Peroxide Method

Directions for Using the Parr Standard Calorimeter,[1] New Form
General Arrangement

The calorimeter should be placed on a good, firm desk in a room where fluctuations of temperature may be avoided. The general arrangement of

FIG. 213.   Parr Calorimeter.   FIG. 213a.

parts is shown in Fig. 214. However, it is better to remove the can (*5 C*) from the instrument for filling with water. The outside of the can should be dry, and no water should be allowed to spill over into the air spaces of the insulating vessels.

Exactly two liters of water (preferably distilled) are used, and it should have a temperature of 2° or 3° F. below that of the room. The thermometer (*46 C*) should extend a little over halfway to the bottom of the can. The

[1] Cuts and description have been furnished through courtesy of The McGraw-Hill Book Co. and The Standard Calorimeter Company.

Chapter contributed by S. W. Parr.

pulley (*37C*) is connected by a light, flexible cord with a small electric or water motor. Stirring is effected by the spring clips with turbine wings (*20AC*) placed on the body. The pulley (*37C*) must be made to revolve at about 150 revolutions per minute. Uniformly maintained, this will insure a complete equalization of temperature throughout the water. The pulley should turn to the right, or as the hands of a watch.

The Chemical: Sodium Peroxide, Na_2O_2

It is absolutely necessary that the chemical employed (sodium peroxide) be kept free from contamination. It has special avidity for moisture, and

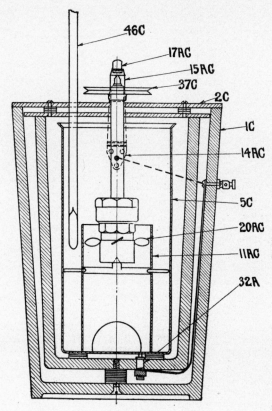

FIG. 214.

the glass jar with lever fastener, shown in Fig. 215, has been found best adapted as a container for this material. The sodium peroxide is furnished in small sealed tins, and the entire contents of a can, upon opening, should be transferred completely to the jar. The half-pound tins will usually be found the most convenient size to use. In any event, the glass jar should be of sufficient size to permit of the complete emptying of the container. Commercial sodium peroxide, or material that has been much exposed to the air so that any considerable amount of moisture has been absorbed, will give variable and uncertain results. The sodium peroxide furnished by The Standard Calorimeter

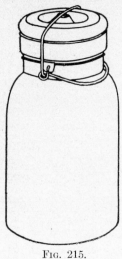

Fig. 215.

Company has been especially prepared under uniform conditions, and enclosed in solder-sealed tins in order that the material may come to the user in the best possible condition.

The Accelerator: Potassium Chlorate, $KClO_3$

In order to secure a combustion that shall be uniformly complete, it has been found desirable to use an accelerator for the purpose of increasing or intensifying the oxidizing effect of the sodium peroxide. While numerous chemicals and mixtures have been tried, a very extended experience has made it evident that potassium chlorate is best adapted for this purpose. It is supplied in finely-divided form, thoroughly dried, chemically pure and standardized. The correction factors to be employed are indicated later under " Calculations." One gram of the accelerator is accurately weighed out, and this amount is employed with all types of coal.

Preparation of the Sample

The usual method for the preparation of the sample is followed. The unground sample as received at the laboratory, usually of buckwheat or pea size and about 5 pounds in amount, is weighed and spread out in a shallow tray over night, or for a few hours, in a current of air raised somewhat above the ordinary temperature, say, to 100° F. The sample thus air-dried is weighed again and the difference taken as the loss on air-drying. After grinding to 10-mesh and thoroughly mixing, two or three ounces of this air-dried sample are ground to pass a 60- or 100-mesh sieve, the finer mesh being essential in the case of the harder types of fuel such as anthracites and coke.

Place in a stoppered bottle to prevent variation in the moisture content. From this sample are weighed out the quantities for moisture, ash, etc., as well as the samples for calorimeter determinations. With the sample thus prepared, ½ gram is carefully weighed out and dried in an oven at 220° F. for one hour. It is then ready to mix with the charge. If the amount of moisture in the air-dried coal is less than 1 or 2%, no drying in the oven is necessary for the determination of caloric value. (See note (h), p. 1645.)

Making Up the Charge

See that the floating bottom *4AC* is in place at the lower end of the bell body, as shown in Fig. 216. The inner surface should be dry so that the fusion cup, when put in place, will be surrounded by an air space with no film of water present. The fusion cup also should be *thoroughly dry* inside before adding the charge. It is well to dry it over a radiator or hot plate,

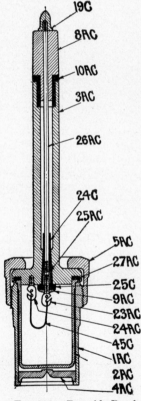

FIG. 216.   Peroxide Bomb.

though it should, of course, be cooled for filling. Add to the fusion cup, not assembled, 1 gram of accelerator and 1 full measure of sodium peroxide.

In filling the measure with peroxide, it should be tapped against the side of the glass jar to insure against the formation of air pockets which might prevent the complete filling of the measure. The measure holds approximately 14 grams. The same precaution also as to the dryness of the measure should be observed as for the fusion cup. It should be rinsed thoroughly with tap water after each using, and dried by heating over a radiator or near a hot plate. If the accelerator is lumpy, it is well to rub it smooth in the bottom of the fusion cup.

Close with the false top and shake *thoroughly* until the ingredients are evenly mixed. Add now $\frac{1}{2}$ gram of oven-dry coal. Replace the false top and shake again. When the mixing is complete, tap the holder lightly on the desk to shake all of the material from the upper part of the container, remove the false cap and put in its place the regular cap with stem and ignition wire $45C$. To attach the ignition wire, take a single length of fuse wire 7 cm. long from the card; pass one end through the eyelet of one of the terminals, $24AC$, so it will extend beyond the eyelet, say, $\frac{1}{4}$ inch. Wrap the free wire around the terminal at the narrow portion formed by the notch, giving it three turns, binding in the free end and bending the wire finally downward in line with the terminal. Repeat the same process with the other end of the wire in the other terminal, $23AC$. Do not have the fuse loop too long. It is better not to extend too far into the charge. It will be noticed that the charge fills the crucible at least two thirds full; hence, $\frac{1}{2}$ inch extension of the fuse wire below the central terminal will be ample.

See that the rubber gasket $27AC$ is in good shape and that the stem cap seats itself properly. It is to be noted that the gasket seals both the upper edge of the crucible and also the upper edge of the bell body. Marring the edges or rims of any of these parts, therefore, must be carefully avoided. Screw down the cap $5AC$ firmly in place by use of the two wrenches; put on the spring clips with the stirring vanes downward, leaving the small holes near the lower edge of the bell body uncovered, and assemble as shown in Fig. 214. In assembling, bring the can to its proper place after adding two liters of distilled water having a temperature of approximately two degrees F. below that of the room. In placing the bomb in the water, hold it at an inclined position so that the lower edge of the body will enter the water at an angle and thus avoid trapping air under the bottom.

Ignition

The current required for igniting the charge should be from 2 to 4 amp., and is most readily obtained by means of a rheostat or sliding resistance coil placed in series in an ordinary lighting circuit of 110 volts.

Make a number of preliminary tests by fastening a loop of fuse wire to the terminals and passing the current without assembling the parts. In this way, the behavior of the fuse wire can be observed. Make a trial with varying resistances. If the wire does not come very quickly to incandescence, decrease the resistance until it melts in only 1 or 2 sec. after closing the circuit.

Temperature Readings

The thermometer is inserted so that the lower end of the bulb will be about midway toward the bottom of the can. The pulley should be allowed o revolve a few minutes before reading the thermometer, in order to equalize the temperature throughout the apparatus. Take readings one minute apart or four or five intervals before igniting the charge, and continue the same for ine or ten minutes subsequent to ignition. The first three or four readings fter ignition are roughly taken, but after the fourth or fifth minute, the emperature should be nearly equalized, and the readings must be carefully aken in order to ascertain the exact maximum and to furnish the necessary ata for making a correction for radiation. If the temperature of the water efore ignition is one or two degrees below that of the room, the temperature t the end of the first minute after ignition will be something above that of he room, and radiation for that period may be considered as self-correcting. Ordinarily, the rise in temperature will continue for about four minutes more, t which time the maximum temperature will have been reached. The radiation for this period is found as follows: Read the fall in temperature for each minute for four minutes after the maximum has been reached. The average drop per minute represents the correction to be added to each minute preceding he maximum, except for the minute immediately following ignition. The final temperature thus corrected for radiation, minus the initial reading before gnition, represents the total rise in temperature due to the reaction in the usion cup.

In reading the thermometer, a suitable lens should be used, preferably mounted in a manner to eliminate errors of the parallax. Tap the thermometer ightly before taking a reading in order to avoid irregularities in the surface of the mercury. It should be remembered that errors in reading the thermometer are multiplied many times in the final computation. Equalization of temperatures should be complete in about 5 minutes. This will always be the case if, in the process of cooling, water has been drawn into the narrow air spaces surrounding the fusion cup. If by some mischance this entrance of the water should fail to take place, it will be indicated by an absence of water within the holder around the bottom and lower part of the fusion cup. It will be evident, also, by a slow, but very evident, rise of the mercury over a period of 10 or 15 minutes, due to the slow conductance of the heat through the limited areas of metal contact between the holder and the cup.

Correction Factors [1]

The method for obtaining the correction for radiation has already been described under Temperature Readings. The other correction components are listed for convenient reference as follows:

Electric fuse wire equals.................... .0030° C. or .005° F.
Per cent ash is multiplied by............... .0025° C. or .005° F.
Per cent sulphur is multiplied by........... .0050° C. or .010° F.
1 gram accelerator equals................... .1500° C. or .270° F.
Hydration factors:
    For all bituminous coals............... .0400° C. or .070° F.
    For black lignites...................... .0560° C. or .100° F

Calculations

From the total rise in temperature, corrected for radiation as indicated under " Temperature Readings," subtract the correction factors for the heat

[1] The correction factors have been re-determined to conform to the altered water equivalent, etc., of the new apparatus.

50

due to the chemical, fuse-wire, etc., as indicated under " Correction Factors, and multiply the remainder by 3100. The product will be the number of British thermal units per pound of coal. (See notes (a) and (b), page 1644

It is to be noted that the heat value as derived refers to the coal in the form in which it is weighed out for making the determination. That is to say, if a coal having 5% of moisture is taken and $\frac{1}{2}$ gram of the same weighed out and dried in the oven at 212° for 1 hour, then burned in the calorimeter, the result obtained refers to the coal on the basis of 5% of moisture and not to the coal as in the oven-dry state.

EXAMPLE

Coal No. 7968.

Ash 13.40%
Sulphur 4.22%

Temperature Readings

Readings.   Room Temp . . . . .72° F
Time

Time	Reading
1	69.45
2	69.50
3	69.60
4	69.75
5	69.90
6	70.00 ←Fired
7	71.00
8	73.50
9	73.90
10	74.20
11	74.25 ←Max.
12	74.25
13	74.20
14	74.10
15	74.00

Initial Temp . . . . .70.00 . . Final 74.25
Certif. Corr . . . . 0.00 . . Corr . . . .—0.01

                                  70.00   74.24

Radiation loss from 11th to 15th min. = 74.25 − 74.00 = 0.06 per minute.
Corr. = 4 × .06 = + 0.24 24

Final Temp. corrected for Rad 74.48

Correction Factors

Fuse Wire 005
Ash, 13.40 × .005 067
Sulphur, 4.22 × .01 042
Accelerator 270
Hydration 070   0.45

                              Corrected Final 74.02
                              Corrected Initial 70.00

                              Corrected Rise 4.02
Constant 3100 × 4.026 = 12,480 B.t.u.

To calculate values to the " dry-coal " basis, divide the number by 100% minus the per cent of moisture present. Thus, a coal having 5% moisture as weighed out, and indicating 12,480 B.t.u., would have 12,480÷.95=13,137 B.t.u. on the " dry-coal " or moisture-free basis.

To Dismantle

Remove the thermometer, pulley and cover; then take out the can and contents entire, so that the lifting out of the cartridge will not drip water into the dry parts of the instrument. Remove the spring clips and unscrew the cap. Remove the fusion cup and place it on its side in the bottom of a beaker and cover with hot water. After the fused material has dissolved, remove the cup and rinse thoroughly with hot water. Wash the face of the cap and

tric terminals thoroughly. For this purpose, a jet of hot water, or sub-
rging in boiling water, is advisable, as the metal is thus left clean and hot,
latter facilitating the drying out of the parts. Place the parts on a radiator
iear a hot plate to insure thorough drying.

Anthracites and Coke

In the case of anthracites and coke, it is well to use 0.3 gram of benzoic
l along with the 1 gram of accelerator and $\frac{1}{2}$ gram of fuel. This substance
ilitates ignition as well as the ultimate combustion. 0.2 gram is usually
ficient, but by using 0.3 gram, all exceptions are taken care of. (See note
p. 1645.) The heat resulting from the combustion of this extra 0.3 gram
benzoic acid is 2.31° F., which is to be corrected for along with the other
iponents. The correction for 0.2 gram of benzoic acid is 1.54° F.
For hard fuels such as coke and anthracites, fine grinding is essential.
is advisable to use an agate mortar for supplementary grinding of the
iple so that it will readily pass a 100-mesh sieve.

For Petroleum Oils

The amount of oil used for a charge should not exceed about 0.3 gram;
m 0.20 to 0.30 gram giving the proper combustion. The weight of oil is
t obtained by means of a small light 15-cc. weighing flask provided with
forated cork and dropping tube with common rubber bulb-cap. Weigh
flask and contents, and by means of the dropping tube discharge 20 to
drops of oil and re-weigh, thus obtaining the weight of oil taken by difference.
termine, by experiment, the height in the dropping tube required for the
proximate amount of oil desired so as to avoid trial weighings.

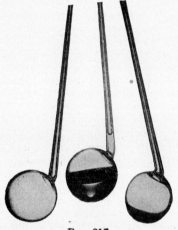

Fig. 217.

One gram of accelerator and one full measure of chemical (sodium peroxide)
e first added and thoroughly shaken as already indicated. Also, to facilitate
e ignition of all oils and at the same time promote the ultimate combustion,
is recommended that a small amount (0.2 gram) of benzoic acid be used as
scribed under "Anthracites and Coke." Add the oil and benzoic acid last

and mix thoroughly by shaking as already indicated and complete the pro
exactly as for coal.

Note that thorough mixing by shaking is not easily accomplished in
case of thick viscous oils. After thorough shaking of the accelerator, chem
and benzoic acid, the thick oil should be added, a few drops at a time,
stirred with a nichrome wire till there is no more tendency of the oil
chemical to segregate into lumps. After closing the bomb, a final sha
will insure an even distribution of the oil throughout the charge.

Compute by means of the formula as follows:

Correcting as under coals for radiation, accelerator, benzoic acid
fuse wire, and letting r represent the rise in temperature; then

$$\frac{r \times 0.73 \times 2123.3}{\text{weight of oil}} = \text{B.t.u. per pound of oil.}$$

To check the value 2123.3, see " Standardization "; also note (j), p. 1
With petroleum oils, a correction for hydration is not required.

Gasoline, Etc.

For gasoline, benzine and other very volatile hydrocarbons, the diffic
of securing an accurate weight of the material taken is met by the follow
procedure: Draw out an ordinary soft-glass tube into a capillary about 1 r
in diameter. By softening the end, it may be blown into a small thin-wa
bulb, as shown in Fig. 217. After a little practice, it is not difficult to b
such bulbs to weigh less than 0.2 gram. They are used as follows: We
the bulb carefully; then, by dipping the capillary end into the liquid
alternately warming gently and cooling the bulb, a quantity of the liq
may be made to flow up into it. When about 0.2 gram is obtained, seal
tip of the capillary in the flame and weigh accurately. Add the accelera
to the fusion cup in the usual manner, reducing any lumps to a fine pow
Add also 0.2 gram carefully weighed standard benzoic acid and the bulb c
taining the liquid fuel; then, over all, the measure of sodium peroxide. P
a glass rod down through the chemical above the bulb just sufficient to br
it. Remove the rod which should be freed from adhering particles by clean
it in the upper part of the sodium peroxide as yet unmixed with any of
other ingredients. Put in place as quickly as possible the ignition top w
fuse wire attached, and clamp firmly in place by means of the screw c
Shake very thoroughly to insure complete mixing of the charge. Tap ligh
on the desk to bring all of the material together, and assemble for the regu
procedure. In calculating, a correction is necessary, in addition to th
normally observed, on account of the heat of fusion due to the glass prese
This amounts to $0.03°$ F. for each 0.1 gram of glass used in the bulb. T
should be subtracted along with the correction for accelerator, benzoic a
and fuse wire. No hydration correction is required. The corrected rise
is then used in the formula as above given for petroleums.

Standardization

A number of methods for the standardization of the peroxide calorime
may be used. (a) By calculating the water equivalent for the metal a v
satisfactory factor is obtained which serves as a constant in calculating the h

ues. The accuracy of this method in connection with the peroxide type of
trument is due to the relatively small amount of metal employed in its
struction, together with the fact that all metal parts are standardized as
weight in the process of manufacture. The total weight of metal not
luding the pulley and insulated part of the stem is approximately 1370
ms. Applying a specific heat value of 0.090 gives a water equivalent for
metal of 123.3, or a total water equivalent value of 2123.3, which is the
is for determining the constant of 3100, as shown under note (a), p. 1644.
A standard coal for which the heat value has been accurately derived by
oxygen-bomb apparatus of the Mahler type. This requires that the
hler value be recently determined owing to the change in the apparent
t value of coal samples upon standing. It has the advantage, however, of
cking the peroxide instrument with respect to the correction factors used
ash, sulphur and water of composition or "hydration." (c) By combustion
a standard material such as sugar or benzoic acid. The latter is usually
ployed. It has the advantage over the first method (a) in that it furnishes
est for the behavior of the thermometer; but with a thermometer of proper
de, the variations on that account are due to uncertain or erroneous reading
temperatures which no method of standardization can correct.

The charge consists of $\frac{1}{2}$ gram of benzoic acid ($C_7H_6O_2$), carefully weighed
t and added to the fusion cup which already contains the accelerator and
lium peroxide thoroughly mixed exactly as in the procedure for coal. After
ding the benzoic acid, the cup is again thoroughly shaken to insure complete
xing of the entire charge.

After combustion in the ordinary manner and correcting the temperature
e for radiation, the accompanying factors are noted as follows:

COMPONENT FACTORS FOR BENZOIC ACID

Fuse wire	0.003° C. or 0.005° F.
Accelerator	0.150° C. or 0.270° F.
Hydration	0.100° C. or 0.180° F.
Total corrections	0.253° C. or 0.455° F.
Heat of reaction	2.040° C. or 3.670° F.
Total rise	2.293° C. or 4.125° F.

From the above, it is seen that the total rise in temperature as corrected
r radiation, after having the normal corrections applied for fuse, accelerator
d hydration, should have a remainder, representing the true heat of com-
astion, of 2.040° C. or 3.670° F., since this value multiplied by the constant
00 gives 6320 Cal. or 11,376 B.t.u., the accepted value for benzoic acid.

If after several check combustions the values indicated by the instrument
ow a consistent variation, the average difference in heat rise should be
lded if + and subtracted if − from the true heat of combustion and the
mainder used as a divisor for the accepted value, thus: With an excess
dication of 0.02° F. we would have:

$$\frac{11,376}{3.690} = 3083.$$

That is, the constant for the instrument is 3083 instead of

$$\frac{11,376}{3.67} = 3100.$$

There are certain cases in making up the charge where it is desired to u benzoic acid as an additional constituent, the heat value of which must corrected for. For instance, 0.2 or 0.3 gram of benzoic acid are used wi anthracites and coke, or with petroleum oils. The value for correction readily obtained from the factors under " Standardization " as follows:

Total rise..4.125° F.
Correction for fuse wire and accelerator................0.275° F.

Heat due to 0.5 gram................................3.850° F.
Heat due to 0.2 gram................................1.540° F.
Heat due to 0.3 gram................................2.310° F.

NOTES

(a) The factor 3100 is deduced as follows: The water used plus the water equivalo of the metal in the instrument amounts to 2123.3 grams. In the reaction, 73% of t heat is due to combustion of the coal and 27% is due to the heat of combination of C and H_2O with the chemical. If now 1/2 gram of coal causes 2123.3 grams of water to r "r" degrees, and if only 73% of this is due to combustion, then .73 × 2123.3 × 2 × " = rise in temperature which would result from combustion of an equal weight (212: grams) of coal. .73 × 2123.3 × 2 = 3100.00. The factor 2 is used instead of t divisor 0.5, the weight of coal taken. If the thermometer used is graduated in t Fahrenheit scale, then obviously multiplying by the factor 3100 will give the result British thermal units. If, however, the thermometer used is graduated in the Centigra scale, then the product derived by use of the factor 3100 will give the result in calori₀

(b) In the process of igniting the charge, prolonged contact of the electric termin should be avoided, otherwise there will be an undue accession of heat from the passa of the current. If the resistance is so adjusted that the wire, in trying out, comes to t melting point in 1 or 2 seconds, then that amount of time is ample for maintaining t electrical contact. A positive rise indicates that combustion has commenced. In su a case, do not make the contact again. It often happens that the fuse wire, aft igniting the charge, extends into the fusion, thus making it possible to complete t electrical circuit a second time.

(c) Do not bring the instrument from a cold room to work at once in a warm roo or vice versa. Sufficient time should be given for equalization of temperatures. D the bomb thoroughly inside and out before putting away. Dry it before using if it h stood for some time, as moisture condenses on the surfaces.

(d) Do not throw a mixture of chemical and unburned coal into water. It ma ignite violently.

(e) Determinations are sometimes required on material too low in carbonaceo matter to support combustion, such as ash residues, etc. If the combustible matter below 20 or 30%, double or treble the quantity, and in calculating, use ½ or ⅓ of t corrected rise. Note that the corrections for ash and sulphur, as indicated under "Co rection Factors," p. 1639, should be doubled or trebled in accord with the doubling trebling of the material taken. Ash residues that have come through the combustio chamber are like coke, in that no hydration factor is applied. It is well also to use 0 or 0.3 gram of benzoic acid as indicated under "Anthracite and Coke," the correctio being 1.54° F. for 0.2 gram, or 2.31° if 0.3 gram is used.

(f) In measuring water from the two-liter flask, read the mark at the bottom of t meniscus. Where two marks are etched on the neck, the upper mark shows the volum at which the required quantity will be discharged from the flask, and, of course, is t one to be used in measurement.

(g) If it is found difficult to differentiate between readings for radiation that a made one minute apart, extend the periods to two or three minutes, making the fin adjustment to cover the time actually to be corrected for.

(h) Concerning the amount of moisture permissible in the fuel sample, it has been indicated [1] that the temperature rise in the apparatus as used, due to the absorption by the chemical, Na_2O_2, of 1 gram of water is 0.663° C. In a ½-gram sample, therefore, 2% of moisture would represent 0.01 gram of water which, if allowed to combine with the Na_2O_2, and it all the heat generated by that absorption were included in the calorimeter process, that amount of moisture would produce a rise of $0.01 \times 0.663 = 0.0066°$ C. This temperature rise would then cause an error of $0.0066 \times 3100 = 20$ cal., which will give sufficient reason for avoiding the use of a coal with a high percentage of moisture. The error for 2% of moisture would be less than the calculated amount, due to dissipation of the heat of absorption before the thermometric readings were taken, but the possibility of an appreciable error is easily guarded against.

(i) Occasionally, a sample of extra hard anthracite or coke is not carried to complete combustion, in which case particles of unburned carbon will be observed on dissolving the fusion. To correct this fault, use 0.3 gram of benzoic acid instead of 0.2 gram in making up the charge. The correction for heat from 0.3 gram benzoic acid is 2.31° F.

(j) The water equivalent of the calorimeter may be calculated directly from the constant for the instrument as determined by standardization with benzoic acid. For example, if the factor so determined is found to be 3100, then divide that constant by $2 \times .73$. Thus:

$$\frac{3100}{2 \times .73} = 2123.3.$$

Reuniting the Mercury Thread of a Thermometer

The thermometers supplied by The Standard Calorimeter Company are nitrogen-filled. Occasionally, due to improper handling, a bubble of the gas gets into the mercury and causes a break in the thread. The presence of this break is shown by a downward flow of mercury in the capillary tube when the thermometer is inverted. By chilling in crushed ice, all of the mercury is drawn down into the bulb, and the gas bubble may be made to float to the top by gently tapping the stem or by shaking vertically with a short, stiff-arm motion. If there are only two or three inches of mercury thread above the break, warm the bulb in hot water or over a very small flame until the bubble has been carried up into the expansion chamber at the top, where it may be made to rise out of the mercury by tapping the stem with finger nail or lead pencil. Be very careful not to force the expansion chamber much more than half full of mercury, as the pressure may burst the glass. To test, invert the thermometer without jarring; if the thread doe s not flow downward by gravity, there is no further break in the mercury.

If the expansion chamber contains mercury which refuses to be dislodged by the above methods, it may be drawn out by a freezing mixture that will produce a temperature low enough to pull some of the thread into the bulb. Crushed ice mixed with coarse salt usually succeeds. Cooling in this mixture, followed by a sharp downward shake, will transfer a droplet of mercury to the bulb. This will make room for gas which will enter the expansion chamber on warming the bulb. Repeat the process until the expansion chamber is free from mercury, and test as above.

[1] Constants of the Parr calorimeter, Jour. Am. Chem. Soc., Vol. XXIX, p. 1616 1907.

Determination of Sulphur and Total Carbon

The combustion of coal by means of sodium peroxide affords a convenient method for the determination of sulphur by reason of the fact that the oxidizing conditions are so pronounced as to insure the complete transformation of all of the sulphur to the sulphate form. This is accomplished in a very few minutes and without possible contamination by accession of sulphur from external sources, as where city gas is employed in the ordinary process.

Making Up the Charge

The procedure for making up the charge is precisely the same as for the determination of the heating value. One gram of accelerator ($KClO_3$) is weighed out and transferred to the fusion cup. After all lumps are reduced by means of a glass rod, one full measure of chemical (about 14 grams sodium peroxide, Na_2O_2) is added and the two thoroughly mixed by putting the cover on and shaking well. One half ($\frac{1}{2}$) gram of coal,[1] accurately weighed, is now added and the shaking continued until the ingredients are evenly mixed. This point of thorough and complete mixing cannot be too strongly insisted upon. It is obvious that a mixture of potassium chlorate and coal alone would have extremely explosive properties. One important function, therefore, of the sodium peroxide is to provide a diluent, thus slowing down the reaction. This function operates most satisfactorily when an even mixture of all three ingredients is secured. After proper mixing, the cover is secured in place and the charge is ready for ignition.

In the case of petroleum, coke and anthracite coals, the procedure in making up the charge is the same as for bituminous coal, with the exception that approximately 0.2 gram of c.p. benzoic acid is added directly after the 14 grams of sodium peroxide. The accelerator, sodium peroxide and benzoic acid are thoroughly mixed by shaking, after which the one half ($\frac{1}{2}$) gram of coal or coke is added and the shaking continued until all four ingredients are evenly mixed. After making sure that the mixture is homogeneous, the cover is secured in place and the charge is ready for ignition.

Igniting the Charge

The bombs, as shown in Fig. 218, have the fusion cup exposed so that a needle flame from a blast lamp may be made to impinge upon the side or bottom, thus producing a red-hot spot from which ignition on the interior may proceed. The use of a pointed flame is preferred to one from a Bunsen burner, since the latter would envelop the fusion cup and heat all parts of the exterior evenly, thus bringing all of the interior surface at once to the ignition point. This may bring about a too violent reaction, especially with coals of the richer type. When ignition is effected, it is shown by the spreading of a faint red over the surface of the fusion cup, more easily observed if done in a

[1] The factor for sulphur, as also for any of the other determinations, is obtained from the sample as weighed out for that determination. In this case, it would be on the air-dry sample, and the result should be calculated back to the condition "as received," thus: Multiply the factor obtained on the "air-dry" basis by (1.00 less loss on air-drying). The result will be the percentage on the "as received" basis. If it is desired to calculate to the moisture-free basis, divide the factor obtained on the air-dry basis by (1.00—per cent moisture).

arkened space. After ten or fifteen seconds, the bomb may be held under
he tap for cooling.

Treatment of the Fused Material

After igniting and cooling the bomb, remove the fusion cup and place on
s side in a beaker of about 300 cc. capacity, add about 50 to 75 cc. of distilled
ater, and cover with a watch glass. Boil over a low flame till the contents
f the cup are dissolved. Rinse the cup well and remove. Continue the
oiling for a few minutes, cool the solution, and add concentrated HCl to
ear the neutral point. For the 14 grams of Na_2O_2 taken, this will require
bout 25 to 28 cc. of HCl (sp.gr. 1.19). Bring to the neutral point and add
bout 1 cc. of acid in excess. From this point the sulphur may be determined
y the regular gravimetric method, or by the photometric method.

Total Carbon

The percentage of total carbon in the coal may be obtained by utilization
f the sodium peroxide fusion in which the total carbon of the coal has been
xidized and combined with chemical to form Na_2CO_3. By liberating the
O_2 under accurately-determined conditions as to temperature and pressure
y means of the apparatus shown in Fig. 219, the amount of carbon present
1ay be derived from the volume of CO_2 discharged. Combustions with
Ja_2O_2 may also be made in a simple piece of apparatus devised for that purpose
nd not involving the elaborations necessary where temperature readings are
1volved. Fig. 218 shows the apparatus for obtaining the fusions.

The total carbon apparatus should be located on a laboratory desk or
able where an even temperature can be maintained.

Fill the jacketing tube J with water slightly acidulated to keep it clear.
ill the leveling tube L with water that has had 2 or 3 cc. of sulphuric acid
dded. A few drops of methyl orange in the leveling tube will impart a color
o the water, greatly facilitating the readings.

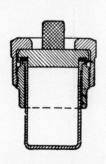 

Fig. 218.

Connect the inlet D with air pressure and adjust so that two or three
ubbles of air per second will enter the jacketing water. This is for the
urpose of keeping the temperature of the water equalized throughout a
1etermination. By reading the thermometer hung in the water, the temperaure of the gas under observation is obtained.

The operation is as follows: The large double pipette P is half filled with 40 per cent solution of caustic potash, or such as is ordinarily used for the absorption of CO_2 gas. By turning the three-way cock T to connect with the pipette P and lowering the leveling tube L, the liquid in P is brought into the right-hand bulb and made to rise in the capillary tube to the mark on the right limb of the capillary. The three-way cock is now closed to the pipette bulb and opened to the tube running to the flask B. By raising the leveling tube L, the liquid in the burette G is made to rise to the three-way cock T thus completely filling the burette. The three-way cock is now closed to retain the liquid in the burette at the zero point, till evolution of the gas is begun.

The cup containing the fused material from a calorimetric determination is placed on its side in the bottom of a small beaker and covered with hot water that has been boiling for 5 or 10 minutes. Contamination with CO_2

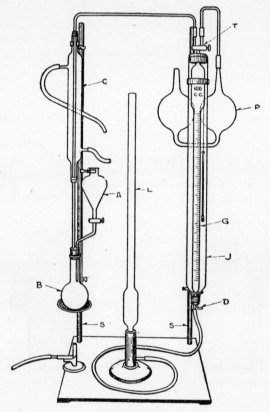

Fig. 219.

from the water used or from contact with the air must be avoided as much as possible. When the fusion is dissolved, remove the cup, rinsing it well, and pour the solution directly into the flask B. Wash out the beaker thoroughly with hot water and pour the washings in with the main portion. Connect the flask with the funnel tube A and bring the ring support with wire gauze in place under the flask. Open the stopcock at the lower end of the funnel and boil the contents of the flask for 3 or 4 minutes. Remove the flame and at once close the funnel cock. In this way the oxygen from the sodium peroxide will be driven off together with the air in the flask. Also, when the three-way cock T is closed, there will be a partial vacuum in the flask.

With the cock to the funnel tube A closed, enough acid is added to A to completely neutralize the alkaline solution in B and leave a distinct excess of acid. Hydrochloric acid is preferred. Thirty cubic centimeters of concentrated hydrochloric acid will be found sufficient.

To operate, lower the leveling tube L, open the three-way cock T to the tube connecting with the flask B and admit acid drop by drop from the funnel A. Meantime, the circulating water for the condenser C should be turned on.

When the evolution of gas has about reached the capacity of the graduated burette G, the acid is shut off, the three-way cock T closed and a reading of the volume of the gas carefully taken by bringing the two surfaces of liquid in the leveling tube and burette exactly on a level. Read also the temperature of the jacketing water and note the barometric pressure. The cock T is now opened to the capillary, and the gas volume forced completely over into the bulb P, where it is held by closing the cock T. Here it is left for complete absorption of the CO_2. The cock T may be again opened to connect with the flask B, the liquid in the burette G being at the zero point as before. The apparatus is now ready for a second evolution and measurement of a gas volume.

A second reading is similarly taken and the volume driven over into P as before, along with the former volume. Repeat the process until no more CO_2 is evolved.

Finally, heat is added to the flask B, and after a few minutes' boiling hot water is added through the funnel A, until the solution is nearly up to the stopper, the flame, of course, being removed. At this point, there should be no water remaining in the funnel A. Lower the leveling tube L to form a partial vacuum and allow air to be drawn through A into B, and thus sweep out the residual gas in the connecting tubes into the burette C. The amount of air thus drawn in should be slightly more than 100 cc. so that after transferring to the bulb P for final absorption of the remaining CO_2, the air returned to the graduated burette will be sufficient in amount to bring the level down upon the graduated portion of the burette for reading. The difference between this volume and the total of the several volumes is the total carbon dioxide present in the fusion.[1]

By referring to pp. 1661, 1662 there is found at the observed temperature and pressure the weight in milligrams of carbon in 1 cc. of CO_2 gas.[2] Multiply this weight by the number of cubic centimeters obtained in the above operation and the product equals the weight in milligrams of pure carbon. From this should be subtracted the weight of carbon found by running a blank in exactly the same manner, using one measure of the sodium peroxide instead of the fusion.

After subtracting the blank, the carbon remaining represents the total carbon present in the fuel. Divide this number by the weight of fuel taken and multiply by 100.   The product is the per cent of carbon present in the sample taken.

Coals with calcium carbonate present should have the CO_2 in that combination determined and the total carbon factor corrected accordingly.   Five grams of coal should be put into the flask and treated precisely as for a fusion. The amount of carbon found from the volume of CO_2 liberated is subtracted from the total carbon as obtained from the fusion.   This, of course, is in addition to the CO_2 found in the blank determination in the Na_2O_2.

Formulae in Ultimate Analysis of Coal, Moisture Free

1. Weight of sulphur $\times$ 2777 = Calories from sulphur as FeS_2.

2. Weight of carbon $\times$ 8080 = Calories from carbon.

3. Total determined calories $-$ (1 + 2) = Calories from available hydrogen.

4. $\dfrac{\text{Calories from available hydrogen}}{34,450}$ = Weight of available hydrogen.

5. Nitrogen present may be assumed as a constant of 1.25 per cent.

6. Then, by difference, 100 $-$ (S + C + H + N + ash as weighed) = (O + H).[3]

7. 8/9 (O + H) = Total oxygen.

8. 1/9 (O + H) = Combined hydrogen.

9. Then, combined hydrogen + available hydrogen (8 + 4) = Total hydrogen.

By deriving the factors as thus indicated, we have all of the constituents as obtained by ultimate analysis and with a degree of accuracye ntirely commensurate with that secured by the longer process.   The apparatus used in the determinations is shown in Figs. 207, 208 and 209.

[1] Apparatus for these determinations may be obtained from The Standard Calorimeter Company, East Molin, Illinois, U. S. A.

[2] See also Parr, S. W., The Weight of Carbon Dioxide with a Table of Calculated Values, Jour. Am. Chem. Soc., Vol. XXI, p. 237, 1909.

[3] The expression (O + H) refers to the total oxygen plus that amount of hydrogen necessary to combine with it to form water.   This hydrogen is referred to as "combined hydrogen" to differentiate it from the "available hydrogen."

The Oxygen Bomb Method

In the Mahler or Berthelot type of instrument, the fuel for combustion is held in a tray supported within a chamber capable of receiving oxygen under a pressure of 25 to 30 atmospheres. Fig. 220 represents such a bomb, the essential parts of which are the cover (2A) held in place by the screw clamp (3A), the supporting wires (4A and 5A) for the fuel tray (43A) which also are the electric terminals for conducting the electric current through the fine

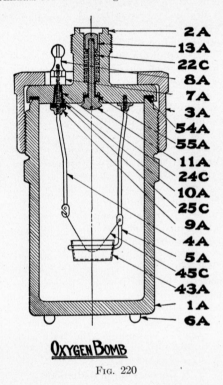

OXYGEN BOMB

FIG. 220

fuse wire (45C). Protection from heat interchanges with the surrounding air is provided by walls of indurated fibre with an air space between, and this arrangement is continuous for sides, bottom and top. Another method of insulation by circulation of water through the jacketing spaces is also to be noted as " Adiabatic Insulation." The fuse wire is No. 34, B. & S. gauge, and is usually of pure iron, though, on some accounts, a wire more resistant to oxidation is desirable. A current of low voltage (10–15 volts) is to be preferred so that arcing within the calorimeter may be avoided.

The capsule should be immune to chemical action, and if of sufficient size, the necessity of compressing the fuel into a tablet is obviated. Trays approximately 1 inch in diameter and 1/2 inch deep should be used.

Definitions

Heat values are expressed in two ways—as calories and as British thermal units. Only the large calorie is made use of in fuel reference, and it represents the amount of heat necessary to raise 1 kilo of water through 1° C. The full expression is, therefore, calories per kilo, or kilo-calories.

The British thermal unit represents the amount of heat necessary to raise 1 pound of water through 1° F. The full expression, therefore, would be B.t.u per pound.

Since the Centigrade degree is 9/5 or 1.8 times as great as the Fahrenheit degree, and the kilo is 2.2046 times the pound, it follows that one calorie would be the equivalent in Fahrenheit degrees of 1.8×2.2046 or 3.968 B.t.u. However, the comparison between units as thus developed is not a comparison between values as made use of in the case of fuels for the reason that the arbitrary amount of coal to which reference is made in both cases is an amount of coal equal to the unit of water involved; that is, a kilo of coal to a kilo of water, a pound of coal to the pound of water. For this reason, therefore, the rise in temperature in each case is the same; that is, a pound of coal will raise the temperature of a pound of water through as many degrees as a kilo of coal will raise a kilo of water, or a ton of coal a ton of water, etc. The difference in heat values as expressed by these two methods, therefore, is simply the difference in the thermometric readings. A reading taken by the Fahrenheit scale will be 9/5 or 1.8 times as great as the reading taken by the Centigrade scale. Therefore, to change fuel values expressed in calories per kilo to B.t.u. per pound, multiply by 1.8.

This relation of 1 to 1.8, it should be observed, refers to solid or liquid fuels only; that is, where the ratio of fuel to total water is that of equivalent quantities. Fortunately, this relationship applies to continental values as well as English and American, so that the transfer from calories to B.t.u. is simple and universally applicable for such material. The matter is quite different, however, in the case of gaseous fuels, where the unit quantity of reference is not the same. For example, the B.t.u. value of a cubic foot of gas must be divided by 3.968 to find the equivalent in calories per cubic foot.

Correction for Radiation

If the system containing the bomb and measured quantity of water is operated at a temperature above or below that of the room, a gain or loss of heat will result, due to radiation. This may be corrected for in a very accurate manner by taking the thermometer readings each minute for a preliminary period of five minutes, and also for a final period of five minutes, with an intervening period usually of about five minutes. The rates of radiation change per minute thus obtained are incorporated into a formula covering the period of combustion and equalization of the system as follows:

The rate of rise for the preliminary period is r_1 and for final period is r_2 The time readings are indicated as (a), (b) and (c). At (a) is noted the time of ignition, at (c) the time of final or maximum reading, and at (b) the time hen the thermometer has reached the point of rise equivalent to 6/10 of the ptal between (a) and (b). In computing, the rate r_1 is multiplied by the me (b-a) in minutes and tenths of a minute, and this product is added to he temperature reading at (a). Similarly, the rate r_2 is multiplied by the me interval (c-b) and the product added to the time (c). Assuming that the hermometer corrections for stem and setting have already been made, the ifference of the two thermometer readings thus corrected gives the total rise f temperature due to combustion. If the temperature was falling at the ime (a), then the system is losing instead of gaining heat, and the correction minus instead of plus, a reduction of the subtrahend operating as a plus orrection. Similarly, if the temperature is rising at the time (c), the system gaining heat and the correction for the period (c-b) should be minus instead f plus. In the case of coals where the approximate total rise is unknown, nd, hence, the time reading (b) at the 6/10 point uncertain, it is only necessary o take readings at 30, 45, 60 and, possibly, 75 seconds after firing. These bservations will enable one to readily locate the 6/10 point when all the eadings are completed. This formula has been devised [1] by Dr. Dickinson f the U. S. Bureau of Standards, and has been adopted by the joint committee f the American Chemical Society and the American Society for Testing Materials on Standard Methods for Coal Analysis.[2] It is exceedingly con-'enient and accurate, and in the report of the committee entirely replaces he very elaborate and tedious method of Pfaundler.[3]

Correction for Acids

Because of the use of pure oxygen at a high pressure and temperature, ertain reactions take place which do not occur in the ordinary process of ombustion. For example, a small amount of residual air present upon 'losing the instrument has free nitrogen which, under the conditions of com-'ustion, is partially oxidized to N_2O_5, or with the moisture present in the omb it becomes HNO_3. Similarly, the nitrogen of the coal burns to a greater r less extent to HNO_3. The sulphur in the coal, which under ordinary con-litions of combustion burns to SO_2, in the calorimeter burns to SO_3, or, with he moisture present, to H_2SO_4. These two highly corroding acids make it necessary to protect the interior surface of the bomb. This is accomplished oy use of an enamel, by a spun lining of gold or platinum, or by constructing the bomb of an acid-resisting alloy equivalent in that respect to gold or olatinum. Where such a precaution is disregarded, as, for example, if the enamel type of protection becomes cracked and scaled off, or if a lining of spun metal, such as nickel, is employed, the solvent property of the acids oecomes active. There are two sources of error which result from such condi-tions—one is the heat of solution resulting from the chemical action. This, of course, should not be credited to the heat of combustion of the coal. It would be relatively small in amount, probably not exceeding 5–10 calories. The other is the masking of the amount of free acid which thus escapes measure-ment and would be uncorrected for. In high sulphur coals, the error from this source may be of considerable moment, frequently equaling, or even exceeding, 100 calories.

[1] Bureau of Standards Scientific Paper No. 230.
[2] A. S. T. M. Standards for 1916, p. 576.
[3] For an excellent presentation of the Pfaundler formula, see White's Gas and Fuel Analysis, p. 268.

The amount of free acid in the bomb washings is first determined b[?] means of a standard solution of Na_2CO_3 made up of such a strength th[?] each cc. represents 1 calorie. The heat of formation for N_2O_5, *aqua*, is 103[?] calories per gram of nitrogen. The reaction for neutralization is:

$$2HNO_3 + Na_2CO_3 = 2NaNO_3 + H_2CO_3,$$
$$28N : 106Na_2CO_3,$$
$$1N : 3.786Na_2CO_3.$$

That is, 1 gram N, burning to HNO_3 and representing 1035 calorie[?] requires 3.786 grams Na_2CO_3. One calorie requires 0.003658 gram of Na_2CO[?] or 3.658 grams per liter in which 1 cc. would represent 1 calorie.

In the calculation thus far it has been assumed that all of the acid presen[?] was HNO_3. The H_2SO_4 must be taken into the account.

When sulphur burns to SO_3, *aqua*, it develops approximately 4450 calori[?] per gram of S. In ordinary combustion, the burning to SO_2 generates onl[?] 2250 calories per gram. The excess heat resulting from conditions withi[?] the bomb would be represented by $4450 - 2250 = 2200$ calories per gram of [?]

But the titration for 1 gram of N as HNO_3 would represent only 7/8 of [?] gram of S as H_2SO_4. This is evident from the ratio:

$$2HNO_3 : H_2SO_4 : 2Na_2CO_3.$$
$$28 : 32.$$

Hence, the titration as HNO_3 for the H_2SO_4 would be only 7/8 of th[?] heat to be credited to the sulphur per gram. This means that 7/8 of th[?] 1035 calories, or 900 calories per gram of sulphur, have been corrected fo[?] Hence, $2200 - 900$ or 1300 would represent the additional correction require[?] for 1 gram of sulphur, or 13 calories per .01 gram of sulphur, equivalent t[?] 13 calories addition for each per cent of sulphur present in the coal.

It is at once obvious that the acid correction is a matter of some momen[?] Coals having from 3 to 5 per cent of sulphur will show a titration of fror[?] 35 to 50 cc. of the standard alkali representing that number of calories. [?] coal having 4 per cent of sulphur would have that correction augmented b[?] 4×13 or 52 calories, or a correction on this account of from 85 to 125 calorie[?]

For complete combustion to H_2SO_4, it is well to note that sufficient nitroge[?] must be present to furnish a proper amount of N_2O_5 as catalyzer for the sulphur.[?]

The correction in calories for the acids formed, together with the correctio[?] for fuse wire, are subtracted from the total observed calories.

Correction for Fuse Wire

The coal in the bomb is ignited by a fuse of iron wire, B. & S. gauge[?] No. 34, and 10 cm. in length. The weight of wire burned is determined wit[?] sufficient accuracy by measuring the length of the unburned wire. Th[?] weight of the total length will be sufficiently constant so that repeated weighing[?] are not necessary. The total observed calories are corrected by subtractin[?] for the iron at the rate of 1600 calories per gram of wire burned.

[1] Jour. Ind. Eng. Chem., Vol. 16, p. 812 (1914).

Procedure for Determining Heat Values by the Oxygen Bomb Calorimeter

When the calorimeter is dismantled, the double cover to the insulating chamber should be supported on a ring-stand, or similar device, as shown in the cut (Fig. 220). This affords a convenient method of handling the stirring device, and insures greater safety for the thermometer.

When the bomb is opened and arranged for receiving the charge of fuel, the cap is most conveniently held on a ring-stand. Thus supported, the fuel capsule and fuse wire are readily adjusted. For coal, approximately 1 gram of the air-dry sample, ground to pass a 60-mesh sieve, is accurately weighed in the capsule (43A, Fig. 220). The fuse wire should be about 10 cm. long. That part of the wire between the terminals should be bent into a somewhat narrow U-shaped loop so that the fuse wire will not touch the sides of the capsule (Fig. 220). Adjust the wire so that the lower part of the fuse loop will just touch the surface of the coal. In using sugar for standardizing purposes, it is well to give the wire a number of short turns in such manner that the spiral will come in contact with the sugar, which is difficult to ignite with the wire in a simple loop. Benzoic acid or naphthalene are easy to ignite and do not need the extra looping of the wire. In the case of naphthalene, to insure against loss of the charge upon igniting, it is well to heat approximately 1 gram in the capsule to the point of incipient fusion and then obtain the accurate weight. The cake-like mass will readily ignite if the wire loop simply touches the surface. Loss by volatilization or spurting is thus avoided.

Ignition

The current required for igniting the charge should be from two to four amperes, which is readily obtained by passing an ordinary lighting current through a resistance or rheostat, before it is led into the bomb. Where a commercial current is not available, six standard dry cells may be used.

Do not allow a full lighting current to pass to the bomb, as this practice will in a short time burn out the terminals. It also has a tendency to cause the ignition wire to burn off close to one of the terminals, so the current cannot pass through the entire wire and an insufficient amount of heat is generated to ignite the charge.

Preliminary to the determination, it is necessary to make a number of test fusions of the ignition wire before the bomb and cover are assembled. Bind about ten centimeters of ignition wire to the terminals as previously directed, and adjust the rheostat to a position where it would be expected to give the proper current for ignition. Now, connect the current through the rheostat to the ignition wire. If the wire does not come very quickly to incandescence, decrease the resistance until the wire melts through practically its entire length with about one-half second's delay after closing the circuit.

In the case of coal or standard material, the amount to be taken is a matter of choice. An exact gram simplifies slightly the calculations, but is apt to prolong unduly the weighing process. A small amount of water—0.5 to 1.0 gram, for absorbing the acids—is added to the bomb, which is placed in the octagon holder for receiving the cover with the fuel and capsule in place. In turning down the cap upon the cover, apply the large wrench, using good, firm pressure, though only moderate force is necessary for securing a perfect seal at the rubber gasket.

51

For filling with oxygen, connection is made with a flexible copper tubing (see Fig. 211), and oxygen is admitted until a pressure of 25–30 atmospheres indicated. In admitting the oxygen, the needle-valve next to the pressure gauge is opened slightly to avoid a sudden rush of gas. After a sufficient amount has been admitted, close the needle-valve and open the pet-cock below the gauge in order to release the oxygen under pressure in the tube and connections. The check valve (Fig. 220, 11A) automatically closes and retains the oxygen at the desired pressure.

Fig. 220a.   Charging the Bomb with Oxygen

Transfer the bomb carefully, without jarring, to the can which has been placed in position in the calorimeter. Make the connection with the electric terminal and add 2000 grams of water, preferably distilled. The temperature of the water should be 1° or 2° C. below that of the room.

The motor is adjusted so as to give the turbine pulley a speed of about 150 revolutions per minute, turning to the right or clockwise. A uniform speed throughout a determination is desirable.

By use of the telescopic lens, readings of the thermometer for the *preliminary period* are taken at one-minute intervals for five minutes. At the fifth reading close the electric circuit for a second or not to exceed two seconds. Ignition of the sample should be indicated by a rise of the mercury, which becomes rapid after 20 or 30 seconds. The *combustion period* extends over 5 or 6 minutes and terminates when the maximum temperature has been reached or when the rate of change has become uniform. The *final period* follows the combustion period. Readings are taken at minute intervals for five minutes.

The temperature readings for these three periods furnish the basis for determining the temperature changes due to radiation.[1]

[1] See report of Committee on Methods of Coal Analysis, Journal of Industrial and Engineering Chemistry, Vol. 5, p. 517 (1913).
Also U. S. Bureau of Standards Circular No. 11.
For a detailed discussion of the various factors involved in calorimetric determinations, reference should be made to "The Analysis of Fuel, Gas, Water and Lubricants," by S. W. Parr, from which these directions have, for the most part, been taken, permission having been granted by courtesy of the publishers, The McGraw-Hill Book Co.

The following notations should be made:

(1) The rate of rise (r_1) for the preliminary period in degrees per minute.

(2) The time (a) at which the last reading of the preliminary period is made, immediately before firing.

(3) The time (b) when the rise of temperature has reached six-tenths of its total amount. This point can generally be determined by adding to the temperature reading at the time of firing 60 per cent of the expected temperature rise and noting the time (b) when this point is reached. If the approximate temperature rise is not known, six-tenths of the total rise, as subsequently developed, when added to the temperature reading at (a), will indicate the time (b) by interpolating readings which should be taken at 15-second intervals for 2 minutes after firing.

(4) The time (c) when the maximum temperature has been reached, or when the rate of change has become uniform, usually about five minutes after firing.

(5) The rate of change (r_2) for the final period in degrees per minute.

Corrections

(a) Apply the corrections as indicated on the thermometer certificate for the initial (a) and final (c) readings.

(b) Determine the correction for radiation as follows:

Multiply the rate (r_1) by the time (b-a) in minutes and tenths of a minute, and add the product to the corrected temperature reading at time (a).

Multiply the rate (r_2) by the time (c-b), and add (or subtract if the temperature was *rising* during the final period) the product to the corrected temperature reading at time (c).

The difference of the two readings thus modified to account for thermometer scale and radiation corrections gives the total rise of temperature.

Multiply the total rise thus found by the water equivalent of the calorimeter, the product giving the total amount of heat liberated. If the thermometer readings were in Fahrenheit degrees, the product gives the heat value in B.t.u. Unless otherwise stated, the readings with the oxygen bomb instrument are considered as Centigrade, and the ultimate values are in calories.

(c) The total heat as obtained under (b) after calculating to calories is to be further corrected on account of the formation of nitric and sulphuric acids in the reaction. Correction for these acids, however, is more conveniently brought to the basis of the heat units involved as follows: Wash the bomb thoroughly with hot distilled water and titrate the washings with a standard solution of sodium carbonate. Make up the sodium carbonate solution by dissolving 3.658 grams of chemically pure Na_2CO_3 in one liter of distilled water. Each cc. of the sodium carbonate solution represents an amount of nitric acid producing 1 calorie in the reaction involved.

The additional correction for sulphuric acid requires that a determination of sulphur be at hand. It can be made from the washings after titrating for the acids either by the gravimetric or photometric method. Multiply the weight [1] of sulphur present by 13. The product equals the number of calories to be combined with the number found by titration. Add also the correction indicated for the fuse wire which will equal substantially 2.8 calories for each centimeter burned. The sum represents the total correction in

[1] Weight of S = amount of fuel taken × sulphur per cent.

calories to be subtracted from the amount obtained from the total correcte temperature under (b).

Finally, note that the total indicated heat as corrected for nitric acid sulphuric acid and fuse wire refers to a quantity of fuel represented by th weight of the charge taken. If this weight were exactly 1 gram, no furthe computation is necessary. If the weight taken varied from an even gram the indicated calories as above derived must be divided at the end of th computation by the weight of fuel taken.

Note especially also that if a thermometer with the Fahrenheit scale i used, the values are in B.t.u., but the corrections for acid and fuse wire mus be changed to correspond. In this case, it will be simpler to make up th standard Na_2CO_3 solution by using 2.032 grams per liter and increasing th titration factor by 23 times the per cent of sulphur. The wire factor als should be taken as 5. units per centimeter of length. Calculations from these values will then all be in B.t.u., which are subtracted from the tota indicated B.t.u. to cover the corrections involved.

Standardization

To standardize the instrument, make a combustion, using a standar substance of known heat value, as pure benzoic acid. Add to the accepte heat value of the quantity taken, say, 1 gram, the heat due to the combustio of the wire and the nitric acid formed. Divide the heat value thus represente by the temperature rise, corrected in the usual manner. The quotient repre sents the total water equivalent made up to the actual grams of water employe 2000 plus the equivalent in water of the metal parts, etc., of the apparatus The substances most commonly used with the values recognized by the U. S Bureau of Standards are:

Benzoic acid.. 6320 calories per gram
Naphthalene.. 9622 calories per gram
Cane sugar... 3949 calories per gram

Variations from these values due to impurities may still permit of the sub stances being used provided the values themselves have been carefully deter mined under properly standardized conditions. Because of its availability i pure form and somewhat simpler procedure, benzoic acid is preferred b many users as a standardizing material.

To Dismantle

After completing the readings, the apparatus is dismantled by removin the double cover from the insulating jacket and placing it in a suitable holde to guard against breaking the thermometer. Transfer the bomb to th octagon holder and release the oxygen from the bomb by pressing down upo the valve (13A, Fig. 220). Do not try to remove screw cap (3A, Fig. 220) unt after the gas pressure has been released.

Upon opening the bomb, if any unburned carbon is found, the determina tion should be rejected.

Gasoline and Volatile Distillates

In order to obtain an accurate weight of the highly volatile fuels, a thin walled glass container should be made use of. Such bulbs (see Fig. 217) ma be readily blown from a piece of soft glass tubing drawn out to a capillary

Make an accurate weighing of the bulb with the capillary end open. It is filled with the liquid by alternately warming and cooling the bulb and having the open end of the capillary dipping into the sample during the cooling process. In this manner, the desired amount of liquid is drawn into the bulb. The capillary is sealed in the glass flame and an accurate weight obtained. Place the bulb in the bottom of a 10-cc. ILLIUM crucible supported on the terminal and loop the fuse wire two or three times around the capillary stem. Attach the ends of the fuse wire to the terminals. Assemble the cover in place, and fill with oxygen as usual.

When ready for ignition, it will be found that upon closing the circuit, the thin-walled capillary is ruptured and the volatile material excapes for simultaneous ignition. The liquid being thus delivered at the bottom of the crucible, spattering or diffusion of the charge without combustion is obviated. Sulphur is not likely to be present, and the nitric acid formed will be very small in amount. However, a titration should be made and the correction applied as for nitric acid only.

Example of Computations

Date—

Lab. No.

Weight of material burned .8 gram.

Sulphur in coal..........4.31%

Room Temp. 23.7° C.

0° of Beckman Ther. 21.8° C.

Water Eqv. 2416.00 grams.

Time	Temperature		
2–11.......	.295		
12.......	.299		
13.......	.303	$r_1 = \dfrac{.018}{5} = 0.0036$	
14.......	.307		
15.......	.310		
(a) 16.......	.313		
	Fired		

Initial Temp.   0.313   Final   2.399

(b)   17.12....1.573[1]   Certif. Corr. − .001   Corr.+ .099

Corr. Initial   .312   Final   2.408

(c) 21.......	2.399		
22.......	2.398		
23.......	2.397	$r_2 = \dfrac{.005}{5} = 0.001$	
24.......	2.397		
25.......	2.395		
26.......	2.394		

$(b\text{-}a) \times r_1 = 1.12 \times .0036 \dots\dots\dots\dots\dots\dots 0.004$

$(c\text{-}b) \times r_2 = 3.48 \times .001 \dots\dots\dots\dots\dots\dots\dots\dots\dots\dots 0.003$

.316   2.411

                      .316

                      2.095

Setting Corr.   +0.001

Stem Corr.   +0.001

Corrected rise.........2.097

[1] The initial temperature is   0.313

60% of the expected rise is   1.260

The time to observe then is   1.573

Total Calories $= 2416 \times 2.097 = 5066.4$
  Acidity titration $= 27.2$ Cal.
  Corr. for wire $= 18.4$ "
  Sulphur Corr. $= 44.8$ "   90.4

    Calories from .8 gram $=$ 4976.
    Calories per gram $=$ 6620.

NOTES. (a) For anthracite coal, a thin pad of asbestos felt should be formed on the inside of the capsule. Take a small amount of asbestos pulp, squeeze out the water and form a felt on the bottom and sides of the capsule, then dry and ignite. This will prevent the lowering of the temperature below the ignition point before combustion is complete.

(b) To insure against loss of oxygen through leakage, keep the needle-valve between the gauge and the oxygen cylinder closed when not drawing out oxygen. For filling the bomb, open the needle-valve gradually, regulating the flow by noting the gauge indicator.

(c) Do not attempt to displace the air in the bomb with oxygen before filling. A certain amount of nitrogen is necessary for the complete oxidation of the sulphur. (See Vol. 6, p. 812, Journal of Industrial and Engineering Chemistry.)

(d) The sulphur correction in the example is $.8 \times 4.31 \times 13 = 44.8$ cals.

Gross and Net Values

In all of the calorimetric considerations thus far, the results as computed give the gross values; that is, with the products of combustion reduced in temperature to approximately that of the surrounding air, 20 to 35° C. This means that the water formed in the reactions has given up to the system its latent heat of vaporization. The weight of water is hydrogen $\times 9$, and the weight of water $\times 580$ represents the latent heat of vaporization in calories to be subtracted from the observed calories. The remainder is the net heat value.

There is not a little disagreement as to which value, the gross or net, is the more important. In ordinary steam-generating installations, where the flue-gases are delivered above the point of condensation, the net values would seem to be required. The engineer, however, in developing his heat balance, takes into account the heat of vaporization of all of the moisture, whether free or formed in the reactions, and it is simpler, therefore, to charge all such heat to the total or gross heat of the coal. It is desirable, on this account, that he be furnished the hydrogen factor as one of the constituents of the chemical analysis. This requires an ultimate analysis of the coal, or a simplified procedure, as described in connection with the apparatus for determining the total carbon in coal (p. 1646. See also formula on page 1650).

Heat Determinations with Petroleum Oils

For all liquid fuels, the capsule container for holding the sample should be replaced by a 10-cc. ILLIUM crucible. In the process of combustion, it is evident that the vapors must rise from the bottom of the crucible and flow over the edge, thus insuring complete combustion of all the hydrocarbons. The amount of material taken should be approximately one gram. In the case of the heavier, or non-volatile, oils, the oil may be weighed directly in the crucible. The crucible and oil are placed in the ring of the supporting terminal, and the fuse wire attached with the loop dipping slightly into the oil.

Assemble the bomb and fill with oxygen as usual. Titrate the bomb washings after combustion with standard alkali, and make the correction for both acids as in the case of coals. This will, of course, necessitate the determination of the sulphur present, either gravimetrically or by means of the photometer, as already described for solid fuels.

CARBON CONVERSION TABLE.

720	722	724	726	728	730	732	734	736	738	740	742	744
.4851	.4864	.4878	.4891	.4905	.4919	.4933	.4947	.4960	.4974	.4987	.5001	.5014
.4829	.4842	.4856	.4869	.4883	.4896	.4910	.4924	.4937	.4951	.4964	.4978	.4991
.4806	.4819	.4833	.4846	.4860	.4873	.4887	.4901	.4914	.4928	.4941	.4955	.4968
.4783	.4796	.4810	.4823	.4837	.4850	.4864	.4878	.4891	.4905	.4918	.4932	.4945
.4760	.4773	.4787	.4800	.4814	.4827	.4841	.4855	.4868	.4882	.4895	.4908	.4921
.4737	.4750	.4764	.4777	.4791	.4804	.4818	.4832	.4845	.4858	.4871	.4884	.4897
.4714	.4727	.4741	.4754	.4768	.4781	.4795	.4808	.4821	.4834	.4847	.4860	.4873
.4691	.4704	.4718	.4731	.4745	.4758	.4771	.4784	.4797	.4810	.4823	.4836	.4849
.4668	.4681	.4694	.4707	.4721	.4734	.4747	.4760	.4773	.4786	.4799	.4812	.4825
.4644	.4657	.4670	.4683	.4697	.4710	.4723	.4736	.4749	.4762	.4775	.4788	.4801
.4620	.4633	.4646	.4660	.4673	.4686	.4699	.4712	.4725	.4738	.4751	.4764	.4777
.4596	.4609	.4622	.4636	.4649	.4662	.4675	.4688	.4701	.4714	.4727	.4740	.4753
.4572	.4585	.4598	.4612	.4625	.4638	.4651	.4664	.4677	.4690	.4703	.4716	.4729
.4548	.4561	.4574	.4587	.4600	.4613	.4626	.4639	.4652	.4665	.4678	.4691	.4704
.4523	.4536	.4549	.4562	.4575	.4588	.4601	.4614	.4627	.4640	.4653	.4666	.4679
.4498	.4511	.4524	.4537	.4550	.4563	.4576	.4589	.4602	.4614	.4627	.4640	.4653
.4473	.4486	.4499	.4512	.4524	.4537	.4550	.4563	.4576	.4588	.4601	.4614	.4627
.4447	.4460	.4473	.4486	.4498	.4511	.4524	.4537	.4550	.4562	.4575	.4588	.4601
.4421	.4434	.4447	.4460	.4472	.4485	.4498	.4511	.4524	.4536	.4549	.4562	.4575
.4395	.4408	.4420	.4433	.4445	.4458	.4471	.4484	.4497	.4509	.4522	.4535	.4548
.4368	.4381	.4393	.4406	.4418	.4431	.4444	.4457	.4470	.4482	.4495	.4508	.4521
.4341	.4354	.4366	.4379	.4391	.4404	.4417	.4430	.4443	.4455	.4468	.4481	.4494
.4314	.4327	.4339	.4352	.4364	.4377	.4390	.4402	.4415	.4427	.4440	.4453	.4466
.4286	.4299	.4311	.4324	.4336	.4349	.4362	.4374	.4387	.4399	.4412	.4425	.4438
.4258	.4271	.4283	.4296	.4308	.4321	.4334	.4346	.4359	.4371	.4384	.4396	.4409
.4230	.4242	.4255	.4267	.4280	.4292	.4305	.4317	.4330	.4342	.4355	.4367	.4380

NOTE. Calculated weight of carbon in milligrams per cubic centimeter of CO_2 om 1.976 g. weight of 1 liter of CO_2 at 41° Lat. Corrected for water vapor and arometer glass scale.

CARBON CONVERSION TABLE—*Continued.*

t\P	746	748	750	752	754	756	758	760	762	764	766	768	77
10	.5028	.5041	.5055	.5069	.5083	.5096	.5110	.5124	.5137	.5151	.5165	.5178	.519
11	.5005	.5028	.5032	.5046	.5060	.5073	.5087	.5101	.5114	.5127	.5141	.5154	.516
12	.4982	.4995	.5009	.5023	.5036	.5049	.5063	.5077	.5090	.5103	.5117	.5130	.514
13	.4959	.4972	.4986	.4999	.5012	.5025	.5039	.5053	.5066	.5079	.5093	.5106	.512
14	.4935	.4948	.4962	.4975	.4988	.5001	.5015	.5029	.5042	.5055	.5069	.5082	.509
15	.4911	.4924	.4938	.4951	.4964	.4977	.4991	.5005	.5018	.5031	.5045	.5058	.507
16	.4887	.4900	.4914	.4927	.4940	.4953	.4967	.4981	.4994	.5007	.5021	.5034	.504
17	.4863	.4876	.4890	.4903	.4916	.4929	.4943	.4957	.4970	.4983	.4997	.5010	.502
18	.4849	.4852	.4866	.4879	.4892	.4905	.4919	.4933	.4946	.4959	.4973	.4986	.499
19	.4815	.4828	.4842	.4855	.4868	.4881	.4895	.4908	.4921	.4934	.4948	.4961	.497
20	.4791	.4804	.4818	.4831	.4844	.4857	.4870	.4883	.4896	.4909	.4923	.4936	.494
21	.4767	.4780	.4793	.4806	.4819	.4832	.4845	.4858	.4871	.4884	.4898	.4911	.492
22	.4742	.4755	.4768	.4781	.4794	.4807	.4820	.4833	.4846	.4859	.4873	.4886	.489
23	.4717	.4730	.4743	.4756	.4769	.4782	.4795	.4808	.4821	.4834	.4847	.4860	.487
24	.4692	.4705	.4718	.4731	.4744	.4757	.4770	.4783	.4795	.4808	.4821	.4834	.484
25	.4666	.4679	.4692	.4705	.4718	.4731	.4744	.4757	.4769	.4782	.4795	.4808	.482
26	.4640	.4653	.4666	.4679	.4692	.4705	.4718	.4731	.4743	.4756	.4769	.4782	.479
27	.4614	.4627	.4639	.4652	.4665	.4678	.4691	.4704	.4716	.4729	.4742	.4755	.476
28	.4587	.4600	.4612	.4625	.4638	.4651	.4664	.4677	.4689	.4702	.4715	.4728	.474
29	.4560	.4573	.4585	.4598	.4611	.4624	.4637	.4650	.4662	.4675	.4688	.4701	.471
30	.4533	.4546	.4558	.4571	.4584	.4597	.4610	.4623	.4635	.4647	.4660	.4673	.468
31	.4506	.4519	.4531	.4544	.4556	.4569	.4582	.4595	.4607	.4619	.4632	.4645	.465
32	.4478	.4491	.4503	.4516	.4528	.4541	.4554	.4567	.4579	.4591	.4604	.4617	.463
33	.4450	.4463	.4475	.4488	.4500	.4512	.4525	.4538	.4550	.4562	.4575	.4588	.460
34	.4421	.4434	.4446	.4459	.4471	.4483	.4496	.4509	.4521	.4533	.4546	.4559	.457
35	.4392	.4405	.4417	.4430	.4442	.4454	.4467	.4479	.4492	.4504	.4517	.4529	.454

See note page 1661.

ELECTROMETRIC METHODS OF ANALYSIS

The Electrometric Determination of Hydrogen Ion Concentration[2]

The electrometric titration of acids and alkalies is based upon the measurement of the electrode potential between the hydrogen on the surface of a hydrogen electrode and the hydrogen ions in the surrounding solution.

If a bar of any metal is dipped into water, it will immediately give off some positively charged ions, thereby leaving the metal negatively charged. The strength of this charge or resulting potential is determined by two factors: The electrolytic solution pressure of the metal and the osmotic pressure of the ions in the solution.

If two similar electrodes are dipped into two solutions of different concentrations with respect to the metal ions, the electrode which is immersed in the more concentrated solution will receive ions from the solution and be positively charged while the electrode dipping into the less concentrated solution will give off positive ions and become negatively charged relative to the other electrode. This will cause a flow of current from the first electrode to the second if they are externally connected. Such a system constitutes a battery, the total electromotive force of which can be calculated by the following formulae:

The potential difference which is produced by the contact of a metal with a solution of its ions is represented by

$$e = \frac{RT}{NF} \log_e \frac{P}{p},$$

where R = gas constant = volts $\times$ coulombs = 8316 Joules,
F = Faraday = 96,540,
N = valence of the metal,
P = electrolytic solution pressure of the metal,
p = osmotic pressure of the ions in solution,
T = absolute temperature.

Substituting the above values, assuming a temperature of 18° and changing to common logarithms

$$e = \frac{0.058}{N} \log \frac{P}{p}.$$

Since the osmotic pressure is proportional to the concentration of the ions, c (concentration) may be substituted for p. Then let C which represents an ionic concentration which just balances the solution pressure P be substituted for P and

$$e = \frac{0.058}{N} \log \frac{C}{c}.$$

This represents a single electrode potential and since the total electromotive force of a cell is the difference between the single electrode potentials

$$E = e_2 - e_1 = \frac{.058}{N} \log \frac{C}{c_2} - \frac{.058}{N} \log \frac{C}{c_1} = \frac{.058}{N} \log \frac{c_1}{c_2}.$$

A platinum or gold electrode, covered with platinum, iridium or palladium

Chapter by G. L. Kelley, chemist, Midvale Steel and Ordnance Company, and J. S. Coye, assistant chemist, General Chemical Company.

black and immersed in an atmosphere of hydrogen, acts as if the hydrogen were a metal and is called a hydrogen electrode. The platinum itself is chemically inert and the electrode potential is due to the contact between the concentration of the hydrogen on the electrode surface and the concentration of the hydrogen ions in the solution. Since the concentration of the hydrogen on the electrode surface can be maintained constant by being kept saturated by the hydrogen gas at a constant pressure and temperature, a potential change will be due to a change of hydrogen ion concentration in the solution and, consequently, the e.m.f. is a direct function of the hydrogen ion concentration of the solution and thus its acidity or alkalinity. Now if one hydrogen electrode dips into a solution having a known hydrogen ion concentration of one and a second into a solution of unknown hydrogen ion concentration and the two solutions are connected by a salt bridge (saturated solution of potassium chloride) the total electromotive force will be

$$E = .058 \log \frac{1}{C},$$

and a measurement of the e.m.f. furnishes a means by which the hydrogen ion concentration of the unknown solution can be determined.

In practice it is more convenient to use the more constant calomel electrode instead of a hydrogen electrode having a hydrogen ion concentration of one. The potential of the calomel electrode has been determined in terms of the normal hydrogen electrode, e.g., the 0.1 N calomel electrode has a potential of .337 volts greater than the normal hydrogen electrode at 25° C.

Therefore, by measuring the electromotive force of the system,

0.1 N calomel electrode / saturated solution of KCl / hydrogen electrode / solution of H−ions at 25° C.

$$E = .05816 \log \frac{1}{c} + .337$$

and the hydrogen ion concentration can be readily calculated, or

$$\frac{E - .337}{.05816} = \log \frac{1}{C}.$$

The value $\log (1/C)$ is widely used to characterize the hydrogen ion concentration without solving for C and has been generally designated P_H. When making an electrometric titration of an acid or a base by means of the hydrogen electrode, this value P_H or the value E in volts may be plotted against the number of cc. of acid or alkali used in the titration and a curve obtained from which the endpoint may be readily observed. Figure 1 shows two such curves. Curve V was obtained by titrating a solution of phosphoric acid, to which a slight excess of alkali had been added, with N/10 HCl. Curve VI was then obtained by titrating the resulting solution with N/10 NaOH.

All phosphate exists as disodium phosphate at B and as monosodium phosphate at A, therefore, the hydrogen ion concentration of disodium and monosodium phosphate solutions may be determined from the e.m.f. at these points. But the principal value of these curves is that they provide a means by which phosphates may be titrated without the use of indicators.

The constants of the above equation are influenced by temperature and by any potential existing between the 0.1 KCl solution of the calomel electrode or the solution being measured and the connecting solution. The latter is practically eliminated by the use of a saturated solution of KCl, while the former may be readily determined and corrections made. It should also be

oted that the electrolytic solution tension of the hydrogen is dependent upon
1e pressure of the gaseous hydrogen at the electrode.   760 mm. partial pres-
1re is the standard pressure for the hydrogen in the standard hydrogen
ectrode.   Corrections for the e.m.f. may be applied for varying hydrogen
ressures, but for all work except that of the high precision this may be dis-
garded.

The hydrogen gas to be used for keeping the hydrogen electrode saturated
1ust be of highest possible purity.   Hydrogen generated by electrolyzing a
0% NaOH solution or the ordinary compressed hydrogen from cylinders
ave been found satisfactory after removing the last traces of oxygen by
assing it through heated palladized asbestos or over a heated platinum spiral.

For the measurement of hydrogen ion concentrations a calomel electrode,
hydrogen electrode and a potentiometer for measuring the voltage between
hem are necessary.   For measurements of highest precision a constant tem-
erature bath is also required.   Fig. 222 shows, diagrammatically, the usual
rrangement of apparatus for this work.

The chief advantages of electrometric titrations for hydrogen ion con-
entration are:

1. The "personal equation," which is always a factor when titrating by
neans of indicators does not enter into the measurements.

2. Measurements may be made without regard to the opacity of solutions
nd under poor or troublesome light conditions.   Precipitation does not appre-
iably interfere with the measurement.

3. The method is fundamental.   To it all colorimetric methods must be
eferred for standardization.

4. The potentiometer covers the entire range of hydrogen ion concentrations
r P_H values, whereas any indicator is useful over a limited range only and its
articular color change as interpreted by the normal eye in many instances
oes not correspond to the hydrogen ion concentrations of the true end-point.

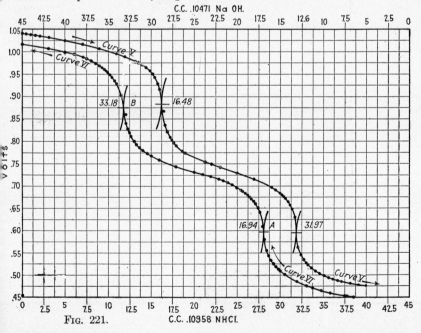

FIG. 221.

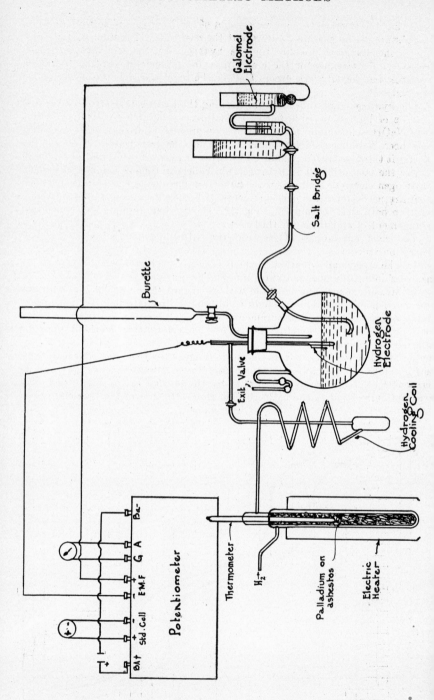

The Electrometric Method of Titration in Oxidation and Reduction Reactions[1]

The electrometric method of oxidation and reduction titrations is similar to that for determining hydrogen ion concentrations since it is based upon the measurement of electrode potentials whereby relative ionic concentrations are determined.

In general, oxidation is a gain of valence or a loss of electrons while reduction is a loss of valence or a gain of electrons. The electric current may effect both oxidation and reduction, the former at the cathode where ions give up their electrons, and the latter at the anode where ions receive electrons, from the circuit. In a solution containing both ferrous and ferric ions the former will be oxidized at the cathode and the latter reduced at the anode. If no external electromotive force is applied and a single platinum wire is inserted into such a solution, the wire will acquire a positive or a negative potential, depending on the relative concentrations of the ferrous and ferric ions, the former tending to give up electrons, thus charging the wire negatively, and the latter tending to take electrons from it, thus giving the wire a positive charge. This can readily be demonstrated by connecting two such solutions possessing different relative concentrations of ferrous and ferric ions by a solution of potassium or sodium chloride and then connecting the electrodes in the solution by closing a circuit through a sensitive voltmeter. The voltmeter will now indicate a flow of current because the tendency for the ferrous ions to give up electrons will be relatively the greater in one solution, and the tendency for the ferric ions to take up electrons from the wire will be the greater in the other solution. The system therefore constitutes a cell whose potential can be measured. If the concentrations of ferrous and ferric ions could be kept constant in one of the solutions, it could become the standard whereby the ferric or ferrous ions of the other could be determined. Such a standard is experimentally impossible and instead of using such a system, a single ferrous-ferric solution is connected with a normal calomel electrode as follows:

Normal calomel electrode/saturated KCl sol./ferric-ferrous solution − Pt.

The potential of such a cell is given by the formula:

$$E = P + \frac{RT}{NF} \log_e \frac{Co}{Ci}.$$

E = E.M.F. produced by the change from the "ous" to the "ic" state.

P = a constant and is equal to the potential when the concentrations Co and Ci are equal; thereby the second term of the second member becomes zero.

Co and Ci = the ionic concentrations of the lower and higher states of oxidation respectively.

N = the increase or decrease of valence.

R = gas constant = volts $\times$ coulombs = 8316 joules.

F = Faraday = 96,540.

T = absolute temperature.

In the case of the ferrous-ferric cell the equation then becomes, after converting to common logarithms.

$$E = P + 0.058 \log \frac{Co}{Ci}.$$

[1] J. S. Coye.

By measuring the E of such a system when the ferrous and ferric ioni concentrations are equal and using a normal calomel electrode the value o P has been found to be .47 volts and the equation then becomes:

$$E = 0.47 + 0.058 \log \frac{Co}{Ci}.$$

The potential of such a system may thus be used as a measure of the relative concentrations of ferrous and ferric ions.

As an illustration, consider the case of titrating the ferrous iron in a hydro chloric acid solution with a standard solution of potassium bichromate, ferri iron being either absent or present. The potential at the beginning of the reaction will depend upon the nature and concentration of the anions as well a upon the concentrations of the ferrous and ferric ions. As the potassium bichromate solution is added the ferrous ions decrease and the ferric ion increase. The term $0.058 \log Co/Ci$, which is the only varying term gradually decreases to zero when the concentration of ferrous and ferric ions become equa and then very slowly decreases until Co becomes equal to zero when there i an abrupt change in voltage and the endpoint is reached. The endpoint may be readily redetermined by adding a slight excess of the potassium bichromate and titrating back with a standard solution of ferrous ammonium sulphate A similar condition exists for all oxidation and reduction reactions. The constant P will, of course, be different for each reaction so that the potentia readings will be different but the abrupt voltage change at the endpoint i common to all. Several forms of apparatus have been designed and described by different investigators for this type of work.

The advantages of this method are:

1. A high degree of accuracy can be obtained without sacrificing rapidity

2. It is applicable to many reactions with only very slight adjustments.

3. The necessity of determining and making corrections for indicators i eliminated.

4. It is possible to determine very small amounts of iron and other metal possessing two states of oxidation, in many raw materials without employing the usual tedious methods of separation.

THE KELLEY ELECTROMETRIC TITRATION APPARATUS

This outfit is the result of work which was undertaken by Dr. G. L. Kelley, Chief Chemist of the Midvale Steel and Ordnance Company, and his associates, in adapting the principles of electrometric titration to commercial methods of steel analysis. The problems encountered in this development work pointed out the desirable features of design in a commercial equipment. With the suggestions of Dr. Kelley as a basis, Leeds & Northrup Company designed the apparatus, developed the necessary equipment for adapting it to conductivity and hydrogen-ion measurements, and now manufacture it.

The principle involved is the change of oxidation potential.

The device has been successfully applied to the determination of chromium, vanadium and manganese in steel and ferrous alloys. Determinations of chromium and vanadium in steel may be made on samples containing one or both of these elements. The presence of molybdenum and tungsten does not interfere. Manganese can be determined readily in the presence of both vanadium and chromium.

Although the apparatus is especially valuable in the analysis of steel and ferrous alloys, the principle involved in the operation of the apparatus has been applied in the determination of other elements than those already mentioned. This is notably the case with zinc. It is also possible, with the addition of certain accessory apparatus, to use this outfit for the measurement of the conductivity of electrolytes, and for the determination of hydrogen-ion concentrations. It is probable that other important applications will also be found.

General Description

The apparatus consists of a wooden case with an upright carrying the motor burettes and electrodes. In the case are two dry cells, an adjustable resistance, and a reflecting galvanometer. On the upper surface of the case is a ground glass scale on which the light from the galvanometer is thrown. A knurled head inside of the case permits of adjusting the zero point of the galvanometer and another on the side controls the resistance.

The standard carries the burettes, the electrodes, and the motor for driving the stirrer. In addition, provision has been made for a reservoir of the electrolyte which is used in the calomel cell. This makes possible, without change in its potential, the displacement of the impure electrolyte which may have accumulated in the tip of the electrode. A pan on an adjustable support, specially treated to resist acids, carries the beaker in which the titration is made. Two switches are mounted on the sides of the case, one of which controls the galvanometer light and motor, while the other closes the potentiometer circuit.

To operate the instrument, a beaker containing the solution to be analyzed is placed on the pan and the support raised and locked in position. The switch controlling the galvanometer light and motor is then closed. The other switch closes the potentiometer circuit and a slight turn of the knob controlling the resistance is sufficient to bring the beam of light on the scale. In titrating a series of solutions, this latter adjustment need be made only once. During the operation, which is quick, certain and convenient, the analyst watches

the beam of light until a permanent change of potential is noted.   In general
the first permanent large change marks the end point of the reaction.

A rheostat for varying the speed of the motor stirrer is mounted on a
casting attached to the box.

Description of Components

Calomel Electrode Cell.   The calomel electrode rests in a metal collar
attached to the upright at E.   The glass stopcock at B allows liquid to flow
into the cell from the reservoir to which it is connected by rubber tubing at A.
When this stopcock is opened, the capillary tube at D is flushed, thus insuring
the purity of the electrolyte in the cell.   The cell may be filled through the
opening at C, which is then closed.   A platinum-tipped wire at F makes
contact with the external circuit.   The capacity of the cell is about 100 ml.
A small amount of mercury is placed in the bottom of the cell and covered
with Hg_2Cl_2.   The cell is then filled with the neutral liquid, a normal solution
of KCl.   This gives a constant potential difference of about .56 volt between
the Hg and the liquid, the Hg being $+$ to the liquid.

Potentiometer.   The E.M.F. of the electrolytic cell is balanced against the
fall of potential across a slide wire in circuit with two dry cells and a resistance.
The total resistance of the slide wire is about 50 ohms.   This resistance can
be varied, to secure a balance, by means of a knurled head on the outside of
the case.

Galvanometer.   A Leeds & Northrup Co. Reflecting Galvanometer is
furnished with this outfit.   This instrument is sufficiently sensitive for the
purpose and has the further advantage of a very short period.   It is rugged
in construction and will withstand as much rough usage as an ordinary voltmeter.   The image of the lamp filament is reflected to a translucent scale
which is placed on the top of the box.   This places the scale where it can
most easily be seen by the operator while titrating.   The lamp furnished with
this instrument has a single straight filament of high brilliancy.

Heating Unit.   A heating unit is mounted on a socket on the inside of
the box for the purpose of keeping the galvanometer circuit dry at all times
and preventing possible " leakage " due to moisture.

Motor and Stirrer.   The stirrer consists of a three-bladed glass propeller
cemented into a brass rod and belted to a small electric motor.   This motor
is securely attached to the upright and is equipped with a rheostat for variable
speeds.

Reservoir.   The reservoir consists of an aspirator bottle, 500 ml. capacity,
firmly attached to the upright.

Switches and Connections.   Two switches are mounted on the box; one
controls the motor and galvanometer light, and the other throws in the potentiometer circuit.   All connections, except to dry cells, are soldered and the
insulation is designed to prevent all possible " leaks."   All metal parts are
treated with a special acid-resisting varnish.   The measuring circuit is carefully insulated from the motor circuit.

Discussion of Oxidation Potential

If platinum and calomel electrodes are placed in an oxidizing solution such as chromic acid, we have a cell with a definite E.M.F. On adding a reducing agent such as ferrous sulphate, the change in potential will be small until the first excess of the reducing agent appears in the solution. The change is then very striking, for the voltage of the cell which originally contained the oxidizing agent drops very markedly from its first value.

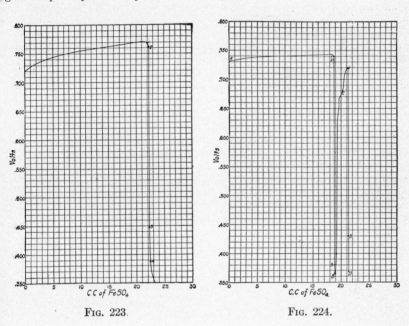

FIG. 223.   FIG. 224.

The calomel electrode, which makes contact with the oxidizing solution through a siphon arm containing KCl or some other neutral salt, has a constant potential (.56 volt if normal KCl solution is used). Since this salt does not enter into the reaction, the potential of the calomel electrode remains fixed throughout the reaction, all changes taking place at the platinum electrode.

It is interesting to follow graphically the changes in potential which are known to take place during a titration. For this reason various curves were plotted, using the Kelley apparatus, and a voltmeter with a range of 1.5 volts. Electromotive forces were plotted as ordinates and ml. of reducing solution as abscissæ. The curves, therefore, show the changes in potential due to the reduction of the oxidizing solution. It should be noted in every case that at the end point of the reaction a very small amount of the titrating solution caused a large drop in potential.

Fig. 223 illustrates the changes that occur when a solution of $K_2Cr_2O_7$ is titrated with $FeSO_4$. The titration was carried out in a volume of 200 ml. in the presence of 25 ml. of H_2SO_4 (sp.gr. 1.58). One ml. of the chromate

52

solution corresponded to .000339 gr. of Cr and the FeSO₄ was of approximately the same strength.

Twenty-three ml. of the chromate solution was used. Point (1) on the curve corresponds to a potential of .766 volt, the difference between it and point (2) is .1 ml. and only .004 volt.

The further addition of .1 ml. of the reducing solution gives point (3 causing a change in potential of .313 volt, a very striking drop. This mark the end point of the reaction. After the end point is reached, the addition of an excess of FeSO₄ causes relatively little change in the potential, as i shown by the curve.

Fig. 224 gives the curve representing the titration of a solution of $K_2Cr_2O_7$ 1 ml. equivalent to .001 gr. Cr, by FeSO₄ of approximately equal strength The portion from A to B represents the direct titration of 21 ml. of the chromate solution. The difference between points (1) and (2) on this portion o the curve corresponds to .05 ml. and .005 volt. The addition of .1 ml. more of the FeSO₄ caused a drop of .335 volt, again a very striking change. When past the end point by several drops of FeSO₄, more $K_2Cr_2O_7$ was added represented by the portion BC of the curve. Then more FeSO₄ was added shown by the portion of the curve (CD), again causing the large decrease in potential from point (1) to point (2) of .29 volt for .05 ml. FeSO₄.

In obtaining the data for these curves no attempt was made to measure with extreme accuracy the absolute potentials. The relative values of the potentials are, however, correct as given.

Directions for Assembling

Unpack the apparatus carefully, giving particular attention to the glass-
are. The various parts are shown assembled in Figs. 225 and 226. To
·gin the assembly place the upright support (13) into its socket in the metal

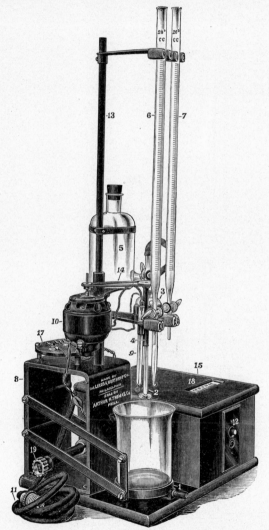

By Courtesy of Arthur H. Thomas Co.

FIG. 225. Apparatus for Electrometric Titration. Front view.

ame (8), and clamp with the set screw on the under side of the frame. Then
lace the right- and left-hand burettes (6) and (7) in their positions. Place
e calomel electrode cell (3) and the platinum electrode tube (9) in their

holding devices. Fasten the stirrer propeller (2) to the stirring shaft (4)
using the small screw on the propeller mounting. Belt up the stirring mot
to the stirrer, using the small coil spring belt (14). Place the reservoir bott
(5) on its support and connect its outlet to the inlet tube of the calomel c
above the stopcock.

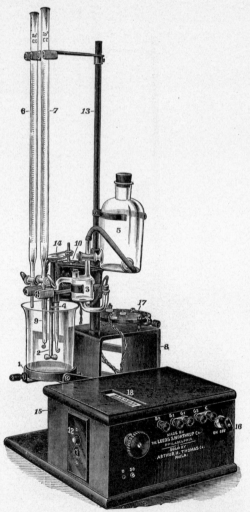

By Courtesy of Arthur H. Thomas Co.

FIG. 226. Apparatus for Electrometric Titration. Rear view.

Raise the beaker support (1) to the upper limit of its motion and latch
into position. The upright support (13) carrying the motor, bottle, cell, etc
should be raised or lowered after loosening the set screws until the stirre
cell tube, and electrode are about $\frac{3}{4}$ inch above the wooden tray on the beak
support. (See Fig. 225.)

Place the platinum-tipped wires into the ends of the electrode tube and the U-shaped tube of the calomel cell. Open the lid of the potentiometer box (15) and connect the loose wire to the dry cell terminal.

If the apparatus is to be used on 110 volts, plug the attachment on the end of the flexible cord (11) into the 110-volt circuit, A.C. or D.C. as marked on the motor. If the apparatus is to be used on 220 volts A.C., connect the plug and cord (11) into the receptacle furnished with the transformer. The other terminals of the transformer are to be connected to the 220-volt A.C. circuit. For 220-volt D.C. circuits the motor will be supplied and marked for 220 volts D.C. Fig. 227 shows the circuits for the motor and lamp circuits. Screw the resistance unit (19) in the receptacle located inside of the metal frame behind the beaker support.

110 Volt Circuit

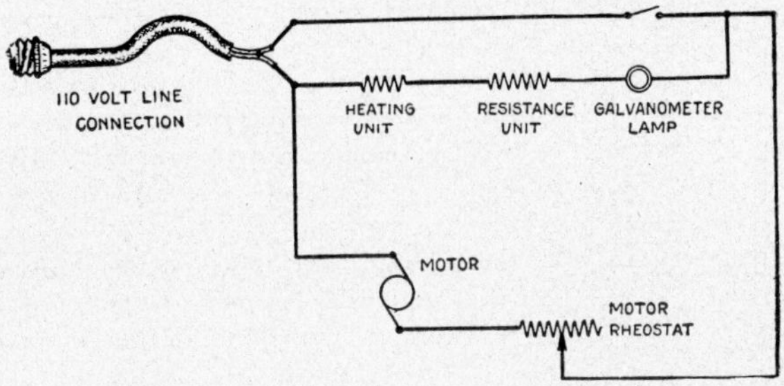

Fig. 227. Diagram showing the circuits for the motor and lamp circuits.

Potientiometer Circuit

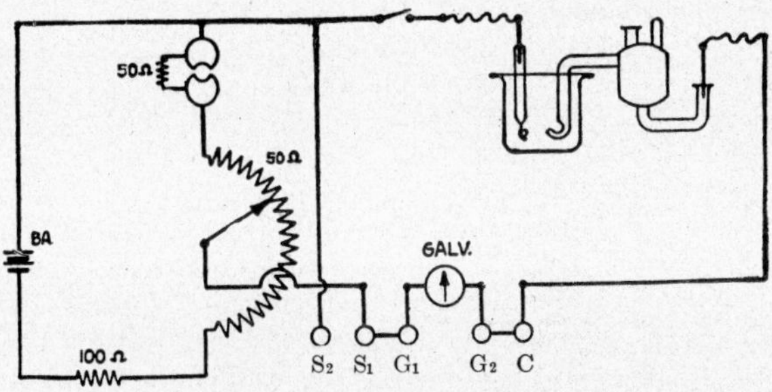

Fig. 228. Diagram showing the galvanometer circuit.

Close the push-button switch (12) on the front of the potentiometer box. This switch controls the galvanometer lamp and the stirring motor. To adjust the speed of the stirring motor vary the setting of the rheostat (17). See that the galvanometer switch (16) on the side of the box is set to the " Off " position. This switch opens and closes the galvanometer circuit (Fig. 228). The reflected beam of light from the galvanometer mirror should appear on the center of the ground glass scale (18). If not, open the lid and adjust the knurled head galvanometer top until the beam is reflected to the center of the scale.

The glass tube of the platinum electrode should be filled with mercury for contact. Then immerse the platinum tip in a solution of $K_2Cr_2O_7$ in H_2SO_4 until the remainder of the apparatus is ready for operation. Before titration the electrode should be washed thoroughly and dipped into $FeSO_4$ solution.

Prepare a normal solution of c.p. KCl with a volume sufficient to fill both the Calomel Electrode Cell and the reservoir bottle. It is convenient to make up a liter, placing the surplus in a stock bottle from which the reservoir can be easily refilled. Shake about 250 ml. of this solution with calomel, preferably freshly precipitated calomel. Allow this to stand until the calomel settles. Fill the calomel cell with clean mercury to a depth of about $\frac{1}{4}$ inch, allowing the mercury to rise to the same level in the glass tube connected to the bottom of the cell. Then place a thin layer of calomel over the mercury and fill the cell with the clear solution of KCl and Hg_2Cl_2, being careful to fill the capillary tube. A freshly made calomel cell does not give as good results upon titration as one that has been made up for 24 hours or more.

Fill the reservoir bottle with a solution of KCl. The capillary tube can be flushed by opening the stopcock of the cell, thus keeping the electrolyte free from diffusion. Other salts may be substituted for KCl, i.e., KNO_3, NaCl, $NaNO_3$, $NaSO_4$. The strength may vary from N to 4N, but should be the same in the reservoir as in the electrode. In titrating permanganate, chlorides are undesirable.

Fill the burette tubes with the titrating solution and the equivalent solution for back titration. Place the beaker of the solution to be titrated on the beaker stand and raise it to a position where the stirrer and the electrodes clear the bottom of the beaker. Close both switches, thus setting the motor into operation and lighting the galvanometer lamp. The speed of the stirrer can be varied by moving the lever of the rheostat. Stirring should be as fast as is possible without drawing air over the platinum electrode. Put the platinum-tipped flexibles into the mercury-filled tubes of the platinum electrode and the calomel cell. Adjust the resistance handle until the galvanometer indicates about zero on the scale. Should this be impossible, reverse the flexible wires leading to the electrode and the calomel cell. When the galvanometer deflection has been adjusted, the two potentials are nearly balanced and the titration can be started. By changing the position of the screw on the side of the potentiometer box, the range of the potential can be varied. With the screw in the 50 position, the full motion of the knob covers a range from .75 to 1.5 volts. With the screw in the other position, a range of 0 to 1.0 volt is secured.

When titrating, observe the change of the galvanometer position. At the neutral or end point there is, in general, a sudden, large, permanent deflection of the galvanometer. Deflections followed by an immediate return to the original position must be disregarded. The capillary tube should be flushed out frequently. A drop or two of liquid which is allowed to escape by opening the stopcock in the cell easily accomplishes this result. Five hundred ml. of the reservoir liquid should last for about 2000 determinations. It is entirely unnecessary to wash the stirrer or electrodes after a titration has been made.

If the cell is not to be used for a considerable time, it is best to disconnect the leads to the dry cells and place the platinum electrode in an H_2SO_4 solution of $K_2Cr_2O_7$. This is unnecessary, however, if the apparatus is in daily use.

Methods for Analysis

The Determination of Chromium in Steel

Solutions: *Silver Nitrate Solution:* Dissolve 2.5 g. $AgNO_3$ in 1 liter H_2O.

Ammonium Persulphate Solution: Dissolve 100 g. in enough cold water to make 1 liter.

Chromate Solution: Dissolve 2.829 g. $K_2Cr_2O_7$ and 5 g. Na_2CO_3 in water to make exactly 1 liter.

Ferrous Sulphate Solution: Dissolve 23 g. $(NH_4)_2SO_4FeSO_46H_2O$ and 100 ml. H_2SO_4 (sp.gr. 1.58) in enough water to make 1 liter. Compare this solution with 30 ml. of chromate solution by electrometric titration. Add water to the iron solution to make the strength equal. The difference should not be greater than 0.1 ml. in 30 ml. of solution. This comparison and adjustment of the iron solution should be made at least once each day.

Method of Procedure. Take 2 g. of samples containing less than .50% Cr, 1 g. of samples containing .5 to 5.0% and $\frac{1}{4}$ g. of samples containing 10 to 20%. Samples containing 10% or more should be weighed accurately to .001 g., all others to .002 g. Dissolve 1 g. or smaller samples in 70 ml. of sulphuric acid (sp.gr. 1.20). For 2 g. samples 100 ml. may be used.

To break up carbides it is safer to evaporate after solution is complete until salts separate. This is always necessary when the Cr is .5% or higher. The solution is then diluted cautiously with hot water to about 50 ml., and while still boiling 2 or 3 ml. nitric acid is added drop by drop to oxidize the iron. If time permits, it is desirable to evaporate a second time until salts separate. This becomes more important with a higher chromium content, as in 15% Cr steel. In both evaporations, great care must be taken to avoid spattering. This care is especially necessary in the second evaporation.

When the decomposition of carbides is complete, dilute carefully with hot water to 250 ml. or 300 ml. volume. To the boiling solution add 10 ml. $AgNO_3$ solution and 20 ml. of the ammonium persulphate solution. This order must not be reversed. When manganese is present, the success of the oxidation is indicated by the formation of permanganic acid. If this is not formed, add more of both solutions. Boil at least 8 minutes. While still boiling, add 5 ml. of dil. HCl (1 to 3) and continue boiling at least 5 minutes. Cool to about 20° C.

To titrate, bring the beam of light near the left end of the scale. Add ferrous sulphate gradually until the beam has permanently moved to the right. Chromate solution is then added slowly drop by drop until the beam will move no further towards the left. The *first* drop of ferrous sulphate which produces even a *small permanent displacement* towards the right of the position taken after adding chromate represents the end point. It is *not* necessary to deflect the beam from the scale.

To calculate, subtract the chromate used from the ferrous sulphate, divide by the number of grams in the sample and by 10. Each ml. of solution represents 0.1% Cr in a 1 g. sample.

Notes and Precautions

If vanadium is present, it will be titrated. In this event use the end point described in the vanadium determination. The chromium may be calculated as follows: Multiply the vanadium titration as found in a separate determination of vanadium by .339, which gives the amount to be subtracted from the titration of chromium and vanadium together.

Carbides are often difficult to decompose. Every solution should be examined for undecomposed carbides before oxidizing with ammonium persulphate.

An alternative method available for steels containing large amounts of Cr (10%) consists in dissolving in HCl, oxidizing with HNO_3 and evaporating with H_2SO_4 to fumes to remove HCl. The removal of the latter must be practically complete.

The more rapid the solution the more readily are carbides decomposed. It is therefore a good plan to add hot acid to the drillings.

The oxidation with persulphate is not successful in the presence of a too concentrated solution of acid. Dilution to at least 250 ml. is necessary when 70 ml. of acid is used.

Tungsten does not interfere with this determination if the volume of the solution is not too great at the time of oxidation with nitric acid.

Tungsten oxide does not occlude chromium, although it does occlude vanadium. When chromium and vanadium are oxidized together by ammonium persulphate and silver nitrate, the oxidation of chromium is complete, and of the vanadium only that part which is retained by the WO_3 remains unoxidized.

Although the chromate solution is taken as the standard, it undergoes changes in strength and should be renewed at least once each week.

In the case of tungsten steel it is not necessary to evaporate until sulphates separate.

If the end point obtained on titrating is not sharp, 25 ml. of sulphuric acid (sp.gr. 1.58) may be added.

Rapid Method for the Determination of Chromium in Steel

Solutions: *Manganese-Nitric Acid Solution:* Manganous Sulphate, 0.20 g.; Dilute Nitric Acid (sp.gr. 1.13), 1 liter. Contains .0025 Mn in 50 ml.

Sulphuric Acid, sp.gr. 1.58.

Dilute Hydrochloric Acid: Concentrated Hydrochloric Acid, 250 ml.; Water, 750 ml.

Chromate Solution: 2.829 g. $K_2Cr_2O_7$ in 1 liter H_2O. Make fresh each week.

Ferrous Ammonium Sulphate: 23 g. $Fe(NH_4)_2(SO_4)_2$, $6H_2O$ and 10 ml. H_2SO_4 1.58 in water to make 1 liter. Compare each day with $K_2Cr_2O_7$.

Method of Procedure. Dissolve 1 g. of the sample in 50 ml. of Manganese-Nitric Acid Solution with heat, and boil one minute after solution is complete. Add 20 ml. water and heat only to boiling. Remove from the hot part of the plate and add 2 g. sodium bismuthate. Boil gently at least two minutes. If the color of permanganic acid is not pronounced at the end of this time, make a second addition of sodium bismuthate and boil again. The color of permanganic acid should be marked at the time of taking the next step in the determination. This consists in adding enough boiling water to make 200 ml., followed by 40 ml. of sulphuric acid and 15 ml. of dilute hydrochloric acid. Boil two minutes after the color of permanganic acid disappears. Then add finely crushed ice and titrate electrometrically.

Notes and Precautions

The method is applicable to steels containing 2.5% of chromium and which have not been forged or subjected to complete heat treatment. In the latter case carbides cause low results. Heating a cast piece above the critical temperature, quenching and drawing do not prevent analysis by this method.

If vanadium is present, this will be oxidized and titrated along with chromium.

Manganese is added to the nitric acid to insure the presence of .3 to .6% of manganese in the sample to be analyzed. The manganese, through the formation of permanganic acid, is a convenient indicator of the success of the oxidation. If present in amounts greater than .75%, the MnO_2 is precipitated in a form which resists solution by dilute hydrochloric acid. It is possible that the permanganic acid assists in the decomposition of carbides.

The 20 ml. of water is added to facilitate the oxidation of the manganese to permanganic acid. If the water is added in a more dilute nitric acid, solution is delayed and carbides are not attacked. If the amount of water is greater, the bismuthate and permanganic acid do not decompose the chromium carbides. If the amount of water is less, more manganese dioxide is formed and there is an incomplete oxidation of the chromium present as carbide.

When the amount of chromium carbides is small, one addition of sodium bismuthate will be sufficient. The index of the presence of sufficient bismuthate is the persistence of the color of permanganic acid during two minutes of gentle boiling. When it does not persist, a second addition must be made. Gentle boiling prevents a too great change in concentration by evaporation. In the case of samples taken from preliminary tests a second addition will generally not be necessary, but no rule as to this can be laid down.

When oxidation is complete and water is added, a precipitate of bismuth subnitrate appears. This dissolves upon the addition of sulphuric acid. At this point the color of the solution should indicate an appreciable quantity of undecomposed permanganic acid. Turbidity may be due to carbides or manganese dioxide. Carbides will not be present when the method is properly applied to the classes of steel for which it has been found suitable. Manganese dioxide will be formed only in small amounts under the conditions described, when the total amount of Mn present does not exceed .75%. Such amounts as do form may be readily decomposed along with the permanganic acid by boiling two minutes after the addition of hydrochloric acid.

The sulphuric acid prevents the precipitation of bismuth oxychloride during boiling to decompose manganese compounds.

The finished solution should have a bright yellow or orange color, and turbidity or undissolved material should be due only to the presence of a precipitate of bismuth oxychloride.

The Determination of Vanadium in Steel

Solutions: *Chromate Solution:* Dissolve .9609 g. $K_2Cr_2O_7$ in 1 liter of distilled water. Although the chromate solution is the standard, it is subject to change and should be renewed at least once a week. One ml. of the solution is equal to 0.1% of V in a 1 g. sample. To convert this chromate solution into one containing Cr equivalent to .1% of chromium in a 1 g. sample, multiply by .339 (or .34).

Ferrous Ammonium Sulphate Solution: Dissolve 8 g. of ferrous ammonium sulphate and 50 ml. H_2SO_4 in 1 liter of water. The factor showing the relation of ferrous sulphate and potassium dichromate should be obtained each day by titrating a 30 or 40 ml. portion of the chromate solution.

Method of Procedure. In steels containing amounts of vanadium less than .5%, use a 2 g. sample. Dissolve this in 40 ml. H_2SO_4 (sp.gr. 1.58) and 60 ml. H_2O. When solution is complete, oxidize with 3 ml. conc. HNO_3 added slowly. Boil a few minutes, dilute to 200 ml. and add 40 ml. of conc. HNO_3. Boil during one hour at such a rate that at the end the volume will be between 100 and 125 ml. Cool, dilute to 300 ml. with ice water, and titrate.

When the vanadium is higher, use a 1 g. sample and dissolve in 30 ml. H_2SO_4 and 50 ml. H_2O. When solution is complete, add 2 ml. conc. HNO_3 gradually. Tungsten does not interfere and need not be removed. Boil this solution until the tungsten, if there is any present, is thoroughly oxidized. Dilute now to 200 ml. with hot water, add 40 ml. HNO_3 and boil at least one hour at such a rate that the final volume will be between 100 ml. and 125 ml. Cool, dilute to 300 ml. with ice water, and titrate.

The directions given above result in the oxidization of 99% of the vanadium in the solution. Accordingly this may be corrected by dividing by .99, or approximated by adding one per cent of the figure. When tungsten is present, a certain amount of vanadium is occluded by the tungstic oxide. This amounts to .015% in the case of steels containing 11 to 15% tungsten. This amount should be added to the corrected amount as determined by titration. When the tungsten present is as high as 20%, the correction should be .02%.

Notes and Precautions

Unless the given proportions of water and sulphuric acid are closely followed, the tungsten may precipitate in such a form as to cause interference with titration.

Do not boil less than one hour. No harm follows boiling longer.

Do not let the volume fall below 100 ml., for at volumes less than this chromium may be oxidized.

Do not fail to renew the chromate solution weekly.

In case of difficulty with the end point, 25 ml. H_2SO_4 may be added at the time of titration.

The temperature at titration should be 20° C. or lower, the colder the better.

During titration there is at first a gradual fall of potential. After a time the beam of light comes to rest. Continued addition of ferrous sulphate at length causes the light to move again. When this occurs, chromate enough is added to cause the light to return to its original position. After this the titration may be completed by the dropwise addition of ferrous sulphate. The first large movement is taken as the end point.

The Determination of Manganese in Steel

Solutions: *Ammonium Persulphate:* 50 g. $(NH_4)_2S_2O_8$, 475 ml. H_2O.

Sodium Thiosulphate: Saturated Solution.

Treated 3 per cent. Nitric Acid: 30 ml. HNO_3; 970 ml. H_2O and 1 g. Bismuthate.

Treated 25 per cent. Nitric Acid: 250 ml. HNO_3; 750 ml. H_2O and 2 g. Bismuthate.

Mercurous Nitrate: Dissolve 10.5 g. mercurous nitrate in 150 ml. H_2O, to which 2 ml. of HNO_3 has been added. Decant clear portion and make up to 1 liter. Adjust strength to equal permanganate.

Permanganate: 3 g. $KMnO_4$, 2000 ml. H_2O. After 3 days filter through asbestos. Adjust strength until 39.33 ml. is equivalent to .1200 g. sodium oxalate. It then contains .0005 g. Mn per ml.

Method of Procedure. Dissolve 1 g. of steel in 50 ml. of HNO_3 (sp.gr. 1.13), add 10 ml. of persulphate solution and boil until the persulphate is broken up. Reduce with thiosulphate solution, boiling 3 minutes afterwards. Add 50 ml. of " treated 25% nitric acid," and cool in a pan to 20° to 30° C. Oxidize with 1 g. sod. bismuthate, and filter through an asbestos mat, washing the beaker and asbestos with 100 ml. of " treated 3% nitric acid." To the filtrate add 50 ml. of H_2SO_4 (sp.gr. 1.58), ice enough to cool the solution to 20° or 30° C., and titrate electrometrically with mercurous nitrate. To titrate, place the beam of light on the scale. Near the end of the titration successive additions of mercurous nitrate cause the light to leave the scale, after which it returns slowly. Dropwise addition should then be made until the light remains off the scale. Then add one or two drops of permanganate to return the light to the original position, followed by enough mercurous nitrate to move the light permanently at least 5 large divisions from the original position.

To calculate, multiply the mercurous nitrate used by the factor, subtract the permanganate used, divide the result by 2 and move the decimal point one place toward the left. The factor is found by dividing the ml. of permanganate by the ml. of mercurous salt to which it is equivalent. Compare the standard solutions by making the titration of permanganate in a medium made up of 50 ml. sulphuric acid (sp.gr. 1.58), ice water 250 ml., and 25 ml. of nitric acid (conc.) which has been previously treated with sodium bismuthate to free it from nitrous acid. Of course, there must not be any undissolved sodium bismuthate present at the time of titration. The factor should be found each day on 10 and 20 ml. of solution.

Notes and Precautions

Be sure of the factor.

Oxidize with sodium bismuthate during at least one minute between 20° and 30° C. There is no occasion for haste in filtering. At temperatures below 20° C. the oxidation of the manganese may be incomplete.

After filtering, the titration must be made quickly, and it is better that the solution should be cold, as the permanganic acid is reduced by chromic salts.

In locating the end point, overrun as little as possible. Repeated back-titration gives poor results.

Dissolve high chromium steel (15% Cr) in HCl and evaporate 3 times with nitric acid. Then proceed as usual.

When cobalt is present, the manganese must be separated.

The Determination of Vanadium and Chromium in Ferro-Vanadium

Method of Procedure. Dissolve 3 g. of the sample in 75 ml. of nitric acid (sp.gr. 1.13). When solution is almost complete, add 10 ml. of HCl to assist in decomposing carbides. After the volume has been reduced about one-half, add a few drops of hydrofluoric acid to remove silica. Then add 50 ml. of sulphuric acid and evaporate until fumes of sulphuric acid appear, with the object of removing all hydrochloric acid. Dilute in a standardized flask with water to one liter. With a standardized pipette remove 2 one hundred ml. portions.

To 100 ml. add 20 ml. sulphuric acid and water to make 300 ml. Boil and add silver nitrate and ammonium persulphate to oxidize chromium, vanadium, and manganese. After ten minutes' boiling, add 3 ml. one to three hydrochloric acid to decompose permanganic acid. Boil ten minutes longer, cool, add 25 ml. sulphuric acid, and titrate at 5° C. with a ferrous sulphate solution equivalent to dichromate solution containing .001 g. Cr per ml. The titration includes chromium and vanadium. Divide the titration by 3 and multiply by 2.943. This converts both chromium and vanadium into the equivalent percentage of vanadium.

To a second 100 ml. portion add a few ml. of ferrous sulphate solution to reduce any chromium existing in the oxidized condition and follow this with 20 ml. of sulphuric acid and 40 ml. of nitric acid together with water enough to give a volume of 200 ml. Evaporate by boiling quietly at such a rate that in one hour the volume is reduced to 100 ml. Under these conditions 99.5% of the vanadium is oxidized. Cool to 5° C. and titrate with ferrous sulphate. To calculate, divide by .995 and by 3 and multiply by 2.943. This gives the percentage of vanadium.

The percentage of chromium may be calculated by subtracting the per cent obtained by the second oxidation from that obtained by the first and dividing the difference by 2.943.

Notes and Precautions

In oxidizing with ammonium persulphate and silver nitrate it is important to have the sulphuric acid and water in the proportions given. After adding the ammonium persulphate, and after adding the hydrochloric acid, the solution should be boiled at least ten minutes.

The concentration of nitric acid, the initial and final volumes, and the rate of evaporation are important as steps in securing a regular oxidation of vanadium by nitric acid.

Any insoluble matter in the ferro-vanadium suspected of containing vanadium should be fused with sodium peroxide. After leaching, boil the alkaline solution for twenty minutes. Then acidify with sulphuric acid and add to the main portion of the solution before making up to volume. It is rare that this treatment is necessary.

If a solution containing 2.883 g. of potassium dichromate in one liter should be used, each milliliter would correspond to one per cent of vanadium when a sample weighing .3 g. is used.

A detailed discussion of this method will soon be published by Dr. G. L. Kelley and his collaborators.

The Determination of Chromium in Ferrochromium by Electrometric Titration [1]

A paper on the determination of vanadium and chromium in steel was published by Kelley and Conant,[2] and more recently a paper by Kelley and other collaborators [3] describes the determination of vanadium and chromium in ferrovanadium. In these cases the end-point was determined electrometrically. The present paper describes a method for the determination of chromium in ferrochromium in which the end-point in the titration is taken as the point of greatest change in the oxidation-reduction potential during the titration of the chromic acid with ferrous sulphate. The description of apparatus suited to this determination has been given by Kelley, Adams and Wiley.[4]

Standard Solutions

Potassium Dichromate Solution. 5.6586 g. of the recrystallized and fused salt in enough water to make one liter.

Ferrous Ammonium Sulphate Solution. 47 g. of ferrous ammonium sulphate and 100 cc. of sulphuric acid (sp.gr. 1.58) in enough water to make one liter. This should be standardized daily by comparison with the dichromate solution which is used as the standard of reference.

Hydrochloric Acid Solution. One part of concentrated acid and three parts of water.

Silver Nitrate Solution. 2.5 g. of silver nitrate in enough water to make one liter.

Ammonium Persulphate Solution. 100 g. of ammonium persulphate and water enough to make one liter.

Method

Use a nickel crucible of about 60 cc. capacity, preferably free from manganese. Fuse 20 g. of sodium carbonate in the crucible, and during cooling rotate it in such a manner as to produce a lining on the crucible. When cool, place 16 g. of sodium peroxide in the crucible. Make a hole in the center of this and place in it 1 g. of ferrochromium, ground to pass a 100-mesh sieve. Mix the ferro-alloy with the peroxide by stirring with a stiff platinum wire, taking care that the alloy does not sink to the bottom. Fuse over a blast lamp until fusion is complete, and apply heat enough to maintain the melt in a state of quiet fusion for 3 min., rotating gently meanwhile. Avoid fusing the lining as this is detrimental to the crucible. During cooling, cause the molten mass to flow in thin layers on the surface of the crucible. When cold, wipe the outside of the crucible clean, and place it in 300 cc. of water contained in a 600-cc. beaker. Warm to complete the solution of the mass, and remove the crucible after rinsing. Boil the solution at least 30 min. Cool to room temperature, and add gradually 80 cc. of sulphuric acid (sp.gr. 1.58). Boil 5 min., cool, filter through asbestos, and make the volume up to exactly 1 liter.

[1] By G. L. Kelley and J. A. Wiley.
[2] Journal of Industrial and Engineering Chemistry, **8** (1916), 719.
[3] Ibid., **13** (1921), 939.
[4] Ibid., **9** (1917), 780.

Analyze the solution as soon as it is prepared. The oxidation value of the solution falls slowly on standing. Remove a 100-cc. portion, add 25 cc. of sulphuric acid, and titrate electrometrically with ferrous ammonium sulphate and potassium dichromate.

A modification of the method involves the following procedure: To 100 cc. of the solution add 25 cc. of sulphuric acid, 10 cc. of silver nitrate solution, and 40 cc. of ammonium persulphate solution. Boil 10 min. after the permanganic acid color appears. Then add 5 cc. of 1 : 3 hydrochloric acid, boil an additional 5 min., cool, and titrate electrometrically with ferrous sulphate.

For the highest accuracy, the potassium dichromate should be recrystallized and fused. The dichromate solution is of such strength that each cubic centimeter corresponds to 2.00 per cent of chromium in a 0.10-g. sample. To calculate, multiply by 2 the cubic centimeters of dichromate solution to which the ferrous sulphate solution used is equivalent. This gives the result directly in per cent.

Vanadium is rarely present in ferrochromium in quantities warranting its determination. When it is desirable to determine it, this may be done, after reduction of the chromate and vanadate with ferrous sulphate, by oxidizing the vanadium alone by means of nitric acid. It is then titrated electrometrically with ferrous sulphate. This procedure has already been described elsewhere [1] by one of us.

[1] Journal of Industrial and Engineering Chemistry, **11** (1919), 632.

STANDARD LABORATORY APPARATUS[1]

VOLUMETRIC APPARATUS

Very great advances have been made in the United States toward the standardization of volumetric apparatus, first by the U. S. Bureau of Standards and more recently by a committee representing manufacturing chemists. The latter, in coöperation with the manufacturers and dealers of chemical apparatus, has completed its recommendations for the standardization of several types of volumetric glassware, in regard to types, quality, design, workmanship and units of capacity. This is a commendable advance but while it will insure a supply of standard volumetric glassware, if the movement is generally supported by both makers and users, it does not preclude the necessity of recalibration or verification by the chemist himself. This is especially evident when we recall the fact that volumetric chemical analyses are often reliably calculated to 0.01%, whereas the volumetric glassware may be in error to such an extent as to make the 0.10% figure unreliable.

The following principles, procedures and tables for testing and calibrating volumetric apparatus, except for a few additions, were obtained from publications of the U. S. Bureau of Standards.

Preparation of Apparatus. Having selected standard apparatus, it should be thoroughly prepared for calibration by removing all foreign material, dirt, grease, etc., from the surface by one of the following methods:

1. By immersion for several hours in a concentrated solution of caustic soda in 95% alcohol, after which it should be washed with sulphuric acid and water and allowed to drain until dry.

2. By immersion in fuming sulphuric acid for a few minutes, washing with water, then with caustic soda solution and finally with water and allowing to drain until dry.

3. Concentrated sulphuric acid saturated with chromic acid is a very efficient cleaning solution. This may be substituted for the fuming sulphuric acid in the above procedure.

4. Another method by which small apparatus, such as flasks, burettes, pipettes, etc., may be quickly and thoroughly cleaned but with which great precaution should be exercised is as follows: To two volumes (10–20 cc.) of 95% alcohol in the apparatus add one volume (5–10 cc.) of concentrated nitric acid. This mixture develops a rather violent action in from one to five minutes, generates much heat and thoroughly cleans the surface with which it comes in contact. This mixture should be used very cautiously and sparingly and should not be confined. The action is accelerated by warming and is almost explosive at times. The change in volume of the apparatus and thermal hysteresis due to the heating by this method of cleaning can usually be neglected if a sufficient drainage and cooling period is employed.

[1] Contributed by R. M. Meiklejohn and J. S. Coye.

1685

Stopcock Grease. Soft grease. Thoroughly mix, by melting and stirring, three parts of vaseline and one part of beeswax.

Hard grease. Add one part (*i.e.*, 1:4) of soft black rubber in small bits to the above mixture, heat to 140–150° C., and stir constantly until thoroughly incorporated.

Measurement of Capacity. There are two general methods in use by which the capacity of an apparatus is determined, the choice being determined by the character of the apparatus; namely, direct measurement and calculation of capacity from the weight of water which it contains or delivers.

Direct Measurement. This method is especially applicable to the testing or calibration of flasks and consists in allowing water at a constant temperature

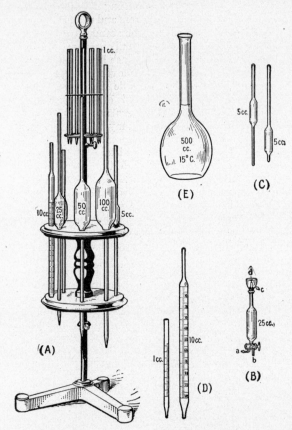

FIG. 229. Volumetric Measuring Apparatus.

to flow from a standard pipette, which is graduated at the lower end, into the flask at a rate of flow standard for the pipette until the flask is filled to its graduation mark. The volume (capacity) of the flask is then read off on the

raduation of the standard pipette, making any instrumental correction apply-
ng to the standard pipette as determined by the procedure of calculation of
apacity at 20° C. from the weight of water delivered under the standard
onditions of outflow.   It is evident that this method gives a direct measure-
nent of capacity at the standard temperature of 20° C. regardless of the
emperature of water except that the water should be maintained at a constant
emperature throughout the entire operation.   This change of temperature is
he only inherent error in the procedure, except the error of unequal expansion
f the two glasses, which is assumed to be negligible.   The chief disadvantage
n the procedure is that a separate standard pipette is necessary for each size of
lask, and consequently is only applicable when a large number of flasks are to
pe calibrated.

Calculation from Weight of Water.   The quantity sought in this case is the
actual volume of water contained or delivered by the apparatus at the standard
emperature of 20° C. and is calculated from quantities observed, obtained
rom tables, and calculated.

Quantities observed.
V = nominal capacity of apparatus (milliliters).
t = temperature of water weighed.
a = apparent weight in air of water.
b = buoyancy constant (Table 1).
Quantities obtained from Tables.
d_t = density of water at $t°$ C. (Table 2).
M = mass of water having a volume V at $t°$ C. (Table 2 $d_t \times V$).
A = apparent weight in air of water having volume V at $t°$ C. (Table 3).
Quantities calculated.
v = volume of water at $t°$ C. (milliliters).
C = capacity of instrument at standard temperature 20° C.

The capacity v at the observed temperature $t°$ C. is first calculated.   This
nay be accomplished by one of three formulæ according to the precision
lesired.

In all cases where the greatest precision is desired the following fomula is
used.

1. $$v = \frac{a}{d_t - b}.$$

d_t is obtained from a table of water densities.

b may be obtained from tables or may be observed directly as follows:
Place a hollow sealed glass bulb of known volume (about 1000 ml.) and mass on
ne pan of a balance and an equal mass of brass weights on the other pan of the
palance.   The additional weight w required on the bulb pan for a balance is
hen the buoyancy of the volume v of the bulb for the atmospheric conditions
prevailing, or $b = \dfrac{w}{v}$ = grams per milliliter.   The mass of the bulb is its true
weight in vacuum and may be calculated from its apparent weight by adding,
o its apparent weight in air, the weight of an equivalent volume of air at the
emperature and atmospheric conditions prevailing at the time the apparent
weight was obtained minus the weight of a volume of air equal to the volume
of brass weights used in obtaining the weight in air.

53

Example:

Volume displaced by the bulb = 950 ml. = .950 liter = V_b.

Apparent weight of bulb at 22° C. and 740 mm. mercury (corrected to 0° C and standard gravity) with brass weights = 218.124 gms.

Then $\dfrac{218.124}{8.4}$ = 25.95 ml. = .02595 liter = V_w or volume of brass weights.

Then $218.124 + \dfrac{(V_b - V_w) \times 1.2930}{1 + .00367 \times t} \times \dfrac{P}{760}$ = true weight of bulb.

Or $218.124 + \dfrac{(.950 - .02595) \times 1.2930}{1 + .00367 \times 22} \times \dfrac{740}{760}$ = 219.2005.

This true weight or mass of the bulb is then the value to be used in determining the buoyancy constant for the particular atmospheric condition prevailing or

$$\text{buoyancy constant} = \dfrac{219.2005 - 218.124}{950.} = .001133 \text{ gm.}$$

or 1.133 mgs. per milliliter.

This figure is obtained by assuming the air to be dry and free from carbon dioxide. The value of 1.2930 gms. as the weight of one liter of air at 0° C and 760 mm. pressure at sea level is obtained only under these conditions and consequently requires corrections for the carbon dioxide and moisture content of the air at the time the weight is taken. For ordinary work Table 1, as prepared by the U. S. Bureau of Standards, gives the buoyancy constant of sufficient accuracy.

When V is a round number, the following approximate formula simplifies the calculation.

2. $v = V + a + (V \times b) - M$.

M = the mass of water having a volume V at $t°$ C. and may be calculated from water density tables.   (Table 2 $d_t \times V$.)

b is obtained as above.

If $v - V$ is less than $1/1000\,v$, the error will not be greater than $1/200,000\,v$

When V is a round number and the buoyancy constant is not observed, the following formula may be applied.

3. $v = V + a - A$.

A may be obtained from tables.   (Table 3.)   The values obtained by this formula are equal in accuracy to those obtained by formula 2.

After calculating v by one of the above formulæ, the capacity C of the apparatus at 20° C. is calculated by the formula

$$C = v + .000025\,v\,(20 - t).$$

The value .000025 is taken as the average cubical expansion of glass.

Values for .000025 v (20 − t) have been calculated and tabulated by the U S. Bureau of Standards.

Flasks.   Flasks are most readily tested or calibrated by direct measurement from a standard pipette as previously described.   When the weighing method

employed, the procedure is as follows: The flask is suspended from the left
m of the balance, thus leaving space for weights on the balance pan. A
eight somewhat greater than the total weight of the flask when filled to the
ark with water is placed on the right balance pan. The clean, dry, empty flask
ith stopper is then balanced by placing the necessary weights on the pan
rrying the flask. The flask is next filled to the mark with water at a definite
nstant temperature $t°$ C. and again balanced by removing weights. The
eights removed give the apparent weight (a) in air of the water at temperature
C. and p barometric pressure (uncorrected). The capacity C at 20° C. of
e flask of nominal volume V is then calculated as previously described.

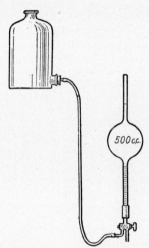

FIG. 230. Morse-Blalock Apparatus in Position for Calibrating Flasks.

Example: (500 ml. flask).

519.710
20.950

$a =$ 498.760 apparent weight in air of water at 17° C. and 735 mm.
$d_t =$ .9988 density of water at 17° C. (gms. per milliliter).
$b =$ .001037 buoyancy constant. (See Table 1.)

Then

$$v = \frac{a}{d_t - b} = \frac{498.760}{9988 - .0010} = 499.88 \text{ ml. at 17° C.}$$

nd

$$C = v + .000025\, v\, (20 - t) = 499.88 + (.000025 \times 499.88 \times 3) = 499.02$$
ml. at 20° C.

Another procedure of calculating the capacity of a flask from the weight in air of the water contained or delivered which eliminates any error in weighing due to condensation of moisture on the flask is as follows:

A flask of similar type and equal volume is used as the counterpoise on the opposite balance arm when obtaining the weight " a " of water at the temperature of the air.

Then

$$v = \frac{a}{d_t - b} = \text{capacity in ml. at } t° \text{ C.}$$

and

$$C = v + .000025 \ V \ (20 - t) = \text{ml. at } 20° \text{ C.}$$

The water used for this work should be pure and freed from dissolved air by previous boiling and should not be allowed to wet the flask above the graduation mark. When filling the flask it should be shaken occasionally to insure complete wetting and removal of any dust, etc., from the glass surface, which might cause the occlusion of minute air bubbles. When possible, these dust particles should be floated off from the top of the water before making up to the graduation mark. If the graduation mark is found to be in error, it may be corrected by making a preliminary mark and subsequently verifying by the above procedure.

Pipette. Pipettes are most conveniently tested and calibrated by filling once with water at constant temperature $t°$ C. and emptying, then filling again to the mark and emptying into a tared flask. By weighing the flask the apparent weight of water at $t°$ C. delivered is obtained. The capacity of the pipette at 20° C. is then calculated as previously described.

Example:

Standardization of Pipette B–902.

$a = 49.8283 = $ wt. of water delivered at 24.1° C. and 740 mm. pressure.
From Tables 1 and 2:
$b = .00101$ gm.
$d_t = .99732.$

Then

$$V = \frac{a}{d_t - b} = \frac{49.8283}{.99631} = 50.0128 \text{ ml. at } 24.1° \text{ C.}$$

and

$$C = v + .000025 \times V \times (20 - t) = 50.0128 - .005 = 50.008 \text{ ml. at } 20° \text{ C.}$$

The method of draining the pipette should be the same when calibrating as when being used. The most generally accepted method of draining a pipette is to allow it to run out freely until emptied, then the tip is touched against the wetted wall of the vessel into which delivery is being made. The shape and character of the tip and size of the meniscus stem should be as specified by the U. S. Bureau of Standards [1] and the committee representing the Manufacturing Chemists.[2]

[1] Committee on Apparatus Standardization of the Manufacturing Chemists' Association of the U. S.

[2] Scientific Papers No. 92 and Circular No. 19.

A pipette may also be calibrated by connecting up with a standard pipette shown in Fig. 231. The water from the standard is allowed to flow by

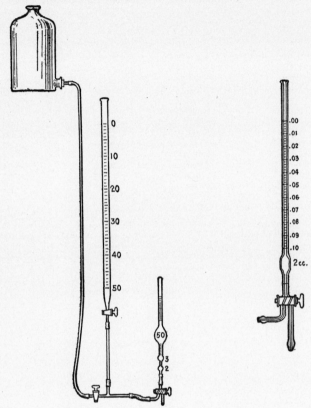

FIG. 231. Volumetric Calibrating Apparatus.

gravity into the pipette being tested, the standardization being conducted at 20° C.

Burettes. Type, design, size, etc., of burettes have been standardized by the U. S. Bureau of Standards and the committee representing the chemical manufacturers to such an extent as to make the calibration of them simple and reliable. These specifications are such as to give the proper rate of out-flow to make the residue and after-flow negligible when calibrated under conditions of out-flow indicated for each particular type of burette.

In calibrating a burette, the weight of water at constant temperature and pressure which is delivered under standard conditions of out-flow is determined for each graduation of the burette as desired, always beginning at the zero graduation each time. The volume of water for each increment is then calculated as previously described. It is very important that the burette types which have been specified by the standardization committee be selected for calibration.

Example:

Standardization of Burette 1394.

Each increment is weighed and the weight, temperature and pressure corded, d_t and b obtained from Tables 1 and 2 and the formula $v = \dfrac{a}{d_t - b}$ a $C = vt$ .000025 $\times V \times (20 - t)$ applied to each increment. The results m be tabulated as follows:

Point	a	C	Error
5 ml.	4.9562	4.98	− .02
10 "	9.9463	9.99	− .01
15 "	14.9220	14.98	− .02
20 "	19.9158	20.00	− .00
25 "	24.9019	25.00	− .00
30 "	29.8572	29.98	− .02
35 "	34.8254	34.96	− .04
40 "	39.8001	39.96	− .04
45 "	44.8419	45.02	+ .02
50 "	49.7809	49.99	− .01

TABLE 1.   BUOYANCY CONSTANTS (mg./ml.)

Difference in milligrams between the mass and the apparent weight of 1 milliliter water weighed with brass weights ($d = 8.4$) in air at various temperatures and barome readings (unreduced). A humidity of 50% saturation is assumed. To find the weig of 1 milliliter of air under the conditions assumed in this table, multiply the buoyan constant by 1.135 (42/37).

Pressure	Temperature in Degrees Centigrade			
	15	20	25	30
640..............	0.904	0.886	0.869	0.852
650..............	0.918	0.900	0.883	0.866
660..............	0.932	0.914	0.897	0.879
670..............	0.946	0.928	0.911	0.893
680..............	0.960	0.942	0.924	0.906
690..............	0.975	0.956	0.938	0.920
700..............	0.989	0.970	0.952	0.933
705..............	0.996	0.977	0.958	0.940
710..............	1.003	0.984	0.965	0.947
715..............	1.010	0.991	0.972	0.953
720..............	1.017	0.998	0.979	0.960
725..............	1.024	1.004	0.985	0.967
730..............	1.031	1.011	0.992	0.973
735..............	1.038	1.018	0.999	0.980
740..............	1.045	1.025	1.006	0.987
745..............	1.052	1.032	1.013	0.994
750..............	1.059	1.039	1.020	1.000
755..............	1.067	1.046	1.027	1.007
760..............	1.074	1.053	1.034	1.014
765..............	1.081	1.060	1.040	1.020
770..............	1.088	1.067	1.047	1.027
775..............	1.095	1.074	1.054	1.034
780..............	1.102	1.081	1.061	1.041

A burette may be standardized against a second standard burette or pipette by filling the one to be tested with water (20° C.) and after connecting to the standard allowing the water to flow into the standard. The connections should be filled with water (free from air bubbles) and the water should stand at the 0 point in the measuring apparatus. See Fig. 231. The upper mark of the measuring standard should be below the level of the lowest mark of the vessel being tested. A two-way stopcock makes it possible to empty the measuring standard, the total capacity of which may be only a fraction of that of the burette to be tested.

TABLE 2.   DENSITY (in gms. per milliliter) OF WATER AT TEMPERATURES FROM 0° TO 102° C.

Temp. °C.	Density	Temp. °C.	Density	Temp. °C.	Density
0	0.99987	35	0.99406	70	0.97781
1	0.99993	36	0.99371	71	0.97723
2	0.99997	37	0.99336	72	0.97666
3	0.99999	38	0.99299	73	0.97607
4	1.00000	39	0.99262	74	0.97548
5	0.99999	40	0.99224	75	0.97489
6	0.99997	41	0.99186	76	0.97428
7	0.99993	42	0.99147	77	0.97368
8	0.99988	43	0.99107	78	0.97307
9	0.99981	44	0.99066	79	0.97245
10	0.99973	45	0.99024	80	0.97183
11	0.99963	46	0.98982	81	0.97120
12	0.99952	47	0.98940	82	0.97057
13	0.99940	48	0.98896	83	0.96994
14	0.99927	49	0.98852	84	0.96930
15	0.99913	50	0.98807	85	0.96865
16	0.99897	51	0.98762	86	0.96800
17	0.99880	52	0.98715	87	0.96734
18	0.99862	53	0.98669	88	0.96668
19	0.99843	54	0.98621	89	0.96601
20	0.99823	55	0.98573	90	0.96534
21	0.99802	56	0.98524	91	0.96467
22	0.99780	57	0.98478	92	0.96399
23	0.99756	58	0.98425	93	0.96330
24	0.99732	59	0.98375	94	0.96261
25	0.99707	60	0.98324	95	0.96192
26	0.99681	61	0.98272	96	0.96122
27	0.99654	62	0.98220	97	0.96051
28	0.99626	63	0.98167	98	0.95981
29	0.99597	64	0.98113	99	0.95909
30	0.99567	65	0.98059	100	0.95838
31	0.99537	66	0.98005	101	0.95765
32	0.99505	67	0.97950	102	0.95693
33	0.99473	68	0.97894		
34	0.99440	69	0.97838		
35	0.99406	70	0 97781		

TABLE 3. APPARENT WEIGHT (in gms.) OF WATER IN AIR

(This table gives the apparent weight, for temperatures between 15° and 30° C. humidity 50 per cent, unreduced barometer reading 76 cm., of certain volumes of water weighed with brass weights. This table is based on the data given in Tables 1 and 2, and may be conveniently employed to determine definite volumes of water for calibrating instruments. The table assumes the air to be at the same temperature as the water.)

Temp. in Degrees C.	2000 ml.	1000 ml.	500 ml.	400 ml.	300 ml.	250 ml.	150 ml.
15...........	1996.11	998.05	499.03	399.22	299.42	249.51	149.71
16...........	1995.80	997.90	498.95	399.16	299.37	249.48	149.68
17...........	1995.48	997.74	498.87	399.10	299.32	249.43	149.66
18...........	1995.13	997.56	498.78	399.03	299.27	249.39	149.63
19...........	1994.76	997.38	498.69	398.95	299.21	249.34	149.61
20...........	1994.36	997.18	498.59	398.87	299.15	249.30	149.58
21...........	1993.95	996.97	498.49	398.79	299.09	249.24	149.55
22...........	1993.51	996.76	498.38	398.70	299.03	249.19	149.51
23...........	1993.06	996.53	498.28	398.61	298.96	249.13	149.48
24...........	1992.58	996.29	498.15	398.52	298.89	249.07	149.44
25...........	1992.09	996.04	498.02	398.42	298.81	249.01	149.41
26...........	1991.57	995.79	497.89	398.31	298.74	248.95	149.37
27...........	1991.04	995.52	497.76	398.21	298.66	248.88	149.33
28...........	1990.49	995.24	497.62	398.10	298.57	248.81	149.29
29...........	1989.92	994.96	497.48	397.98	298.49	248.74	149.24
30...........	1989.33	994.66	497.33	397.87	298.40	248.67	149.20

NOTE. The term milliliter, ml, 1/1000 liter, based on the volume occupied by a kilogram of water at its greatest density, has been adopted by the Bureau of Standards and is frequently found on calibrated apparatus. This form has been used in the section on volumetric apparatus in place of the term cc., generally used throughout this book. Owing to the expansion of water, 1000 grams would occupy a greater volume at room temperature than at 4° C. so that 1 cc. would be less than 1/1000 of this expanded volume. The difference of 1 ml and 1 cc., under convenient workable temperatures, could not be measured by the ordinary burette, so that for practical purposes the volumes represented by ml and cc. may be considered the same. This expansion has been taken into consideration in calibration of apparatus, the cc. and the liter being volumes in ratio of 1 : 1000, a relativity demanded in volumetric analysis, so that the terminology is of little importance, provided the apparatus used is thus calibrated.

EDITOR.

STANDARDIZATION OF WEIGHTS

Precision measurement of mass is the first requisite in accurate analysis. The chemist has at his command instruments for the measurement of mass which by far surpass in accuracy the major operations of his work. This is probably largely responsible for the negligence in the care of the balance and weights too frequently observed in the technical laboratory. It is often the case that the average technical laboratory uses analyses calculated to one decimal place more than warranted by the accuracy of the weights used. Assuming all other operations without error, an analysis made on a 1-gram sample and reported as 98.53% requires a weight accuracy of .0001 gram if the last figure is intended to have any significance.

Laboratories doing accurate analytical or research work should always be in possession of a set of standard weights and these weights should be used only in standardizing those in constant use. Where a large number of balances are used, it is advisable to have two sets of standard weights, a Primary and a Secondary set, each ranging from 100 grams to 1 milligram. The Primary set is used exclusively for checking the Secondary set and is checked annually by the Bureau of Standards at Washington, D. C. The Secondary set is used for standardizing the weights assigned to the various balances. Where balances are used constantly, it is advisable to have the weights checked at least monthly against the Secondary set, and the Secondary likewise checked monthly against the Primary set. While this frequent checking may appear excessive, it is quite inexpensive insurance against errors which cannot easily be detected in any other way.

It is advisable to use one-piece gold-plated weights for the Primary Standard. The type designated Class M by the Bureau of Standards is very satisfactory. Lacquered brass weights are very satisfactory for general use.

The practice frequently observed in chemical laboratories of setting out the weights on the balance plate is very bad. While it expedites weighing, the chance of contaminating and changing the accuracy of the weights more than counterbalances the advantage of speed.

Students are frequently taught that it is not necessary for weights to bear true values so long as they are comparable to one another; that is, to bear true relation to each other. This contention holds good so long as all work done by the chemist is related to his balance. This condition does not exist in the majority of technical laboratories. The chemist frequently uses standard solutions made by use of other balances and for this reason his weighings must be comparable to others in the laboratory. This condition necessitates the standardization of all weights to true values.

Although there are several methods for weighing in use in the various technical laboratories, that of the double swing or vibration is probably the best for standardization of weights.

Standardization

There are three methods for standardizing weights:

1. Standardizing the weights to true or absolute values.
2. Standardizing the weights to weigh true or absolute weights.
3. Standardizing the weights to bear true relation to each other.

The procedure followed in the first method is dependent upon the comparative arm lengths of the balance. If the arm lengths are equal, the weights are standardized by direct weighing or balancing on the opposite pans. If unequal, by substitution weighing or having both weights, when placed alternately on the left pan, balance a given mass on the right pan.

The standardization of the weights by the second method is independent of arm length. The weights are standardized by adjusting them so that when they are placed on the right pan they balance the standard weights of a similar denomination placed on the left pan.

In small laboratories where there is but one balance used for fine work, or for students' use, the third method is very satisfactory.

In the first two methods of standardization, each weight is standardized independently.

In all cases of two or more weights of one denomination, the second and third should be marked with one and two dots respectively.

It is, of course, assumed that high-grade balances are used and are thoroughly understood by the chemist, and that in weighing, objects to be weighed are placed on the left pan.

First Method. (Assuming the arm lengths unequal.) It is both convenient and time saving in this work to have an extra set of weights to use as counterpoises.

Place a standard 5 or 10 mgm. weight on the left pan and the 5 or 10 mgm. rider on the right beam. Adjust the weight of the rider until it balances the weight on the left pan when it is located at a point indicating that denomination. Remove both weights. Place the standard 100-gram weight on the left pan and balance it with the counterpoise set. Replace the standard with the 100-gram weight to be standardized and adjust the weight until it balances the counterpoise. Continue in this manner throughout the entire set.

In case the balance arms are equal, the counterpoise set may be dispensed with and the set being standardized placed on the right pan. Of course when weights of absolute value are used on a balance having unequal arm lengths, corrections must be made on all weighings.

Second Method. This method is the more practical since it is independent of arm length. However weights standardized in this way can only be used on the balance on which they have been standardized.

Place the standard 5 or 10 mgm. weight on the left pan and the 5 or 10 mgm. rider on the right beam, adjust the rider until it balances the weight on the left pan when it is on the point indicating the denomination of that weight. Remove both weights. Place the standard 100 gram weight on the left pan and the 100 gram weight to be standardized on the right pan. Adjust the weight until it balances the standard. Continue with all other weights in the same manner one at a time.

Adjustment of Weights. Since it is not practical in commercial work to use corrections on weights, they should be adjusted when standardized. In the case of brass weights, by removing the top and either adding or removing granulated aluminum or lead (20–40-mesh) as required, and in the case of platinum fractional weights, fusing on gold shavings cut from foil or wire, if light, or removing platinum with a small file if heavy. When aluminum is used for fractional weights and one is found light, it is advisable to destroy it and replace with another.

When making the adjustment of the brass weight, the weight should be gripped with pieces of heavy linen cloth or chamois skin, never with the fingers. The metal should be added or removed with a pair of tweezers and the weight allowed to stand 15 minutes before final checking. While it is standing other weights may be adjusted. In this way little time is lost.

Third Method. If the arms of the balance are equal, the weights may be compared with each other. If, however, they are unequal, the method of substitution must be used and another set of weights will be required. In the latter case the counterbalance weights are placed in the left pan and the set being standardized on the right.

The following method assumes the arm lengths equal or practically so:

Place the 5 or 10 mgm. weight on the left pan and the 5 or 10 mgm. rider on the right beam. Adjust the rider with fine emery cloth until it balances the weight when on the point indicating its denomination. Take a 10 mgm. weight from another box for use as a tare and call it T. Place T on the left pan and one of the 10 mgm. weights on the right and balance with the rider if necessary. Record the weight, *e.g.*,

$$0.01 = T + 0.0001.$$

Replace the weight on the right with the other 10 mgm. weight and again balance.

Record the weight, *e.g.*,

$$0.01_2 = T + 0.0001.$$

Replace the tare with the 20 mgm. weight and put both 10 mgm. weights on the right pan and balance. Record weights as follows:

$$0.02 = 0.01 + 0.01_2 + 0.0001$$

or

$$0.02 = 2T + 0.0003.$$

Replace the 20 mgm. weight with the 50 mgm. weight and place the 20 mgm. weight and tare on the right pan with the two ten mgm. weights. Balance and record the weights, *e.g.*,

$$0.05 = 0.02 + 0.01 + 0.01_2 + T + 0.0000$$

or

$$0.05 = 5T + 0.0005.$$

Place the 50 mgm. weight on the right pan and the 100 mgm. weight on the left pan. Balance and record the weight, e.g.,

$$0.10 = 0.05 + 0.02 + 0.01 + 0.01_2 + T - 0.0003$$

or

$$0.10 = 10T + 0.0007.$$

The remaining decigram and gram weights are tested in this manner and the results compiled as follows:

Nominal Value	Value Found on Test	Values Using $T = 0.01$	Corrected Using 1.0005 as Std.	Corrections
0.01	$T + 0.0001$	0.0101	0.0100	$+ 0.0001$
0.01$_2$	$T + 0.0001$	0.0101	0.0100	$+ 0.0001$
0.02	$2T + 0.0003$	0.0203	0.0200	$+ 0.0003$
0.05	$5T + 0.0005$	0.0505	0.0500	$+ 0.0005$
0.10	$10T + 0.0007$	0.1007	0.1001	$+ 0.0006$
0.10$_2$	$10T + 0.0006$	0.1006	0.1001	$+ 0.0005$
0.20	$20T + 0.0007$	0.2007	0.2001	$+ 0.0006$
0.50	$50T + 0.0004$	0.5004	0.5003	$+ 0.0001$
1.00	$100T + 0.0005$	1.0005	1.0005	$+ 0.0000$
2.00	$200T + 0.0006$	2.0006	2.0010	$- 0.0004$
2.00$_2$	$200T + 0.0009$	2.0009	2.0010	$- 0.0001$
etc.				

Effect of Buoyancy. In making accurate weighings the buoyant effect of air on the weight and mass being weighed must be considered. When the mass being weighed has a specific gravity differing with that of the weights, the buoyancy of the air on the two masses will affect the accuracy of the weighing. Thus the weighing of a 1 gram sample of potassium chloride with brass weights without correction for buoyancy results in an error of .00046 gram or approximately .05%.

The following formula may be used in making this correction for general work carried on under normal conditions:

$$\text{Correct weight} = W + .0012\frac{W}{S} - \frac{W}{S_1},$$

where $W =$ the apparent weight of the object, S and S_1 the specific gravities of the object and weights respectively.

.0012 is the weight of 1 cc. of air at normal laboratory conditions.

The specific gravities of metal generally used in weights are Platinum 21.5, Brass 8.4 and Aluminum 2.7.

Precision and Tolerances of Weights. The following is a table of the Precision of Corrections and Tolerances of Class S analytical weights issued by the U. S. Bureau of Standards, Washington, D. C. While it is quite evident that the Precision of Correction is beyond the accuracy of a 1/10 mgm. or even a 1/20 mgm. balance, it is however advisable to standardize the weights to the limit of sensitiveness of the balance.

Denomination	Tolerance	Precision of Correction
100 grams	0.5 mgm.	0.1 mgm.
50	0.3	0.1
20	0.2	0.1
10	0.15	0.05
5	0.15	0.05
2	0.1	0.05
1	0.1	0.05
500 mgms.	0.05	0.01
200	0.05	0.01
100	0.05	0.01
50	0.03	0.01
20	0.03	0.01
10	0.02	0.01
5	0.02	0.01
2	0.01	0.01
1	0.01	0.01

Fig. 231a.   Ainsworth's analytical balance, with improved multiple rider carrier.

Atomic Numbers of the Elements and the Nuclear Theory of the Atom [1]

The nuclear theory assumes the atom to consist of a positively charged nucleus surrounded by a system of electrons which are kept together by attractive forces from the nucleus. This theory was proposed by Rutherford and has been elaborated by Bohr, Moseley and Darwin. Bohr made the following assumptions after considerable investigation: (1) The electrons revolve in circular orbits about the positive nucleus, with an angular momentum which is the same for all the electrons in the atom. (2) The frequency and linear dimensions of the rings are completely determined when the nuclear charge and the number of electrons in the different rings are given. (3) The nuclear charge of the atom of any element corresponds to the position of the element in the series of increasing atomic weights. Thus oxygen being 8th in the series should have a nuclear charge of eight unit charges and eight electrons.

The order of the elements in the periodic table corresponds to the number of unit positive charges of the nucleus. According to Bohr the physical and chemical properties of the atom depend upon the magnitude of this nuclear number. It follows that since any given number of electrons may assume different configurations two or more elements can exist having the same nuclear charge but possessing different atomic weights. Such elements are designated by Soddy as isotopes.

This gives the atomic weight a secondary significance and shows that the nuclear charge (atomic number) is the important property of an element. It was thought that if the elements were arranged in order of increasing nuclear charge a much closer approximation to a perfect periodic arrangement could be obtained.

That a definite relation must exist between the charge on the nucleus and the frequency of the characteristic X-rays emitted by the element has been shown by Bohr.

Following this assumption H. G. J. Moseley carried out a series of experiments with the object of accurately measuring the characteristic X-rays emitted by the different elements when they were made anti-cathodes in an X-ray tube. In this way he determined the atomic numbers of a great many elements.

The experiments of Moseley are reported in the Philosophical Magazine, Vol. 27, 1914. In this paper the results are summarized as follows:

(1) Every element from aluminium to gold is characterized by an integer N which determines its X-ray spectrum. Every detail in the spectrum of an element can therefore be predicted from the spectra of its neighborhood.

(2) This integer N, the atomic number of the element, is identified with the number of positive units of electricity contained in the atomic nucleus.

(3) The atomic numbers for all elements from aluminium to gold have been tabulated on the assumption that N for aluminium is 13.

(4) The order of the atomic numbers is the same as that of the atomic weights, except where the latter disagrees with the order of the chemical properties.

(5) Known elements correspond with all the numbers between 13 and 79 except 3. There are here three possible elements still undiscovered.

(6) The frequency of any line in the X-ray spectrum is approximately proportional to $A(N - b)^2$, where A and b are constants.

[1] By William C. Wells, Jr. See table on front cover. Lefax, July, 1918.

METALLOGRAPHY

Metallography is that branch of the science of metallurgy which treats of the constitution and internal structures of metals and their relations to the physical properties. The success of its application to the examination of metals or alloys is dependent to a great extent not only upon a knowledge of their chemical composition, method of manufacture, and mechanical or thermal treatment, but also on the fundamental laws which relate to their fusion and solidification and the internal changes which occur while whole or partly solid.

THE MICROSCOPE

The application of the compound microscope to the study of opaque objects examined by reflected light introduces conditions somewhat different from those where thin transparent sections are used. The fundamental laws pertaining to the manipulation and use of the microscope are, however, applicable in either case.

There are two methods of illumination: (1) *normal* or *vertical* illumination in which the light is directed on to the specimen at right angles to its surface; (2) *oblique* illumination in which the light is directed obliquely to the specimen from a source outside the lenses of the instrument. Fig. 232 is a sketch showing the two methods.

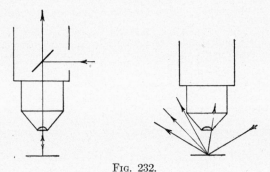

Fig. 232.

Oblique illumination is the simplest because no special attachments to the microscope are necessary, but it is valuable only when low magnifications are used and where it is a question of examining small differences in level on the polished and etched surface. Vertical illumination is the method more commonly used. In this system the light enters the instrument through an aperture in the side of the tube and strikes a disc of glass set at an angle of

Chapter by Joseph Winlock, Research Metallurgist, Edward G. Budd Manufacturing Co.

45 degrees which reflects the light downward to the specimen. The light reflected by the surface of the specimen then passes upward through the disc and forms the image. If desired, a totally reflecting prism may be used instead of the plain glass disc.[1]

The choice of lenses depends upon the character of the metal and upon the magnification desired, but for ordinary work the following types [2] are suggested as being suitable:

(*a*) For magnifications from 0 to 10: a photographic lens of approximately 72 mm. focal length to be used without ocular.

(*b*) For magnifications from 10 to 30: a photographic lens of approximately 35 mm. focal length to be used without ocular.

(*c*) For magnifications from 30 to 75: an achromatic [3] objective of approximately 32 mm. focal length with Huyghens ocular (approximately ×5).

(*d*) For magnifications from 75 to 150: an achromatic objective of approximately 16 mm. focal length with Huyghens ocular (approximately ×5).

(*e*) For magnifications from 150 to 1000: an apochromatic [4] objective of approximately 4 mm. focal length with an ocular compensated for apochromatic objectives.

The magnifications in microphotography should be accurately determined by measuring the image of a stage micrometer scale and not by calculations from lens combinations and projection distances.

In order to overcome slight degrees of chromatic aberration even in apochromatic objectives, the use of monochromatic light is preferable and for this purpose the light before reaching the specimen should be allowed to pass through a colored glass screen. Filters having a dominant wave-length of 5500 Å. U. (i.e., yellowish green) are very satisfactory for general use. In very high magnification a violet or blue filter is recommended.

[1] A slight degree of oblique illumination may be obtained by rotating the reflector of the vertical illuminator.

[2] It should be borne in mind that increasing the magnification by increasing the bellows length of the camera adds nothing to the detail of micrograph. This depends for the most part upon the resolving power of the objective used. See also Patterson, W. L., Trans. A. S. S. T., Vol. 11, No. 2, Sept., 1921.

[3] Achromatic lenses are those corrected for two colors.

[4] Apochromatic lenses are those corrected for three colors.

PHOTOGRAPHIC MATERIALS

A medium speed, moderately fine-grained orthochromatic photographic plate such as Eastman's D.C. double-coated ortho should be used. In order to bring out the details of the structure, a printing paper with a glossy surface should be used, e.g., Eastman's Regular Glossy Velox. The maximum degree of gloss may be obtained by drying the prints on " ferrotype " plates which have been previously wiped with a solution of paraffin in benzol and then polished with a clean dry cloth.

Complete directions regarding the process of developing and printing are furnished with each box of plates and paper and for the best results should be rigorously adhered to.

Full information regarding magnification, type and kind of ocular and objective used should accompany each microphotograph.

PREPARATION OF SPECIMENS FOR MICROSCOPICAL EXAMINATION

The sample chosen for microscopical examination should be as characteristic of the specimen it represents as is a sample for chemical analysis,—the size and location depending upon the nature of the article to be examined. Samples of rolled objects, for example, are usually taken so that the surface examined is longitudinal to the direction of work. For convenience in handling, a sample from $\frac{1}{2}$ to $\frac{3}{4}$ inch square and $\frac{1}{4}$ of an inch thick is best.

Soft metals may be cut with a hand or power hacksaw and hard material by means of a thin emery disc or broken with a hammer. Great care should be taken at all times to prevent the metal from becoming unduly heated during the cutting operation on account of the change in structure which might result. If the sample is small, such as wire or thin sheets, some sort of mounting device such as a clamp or small container filled with a low melting alloy [1] in which the sample may be imbedded is desirable. If the edge of the sample is to be examined, it is sometimes convenient—particularly with iron and steel— to plate the sample with a thin coating of copper to prevent the edges from becoming rounded off during the grinding and polishing operations.

The coarse scratches caused by the saw or emery disc are removed by grinding on a fine grade emery wheel such as alundum grade 80 P revolving at a speed of approximately 1000 r.p.m. From the emery wheel [2] the sample is taken to a canvas-covered disc revolving at a speed of about 400 r.p.m. armed with flour emery suspended in water.

[1] A very satisfactory alloy melting at about 50° C. can be made up as follows: Lead 30 grams, bismuth 50 grams, tin 25 grams, and zinc 3 grams.

[2] Between each grinding or polishing operation the sample should be thoroughly washed in water. Subsequent polishing scratches should always be at 90° to those immediately preceding.

Mechanical polishing is generally much more convenient and satisfactor than hand polishing. For mechanical polishing a disc of any convenient siz covered with a fine-grade broadcloth and revolving at about 400 r.p.m. ha been found to be suitable. Jeweler's rouge or levigated alumina are th principal powders used. The 6-hour alumina is a rapid polishing powder an is used on steel and hard materials. Two ounces of the powder are taken fo 100 ounces of distilled water. The 12-hour alumina is more comparable t jeweler's rouge and is generally preferred. It is particularly useful for th non-ferrous alloys such as brass, bronze, German silver, etc. One ounce o the powder is taken for 100 ounces of distilled water. The 24-hour alumin is very fine and is therefore used only in special cases such as preparing section for examination under high magnifications or for polishing very soft alloys Six-tenths of an ounce of the powder are taken for 100 ounces of distilled water Certain alloys such as those rich in lead become tarnished if water is used fo polishing in which case the water should be replaced by alcohol or a thin oil

With hand grinding and polishing, the sample is rubbed on each of th following emery papers in the order given:

1. Rough commercial   No. 0.
2. Smooth commercial   No. 00.
3. French-Hubert   No. 0.
4. French-Hubert   No. 00.
5. French-Hubert   No. 000.

Final polishing may be conducted on a block of wood covered with broad cloth armed with jeweler's rouge or levigated alumina.

After grinding and polishing, the samples should be carefully washed in alcohol and dried in an air blast or with a soft cloth. They should be kept in a desiccator until ready for miscroscopical examination.

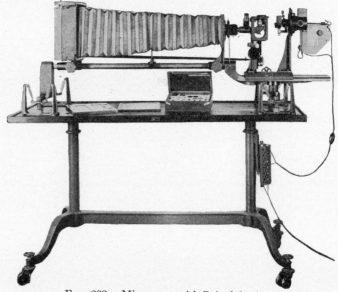

Fig. 233.   Microscope with Paired Oculars.

ETCHING SAMPLE FOR EXAMINATION

There are occasions when the sample is examined without etching, e.g., if the metal is thought to contain an excessive amount of dirt, slag, or other non-metallic inclusions. The graphite in gray cast iron or malleable castings or manganese sulphide in steel, etc., may also be seen before the sample has been etched.

In the majority of cases, however, some suitable etching medium is employed to reveal the internal structure by differentially attacking the constituents or crystalline grains of the metal. A few of the more important etching reagents are given in the following list.

Nitric Acid and Alcohol. A 3% alcoholic solution of nitric acid is used for etching plain carbon, alloy steels and cast iron. The sample is dipped in the solution from two to ten seconds, washed in alcohol and dried in air blast or with soft cloth.

Picric Acid and Alcohol. A 5% alcoholic solution of picric acid is also used for steels and has been found especially valuable in revealing the structure of pearlite and sorbite.

Concentrated Nitric Acid (sp.gr. 1.42) (after Sauveur). Used for etching iron and steel. Sample is dipped in acid where it assumes the passive state. Then held in stream of running water causing it to be momentarily vigorously attacked. It is then washed in alcohol and dried.

Sodium Picrate. Solution made by adding 2 parts of picric acid to 98 parts of a solution containing 25% of caustic soda. Sample is immersed from 4 to 6 minutes in solution heated to boiling, then washed in alcohol and dried. Colors cementite black, leaving ferrite unaffected.

Yatsevitch's Reagent. Ten cubic centimeters of hydrogen peroxide added to 20 cubic centimeters of a 10% solution of sodium hydrate in water. Sample is immersed from 10 to 20 minutes in solution, washed in alcohol and dried. Reagent should be prepared fresh every day. Used for high-speed steels, coloring the special carbides brown or black.

Le Chatelier No. 1. 200 cc. methyl alcohol, 20 cc. distilled water, 4 cc. hydrochloric acid (sp.gr. 1.18), 2 grams cupric chloride, 8 grams magnesium chloride and 1 gram of picric acid. This solution is used to reveal the macro-structure (structure visible to naked eye) and local segregations, particularly phosphorous. Sample is immersed in reagent until a thin film of copper has been deposited on entire surface. Copper then washed from specimen with a piece of absorbent cotton dipped in ammonia. Sample then washed in water, alcohol and dried. Operation is repeated until structure is plainly visible.

Ferric Chloride (Moore and Gilligan). 40 grams of ferric chloride, 3 grams cupric chloride, 40 cc. hydrochloric acid, and 500 cc. of distilled water. The *modus operandi* is the same as with Le Chatelier No. 1.

Ammonia. Used for etching copper alloys, gun metal, bell metal, cast bronze, etc. To 5 cc. of ammonia are added a few drops of hydrogen peroxide and applied to sample with a small wad of absorbent cotton.

EQUILIBRIUM DIAGRAMS

The equilibrium diagrams are based on thermal and microscopical data and show the changes observed in many alloys of the same series [1] when passing from the liquid to the solid state (or vice versa) and, if any, those taking place after the metal has completely solidified.

There are three main types of equilibrium diagrams relating to the solidification of metals and alloys, viz., those binary alloys (1) whose component metals are completely soluble in each other when solid; (2) whose component metals are partly soluble in each other when solid; and (3) whose component metals form a definite compound.

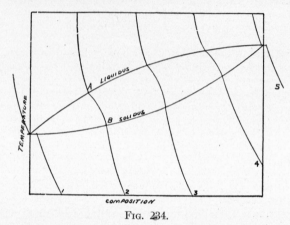

Fig. 234.

Figure 234 [2] shows the equilibrium diagram obtained by plotting several cooling curves of alloys whose component metals are completely soluble in the solid state. It will be noticed that the pure metals at each end of the series solidify at definite temperatures,[3] and not over a temperature range as in the case of an alloy (the portion of curve 2 from A to B).

[1] With the few exceptions where a pure metal is used, the metals or alloys used in commercial practice are composed chiefly of two elements. The other elements often added to impart special properties and those whose presence is due to the prohibitive cost of removal may be considered separately.

[2] After Sauveur.

[3] "Surfusion" or undercooling may take place if the cooling is slow and undisturbed. Surfusion or superfusion is the unstable condition of a body which, under certain conditions, e.g., slow and undisturbed cooling, may remain liquid after the temperature has fallen below the freezing point.

The appearance under the microscope of alloys of this series is similar to that of a pure metal as in Fig. 235 which shows the structure of almost pure iron magnified 100 diameters. The microphotograph shows a polygonal network, indicating that the metal itself is composed of irregular polyhedral crystalline grains, each polygon representing a section through a polyhedron. The dissimilarity in shade of the grains is due to the varying orientation of the different grains.

FIG. 235.—Microphotograph of Almost Pure Iron Magnified 100 Diameters, Etched in a 4% Alcoholic Solution of Nitric Acid.

The alloys of which this diagram is typical are those of gold and platinum, copper and nickel, gold and silver, etc.

The equilibrium diagram of alloys whose component metals are partly soluble in the solid state is shown in Fig. 236.

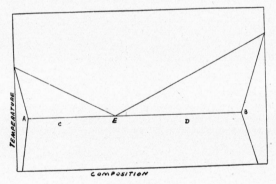

FIG. 236.

The portions at each end of the diagram appear similar to that shown in Fig. 234 of alloys whose component metals are completely soluble in the solid state whereas the middle portions show the diagram typical of those alloys whose component metals form a eutectic. A photomicrograph taken at C would appear as in Fig. 237.[1] Here the metal in excess of the eutectic ratio has solidified first, forming the major portion of the alloy with the matrix composed

[1] After Sauveur.

of the eutectic [1] of the two metals which solidifies along the line AB. At E the structure would be composed entirely of eutectic as shown in Fig. 238.

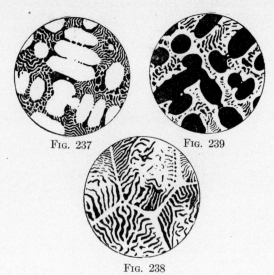

FIG. 237　　　　　　　　FIG. 239

FIG. 238

At D the reverse of the conditions appearing at C would have taken place and the structure would appear as in Fig. 239.

The alloys of which this diagram is typical are those of silver and copper, lead and antimony, etc.

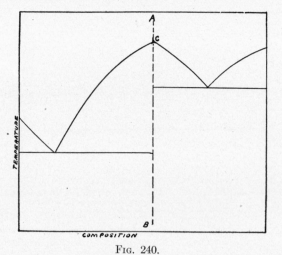

FIG. 240.

[1] EUTECTIC (from the Greek εὔτηκτος, easily melting), the alloy of a certain series possessing the lowest temperature of solidification. Their structures are made up of alternate plates or "lamellae" of the different constituents.

The equilibrium diagram of alloys whose component metals form a definite compound is shown in Fig. 240—the definite compound being formed at C. If this diagram is divided into two parts at the line AB, it is noticed that each of the parts resembles Fig. 236. The diagram, then, resolves itself into two systems, viz., alloys of one pure metal and the eutectic of that metal and the definite compound of the two metals, and alloys of the other pure metal and the eutectic of that metal and the definite compound.

The alloys of magnesium and tin form the definite compound of Mg_2Sn.

In addition to the phenomena observed in the transition from the liquid to the solid state, further changes occur in many alloys and upon which to a great extent their usefulness depends. These changes, usually accompanied by allotropic[1] modifications and consequently accompanied by changes in physical properties, are also marked by evolutions of heat on cooling (absorptions of heat on heating) and are attended by variations in structure often readily discernible by means of a metallographic examination. It is due to a knowledge of the laws governing these modifications that it is possible to regulate and control the physical properties of an alloy by means of heat treatment.

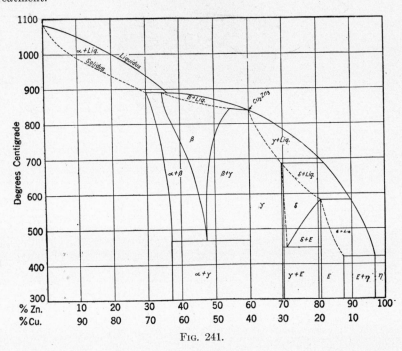

FIG. 241.

[1] ALLOTROPY. A change in the properties of an element without change of state. Probably due to a change in the number or in the arrangement of the atoms in the molecule. Best defined by the example of the three allotropic forms of carbon, viz., diamond, graphite, coke (amorphous).

COPPER=ZINC ALLOYS

The application of the principles of metallography in connection with only one of the commercial non-ferrous alloys will be discussed and in a general way due to the somewhat greater importance of iron and steel in the industrial world and because the metallography of iron and steel embodies in a greater degree all the principles found in the metallography of the non-ferrous alloys.

Figure 241 [1] shows the equilibrium diagram of the brasses, an examination of which will show that the shape of the liquidus and solidus curves is of the type indicating the formation of a solid solution, except that in this case there are several solid solutions occurring instead of one. Below the solidus the existence of several different constituents can be noted which are formed after the metal has solidified and known as alpha, beta and gamma, etc. There are, however, practically no commercial alloys containing more than 60% zinc and so it is only necessary that attention be given to the alloys containing less than that amount.

Fig. 242.—Microphotograph of Brass Cold Rolled and Annealed. Magnified 100 diameters. Etched with ammonia and hydrogen peroxide.

Here there are three solid solutions, alpha, beta and gamma. The color of the alpha brasses varies from a pale yellow to a yellowish red, the color becoming redder as the copper content increases. These brasses have moderate tensile strength, high ductility and are suitable for cold rolling. Figure 242 is a microphotograph of a section of alpha brass which has been cold rolled and annealed. Alloys containing the beta solution are somewhat harder and when cold are much less malleable and ductile. Beta brass has a greenish-red color and is darkened more quickly by the etching reagents than the alpha variety. Brasses containing the gamma solution being very brittle are without mechanical value and are only employed for castings of a purely ornamental character.

By regulating the amounts of copper and zinc and the temperature to which the alloy is heated and the rate of cooling from that temperature, the most advantageous properties of each of the constituents can be imparted to the metal. Mechanical working also improves the physical properties. Other metals are often added to copper-zinc alloys to make the alloy more suitable for the purpose for which it is to be used, e.g., iron, manganese, and aluminum are added in small quantities and increase the tenacity of the alloys considerably.

[1] After Hofman.

IRON=CARBON ALLOYS

The equilibrium diagram of the iron-carbon alloys is shown in Fig. 243.[1] By comparing the shape of the curves of the liquidus and solidus with those in Figs. 234 and 236, it may be seen that in the region embracing the steels, the alloys solidify as solid solutions; and in the region containing from about 2% to 5% carbon and in which fall the cast irons, a eutectic is formed.[2] Imme-

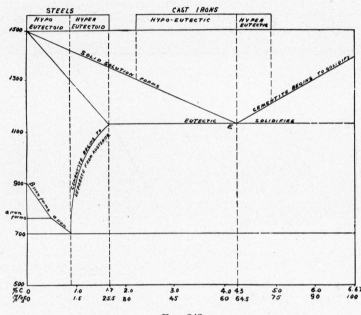

FIG. 243.

diately after solidification has taken place the steels consist of a solid solution of carbon in gamma iron.[3] Gamma iron, then, will dissolve carbon until a total content of approximately 1.7% is reached at which point the solid solution becomes saturated and further increase in the amount of carbon results in the precipitation of the carbon in the form of the carbide of iron (Fe_3C) (called cementite) which forms a eutectic with the saturated austenite. At the point E the alloys solidify as 100% eutectic. With more than 4.3% carbon the constituent in excess of that necessary to form the eutectic is the carbide of iron.

[1] After Sauveur.
[2] The division between the steel series and the cast iron series is a purely arbitrary one, but the fact that there are very few commercial products containing between 1.7% and 2.5% carbon makes it a particularly convenient one.
[3] Many authorities define austenite as a solid solution of Fe_3C in gamma iron. Recent research, however, on crystal structure founded on X-ray examinations shows that independent molecules of Fe_3C do not exist in austenite. Z. Jeffries and R. S. Archer, Chem. and Met. Eng., 24 (1921), 1057; 26 (1922), 249.

In Fig. 244 is shown on a larger scale than Fig. 243 the transformation which take place after the metal has solidified. The shaded portions indicate the intensity of the critical points. It may be seen that pure iron has two critical points on cooling to atmospheric temperature, one occurring at about 900° C. and another at about 760° C. This indicates that iron exists in three allotropic forms—alpha, beta,[1] and gamma. The point marking the division between gamma and beta iron is known as the Ar_3 point [2] and the point marking the division between the beta and alpha iron is known as the Ar_2 point. As soon as any carbon is present, another point appears at about 690° C. (1274° F.) known as the Ar_1 point. When the carbon content reaches 0.4%, the two upper

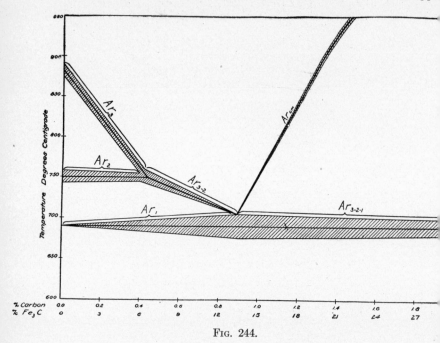

FIG. 244.

points merge forming a single point, $Ar_{3.2}$, which in turn merges at 0.85% carbon content with the Ar_1 point forming the $Ar_{3.2.1}$ point. From 0.85% carbon to about 2.0% carbon there are two points—the new point being known as the Ar_{cm} point.

It may be seen that the shape of these curves closely resembles that shown in the diagram illustrating the general type of curve representing the formation

[1] There is much controversy as to the presence of more than two allotropic forms. Some authorities contend that beta iron does not exist. Recently another allotropic modification has been noted as occurring at 1400° C. (2552° F.), denoting the presence of delta iron.

[2] The "r" in "Ar_3" etc. is the first letter of the French word "refroidissement." The points obtained on heating are "Ac_3" etc., the "c" being the first letter of the French word "chauffage." Due to hysteresis the transformation points occur at somewhat lower temperatures on cooling than on heating.

a eutectic. On account of its analogy to this diagram as evidenced by the mechanism of the formation of the different constituents, and the thermal phenomena noted, the laminated structure formed on cooling 0.85% carbon steel has been named eutectoid.

FIG. 245.—Microphotograph of 0.40% Carbon Steel (Cast). Magnified 100 diameters. Etched in a 4% alcoholic solution of nitric acid.

The four microphotographs shown in Figs. 245, 246, 247, and 248 illustrate the structure of cast steel slowly cooled containing varying amounts of carbon.

The black constituent in the above microphotograph is the eutectoid of iron and the carbide of iron called " pearlite " because of its resemblance in color with the naked eye to mother-of-pearl; the white constituent is made

FIG. 246.—Microphotograph of 0.85% Carbon Steel (Cast). Magnified 100 diameters. Etched in a 4% alcoholic solution of nitric acid.

up of the crystals of iron (in excess of the eutectoid ratio) and is called " ferrite." Pearlite is relatively strong and hard, whereas ferrite is weak and soft.

Figure 246 shows the structure of slowly cooled steel which is made up of the single constituent pearlite, and Fig. 247 shows the same steel under a higher

magnification which brings out the characteristic laminations. In this microphotograph the white constituent is the cementite and the dark constituen
is the ferrite. (The ferrite is dark here because of its greater solubility in
the etching reagent than the cementite and is consequently thrown in shadow.
Cementite is hard and strong, but very brittle.

FIG. 247.—Microphotograph of 0.85% Carbon Steel. Magnified 500 diameters.
Etched with a 4% alcoholic solution of nitric acid.

The excess constituent is cementite—the needle-like forms in the grains o
pearlite and the white substance at the grain boundaries.

FIG. 248.—Microphotograph of 1.25% Carbon Steel (Cast). Magnified 100 diameters
Etched in a 4% alcoholic solution of nitric acid.

The carbide of iron is an unstable compound and in the case of the cast
irons at high temperatures is readily decomposed into graphite and iron
The result of this decomposition is that when the iron has cooled to atmospheri
temperature, part of the carbon is present as Fe_3C, and part as free graphite
Certain impurities as well as the rate of cooling influence the breaking up o
the carbide, e.g., silicon and slow cooling promote the formation of graphite
and manganese and fast cooling tend to keep the carbon in the combined

ondition. Fig. 249 shows the structure of cast iron and explains why this metal is weak, lacks ductility and cannot be forged or hammered. The black plates of graphite break up the continuity of the mass rendering it soft and weak.

 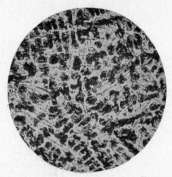

Fig. 249. — Magnified 100 diameters. Etched with a 4% alcoholic solution of nitric acid.

Fig. 250. — Magnified 100 diameters. Etched with a 4% alcoholic solution of nitric acid

If the percentage of silicon is low and the percentage of manganese is high, the carbon, in spite of a fast rate of cooling, will remain in the combined condition and the resultant product is " white " cast iron (so called from the appearance of its fracture as contrasted with that of " gray " cast iron). This metal although too brittle for commercial purposes is used for the production of the so-called malleable castings. Castings of this material are heated in large containers together with an oxidizing packing material to a

 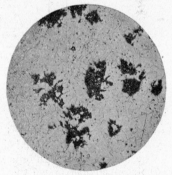

Fig. 251. — Magnified 100 diameters. Etched with a 4% alcoholic solution of nitric acid.

Fig. 252. — Magnified 100 diameters. Etched with a 4% alcoholic solution of nitric acid.

high temperature for forty-eight hours or more, causing the carbide of iron to decompose into iron and graphite and a small amount of carbon to be removed from the surface. The graphite particles resulting from this decomposition due to their size and shape are less detrimental to the physical properties than the plates present in gray cast iron. This may readily be seen in Figs. 2⁵ and 252. The dark constituent in Fig. 250 is pearlite and the white is the carbic of iron. In Fig. 252 the black constituent is the graphite resulting from tl breaking up of the Fe_3C and the white the ferrite.

Fig. 251 shows the process only partly completed. The black areas a graphite, the lighter areas pearlite, and the white areas ferrite.

INFLUENCE OF MECHANICAL WORK

The purpose of hot work [1] such as forging, hammering, etc., is to shap tne metal into useful articles and to decrease the size of the grains whic greatly improves the physical properties, increasing the tensile strength an elastic limit. The diagram shown in Fig. 253 [2] depicts the influence of hc work on the structure of steel. While this is not strictly true for alloys othe than steel, the same principles are involved.

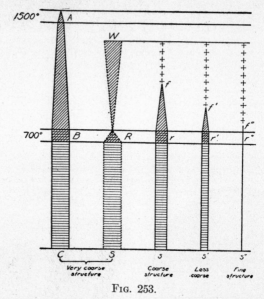

FIG. 253.

As the steel solidifies at A (or is reheated to W after the steel has cooled the crystalline grains of the solid solution increase in size as the temperature falls to the critical range. In order to reduce this growth to a minimum, work should be stopped just above the critical range. If the work is stopped at f or f', a larger grain growth will result than if the work is stopped at f''. Work performed below the critical range when the metal is composed of an aggregate distorts the grains into elongated masses producing harmful internal strains.

In Figs. 254, 255, 256 are shown the structure resulting from hot working steels of different carbon content.

[1] The term "Hot Work" as used here denotes work performed above the critica range and "Cold Work" that performed below the critical range.
[2] After Sauveur.

Cold work is performed in wire drawing, rolling sheet steel, etc. It increases the elastic limit, tensile strength and hardness, and decreases the ductility as represented by the elongation and reduction of area.

FIG. 254.—Microphotograph Showing Structure of Hot Worked .030% Carbon Steel. Magnified 100 diameters. Etched with a 4% alcoholic solution of nitric acid. Pearlite dark; ferrite white.

FIG. 255.—Microphotograph Showing Structure of Hot Worked Eutectoid Steel. Magnified 100 diameters Etched with a 4% alcoholic solution of nitric acid.

The permanent deformation of metals results in the occurrence of certain characteristic changes in structure some of which are discernible under the microscope. The most important of these are: (1) Slip bands;[1] (2) Neumann lines; and so-called critical or exaggerated grain growth.[2]

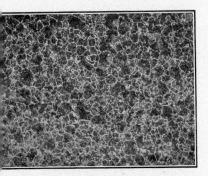 

FIG. 256.—Microphotograph Showing the Structure of Hot Worked 1.25% Carbon Steel. Magnified 100 diameters. Etched with a 4% alcoholic solution of nitric acid. Pearlite dark; cementite white.

FIG. 257.—Microphotograph Showing the Structure Produced by Cold Work in a Steel Containing about 0.20% Carbon Magnified 100 Diameters. Etched with a 4% alcoholic solution of nitric acid. Pearlite dark; ferrite light.

Slip Bands. Deformation under a slowly applied load is accomplished by a process of slip, i.e., the crystalline fragments of the grains slide on each other in much the same manner as a pile of books evenly stacked will slide on

[1] Z. Jeffries and R. S. Archer, Chem. and Met. Eng., Vol. 27, No. 18, p. 882.
[2] Sauveur, Met. of Iron and Steel, p. 265.

one another if a force is exerted which disturbs them. The slip bands appear on polished and etched surfaces after the metal has been deformed as small hair lines (actually differences in level) for the most part running in one direction in the same grain, but in different directions in different grains. In some metals such as brass (see Fig. 242) annealing after cold work results in the

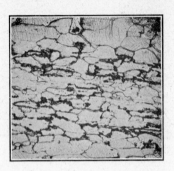

FIG. 258.—Microphotograph Showing Small Strip of Steel Slightly Bent after Polishing and Etching. Slip bands appear as black lines in those grains where the strain was greatest. Magnified 100 diameters. Etched with a 4% alcoholic solution of nitric acid.

formation of twins produced by part of the crystal having rotated through an angle of ₁₈0°.

Neumann Lines. The appearance of these under the microscope is much the same as slip bands. They are, however, still present after repolishing

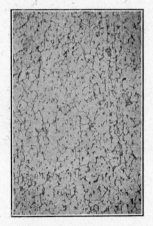

FIG. 259.—Magnified 100 diameters. Etched with a 4% alcoholic solution of nitric acid.

FIG. 260.—Magnified 100 diameters. Etched with a 4% alcoholic solution of nitric acid.

and etching whereas slip bands disappear. Their exact nature is not known but they are probably caused by a suddenly produced deformation, which may or may not have been accompanied by fracture.

Critical or Exaggerated Grain Growth. This condition occurs in low carbon steel (.08% to 0.12%) strained by cold work corresponding to a 5 to 15% reduction and subsequently annealed at a temperature varying from 325° C. to 775° C. Steels composed of very large grains resulting from this treatment are said to give poor results under both shock and fatigue stresses. Fig. 259 shows a low carbon steel in the normal condition and Fig. 260 after critical grain growth has taken place.

HEAT TREATMENT OF STEEL

Heat treatment as defined by Tiemann is " the change, or series of changes, in temperature, also the rate of cooling from one temperature to another brought about to secure certain desired conditions or properties in a metal or alloy." Heat treatment, in general, may be conveniently divided into three classes: (1) softening treatment; (2) hardening treatment; and (3) strengthening treatment.

There are three structural transformation changes that take place in steel as the metal cools through the critical range, each of which has definite physical properties and characteristic appearance under the microscope. Either one of these constituents or any combination of them may be retained in the metal when cold by cooling the steel through the critical range at different speeds, or by hardening followed by tempering. The names of the transformation constituents are martensite, troostite, and sorbite.

FIG. 261.—Microphotograph of 1.25 % Carbon Steel Quenched in Water from Above the Critical Range. Magnified 100 diameters. Etched with a 4 % alcoholic solution of nitric acid. Martensite light; troostite dark.

FIG. 262.—Microphotograph of 0.75 % Carbon Steel Quenched in Oil from Above Its Critical Range and Reheated to 525° C. Magnified 100 diameters. Etched in a 4 % alcoholic solution of nitric acid.

In order to produce maximum softness a very slow rate of cooling through the range is used which produces pearlite. To produce maximum hardness, the steel should be in the martensitic condition. This is obtained by cooling through the range at a fast rate, i.e., by quenching in water or oil. Such cooling should, theoretically, prevent any transformation from taking place, but in plain carbon steels partial transformation always occurs. If austenite is desired, certain other metals must be added which act as retarding agents on the transformation.

Steel containing 12% manganese or 25% nickel, for example, will remain austenitic even after slow cooling. Austenite is mineralogically softer than martensite, but is more resistant to abrasion. Under the microscope it has the general characteristics of a solid solution. Troostite is often present along with martensite in hardened steel and possesses similar physical properties, but in a lesser degree. Fig. 261 shows the appearance of martensite and troostite.

Maximum strength combined with maximum ductility is obtained by producing the constituent sorbite. This can be done by cooling through the range at the proper speed, but more exactly by hardening followed by heating to a temperature between 400 and 600° C. according to the composition of the steel and the properties desired. Troostite may also be formed in such a manner if a lower reheating or " drawing " temperature is used. The appearance of sorbite when examined under the microscope is shown in Fig. 262.

CASE HARDENING

Case hardening, as the name implies, is the production of a hard case or shell on the surface of a soft steel in order to make it more resistant to wear without materially reducing its toughness and resistance to shock. Case hardening is made possible by the ability of iron when in the gamma condition to absorb carbon. The article to be so treated is packed in a suitable carbonaceous material and heated to a high temperature (about 950° C.) for a time depending upon the depth of case desired.

Fig. 263.—Microphotograph Showing the Edge of a Case-hardened Sample of Steel. Magnified 100 diameters. Etched with a 4% alcoholic solution of nitric acid.

The core and case may then be heat treated to further improve the physical properties. Case-hardened objects appear under the microscope as in Fig. 263.

INFLUENCE OF SOME ELEMENTS ON IRON AND STEEL

Manganese has a greater affinity for sulphur than iron and, therefore, if sulphur is present, manganese sulphide is formed. Under the microscope this appears in castings as small round areas, pale gray in color, and in forgings as elongated streaks of the same color. If there is any manganese remaining after the sulphide has formed, the carbide of manganese (Mn_3C) is produced, which forms a solid solution with the iron.

Sulphur, when present in small amounts (e.g., less than 0.08%), combines with the manganese as explained, but if in excess of this amount, the sulphide of iron (FeS) is produced which forms around the grains. Steel containing iron sulphide is weak and brittle at high temperatures. FeS appears as a reddish brown under the microscope.

Phosphorus is present in solid solution as the phosphide of iron (Fe_3P). In cast irons, due to the large amount of carbon present, a eutectic of iron and the phosphide of iron is formed. Iron phosphide makes the steel brittle, especially when cold.

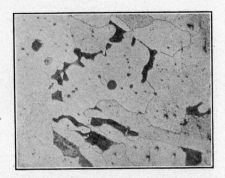

Fig. 264.—Microphotograph Showing Appearance of Manganese Sulphide (Small Round Areas Pale Gray in Color) in Low Carbon Cast Steel. Magnified 100 diameters. Etched with a 4% alcoholic solution of nitric acid.

Silicon is present as FeSi, which enters into solid solution with the iron. When in small amounts, silicon produces no marked influence on the physical properties.

Other elements such as nickel, chromium, vanadium, tungsten, and molybdenum are added to steel usually in amounts less than 5.0% which

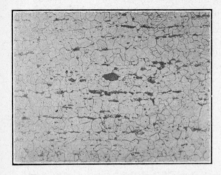

FIG. 265.—Microphotograph Showing Appearance of Manganese Sulphide in Forged Low Carbon Steel (over 1.0 % Sulphur). Pale gray colored areas drawn out in the direction of rolling. Magnified 100 diameters. Etched with a 4 % alcoholic solution of nitric acid.

FIG. 266.—Microphotograph Showing Structure of Cast Manganese Steel (Manganese 12 %) Austenitic. Small spots are undissolved carbides. Magnified 100 diameters. Etched with a 10 % alcoholic solution of nitric acid.

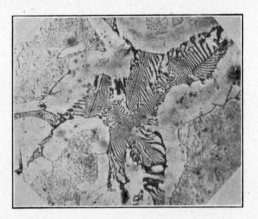

FIG. 267.—Microphotograph Showing Structure of Cast High Speed Steel. Magnified 500 diameters. Etched with Yatsevitch's Reagent.

impart to the metal specially desired properties such as increase in hardness, without decrease in ductility, machine tools capable of cutting at a high rate of speed, and for greater shock and fatigue-resisting properties.

POISONS

THEIR DETECTION AND ESTIMATION

With Special Reference to Organic Poisons [1]

Samples for toxicological examination should be placed in clean glass jars, having airtight glass covers. The jars should be sealed, numbered and labeled, and the sealer should affix his initials. The portions of the body to be preserved for the chemical examination are, as a rule, the stomach and contents, a portion or all of the intestinal tract, about one fourth of the liver, both kidneys, the spleen, the brain, the bladder contents, and occasionally the heart, lungs and a portion or all of the spinal cord.

A preliminary examination should precede the analysis, noting the appearance, odor, color, and reaction to litmus of the samples. Opium, hydrocyanic acid, carbolic acid, chloroform, alcohol, nitrobenzole, benzaldehyde and nicotine may be suggested by the odor.

Salts of copper, portions of insects, or certain arsenical preparations or other coloring matter may be suggested by the color.

The lining of the stomach should be examined; corrosion may indicate caustic alkalies, acids, or other corrosive substances; a reddening of the lining may indicate cyanide; a " toughened " stomach lining may indicate mercury salts.

The color of the blood should be noted, red indicating possible hydrocyanic acid or carbon monoxide poisoning.

The odor of such poisons as hydrocyanic acid and chloroform can often be detected better in the brain than any other portion of the body.

All available information as to symptoms should be obtained and considered since this information will usually point to a particular class of poison or even to a particular poison. Thus the work of the identification may be lessened and, what is more important, valuable and unreplaceable material will not be wasted in useless tests. It is usually safe to assume that but one poison is present. However, a quantity of a poison insufficient to cause death may be found, in which case the examination should be continued.

Food materials suspected of containing poisons may be examined by the methods given but it is well to remember that in cases of intentional poisoning the quantity of poison is usually large and the analyst should not be misled by finding traces, as of arsenic, for instance, which might easily occur in a food material due to the very common practice of using arsenical spray on fruits and vegetables.

[1] By Arthur R. Maas, Professor of Pharmacy and Toxicology, University of Southern California.

Classification of Poisons

Nearly all of the common poisons may be placed in one of three groups:

Group I.   Poisons volatilized without decomposition by distillation with steam from an acid solution.

Group II.   Organic poisons.   Most of the poisons in this group can be separated from extraneous matter by treatment with hot alcohol containing tartaric acid.   Alkaloids, glucosides, bitter principles and many organic compounds come in this group.

Group III.   All poisonous metals.

NOTE.   Caustic alkalies, mineral acids, and a few special poisons such as oxalic acid do not adapt themselves to the above scheme and will have to be treated separately.

General Procedure

Organs of the human body should first be weighed and then a representative weighed sample reduced to a finely divided mass (a clean small meat grinder answers nicely for this purpose).

It is advisable to always preserve a portion of the material in its original form for possible further examination.

About one tenth of the thoroughly mixed material is used in testing for each one of the three groups, the balance being reserved for checking.   If only a small amount of the original material is available, tests for all three groups of poisons may be made with the same portion.   In this case, after removal of volatile poisons, the residue should be divided into two unequal portions, the larger being used for non-volatile organic poisons and the smaller, together with the residue from the non-volatile organic, for metallic poisons.

Blank tests should be run upon *all* reagents used and the chemist should familiarize himself with the various tests before applying them to the unknown. At least three confirmatory tests, different in character, should be applied to the unknown substance before the presence of a poison can be definitely established. Whenever possible these confirmatory tests should include form, color, odor or taste.

Group I

Place some distilled water in a clean round-bottomed flask connected with a Liebig condenser.   Distil about 10 cc. and test distillate with silver nitrate solution.   Absence of a precipitate indicates that the apparatus is clean. Next pour out the distilled water and transfer a weighed portion of the finely divided and thoroughly mixed material to the flask, adding enough distilled water for free distillation.   Then add tartaric acid solution gradually until the mixture is acid after thorough shaking.   The distillate should be received in a test tube in which a little distilled water has been placed.   The distillate may contain:

Yellow Phosphorus	Carbolic Acid
Hydrocyanic Acid	Aniline
Chloroform	Chloral Hydrate
Ethyl Alcohol	Carbon Disulphide
Methyl Alcohol	Benzaldehyde
Acetone	Amyl Nitrite
Iodoform	Amyl Alcohol
Nitrobenzene	

Collect the distillate in several portions. Test the first portion of 5–10 cc. for hydrocyanic acid, chloroform, ethyl alcohol, methyl alcohol, acetone, iodoform and nitrobenzene. The other portions of 10–20 cc. will contain the less volatile substances, carbolic acid, etc. Observe the reaction of the distillate; if acid, test for hydrocyanic acid. Observe the odor of the distillate. A number of the above substances have characteristic odors. When there is reason to believe that a certain substance is present, confirm the results by making other characteristic tests. It is seldom necessary to test for all members of the group. Test a portion of the first distillate with silver nitrate T. S. Failure to obtain a precipitate eliminates hydrocyanic acid.

YELLOW PHOSPHORUS

Average dose, 1/120 grain.

Lethal dose, 1/8 to $1\frac{1}{2}$ grains.[1]

Preliminary Test: (Sherer's Test.) Place the finely divided material in a small flask and cover with water if necessary. Suspend in the neck of the flask by means of a cork with a V-shaped slit two prepared strips of filter paper in such a manner as to avoid touching the sides of the flask. One strip is moistened with $AgNO_3$ solution and the other with a solution prepared by adding an excess of NaOH solution to a solution of a lead salt. Warm the flask gently to 40°–50° C. on a water bath. If both strips darken, phosphorus may be present together with H_2S. If the $AgNO_3$ strip darkens and the Pb strip does not, phosphorus *may* be present. If neither strip darkens, phosphorus *is not* present. In case there is an indication of phosphorus, proceed as follows:

Make a separate portion of the finely divided material quite liquid with water to which a little H_2SO_4 has been added to neutralize any NH_3 present. Transfer to a flask or retort fitted with a long condenser terminating in a receiver containing a dilute solution of $AgNO_3$. The distillation is carried out in a darkened room. Phosphorus may be detected by a phosphorescent ring at the point where the vapors are condensing. Care must be taken to avoid reflections of light which may be taken for phosphorescence. If a distinct phosphorescence is observed, it is positive proof that elementary phosphorus is present, but the absence of phosphorescence is not a good negative test, as many substances like alcohol, oil of turpentine, H_2S, etc., may entirely prevent this indication. If the preliminary test is positive and no indication is obtained on distillation, more complete works like Autenrieth or Witthaus should be consulted for further tests which include elementary phosphorus, phosphorus, and hypophosphorus acids.

HYDROCYANIC ACID

Average dose of 2% U. S. P. acid, $1\frac{1}{2}$ minims.

Lethal dose of 2% U. S. P. acid, 40 minims.

Lethal dose of anhydrous acid, 6/10 to 9/10 grain.

In testing for hydrocyanic acid examine the brain, the contents of the stomach and intestines, and organs rich in blood such as the liver, and heart.

---

[1] Where doses are given, it means average adult doses. The lethal dose given represents the amount that would under average conditions probably be fatal to an adult.

Examination should be made as soon as possible, as hydrocyanic acid rapidly disappears through volatilization and combination with sulphur of proteins during putrefaction forming sulphocyanates.

Note cautiously the odor of the material as well as the odor of the distillate. Hydrocyanic acid has a characteristic " peach kernel " odor.

Apply the following tests:

1. *Schonbein-Pagenstecher Test*

In case of suspected cyanide poisoning this test should precede the distillation. A small quantity (15 grams) of the finely divided material is placed in a small flask together with enough tartaric acid solution to thoroughly moisten it and a piece of guaiac-copper " paper " [1] is suspended in the neck of the flask in such a manner as not to touch the liquid. The flask and contents are then gently warmed on the water bath. If the paper is not turned blue or bluish green, it is positive proof that neither HCN nor a readily decomposed cyanide is present. A positive test means only that HCN or cyanide *may* be present as many substances such as Cl, HCl, NH_3 and HNO_3 produce this same change in color.

2. *Prussian Blue Test* [2]

To a small portion (3 cc.) of the distillate in a test tube add a few drops of KOH solution, then 1 or 2 drops of a $FeSO_4$ solution and 1 drop of a $FeCl_3$ solution. Shake and warm gently. Acidify with dilute HCl. If cyanide is present in quantity a precipitate of Prussian blue will appear immediately, but if present only in traces the solution will acquire a blue or bluish green color which on standing 10 to 24 hours will throw down a flocculent precipitate of Prussian blue. The maximum sensitivity of this reaction is 1: 5,000,000.

Since formaldehyde is the principal ingredient of most embalming fluids, the Prussian blue test cannot be relied upon as a negative test when working with embalmed tissues.

3. *Sulphocyanate Test*

To another portion of the distillate in a small evaporating dish add 2 or 3 drops of KOH solution, enough yellow ammonium sulphide to color the solution yellow and evaporate to dryness on the steam bath. Dissolve in a few drops of water and acidify with a little dilute HCl. Filter through a double filter paper into another small evaporating dish. Add 2 or 3 drops of dilute $FeCl_3$ solution. If HCN is present in the distillate, a reddish to blood-red color will appear, which is discharged upon the addition of a few drops of $HgCl_2$ solution. The color so produced is due to ferric sulphocyanate. The maximum sensitivity of this test is 1: 4,000,000 and is not affected by the presence of formaldehyde.

[1] "Guaiac-copper" paper is prepared by saturating strips of filter paper with a freshly prepared 10% alcoholic tincture of resin of guaiac, drying and, just before using, moistening with a 1 to 1000 $CuSO_4$ solution.

[2] The author has found that hydrocyanic acid fails to respond to this test in the presence of formaldehyde, due probably to the following reactions:

$$HCOH + HCN = HOCH_2CN.$$

4. *Silver Nitrate Test*

Acidify 1 cc. of the distillate with dilute HNO_3 in a small test tube and add or 3 drops of $AgNO_3$ solution. If HCN is present, a white curdy precipitate resembling that of AgCl is produced which dissolves in NH_4OH. This reaction cannot be due to HCl because when a very dilute solution of HCl is distilled HCl is not found in the distillate. The maximum sensitivity of this test is 1:250,000.

5. *Silver Cyanide Crystal Test*

Acidify 1 cc. of the distillate with dilute HNO_3 in a small test tube. Place a drop of dilute $AgNO_3$ on a microscope slide and carefully invert the drop over the center of the tube so as to avoid touching the side of the tube. Allow to stand for 15 to 20 minutes, then cover with a coverglass and examine under the microscope, using a power of from 50 to 100 diameters. If HCN is present, characteristic crystals of AgCN will appear under the microscope. (See Fig. 276.)

6. *Detection of Hydrocyanic Acid in the Presence of Potassium Ferrocyanide*

Should the material contain potassium ferrocyanide (which is not a poison), the ordinary tartaric acid distillation will show the presence of HCN even though there is none present before distillation. Therefore, in medico-legal cases where cyanide is found it is well to test the original material for potassium ferrocyanide as follows:

Shake a small portion with water, filter and test with $FeCl_3$ and dilute HCl for the Prussian blue reaction. If there is an indication of a ferrocyanide, distil a fresh portion of the material with an excess of $NaHCO_3$ and repeat the tests for cyanides.

7. *Detection of Mercuric Cyanide*

In cases of suspected mercuric cyanide poisoning a few cc. of a freshly prepared saturated aqueous solution of H_2S should be added to the contents of the flask and distillation continued. If mercuric cyanide is present, HCN will be found in this second distillation. This step is made necessary because mercuric cyanide in dilute solution is not decomposed by either tartaric acid or sodium bicarbonate.

8. *Estimation of Hydrocyanic Acid*

When HCN is found, it is always well to determine as accurately as possible the amount present.

Acidify a weighed portion of the material with sulphuric or tartaric acid and distil into dilute NaOH free from chlorides. Determine the cyanide in the distillate by a good volumetric method. If chlorides are present in the distillate, they may be removed by one redistillation over borax.

CHLOROFORM

Average dose, 5 minims.
Lethal dose by inhalation, from 15 drops up.
Lethal dose by mouth, 2 to 8 drachms.

Distribution: When inhaled, chloroform passes from the air into the blood-plasma, then to the red blood corpuscles. It can often be found in the brain.

Phenylisocyanide Test

To a small portion of the distillate add 1–2 drops of aniline oil and a few cc of KOH solution and heat gently. If chloroform is present, the offensive characteristic odor of phenylisocyanide is produced. This test is sensitive to 1 in 5000. This odor is produced by other substances such as chloral and chloral hydrate and for this reason other tests should be applied.

Schwarz's Resorcinol Test

To 2 cc. of a 5% solution of resorcinol add a few drops of NaOH solution and a small portion of the distillate and heat to boiling. If chloroform is present even in small quantity, a yellowish red color is produced. Chloral, bromal, bromoform, and iodoform also give this test.

Nicloux's Method (Quantitative)

To 20 cc. of blood or other aqueous liquid add about 95 cc. of alcohol and 5 cc. of a 5% solution of tartaric acid in alcohol. Distil 40 cc. into 10 cc. of alcohol, using a condenser with an adapter dipping beneath the surface of the alcohol so that none of the chloroform may be lost. To the distillate add 10 cc. of a 10% alcoholic solution of KOH (free from chlorides) and boil under a reflux condenser for 30 minutes, cool, add 15 cc. of distilled water, neutralize to phenolphthalein with dilute H_2SO_4, add a few drops of neutral potassium chromate solution and titrate with standard silver nitrate solution.

$$3Cl = 1 \ CHCl_3 \quad CHCl_3 + 4KOH = HCO \ OK + 3KCl + H_2O.$$

Ethyl Alcohol

Lethal dose, $3\frac{1}{2}$ to 7 fluid ounces.

Distribution: Ethyl alcohol may be found in the brain, liver and blood.

Detection

1. Lieben's Iodoform Test

Warm a small portion of the first distillate to 40° or 50° C. Add 1–2 cc. of an aqueous iodo-potassium iodide solution and enough KOH solution to give a distinct yellow to brownish color. If alcohol is present, a yellowish white to lemon yellow precipitate of iodoform is formed. If the solution is very dilute, some time may be required to form the precipitate. When formed slowly the crystals may be identified under the microscope. This test is very delicate but is not characteristic of ethyl alcohol because other primary alcohols (except methyl alcohol) and many secondary alcohols produce this reaction. (See Fig. 274.)

2. Chromic Acid Test

Warm a small portion of the distillate with dilute H_2SO_4 or HCl and add 1–2 drops of a very dilute $K_2Cr_2O_7$ solution. The color of the liquid will change from red to green and give off the odor of acetaldehyde. Many other volatile organic compounds react in this manner.

3. *Ethyl Acetate Test*

Mix a small portion of the distillate with an equal volume of concentrated $_2SO_4$. Add a very small quantity of anhydrous sodium acetate and heat. he odor of ethyl acetate is produced if alcohol is present.

4. *Vitali's Test*

Thoroughly mix a small portion of the distillate in a glass dish with a small iece of solid KOH and 2 or 3 drops of CS_2. Let stand a short time without arming. When most of the CS_2 has evaporated add a drop of ammonium nolybdate solution and then an excess of dilute H_2SO_4. A red color is produced alcohol is present. Acetone and acetaldehyde will produce a similar color. . 5% solution of alcohol gives this test distinctly.

METHYL ALCOHOL (WOOD ALCOHOL)

Fatal dose, 1 fluid ounce.

Methyl alcohol is found in methylated spirit, which contains 10 parts nethyl alcohol and 90 parts ethyl alcohol. It is also found in some other forms f denatured alcohol. It may poison either from external application or internal administration. One teaspoonful has produced blindness and one ounce leath.

Detection

To 5 cc. of the first distillate add 1 cc. of 25% H_2SO_4 and 4 cc. of N/5 KMnO$_4$; allow to stand 10 minutes and filter. (Decolorize with H_2SO_3 if necessary.) To 5 cc. of the filtrate add 1 drop $FeCl_3$ solution and about 5 cc. nilk. Underlay this mixture with concentrated H_2SO_4. A violet ring at line of contact indicates formaldehyde (oxidation product of methyl alcohol).

To the balance of the filtrate (5 cc.) add 8 drops of an aqueous solution of resorcinol (1–200) and then carefully pour this upon 5 cc. of concentrated sulphuric acid contained in a test tube in such a manner that the two liquids do not mix. After standing for three minutes a rose-red ring at line of contact indicates formaldehyde (oxidation product of methyl alcohol).

CARBOLIC ACID (PHENOL)

Average dose, 1 grain.
Fatal dose, 1–4 drachms.

Distribution: Carbolic acid is very rapidly absorbed by the skin and gastrointestinal tract and appears in the liver, stomach, blood, kidneys, brain and urine in a very short time after taking.

1. If present in quantity, this acid may be recognized by its odor.

2. *Millon's Test*

Heat 1 cc. of the distillate with a few drops of Millon's Reagent. (See Special Reagents.) If carbolic acid is present even in minute quantity, a distinct red color is produced. The absence of this color is an excellent indication of the absence of phenol but other substances such as the three cresols and salicylic acid may produce this color and for this reason other tests should be applied if this test is positive.

3. *Bromine Test*

To 1 cc. of the distillate add 1 or 2 drops of freshly prepared saturate bromine water. If phenol is present in quantity a yellowish white precipitat is immediately thrown down, but if highly diluted some time may be required The precipitate should be examined under the microscope for characteristi crystals of tribromophenol. (See Fig. 275.)

Phenol in a dilution of 1:50,000 yields on standing a precipitate containin some of the characteristic crystals.

Substances like salicylic aldehyde and salicylic acid also produce this pre cipitate and other tests should, therefore, be applied.

4. *Ferric Chloride Test*

To a small portion of the distillate add a very dilute solution of $FeCl_3$ droj by drop. If phenol is present to the extent of 1:1000, a blue-violet color is pro duced. Dilute HCl and H_2SO_4 change the color to yellow. This test is entirel\ negative in the presence of mineral acids.

5. *Hypochlorite Test*

Add a little NH_4OH to a small portion of the distillate and then 2–3 drops o freshly prepared solution of calcium or sodium hypochlorite and warm. I phenol is present in quantity a blue color is produced, but if very dilute onl\ green or blue-green color appears. The maximum sensitivity of this reactio\ is 1:1000.

6. *Nitrite Test*

To a small portion of the distillate add a few drops of a dilute alcoholic solu tion of ethyl nitrite and underlay the mixture in a test tube with concentrated H_2SO_4. If phenol is present, a red zone will appear at the point of contact of the two liquids. The maximum sensitivity of this reaction is 1:10,000.

7. *Quantitative Estimation of Phenol*

For the quantitative estimation of phenol the analyst is referred to the Beckurts-Koppeschaar Volumetric Method as described in Autenrieth-Warren, "The Detection of Poisons and Powerful Drugs," page 31.

CHLORAL HYDRATE

Average dose, 8 grains.
Fatal dose, $\frac{1}{2}$ to 2 drachms.

Distribution: Chloral hydrate may be found in the stomach, blood, brain and spinal cord.

Detection

Chloral hydrate gives the phenylisocyanide and resorcinol test for chloro- form but the distillate does not have the characteristic odor of chloroform.

Add a few drops of Nessler's solution to a small quantity of the second dis- tillate and shake. If chloral hydrate is present, a yellowish red precipitate is produced which on standing changes to dirty yellowish green. Formaldehyde gives a brownish precipitate with this reagent. Boil a small portion of the dis- tillate with 0.2–0.3 g. solid sodium thiosulphate. If chloral hydrate is present, a urbid liquid of brick red color is produced.   A few drops of **KOH** solution will emove the turbidity and change the color to brownish red.

Decomposition of Chloral Hydrate

Heat a small portion of the distillate with calcined MgO for 30 minutes on he steam bath with a reflux condenser.   The chloral hydrate is decomposed nto magnesium formate and chloroform.   Test as follows:

Distil a few cc. of the decomposed liquid and test the distillate for chloro- orm.   Filter the residue, concentrate to a small bulk and divide into two parts. To one part add 1–2 drops of $HgCl_2$ solution and warm.   Formic acid reduces IgCl$_2$ to HgCl, producing a white precipitate.   To the other part add 2–3 drops f $AgNO_3$ solution and warm.   Formic acid reduces $AgNO_3$ to metallic silver, lepositing a mirror on the test tube.

Group II

ALKALOIDS, GLUCOSIDES AND OTHER ORGANIC COMPOUNDS

Alkaloids form salts with tartaric acid insoluble in ether and chloroform but oluble in alcohol and water.   These alkaloidal salts are decomposed by alkalies iberating the alkaloid which is insoluble in water, but soluble in ether or chloro- orm.   The above is the principle by which alkaloids are separated from oreign material.

Method of Analysis

The substance is finely hashed, if solid, and then treated with several volumes of purified alcohol [1] and made slightly acid with tartaric acid.   The mixture is placed in a flask and heated under a reflux condenser for about 30 minutes.   After cooling it is filtered and the residue washed with purified alcohol.   The alcoholic extract is evaporated on a water bath to the consistence of a syrup.   From 3 to 4 volumes of purified alcohol are then gradually stirred n, the solution allowed to stand an hour or more, filtered and carefully evapo- rated on a water bath to a thin syrup.   This syrup is now treated with about 50 cc. of distilled water and filtered.

NOTE.   If croton oil or nitroglycerine are suspected, they should be looked for in the residue insoluble in water.

The filtered aqueous acid solution should be placed in a separatory funnel and extracted with ether, and the extractions repeated until the ether on evapo- ration gives no residue.

Unite the ether extractions, wash once with a small quantity of water, filter through dry paper and evaporate.   The residue may contain:

Fats and Oils	Acetanilid	Antipyrine
Ptomaines	Phenacetine	Salicylic Acid
Picrotoxin	Chloretone	Benzoic Acid
Colchicine	Brometone	Veronal
Picric Acid	Essential Oils	Trional
Menthol	Cantharidin	Sulphonal
Camphor		
Phenol		
Cresol		
Thymol		

[1] The alcohol used should be purified by treating it with about 0.1% of tartaric acid, allowing to stand 24 hours and then distilling.

Note the general appearance and taste of the residue. If bitter, test fo
picrotoxin and colchicine. Veronal and trional have a bitter taste and give
characteristic crystals. Sulphonal is tasteless and gives prismatic crystals.

The aqueous liquid is next rendered slightly alkaline with NaOH and ex
tracted with ether as before.

The extracted substances from which the solvent has been evaporated should
be weighed so as to determine the amount present. If material so recovered
is crystalline, the weight may be taken as representing the actual amount
present. If not crystalline, the extract may be purified in most cases by dis
solving in dilute acid, making the solution alkaline as before and re-extracting
with the volatile solvent.

The residue from the evaporation of the ether may contain any of the follow
ing substances:

Ptomaines	Atropine	Codeine	Antipyrine
Coniine	Hyoscyamine	Narcotine	Quinine
Nicotine	Scopolamine	Pilocarpine	
Aniline	Cocaine	Sanguinarine	
Toluidine	Physostigmine	Berberine	
Veratrine	Brucine		
Strychnine	Hydrastine		

Carefully acidify the aqueous alkaline residue remaining from the preceding
ether extraction with dilute HCl and then make alkaline with dilute NH_4OH
using litmus paper for both tests. Extract repeatedly with hot chloroform
containing 10% by volume of alcohol.

The residue from the evaporation of the chloroform may contain:

Morphine
Apomorphine
Narceine

ACETANILID

Dose, 2–10 grains
Lethal dose, 60 grains has proven fatal, less is dangerous to a person with a
weak heart.

Phenylisocyanide Test

Dissolve a small portion of the residue in 5–6 cc. of a boiling solution of
alcoholic potash. Cool, add 2 or 3 drops of chloroform and again heat. If
acetanilid is present, the offensive odor of phenylisocyanide is produced. The
alcoholic potash decomposes acetanilid into aniline and potassium acetate.
The former with chloroform gives phenylisocyanide.

Bichromate-Sulphuric Acid Test

To a small portion of the residue add 1–2 drops of concentrated H_2SO_4 con
taining a little $K_2Cr_2O_7$. Acetanilid produces a red color changing to brown and
finally dirty green.

VERONAL

Dose, 8 to 15 grains.
Lethal dose, 120 grains has proven fatal.

Distribution: Veronal should be looked for in the stomach and bladder
contents.

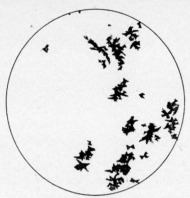

Fig. 268.   Atropine 1:500.   With
Wagner's Reagent.

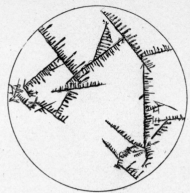

Fig. 269.   Cocaine 1:1000.   With
Gold Chloride.

Fig. 270.   Codeine 1:200.   With
Maime's Reagent.

Fig. 271.   Narcotine 1:1000.   With
Sodium Carbonate.

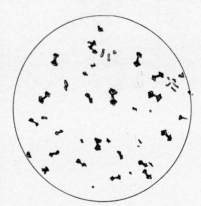

Fig. 272.   Nicotine 1:1000.   With
Gold Chloride.

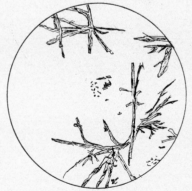

Fig. 273.   Strychnine 1:500.   With
Ammonium Thiocyanate.

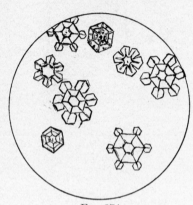

FIG. 274.

Iodoform Crystals.

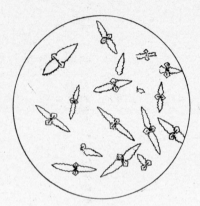

FIG. 275.

Tribromphenol Crystals.

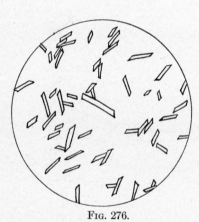

FIG. 276.

Silver Cyanide Crystals.

FIG. 277.

Morphine Crystals.

Purification and Detection

Dissolve a portion of the residue from the acid ether extraction in the smallest possible quantity of hot water. If colored, decolorize by boiling a few minutes with animal charcoal, filter hot and allow the solution to cool. If no crystals are deposited, evaporate further and cool. Make the following tests on any pure crystals obtained:

Dissolve a few crystals in a few drops of water and test with sensitive litmus paper. An aqueous solution of veronal has a faintly acid reaction.

Dissolve a few crystals in a few drops of dilute NaOH solution and acidify the clear solution with dilute HCl. Veronal is precipitated.

Determine the melting point on a few of the crystals. Pure veronal melts between 188° and 189° C.

Mix a few of the crystals with a few crystals of pure veronal and determine the melting point of the mixture. The mixture should have the same melting point as the unknown if the unknown is pure veronal. Carefully sublime a number of the crystals in a dry test tube and compare with crystals known to be pure veronal. A low power microscope is used for this purpose. Fuse some of the crystals with metallic sodium in a dry test tube. Cool, dissolve carefully in water and test for sodium cyanide by the methods given on pages 1725–1727. Veronal contains nitrogen which reacts to form sodium cyanide.

Extraction of Veronal from the Bladder Contents

Evaporate a considerable quantity of the urine on the steam bath to 1/5 its volume and extract several times with ether, using a large volume for each extraction because veronal is not very soluble in this solvent. Evaporate the extract and proceed with the residue as directed under " Purification and Detection " given above.

NICOTINE

Dose, 1/20 to 1/10 grain.
Lethal dose, 2–3 drops pure alkaloid.

Distribution

Nicotine should be sought in the stomach, lungs and liver.

Detection

If present in large quantities, nicotine may be detected by its odor. If nicotine is suspected, the ether extract from NaOH solution should be evaporated without heat. If nicotine is present, oily drops of a colorless or yellowish liquid which reddens phenolphthalein and has a peculiar odor somewhat resembling stale tobacco smoke will remain in the residue. If exposed to the light, the oil becomes yellow or brown, thicker and finally resinous. If heated, it volatilizes completely, giving off white fumes.

If a drop of HCl be placed on a watch glass and inverted over a similar watch glass containing nicotine alkaloid, a white cloud is produced which is, however, not so dense as that produced by coniine under like conditions and no crystals are produced as with coniine.

Place a drop of an aqueous extract of the oily residue on a microscope slide, add a drop of a solution of gold chloride, let stand for several minutes and examine under the microscope. If nicotine is present, small characteristic crystals will appear upon standing.

STRYCHNINE

Dose, 1/60 to 1/12 grain.
Minimum lethal dose for an adult, $\frac{1}{2}$ grain.

Distribution

Strychnine should be looked for in the stomach and contents and organs rich in blood such as the liver and heart.

Detection

Strychnine has a very bitter taste and may be detected even in a dilution of one in 700,000 by the taste.

Bloxam's Test

Add 1–2 drops strong HNO_3 to a portion of the solid residue in a porcelain dish and gently warm. On adding a small crystal of $KClO_3$, a scarlet color is produced if strychnine is present. NH_4OH changes the color to brown and a brown precipitate falls. On evaporating slowly to dryness, a dark green residue is left. This residue is soluble in water, forming a green solution which is changed to orange-brown by KOH and green again by HNO_3. This reaction distinguishes strychnine from any of the alkaloids commonly occurring in cases of poisoning.

Bichromate Test

Place a drop of an acid extraction of the residue on a microscope slide and add a drop of a dilute solution of $K_2Cr_2O_7$. Let stand for a few minutes and examine under the microscope. If strychnine is present, characteristic crystals will be found. Dry the crystals and add a drop of concentrated H_2SO_4, holding the slide over a white surface. A deep blue color which changes through deep violet, purplish red, orange to yellow is produced if strychnine is present.

NOTE. A mixture of hydrastine and morphine causes this same color reaction but this mixture is not possible if the extractions have been properly carried out.

Sulphocyanate Test

Place a few drops of the acid extraction on a microscope slide and add a drop of a dilute solution of ammonium sulphocyanate. Strychnine sulphocyanate produces characteristic needle-shaped crystals.

BRUCINE

Dose, 1/12 to $\frac{1}{2}$ grain.

Detection

Dissolve a small quantity of the residue in 1 or 2 drops of concentrated HNO_3. If brucine is present, a blood red color will appear, which soon changes to yellowish red and finally to yellow. Add a few drops of a freshly prepared dilute solution of stannous chloride to the yellowish red or yellow solution. An intense violet color will appear. Heat usually changes this color to yellowish red but more stannous chloride solution restores the violet color.

Dissolve a small portion of the residue in 2 drops of dilute HCl. Place a drop of this solution on a microscope slide and add a drop of platinum chloride solution. If brucine is present, characteristic rod-like crystals separate and may be compared under the microscope with those produced in a solution of brucine. These crystals are formed in solutions as dilute as 1 to 20,000. The best crystals are obtained from the more dilute solutions.

ATROPINE

Dose, 1/120 to 1/60 grain.
Lethal dose, 1/20 grain. Much larger doses have been followed by recovery.

Detection

Vitali's Test

Dissolve a small portion of the dry residue from the ether extraction of solution made alkaline with NaOH in a few drops of fuming HNO_3 and evaporate to dryness on the steam bath. Cool and moisten the yellowish residue with a few drops of a 4% solution of KOH in absolute alcohol. If atropine is present, an evanescent violet color will appear. This color reaction is also obtained with hyoscyamine, scopolamine, strychnine and veratrine, and therefore other tests should be applied.

Physiological Test

Dissolve a small portion of the residue in a few drops of very dilute H_2SO_4 and place a drop of this solution in a dog's or cat's eye. If atropine is present, a noticeable enlargement of the pupil will be observed. (Note: Great care must be exercised if this test is applied to the human eye.) One drop of a 1: 130,000 solution of atropine will produce this enlargement.

Dissolve a small portion of the residue in 2 drops of dilute H_2SO_4. Place a drop of this solution on a microscope slide and add a drop of Wagner's Reagent. If atropine is present, an amorphous precipitate appears and slowly forms numbers of small characteristic crystals which may be observed under the microscope. This test is sensitive to 1 in 8000.

COCAINE

Dose, 1/8 to 1 grain.
Lethal dose, 15 grains.

Detection

The material should be examined for cocaine as soon as possible because cocaine undergoes changes in the viscera which are said to change it rapidly into ecgonine.

Dissolve a small portion of the residue in water and touch it to the tongue. Cocaine produces a temporary anesthesia.

To a small portion of the residue in a porcelain dish add a few drops of strong HNO_3 and evaporate carefully to dryness. Treat the residue with a few drops of alcoholic potash and warm. If cocaine is present, a characteristic sweet odor will be given off.

Dissolve a small portion of the residue in 1 or 2 drops of dilute HCl. Place a drop on a microscope slide and add a drop of gold chloride solution. Cocaine produces after a short time very characteristic crystals, the form depending on the dilution. This test is sensitive 1: 20,000.

CODEINE

Dose, $\frac{1}{2}$ to 1 grain.

Lethal dose, 5 grains. Much larger doses have been recovered from.

Detection

Nitric Acid Test

To a small portion of the residue in a porcelain dish add a few drops of a cold 25% solution of nitric acid. Codeine produces a yellow color which soon changes to red. Concentrated nitric acid produces a reddish brown color.

Froehde's Test

To a small portion of the residue in a porcelain dish add a few drops of Froehde's Reagent (see Special Reagents) and warm very gently over a very small flame. Codeine produces a yellowish color which soon changes to green and finally to blue.

Formaldehyde-Sulphuric Acid Test

To a small portion of the residue in a small porcelain dish add a few drops of concentrated sulphuric acid to which has been added a trace of formaldehyde. Codeine produces a reddish violet color which changes to blue-violet.

Marme's Reagent Test

Dissolve a small portion of the residue in 2 drops of dilute H_2SO_4. Place a drop of this solution on a microscope slide and add a drop of Marme's Reagent (see Special Reagents). Characteristic crystals soon begin to form in solution of codeine as dilute as 1: 2000 and may be observed under the microscope.

NARCOTINE

Dose, 2 to 15 grains.

Detection

Dilute Sulphuric Acid Test

Dissolve a small portion of the residue obtained from the ether extraction of the NaOH solution in a little dilute H_2SO_4 and evaporate in a small porcelain dish on the steam bath. If narcotine is present, the residue has a reddish yellow color which changes on stronger heating to crimson red. As the acid begins to evaporate, blue-violet streaks radiate from the margin and the entire liquid finally assumes a dirty red-violet color.

Froehde's Reaction

To a small portion of the residue in a porcelain dish add a few drops of Froehde's reagent. If narcotine is present, a greenish color is produced which immediately changes to cherry red. Gentle heat hastens the appearance of the cherry red color which is quite persistent.

Selenious Acid-Sulphuric Acid Test

To a small portion of the residue add a few drops of selenious acid-sulphuric acid reagent (see Special Reagents). If narcotine is present, a greenish steel blue color appears which, after a time, changes to cherry red. Heat destroys the cherry red color immediately.

Sodium Carbonate Test

Dissolve a small portion of the residue in 2–3 drops of very dilute HCl. Place a drop of this solution on a microscope slide and add a drop of a 5% solution of Na_2CO_3. If narcotine is present, small characteristic crystals are precipitated in solutions as dilute as 1 to 20,000. These crystals should be compared under the microscope with crystals obtained from solutions of narcotine of different concentrations.

MORPHINE

Dose, 1/20 to $\frac{1}{2}$ grain.
Average lethal dose, 1 to 4 grains. Recovery may follow after taking a much larger quantity.

Detection

Formaldehyde-Sulphuric Acid Test

To a small portion of the residue from the chloroform extraction in a small porcelain dish add a few drops concentrated H_2SO_4 containing 2 or 3 drops of 40% formaldehyde solution to 5 cc. acid. A trace of morphine produces a purple red color which changes to violet and finally becomes pure blue. If this test is negative morphine is not present, but a positive reaction must be confirmed by other tests because codeine, heroin and apomorphine produce a similar color.

Froehde's Test

To a small portion of the residue in a porcelain dish add a drop of Froehde's Reagent. Morphine produces a violet color which changes through blue to dirty green and faint red. Other alkaloids of the opium group give similar color reactions.

Iodic Acid Test

Dissolve a small quantity of the residue in dilute H_2SO_4, add a few drops of iodic acid and shake with chloroform. A violet color appearing in the chloroform layer may be due to other reducing agents as well as morphine.

Ferric Chloride Test

Dissolve a small quantity of the residue in dilute HCl and evaporate to dryness on the steam bath. Take up with a few drops of distilled water and add a drop of neutral FeCl₃ solution. If morphine is present, a blue color will appear.

Nitric Acid Test

To a small portion of the residue add 1–2 drops of concentrated HNO_3. Morphine gives a blood red color which gradually changes to yellow.

Marme's Test

Dissolve a small portion of the residue in 2 drops of dilute HCl. Place one drop of this solution on a microscope slide and add a drop of Marme's Reagent. If morphine is present in solution to the extent of 1 to 1000, delicate silvery needle-shaped crystals will form slowly around the edges of the drop and in more concentrated solutions these crystals group together to form rosettes as shown in Fig. 277.

OPIUM

Dose, 1 grain.

Lethal dose, 4 grains has produced death. Larger amounts have been recovered from.

The principal constituents of opium are morphine, codeine, narcotine, narceine, and meconic acid.

Narcotine can be extracted from an aqueous solution of opium by shaking out with ether, and evaporating the ether. Meconic acid can be obtained by adding lead acetate to an aqueous solution of opium and filtering off the precipitate of lead meconate (the filtrate will contain morphine acetate). The precipitate of lead meconate is decomposed by treating it with dilute sulphuric acid and gently boiling the mixture, filtering and neutralizing. On adding a drop of ferric chloride solution, a deep red color, not easily destroyed by a solution of mercuric chloride or hot dilute sulphuric acid, indicates meconic acid. Mercuric chloride instantly bleaches the color caused by sulphocyanates while the boiling dilute sulphuric acid destroys that due to acetates by decomposing the acetate and expelling acetic acid.

The solution of morphine acetate should be treated with hydrogen sulphide to remove excess of lead, the solution filtered and the filtrate evaporated to a soft extract on a water bath. This extract treated with alcohol, filtered and evaporated will give morphine acetate to which the characteristic tests for morphine should be applied.

The presence of morphine, narcotine and meconic acid definitely establishes the presence of opium.

PTOMAINES

The consideration of ptomaines is very important in toxicology because of the similarity of these substances to alkaloids. Ptomaines contain nitrogen and are basic in character and may or may not be toxic. They are products of decomposition occurring especially in advanced stages of putrefaction of a dead body. Probably they are always present in cadavers and it seems probable that they are normal products of bacterial life processes.

Great care should be exercised especially in legal-chemical cases not to report an alkaloid present if there is any possibility of the identifying reactions being caused by a ptomaine. No positive report should be made until every characteristic chemical test of the suspected alkaloids has been confirmed, and in case there is even a remote possibility that the suspected substance may be a ptomaine, a physiological test should be made in order to confirm the chemical examination.

A ptomaine may resemble an alkaloid chemically but usually it will have an entirely different physiological action. Ptomaines resembling to a certain degree the following alkaloids have been isolated: atropine, codeine, coniine, delphinine, hyoscyamine, morphine, narceine, nicotine, strychnine and veratrine.

Frequently the resemblance between a ptomaine and an alkaloid lies in one reaction only but an animal decomposition product has been found that resembles morphine in its characteristic solubilities and also liberates iodine from iodic acid but does not give the reactions that are characteristic of morphine alone.

Ptomaines may resemble alkaloids in the following characteristics: they give precipitates with reagents that precipitate alkaloids, their separation with various solvents from both acid and alkaline solution resembles various alkaloids and many ptomaines are strong reducing agents and give the Prussian blue test in common with certain alkaloids.

When it is possible to isolate the alkaloid in a pure state, its identity can be established beyond a doubt.

Group III

This group contains all metals. Arsenic however is best tested for on a small separate portion of the original material.

Preparation of Solution

Place from 50 to 100 gm. of the finely chopped material in a 1000-cc. boiling flask. Dilute with water if necessary until a fluid mixture is obtained and add pure concentrated HCl and crystalline $KClO_3$ in the proportion of 25 cc. HCl and 2 g. $KClO_3$ to every 100 g. Allow the mixture to stand cool for 24 hours and heat on the steam bath (preferably under a reflux condenser) with frequent agitation and the occasional addition of $KClO_3$ (0.5 g. at a time) until the contents of the flask are yellow and fluid except for fatty and white granular matter in suspension and until the liquid does not darken on heating for half an hour without adding $KClO_3$. If, during the heating, the addition of $KClO_3$ does not produce any visible reaction, add more concentrated HCl in the proportion of 10 cc. HCl to every 100 g. material used and continue as directed above. Care should be used to keep the quantities of HCl and $KClO_3$ as small as possible, as an excess of HCl may prevent the precipitation of some of the metals by H_2S. Expel the excess of chlorine by passing a rapid stream of CO_2 through the cool liquid or by adding small quantities of $NaHSO_3$ until a distinct odor of SO_2 is obtained. Filter the solution through a wet filter and wash the residue thoroughly with hot water. If a large amount of fatty residue is left, it should be extracted two or three times with small quantities of hot water acidulated with HCl and these filtered extracts added to the main filtrate. If silver and small quantities of lead, thallium, mercury or barium are suspected, this residue should be examined qualitatively for these metals. If a large excess of HCl is present, add a concentrated solution of Na_2CO_3 to such an extent that the reaction still remains distinctly acid. Place the liquid in a flask fitted with a two-hole rubber stopper and tube dipping below the liquid and pass pure H_2S through it at the temperature of the steam bath for 2 hours. Allow to stand cold for eight or ten hours and filter. A colored precipitate at this stage may mean nothing, as it may be due to organic thio-compounds, and therefore the precipitate and filtrate should be tested by any good method of qualitative analysis for metals.

Detection of Arsenic

Place 10 grams of the finely divided material in a 150-cc. beaker, add 10 cc. of concentrated HNO_3, cover and allow to stand over night. Then add 5 cc. concentrated H_2SO_4 and warm. When the material starts to turn brown, add concentrated HNO_3 1 cc. at a time until SO_3 fumes are given off without the solution turning brown. Cool; carefully add 10 cc. of water and boil down to SO_3 fumes. Cool, dilute, add 0.5 g. Kl, warm to 90° C., add dilute solution of $SnCl_2$ to decolorize, cool and run in the regular small Gutzeit apparatus.

DETERMINATION OF CARBON MONOXIDE IN AIR

(Sayers, Yant and Jones, Public Health Reports, Vol. 38, No. 40, Oct. 5, 1923)

The following method slightly abridged from that of the original authors will give approximate results where the percentage of CO in air is less than 0.2%.

Blood Solution

Saturate a small amount of defibrinated blood with CO. This is done readily by passing house gas containing CO through blood for a minute or two or preferably by using air containing 3 to 5% of CO. Prepare a 1 to 20 dilution of this blood with water. Also prepare a 1 to 20 dilution of CO-free blood. For standards set up a series of nine test tubes containing 0.0, 0.2, 0.4 . . . 1.6 cc. of CO-blood dilution, each made up to a final volume of 2 cc. with the CO-free blood dilution. To each of these tubes add 40 mg. of a mixture of equal parts of tannic and pyrogallic acids. Invert the tube 4 or 5 times to mix. These standards give a series in which the proportion of saturation with CO varies from 0 to 80 in steps of 10%. If air is excluded by a paraffin seal on the surface of the liquid, these standards will be sufficiently permanent for a week or two, but it is little trouble to prepare them fresh for an occasional sample.

A sample of air to be examined is obtained in a 250-cc. bottle, using an aspirator bulb and discharging the bulb at least 25 times into the bottom of the bottle. The bottle is closed with a rubber stopper or with a well-vaselined glass stopper if preferred. Such a sample will keep well. When ready for the test, add to the bottle 2 cc. of the 1–20 CO-free blood dilution, avoiding as much as possible the escape of the air-gas mixture from the bottle. Slowly turn the bottle so that the blood solution flows over the surface of the inside of the bottle, avoiding violent shaking. After 15 or 20 minutes' rotation, transfer the blood solution to a test tube of the same size as the standards, add 40 mg. of the tannic-pyrogallic mixture, invert for mixing as with the standards, and, after standing 15 minutes, compare with the standards and determine the approximate saturation of the blood solution. This may be done with an accuracy of

% by estimating the degree of color as equal to a standard tube or between two such tubes. The following table gives the approximate percentage of CO in the air corresponding to the percentage of saturation of the blood when the temperature at the time of making the test is not far removed from 20° C. and the air is otherwise of fairly normal composition, say, containing at least 19% of oxygen.

Saturation %	CO %
0	0.00
10	0.007
20	0.015
30	0.028
40	0.045
50	0.066
60	0.090
70	0.152
75	0.200

Corrections for variations in temperature and composition may be found in the original (loc. cit.).

DETERMINATION OF CO IN BLOOD

Dilute 0.1 cc. of blood of a supposed victim of CO poisoning to 2 cc. with .03% solution of sodium fluoride or 0.05% solution of potassium oxalate (to prevent coagulation). Add 40 mg. of tannic-pyrogallic acid mixture (1–1), invert 4 or 5 times and after 15 minutes compare with standards made up as in the method for CO in air, except that sodium fluoride or potassium oxalate solution of the above strength is used instead of water in making up the blood solutions. Report the percentage of saturation with CO.

In general, slight symptoms may be noted when the hemoglobin of the blood is saturated to the extent of 25%, while 50% saturation gives violent symptoms and a dangerous condition.

Special Reagents

MILLON'S REAGENT

Dissolve 1 part of mercury in 1 part of cold, fuming nitric acid. Dilute with twice the volume of water and decant the clear solution after 24 hours.

FROEHDE'S REAGENT

A solution of molybdic acid in sulphuric acid, prepared by dissolving 5 mg. of molybdic acid, or sodium molybdate, in 1 cc. of hot pure concentrated sulphuric acid. This solution, which should be colorless, does not keep long.

MARME'S REAGENT

Dissolve 30 gms. of cadmium iodide and 60 gms. of potassium iodide in 180 cc. of water.

SELENIOUS-SULPHURIC ACID REAGENT

Dissolve 5 mg. of selenious acid ($H_2Se_2O_3$) in 1 cc. of concentrated sulphuric acid.

Iodo-Potassium Iodide Reagent

Dissolve 5 g. of iodine and 10 g. of potassium iodide in 100 cc. of water.

Mayer's Reagent

Dissolve 1.358 g. of mercuric chloride in 60 cc. of water and 5 g. of potassium iodide in 10 cc. of water. Mix the two solutions and dilute to 100 cc.

MISCELLANEOUS*

ALCOHOL

Detection and Estimation of Alcohol

Detection of Alcohol. Ethyl or "grain alcohol" C_2H_5OH boils at 78.4° C. so that it readily distills with steam. If an appreciable amount of alcohol is present in the liquor it may be detected by the odor of the solution or in the first fraction of its distillate.

Iodoform Test. A few cc. of the liquor are distilled and to this distillate is added a small crystal of iodine or a few cc. of aqueous solution of iodine-potassium iodide solution, followed by sufficient potassium hydroxide to give the liquid a distinct yellow to brownish color. The solution is warmed gently. If alcohol is present a whitish to lemon yellow precipitate of iodoform will appear. The odor of iodoform may be noted. If the crystals form slowly they are deposited in form of perfect stars and hexagonal plates. This test is not conclusive of alcohol as other organic materials also give iodoform.

Berthelot's Test. The distillate of the liquid is vigorously agitated with a few drops of benzoyl chloride and 4 or 5 drops of 10% solution of sodium hydroxide, until the penetrating odor of benzoyl chloride has disappeared. The characteristic odor of ethyl benzoate will be detected if alcohol is present in the liquid tested.

Reaction: $C_2H_5OH + C_6H_5.COCl + KOH = C_6H_5.CO.OC_2H_5 + KCl + H_2O.$

Ethyl Acetate Test. The liquid (distillate) is mixed with the same volume of concentrated sulphuric acid. A very small quantity of anhydrous (fused) sodium acetate is added and the mixture warmed. The odor of ethyl acetate will be recognized if alcohol was present in the liquid tested.

Reactions: $C_2H_5OH + H_2SO_4 = C_2H_5O.SO_2.OH,$
$C_2H_5O.SO_2.OH + CH_3.CO.ONa = CH_3.CO.OC_2H_5 + NaHSO_4.$

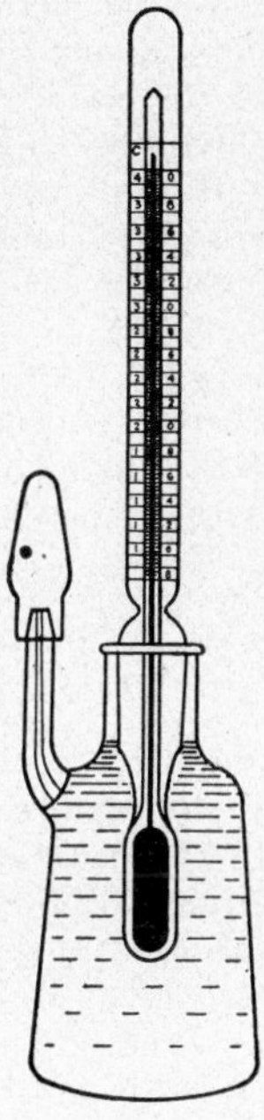

FIG. 278. Pycnometer.

Determination of Alcohol

In carbonated liquids the carbon dioxide should first be expelled by pouring the liquor back and forth from one beaker to another, or by vigorously shaking the sample in a large separatory funnel and drawing off the lower portion, repeating this several times if necessary. After treatment the liquid should be free from foam.

Distillation Method. This is the most accurate method for determination of alcohol. A convenient quantity of the sample is accurately measured or weighed, according to whether the per cent by weight or measure is desired.

*Edited by Wilfred W. Scott.

The weight taken varies from 25 to 100 grams, according to the alcohol content of the sample.

The sample is placed in a 250 to 400 cc. round-bottom flask and diluted to 150 cc. The flask is connected to a condenser and 90 to 95 cc. of the liquid is distilled into a narrow-necked flask. The distillate is made to exactly 100 cc. with distilled water.

The specific gravity of the thoroughly mixed distillate is taken by means of the pycnometer or by the Westphal balance, the temperature of the liquid being exactly 15.6° C. From the specific gravity the corresponding percentage of alcohol by weight or by volume, or the grams per 100 cc. in the distillate, is ascertained from the accompanying tables.

The percentage of alcohol by weight in the sample is obtained by multiplying the per cent by weight in the distillate by the weight of the distillate, and dividing by the weight of the sample taken. The per cent by volume is obtained by multiplying the per cent by volume in the distillate by 100 and dividing by the volume of the sample taken.

Evaporation Method. Should a distillation apparatus not be available the following method may be used. The specific gravity of the original sample is determined, the temperature being regulated to 15.6° C. A measured portion of the liquor (50–100 cc.) is placed in a porcelain dish over a water bath and three fourths of its volume evaporated off. The concentrate is diluted to exactly its original volume and its specific gravity again taken at 15.6° C. To apply the table add 1 to the original specific gravity and from this total subtract the second specific gravity. The difference is the specific gravity corresponding to the alcohol in the liquor. For example if the specific gravity of the original solution was 0.9989 and the de-alcoholized sample was 1.0005. Then $1.9989 - 1.0005 = .9984 = 1.06\%$ alcohol, by volume.

If the liquor is free from residue its specific gravity may be taken directly without distillation and the alcohol content determined, provided it is a mixture of water and alcohol.

Analysis of Grain Alcohol (Ethyl Alcohol, Spirits of Wine, Cologne Spirits)

Per cent Ethyl Alcohol. The method of determining per cent of alcohol by the distillation of the alcohol from liquors has already been discussed. In straight grain alcohol the specific gravity may be taken directly by means of the Westphal balance or by means of the pycnometer and the amount of alcohol by weight or volume obtained from the tables on page 1526.

Proof. This is obtained by multiplying the per cent by volume of the ethyl alcohol by 2.

Non-volatile Residue. 100 cc. of the sample, in a large platinum (tared) dish are evaporated on the water bath to a moist residue. The evaporation to dryness is accomplished in a water oven for two and a half hours at 100° C. The weight of the residue divided by the specific gravity gives per cent of non-volatile residue.

Acidity Expressed as Acetic Acid. 10 cc. of the alcohol are titrated with N/10 NaOH in presence of phenolphthalein indicator.

$$1 \text{ cc. N/10 NaOH} = 0.006 \text{ gram acetic acid.}$$

Distilled Solution for Determining Aldehydes, Furfural and Esters (A). To 250 cc. of the sample 30 cc. of water are added and the liquor distilled into a 250 cc. volumetric flask. When the distillate has almost reached the mark the distillation is discontinued and the volume made up to mark by addition of water. The distillate contains all the aldehyde, furfural and esters. 1 cc. of this solution is equivalent to 1 cc. of the original sample.

ALDEHYDES

Qualitative Examination

Alkaline Silver Nitrate Reagent. Three grams of $AgNO_3$ are dissolved in a little water in a 100 cc. volumetric flask, 3 grams of pure NaOH are added followed by 20 cc. of strong NaOH and the whole made to 100 cc.

Test. Ten cc. of the sample are diluted with an equal volume of water in a glass stoppered bottle, 1 cc. of the alkaline silver reagent added, and the bottle is closed and placed in a dark chamber for an hour. The liquid is now filtered and the filtrate made acid with HNO_3 and a few drops of HCl added. A precipitate of AgCl indicates the non-reduction of the silver salt and consequently a negligible amount of aldehyde in the sample.

Quantitative Determination of Aldehyde

Reagents. Alcohol—Aldehyde-free. To 1.5 liters of 95% ethyl alcohol are added 25 grams of NaOH in a large distilling flask and all but 100 cc. distilled over. To this distillate are added 2.5 grams of meta-phenylenediamine hydrochloride, the sample being placed in a large flask with reflux condenser. After heating on a steam bath for several hours the solution is distilled down to about 200 cc. The distillate (rejecting the first 100 cc.) is placed in a stoppered bottle for use.

Fuchsin-Sulphite Solution. To 0.5 gram of fuchsin dissolved in 500 cc. of water are added 5 grams of SO_2 dissolved in water. (100 cc. H_2O saturated with SO_2 at 20° C. contains 11.29 g. SO_2, at 15° C. = 13.5 g. SO_2—Seidell. Determine by titrating with N/10 iodine sol. 1 cc. = .0032 g. SO_2.) Dilute to 1000 cc. and allow to stand until colorless. The solution retains its strength only a few days, so should be made up in small quantities at a time.

Standard Acetaldehyde Solution. Five grams of aldehyde ammonia are purified by repeated extraction with ether, grinding the salt with the ether in a mortar and decanting off the ether. The salt is dried by blowing air over it and finally placing it in a vacuum desiccator over strong H_2SO_4. 1.386 gram of the purified salt is dissolved in 50 cc. of the 95% alcohol reagent prepared as stated above. To this are added 22.7 cc. of N alcoholic H_2SO_4 (49.04 grams H_2SO_4 made up to 1000 cc. with 95% alcohol) and the solution made to 100 cc. with 95% alcohol. To compensate for the $(NH_4)_2SO_4$ precipitated 0.8 cc. alcohol is added. After standing all night the solution is filtered. 100 cc. of this reagent contains 1 gram of acetaldehyde. It retains its strength.

Reagent for Standard. Two cc. of the above solution diluted with 50% alcohol to 100 cc. 1 cc. contains 0.0002 gram acetaldehyde. Make up fresh for use.

Procedure for Aldehydes

Ten cc. of the solution A are diluted to 50 cc. with the aldehyde free alcohol (diluted to 50% by volume) 25 cc. of fuchsin reagent are added and the mixture allowed to stand for 15 minutes (all reagents and the sample should be at 15° C.). The solution is now compared colorimetrically with standards made up in the same way. Nessler tubes may be used. Comparison may be made in a colorimeter. From this the per cent aldehyde is readily calculated.

Determination of Furfural

Standard Furfural Reagents. One gram of freshly redistilled furfural is dissolved in 100 cc. 95% alcohol (furfural free). This solution keeps.

One cc. of the strong solution is diluted to 100 cc. with 50% (by volume) alcohol. 1 cc. = 0.0001 gram furfural.

Procedure. Twenty cc. of the distilled solution (A) are diluted to 50 cc. with 50% (by volume) of furfural-free alcohol. To this are added 2 cc. of colorless aniline and 0.5 cc. of dilute HCl (5 : 4) and the mixture placed in a water bath at 15° C. for fifteen minutes. Colorimetric comparison is now made with standards containing known amounts of furfural, the solutions being prepared in the same way as the sample.

Determination of Esters Expressed as Ethyl Acetate

Fifty cc. of the distilled solution (A) in an Erlenmeyer flask are exactly neutralized with N/10 NaOH (phenolphthalein indicator) and about 50 cc. excess added, the exact amount being recorded. The solution is boiled for an hour with reflux condenser. After cooling, the excess of alkali is titrated with N/10 acid. The cc. N/10 NaOH consumed in the saponification, multiplied by 0.0088 gives the gram weight of esters calculated as ethyl acetate. This weight divided by the specific gravity of the sample and multiplied by 2 gives per cent.

Determination of Fusel Oil

Fifty cc. of the original sample, in an Erlenmeyer flask, are diluted with an equal volume of water and 20 cc. of N/5 NaOH added. The mixture is now saponified by boiling for an hour with reflux condenser. The flask is connected to a condenser and about 90 cc. distilled into a deep beaker. 25 cc. of water are added to the flask and the distillation continued until the total volume of the distillate is 115 cc. Finely ground salt (NaCl) is now added until the solution is almost saturated and a saturated solution of NaCl added until the specific gravity of the solution is 1.10. The solution placed in a separatory funnel is extracted four times with carbon tetrachloride, CCl₄, using 40, 30, 20 and 10 cc. CCl₄ respectively. To the extract in a separatory funnel 10 cc. of KOH solution (1 : 1) are added. This solution is cooled in ice water to 0° C. and at the same time 100 cc., accurately measured, of KMnO₄ solution (20 grams per liter) in a flask. When cooled to 0° C. the bulk of the KMnO₄ solution is added to the extract, leaving the rinsing out of the flask until later. The mixture removed from the ice bath is shaken vigorously for five minutes, then set aside for half an hour allowing it to warm up to room temperature (20–25° C.).

Into a liter Erlenmeyer flask are measured accurately 100 cc. of H_2O_2 solution (2% stronger than the $KMnO_4$ solution) followed by 100 cc. of. 25% H_2SO_4 and to this mixture are added slowly the contents of the separatory funnel, swirling to get an even distribution. (The acid solution should be constantly in excess.) The rinsing of the separatory funnel and the flask containing the residue of the $KMnO_4$ are added and the excess of the H_2O_2 determined by titration with standard $KMnO_4$ solution (10 grams $KMnO_4$ per liter).

Blank. The same amounts of stronger $KMnO_4$, KOH, H_2O_2 and H_2SO_4 are mixed side by side with the sample and the residual H_2O_2 determined with the standard $KMnO_4$ to determine the blank. This is subtracted from the first titration and the difference multiplied by the value of the standard $KMnO_4$. If this is exactly 10 grams per liter as determined by titration with N $H_2C_2O_4$ then—

1 cc. $KMnO_4$ = 0.696 gram amyl alcohol. ($KMnO_4$ 10 g. per liter.)

Note. 1 cc. N $H_2C_2O_4$ = 0.03161 g. $KMnO_4$. The standard $KMnO_4$ should contain 0.01 g. per cc. of the reagent.

Detection of Nitrates in Grain Alcohol

Fifty cc. of the sample are neutralized with N/10 NaOH (phenolphthalein indicator) and evaporated to a moist residue. A little distilled water is added and 1 cc. of phenoldisulphonic acid and the mix made alkaline with NH_4OH. A bright orange color indicates the presence of nitrates. Run a blank on the water used. See subject of nitrates in the chapter of Water.

Determination of Sulphur Compounds in Grain Alcohol

A hundred cc. of the alcohol are made slightly alkaline with N/10 NaOH (phenolphthalein) and 5 cc. H_2O_2 added, preferably in a large platinum dish. The residue is ignited over an alcohol flame then taken up with 50 cc. of water, 5 cc. dilute HCl added and 5 cc. 10% $BaCl_2$. The precipitated $BaSO_4$ is filtered off, ignited and weighed according to the customary procedure.

$$BaSO_4 \times 0.1373 = S.$$

Determination of Methyl Alcohol, Wood Spirit, Wood Naphtha, Wood Alcohol, Etc.

See Methyl Alcohol in section following the tables on alcohol.

PERCENTAGE OF ALCOHOL BY VOLUME AND BY WEIGHT*

GILPIN, DRINKWATER, AND SQUIBB

Specific Gravity at 60°/60° F.	Alcohol per cent by volume.	per cent by weight.	Grams per 100 cc.	Specific Gravity at 60°/60° F.	Alcohol per cent by volume.	per cent by weight.	Grams per 100 cc.
1.00000	0.00	0.00	0.00	.99473	3.60	2.88	2.86
0.99984	0.10	0.08	0.08	.99459	3.70	2.96	2.94
.99968	0.20	0.16	0.16	.99445	3.80	3.04	3.02
.99953	0.30	0.24	0.24	.99431	3.90	3.12	3.10
.99937	0.40	0.32	0.32	.99417	4.00	3.20	3.18
.99923	0.50	0.40	0.40	.99403	4.10	3.28	3.26
.99907	0.60	0.48	0.48	.99390	4.20	3.36	3.34
.99892	0.70	0.56	0.56	.99376	4.30	3.44	3.42
.99877	0.80	0.64	0.64	.99363	4.40	3.52	3.50
.99861	0.90	0.71	0.71	.99349	4.50	3.60	3.58
.99849	1.00	0.79	0.79	.99335	4.60	3.68	3.66
.99834	1.10	0.87	0.87	.99322	4.70	3.76	3.74
.99819	1.20	0.95	0.95	.99308	4.80	3.84	3.81
.99805	1.30	1.03	1.03	.99295	4.90	3.92	3.89
.99790	1.40	1.11	1.11	.99281	5.00	4.00	3.97
.99775	1.50	1.19	1.19	.99268	5.10	4.08	4.05
.99760	1.60	1.27	1.27	.99255	5.20	4.16	4.13
.99745	1.70	1.35	1.35	.99241	5.30	4.24	4.21
.99731	1.80	1.43	1.43	.99228	5.40	4.32	4.29
.99716	1.90	1.51	1.51	.99215	5.50	4.40	4.37
.99701	2.00	1.59	1.59	.99202	5.60	4.48	4.44
.99687	2.10	1.67	1.66	.99189	5.70	4.56	4.52
.99672	2.20	1.75	1.74	.99175	5.80	4.64	4.60
.99658	2.30	1.83	1.82	.99162	5.90	4.72	4.68
.99643	2.40	1.91	1.90	.99149	6.00	4.80	4.76
.99629	2.50	1.99	1.98	.99136	6.10	4.88	4.84
.99615	2.60	2.07	2.06	.99123	6.20	4.96	4.92
.99600	2.70	2.15	2.14	.99111	6.30	5.05	5.00
.99586	2.80	2.23	2.22	.99098	6.40	5.13	5.08
.99571	2.90	2.31	2.30	.99085	6.50	5.21	5.16
.99557	3.00	2.39	2.38	.99072	6.60	5.29	5.24
.99543	3.10	2.47	2.46	.99059	6.70	5.37	5.32
.99529	3.20	2.55	2.54	.99047	6.80	5.45	5.40
.99515	3.30	2.64	2.62	.99034	6.90	5.53	5.48
.99501	3.40	2.72	2.70	.99021	7.00	5.61	5.56
.99487	3.50	2.80	2.78	.99009	7.10	5.69	5.64
.98996	7.20	5.77	5.72	.98513	11.30	9.11	8.97
.98984	7.30	5.86	5.80	.98502	11.40	9.19	9.05
.98971	7.40	5.94	5.88	.98491	11.50	9.27	9.13
.98959	7.50	6.02	5.96	.98479	11.60	9.35	9.21
.98947	7.60	6.10	6.04	.98468	11.70	9.43	9.29
.98934	7.70	6.18	6.11	.98457	11.80	9.51	9.36
.98922	7.80	6.26	6.19	.98446	11.90	9.59	9.44
.98909	7.90	6.34	6.27	.98435	12.00	9.67	9.52
.98897	8.00	6.42	6.35	.98424	12.10	9.75	9.60
.98885	8.10	6.50	6.43	.98413	12.20	9.83	9.68
.98873	8.20	6.58	6.51	.98402	12.30	9.92	9.76
.98861	8.30	6.67	6.59	.98391	12.40	10.00	9.84
.98849	8.40	6.75	6.67	.98381	12.50	10.08	9.92
.98837	8.50	6.83	6.75	.98370	12.60	10.16	10.00

* Bulletin No. 65, U. S. Department of Agriculture.

PERCENTAGE OF ALCOHOL BY VOLUME AND BY WEIGHT

(Continued)

Specific Gravity at 60°/60° F.	Alcohol			Specific Gravity at 60°/60° F.	Alcohol		
	per cent by volume.	per cent by weight.	Grams per 100 cc.		per cent by volume.	per cent by weight.	Grams per 100 cc.
.98825	8.60	6.91	6.83	.98359	12.70	10.24	10.07
.98813	8.70	6.99	6.91	.98348	12.80	10.33	10.15
.98801	8.80	7.07	6.99	.98337	12.90	10.41	10.23
.98789	8.90	7.15	7.07	.98326	13.00	10.49	10.31
.98777	9.00	7.23	7.14	.98315	13.10	10.57	10.39
.98765	9.10	7.31	7.22	.98305	13.20	10.65	10.47
.98754	9.20	7.39	7.30	.98294	13.30	10.74	10.55
.98742	9.30	7.48	7.38	.98283	13.40	10.82	10.63
.98730	9.40	7.56	7.46	.98273	13.50	10.90	10.71
.98719	9.50	7.64	7.54	.98262	13.60	10.98	10.79
.98707	9.60	7.72	7.62	.98251	13.70	11.06	10.87
.98695	9.70	7.80	7.70	.98240	13.80	11.15	10.95
.98683	9.80	7.88	7.78	.98230	13.90	11.23	11.03
.98672	9.90	7.96	7.85	.98219	14.00	11.31	11.11
.98660	10.00	8.04	7.93	.98209	14.10	11.39	11.19
.98649	10.10	8.12	8.01	.98198	14.20	11.47	11.27
.98637	10.20	8.20	8.09	.98188	14.30	11.56	11.35
.98626	10.30	8.29	8.17	.98177	14.40	11.64	11.43
.98614	10.40	8.37	8.25	.98167	14.50	11.72	11.51
.98603	10.50	8.45	8.33	.98156	14.60	11.80	11.59
.98592	10.60	8.53	8.41	.98146	14.70	11.88	11.67
.98580	10.70	8.61	8.49	.98135	14.80	11.97	11.75
.98569	10.80	8.70	8.57	.98125	14.90	12.05	11.82
.98557	10.90	8.78	8.65	.98114	15.00	12.13	11.90
.98546	11.00	8.86	8.73	.98104	15.10	12.21	11.98
.98535	11.10	8.94	8.81	.98093	15.20	12.29	12.06
.98524	11.20	9.02	8.89	.98083	15.30	12.38	12.14
.98073	15.40	12.46	12.22	.97658	19.50	15.84	15.47
.98063	15.50	12.54	12.30	.97648	19.60	15.93	15.55
.93052	15.60	12.62	12.37	.97638	19.70	16.01	15.63
.98042	15.70	12.70	12.45	.97628	19.80	16.09	15.71
.98032	15.80	12.79	12.53	.97618	19.90	16.18	15.79
.98021	15.90	12.87	12.61	.97608	20.00	16.26	15.87
.98011	16.00	12.95	12.69	.97598	20.10	16.34	15.95
.98001	16.10	13.03	12.77	.97588	20.20	16.42	16.03
.97991	16.20	13.12	12.85	.97578	20.30	16.51	16.10
.97980	16.30	13.20	12.93	.97568	20.40	16.59	16.18
.97970	16.40	13.29	13.01	.97558	20.50	16.67	16.26
.97960	16.50	13.37	13.09	.97547	20.60	16.75	16.34
.97950	16.60	13.45	13.17	.97537	20.70	16.84	16.42
.97940	16.70	13.53	13.25	.97527	20.80	16.92	16.50
.97929	16.80	13.62	13.33	.97517	20.90	17.01	16.58
.97919	16.90	13.70	13.41	.97507	21.00	17.09	16.66
.97909	17.00	13.78	13.49	.97497	21.10	17.17	16.74
.97899	17.10	13.86	13.57	.97487	21.20	17.26	16.82
.97889	17.20	13.94	13.65	.97477	21.30	17.34	16.90
.97879	17.30	14.03	13.73	.97467	21.40	17.43	16.98
.97869	17.40	14.11	13.81	.97457	21.50	17.51	17.06
.97859	17.50	14.19	13.89	.97446	21.60	17.59	17.14
.97848	17.60	14.27	13.96	.97436	21.70	17.67	17.22
.97838	17.70	14.35	14.04	.97426	21.80	17.76	17.30
.97828	17.80	14.44	14.12	.97416	21.90	17.84	17.38
.97818	17.90	14.52	14.20	.97406	22.00	17.92	17.46

PERCENTAGE OF ALCOHOL BY VOLUME AND BY WEIGHT

(Continued)

Specific Gravity at 60°/60° F.	Alcohol per cent by volume.	Alcohol per cent by weight.	Grams per 100 cc.	Specific Gravity at 60°/60° F.	Alcohol per cent by volume.	Alcohol per cent by weight.	Grams per 100 cc.
.97808	18.00	14.60	14.28	.97396	22.10	18.00	17.54
.97798	18.10	14.68	14.36	.97386	22.20	18.09	17.62
.97788	18.20	14.77	14.44	.97375	22.30	18.17	17.70
.97778	18.30	14.85	14.52	.97365	22.40	18.26	17.78
.97768	18.40	14.94	14.60	.97355	22.50	18.34	17.86
.97758	18.50	15.02	14.68	.97345	22.60	18.42	17.94
.97748	18.60	15.10	14.76	.97335	22.70	18.51	18.02
.97738	18.70	15.18	14.84	.97324	22.80	18.59	18.10
.97728	18.80	15.27	14.92	.97314	22.90	18.68	18.18
.97718	18.90	15.38	15.00	.97304	23.00	18.76	18.26
.97708	19.00	15.43	15.08	.97294	23.10	18.84	18.33
.97698	19.10	15.51	15.15	.97283	23.20	18.92	18.41
.97688	19.20	15.59	15.23	.97273	23.30	19.01	18.49
.97678	19.30	15.68	15.31	.97263	23.40	19.09	18.57
.97668	19.40	15.76	15.39	.97253	23.50	19.17	18.65
.97242	23.60	19.25	18.73	.96805	27.70	22.71	21.98
.97232	23.70	19.34	18.81	.96794	27.80	22.79	22.06
.97222	23.80	19.42	18.88	.96783	27.90	22.88	22.14
.97211	23.90	19.51	18.96	.96772	28.00	22.96	22.22
.97201	24.00	19.59	19.04	.96761	28.10	23.04	22.30
.97191	24.10	19.67	19.12	.96749	28.20	23.13	22.38
.97180	24.20	19.76	19.20	.96738	28.30	23.21	22.45
.97170	24.30	19.84	19.28	.96726	28.40	23.30	22.53
.97159	24.40	19.93	19.36	.96715	28.50	23.38	22.61
.97149	24.50	20.01	19.44	.96704	28.60	23.47	22.69
.97139	24.60	20.09	19.52	.96692	28.70	23.55	22.77
.97128	24.70	20.18	19.60	.96681	28.80	23.64	22.85
.97118	24.80	20.26	19.68	.96669	28.90	23.72	22.93
.97107	24.90	20.35	19.76	.96658	29.00	23.81	23.01
.97097	25.00	20.43	19.84	.96646	29.10	23.89	23.09
.97086	25.10	20.51	19.92	.96635	29.20	23.98	23.17
.97076	25.20	20.60	20.00	.96623	29.30	24.06	23.25
.97065	25.30	20.68	20.08	.96611	29.40	24.15	23.33
.97055	25.40	20.77	20.16	.96600	29.50	24.23	23.41
.97044	25.50	20.85	20.24	.96587	29.60	24.32	23.49
.97033	25.60	20.93	20.32	.96576	29.70	24.40	23.57
.97023	25.70	21.02	20.40	.96564	29.80	24.49	23.65
.97012	25.80	21.10	20.47	.96553	29.90	24.57	23.73
.97001	25.90	21.19	20.55	.96541	30.00	24.66	23.81
.96991	26.00	21.27	20.63	.96529	30.10	24.74	23.89
.96980	26.10	21.35	20.71	.96517	30.20	24.83	23.97
.96969	26.20	21.44	20.79	.96505	30.30	24.91	24.04
.96959	26.30	21.52	20.87	.96493	30.40	25.00	24.12
.96949	26.40	21.61	20.95	.96481	30.50	25.08	24.20
.96937	26.50	21.69	21.03	.96469	30.60	25.17	24.28
.96926	26.60	21.77	21.11	.96457	30.70	25.25	24.36
.96915	26.70	21.86	21.19	.96445	30.80	25.34	24.44
.96905	26.80	21.94	21.27	.96433	30.90	25.42	24.52
.96894	26.90	22.03	21.35	.96421	31.00	25.51	24.60
.96883	27.00	22.11	21.43	.96409	31.10	25.60	24.68
.96872	27.10	22.20	21.51	.96396	31.20	25.68	24.76
.96861	27.20	22.28	21.59	.96384	31.30	25.77	24.84
.96850	27.30	22.37	21.67	.96372	31.40	25.85	24.92

PERCENTAGE OF ALCOHOL BY VOLUME AND BY WEIGHT

(Continued)

Specific Gravity at 60°/60° F.	Alcohol			Specific Gravity at 60°/60° F.	Alcohol		
	per cent by volume.	per cent by weight.	Grams per 100 cc.		per cent by volume.	per cent by weight.	Grams per 100 cc.
.96839	27.40	22.45	21.75	.96360	31.50	25.94	25.00
.96828	27.50	22.54	21.83	.96347	31.60	26.03	25.08
.96816	27.60	22.62	21.90	.96335	31.70	26.11	25.16
.96323	31.80	26.20	25.24	.95787	35.90	29.74	28.49
.96310	31.90	26.28	25.32	.95773	36.00	29.83	28.57
.96298	32.00	26.37	25.40	.95759	36.10	29.92	28.65
.96285	32.10	26.46	25.48	.95745	36.20	30.00	28.73
.96273	32.20	26.54	25.56	.95731	36.30	30.09	28.81
.96260	32.30	26.63	25.64	.95717	36.40	30.17	28.88
.96248	32.40	26.71	25.71	.95703	36.50	30.26	28.96
.96235	32.50	26.80	25.79	.95688	36.60	30.35	29.04
.96222	32.60	26.89	25.87	.95674	36.70	30.44	29.12
.96210	32.70	26.97	25.95	.95660	36.80	30.52	29.20
.96197	32.80	27.06	26.03	.95646	36.90	30.61	29.29
.96185	32.90	27.14	26.11	.95632	37.00	30.70	29.36
.96172	33.00	27.23	26.19	.95618	37.10	30.79	29.44
.96159	33.10	27.32	26.27	.95603	37.20	30.88	29.52
.96146	33.20	27.40	26.35	.95589	37.30	30.96	29.60
.96133	33.30	27.49	26.43	.95574	37.40	31.05	29.68
.96120	33.40	27.57	26.51	.95560	37.50	31.14	29.76
.96108	33.50	27.66	26.59	.95545	37.60	31.23	29.84
.96095	33.60	27.75	26.67	.95531	37.70	31.32	29.92
.96082	33.70	27.83	26.75	.95516	37.80	31.40	30.00
.96069	33.80	27.92	26.82	.95502	37.90	31.49	30.08
.96056	33.90	28.00	26.90	.95487	38.00	31.58	30.16
.96043	34.00	28.09	26.98	.95472	38.10	31.67	30.24
.96030	34.10	28.18	27.06	.95457	38.20	31.76	30.32
.96016	34.20	28.26	27.14	.95442	38.30	31.85	30.40
.96003	34.30	28.35	27.22	.95427	38.40	31.94	30.48
.95990	34.40	28.43	27.30	.95413	38.50	32.03	30.56
.95977	34.50	28.52	27.38	.95398	38.60	32.12	30.64
.95963	34.60	28.61	27.46	.95383	38.70	32.20	30.72
.95950	34.70	28.70	27.54	.95368	38.80	32.29	30.79
.95937	34.80	28.78	27.62	.05353	38.90	32.37	30.87
.95923	34.90	28.87	27.70	.95338	39.00	32.46	30.95
.95910	35.00	28.96	27.78	.95323	39.10	32.55	31.03
.95896	35.10	29.05	27.86	.95307	39.20	32.64	31.11
.95883	35.20	29.13	27.94	.95292	39.30	32.72	31.18
.95869	35.30	29.22	28.02	.95277	39.40	32.81	31.26
.95855	35.40	29.30	28.09	.95262	39.50	32.90	31.34
.95842	35.50	29.38	28.17	.95246	39.60	32.99	31.42
.95828	35.60	29.48	28.25	.95231	39.70	33.08	31.50
.95814	35.70	29.57	28.33	.95216	39.80	33.17	31.58
.95800	35.80	29.65	28.41	.95200	39.90	33.27	31.66
.95185	40.00	33.35	31.74	.94519	44.10	37.02	34.99
.95169	40.10	33.44	31.82	.94502	44.20	37.11	35.07
.95154	40.20	33.53	31.90	.94484	44.30	37.21	35.15
.95138	40.30	33.61	31.98	.94467	44.40	37.30	35.23
.95122	40.40	33.70	32.06	.94450	44.50	37.39	35.31
.95107	40.50	33.79	32.14	.94433	44.60	37.48	35.39
.95091	40.60	33.88	32.22	.94416	44.70	35.57	35.47
.95075	40.70	33.97	32.30	.94398	44.80	37.66	35.55
.95059	40.80	34.06	32.38	.94381	44.90	37.76	35.63

PERCENTAGE OF ALCOHOL BY VOLUME AND BY WEIGHT*

(Continued)

Specific Gravity at $\frac{60°}{60°}$ F.	Alcohol			Specific Gravity at $\frac{60°}{60°}$ F.	Alcohol		
	per cent by volume.	per cent by weight.	Grams per 100 cc.		per cent by volume.	per cent by weight.	Grams per 100 cc.
.95044	40.90	34.15	32.46	.94364	45.00	37.84	35.71
.95028	41.00	34.24	32.54	.94346	45.10	37.93	35.79
.95012	41.10	34.33	32.62	.94329	45.20	38.02	35.87
.94996	41.20	34.42	32.70	.94311	45.30	38.12	35.95
.94980	41.30	34.50	32.78	.94294	45.40	38.21	36.03
.94964	41.40	34.59	32.86	.94276	45.50	38.30	36.11
.94948	41.50	34.68	32.93	.94258	45.60	38.39	36.19
.94932	41.60	34.77	33.01	.94241	45.70	38.48	36.26
.94916	41.70	34.86	33.09	.94223	45.80	38.57	36.34
.94900	41.80	34.95	33.17	.94206	45.90	38.66	36.42
.94884	41.90	35.04	33.25	.94188	46.00	38.75	36.50
.94868	42.00	35.13	33.33	.94170	46.10	38.84	36.58
.94852	42.10	35.22	33.41	.94152	46.20	38.93	36.66
.94835	42.20	35.31	33.49	.94134	46.30	39.03	36.74
.94810	42.30	35.40	33.57	.94116	46.40	39.12	36.82
.94802	42.40	35.49	33.65	.94098	46.50	39.21	36.90
.94786	42.50	35.58	33.73	.94080	46.60	39.30	36.98
.94770	42.60	35.67	33.81	.94062	46.70	39.39	37.06
.94753	42.70	35.76	33.89	.94044	46.80	39.49	37.13
.94737	42.80	35.85	33.97	.94026	46.90	39.58	37.21
.94720	42.90	35.94	34.04	.94008	47.00	39.67	37.29
.94704	43.00	36.03	34.12	.93990	47.10	39.76	37.37
.94687	43.10	36.12	34.20	.93971	47.20	39.85	37.45
.94670	43.20	36.21	34.28	.93953	47.30	39.95	37.53
.94654	43.30	36.30	34.36	.93934	47.40	40.04	37.61
.94637	43.40	36.39	34.44	.93916	47.50	40.13	37.69
.94620	43.50	36.48	34.52	.93898	47.60	40.22	37.77
.94603	43.60	36.57	34.60	.93879	47.70	40.32	37.85
.94586	43.70	36.66	34.68	.93861	47.80	40.41	37.93
.94570	43.80	36.75	34.76	.93842	47.90	40.51	38.01
.94553	43.90	36.84	34.84	.93824	48.00	40.60	38.09
.94536	44.00	36.93	34.91	.93805	48.10	40.69	38.17
.93786	48.20	40.78	38.25	.93617	49.10	41.61	38.96
.93768	48.30	40.88	38.33	.93598	49.20	41.71	39.04
.93749	48.40	40.97	38.41	.93578	49.30	41.80	39.12
.93730	48.50	41.06	38.49	.93559	49.40	41.90	39.20
.93711	48.60	41.15	38.57	.93540	49.50	41.99	39.28
.93692	48.70	41.24	38.65	.93521	49.60	42.08	39.36
.93679	48.80	41.34	38.72	.93502	49.70	42.18	39.44
.93655	48.90	41.43	38.80	.93482	49.80	42.27	39.52
.93636	49.00	41.52	38.88	.93463	49.90	42.37	39.60

* See additional tables in Chem. Annual, D. Van Nostrand Co.

METHYL ALCOHOL

Detection of Methyl Alcohol—Method of Riche and Bardy[1]

The following method for the detection of methyl alcohol in commercial
spirit of wine depends on the formation of methyl-anilin violet:

Place 10 cc. of the sample, previously rectified over potassium carbonate if
necessary, in a small flask with 15 grams of iodine and 2 grams of red phos-
horus. Keep in ice water for from ten to fifteen minutes until action has
ceased. Distil on a water bath the methyl and ethyl iodides formed into about
10 cc. of water. Wash with dilute alkali to eliminate free iodine. Separate
the heavy oily liquid which settles and transfer to a flask containing 5 cc.

FIG. 279.   Pyc-
nometer.

of anilin. The flask should be placed in cold water, in case the
action should be violent, or, if necessary, the reaction may be
stimulated by gently warming the flask. After one hour boil
the product with water and add about 20 cc. of a 15 per cent
solution of soda; when the bases rise to the top as an oily layer
fill the flask up to the neck with water and draw them off with
a pipette. Oxidize 1 cc. of the oily liquid by adding 10 grams
of a mixture of 100 parts of clean sand, 2 of common salt,
and 3 of cupric nitrate; mix thoroughly, introduce into a
glass tube, and heat to 90° C. for eight or ten hours. Exhaust
the product with warm alcohol, filter, and make up with alcohol to 100 cc. If the sample of spirits be pure the liquid is
of a red tint, but in the presence of 1 per cent of methyl
alcohol it has a distinct violet shade; with 2.5 per cent the
shade is very distinct, and still more so with 5 per cent. To

detect more minute quantities of methyl alcohol, dilute 5 cc. of the colored
liquid to 100 cc. with water, and dilute 5 cc. of this again to 400 cc. Heat the
liquid thus obtained in porcelain and immerse a fragment of white merino (free
from sulphur) in it for half an hour. If the alcohol be pure the wool will remain
white, but if methylated the fiber will become violet, the depth of tint giving a
fair approximate indication of the proportion of methyl alcohol present.

Detection of Methanol (" Methyl Alcohol ") Oxidation Method

Twenty-five cc. of the sample are diluted to about 100 cc. in a small distillation flask and about 10 grams of chromic acid added. Methyl alcohol, if
present, is oxidized to formaldehyde. 15 to 20 cc. of the solution are distilled
into a large test tube and a 5 to 10 cc. portion tested for formaldehyde by one
of the methods outlined on the following page.

Detection of Methanol (" Wood Alcohol ") in the Presence of Ethyl Alcohol [2]

Dilute 1 cc. of the alcohol with water to 100 cc. To 2 cc. of this solution add
2 cc. $KMnO_4$ (25 g. per l.) and 0.4 cc. 50% H_2SO_4. After 3 minutes destroy
excess of $KMnO_4$ with oxalic acid, add 1 cc. of H_2SO_4 and 5 cc. of Schiff's
fuchsin bisulphite reagent. In the presence of CH_3OH a violet color is produced on long standing (HCHO formed). Ethyl alcohol produces no color.
1% CH_3OH may be detected. 3% gives an intense color.

    Reagent. Schiff's Fuchsin Bisulphite—0.5 fuchsin in 500 cc. of water, add
sufficient SO_2 to bleach the solution, make up to 1000 cc.

[1] Allen's Commercial Organic Analysis, 3d ed., **1**: 80.
[2] A. Kling and A. Lassieur, C. A., **18**, 1801 (June 20, 1924).

FORMALDEHYDE

Detection of Formaldehyde[1]

Leach's Test. The solution in which formaldehyde is suspected, obtained by distillation if necessary, is tested as follows: To a 10 cc. portion, in a casserole, an equal volume of pure milk is added followed by 10 cc. hydrochloric acid (sp. gr. 1.2) containing about 1 cc. of 10% ferric chloride solution per 50 of the acid. The mixture is heated to 80–90° C., the curd being broken up by agitation. A violet-colored solution indicates formaldehyde.

Hehner's Test. Five cc. of the solution in a large test tube is mixed with about 50 cc. of pure milk, the tube tilted to a side and strong sulphuric acid carefully added so as to run down the wall of the tube without mixing with the milk. At the juncture of the acid and milk a violet color will appear if aldehyde is present.

Morphine-Sulphate Test. To 5 cc. of morphine sulphate reagent [0.5 gram of morphine sulphate in 500 cc. sulphuric acid (sp. gr. 1.82)] a 2 cc. portion of the solution to be tested is added. The presence of formaldehyde is indicated by a violet color that developes on standing.

Estimation of Formaldehyde in Solution

Formaldehyde, HCHO, is a gas sold in aqueous solution (37% HCHO or over). The solution generally contains alcohol to prevent polymerization.

Determination of Formaldehyde

Hydrogen Peroxide Method.[2] To 50 cc. of normal NaOH in an Erlenmeyer flask are added 50 cc. of neutral H_2O_2 (3% sol.) and 3 cc. of the formaldehyde solution under examination, care being taken to add the sample with the tip of the measuring pipette near the surface of the reagents. A funnel is placed in the neck of the flask and the mixture heated for five minutes on the steam bath, with occasional shaking. The solution is now cooled, the funnel rinsed down, and the excess of N NaOH titrated by normal H_2SO_4, in presence of purified litmus indicator

$$1 \text{ cc. N NaOH} = 0.03002 \text{ gram HCHO.}$$

[1] Carry out the tests with blanks of pure ethyl alcohol and ethyl alcohol containing a little methyl alcohol.

[2] J. Assoc. Official Agr. Chemists, Methods of Analysis (1916), page 75.

GLYCEROL

There are two recognized methods for the determination of glycerol:

A. Acetin method, depending upon the conversion of glycerol to triacetin by means of acetic anhydride and sodium acetate and a quantitative saponification of the triacetin. This method is recommended by the International Committee on glycerol as giving results nearer the truth and should be employed for crude and refined glycerines of over 40% strength.

B. Bichromate method, which is based on the fact that glycerole is completely oxidized to CO_2 and H_2O by $K_2Cr_2O_7$ in presence of H_2SO_4. The method is applicable for determination of glycerines in soap lyes.

The following procedures are taken from the report as recommended.[1]

Acetin Process for the Determination of Glycerol[2]

Reagents Required

(A) Best Acetic Anhydride. This should be carefully selected. A good sample must not require more than 0.1 cc. normal NaOH for saponification of the impurities when a blank is run on 7.5 cc. Only a slight color should develop during digestion of the blank.

The anhydride may be tested for strength by the following method: Into a weighed stoppered vessel, containing 10 to 20 cc. of water, run about 2 cc. of the anhydride, replace the stopper and weigh. Let stand with occasional shaking, for several hours, to permit the hydrolysis of all the anhydride; then dilute to about 200 cc., add phenolphthalein and titrate with N/1 NaOH. This gives the total acidity due to free acetic acid and acid formed from the anhydride. It is worthy of note that in the presence of much free anhydride a compound is formed with phenolphthalein, soluble in alkali and acetic acid, but insoluble in neutral solutions. If a turbidity is noticed toward the end of the neutralization it is an indication that the anhydride is incompletely hydrolyzed and inasmuch as the indicator is withdrawn from the solution, results may be incorrect.

Into a stoppered weighing bottle containing a known weight of recently distilled aniline (from 10 to 20 cc.) measure about 2 cc. of the sample, stopper, mix, cool and weigh. Wash the contents into about 200 cc. of cold water, and titrate the acidity as before. This yields the acidity due to the original, preformed, acetic acid plus one-half the acid due to anhydride (the other half having formed acetanilide); subtract the second result from the first (both calculated to 100 grams) and double the result, obtaining the cc. N/1 NaOH per 100 grams of the sample. 1 cc. N/NaOH equals 0.0510 anhydride.

(B) Pure Fused Sodium Acetate. The purchased salt is again completely fused in a platinum, silica or nickel dish, avoiding charring, powdered quickly and kept in a stoppered bottle or desiccator. It is most important that the sodium acetate be anhydrous.

(C) A Solution of Caustic Soda for Neutralizing, of about N/1 Strength, Free from Carbonate. This can be readily made by dissolving pure sodium hydroxide in its own weight of water (preferably water free from carbon dioxide) and allowing to settle until clear, or filtering through an asbestos or

---

[1] Jour. Ind. Chem. Eng., 3, 679–685, 1911.
[2] Jour. Ind. Eng. Chem., Sept., 1911, pp. 683–685.

paper filter. The clear solution is diluted with water free from carbon dioxide to the strength required.

(D) N/1 Caustic Soda Free from Carbonate. Prepared as above and carefully standardized. Some caustic soda solutions show a marked diminution in strength after being boiled; such solutions should be rejected.

(E) N/1 Acid. Carefully standardized.

(F) Phenolphthalein Solution. 0.5 per cent phenolphthalein in alcohol and neutralized.

The Method

In a narrow-mouthed flask (preferably round-bottomed), capacity about 120 cc., which has been thoroughly cleaned and dried, weigh accurately and as rapidly as possible 1.25 to 1.5 grams of the glycerine. A Grethan or Lunge pipette will be found convenient. Add about 3 grams of the anhydrous sodium acetate, then 7.5 cc. of the acetic anhydride, and connect the flask with an upright Liebig condenser. For convenience the inner tube of this condenser should not be over 50 cm. long and 9 to 10 mm. inside diameter. The flask is connected to the condenser by either a ground glass joint (preferably) or a rubber stopper. If a rubber stopper is used it should have had a preliminary treatment with hot acetic anhydride vapor.

Heat the contents and keep just boiling for one hour, taking precautions to prevent the salts drying on the sides of the flask.

Allow the flask to cool somewhat, and through the condenser tube add 50 cc. of distilled water free from carbon dioxide at a temperature of about 80° C., taking care that the flask is not loosened from the condenser. The object of cooling is to avoid any sudden rush of vapors from the flask on adding water, and to avoid breaking the flask. Time is saved by adding the water before the contents of the flask solidify, but the contents may be allowed to solidify and the test proceeded with the next day without detriment, bearing in mind that the anhydride in excess is much more effectively hydrolyzed in hot than in cold water. The contents of the flask may be warmed to, but must not exceed, 80° C., until the solution is complete, except a few dark flocks representing organic impurities in the crude. By giving the flask a rotary motion, solution is more quickly effected.

Cool the flask and contents without loosening from the condenser. When quite cold wash down the inside of the condenser tube, detach the flask, wash off the stopper or ground glass connection into the flask, and filter the contents through an acid-washed filter into a Jena glass flask of about 1 liter capacity. Wash thoroughly with cold distilled water free from carbon dioxide. Add 2 cc. of phenolphthalein solution (*F*), then run in caustic soda solution (*C*) or (*D*) until a faint pinkish yellow color appears throughout the solution. This neutralization must be done most carefully; the alkali should be run down the sides of the flask, the contents of which are kept rapidly swirling with occasional agitation or change of motion until the solution is nearly neutralized, as indicated by the slower disappearance of the color developed locally by the alkali running into the mixture. When this point is reached the sides of the flask are washed down with carbon dioxide-free water and the alkali subsequently added drop by drop, mixing after each drop until the desired tint is obtained.

Now run in from a burette 50 cc. or a calculated excess of N/1 NaOH (D) and note carefully the exact amount. Boil gently for 15 minutes, the flask being fitted with a glass tube acting as a partial condenser. Cool as quickly as possible and titrate the excess of NaOH with N/1 acid (E) until the pinkish yellow or chosen end-point color just remains.[1] A further addition of the indicator at this point will cause an increase of the pink color; this must be neglected, and the first end-point taken.

From the N/1 NaOH consumed calculate the percentage of glycerol (including acetylizable impurities) after making the correction for the blank test described below.

1 cc. N/1 NaOH = 0.03069 gram glycerol.

The coefficient of expansion for normal solutions is 0.00033 per cc. for each degree centigrade. A correction should be made on this account if necessary.

Blank Test. As the acetic anhydride and sodium acetate may contain impurities which affect the result, it is necessary to make a blank test, using the same quantities of acetic anhydride, sodium acetate and water as in the analysis. It is not necessary to filter the solution of the melt in this case, but sufficient time must be allowed for the hydrolysis of the anhydride before proceeding with the neutralization. After neutralization it is not necessary to add more than 10 cc. of the N/1 alkali (D), as this represents the excess usually present after the saponification of the average soap lye crude. In determining the acid equivalent of the N/1 NaOH, however, the entire amount taken in the analysis, 50 cc., should be titrated after dilution with 300 cc. water free from carbon dioxide and without boiling.

Determination of the Glycerol Value of the Acetylizable Impurities. The total residue at 160° C. is dissolved in 1 or 2 cc. of water, washed into the acetylizing flask and evaporated to dryness. Then add anhydrous sodium acetate and acetic anhydride in the usual amounts and proceed as described in the regular analysis. After correcting for the blank, calculate the result to glycerol.

Instructions for Calculating the Actual Glycerol Content

(1) Determine the apparent percentage of glycerol in the sample by the acetin process as described. The result will include acetylizable impurities if any are present.

(2) Determine the total residue at 160° C.

(3) Determine the acetin value of the residue at (2) in terms of glycerol.

(4) Deduct the result found at (3) from the percentage obtained at (1) and report this corrected figure as glycerol. If volatile acetylizable impurities are present these are included in this figure.

Trimethylenglycol is more volatile than glycerine and can therefore be concentrated by fractional distillation. An approximation to the quantity can be obtained from the spread between the acetin and bichromate results on such distillates. The spread multiplied by 1.736 will give the glycol.

[1] A precipitate at this point is an indication of the presence of iron or alumina, and high results will be obtained unless a correction is made as described below.

Bichromate Process for Glycerol Determination. Reagents Required

(A) **Pure potassium bichromate** powdered and dried in air free from dust or organic vapors, at 110° to 120° C. This is taken as the standard.

(B) **Dilute Bichromate Solution.** 7.4564 grams of the above bichromate are dissolved in distilled water and the solution made up to one liter at 15.5° C.

(C) **Ferrous Ammonium Sulphate.** It is never safe to assume this salt to be constant in composition and it must be standardized against the bichromate as follows: dissolve 3.7282 grams of bichromate (A) in 50 cc. of water. Add 50 cc. of 50 per cent. sulphuric acid (by volume), and to the cold undiluted solution add from a weighing bottle a moderate excess of the ferrous ammonium sulphate, and titrate back with the dilute bichromate (B). Calculate the value of the ferrous salt in terms of bichromate.

(D) **Silver Carbonate.** This is prepared as required for each test from 140 cc. of 0.5 per cent. silver sulphate solution by precipitation with about 4.9 cc. N/1 sodium carbonate solution (a little less than the calculated quantity of N/1 sodium carbonate should be used as an excess prevents rapid settling). Settle, decant and wash once by decantation.

(E) **Subacetate of Lead.** Boil a 10 per cent. solution of pure lead acetate with an excess of litharge for one hour, keeping the volume constant, and filter while hot. Disregard any precipitate which subsequently forms. Preserve out of contact with carbon dioxide.

(F) **Potassium Ferricyanide.** A very dilute, freshly prepared solution containing about 0.1 per cent.

The Method

Weigh 20 grams of the glycerine, dilute to 250 cc. and take 25 cc. Add the silver carbonate, allow to stand, with occasional agitation, for about 10 minutes, and add a slight excess (about 5 cc. in most cases) of the basic lead acetate (E), allow to stand a few minutes, dilute with distilled water to 100 cc., and then add 0.15 cc. to compensate for the volume of the precipitate, mix thoroughly, filter through an air-dry filter into a suitable narrow-mouthed vessel, rejecting the first 10 cc., and return the filtrate if not clear and bright. Test a portion of the filtrate with a little basic lead acetate, which should produce no further precipitate (in the great majority of cases 5 cc. are ample, but occasionally a crude will be found requiring more, and in this case another aliquot of 25 cc. of the dilute glycerine should be taken and purified with 6 cc. of the basic acetate). Care must be taken to avoid a marked excess of basic acetate.

Measure off 25 cc. of the clear filtrate into a flask or beaker (previously cleaned with potassium bichromate and sulphuric acid). Add 12 drops of sulphuric acid (1 : 4) to precipitate the small excess of lead as sulphate. Add 3.7282 grams of the powdered potassium bichromate (A). Rinse down the bichromate with 25 cc. of water and let stand with occasional shaking until all the bichromate is dissolved (no reduction will take place in the cold).

Now add 50 cc. of 50 per cent. sulphuric acid (by volume) and immerse the vessel in boiling water for two hours and keep protected from dust and organic vapors, such as alcohol, till the titration is completed. Add from a weighing bottle a slight excess of the ferrous ammonium sulphate (C), making spot tests on a porcelain plate with the potassium ferricyanide (F). Titrate back with the dilute bichromate. From the amount of bichromate reduced calculate the percentage of glycerol.

1 gram glycerol = 7.4564 grams bichromate.

1 gram bichromate = 0.13411 gram glycerol.

The percentage of glycerol obtained above includes any oxidizable impurities present after the purification. A correction for the non-volatile impurities may be made by running a bichromate test on the residue at 160° C.

For complete analysis see Journal of Industrial and Engineering Chemistry, Sept., 1911, pages 679–683.

NOTES. (1) It is important that the concentration of acid in the oxidation mixture and the time of oxidation should be strictly adhered to.

(2) Before the bichromate is added to the glycerine solution it is essential that the slight excess of lead be precipitated with sulphuric acid, as stipulated.

(3) For crudes practically free from chlorides the quantity of silver carbonate may be reduced to one-fifth and the basic lead acetate to 0.5 cc.

(4) It is sometimes advisable to add a little potassium sulphate to insure a clear filtrate.

ACETONE

Analysis of Acetone by Messinger's Method

An amount of acetone in aqueous solution, equivalent to 30–40 mg. is pipetted or added to 50 cc. of N sodium hydroxide solution contained in a glass bottle which can be closed with a ground glass stopper. After standing for 5 minutes, about 25% excess of a 0.1 N solution of iodine is run in from a burette with continual shaking. It is essential to shake properly or to keep the liquid in continuous rotation. The excess of iodine is needed to complete the reaction.[1] The bottle is then stoppered and the solution allowed to stand for at least 10 minutes (20 minutes in cold weather).

Twenty-five cc. of 2 N sulphuric acid is then added from a measuring cylinder, 0.3–0.4 cc. being added in excess of the amount found necessary to neutralize the 50 cc. of caustic soda solution. A 0.05 N solution of sodium thiosulphate is then added from a burette until the yellow color just remains visible. Freshly prepared starch solution is now added and the titration finished. 1 cc. of 0.1 N iodine = 0.96747 mg. of acetone.

If a larger excess of sulphuric acid is added, too much thiosulphate is required, and the real amount of iodine solution required is thus reduced (see below).

If the bottle is not shaken vigorously while adding the iodine solution, the iodine cannot act completely on the acetone.

[1] L. F. Goodwin, Jour. Am. Chem. Soc., 42, 39–45 (Jan., 1920).

TANNIC ACID[1]

The following procedure is applicable for the examination of pure tannic acid solutions and tannins.

Reagents

Potassium Permanganate. Approximately N/10 $KMnO_4$. Standardize against N/10 oxalic acid solution.

Indigo Carmin Solution. 5 grams of pure indigo carmin dissolved in water, 50 grams of conc. H_2SO_4 are added and the solution diluted to 1000 cc.

Gelatin Solution. 20 grams of pure gelatine dissolved in hot water and diluted to 1 liter.

Saturate NaCl Acid Solution. 5 per cent H_2SO_4 solution saturated with NaCl.

Total Astringency—Lowenthal=Proctor Method

Standardization of the Indigo Carmin Solution. The filtered solution should give a yellow color free from brown when oxidized with $KMnO_4$.

Twenty-five cc. of the reagent in a porcelain casserole are diluted to 750 cc. with water and the $KMnO_4$ reagent added drop by drop from a burette with constant stirring until a pure yellow color is obtained. The rate of titration should be uniform in all tests and should be carried out very cautiously as the endpoint is approached. This is recognized by a faint pinkish rim appearing, best seen on the shaded side of the casserole.

Procedure for Astringency. 1 gram of solid (or 2–5 grams of solution sumac extract) is dissolved in water and diluted to 1 liter. 10 cc. of this solution is placed in a large casserole containing 750 cc. of water. 25 cc. of the carmin solution are added and the mixture titrated with N/10 $KMnO_4$ as described for standardization of the indigo carmin reagent. From this titration the number of cc. $KMnO_4$ required by 25 cc. of indigo carmin reagent are subtracted and the difference represents the $KMnO_4$ required by the sample. Multiply cc. $KMnO_4$ required by sample by $0.004157 = A$.

Astringent Non-tannins. To 50 cc. of the solution (in an 8 oz. bottle) made as stated in the previous determination are added 25 cc. of 2% gelatin solution and 25 cc. of the saturated NaCl acid reagent followed by 10 grams of china clay. The bottle is stoppered and the mixture shaken for five minutes and then filtered through a dry filter, thus removing the tannins. The filtrate is tested with more gelatin solution to see that the tannin is completely precipitated. (A stronger gelatin solution should be used if tannin is evident and the test repeated with 25 cc. of this.) 20 cc. of the filtrate, equivalent to 10 cc. of the original solution, are titrated with N/10 $KMnO_4$ exactly as in the preceding test and the cc. $KMnO_4$ consumed by the non-tannins is multiplied by the value of the $KMnO_4$ (N/10 = 0.004157) and the result recorded as B.

Tannic Acid or Tannins. The difference between the total astringency, calculated as tannin, and the astringent non-tannins gives the amount of tannins, namely result A minus result B = gram tannin. Calculate to percentage.

$$1 \text{ cc. N/10 } KMnO_4 = 0.004157 \text{ gram tannin.}$$

[1] References: H. R. Proctor, "Leather Industries Laboratory Book of Analytical and Experimental Methods."

Knecht-Rawson-Lowenthal, "Manual of Dyeing," Vol. II, pp. 802, Eighth Edition.

Leach, "Food Inspection and Analysis," p. 282.

DETERMINATION OF PEROXIDES

Determination of Hydrogen Peroxide.
Kingzett's Iodide Method[1]

The method depends upon the reaction—

$$H_2O_2 + 2KI + H_2SO_4 = I_2 + K_2SO_4 + 2H_2O.$$

Procedure. Approximately 2 grams of potassium iodide are dissolved in 200 cc. of water, conveniently in an Erlenmeyer flask, and 30 cc. of dilute sulphuric acid (1 : 2) are added. Ten cc. of hydrogen peroxide solution (the sample having been diluted to contain approximately 0.6 per cent by weight of H_2O_2) are run in from a burette, agitating the mixture during the addition. After standing five minutes, the liberated iodine is titrated with N/10 thiosulphate.

1 cc. N/10 $Na_2S_2O_3 = 0.001701$ gram H_2O_2.

Determination of Hydrogen Peroxide by the Arseneous Acid Method of Jamieson[2]

The method is based on the reactions—

$$As_2O_3 + 2H_2O_2 = As_2O_5 + 2H_2O$$

and

$$As_2O_3 + KIO_3 + 2HCl = As_2O_5 + ICl + KCl + H_2O.$$

Procedure. A measured quantity of N/5 solution of As_2O_3, which must be in excess of that required by the peroxide taken for analysis, is placed in a 500 cc. glass stoppered bottle, and 10 cc. of 10% NaOH added, followed by a measured volume of the peroxide from a burette (15–20 cc. of the solution made by diluting 50 cc. of the commercial peroxide to 500 cc.) with gentle agitation of the contents of the bottle. After standing two minutes, 40 cc. of concentrated HCl are added and the stopper inserted in the bottle. The contents of the bottle are shaken violently, holding the stopper in place. The stopper is now cautiously released and the confined gas allowed to escape. Six to seven cc. of chloroform are added and the unoxidized As_2O_3 is titrated with N/5 KIO_3 solution, shaking the closed bottle after each addition, until the iodine color in the chloroform has disappeared.

The cc. As_2O_3 solution used minus the cc. equivalent of KIO_3 gives the cc. of arsenous acid required by the hydrogen peroxide.

1 cc. N/5 $As_2O_3 = 0.0034016$ gram H_2O_2.

This method is not influenced by the presence of organic preservatives as is the permanganate method which follows.

*Selections by W. W. Scott.

[1] J. Chem. Soc., 1880, 792.   [2] Am. Jour. Sci., 44, 150–2 (1917).

Permanganate Method for Determination of Hydrogen Peroxide

The procedure depends upon the reaction—

$$5H_2O_2 + 2KMnO_4 + 4H_2SO_4 = 2KHSO_4 + 2MnSO_4 + 5O_2 + 8H_2O.$$

Procedure. Fifty cc. of the commercial peroxide are diluted to 500 cc. 10 cc. of this diluted solution are taken for the test. This sample is further diluted to 400 cc. in a beaker, 10 cc. of dilute sulphuric acid (1 : 4) are added and the mixture titrated with N/10 $KMnO_4$ reagent to a pink coloration.

Should the first drop or of permanganate cause a pink color it indicates that an insufficient quantity of sulphuric acid is present and an additional amount should be added.

$$1 \text{ cc. N/10 } KMnO_4 = 0.001701 \text{ gram } H_2O_2.$$

NOTES. If it is required to report the number of volumes of oxygen liberated by one volume of the peroxide "per cent per volume," multiply the per cent weight of H_2O_2 by 112 and divide the result by 34.

Since H_2O_2 decomposes to $H_2O + O$, one gram molecule of peroxide sets free one gram atom of oxygen, equivalent to 11,200 cc. Therefore 100 grams commercial $H_2O_2 = \% H_2O_2 \times 11,200$ divided by 34, and 1 gram = 1/100 of this.

Analysis of Sodium Sulphide [1]

The portions of the sample used for the determination of sodium sulphide and sodium thiosulphate are freed from sodium sulphite by treatment with barium chloride. The sulphide is evolved as hydrogen sulphide, using ammonium chloride which does not attack the thiosulphate, the H_2S being absorbed in ammoniacal cadmium chloride solution forming CdS, which is titrated with iodine according to the procedure given for determining sulphur in steel by the evolution method. The thiosulphate is titrated with iodine after the removal of the sulphide in a larger sample by treatment with ammonium chloride and evolution under reduced pressure. The sodium sulphide is determined by direct precipitation as barium sulphite in a medium of ammonium acetate solution made alkaline with ammonia, and subsequently titrated with standard iodine solution. Sodium carbonate is precipitated as barium carbonate under the conditions for precipitation of barium sulphite. The acid consuming value of the precipitate is determined and the sodium carbonate content calculated after deducting the equivalent acid consuming value of the sodium sulphite as previously determined by the iodine titration. Accuracy to 0.3% is claimed for each of the constituents.

[1] W. S. Colcott, F. L. English, F. B. Downing, Ind. Eng. Chem., **17**, 176 (Feb., 1925).

BEAM TEST FOR DETERMINING THE PRESENCE OF SUSPENDED MATTER IN GASES[1]

Tyndall demonstrated that dust particles are responsible for the visibility of rays of light, such as the sun beam or the beam of the searchlight. He did not make clear the best conditions enabling one to see the beam produced by minute amounts of suspended matter in purified gases, nor did he show that a gas free of dust may still produce a beam in presence of liquid mist. The opinion commonly current regarding the conditions necessary to see the beam produced by light rays in purified gas, is that the rays should be parallel and should be viewed with the visual axis at right angles to this beam. Observing these conditions the author[1] failed to see the beam using direct sunlight, but discovered that a cone of light from an arc light gave a distinct beam. This led to the discovery that the beam is best viewed by glancing towards the source of light. Accordingly the apparatus shown in Fig. 280 was designed.

For the examination of a corrosive gas, it is advisable to have the chamber of the camera made of a material not affected by that gas. For example, in examining purified contact gas a lead chamber is recommended. The interior of the chamber is blackened with dull paint that is a poor light reflector. In the apparatus shown, circular glass discs close the ends of the tubes "a," "b" and "c." The gas examined enters near the eyepiece "b" and passes out at the opposite large end. The ray of light is directed through a small opening, either circular (diam. 1 cm.) or a narrow slit, located at "a" and passes through the arm of the tube and out through a glass window at "c." The idea is to avoid light reflection in the chamber, as this would cause a glow in the tube and greatly reduce the sensibility of the test.

The beam caused by liquid mist alone appears as a uniform pencil or band of light, whereas dust particles produce a sparkling effect or irregular flashes of light. The beam is more intense with the gas in motion. Within certain limits the intensity of the beam is directly proportional to amount of suspended matter in the gas.

If the gas is dry the beam is completely removed by passing the gas through a three-inch mat of loosely carded purified asbestos. If the gas, thus purified of solid matter, is passed through a liquid the beam again becomes apparent. From this it is evident that the test must be applied to dry gas if it is desired to ascertain the presence of solid matter in suspension.

Fig. 284 shows the apparatus set up for ascertaining the effectiveness of a scrubber in a quantitative determination of the solid and liquid suspended matter in a gas. The apparatus is so arranged that comparisons may be made of the unfiltered gas, by means of a bypass with that of the filtered or purified gas. Advantage is taken of the difference in pressures at A and B, so that a continuous sample may be taken of the gas without the necessity of an aspirator. A hand arc light shown on the left furnishes the rays of light which enter at "a" and pass out into the air at "c." The beam is viewed through the eyepiece "b." The meter measures the volume of gas aspirated.

[1] Contributed by Wilfred W. Scott.

Beam Test for Suspended Matters in Gases.

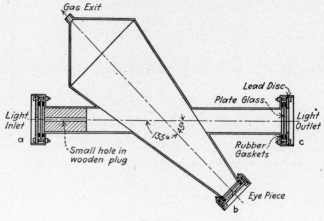

FIG. 280.

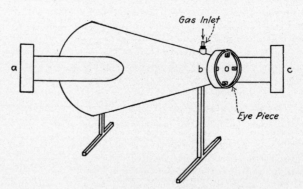

FIG. 281.   Apparatus for ascertaining the pressure of suspended material in a gas by
means of a beam of light.

DETERMINATION OF SOLID AND LIQUID IMPURITIES IN A GAS[1]

Solid or liquid impurities suspended in a gas may be removed quantitatively by passing the gas through a filter of loosely carded dry asbestos. A filter two inches thick and $1\frac{1}{4}$ inches in diameter is effective in removing suspended matter completely with gas passing through it at the rate of 2 to 3 liters per second (5 to 7 cubic feet per minute). It is essential that the asbestos be free from condensed moisture as a soggy filter is not effective for gas filtration.

Determination of Sulphuric Acid Mist in Gas. The gas is aspirated through a filter of well-carded, blue fibre, purified asbestos, the asbestos extracted with water and the extract titrated with standard alkali.

Apparatus. An ordinary $1\frac{1}{4}$ inch filter tube funnel (see Fig. 283) with long stem, to permit a sample being drawn directly from the flue may be used. If the gas is supersaturated with moisture it is advisable to use the form of apparatus shown in Fig. 282, the bottle serving as a condensing chamber to avoid water condensation on the asbestos. Occasionally it is necessary to pass the gas through two such chambers to remove the condensed moisture from warm moist gases.

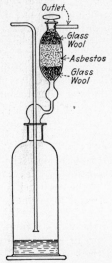

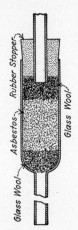

Fig. 282. Apparatus for determining solids and liquid mist in wet gases.

Fig. 283. Filter for gases.

The funnel is packed first with a layer of glass wool, followed by a two-inch layer of well-carded, purified, blue asbestos, and finally a second layer of glass wool. The glass wool prevents the asbestos plugging the inlet and exit openings. Perforated disks may be used in place of the glass wool.

The asbestos is the blue African form. White asbestos will not give accurate results as this is attacked slightly by dilute sulphuric acid and decidedly so by strong sulphuric. The blue form is not appreciably attacked so that the acid may be extracted as free acid by water. The asbestos is purified by digesting with nitric acid, followed by a second digestion with hydrochloric

[1] Contributed by Wilfred W. Scott.

Impurities in Gases.

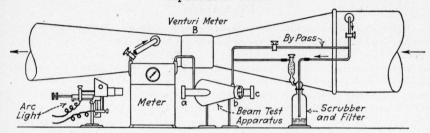

Fig. 284. Apparatus for determining solid or liquid impurities in gases.

acid. The material is now thoroughly washed to remove the acids and is dried. The dry asbestos is placed in wide mouth bottles until required. Before using it is carded or fluffed out by means of a pick and then placed loosely in the funnel to be used in the test.

The Test. The gas is aspirated through the filter at the rate of about five cubic feet per minute, the gas being measured by a dry gas meter following the apparatus. When a volume of 10 to 100 cubic feet of gas has been aspirated, the amount depending upon the amount of acid mist present in the gas, the asbestos filter is placed in a beaker. (If SO_2 is present in the gas, as is the case in contact sulphur gases, air is first passed through the asbestos to remove the SO_2.) The tube is rinsed out, the rinsings added to the asbestos. The contents of the beaker is now transferred to a two-inch Buechner funnel in position on a half-liter capacity suction bottle. The water is drawn out of the asbestos and the filtrate passed through the mat, thus formed, to remove the asbestos fibers. The mat is washed with small portions of pure water, until free of acid and the extract, transferred to a beaker, is titrated with standard alkali. N/20 alkali has been found to be satisfactory. Methyl orange is used as an indicator.

Determination of Arsenic in Gas. The test is the same as the one described for determining sulphuric acid. An aliquot portion of the water extract is taken for a Gutzeit determination of arsenic. The Gutzeit method is described in full in the chapter on arsenic, Volume I. Arsenic in purified contact gas is carried in the acid mist.

Determination of Chlorides. A portion of the water extract, obtained by the procedure described under the test for acid in gas and filtered through paper if necessary, is examined for chloride by the turbidity test by addition of nitric acid followed by silver nitrate reagent. Comparison is made with a standard using either Nessler tubes or a colorimeter. If the amount of chloride is too great for a turbidity test a gravimetric determination should be made, or the aliquot portion taken should be sufficiently diluted with water to enable the turbidity test to be made. The standard should contain the same amount of sulphuric acid as the sample. The extract should be free of asbestos fibre.

Composition of Asbestos.

[2] Asbestos	SiO_2,	CaO,	MgO,	FeO,	Al_2O_3,	MnO,	H_2O
Blue—African	49.0	1.2	2.7	24.4	11.9	—	—
White—Canadian	40.3	—	43.4	.9	2.3	—	13.7
White—Italian	55.9	17.8	20.3	—	4.3	1.1	—

Preparation of a Gooch Crucible

Asbestos Fibre.   The asbestos for use in Gooch crucibles should be carefully selected.   The fibres should be moderately stiff, not the " cottony " type. Cut the fibre into pieces about $\frac{1}{4}$ inch long.   Ignite the asbestos in a platinum dish at low red heat.   Cool and transfer to a clean porcelain mortar and macerate to a pulp with strong hydrochloric acid.   Dilute with water and transfer to a large beaker containing 600–800 cc. of water.   Stir thoroughly, allow to settle and pour off the milky water.   Repeat the washing with water until the milkiness, due to powdered fibres, is scarcely evident.   Now filter off the asbestos onto a Buechner funnel.   Again wash with water until free of acid. Transfer to a wide mouth bottle, add water in sufficient amount to form with the stirred up fibre a thin suspension of asbestos.   This is now ready for use. If preferred the asbestos may be dried and kept in this form until desired.

Preparation of the Filter.   The Gooch crucible, either of platinum or porcelain, having a perforated bottom, is placed in a funnel tube and the apparatus set up as is shown in Fig. 285.   The suction bottle holding the Gooch

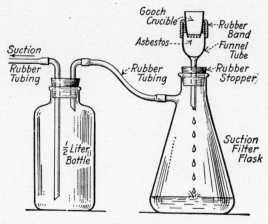

Fɪɢ. 285.

is attached to a second bottle, if a water filter pump is used to obtain the vacuum, as there is danger of water being sucked into the apparatus from the tap.   Suction is now applied and a small amount of the finely suspended asbestos is poured into the crucible, in amount sufficient to form a thin pad of the material about $\frac{1}{16}$ inch thick over the bottom of the Gooch.   The felt is washed with distilled water, the asbestos drawn down hard.   It is possible to see light through the bottom of a properly made filter.   The crucible is placed in an oven and the filter dried to constant weight at 110° C.   For BaSO₄ and AgCl determinations it is advisable to make the filter about twice the above thickness to prevent the precipitate from passing through.   Whenever the Gooch crucible is used, suction should be applied before pouring material into the crucible and the suction continued during the washing of the precipitate.

DETERMINATION OF MOISTURE AND WATER OF CRYSTALLIZATION

1. Moisture. The moisture is best determined on a 10–100 gram sample. The sample is weighed and placed in a watch or clock glass and heated to constant weight in oven at 105–110° C. The loss of weight is calculated to per cent on a 10 gram sample by multiplying by 10 and directly on 100 gram sample.

2. Water of Crystallization. Many of the crystallized salts do not give up all of their water of crystallization until heated considerably above the boiling point of water. Two methods of procedure will be considered.

(a) *The Loss Method*, which consists in heating the salt to a temperature at which the water is completely driven off and obtaining the loss of weight by weighing the anhydrous salt. By this method error may result owing to the fact that the anhydrides generally absorb moisture rapidly from the air, so that the salt must be transferred hot to the desiccator, cooled and then weighed as rapidly as possible.

(b) *Absorption or Direct Method*, which consists in heating the salt in a boat in an enclosed tube, passing a current of dry air over the sample which carries the moisture to a tube containing a dehydrating ·agent, where the water is absorbed and may be weighed directly.

3. The Loss Method in Detail. For practice a sample of either barium chloride or copper sulphate will be taken. $BaCl_2.2H_2O$, $CuSO_4.5H_2O$. The determination should be made in duplicate.

Procedure. Carefully clean and dry a weighing bottle. Place in this 5–10 grams of the crystals. If the crystals are large they should be broken down to about the consistency of coarse sand.

Heat the crucible on a pipestem triangle to redness and cool the crucible in a desiccator containing calcium chloride. Weigh and record the weight in a notebook.

Place in the crucible 1–2 grams of the sample from the weighing bottle. Make note of the exact amount by deducting the weight of the crucible from the total weight of crucible and salt.

Place the crucible in a clean crucible of iron or nickel of sufficient capacity to allow an air space of $\frac{1}{4}$ inch around the vessel containing the salt. A thin asbestos pad is placed at the bottom of the larger crucible, separating it from the smaller.

Place the larger crucible with its contents on the triangle of a tripod and heat to low redness, applying the heat gradually, keeping the temperature within the crucible at 100–120° C. for 10 minutes or more, then increasing to 250° C., the outer crucible becoming red hot. Keep the large crucible at red heat for about 10 minutes.

Cool in a desiccator and then weigh the smaller crucible with its contents and note the loss of weight.

Repeat the heating in the larger crucible until the weight of the sample becomes constant. Calculate the loss of weight and report as per cent water. (Loss × 100 divided by Wt. taken.)

Note: It is frequently necessary to cover the inner crucible during the initial heating to prevent loss of salt due to " snapping out," decrepitation. The crucible cover should also be weighed.

§ 38. Determination of Water. Absorption Method.[1] The apparatus for this determination is shown below. (Fig. 286.) The combustion tube C is attached to the calcium chloride or phosphorus pentachloride tubes A and D. The former to dry the air entering C and the latter, D, to retain the moisture swept from the sample in the boat B. The carboy E is used as an aspirator by allowing an outflow of water (about five drops per second) from a stopcock at the bottom.

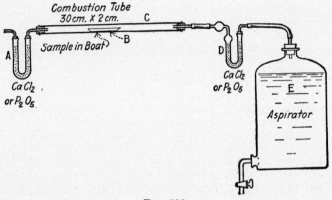

FIG. 286.

Procedure. The combustion boat B is dried and weighed. Meantime the apparatus is swept out with dry air for about 10–15 minutes.

The tube D is detached and carefully weighed, preferably using a counter-weight calcium chloride or phosphorus pentachloride tube, which is kept alongside of D. The tube D contains calcium chloride in small lumps. The ends of the tube are packed loosely with cotton or glass wool. Tube A is prepared in the same way.

Place in B 1–2 grams of the sample. Insert in the tube C. Attach the weighed tube D. See that the apparatus is properly connected and tight.

Gently apply heat to the portion of the tube adjacent to B. Increase the heat as desired by means of a Meeker burner, aspirating air through the apparatus by allowing an outflow of water from E at the rate of five drops per second.

If any moisture condenses in C, drive it forward to D by heating the tube, but be careful not to heat the tube too much near the rubber stopper, as fumes from the rubber would cause an error in results.

Forty minutes to an hour should be ample for the expulsion of water. The temperature finally obtained should be not over 300° C. for most salts. Higher heat may be necessary for certain oxides, but for such the ignition method in an open crucible is recommended.

The tube D is disconnected and weighed. (Using the tare weight counter balance, as suggested.) The increased weight is due to the water of the sample.

[1] These methods are not applicable to compounds decomposing on heating.

Calculation of Percentage of Material Determined in the Original Sample to the Dry Basis, or if Determined on a Dried Sample to the Original Form Including Water. Frequently a chemist is required to report the percentage of constituent both on the dried sample and in its original form containing water. The following formulæ will be of assistance in these calculations:

Let a = percentage of material found (determined on the dry basis, or in the original sample, as the case may be).

b = percentage of total dry material with water expelled.

c = per cent of water in the original sample, $100 - c = b$.

Then $\dfrac{100 \times a}{b}$ = per cent calculated from wet basis to dry.

$\dfrac{a \times b}{100}$ = per cent calculated from dry basis to wet.

Direct Determination of Moisture. Bidwell and Sterling [1] suggest a direct determination of moisture as actual water by adding toluene to the material in a pyrex Erlenmeyer flask, connected with a calibrated receiving tube and a condenser. The mixture is heated, the water is condensed and runs into the calibrated tube where its volume is measured.

DETERMINATION OF MOISTURE IN GASES

§ 39. The gas to be tested is passed through a dehydrating agent such as phosphorus pentoxide, P_2O_5, alumina, Al_2O_3, or lime, CaO, contained in a weighed U-tube. The following facts should be borne in mind in selecting the dehydrating agent: (a) It should not absorb the gas; (b) it should not react chemically with the gas. For example, lime or alumina could not be used for determining moisture in sulphur dioxide, nor could phosphorus pentoxide be used in determining moisture in ammonia. For the former, phosphorus pentoxide is best, and for the latter, lime. Alumina that has been carefully heated to 1400° is useful for determining moisture in neutral gases. It should be remembered that gases dried over calcium chloride will give up moisture to strong sulphuric acid, and these in turn will give up moisture to phosphorus pentoxide: Professor Morley has even determined the amount of moisture that is left after this latter treatment.

Procedure. The volume of the gases required for the test varies widely according to the percentage of moisture in the gas, 1000 cc. to 10,000 cc. is generally required. For minute amounts of moisture it may be necessary to lead the gas over the dehydrating agent for a given length of time, using a manometer or difference gauge, or a gas meter. The absorption tube is weighed before and after the test and the increase in weight taken as the moisture content of the gas.

[1] G. L. Bidwell and W. F. Sterling, Ind. Eng. Chem., **17**, 147 (Feb. 1925).

LIGHT OIL IN COKE=OVEN GAS [1]

Use of Activated Carbon in Its Determination

The quantity of the light oil in coke-oven gas, before and after scrubbing with straw oil, is generally determined by passing a definite quantity of the gas through straw oil contained in a train of bottles packed in ice, and subsequently separating the light oil from the straw oil by distillation. The removal of the light oil from the gas approaches completeness only when the flow of gas is extremely slow, and under all conditions the method of procedure is cumbersome.

The light oil present in the gas may be determined readily and accurately by the absorption of the condensable vapor in a definite quantity of gas by activated carbon, with subsequent removal by distillation of the carbon with U. S. P. cresol. Carbon of activity 40 to 50, screened 8 to 14 mesh, is suitable.

Apparatus

The absorption requires a 0.1-cu. ft. gas meter and two activated carbon tubes complete. The carbon tubes are cylindrical containers, 1.5 in. in diameter and 12 in. in length over all, fitted with a 20-mesh screen in one end, with 1-in. breasts and screw caps on both ends. Four connecting caps consisting of 1-in. screw caps carrying $\frac{5}{16}$ x $\frac{3}{4}$-in. copper tubes soldered in the centers and fitted with $\frac{1}{16}$-in. rubber gaskets are used on each carbon tube during the absorption proper.

The distillation of the enriched activated carbon with cresol to remove the light oil is made, using a 500-cc., round-bottom, side-neck, Pyrex distilling flask; a 4-in. ring burner; a 200° C. thermometer; a " Barrett standard " condenser; a 200-cc. separatory funnel graduated to 100 cc.; U. S. P. cresol; and sodium hydroxide solution of specific gravity 1.10 to 1.15.

Procedure

Absorption. Place 300 cc. of activated carbon in each of the two carbon tubes. Screw a connecting cap with rubber gasket to each end of each tube, and tighten with a pair of combination pliers.

Connect the inlet of the wet gas meter to the gas sampling tube and allow gas to pass through for several minutes to insure a thorough displacement of air. Turn off the gas, set the indicating hands of the meter to the zero position. (*Caution:* See that the hands are reasonably loose before turning so that the driving shafts will not be twisted.) Connect the top of the first carbon tube to the outlet of the gas meter, the bottom of the first tube to the bottom of the second tube, and either allow the residual gas coming from the top of the second tube to escape or be conducted away by an attached exit tube. *Keep the tubes in a vertical position.*

Pass an amount of gas containing approximately 30 to 40 cc. of light oil through the absorption tubes, at the rate of 10 to 15 cu. ft. per hr. At the

[1] By Arthur L. Davis, Standard Oil Company (Indiana), Wood River, Ill.
[Reprinted from Industrial and Engineering Chemistry,
Vol. 15, No. 7, page 689. July, 1923.]

completion of the absorption note the volume of gas passed, the temperature of the gas, and the barometric pressure.

Distillation. Place the enriched carbon from the first tube in a 500-cc., side-neck, Pyrex distilling flask, add 125 cc. of cresol, *mix thoroughly by shaking in the flask,* insert the thermometer in neck of the flask, and connect to a " Barrett standard " condenser. Heat carefully with the ring burner and distil at a moderate rate till the temperature of 180° C. is reached. Collect the distillate in the 200-cc. separatory funnel, which is graduated to 100 cc. Add 125 cc. of sodium hydroxide solution, specific gravity 1.10 to 1.15 (8 to 13 per cent), and agitate thrroughly. Care should be taken to release the pressure of the gas which is often built up. Allow to stand for a few minutes, run off the sodium hydroxide solution, and record the volume of light oil obtained.

Repeat the foregoing procedure with the second carbon tube. Record the volume of light oil obtained separately.

The sum of the two volumes of light oil obtained above gives the total volume of light oil from the volume of gas passed at the temperature and barometric pressure recorded.

Calculation. The amount of light oil present in the gas (volume corrected to 15.5° C. (760 mm.)) is calculated as follows:

Total volume of light oil $\times$ 0.264 = Gal. light oil per 1000 cu. ft. gas.

$$\text{Cu. ft. gas} \times \frac{288.5}{273 + \text{temp. ° C.}} \times \frac{\text{Bar. press.}}{760}.$$

Gal. light oil per 1000 cu. ft. $\times$ 12 = Gal. light oil per ton of coal. (One ton of coal produces approximately 12,000 cu. ft. of gas.)

Volume of Gas Required

In order that the time required for making an absorption may be fairly accurately determined before making a test, the volume of gas containing a certain amount of condensable vapor should be known. The volume of gas containing approximately 30 to 40 cc. of light oil is shown in the table.

In making routine analysis by this method it is advised that the determination of the gas entering the scrubbers and the gas leaving the scrubbers be made simultaneously.

VOLUME OF COKE-OVEN GAS REQUIRED FOR CHARCOAL ABSORPTION METHOD

Gal. Light Oil per Ton Coal (12,000 Cu. Ft.)	Cu. Ft. Gas Required for Determination
0.5	190–250
1.0	95–125
1.5	63–83
2.0	47–60
2.5	38–50
3.0	31–41
3.5	27–36
4.0	24–31
4.5	21–28

The spent activated carbon containing cresol may be revivified, but it is more satisfactory to use fresh material for each determination.

METHODS FOR TESTING PAPER-MAKING MATERIALS [1]
Aluminum Sulphate

Sampling. Five per cent of the packages in the shipment should be sampled in the case of ground alum. The portions from the various barrels or bags shall be mixed together in one composite sample representing the shipment.

Twelve fragments, each chipped off from an ingot taken at random, shall be taken as a representative sample of alum for each carload shipment of ingot alum. These fragments shall be ground together in one composite sample representing the shipment.

Insoluble Matter. Weigh out 25 grams of the alum in a beaker and dissolve in about 200 cc. of hot distilled water. Filter through a weighed Gooch or alundum crucible, using suction to hasten filtration; wash well, dry to constant weight and calculate per cent insoluble matter.

Alumina and Iron Oxide. The filtrate from the foregoing should be poured into a 500-cc. graduated flask, carefully rinsing the last traces of the filtrate into the flask. The flask is brought to the temperature of calibration, the liquid diluted to the mark, and well shaken. Draw out 100 cc. of the solution by means of a pipette and dilute to 500 cc. in a calibrated flask. From this second flask 50 cc. (corresponding to 0.5 gm.) is drawn with a pipette, and transferred to a beaker.

Dilute to about 150 cc., add 5 cc. of concentrated hydrochloric acid and a few drops of concentrated nitric acid; heat solution to boiling, and add slowly dilute ammonia until a slight excess is present; continue boiling until there is only a faint odor of ammonia preceptible. Remove beaker from source of heat, and filter on an 11 cm. washed filter, using suction in conjunction with a platinum filter cone; wash with hot water until free from chlorides, and ignite the moist precipitate in a platinum crucible over a Bunsen burner. When the filter has been entirely consumed, ignite over the highest heat of the blast or No. 4 Meeker burner, to constant weight. Calculate percentage of Al_2O_3 $+Fe_2O_3$. (We have found by experiments that igniting for $\frac{1}{2}$ hour over a blast or No. 4 Meeker burner is sufficient to dehydrate the alumina.)

NOTE. Before precipitating with NH_4OH, if a little tannin is added, the precipitate will be more granular and easily filtered.

Iron. From the first 500-cc. flask, transfer to a beaker 100 cc. (corresponding to 5 gm.) with a pipette, add 5 cc. of concentrated sulphuric acid, and heat solution nearly to boiling. Add permanganate drop by drop till permanent strong pink color, to oxidize any possible reducing matter. Run through a Jones reductor in the usual manner, cool and titrate with standard potassium permanganate solution.

Calculate percentage of Fe_2O_3.

For alum containing less than 0.1% iron, use the following method adapted from that of Stokes and Cain, J. A. C. S., 29, 4, 409–447 (April, 1907), making

[1] Report of Comm. on Standard Methods for Testing Materials of Tech. Asso. Pulp and Paper Industry.

use of a colorimeter consisting of two test tubes, 8 inch by 1 inch, whose diameters are very nearly alike, are employed:

A solution containing 0.1000 gm. ferrous iron per liter is made by dissolving 0.7026 gm. ferrous ammonium sulphate in a liter of water. By diluting 10 cc. of this solution to 500 cc., 10 cc. of the resulting solution will contain .00002 gm. of iron. This produces about the proper depth of color for comparison.

Into one of the test tubes 10 cc. of the above solution is put, together with 10 cc. of water, 5 cc. of sulphocyanic acid solution (saturated with mercuric sulphocyanate), (see also chapter on Iron, Vol. I), .01 gm. ammonium persulphate, and 10 cc. amyl alcohol. Into the other tube .5 cc. of the alum solution is run from a 10-cc. burette, and 19.5 cc. water, 5 cc. sulphocyanic acid solution, .01 gm. ammonium persulphate, and 10 cc. of amyl alcohol added. Both tubes are then thoroughly shaken and comparison of the colors in the colorimeter is made as soon as the amyl alcohol layer is clear. If the color of the alum solution is weak, it is adjusted to standard by adding alum solution, 1 cc. at a time, and shaking well. If the color is too strong, the alum solution may be added to the iron standard until the colors match, and then considering the " alum solution used " to be the difference between the amount of alum solution in one tube and the amount added to the iron standard tube. By dividing .00002 by the number of grammes of alum represented by the alum solution used, and multiplying this quotient by 100, the percentage of iron in the alum is obtained. This number multiplied by 1.43 (the ratio of ferric oxide to iron) gives the per cent of iron calculated as iron oxide, Fe_2O_3.

Sulphuric Anhydride. 50 cc. of the 1% alum solution is drawn out with a pipette and transferred to a beaker. Dilute to about 200 cc., add 1 cc. concentrated hydrochloric acid, bring to boil and then add drop by drop 10 cc. of a 5% barium chloride solution. Allow the precipitate to settle. Filter, wash, and ignite in the usual manner. See chapter on Sulphur, Vol. I.

Free Sulphuric Acid. 3.4038 gm. finely ground sample or an equivalent amount in solution (100 cc. sample containing 34.038 gm. per liter) are taken. The powder is dissolved by boiling with 100 cc. of distilled water in a 4-in. casserole with clock glass cover. To the hot solution 10 cc. of N/2 H_2SO_4 are added, and after cooling to room temperature (20° C.), 18 to 20 cc. of the potassium fluoride reagent are added and $\frac{1}{2}$ cc. of phenolphthalein indicator. The solution is now titrated with N/2 KOH, added drop by drop until a delicate pink color, persisting for one minute, is obtained. This titration shows whether the product is basic or acid. See chapter on Aluminum, Vol. I.

$$\text{Free Acid} = (\text{Cc. KOH} - \text{Cc. } H_2SO_4) \times 0.72.$$

NOTE. In alums containing small amounts of iron the error is not serious, if all the iron is considered as being in the ferrous state of oxidation and combined with sulphuric anhydride as ferrous sulphate.

The aluminum sulphate should be calculated from the SO_3 left by subtracting the SO_3 combined as ferrous sulphate and free acid from the total SO_3 as determined above.

Potassium Fluoride. The reagent may be prepared by dissolving 1000 grams of potassium fluoride in 1200 cc. of hot CO_2-free water, then neutralizing the solution with alkali or hydrofluoric acid as the case may require, using 5 cc. of phenolphthalein indicator. Dilute sulphuric acid may be used in place of hydrofluoric acid, in the final adjustment, to get a neutral product: 1 cc. of the solution in 10 cc. of CO_2-free water should appear a faint pink. The concentrated mix is filtered, if necessary, and then diluted to 2000 cc. with CO_2-free water. The gravity will now be approximately 1.32 (about 35° Be.): 1 cc. contains 0.5 gm. potassium fluoride salt.

Rosin

Sampling. Five per cent of the barrels should be taken, the rosin broken up on a clean floor, quartered and sampled down to a 2-lb. laboratory sample.

Grade. Rosins are graded according to color. The grades are as follows: WW, WG, N, M, K, I, H, G, F, E, D, and B. WW is the best and palest grade. B is the cheapest and darkest grade. Grades G, F, and E are most frequently used for papermaking. Yaryan extract rosin is sometimes met with; it grades between E and F and is ruby red in color.

To determine the grade of rosin a set of standard cubes of rosin of the various grades must be available. The rosin under test is cast into a cube in a mold of sheet aluminum and compared as to color with the standards by looking through the cubes toward the light. Care must be taken to heat the rosin only just enough to pour. Overheating darkens the color.

Dirt and Foreign Matter. Unless the rosin is quite dirty no quantitative estimation is necessary. In case quantitative estimation is desired, dissolve 25 grams of rosin in warm alcohol, filter through a tared filter paper, wash with alcohol, dry and weigh the residue.

Saponification Number. Weigh 2 grams of powdered rosin into an Erlenmeyer flask of 300 cc. capacity. Add 25 cc. half-normal alcoholic KOH and boil for two hours, using a reflux condenser. Shake the flask frequently with a swirling motion to prevent the rosin from sticking to the sides of the flask above the liquor line. Cool and titrate the excess KOH with half-normal acid and phenolphthalein. Calculate the milligrams of KOH consumed per gram of rosin. This is the saponification number. In each case run a blank on the KOH solution by boiling 25 cc. of the solution for two hours in exactly the same manner as the saponification proper is carried out and titrating.

Acid Number. Dissolve one gram of powdered rosin in warm alcohol (neutral to phenolphthalein), cool and titrate the solution with half-normal alcoholic KOH, using phenolphthalein. Express the result as milligrams of KOH consumed per gram of rosin. This is the acid number.

Ester Number. The ester number is the difference between the saponification number and the acid number.

Unsaponifiable Matter. Saponify about 5 grams of rosin by boiling for two hours with excess of half-normal alcoholic potash. Evaporate most of the alcohol, add about 100 cc. of water, extract in a separatory funnel with acid-free ether exactly as in the determination of free rosin in rosin size.

Ash. The determination of ash is seldom necessary. It is accomplished by igniting 5 gm. in a platinum crucible to a white or light gray residue. Cool in a desiccator and weigh.

Practical Sizing Tests of Rosin. For this purpose a small beating engine is desirable, though the work can be done by using a cream whipper. Twenty-five or fifty grams dry weight of unbleached sulphite pulp is thoroughly disintegrated in the beater or cream whipper and 2% of rosin sizing in the form of a thin milk added. After thorough mixing, 3% of a standard alum is added in solution and thoroughly mixed. The pulp is then thinned, made into hand sheets and the sheets dried and tested for ink penetration. Two sets of sheets are made, one with size made from a standard rosin and one with size made from the rosin under test.

The size is made by cooking a given weight of powdered rosin in a container surrounded by boiling water for four hours with that weight of soda ash which will yield a size containing 25% free rosin, dry basis. The water used in its making should be sufficient to give a finished thick size containing 70% dry matter. The thick size is diluted to a milk by stirring with water at 70° F. before adding to the pulp.

Rosin Size

Sampling. Any barrel or drum of the lot, containing size of the same cook, shall be taken as representative of the quality of the size. This barrel or drum is opened, the size thoroughly mixed by careful stirring and a pint sample inclosed in a fruit jar or friction-top, airtight tin can, so that no loss of water can take place between time of sampling and test for moisture.

Solubility. Dissolve 10 grams of rosin size in 300 cc. water at 85° to 90° C. and allow to stand twelve hours; pour off and see if lumps remain, or any grains which will not stir up to a fine milk with cold water.

Color is examined in tubes; 20 cc. of the size milk is diluted with 200 cc. cold water, and 10 to 20 cc. of a 5% alum solution gradually stirred in. A pure white finely divided precipitate should result, settling slowly, which should readily mix again on stirring; it should not be yellowish or curdy in appearance.

Free Rosin. Weigh out approximately 10 grams of size and mix with 30 cc. of water; wash with as small an amount of water as possible into a 500-cc. separatory funnel, free from any trace of acid or alkali. Extract with 25 cc. of acid-free ether; draw off the water into a second separatory funnel and wash the ether extract with two 25 cc. portions of water, adding the wash waters to the second separatory funnel. Pour the first ether extract into a weighed Soxhlet flask. Extract the solution a second time with 25 cc. of acid-free ether which has been used to rinse out the first funnel; draw off the solution into the first separatory funnel, wash the ether extract twice with 25 cc. portions of water as above, running the water into the main solution and pouring the ether extract into the Soxhlet flask. Repeat the extraction and washings once more. Immerse the Soxhlet flask in warm water and distil off the ether through a condenser. Dry the flask at not over 105° C. to constant weight, cool in desiccator and weigh the free rosin.

NOTE. It is especially important that the ether used in this determination shall have been specially prepared by washing once with sodium carbonate solution, once with water, and then redistilled to free it from all acid. A moist piece of sensitive blue litmus paper should not change color when completely submerged in the ether for fifteen minutes.

Moisture. Run the residue from the free rosin determination into a 250-cc. graduated flask (or a 500-cc. flask, if necessary), dilute to the mark and mix thoroughly. Pipette 25 cc. of this solution (or 50 cc.) into a weighed platinum dish, evaporate to dryness on the water bath and place in a water oven and dry at 105° C. to constant weight. Two hours' drying ought to be sufficient.

Divide this weight by 25/250 of the weight of sample taken and multiply by 100; this gives percentage of dry matter in the size, exclusive of free rosin. Add the percentage of free rosin, as above determined, and subtract from 100; the difference will be the percentage of water.

Total Alkali. Ignite the residue from the moisture determination until all carbonaceous matter is burned off. Dry in a desiccator and weigh. Dissolve the residue in a few cc. of water and titrate with N/10 acid, using methyl orange as indicator. Calculate the titration direct to Na_2CO_3. This weight should check the weight of the ash reasonably closely unless the size contains insoluble or other foreign matter. Calculate the titration also to Na_2O; divide the weight thus obtained by 25/250 of the original sample taken and multiply by 100; this gives percentage of Na_2O in the size.

1 cc. N/10 acid = 0.0031 gram Na_2O.　　Log = 7.49136.

1 cc. N/10 acid = 0.0053 gram Na_2CO_3.　　Log = 7.72428.

Combined Rosin. Pipette 200 cc. of the soap solution from the determination of free rosin into a separatory funnel and acidify with 10 cc. of dilute (1–5) sulphuric acid. Add 25 cc. of ether, shake well and allow to stand until the two layers are completely separated. Draw off the water solution into a second separatory funnel and wash the ether with two 25 cc. portions of water, drawing off the water into the second funnel and pouring the ether extract into a weighed Soxhlet. Rinse the first funnel with 25 cc. of ether into the second funnel. Shake well and draw off the water layer into the first funnel. Wash as above with two 25 cc. portions of water. Repeat once more. Evaporate the ether from the combined extracts as in the Free Rosin determination. Dry to constant weight at not over 105° C. Divide the weight obtained by 200/250 of the original weight taken and multiply by 100 to obtain the percentage of combined rosin.

NOTE. The ether in this case does not need to be specially purified though it should be free from any non-volatile residue.

Free Alkali. Weigh out 10 grams of size into 200 cc. of acid-free absolute alcohol. Allow the solution to stand eight or ten hours, or over night if possible, protected from acid fumes. Filter on a weighed filter and wash thoroughly with absolute alcohol; pour boiling water through the filter and after cooling titrate the aqueous solution with N/10 acid, using methyl orange as indicator. Calculate to Na_2CO_3.

1 cc. N/10 H_2SO_4 = 0.0053 gram Na_2CO_3.　　Log = 7.72428.

Insoluble Matter. This will be left on the weighed filter in the above determination and may be dried and weighed. In order to determine whether this is mineral matter, it may be ignited and the mineral matter weighed.

Rapid Methods for Rosin and Moisture in Size

Total Rosin. Weigh about 10 grams of the size in a small beaker. Dissolve in hot distilled water; pour the solution into a 250-cc. graduated flask, thoroughly rinsing out the beaker; cool the flask and make up to mark. Pipette 25 cc. of the dilute size, run into a 150-cc. beaker, add sufficient N/NaOH to dissolve all free rosin; heat until solution is complete.

Add 75 cc. of cold, distilled water and precipitate with an excess of normal H_2SO_4. The precipitate should settle, leaving a clear supernatant liquid. The solution and precipitate are then filtered on a filter paper which had been previously dried and weighed in a glass-stoppered weighing bottle. Wash the precipitate free of sulphates, place in the weighing bottle and dry to constant weight at 105° C. Divide the weight obtained by 25/250 of the weight of sample taken and multiply by 100 to get per cent total rosin. It has been found that the weight of total rosin divided by 0.97 will give the actual weight of G rosin when size is made from that grade.

If preferred, the solution and precipitate may be filtered through two filter papers, which have been carefully counterpoised previously by removing a sufficient amount from the heavier filter paper so that they accurately balance, then folding together and placing in the funnel. The precipitate is washed free from sulphates, then dried with filter papers in vacuo over concentrated sulphuric acid to constant weight which may take from twelve to fourteen hours. The filter papers are then separated, one being placed on each pan of balance, and the weight of rosin determined. If the proper filter paper is selected and the filtration is carefully handled, there is no danger of the rosin running through the top filter paper on to the bottom one. Drying in vacuo over sulphuric acid to constant weight, while consuming much more time, is more accurate than drying in an oven at 105° C., as it is not always possible to remove all traces of water owing to the fusing of the rosin at that temperature.

Moisture. Pipette 25 cc. of the solution made for Total Rosin Determ. into a weighed platinum dish, evaporate to dryness on water bath and dry at 105° C. to constant weight.

Free Rosin. Five grams of the sample are dissolved in about 100 cc. of neutral 96% alcohol and titrated with normal NaOH, using phenolphthalein as the indicator. The alcoholic solution from this titration is evaporated to dryness and the residue dissolved in a small amount of warm distilled water, then diluted with cold water, and all of the rosin precipitated with an excess of normal H_2SO_4. Heat on steam bath until the precipitated rosin has collected together into a lump, cool, and titrate back with normal NaOH.

From these figures, assuming that the acid number of the combined rosin is the same as that of the free rosin, the relative amounts of free and combined rosin can be determined.

Bleaching Powder

Sampling. Twenty per cent of the packages in the shipment should be sampled. The sample shall be taken by boring or cutting a two-inch hole through the side of the wooden cask or iron drum midway from the ends, or through the head near the center. The sampler, which consists of a stout iron scoop about one and a half inches wide and eighteen inches long, shall be inserted for two or three inches, withdrawn, and the bleach removed discarded. The sampler shall be inserted again as far as it will go, removed, the bleach transferred to a glass fruit jar, and the jar closed until the next cask is sampled. The portions from the several casks shall all be mixed together to make one composite sample representing the shipment.

Available Chlorine. Ten grams of bleaching powder from the well-mixed sample is weighed out and triturated in a mortar, adding small quantities of distilled water at a time and grinding thoroughly after each addition until the powder is converted to a voluminous paste free from dense particles. The liquor after each trituration is poured off into a 1000-cc. graduated volumetric flask, and the paste is finally washed into flask. Fill the flask to the mark with distilled water, shake well and draw off an aliquot portion by means of a 50-cc. pipette for analysis, observing the precaution that the liquor drawn off contains its proportion of suspended matter. The available chlorine is determined by titration with N/10 sodium arsenite solution, using starch iodide paper as an indicator.

NOTE. The N/10 sodium arsenite solution is made by drying arsenic trioxide, which answers Krauch's requirements for purity, in a desiccator over night, 4.95 grams being weighed out and dissolved in 200 cc. distilled water with 20 grams of pure sodium carbonate, the solution cooled and made up to 1 liter, then standardized with resublimed iodine.

One gram of potato starch is mixed with distilled water to a cream and then poured slowly into 100 cc. of boiling water and the liquid allowed to boil gently for two minutes when 1 gram of c.p. potassium iodide, dissolved in a little distilled water, is poured in. The liquid is then thoroughly mixed, allowed to settle and strips of unsized paper are soaked in the solution and hung up to dry, out of contact of fumes.

Chlorates. The solution in which the available chlorine has been determined by means of N/10 sodium arsenite is slightly acidified with sulphuric acid, the solution transferred to a narrow-mouth flask, and a quantity of pure ammonium ferrous sulphate is added in excess of that required to reduce all chlorates to chlorides. The flask is then stoppered with a 2-hole rubber stopper, which is fitted with a small separatory funnel through one opening, and a small glass tube ending in a short piece of rubber tubing (which may be clamped tight when needed) is fixed in the other opening. The liquid is then brought to boiling and 15 cc. of 1.29 sulphuric acid is added drop by drop, through the funnel. When acid is all in, close opening in funnel and clamp rubber tubing on vent, cool, and titrate back the excess of ferrous ammonium sulphate with N/10 potassium permanganate.

Total Chlorides. The slight pink color produced by the permanganate is removed by the addition of a drop or two of N/10 ferrous ammonium sulphate, and an excess of N/10 silver nitrate solution is added.

The silver chloride is filtered off, washed well and the excess silver nitrate is determined by means of N/10 potassium thiocyanate, the iron in solution acting as an indicator. See chapter on Chlorine, Vol. I.

NOTE. The chlorine as chlorates plus the available chlorine subtracted from the total chlorine as chlorides gives the chlorine present originally in the bleach as chlorides.

Determination of Bases and Silica. To 2 grams of bleaching powder add 25 cc. 1.12 HCl and 50 cc. of 3% H_2O_2. Digest and evaporate on steam bath or hot plate. Dehydrate the silica and determine the silica, alumina, iron, calcium oxide, and magnesia as in lime analysis.

Free Lime. To 100 cc. of bleach liquor made up for the available chlorine determination add 25 cc. hydrogen peroxide, bring to boil and oxidize the hypochlorite. The solution is then titrated with standard acid. At the same time the acidity of the H_2O_2 used should be determined and a correction made for the amount used in destroying the hypochlorite. The free lime is calculated from the acid consumption.

Quality of Powder for Producing Bleach Liquor. Sixty grams of bleaching powder is weighed out and added to 1000 cc. distilled water in a glass jar $4\frac{1}{2}$ inches in diameter and 5 inches deep. The mixture is stirred vigorously by means of a glass rod bent so that it just clears the bottom and sides of the jar, driven by power from electric or water motor at 250 r.p.m. for exactly 15 minutes. The jar is then placed on a bench free from vibration and the time required for the dregs to settle to the bottom noted; 25 cc. of the clear bleach liquor is then measured out and tested in the usual way for available chlorine.

Determination of Wood and Coarse Impurities. 100 grams of the powder is triturated in a porcelain mortar, washed through a 60-mesh sieve, residue is dried and weighed.

Proximate Analysis for Sand and Grit. To 10 grams of the powder add 75 cc. of 1.12 hydrochloric acid, and warm until all lime salts are dissolved, dilute to 200 cc. with distilled water, pour off the supernatant liquid, again dilute to 200 cc. with distilled water, filter, wash, and ignite the residue.

NOTE. If preferred, a potassium iodide-starch solution preserved with a drop of CCl_4 or CS_2 may be used as the indicator in the determination of available chlorine by testing a drop of the bleach liquor with a drop of the indicator on a pill tile rather than the use of the potassium iodide-starch paper. If desired, soluble starch, which dissolves readily in hot water, may be used in the preparation of this indicator.

Starch and Starch Products

Starch is used in the paper industry for four purposes: (1) Engine sizing; (2) tub sizing; (3) pasting, and (4) coating. It is necessary to divide it into two main classes, with a method of analysis for each class. The first to be known as raw starch and to include all starches which have not been treated in any other way than by the purifying methods used in their manufacture. The second to be known as converted starches with subclasses. The method of sampling for all kinds of starch products to be the same, and to be embodied as part of the method of analysis.

Sampling. Ten bags or barrels are taken from different parts of a car. These are sampled by means of a 1-inch tryer 12 inches long. One filling of the tryer is to be taken from each bag or barrel. Samples so obtained are mixed, bottled and sealed in three jars, one for each party to the transaction, and one for reference. For smaller deliveries than a carload 10% at least of the bags or barrels should be sampled.

Preliminary Examination. Raw Starch: (a) Spread out 100 grams of the sample on a sheet of white glazed paper, and examine for foreign material.

(b) Mix this sample with 500 cc. of water to a smooth cream and strain through a 200-mesh silk bolting cloth. Compare residue on silk with standard sample of the same grade, treated in the same manner, at the same time.

(c) Stir filtrate from above for two seconds with a circular motion, and let stand thirty seconds. Decant carefully, and compare residue with a standard sample of the same grade of starch, treated in the same manner, at the same time.

Moisture. Dry approximately 5 grams to constant weight at 100° C. Loss in weight is calculated as moisture.

Ash. Weigh out 1 gram of the sample; transfer to a platinum crucible; ignite to constant weight.

Acidity. Weigh out 20 grams on a watchglass. Transfer to a 250-cc. porcelain dish. Add approximately 200 cc. of water, and stir until starch forms a smooth cream. Titrate with N/10 caustic soda, using phenolphthalein as indicator until a faint pink color persists for twenty seconds.

Alkalinity. Method is same as for acidity, except that sample should be titrated with N/10 sulphuric acid until the pink coloration just disappears.

Test for the Presence of Alkaline Starch or Alkali. Add a few drops of phenolphthalein solution to water in a white porcelain dish; sprinkle in a little of the dry sample. If some of the grains turn pink, it indicates that the sample is a mixture of raw starch and alkaline starch or alkali. If all the particles turn pink, the material is an alkaline finished starch.

Viscosity. Take 12 grams of the sample in 300 cc. of water, bring to boil, then boil for ten minutes with constant stirring in an aluminum beaker over a naked flame. Determine viscosity at 100° C. with 200 cc. of the liquid in a Scott viscosimeter, standardized as follows: Calibrate to hold 200 cc. of water at 100° C. Determine viscosity on first 50 cc. withdrawn. Express result as a ratio. (Starch viscosity) $\div$ (water viscosity) = viscosity number.

Converted Starches. Owing to the number and variety of the products on the market, their classification is a matter of some difficulty. The method of conversion, however, may be used as a means, and thus the following classes can be arranged: (1) Thin boiling starch, mainly used for tub sizing, converted by treatment with weak acid solutions by the "in suspension" or "drying in" process.   (2) Partly dextrinized starches, and dextrins, made by damping the starch with small quantities of acid, and converting at a high temperature by the dry process.   (3) Oxidized starches.   (4) Acetylated starches.   (5) Alkali-treated starches, including products consisting of raw starch mixed with certain quantities of various alkalis and alkaline salts.   (6) Mixtures of starch products and mineral fillers.   (7) Mixture of starch products with glue and casein or other sizing agents.   (8) Products in solution or paste form.

Sampling, Moisture and Ash are the same as for raw starch.

Acidity and Alkalinity.   First method same as for raw starch.

Total Acidity.   Mix 10 grams of the sample in 200 cc. of water and heat on a water bath for five minutes after reaching 75° C.; cool and titrate.   This gives the acidity within the starch granule.

Viscosity.   In determining viscosity the starches are divided into three classes: (a) Low boiling, or laundry starch; (b) medium thin boiling; (c) high thin boiling, with a decrease in viscosity from (a) to (c).   For (a) the viscosity should be determined in a 10% solution; for (b) in a 20% solution; for (c) in a 30% solution.   Otherwise the method is the same as for raw starch.

Added Materials.   These are tested for by the ordinary methods used in separating and identifying mineral fillers, metallic salts, glue, casein, and other vegetable sizes.   The identification of the product in relation to the classification of the process of manufacture involves a more exhaustive analysis including: (1) The identification of the starch by microscopical observation. (2) Combined acid to determine the degree of acetylation of the product. (3) Solubility in cold water and reaction with Fehling's solution, which gives a measure of the degree to which the starch has been hydrolyzed and dextrinized.   (4) Color reaction with iodine and other agents.   (5) *Technical Valuation*—Character of Size.   A sample of the starch product is mixed with four or five times its weight of water, and heated on a water bath, for at least twenty minutes after swelling.

(a) Portions of the size are allowed to cool, and the time of setting observed. This gives a figure for the permanency of the solution.

(b) A little of the size is rubbed out on paper and allowed to dry, when the surface and finish produced is observed.

(c) The solution is run out on a clean glass plate to a thin layer and allowed to dry at room temperature.   Film produced is examined and compared with, say, a gelatin film, for physical characters.

Sizing Strength.   For paper coating the size is prepared under the proper conditions for the particular product and mixed with definite quantities of clay or other filler.   A series of samples is made up at graduated strengths according to the proportions used in practice, and samples of paper are coated by color obtained.   The sizing power of the sample is determined, in comparison with other sizing materials, treated in the same manner, at the same time, by noting the resistance to spirit varnish, or by using the sealing wax test and others.   In most cases, both for coating and tub sizing, the most accurate and reliable results are only obtainable by a working trial under standard conditions.

Soda Ash

Sampling. Five per cent of the bags, or barrels, in the shipment should be sampled by means of a sampling auger in the usual manner.

Moisture. Heat a carefully weighed amount of the soda ash in a covered platinum crucible to constant weight. The heating should be so regulated that the bottom of the crucible when viewed in subdued light shows a very faint trace of color.

Alkalinity. Weigh 5 grams of the soda ash on a watchglass, transfer to a beaker, and dissolve in about 300 cc. of water. Transfer to a 500-cc. graduated flask, cool, and make up to the mark. After thorough agitation, pipette 100 cc. into a beaker and titrate with standard acid, using methyl orange as the indicator. Calculate to per cent of Na_2CO_3 on the dry soda ash.

Sulphuric Acid

Sampling. Contents of carboy shall be well mixed before sampling.

Specific Gravity. Determine by standard hydrometer.

Sediment. A portion of the acid should be taken immediately after agitation and set aside in a tall glass cylinder and the amount of sediment noted.

Acidity. Run 50 grams of the acid into a beaker containing 200 cc. cold distilled water, transfer to a 1000-cc. graduated flask when cooled to room temperature. Make up to the mark with distilled water and mix well. Draw out 100 cc. of this acid by means of a pipette and make up to 500 cc. with distilled water in a graduated flask. Draw out 50 cc. of this acid (equal to 0.5 gm. of the original sample) in a beaker and titrate with standard alkali, using methyl orange as the indicator. Calculate per cent H_2SO_4 in sample.

Iron. Determine colorimetrically by the method given in the procedure for the analysis of aluminum sulphate page 1773.

Caustic Soda

Sampling. Break open the drum, crack off clean pieces and place them in air-tight fruit jars. The pieces should be crushed and ground as rapidly as possible in the laboratory and samples preserved in an air-tight jar or rubber-stoppered bottle.

Alkalinity. Fill a glass-stoppered weighing tube with a portion of the sample and weigh approximately 1 gram of the sample in a 350-cc. beaker. The caustic soda is then dissolved in about 200 cc. water, titrated first with standard acid and phenolphthalein as the indicator, and then completed by titrating for total alkali with methyl orange as the indicator. The titration with phenolphthalein gives the acid consumed by the NaOH and half the Na_2CO_3. The second titration gives the acid consumed by the remaining half of the sodium carbonate. Twice the difference between the two titrations gives the number of cc. of standard acid consumed by the NaOH, from which the percentage of NaOH in the caustic soda may be calculated.

NOTE. If through damage of the drum in transportation the caustic soda has absorbed a considerable amount of moisture, the following procedure should be used: Sample as above. Determine the alkalinity on the dry basis by weighing approximately 1 gram of the sample in a tared, covered silver crucible, heat to fusion and until all moisture is driven off. Cool in desiccator and weigh. The weighed, dry sample is then dissolved in about 200 cc. water and procedure followed as above.

Lime

Sampling. One shovelful out of every tenth wheelbarrow of lime, as it is unloaded from the car, should be taken and placed on a clean floor or canvas. The combined sample should be crushed, preferably by a laboratory crusher, and quartered down to desired amount. The sample should be kept in a well-stoppered bottle or friction-top can.

Moisture and Carbon Dioxide. Ignite about 1 gram of the finely pulverized sample to constant weight in a covered platinum crucible, in the full flame of a blast lamp or No. 4 Meeker burner.

Impurities. A 1 gram sample of the pulverized lime is weighed in a 300-cc. casserole, slightly dampened with water and after covering the casserole with a watchglass, about 25 cc. conc. HCl is carefully poured on the lime. The solution is evaporated to dryness and the residue taken up with a few drops of conc. HCl. The HCl solution is transferred to a beaker, made up to about 300 cc., a few drops of conc. HNO_3 added, and the solution boiled for a few minutes. Add 10 cc. of a 5% NH_4Cl solution and NH_4OH until present in slight excess. Boil until odor of ammonia is barely perceptible. The precipitate is filtered, washed, ignited, and weighed as impurities.

NOTE. In case of dolomite lime, or lime containing a large proportion of magnesia, a double precipitation with NH_4OH is recommended. Dissolve the first precipitate by means of hot dilute HCl on filter paper, catching the solution in beaker used for first precipitation. Wash the filter paper free from acid, make up solution to about 200 cc., bring to boil, precipitate with NH_4OH as before and filter the precipitate on filter paper used previously.

Lime (CaO). To the filtrate, or combined filtrates, from the " impurities " precipitate a few drops of NH_4OH are added, and the solution brought to boiling. To the boiling solution 20 cc. of a saturated solution of ammonium oxalate are added drop by drop, and the boiling continued until the precipitated CaC_2O_4 assumes a well-defined granular form. It is then allowed to stand for thirty minutes, or until the precipitate has settled, decanted through a filter, redissolved with HCl, washing the filter five or six times with hot water, and a final wash with ammonia water. The solution is then made up to 250 cc. with water and brought to boiling. Add 1 cc. ammonium oxalate solution and ammonia drop by drop until present in slight excess, and boil for two or three minutes. Allow to stand for thirty minutes or until the precipitate has settled, filter and wash (the volume of wash-water should not be too large), weigh as oxide by ignition and blasting in a covered crucible to constant weight, or determine with dilute standard permanganate.

NOTE. In the absence of magnesia the second precipitation may be omitted.

Magnesia (MgO). The combined filtrates from the calcium precipitates are acidified with HCl and concentrated on the steam bath to about 150 cc., 10 cc. of a saturated solution of $Na(NH_4)HPO_4$ are added, and the solution boiled for several minutes. It is then removed from the flame and cooled by placing the beaker in ice water. After cooling, NH_4OH is added drop by drop with constant stirring until the crystalline ammonium-magnesium ortho-phosphate begins to form, and then in moderate excess, the stirring being continued for several minutes. It is then set aside for several hours in ice water and filtered. The precipitate is redissolved in hot dilute HCl, the solution made up to about 100 cc., 1 cc. of a saturated solution of $Na(NH_4)HPO_4$ added, and ammonia drop by drop, with constant stirring, until the precipitate is again formed as described and the ammonia is in moderate excess. It is then allowed to stand for about four hours in ice water, when it is filtered on a paper or a Gooch crucible, ignited to constant weight over blast or No. 4 Meeker burner, cooled and weighed as $Mg_2P_2O_7$.

NOTE. To avoid danger of injury to platinum crucible, when the precipitate is filtered on paper, it is advisable to dry the precipitate and filter paper, and separate the precipitate from the filter paper, igniting the paper in the crucible, then adding the precipitate to the ash in the crucible and igniting to constant weight.

Causticizing Test. Boil 4 grams of the lime with 8 grams of dry soda ash in 500 cc. water in a covered beaker for 1 hour. Cool, make up to 500 cc. in a graduated flask, mix, allow to settle clear, draw out 50 cc. of the clear solution by means of a pipette, and titrate for NaOH with standard acid as given in procedure under caustic soda. Knowing the weights of both lime and soda ash used, it is easy to calculate the amount of lime required to completely causticize a given amount of soda ash.

Rapid Methods for a Calcium Lime Containing Less than One Per Cent Magnesia

Free Lime. Five grams of the lime is made into a milk and diluted to 500 cc. in a graduated flask. Aliquot portions are pipetted from the well-shaken milk and titrated with standard oxalic acid and phenolphthalein. Calculate to per cent CaO.

Calcium Carbonate. An aliquot portion of the milk is dissolved in an excess of standard HCl boiled to remove CO_2, and the excess acid is titrated with standard alkali and methyl orange.

This value for total CaO, less the free CaO already determined, gives the CaO combined as $CaCO_3$.

Moisture. From loss on ignition subtract the CO_2, calculated from the $CaCO_3$ as determined above.

ANALYSIS OF CLAY [1]

Chemical Analysis. The sample should be finely ground, if necessary a large quantity, 2 to 10 pounds, should be weighed and dried on steam table, weighed again and loss in moisture calculated to percentage; it may then be finely ground.

A weighed quantity, 1 to 10 grams, should now be dried at 100° C. to constant weight, this loss calculated to percentage and added to that from the first drying and is the moisture. A weighed portion, 1 to 2 grams, of the moisture-free powder is heated, in a covered crucible, to bright redness for 10 minutes, cooled and reweighed; loss = combined water and organic matter. Or a weighed quantity is put in a boat which is heated in a tube in a current of dry air and drawn through a weighed $CaCl_2$ tube; gain in weight = combined moisture.

Mix 1 gram dry clay with 5 gms. $Na_2CO_3 + \frac{1}{2}$ gm. KNO_3 in a platinum crucible, fuse 30 to 40 minutes, cool, detach melt from crucible. Wash crucible with H_2O, then HCl, then H_2O, pouring all washings into a porcelain dish, add the melt. Cover dish, add HCl little at a time until in considerable excess. Evaporate dry, bake 1 hour at 120° C. Cool, moisten well with HCl. Evaporate and bake again. Cool, moisten HCl, take up in H_2O, boil 10 minutes, filter, wash hot HCl (1 to 1), cold H_2O, hot HCl, cold H_2O, then 5 to 6 times hot H_2O, ignite in a weighed platinum crucible and hold.

Evaporate the filtrate and washing in a dish, bake as above, moisten HCl, evaporate and bake again. Take up HCl + H_2O filter and wash as above. Burn this filter in same crucible, cool, weigh = crude SiO_2. Moisten with few drops H_2SO_4 (1 to 4), then H_2O to make a thin mud; add enough HF to fill crucible $\frac{2}{3}$ full, evaporate at gentle heat; heat cautiously over lamp—to avoid spattering—raising heat slowly to full heat of lamp. Loss in weight = SiO_2.

If any residue remains in the crucible, fuse with $KHSO_4$. Leach melt with H_2O and add to main filtrate.

Boil filtrate from silica, add 1 to 3 cc. HNO_3, boil 10 minutes. Add NH_4OH in slight excess, boil 3 minutes, let settle in warm place, decant through a filter. Add hot water to precipitate, stir, let settle, filter, dissolve precipitate in HCl (1 to 1). Dilute to 250 cc., boil, reprecipitate as above, repeat again, wash thoroughly with hot H_2O. Ignite and weigh precipitate = $Fe_2O_3Al_2O_3$-($P_2O_5.TiO_2$).

Fuse with $KHSO_4$, leach with H_2O, reduce in Jones reductor. Titrate Fe with $KMnO_4$. $Fe/0.7 = Fe_2O_3$.

Fuse 2 to 5 grams dry sample with 5 wts. $Na_2CO_3 + \frac{1}{2}$ wt. KNO_3. Leach melt with H_2O, filter, wash with $H_2O + Na_2CO_3$. Save residue for Ti. Acidify filtrate with HNO_3, boil off CO_2, add Fe_2Cl_6 solution (free from Phos.), boil. Add NH_4OH, filter, take up precipitate in HNO_3. Boil well and precipitate the phosphorus with ammonium molybdate. Determine phosphorus.

$$P \times 2.29 = P_2O_5.$$
$$(Al_2O_3 + Fe_2O_3 + P_2O_5 + TiO_2) - (Fe_2O_3 + P_2O_5 + TiO_2) = Al_2O_3.$$

Evaporate united filtrates from Al_2O_3, etc., to 100 cc. Make ammoniacal, add Br in excess, then 60 to 70 cc. NH_4OH, boil 20 minutes, filter, wash with hot H_2O. Ignite and weigh Mn_3O_4. $Mn_3O_4 \times 0.93006 = MnO$.

[1] By J. M. Wilson, Lefax, 9-196, June, 1919. By courtesy of Lefax, Philadelphia.

Acidify filtrate from MnO_2, evaporate dry, take up in $HCl + H_2O$ (volume 150 cc.), boil, add NH_4OH till neutral, then ammonium oxalate. Boil 10 minutes, cool 2 hours, decant close as possible through filter. Dissolve precipitate in HCl, dilute to 100 cc., add ammonium oxalate, boil. Precipitate with NH_4OH, boil 10 minutes, filter after 2 hours, wash twice with cold H_2O, then 5 or 6 times with hot H_2O. Ignite strongly, weigh while still warm, repeat ignition and weighing = CaO. Or dissolve precipitate in least quantity HCl (1 to 1) through filter into an Erlenmeyer flask. Wash with H_2O, add 25 cc. H_2SO_4 (1 to 4), heat to 80° C., titrate with $KMnO_4$. Fe value $KMnO_4/2 = CaO$.

Evaporate combined filtrates from CaO to small volume (15 to 20 cc.), add 1 gram ammonium phosphate $(NH_4)_2HPO_4$, then NH_4OH till solution is neutral. Cool under tap, stir till precipitate forms, set aside 15 minutes, stirring occasionally. Add $\frac{1}{2}$ volume NH_4OH, stir, let stand 4 hours, filter but do not wash. Dissolve through filter in HCl into vessel in which precipitation was conducted. Wash filter with H_2O, reprecipitate with NH_4OH as before, filter on weighed Gooch felt. Wash with (NH_4NO_3, 60 gms.; H_2O, 80 cc.; NH_4OH, 1–3, to 600 cc.), dry at 100° C., ignite carefully till a glow passes over the precipitate, cool and weigh $Mg_2P_2O_7$.

$$Mg_2P_2O_7 \times 0.36207 = MgO.$$

Alkalies. Weigh 1 gram clay, 1 gram NH_4Cl into a platinum crucible, mix thoroughly. Add 6 grams $CaCO_3$ (free from alkalies), mix, cover with 2 grams $CaCO_3$. Heat covered crucible very gently till no more fumes are given off. Raise heat slowly till lower third of crucible is at good red heat. Maintain this heat for 15 minutes, cool, transfer sintered mass to a porcelain dish. Wash out crucible with water into dish, add more water till volume is 200–300 cc. Digest at 100° C., breaking lumps with a glass rod, then boil 5 to 10 minutes, add $(NH_4)_2CO_3$, allow to stand 20 to 30 minutes. Filter into a porcelain dish, wash thoroughly with hot H_2O containing $(NH_4)_2CO_3$. Evaporate nearly dry, add NH_4OH + ammonium oxalate, filter into a platinum dish. Evaporate dry, ignite gently to drive off ammonium salts, cool, add $(NH_4)_2CO_3$ + ammonium oxalate, filter through very small filter into a weighed platinum dish. Evaporate dry, ignite gently till ammonium salts are volatilized, raise heat till bottom of dish is a faint red, cool and weigh. Moisten with a drop or two of HCl, heat again and weigh = NaCl + KCl. Separate 1st by $PtCl_4$, 2d by perchloric acid, 3d by titration of Cl with $AgNO_3$, or 4th by conversion into sulphates and determining the SO_3 with $BaCl_2$.

Titanium. Decomposition, (1) by fusion with 5 wts. $Na_2CO_3 + \frac{1}{2}$ wt. KNO_3, leaching with H_2O, and extracting TiO_2 from residue, (2) by fusion with $KHSO_4$, leaching with $H_2O + H_2SO_4$, filtering and precipitating TiO_2 from filtrate, (3) by moistening with dilute H_2SO_4 and evaporating with HF to remove SiO_2 and decompose silicates.

Precipitate, add NH_4OH to solution until a faint precipitate is produced, then HCl to redissolve the precipitate and leave a slight excess. Dilute to 250 cc., add strong solution $Na_2S_2O_3$ and boil 20 minutes. Let settle, decant through a filter, wash once by decantation, keeping as much of the precipitate in the beaker as possible. When filter has drained, place beaker, in which the precipitation was made, under the funnel and treat filter with concentrated HCl. Allow to act 15 to 20 minutes, wash filter thoroughly with cold H_2O, repeat the precipitation as above, filter, wash well with hot H_2O, ignite and weigh TiO_2.

When TiO_2 is present in small amount, it may be determined by color: Standard $TiSO_4$ solution made as follows: Fuse $\frac{1}{2}$ gram rutile with Na_2CO_3, leach melt with H_2O, filter, take up insoluble in H_2SO_4 (1 to 4), evaporate to fumes, cool, take up with H_2O + H_2SO_4, filter if necessary, dilute till 1 cc. = 0.001 gram Ti. Decompose clay by fusion with Na_2CO_3 and treat the residue with H_2SO_4. Evaporate to fumes, take up with H_2O + H_2SO_4, pour into a Nessler tube. Fill another Nessler tube nearly to same volume with H_2O. To each add 5 cc. H_2O_2 and to the standard add the standard $TiSO_4$ from a burette until the brown colors match, when the volumes are equal. The burette reading will then give the number of milligrams of Ti in the clay from which the percentage may be calculated.

State of Silica. A—Combined with bases in the clay, B—Hydrated silica, C—Sand or silicates. Moisten 2 grams dry powder with H_2O, add 20 cc. H_2SO_4 (conc.), cover dish, heat 10 hours, remove cover, evaporate dry, cool, take up in H_2O, filter, wash with H_2O, ignite and weigh = $A + B + C$.

Boil with Na_2CO_3 solution, allow to settle, decant through a weighed Gooch felt or alundum crucible, repeat boiling and decantation until a portion of the filtrate gives no precipitate with NH_4Cl on standing. Transfer residue to filter and wash thoroughly with hot H_2O, acid, then hot H_2O. Ignite and weigh = C. A and B are in filtrate.

Boil 4 to 5 grams dry powder with strong solution of Na_2CO_3, filter, wash with hot H_2O. Acidify filtrate with HCl, evaporate dry, bake at 120° C., cool, moisten with HCl, evaporate dry, bake again. Take up in HCl and H_2O, filter, wash, ignite; weigh as $SiO_2 = B$. $(A + B + C) - (B + C) = A$.

If $A + B + C$ = total SiO_2 found on analysis, C is quartz. If $A + B + C$ is greater than total SiO_2, C is in form of silicate and weight of SiO_2 as silicates = $A + B + C -$ total SiO_2 found in 1 gram.

ANALYSIS OF GLASS [1]

An exact definition of glass is a decidedly perplexing problem as it consists of such a variety of substances. Neither can a formula be written for such a substance, because it may contain so many different radicals and also because glass is a mixture of silicates and not a definite compound.

It is also quite a problem to write up an analysis of glass that will embrace all glasses. The most common substances usually found in clear glasses are Silica, Lead, Alumina, Calcium, Magnesia, Soda, Potash, Iron as an impurity, and other substances found in special glasses and colored glasses such as Barium, Borax, Manganese, Sulphur, Zinc, Tin, Copper, Chromium, Gold, and Uranium, Fluorides, Phosphates, Lithium and Strontium are also occasionally found. Antimony, Arsenic, Cobalt, Selenium, Titanium, etc., are not uncommon but are usually present in such small quantities that they are seldom determined or even looked for.

In the following analysis only the substances most frequently encountered by the glass chemist will be considered. They are—Silica, Lead, Iron, Alumina, Calcium, Magnesia, Soda, Potash, Barium, Borax, Manganese and Sulphur. If an unknown glass is to be analyzed, it is always necessary to make a qualitative examination of the sample before any quantitative work should be attempted.

Density or Specific Gravity. The value and importance of knowing the specific gravity of a glass is quite often overlooked but its value becomes more evident as one continues to make the determinations and link them up with the analysis of the glass in question. It is always advantageous to take the specific gravity before the glass is analyzed as it quite often gives a clue as to the type of glass, especially to the person who is familiar with linking gravity and analysis. It is always interesting to calculate the specific gravity from the percentages of constituents in the analysis. This can be done by any who have the proper tables and formula at hand.

The specific gravity can be very accurately determined on the analytical balance on a piece of glass weighing as little as 8 grams. By making substitution in the equation:

$$D = \frac{W_1 - W_2}{W_1},$$

where D = specific gravity, W_1 = weight in air, W_2 = weight in water, the density is easily computed. Duplicate computations should check within five points in the third decimal place.

Preparation of Sample and the Determination of Silica. Grind the sample of glass to an impalpable flour with a mortar and pestle. Weigh out 1 gram of the finely powdered glass into a platinum crucible. Weigh out 4 grams of sodium potassium carbonate fusion mixture and about half a gram of potassium chlorate and transfer to the same crucible. Mix thoroughly and take care not to lose any. Fuse this and keep it hot till the mass is a liquid in the bottom of the crucible. Allow the mass to cool off considerably and then take up the melt with 50 to 100 cc. of hot water containing about 10 cc. of hydrochloric acid. If borates are present, refer to the removal of borates under " Determination of B_2O_3." Transfer to an evaporating dish and evaporate to

[1] By G. E. Fisher, Lefax, 11–319. By courtesy of J. C. Parker, President Lefax, Philadelphia.

dryness on a steam bath and then bake for at least half an hour on a hot plate at 110° C. Then take up with dilute hydrochloric acid and water and filter. Wash the residue with hot water until free from chlorides. Save this residue. Transfer the filtrate to the evaporating dish and evaporate and bake as before. Take this up with water and hydrochloric acid and filter and wash with hot water until free from chlorides. Combine this residue with the first one and ignite to constant weight in a previously ignited platinum crucible. After weighing, moisten with *dilute* sulphuric acid and then fill the crucible three quarters full with hydrofluoric acid and evaporate to dryness in an iron cone and ignite and weigh. Deduct the weight of this residue from that of the above weighing. The difference in weights is the weight for corrected silica from which the percentage is easily calculated. Fuse the residue which remains in the crucible with about 2 grams of potassium bisulphate, take up with dilute hydrochloric acid and add it to the main solution. If the sodium potassium carbonate fusion mixture is not known to be pure, it should be analyzed and corrections made accordingly.

Determination of PbO. Neutralize the solution, then make it just acid with 1 drop of hydrochloric acid. Pass in hydrogen sulphide gas for several minutes to insure complete precipitation. Allow the lead sulphide to settle, then filter on a Gooch crucible. Wash the residue with water saturated with hydrogen sulphide. Again pass hydrogen sulphide into this filtrate to be sure precipitation is complete. Preserve the filtrate for the estimation of iron, etc. Dissolve the lead sulphide in dilute nitric acid (1 to 4). Filter this solution to remove the asbestos used in the Gooch. Precipitate lead sulphate from this solution by adding dilute sulphuric acid with constant stirring. Then add 100% by volume of 98% ethyl alcohol to the *cold* solution. Allow the precipitate to settle for an hour and filter on a weighed Gooch previously ignited at a red heat. Wash with 50% alcohol. Heat the residue slowly and ignite at a dull red heat until the residue is white. Cool and weigh as lead sulphate. Calculate the percentage of PbO by using the proper factors which may be found in the table below.

Determination of Fe_2O_3 and $Al_2O_3(R_2O_3)$. Boil this solution with 2 or 3 cc. of nitric acid to remove the sulphur and oxidize the iron. Cool the solution. Add about 5 grams of ammonium chloride and then add ammonium hydroxide until the solution is slightly ammoniacal. Boil cautiously for about 5 minutes. Allow the precipitate to settle. Filter and wash with hot water or hot 2% ammonium nitrate solution. Preserve this filtrate for the determination of calcium. Ignite the residue in a weighed platinum crucible. Cool and weigh as Fe_2O_3 and Al_2O_3. Fuse this residue with potassium bisulphate and digest with dilute sulphuric acid. Transfer to a 250-cc. Erlenmeyer flask. Pass in hydrogen sulphide gas to reduce the iron. Then fit a Bunsen valve to the flask and boil to a small volume to drive off the excess hydrogen sulphide. Cool and add a pinch of sodium bicarbonate and titrate with standard N/200 potassium permanganate solution. From the amount of standard solution used calculate the percentage of iron oxide. Deduct the percentage of iron oxide from ($Fe_2O_3 - Al_2O_3$) and the difference is the per cent Al_2O_3.

Determination of CaO. Bring the solution to boiling. While hot add 10 to 20 cc. of hot saturated ammonium oxalate solution with constant stirring.

Then add about 5 cc. of ammonium hydroxide. Allow to stand for several hours or preferably over night. Filter off the calcium oxalate and wash with a 2% ammonia water. Preserve the filtrate for the determination of magnesia. Ignite the residue at full blast in a previously ignited and weighed platinum crucible to constant weight. Weigh as calcium oxide.

Determination of MgO. Concentrate the solution by boiling and while hot add 10 to 20 cc. of saturated microcosmic salt solution with constant stirring. Then add ammonia and stir vigorously, taking care not to strike the sides of the beaker. Allow the precipitate to settle for several hours or preferably over night. Filter and wash with a 2% solution of ammonia water. Dry the residue and filter paper. Ignite slowly at first and then at full heat in a weighed porcelain or platinum crucible, until constant weight. Cool and weigh up as magnesium pyrophosphate. Calculate the percentage of MgO by using the factor found in the table below. If large amounts are to be ignited, it is best to ignite the residue and paper separately in a porcelain crucible.

Determination of the Alkalies. The method in general use is that of Sullivan and Taylor. Weigh out 1 gram of finely powdered glass in a platinum crucible of about 40 cc. capacity, moisten with water and add 2 grams of oxalic acid crystals and enough 48% hydrofluoric acid to fill the crucible half full. This is evaporated to dryness and warmed to a temperature which is just high enough to expel the excess oxalic acid. When all the acid is expelled, the crucible is cooled and the evaporation repeated twice more with oxalic acid and water. The amount of oxalic acid used is about 5 grams in all. After the third evaporation when all the excess of oxalic acid is expelled, the remaining oxalates are taken up with hot water, allowed to cool and filtered. The residue which consists of lead oxalate and calcium oxalate is filtered off. The filtrate is evaporated to dryness in a platinum dish and then heated over a free flame until oxalates are decomposed to carbonates. The insoluble carbonates are filtered off and the alkali carbonates are in the filtrate. The filtrate is made acid with hydrochloric and evaporated to dryness to remove traces of silica. The filtrate is evaporated to dryness in a platinum dish, the sodium chloride and potassium chloride heated to incipient fusion, cooled and weighed. This gives the weight of the combined alkali chlorides. The chlorides are dissolved in about 25 cc. of water and 4–5 cc. of chloroplatinic acid (1 gram Pt in 10 cc.) added and the solution evaporated to a syrupy consistency. The insoluble potassium chloroplatinate is filtered on a Gooch. Wash by decantation with 85% ethyl alcohol until the washings are colorless. The Gooch is dried at 130° C. to constant weight. The potassium chloroplatinate is computed to potassium chloride, and the sodium chloride found by difference from the weight of the combined alkali chlorides. Both potassium chloride and sodium chloride are computed to their respective oxide.

Determination of B_2O_3. Before proceeding with any of the determinations, boric acid must be removed. This is done by adding 25 cc. of methyl alcohol in both dehydrations of silica. Then proceed as usual. The determination of B_2O_3 must be made as follows on a separate sample of glass. Fuse .5 gram sample with about 4 grams of sodium carbonate. Take up with 20–30 cc. dilute hydrochloric acid and add a few drops of nitric acid to oxidize the iron. Place the whole in a 250-cc. round bottom flask. Heat nearly to boiling and add dry precipitated calcium carbonate in moderate excess. *Connect with a reflux condenser and boil vigorously for ten minutes to remove CO_2 from the solution. Filter off precipitate through a small Buchner funnel, washing several times with hot water. Keep the volume below 100 cc. Return the filtrate to the flask and add a small amount of calcium carbonate and again heat to boiling. Connect up to a filter pump, through a splash trap, and continue suction cautiously, until boiling has nearly ceased, to remove the last traces of CO_2 in the solution. Cool to room temperature and filter if necessary. Add 4–5 drops of phenolphthalein indicator and run in slowly N/10 standard sodium hydroxide solution until the liquid is decidedly pink. Add about 1 gram of mannite or 10 cc. glycerol and shake. The pink color will disappear. Then run in more standard NaOH till pink and then more glycerol. Continue this until the pink is permanent. The glycerol must be neutral. The standard NaOH should be standardized against a standard sample of B_2O_3. The percentage B_2O_3 can then be computed.

This method is unsatisfactory when zinc or lead are present in the glass as high results are obtained. Fuse a half-gram sample with 4 grams of sodium carbonate. Digest with 20–30 cc. of hot water and when the melt is entirely decomposed filter off any insoluble oxides. After washing, transfer the filtrate to a 250-cc. round bottom flask. Add about 7 cc. concentrated hydrochloric acid. Heat nearly to boiling and add a moderate amount of calcium carbonate in excess; from here proceed as above from asterisk *.

Determination of MnO_2. The iron and alumina precipitation with ammonia also effects the precipitation of manganese. It is then necessary to separate these three substances. The residue containing Fe_2O_3, Al_2O_3, MnO_2 is dissolved in dilute nitric acid. It is necessary that the solution be free from ferrous iron. To this solution add as much sodium carbonate as possible without any precipitation taking place. This must be added very cautiously drop by drop. Dilute and add one-half gram of sodium acetate and boil. Let settle and filter. Wash with a $\frac{1}{2}\%$ solution of ammonium acetate. The filtrate should now be neutral to methyl orange. The residue contains the iron and alumina. The filtrate contains the manganese. Dissolve the residue in dilute hydrochloric acid and determine iron and alumina by the foregoing method. The filtrate should be concentrated. Add 10 grams of sodium acetate. The solution should now have a volume of about 200 cc. Bromine water is then added until the color is distinct. The solution is then boiled for about 15 minutes, with small additions of bromine water. The precipitate is then allowed to settle. Filter and wash. Dissolve the residue in hot dilute hydrochloric acid containing a little bisulphite. Add ammonium phosphate, then ammonia slowly, with heating and constant stirring. Allow it to settle a few hours, then filter and wash with a dilute solution of ammonia water. Ignite in a weighed porcelain crucible, as manganese pyrophosphate, and compute the percentage of MnO_2 from the factor in the table below.

Determination of Sulphur. A separate sample should be used for the estimation of sulphur. Weigh out a 2 gram sample, mix with 5 grams of sodium potassium carbonate fusion mixture and a half gram of potassium nitrate. During fusion the charge should be protected from the flame by an asbestos board provided with a hole to accommodate the crucible. Take up the fusion with water, transfer to an evaporating dish and dehydrate. Take up with dilute hydrochloric acid, filter and wash. Dehydrate the filtrate the second time, take up with dilute hydrochloric acid, boil to drive off carbon dioxide, filter and wash. To the hot filtrate add enough barium chloride solution to completely precipitate the sulphur. The barium chloride should be added very slowly and with constant stirring. Allow the barium sulphate to settle several hours and then filter on a weighed ignited Gooch. Wash with a dilute alcohol solution. Ignite at a temperature of about 800° C. Cool and weigh as barium sulphate. Compute percentages from the table given below.

Determination of BaO and Separation of Barium from Calcium. This separation is made from the solution from which iron and alumina have been precipitated. Boil this solution sufficiently to remove the ammonia. Evaporate the filtrate nearly to dryness. Then take up with about 300 cc. of water and add 5–6 drops of acetic acid with enough ammonia acetate to neutralize any free mineral acid present. Heat the solution and add an excess of ammonium chromate. Allow the barium chromate precipitate to settle for an hour or more. Filter on a weighed Gooch and wash with water containing ammonium chromate, until free from calcium. Then wash with water until free from ammonium chromate. Dry the precipitate at 110° C. and ignite gently at first and finally to a dull red heat. Weigh as barium chromate and compute the percentage of BaO from table.

TABLE OF COMPUTATION FACTORS

$BaSO_4$	× 0.1373 = S		$PbSO_4$	× 0.736 = PbO	
	× 0.2744 = SO_4			× 0.683 = Pb	
	× 0.3430 = SO_3		$Mg_2P_2O_7$	× 0.218 = Mg	
	× 0.4115 = SO_4			× 0.362 = MgO	
	× 0.4202 = H_2SO_4		$Mn_2P_2O_7$	× 0.387 = Mn	
	× 0.821 = Na_2SO_4			× 0.612 = MnO_2	
	× 0.747 = K_2SO_4		K_2PtCl_6	× 0.306 = KCl	
	× 0.892 = $BaCl_2$			× 0.193 = K_2O	
$BaCrO_4$	× 0.541 = Ba		KCl	× 0.631 = K_2O	
	× 0.605 = BaO		NaCl	× 0.530 = Na_2O	

ANALYSIS OF THE MOST IMPORTANT GLASS= MAKING MATERIALS [1]

Potash (**Potassium Carbonate**) Water Insoluble. Dissolve five grams of the sample in 100 cc. of distilled water and filter off any insoluble matter on a tared Gooch crucible. Dry, cool and weigh.

Moisture. Weigh out a five gram sample into a tared porcelain crucible or a small evaporating dish and heat in an electric oven at 110° C. for several hours. Cool and weigh and report the loss in weight as moisture.

Chlorides. Dissolve a five gram sample in 100 cc. of distilled water. Filter if necessary. To the filtrate add a few cubic centimeters of nitric acid until the solution is acid and then add silver nitrate solution until precipitation of the chlorides is complete. Heat the solution to boiling and stir vigorously to coagulate the silver chloride. Let the precipitate settle (in a dark place) and filter on a tared Gooch crucible and dry on a hot plate. Cool and weigh and calculate the percentage of potassium chloride. Factor 0.519.

Sulphates. Dissolve five grams of the sample in 100 cc. of distilled water. Filter if necessary. To the filtrate add hydrochloric acid until the solution is slightly acid. Heat the solution to boiling and precipitate the sulphates by adding barium chloride solution slowly and with vigorous stirring. Allow to set on a hot plate to settle. Filter on a previously ignited and weighed Gooch crucible. Ignite at a red heat to constant weight and cool and weigh as barium sulphate. Calculate the percentage of potassium sulphate by using the factor 0.747.

When the Sulphates are Under 1%. A two and one-half gram sample is dissolved in about 100 cc. of distilled water and then made slightly acid with hydrochloric acid. Filter if necessary. Transfer the solution to a 250-cc. volumetric measuring flask and dilute to 250 cc. From this solution draw off 25 cc. with a pipette and drain into a previously ignited and weighed platinum dish. Evaporate the solution to dryness and then heat gently (to avoid spattering of the residue) to low redness or to the point where the chlorides just begin to fuse. Cool and weigh and note as combined chlorides.

The precipitate in the platinum dish should then be taken up with the smallest possible amount of water and to it add seventeen times the weight of the combined chlorides, a solution of chloroplatinic acid (1 gram platinum to 10 cc.). Evaporate this solution to a thick syrup, and take it up with 25 cc. of 95% alcohol and filter through a tared Gooch crucible and wash with 95% alcohol until the washings are colorless. It is then dried at about 160° C., cooled and weighed. The washings and residues should be preserved for the recovery of the platinum.

$$K_2PtCl_6 \times 0.307 = KCl.$$

$$KCl - \left\{ \begin{array}{l} K_2SO_4 \text{ reduced to chlorides} \\ KCl \text{ as impurity} \end{array} \right\} = KCl \text{ as } K_2CO_3.$$

$$\frac{KCl \times 0.926 \times 100}{0.25} = \% \ K_2CO_3.$$

[1] By G. E. Fisher, Lefax, 12–561. By courtesy of J. C. Parker, President Lefax, Philadelphia.

Combined chlorides—KCl = NaCl.

$$\frac{NaCl \times 0.905 \times 100}{0.25} = \% \ Na_2CO_3.$$

When the Sulphates are Over 1%. To the 25 cc. as obtained above and heated to boiling add barium chloride in slight excess. Let it settle and filter. Then to the filtrate add ammonium carbonate in excess to precipitate the excess of barium. Filter. Evaporate this filtrate to dryness and ignite very carefully to decompose the excess ammonium carbonate and fuse the combined chlorides. Then proceed as outlined above when the sulphates are not in excess of 1%.

The potash residues and washings should be saved and the platinum recovered as follows: The washings and residues are combined and dissolved in hot distilled water. Add sodium formate and sodium hydrate and heat the solution until the platinum is precipitated. Filter and ignite, cool and weigh. Dissolve this residue in aqua regia and evaporate with successive additions of hydrochloric acid until all the nitric is expelled. Then pass chlorine through the solution and evaporate to a syrup to decompose the excess hydrochloric acid. Filter and ignite and weigh and correct for the amount not dissolved. Make up the solution with distilled water so that 10 cc. contains 1 gram of platinum.

Feldspar, Kaolin and China Clay. These are the chief sources of alumina in glass batches and their frequent examination is to be encouraged. They all contain silica, iron and alumina but in different proportions. Kaolin and China clays are examined for moisture whereas feldspar usually is not. Therefore the same methods of analysis may be carried out for these three materials.

Not more than 0.5 gram sample should be weighed out. (This is done because the alumina precipitate is so voluminous that if larger samples are taken the precipitate is too bulky to handle well and losses may occur.) This is mixed thoroughly with about four grams of sodium potassium carbonate in a platinum crucible and fused. Digest the fusion in dilute hydrochloric acid and distilled water. Then transfer to a porcelain evaporating dish and evaporate to dryness and bake for about half an hour. Take it up with hot distilled water and dilute hydrochloric acid and filter. Wash the residue with hot water until entirely free from chlorides. Preserve the residue. Make a second dehydration on the filtrate and digest as above, filtering and washing. Combine the residues from the two filtrations and ignite them slowly at first in a clean platinum crucible. When the residue is snow white and to constant weight, cool and weigh. Then moisten the residue with dilute sulphuric acid and make the crucible three quarters full of hydrofluoric acid and evaporate to dryness. (Sometimes it may be necessary to make a second hydrofluoric evaporation.) Ignite, cool and weigh and report the loss in weight as silica. The residue remaining in the crucible may be fused with potassium bisulphate or sodium potassium carbonate and the fusion added to the filtrate remaining from the silica.

To this solution then cautiously add ammonium hydroxide until it is just alkaline and a dense voluminous precipitate comes down. Transfer the beaker to a flame and boil the solution for a few minutes. Allow the precipitate to settle and then filter and wash with hot distilled water. Preserve the filtrate. After the residue is thoroughly washed, place a clean beaker under the funnel and pierce a hole in the paper and wash the residue through with hot water and dilute hydrochloric acid. Be sure to wash the paper thoroughly because any residue remaining and lost will make the results inaccurate. The residue will be dissolved in dilute hydrochloric acid and reprecipitated with ammonium hydroxide, boiled, filtered and washed as described above. The residue is then ignited in a tared platinum crucible, cooled and weighed and reported as (R_2O_3), $Al_2O_3.Fe_2O_3$. This residue should then be fused with potassium bisulphate or sodium potassium carbonate and the fusion taken up with dilute sulphuric acid. The iron may then be reduced by a choice of methods and titrated with a standard solution of potassium permanganate. The filtrate from the second precipitation of alumina should be combined with the main solution.

The solution is then brought to boiling and while hot, add about 20 cc. of a saturated ammonium oxalate solution and stir constantly. Then add a few cubic centimeters of ammonium hydroxide. Allow the precipitate to settle for several hours and then filter. Wash well with a 2% solution of ammonia water. Ignite the residue at full blast, in a tared platinum crucible, until the weight is constant. Cool and weigh as calcium oxide and report it as such.

Concentrate the filtrate by boiling and while hot add a few cubic centimeters of microcosmic salt solution and then ammonium hydroxide. Stir vigorously and constantly. Allow the precipitate to settle for several hours and then filter. Dry the residue and paper before igniting. Then ignite in a tared platinum crucible, cool and weigh as magnesium pyrophosphate. Calculate the percentage of MgO by using the factor 0.362.

If the alkalies in feldspar are desired by other than the difference method, a separate sample may be used and the alkali determined as previously described.

For moisture in kaolins and clays a five gram sample is weighed out and placed in a tared porcelain dish and transferred to a hot plate or oven and heated to about 110° C. for several hours or over night. The loss in weight is reported as moisture.

Barium Carbonate. Weigh out a one gram sample and dissolve it completely in hydrochloric acid. When dissolved, transfer the solution to a porcelain evaporating dish and evaporate to dryness on a hot plate at 110° C. This residue is then taken up in hot dilute hydrochloric acid and filtered and washed with hot water until free from chlorides. Ignite in a previously ignited and weighed platinum crucible and cool and weigh. This residue is then moistened with dilute sulphuric acid and then the crucible is half filled with hydrofluoric acid and evaporated and ignited, cooled and weighed. The loss in weight is reported as silica. If any residue remains, it is fused with sodium potassium carbonate and added to the main solution.

Separation of Iron and Alumina. A small amount of ammonium is added to the solution and precipitation of iron and alumina is effected by ammonium hydroxide in the usual way. After ignition and weighing, the residue is fused in sodium potassium carbonate and the iron reduced and titrated with a standard solution of potassium permanganate in the usual way. Reduction of iron may be accomplished in various ways described in data sheet 543:6–40 (Fluorspar).

Separation of Barium from Strontium and Calcium. Evaporate the filtrate nearly to dryness. Take up with about 300 cc. of distilled water and add 5 or 6 drops of acetic acid with enough ammonium acetate to neutralize any free mineral acid present. Heat the solution and add an excess of ammonium chromate. Allow the barium chromate precipitate to settle for an hour or more, filter on a weighed Gooch crucible and wash with water containing ammonium chromate until free from strontium and calcium. Then wash with distilled water until free from ammonium chromate. Dry the precipitate at 110° C. and ignite gently and finally to a dull red heat. Cool and weigh as barium chromate. Calculate to barium carbonate by using the factor 0.7786.

Separation of Strontium and Calcium. To the filtrate from the barium solution add about one cubric centimeter of nitric acid. Heat the solution and make it alkaline with ammonia followed by ammonium carbonate. Strontium carbonate and calcium carbonate will be precipitated. Dissolve the carbonates in hydrochloric acid and reprecipitate from a hot solution with ammonia and ammonium carbonate. Filter. Wash with hot water. Dissolve the precipitate in the least amount of nitric acid and wash into an evaporating dish. Evaporate to dryness and heat for about an hour at 160° C. Pulverize this mass and mix with a few cubic centimeters of ether-alcohol solution. Make several extractions in this way and decant into a flask. The residue is again dried, pulverized and washed into the flask with ether-alcohol solution. Digest with shaking. Wash the residue onto a filter previously moistened with ether-alcohol solution. Strontium nitrate remains, which is dissolved in water. To this water solution add dilute sulphuric acid in slight excess and then an equal volume of alcohol. Allow the precipitate to settle for several hours. Filter on a previously ignited and weighed Gooch crucible and wash several times with a 50% alcohol solution. Dry thoroughly and weigh as strontium sulphate. Compute the sulphate to carbonate by using the factor 0.803.

Determination of Calcium. Calcium remaining in solution is estimated by making the solution slightly ammoniacal, heating and adding ammonium oxalate with vigorous stirring. Allow the precipitate to settle and then filter and wash with a very dilute ammonia solution. Ignite slowly at first, and finally at full blast. Cool and weigh as calcium oxide. Compute to calcium carbonate by the factor 1.7847.

Determination of Magnesium. The magnesium is determined in the filtrate from the calcium. Boil off the ammonia and while the solution is still hot, add a slight excess of microcosmic salt with constant stirring. Then make the solution alkaline with ammonia and stir. Allow the precipitate to settle over night and filter and wash with a dilute ammonia solution. Dry the residue before igniting. Ignite in a previously ignited and weighed platinum until white. Cool and weigh as magnesium pyrophosphate. Calculate to magnesium carbonate by using the factor 0.75719.

If only the barium content is desired, a short method may be used. After the silica is removed, the filtrate is treated with sulphuric acid, added a drop at a time, and stirred vigorously. The precipitate is allowed to settle and then filtered on a Gooch crucible which has been ignited and weighed. Wash with water containing a few drops of sulphuric acid and finally with hot water. Ignite gently at first and finally at a red heat. Cool and weigh as barium sulphate and compute to barium carbonate by using the factor 0.8455.

Any residue remaining after the hydrofluoric evaporation of silica is calculated as barium sulphate and computed to barium carbonate.

Lime. Weigh out 0.5 gram sample into a beaker. Cover it with 10 cc. of distilled water and then 10 cc. of hydrochloric acid and heat until clear. Filter and wash several times. Transfer the filter paper to a clean platinum crucible and ignite. Then add about 1 gram of sodium potassium carbonate and fuse. Take up the fusion in dilute hydrochloric acid and add it to the main solution which is then transferred to an evaporating dish and evaporated to dryness. Take up the residue with dilute hydrochloric acid and heat and filter. Wash with hot water until free from chlorides. Preserve the residue and perform a second dehydration as above. Filter and wash and add this residue to that of the first dehydration and ignite in a previously ignited and weighed platinum crucible. Cool and weigh up as silica. Correction need not be made on the silica.

To the filtrate from the silica add a small piece of litmus paper and add ammonium hydroxide until it is just alkaline. Heat to boiling and filter. Wash the residue with hot water until free from chlorides. Ignite the residue in a tared platinum crucible. Cool and weigh up as (R_2O_3) the combined oxides of iron and alumina. This residue is fused in sodium potassium carbonate or potassium bisulphate, dissolved and the iron reduced and titrated according to the method given in data sheet 543:6–40 (Analysis of Fluorspar).

The filtrate from the iron and alumina precipitation is heated to boiling and about 20 cc. of a saturated solution of ammonium oxalate is added with vigorous stirring. Allow the precipitate to settle and then filter and wash with hot water. Transfer the precipitate and filter paper to the original beaker and dissolve it in 10 cc. of sulphuric acid and 40 cc. of distilled water. Heat this solution to 70° C. and titrate it with a solution of standard potassium permanganate. Compute the results to calcium oxide.

The filtrate from the calcium is concentrated by boiling. To the hot solution is added a solution of microcosmic salt with constant stirring. It is then made strongly alkaline with ammonium hydroxide. Allow the precipitate to settle for several hours and then filter and wash with a 5% ammonia solution. Dry the precipitate and paper and when dry, separate them and ignite separately. If there is considerable residue, it is advisable to ignite in a porcelain crucible. The residues are cooled and weighed, their weights combined and computed to magnesium oxide.

If it is desired to determine the strontium present, refer to the method outlined under the examination of Barium Carbonate.

ANALYSIS OF PRINTING INKS [1]

1. Separation of Oil and Pigment. Readily effected by mixture of 3 parts ether, 1 part benzene. About 50 gm. of ink (avoiding the hard surface film) is placed in a weighed glass tumbler of about 300 cc. capacity, a small amount of solvent added, and the whole stirred thoroughly until a homogeneous mixture is obtained. The glass is then filled with the solvent to about $\frac{1}{2}$ in. of top, and the whole again stirred. It is next placed in the metal cup of the centrifuging machine, and the space between the glass and metal cups filled with water in order to equalize the pressure of the liquid inside the glass. Placing a rubber disk at the bottom of the metal cup has been found to materially lessen the danger of breakage. The metal cup and contents are then counterbalanced, most conveniently by either a second sample of the same ink or another sample of ink, and then both are placed in the machine. For webpress and flat-bed inks 2000 r.p.m. for 10 minutes is sufficient. Where carbon black has been used, it has frequently been necessary to run the machine at 2600 to 2800 r.p.m. for 20 or 30 minutes. The clear liquid is decanted through a pleated filter into a glass bottle, a further quantity of solvent added, and the process repeated. Usually three treatments suffice to give practically complete separation. The glass and contents are dried at about 90° C. and on cooling, reweighed. The increase in weight is the pigment, which is calculated to percentage. The amount of pigment on filter paper should be negligible if centrifuging has been efficient.

2. Analysis of the Oil. May contain linseed oil, hard gums, rosin, rosin oil, mineral oils, and bituminous substances. The last mentioned, when present, must be judged largely by their color. Sufficient of the solution from the separation of the oil and pigment to leave a residue of about 5 gm. is evaporated in a weighed beaker; 50 cc. of normal alcoholic potash is added, the beaker covered with a watch glass, and heated on a steam bath for several hours, stirring frequently to assist saponification. When the latter is complete, the watch glass is removed and the alcohol distilled off. The residue is transferred to a separatory funnel with successive portions of water, using in all about 100 cc., and extracted with petroleum ether until no further oil is obtainable. Four extractions are usually sufficient. The petroleum ether fractions are united in another funnel, washed with water until the wash water gives no further alkaline reaction, filtered into a weighed beaker, the petroleum ether distilled off, and the residue dried at 95° C., cooled, and weighed. If this unsaponifiable matter is over 2%, it indicates the presence of something else than linseed oil and hard gums. The wash water from the first two washings should be united with the water layer in the first separatory funnel. This unsaponifiable matter is tested for rosin oil by heating a small portion of the oil with 10 cc. of acetic anhydride, allowing it to cool, and adding a drop of H_2SO_4, sp.gr. 1.63. A violet coloration indicates rosin oil.

If the test for rosin is positive, the alkaline water solution which has been extracted with petroleum ether is made acid with HCl (there is usually sufficient dye present from the ink to act as indicator), and the fatty acids which are thus liberated are extracted with successive portions of ethyl ether. These extracts are united, washed free from acid and salts, and evaporated in a small beaker.

[1] By J. B. Tuttle and W. H. Smith. Tech. Paper No. 39, U. S. Bu. of Standards.

A quantitative determination of the rosin may be made as follows: The fatty acids are dissolved in 20 cc. of 95% alcohol, a drop of phenolphthalein is added, and then strong caustic soda (1-NaOH, 2-H$_2$O) until the reaction is just alkaline. The solution is heated for a few minutes, allowed to cool, and then transferred to a 100-cc. stoppered graduated cylinder. The latter is filled to the 100 cc. mark with ether, 2 gm. of powdered silver nitrate crystals is added, and the mixture shaken vigorously for 15 minutes. When the insoluble salts have settled, 50 cc. of clear solution (containing the silver salts of rosin) is pipetted off into a second 100-cc. cylinder, and shaken with 20 cc. dilute HCl (one acid to two water). The ethereal layer is drawn off, and the aqueous layer is shaken twice with ether. The ether extracts are united, washed with water, and the ether distilled off in a weighed beaker. The residue (rosin) is dried at 100° to 115° C., cooled, and weighed. The results are calculated on basis the original weight of oil.

3. **Analysis of the Pigment.** (a) *Black Inks.* Ignite, at the lowest possible temperature, a weighed quantity in a porcelain crucible (presence of Pb prohibits Pt), the loss on ignition represents lampblack, the carbon of boneblack (should there be any present), aniline dyes, and undissolved oils or gums. Prussian blue is decomposed by heat, part of it being volatilized, the iron remaining as iron oxide. The residue from the ignition contains any added mineral matter of the pigment, lead or manganese from the driers, iron oxide from the Prussian blue, or iron oxide added as such (the so-called magnetic pigment), calcium phosphate if boneblack is present, and alkali or calcium carbonates from the soaps present. The ash is analyzed quantitatively for insoluble matter, Pb, Fe, Mn and Ca. One quarter gram of the ash is heated to dull redness in a porcelain crucible for a few minutes, cooled in a desiccator, and weighed. This is transferred to a 250-cc. beaker, using conc. HCl to dissolve any material that may stick to the crucible. About 25 cc. of conc. HCl is added, the beaker covered with a watchglass, and after heating until as much as will go in solution is dissolved, the cover is removed and the solution evaporated to dryness. The residue is moistened with a few drops of strong HCl, 50 to 75 cc. of boiling water added, and the solution is filtered, washing thoroughly with hot water. The filter paper and residue are ignited and weighed, and the product is called " insoluble matter."

Fifty cc. of 10% H$_2$SO$_4$ is added to the filtrate from the previous determination and evaporated down until the solution fumes strongly. This is cooled, diluted carefully with about 100 to 150 cc. of water, and heated on the steam bath until any basic ferric sulphate which sometimes separates is redissolved. The precipitate containing the lead sulphate is now filtered off. It is dissolved in ammonium citrate or acetate, filtered from any insoluble matter, the filtrate made strongly acid with H$_2$SO$_4$ and the precipitated lead sulphate filtered off on a Gooch crucible, ignited, and weighed. The insoluble matter from the ammonium acetate solution should be examined for Ca and Ba.

Another method for the determination of the lead is to nearly neutralize the acid present with sodium carbonate, saturate the solution with hydrogen sulphide, filter off the precipitated lead sulphide, dissolve it in fairly strong nitric acid, and determine the lead as sulphate by the addition of sulphuric acid as above. In this case, solution in ammonium acetate is omitted. The former method is of advantage where qualitative tests show that there is very little manganese present, and it is desired to determine only the iron. The iron is reduced to the ferrous condition by passing the solution through a Jones reductor, and the ferrous sulphate titrated with a standard solution of $KMnO_4$, which has been standardized with sodium oxalate.

Iron is separated from manganese and other metals which may be present by precipitation with ammonia, the precipitate being filtered off, dissolved in HCl, reprecipitated with ammonia, and again filtered. It is now dissolved in HCl, sulphuric acid added, and evaporated down until all the HCl is removed; the solution is diluted and the iron determined as before. Before the addition of the ammonia, if H_2S has been used, the solution should be boiled until it is removed, and nitric acid added to oxidize the iron to the ferric condition. H_2S is now passed into the ammoniacal solution from the iron precipitation. This is allowed to stand over night, and the precipitate, if there is any, is examined for manganese. Should there be much manganese, the sulphide can be filtered off, and the quantitative determination made by conversion into the pyrophosphate.

If it is desired to determine the calcium, this can be done after the filtration from the ammonium sulphide. (If phosphates are present—as, for instance, if boneblack is present—a basic acetate separation is required.) In either case the lead should be separated by H_2S. The filtrate from the manganese sulphide is heated on the steam bath until the H_2S is removed, ammonia and ammonium oxalate are added, and the precipitated Ca oxalate is determined either as oxide or sulphate.

The percentage of ash will be of great assistance in determining the nature of the pigment. Black oxide of iron is only slightly changed on heating, being completely oxidized to ferric oxide. Boneblack is composed largely of calcium phosphate, yielding the greater part of its weight as ash. The presence of any large amount of phosphoric acid will be sufficient evidence that boneblack has been used.

Prussian blue should be tested for qualitatively in the dry pigment. For this purpose 1 gm. of pigment is moistened with 2 or 3 cc. of normal alcoholic potash, heated on the steam bath until the alcohol is removed, 5 cc. of water added, and the insoluble matter filtered off. The filtrate is made acid with HCl, and filtered again if necessary. When ferric chloride is added, a blue precipitate will be obtained if Prussian blue is present. If blue dye obscures the reaction, the solution is again made alkaline and filtered, made acid with HCl as before, and copper sulphate added. The precipitate is filtered and washed thoroughly. In this case we will have reddish-brown copper ferrocyanide. It is advisable, in case of doubt, to add a small amount of Prussian blue to the pigment, and make a check test. In the absence of black oxide of iron we may assume that all of the iron in the filtrate is due to the Prussian blue. The percentage of Fe_2O_3 in the ash, multiplied by the percentage of ash in the pigment, multiplied by the factor 1.53, will give, roughly, the amount of Prussian blue present. The factor 1.53 is obtained by the ratio $Fe_7(CN)_{18}$ to Fe_2O_3. An approximate determination of the dyes can be made by extracting with alcohol. When the presence of oxide iron is suspected, 1 gm. of pigment is wrapped in filter paper and the dye extracted with alcohol. When all of the dye has been extracted, the paper and contents are dried and the nitrogen is determined in the residue by the Kjeldahl method. From the nitrogen thus determined the Prussian blue is calculated, using the factor 3.41. The Fe_2O_3 present in this amount of Prussian blue is deducted from the total Fe_2O_3 found in the ash. The remainder will be the percentage of iron from the magnetic oxide. The formula of the latter is theoretically Fe_3O_4, and proper calculation should be made.

(b) *Blue Inks*. A weighed quantity of pigment is ignited as under black pigments. The ash is analyzed same as before, determining only lead, manganese, and iron if the qualitative tests show that Prussian blue is present. The lead and manganese are reported as metallic driers, the iron is calculated to Prussian blue, and the remainder reported as mineral filler. The presence of ultramarine will be shown by the blue color of the ash. In this case the ash is reported after deducting the $Pb+Mn$. Dyes are determined by alcohol extraction.

(c) *Red Inks*. Vermillion (mercuric sulphide) is readily detected by taking a small quantity of pigment, covering it with 4 or 5 cc. aqua regia, and heating gently. This is diluted with five volumes of water, filtered, and stannous chloride added to the filtrate; a grayish precipitate of mercury will be formed if even a very small amount is present.

Quantitative method: Dissolve the mercuric sulphide in aqua regia, and after nearly neutralizing the diluted solution to precipitate the mercuric sulphide with H_2S, weigh the precipitate on a Gooch crucible, observing all the precautions to eliminate sulphur which separates during the precipitation.

The following procedure has also been found of value: One gm. of the pigment is treated with a slight excess of ammonium sulphide. Sodium hydroxide is then added, while stirring. The beaker is placed upon the steam bath, adding more alkali if necessary, until all the mercuric sulphide has passed into solution. An excess of alkali should be avoided. The solution is allowed to cool, filtered, and the residue washed thoroughly. To the filtrate sufficient ammonium nitrate to reprecipitate the mercuric sulphide is added, and it is then boiled to expel ammonia. The precipitate is allowed to settle, and the supernatant liquid decanted through a weighed Gooch crucible. The residual mercuric sulphide is boiled with a little sodium sulphide solution to remove free sulphur, and is then transferred to the crucible where it is washed with hot water, until it no longer reacts with silver nitrate solution. It is dried at 110° and weighed. The pigment is ignited, and the ash analyzed for lead and manganese. The rest of the ash is reported as mineral filler.

(d) *Green Inks*. The coloring matter may be chrome green, green lake, or dye. Some of the darker shades are obtained by the addition of lampblack. The ash of the pigment is determined as usual. Part of this ash is taken and tested qualitatively for chromium. If present, the ash should be tested for the following substances: $PbCrO_4$, $PbSO_4$, PbO, $BaSO_4$, $CaSO_4$, Fe_2O_3, and Mn_3O_4. For the determination of sulphur, 0.250 gm. of the ash and 5 gm. of a mixture of equal parts of potassium nitrate and sodium carbonate are fused in a porcelain crucible over a sulphur-free flame. The cooled mass is extracted with hot water and filtered. The filtrate is acidified with HCl, heated to boiling, and 10 cc. 10% barium chloride added. After standing over night, the precipitated barium sulphate is filtered off, ignited, and weighed. The solution should be sufficiently acid to prevent any significant contamination of the barium sulphate with barium chromate.

For the determination of barium, the insoluble matter is dissolved in HCl, the solution made nearly neutral with sodium carbonate, and H_2S is passed into the solution until all the lead is precipitated. The lead sulphide is filtered off, the filtrate heated to boiling, and 10 cc. of 10% H_2SO_4 added. The barium sulphate is treated as directed under the determination of sulphur.

A fresh portion of ash is mixed with sodium peroxide and fused in a nickel crucible. The cooled melt is dissolved in hot water and filtered. Carbon dioxide is passed into the filtrate, and the latter heated again on the steam bath in order to precipitate any lead which may be held up by the caustic alkali. Any insoluble matter which may separate is filtered off. The filtrate is made strongly acid with HCl, KI added, and the liberated iodine titrated with a standard $Na_2S_2O_3$ solution. From the amount of thiosulphate used the amount of CrO_3 present is calculated.

The two precipitates from the previous determination are combined and used for the determination of Pb, Fe, Mn, and Ca. They are dissolved off the filter paper with HCl, the solution is nearly neutralized with sodium carbonate, and H_2S passed into the solution. The precipitated lead sulphide is filtered off, dissolved in nitric acid, and determined as sulphate, as directed under black pigments.

The filtrate from the lead sulphide is heated until all the H_2S is boiled off. If any sulphur separates, it is filtered off. Two or three cc. of nitric acid is added and the solution again heated. It is then made alkaline with ammonia and filtered. The precipitate is dissolved in HCl and reprecipitated with ammonia, the precipitate again filtered off and the filtrate united with that from the first precipitation. This solution is reserved for the determination of manganese. The second precipitate of iron is dissolved in HCl, converted into the sulphate, and the iron determined as under black pigments.

The united filtrates from the iron precipitation are saturated with H_2S, allowed to stand over night, and then filtered. If there be a sufficient amount of manganese present, it can be determined quantitatively as pyrophosphate; otherwise qualitative identification will be sufficient.

It is safe to assume that all chromium was present originally as lead chromate, and it should be so calculated. The iron oxide should be calculated to Prussian blue, provided there is a positive qualitative test. Any barium present should be calculated to sulphate; if there is any question as to its being originally present as carbonate, the ash of the pigment is treated with very dilute HCl, the solution filtered and the filtrate tested for barium. Barytes is difficultly soluble in cold dilute HCl. In the absence of barytes the sulphur present is calculated to lead sulphate. The excess of lead over that required for the lead chromate and sulphate may be considered as drier. China clay may be present either as an added part of the chrome green, or as the base of a green lake. In such cases, the undetermined portion of the ash should be reported as mineral filler. Green dyes are determined by extraction as usual. In the absence of chrome green the pigment is ashed, and the ash analyzed for lead and manganese only, the balance being reported as mineral fillers. If lampblack has been used to produce a dark shade of green, it can be tested qualitatively by taking a small portion of the pigment, treating it with strong alkali, and filtering through a Gooch crucible, washing first with hot water, and finally with moderately strong HCl. Lampblack will show a black residue, which will disappear on ignition. It is generally classed with the volatile constituents, which are then reported as aniline dye, lampblack, undissolved oil, etc.

The analytical methods included the essential constituents of inks: the determination of iron, tannic acid, gallic acid, total solids, ash, acidity, etc. The specific gravity of the ink will indicate the amount of dissolved material present. F. F. Rupert, in a paper on the examination of writing inks (Ind. Eng. Chem., **15**, 489, May, 1923), emphasizes the importance of the physical tests of color, permanence, stability and noncorrosiveness. The following tests are suggested.

Streak Tests.   A sheet of a good quality of bond paper placed on a pane of glass and held by clamps serves for taking the streak.   The streak is made by a pipette 25 cm. long, 3.5 mm. in diameter with a file mark 62 mm. from the tip.   Ink filled to the mark (0.6 cc.) is tested by drawing the pipette over the surface of the paper, at the same time allowing the ink to flow.

Penetration and Fluidity.   The ink should penetrate into the fibres of the paper but should not pass through.   A normal ink will give an oval head (where the streak begins) and the width of the line will be uniform.   A poor ink gives a wide head and the streak narrows rapidly.   Stickiness should be observed.

Temporary Color.   The mark should be dark enough to be easily seen. A speckled appearance indicates that the ink contains a dye which is not in solution.

Permanent Color.   The streak is exposed to diffused light for 7 days in an atmosphere free from chemical fumes and dust.   A comparison is made with a standard ink.   The paper is now cut into crosswise strips 1 inch in diameter.   The top and bottom strips are set aside as blanks.

Exposure to Light.   Strips containing the streaks are exposed to sunlight or ultra violet rays for a period 48 hours to two weeks or longer and the ink thus exposed compared with the blanks.

Exposure to Weather.   The exposed sample is inspected weekly.

Exposure to Water and Reagents.   Tests in water, in dilute ammonia (1 : 10), HCl 2% solution, bleaching powder or sodium hypochlorite of 0.005 N available Cl.

Stability.   Note sediment in original.   Filter two portions, one into a bottle which is later stoppered, the other portion into an open bottle covered by a piece of paper.   Filter each after a period of a week or more and note sediment on filter paper.

Corrosion.   The effect of the ink on steel pens, immersed in the ink for a period of time, at least one week.   The pens are weighed before and after the test.

Comparison and Rating.   The system is subordinated to the knowledge of the purpose for which the ink is to be used.   For further details the reader is directed to the article by Rupert.

Zinc Chloride Method for Determining Free Lime in Presence of Calcium Carbonate

The following procedure is of interest to the sugar chemist. The method developed by John C. Bailar, Great Western Sugar Company, depends upon masking by means of a green dye the faint pink color produced by calcium carbonate in water on phenolphthalein. The color of the dye does not interfere in the titration of the alkalinity of calcium hydroxide. The cheapness of the procedure as compared with the iodine method commends its use in the commercial laboratory.

Solutions

Zinc Chloride Solution. This is made by dissolving 25 grams of the salt in a liter of water and filtering. 1 cc. of this solution is equivalent to about 0.01 g. CaO.

Sodium Hydroxide Solution. The solution is made of such strength that 1 cc. is equivalent to 1 cc. of the zinc chloride solution.

Indicator. 5 grams of phenolphthalein are dissolved in 500 cc. of 95% alcohol. This is mixed with a solution containing 2 grams of Alkali Fast Green E dissolved in 500 cc. of water.

Standardization

The sodium hydroxide solution is standardized against a standard acid. The zinc chloride solution is now standardized against the alkali as follows: Into a liter flask containing 500 cc. of boiling hot distilled water 25 to 50 cc. of the NaOH solution are accurately measured from a burette. About 0.5–1.0 cc. of the indicator is added and the zinc chloride is run in until a green color is obtained that persists for half a minute. 10 cc. excess of the $ZnCl_2$ solution are now added and this excess, after vigorous shaking, is titrated with the NaOH solution until a lavender (not pink) color is obtained

Determination

In a dry one-liter flask is placed 1 gram of the sample. 500 cc. of boiling, CO_2-free water are added. As soon as the lime has hydrated, the solution is titrated with zinc chloride solution until a green color appears, an excess of zinc chloride is added and the excess determined with standard NaOH solution as in case of the standardization above. The end point is a lavender color.

NOTES. The flask used with the lime determination must be dry, otherwise the water in small amount reacting with the sample will cause difficulty in the subsequent procedure.

The quantity of indicator in standardization and the determination must be the same, as the quantity influences results. The Alkali Fast Green E dye is made by the National Aniline Company, Buffalo, N. Y.

ANALYSIS OF ALKALINE MIXTURES
Sodium-Carbonate, -Bicarbonate, -Borate.

The determination of sodium carbonate, sodium borate and sodium bicarbonate in solids or in solution together with neutral salts can be carried out by titration with standard acid and alkali.

Sampling. In all determinations in which mixtures of carbonate and bicarbonate are evolved the contact of the sample with the air or moisture must be avoided as far as possible. Solutions of carbonate and bicarbonate will be altered rapidly until an equilibrium is established, which is independent upon the initial composition of the sample.

In the case of solids weigh out 0.5 to 2.0 gms. and make up with carbon dioxide free water to 100 cc. Weigh out a second sample for the bicarbonate determination.

In the case of liquid samples the dilution of 10 cc. to 100 cc. is convenient. The bicarbonate determination requires an undiluted sample, conveniently use 2 or 5 cc.

Procedure. Total Alkali: Titrate a sample with 0.1 normal hydrochloric acid, using as little methyl orange indicator as possible, to the dead neutral point.

Let "a" = cc. of 0.1 n HCl used.

Borax: Use the same sample which has been titrated with the hydrochloric acid to the dead neutral point in the titration for total alkali, boil for 2 or 3 minutes, cool sufficiently, preferably below 20° C., add mannitol [1] (3 gms. for each gram of $Na_2B_4O_7$) or cerelose (30 gms. for each gram borate), followed by phenolphthalein indicator (excess not harmful) and titrate with 0.1 normal sodium hydroxide solution until a pink color is obtained. Add more of the polyhydroxy compound and, if a fading of the pink color occurs, continue the titration with the sodium hydroxide solution until on addition of mannitol or cerelose no more fading takes place.

Let "b" = cc. of 0.1 n NaOH used.

Bicarbonate: The separate samples (as described under "sampling") are used for this determination. The samples are placed into a *dry* flask and at once an excess of 0.1 normal sodium hydroxide solution is added, the solution shaken gently for a few seconds (shaking violently too long will result in absorption of carbon dioxide from the air) followed by a slight excess of neutral barium chloride solution.

Let "c" = cc. of 0.1 n NaOH added.

The solution together with the white precipitate (consisting of barium carbonate (and sulfate)), is titrated with 0.1 normal hydrochloric acid using phenolphthalein as indicator until colorless.

Let "d" = cc. of 0.1 n. HCl used.

Determine the carbonate content of the sodium hydroxide solution by

[1] Mannitol as well as Cerelose should be tested for neutrality.

measuring out 100.0 cc., adding barium chloride and phenolphthalein indicator and titrating with 0.1 n HCl.

Let "e" = cc. of 0.1 n HCl used.

Calculation:

Total alkali Na_2O: "a" times 0.0031 = gms. of Na_2O in sample taken.

Bicarbonate $NaHCO_3$: [("c" + "e"/100) − ("d" − $\frac{1}{2}$ "b") × 0.0084] = gms. of sodium bicarbonate in sample taken. *Note:* The actual weights of the original sample used for the titration on total alkali and borax [2] must be equal to the weight of the undiluted sample taken for the bicarbonate determination, or due allowance for the ration between the number of cubic centimeters used in "a," "b," "c" and "d" must be made, if a different weight is taken.

Borax $Na_2B_4O_7.10H_2O$: "b" times 0.00955 = gms. of sodium tetraborate decahydrate, or "b" times 0.00505 = gms. of anhydrous sodium tetraborate in sample taken.

For more accurate analysis:

$$[("b" \times "e"/100) + \{"b" \times 0.02(100 - "e")\}]$$

times the above given factors equals the grams of borax.

Sodium carbonate Na_2CO_3: "a" − [("c" × "e"/100) − ("d" − "b")] × 0.0053 = gms. of sodium carbonate in sample taken.

H. H. Chesny.

Univ. of Southern California.

[2] In the presence of large amounts of borax the precipitate is filtered off and washed carefully with CO_2 free water.

INDEX

SUBJECT INDEX

Abbé refractometer, 1125
Abraham, H., bituminous substances, 1289–1350
Abraham's ductility test, 1304
Absorption bulbs:
  carbon dioxide, Fleming, Geissler, Gerhardt, Liebig, Vanier, 111, 114
  gas analysis, Friedrich, Hanjkus, Nowicki-Heinz, Varrentrapp, Winkler, Wolff, 1237
Absorption spectrum, carbon monoxide in air, 1274
Accuracy in methods of gas analysis, 1251
Accuracy, limit of, in alloy analysis, 1041
Acetanilid, 1732
Acetate extraction of lead, 273, 279
Acetates, 1547
Acetic acid, complete analysis of acetone, formic acid, furfurol, hydrochloric acid, metals, sulphuric acid, sulphurous acid, 1545–1547
  method for nitrite, 338
  specific gravity table, 673, 1548
Acetic anhydride, analysis of, 1544
Acetin method for det. glycerol, 1755
Acetone, analysis of, 1759
  extraction of rubber, 1576, 1585, 1587
  in acetic acid, 1546
Acetyl value for oils, 1135
Acetylene flame, temperature of, 658
  properties of, 1227g
Acid number in soap analysis, 1604
Acid, free in soap, 1600
Acidimetric and alkalimetric methods for metabisulphites, sulphites, sulphurous acid, 513
  phosphorus in steel, 1364
Acidimetry and alkalimetry, 1491–1560
Acid number, Chinese wood oil (Tung oil), 1169
  linseed oil, 1165
  varnish, 1174
Acid number, linseed oil, 1165
Acidity in explosives, 1394
  in rubber, 1570
  in water, 1429
Acids, chapter on, 1491
  analysis of acetic. See subject above.
  carbolic, 1549
  carbonic, 1549

Acid, citric, 1549
  chlorsulphonic, 1540
  fluosilicic, 1507
  formic, 1542
  hydrochloric, determination of total acidity, arsenic, barium, chloride, chlorine, nitric acid, sulphuric acid, silica, total solids, 1501
  hydrofluoric, determination of acidity, hydrofluosilicic acid, sulphuric acid, sulphurous acid, 1506, 1509
  nitric, determination of acidity, free chlorine, hydrochloric acid, iodine, nitric and nitrous acids, non-volatile solids, sulphuric acid, 1509
  procedure for determining, in arsenic acid, ferrous sulphate method, 1516
  in oleum and mixed acids, 1515
  in phosphoric acid, 1516
  in sulphuric acid, 1514
  nitrous, permanganate titration of, 1510, 1530
  oleum and mixed acids, complete analysis, determination of total acidity, lower oxides, nitric acid, sulphuric acid and free SO_3, calculations, table, 1530–1540
  organic, 1542–1551
  phosphoric acid, analysis of, 1521
  sulphuric acid, analysis of, 1524
    det. lead, iron, arsenic, zinc, selenium, hydrochloric and nitric acids, 1524–1528
  tartaric acid, 1550
Acids—arsenic in acids, 49
  corrections for in calorimetry, 1653
  formulæ for diluting or strengthening of, 1533
  free acids in aluminum salts, estimation of, 12
    in aluminum salts, test for, 13
    in presence of iron salts, estimation of, 1551
  indicators for determination of, 1491
  number in oil analysis. See Oils.
  reactions—tables of, 630, 646–653
  standards, preparation of benzoic, hydrochloric, sulphuric, 1493–1495

Acids—test for, in animal and vegetable oils, 1140
in burning oils, 1113
in Chinese wood oil, 1169
in varnish, 1174
titration of, 1497
tungstic, solution of, 555
strong acids, Blay-Burkhard burette, bulb tube, Deli tube, Lunge-Ray pipette, snake tube, 1498
weighing dilute acids, 1498
Acker process for determination of tin, 531
Adolph's apparatus for fluorine det., 218
modification of Offerman's method for fluorine, 218
Ahlum's method for free acids in presence of iron salts, 1541
Air, composition of, 338
examination of. See Gas Analysis, 1272
oxygen in, hydrogen combustion method, 1247
phosphorus method, 1246
pyrogallate method, 1247
pound per cubic foot of coal burned, calculation of, 1254
sulphur dioxide in, 1283
Air, dry, properties of, 1227f, 1287
saturated, properties of, 1288
Albuminoid ammonia, determination of, in water, 1413
Alcohol, ethyl, detection of, 1728, 1743
determination of distillation and evaporation methods, 1744
specific gravity tables, 1748
Alcoholic–KOH extraction of rubber, 1588
Alcohol-insoluble matter in soap, 1601
methyl, det. of, 1728, 1753
Aldehyde, det. of, 1745
Alexander's volumetric method for determining lead, 277
method for rubber, 1568
Alizarine S for determination of aluminum, 14
test for aluminum, 3
Alkali arsenates, arsenic determination in, 35
standard for acidimetry and alkalimetry, 1493–1496
Alkali combined in soap, 1601
Alkali fluorides, det. of, 224
Alkalies, analysis of, 1552–1560
Alkalies, chapter on, 401, 1552
detection of cæsium, lithium, potassium, rubidium, sodium, 401–403
estimation in alunite, 417
in Portland cement, 1216
in silicates, hydrofluoric acid method, 417
J. Lawrence Smith method, 416
volumetric method, 418, 1552
physical properties, 401

Alkalies, preparation of the sample, fertilizers, 404
plants, ashes of, 405
rocks and insoluble mineral products, 404
saline residues, soluble salts, brines, 405
soils, 404
reaction—tables of, 644
separation from aluminum, chromium, iron, phosphoric acid, titanium, uranium, 406
from barium, calcium, strontium, sulphuric acid, 406
from each other, 408
from the hydrogen sulphide group and silica, 405
from magnesium, 405
test for iridium, 383
for palladium, 382
Alkalimeter, Mohr's, 147
Schroetter's, 147
Alkalimetric method for determining phosphorus, 368
for determining strontium, 491
Alkaline earths. See Barium.
separation from one another, 60
silicates in soap analysis, 1604
Alkalinity determination in water, 1429
Alkaloids, 1731
Allen, method for traces of iron, 244
modification of Devarda's method for nitrates, 346
and Bishop method for sulphur in pyrites and sulphur ores, 498
Allihn's method for sugar in soap, 1159
Alloy steel. See Iron and Steel.
Alloys, 1036–1107
determination of aluminum in, 1090, 1106h
antimony in, 28, 1074, 1086, 1103
arsenic in, 1088
bismuth in, 286, 1047
cadmium in, 1087
carbon in, 1102, 1106g, 1106i
copper in, 1049, 1053, 1058, 1067, 1071, 1076, 1098, 1099, 1106, 1106j
iron in, 1055, 1073, 1082, 1092, 1097, 1106j
lead in, 1051, 1052, 1053, 1061, 1062, 1067, 1071, 1080, 1081, 1106, 1106a, 1106b
magnesium in, 1106c
manganese in, 1056, 1057, 1093, 1100, 1101, 1106d, 1107
nickel in, 1083, 1094, 1106b
phosphorus in, 1059, 1063, 1078, 1084
silicon in, 17e, 1095, 1103
sulphur in, 1075, 1087, 1107
tin in, 1054, 1059, 1060, 1072, 1077, 1079, 1105

Alloys, titanium in, 1096, 1103
  zinc in, 1063, 1094, 1106c
Alloys, decomposition of, 71, 101, 167, 183,
  186, 272, 1040, 1041–1066, 1072
  —detection of bismuth in, 1047
  of gold in, 228
  general, alloys with:
    antimony, 20, 21
    iridium, 388
    iron-titanium, 297
    lead, 21, 272
    manganese, 286. See Alloys.
    molybdenum, 297
    nickel, 331, 336. See Alloys.
    rhodium, 393
    silicon, 297, 1368a
    tin, 21, 536a
    titanium, 540
    tungsten, 297, 554, 556, 558
    vanadium, 297. See chapter on V.
  non-ferrous alloys, 1033–1066
    alloys of antimony, copper, lead and
      tin, 1041–1047
    aluminum alloys, 17, 1090, 1095–1106
    brass and sand castings, 1067–1075
    bronze and bearing metal, 1076–1089
    gun metal, 1058–1063
    manganese bronze, 1047–1057
    monel metal, 1106
    nickel silver and cupro nickel, 1092–
      1094
    phosphorus in alloys, 1063–1066
    white metals, 1047–1048
Alpha benzyldioxime method for determining nickel, 332
  test for nickel, 311
Alumina in bauxite, 15, 17g
  in nitrate of soda, 350
  in phosphate, together with iron, 372
  in Prussian blue, 1197
  in ultramarine blue, 1197
  in sand, 448
  in slag, 1612
  in silicate of soda, 447
  in titaniferous ores, 552
  in water, 1423
  basic, determination of, in aluminum
    salts, 13
Alumina and iron oxide in composite
    white paint, 1189
  in green paint pigments, 1199
  in metallic lead, 290
  in Portland cement, 1216
  together in phosphate rock, 372
Alumina ores, arsenic determination in,
  50
Aluminum, detection of, 3
  estimation, general procedures:
    gravimetric, by hydrolysis with am-
      monium hydroxide, 7
      by hydrolysis with sodium thiosul-
        phate, 9

Aluminum, by precipitation as aluminum
    chloride, 10
  as phosphate, 9
  volumetric, determination of com-
    bined alumina, 11, 15
  free alumina or free acid, 12
  special procedures:
    analysis of metallic aluminum for
      silicon and iron, 17a
    in alloys, 1090, 1106h
    in bronze, 16
    in bauxite, 17g
    in iron and steel, 17a, 268–269
    in metallic aluminum dust, 17e
    in nickel, 336d
    in presence of iron, phenylhydra-
      zine method, 552
  impurities in metallic aluminum, 17a
  industrial application, 3
  occurrence, minerals and ores, 3
  preparation and solution of the sample,
    3–5
    metallic aluminum and its alloys, 5
  properties, 3
    aluminum phosphate, 10
  separation from glucinum, iron, manga-
    nese, nickel, phosphoric acid, silica,
    titanium, uranium, zinc, 5, 6
    from chromium, 158, 159
    from glucinum, 69a
  solubilities, metal and its oxide, 3
  traces, detection and estimation of, with
    alizarine S, 3
Aluminum Company of America, methods
  for aluminum, 17a–17l
  methods for alloys of Al, 17a–17l
Aluminum precipitate of Cu, 184, 193a
Aluminum reduction method for nitrates,
  1416
Aluminum hydrate, analysis of, 17h
Aluminum sulphate, analysis of, 1773
Alunite, alkalies in, 418
American Vanadium Company, methods
  of analysis, 594–596
Amino-nitrosophenyl-h y d r o x y l a m i n e
  method for iron, 250
Ammonia, albuminoid, in water, estimation of, 1413
  free in water, estimation of, 1412, 1434
  gravimetric method for, determining as
    platino-chloride, 342
  reagent for etching, 1705
  total, in ammoniacal liquor, 343
  traces, determination of, in gas, 1261
  volatile, in ammoniacal liquor, 343
  volumetric method, 343
Ammonia, aqua, volumetric method for,
  1560
  in fused zinc chloride, det. of, 617
  conversion to HNO_3, 361c
  specific gravity table, 675, 1559
Ammonia-dynamite, analysis of, 1379

Ammonium chloride, fusion with perchlorate (note), 152
  test for iridium, 389
  test for palladium, 383
  test for platinum, 376
  test for vanadium, 583
hydroxide method for determining traces of copper, 199
  table, 675, 1559
  test for iron, 246
  test for palladium, 382
  test for rhodium, 389
iridium chloride, determination of iridium as, 382
magnesium phosphate, acid titration of, 294
  properties of, 294
nitrate washing solution for aluminum hydroxide, 8
nitrate-pyridine in, 1309
oxalate reagent for oxygen consumed, water analysis, 1417
persulphate method for Mn det., 266, 305
phosphomolybdate method for phosphorus, 366
phosphate method for separating magnesium from alkalies, 408
  method for zirconium, 622a
platinochloride method for determining ammonia, 342
Ammonium nitrate, pyridine in, 360
Ammonium persulphate m. for Mn, 266
Ammonium picrate, analysis of, 1393
Ammonium salts, effect on magnesium precipitation, 293
  effect on sulphur determinations, 497
  determination of ammonia in, 341
  mixtures, ammonia in, 343
sulphate, det. of, in shale, 1350
sulphide group, separation of, 168, 292, 405
sulphide method for mercury, 377
  test for ruthenium, 387
  test for vanadium, 583
sulphocyanate test for cobalt, 166
  test for iron, 246
  table, sp. gr., 1559
Amorphous sulphur, det. of, 519a
Ampre, definition of, 708
Amyl alcohol. See Fusel Oil.
Andrew's method for silver, 463
Andrew-Burgarszk's method for analysis of crude bromide and bromine, 96
Anemometer, 1236
Aniline method for det. acetic anhydride, 1544
Animal and vegetable oils, 1133, 1140d
  analysis of, 1123
  test for, 1134
Anthraquinone, 1325
Antifluorescence, tests for, 1135, 1141

Antilogarithms, table of, 715
Antimonous and antimonic salts, distinction between, 18
Antimony, detection of, by hydrogen sulphide test, hydrolysis, in minerals, traces, 18
estimation, general procedures: gravimetric, electrolytic as metallic antimony, 25
  as trisulphide, Sb_2S_3, 24
  volumetric, bromate method, 26
  indirect evolution method, 28a
  iodide method, 27
  oxidation with iodine, 28
  permanganate method, 28a
estimation, special procedures:
  determination in alloys, in brass and bronze, 28b, 1074, 1086, 1105
  in ash of rubber, 1592
  in copper, 202
  in hard lead, 25
  in metallic lead, 289
  in nickel, 336e   1591
  in rubber goods, 21, 1572, 1580,
  in sulphuric acid, 1526
  in soft solder, 28
  in tartar emetic, 33
  in tin and lead alloys, 28
  in presence of vanadium, 592
industrial application of analysis, 18
occurrence, minerals, ores and alloys, 18
preparation and solution of the sample:
  alloys of antimony, tin, and lead, hard lead, low-grade oxides, mattes, slags, speisses, sulphides, rubber materials, 19–21
properties, antimony trisulphide, 24
separation from members of the subsequent groups, aluminum, chromium, cobalt, iron, manganese, nickel, zinc, alkaline earths and alkalies, 22
  from bismuth, cadmium, copper, lead and mercury, 22
  from arsenic, antimony and tin, 22–23
  from tin in alloys, 1041
solubility of the element and its oxides, 19
solution for standard stains, 31
traces of, in refined copper, 32
traces, determination of, 29
Antimony and calcium oxides in As_2O_3, 54
Antimony oxide pigment, 1193
Antwerp blue, analysis of, 1197
Apothecaries' weight table, 703
Apparatus. See lists following Table of Contents, Vol. 1 and Vol. 2.
  standard, calibrated, 1685–1694
Applebaum, A. F., chromium in steel, 164
Aqua ammonia, 1559–1560
Arc, electric, temperature of, 650

Areas, formulæ for determining, 703
  table of, 702
  triangle, rectangle, parallelogram, trapezoid, circle, 703
Argon in the atmosphere, 358
Arnold-Kjeldahl-Gunning method for nitrogen, 339
Arsenates, alkali, 35
Arsenates, distinction from arsenites, 34
Arsenic acid, alkali arsenates, 37
  commercial As₂O₃, analysis of, 53
Arsenic, detection of, by Gutzeit test, by hydrogen sulphide, volatility test, 34, 1740
  estimation, general procedures:
    gravimetric, determination as arsenic trisulphide, As₂S₃, 41
      determination as magnesium pyroarsenate, 41
    volumetric, oxidation with iodine, Mohr's method, 44
      iodate method, 44
      silver arsenate method, 45
    special procedures:
      determination in alloys, brass and bronze, 1088
      in brimstone, 519
      in copper, 55, 202
      in gases, det. of, 1505
      in hydrochloric acid, 1502
      in iron, 55
      in metallic lead, 287
      in molybdenite and wulfenite, 565
      in molybdenum ores, det. of, 325
      in nickel, 336e
      in presence of vanadium, 593
      in steel, 37, 55
      in sulphuric acid, 1526
      in tungsten ores, 565
    impurities in "arsenic acid," determination of moisture, antimony, arsenic calcium cobalt, copper, iron, lead, nickel and zinc oxides, silica, sulphuric acid, 53–55
  industrial application of methods, 34
  occurrence, minerals, ores, 34
  potassium iodate method, 44
  preparation and solution of the sample, alkali arsenates, arsenic acid, arsenous oxide, hydrochloric and sulphuric acids, pyrites ore, 35, 49
    lead arsenate, zinc arsenite insecticides, copper, iron, 36, 37
  properties, 34
  separation from other elements by distillation, 38, 39b
    from antimony and tin, 40
    from tin in alloys, 1193
  solubility of oxides, sulphides, salts, 34
  solution standard, 1360
  stains, preservation of, for Gutzeit method, 47

Arsenic traces, determination of, by modified Gutzeit method, 46, 52
  Marsh test for, 47
  in acids, hydrochloric, nitric, sulphuric, 49–50
  in baking powders, canned goods, meat, organic matter, etc., 51
  in ores, alumina-bearing, bauxite, cinders, pyrites, 50
  in organic matter, 51
  in refined copper, 202
  in salts, sodium chloride, magnesium sulphate, etc., 51
Arsenite reagent 0.1 N, 240
Arsenous acid, determination of, with iodine, 43
  reduction of bromates with, 96
  chloride, volatility of, 34, 38
  oxide in paint pigments, 1185
  in zinc oxide, 1185
Arsenous method for determining peroxides, 1761
Asbestine paint pigment, 1187
Ash soda, cauterized ash, 1555
Ash, fusibility, 1630
  in black paint pigments, 1197
  in coal, determination of, 1630
  in explosives. See Explosives.
  in linseed oil, 1166
  in plants, determining alkalies in, 282
  of rubber, sulphur in, 1591
Asphalt. See Bituminous substances, 1289
Assaying of gold and silver. See Fire Assay of Gold and Silver.
Astringency of tannic acid, 1760
A.S.T.M. analysis of alloys, 1036–1107
  for gypsum analysis, 108b
A.S.T.M. standards for Chinese wood oil, 1171
  iron and steel analysis, 1351–1371d
  for linseed oil, boiled and raw, 1172
  turpentine, 1174
  vanadium in steel, 595
Atomic weights, international, table of. See front cover
Atropine, 1735
Attack's method for traces of aluminum, 14
Available lime, 108
Avoirdupois weight, table of, 702

Babbit metal, copper in, 211
Bach's test for rapeseed oil, 1144b
  for rosin oil, 1144b
Bacteria, total in water, 1461
Bacteriological exam. of water, 1454–1468
Bahr's app. for solubility determ., 1476–1477
Bailar's iodide method for CaO, 108a
  zinc chloride method for CaO, 1804
Baker's method for tin, 532
Baking powder, arsenic determination in, 51

Baking powder, lead determination in, 281
　phosphate, determination of phos-
　　phoric acid in, 365
Balata, 1371
Ball mill, 1617
Bardy and Riche on det. methyl alcohol,
　1753
Barium, detection of, with sat. sol. of cal-
　cium or strontium sulphates, 56
　with soluble chromates, fluosilicic
　　acid, flame, 56
　spectrum of, 56
　estimation, general procedures:
　　gravimetric, determination as car-
　　　bonate, $BaCO_3$, 63b
　　as chromate, $BaCrO_4$, 63a
　　as sulphate, $BaSO_4$, 64
　　volumetric, acid titration of carbon-
　　　ate, 66
　　dichromate method, 65
　　permanganate method, 65
　　potassium iodide method, 65
　estimation, special procedures:
　　determination in insoluble residue, 62
　　in ores, 63
　　in silicates, 63
　　ore, valuation of. See Barytes.
　industrial application, 56
　occurrence, ores, commercial products,
　　56
　preliminary tests, 59
　preparation and solution of the sample,
　　carbonates, insoluble residue, sul-
　　phates, sulphides, soluble salts, or-
　　ganic matter, 57
　properties, barium sulphate, 56, 64
　　barium chromate, 64
　separations, general considerations, 58
　　from alkalies and magnesium by the
　　　oxalate and sulphate methods,
　　　59, 60
　　from calcium and strontium, 60, 61
　　from molybdenum and from P_2O_5,
　　　62
　solubilities, barium compounds, 56, 64
　traces, detection of, by flame and spec-
　　trum, 56
Barium acetate or chloride test for chro-
　mate, 156
　carbonate in rubber, 1595
　chloride in hydrochloric acid, 1502
　　-potassium chromate method for sul-
　　　phur determination, 505
　　test for bromate, 92
　chromate, determination of chromium
　　as, 160
　　property of, 64
　　solubility of, 64
　　-thiosulphate method for sulphur, 506
　hydroxide reagent for C in steel, 1356,
　　1357
　sulphate in rubber, 1591

Barium hydroxide method for separating
　magnesium from alkalies, 407
　sulphate, apparatus for filtering of, 500
　　decomposition for sulphur det., 496
　　in blanc fixe, 1188
　　in lithopone, 1186
　　properties and solubility of, 64
Barium ores, analysis of, 66
Barker's hydrometer for CO_2 det. in car-
　bonates, 125
B. coli, examination of, 1462
Barnitt, formulæ for solutions, 1533
　chapter on sampling, 1003
Barton, methods for titanium in steel, 547
Barton and Scott, chapter on titanium,
　538
　method for nitrogen in steel, 361a
Barytes, analysis of, determining barium
　carbonate, barium sulphate, iron and
　aluminum oxides, lime, magnesia,
　silica, soluble SO_3, etc., 66–68
　water test for magnesium, 291
Base box, definition (note), 524
Bases, reactions, tables of, 632–645
Basic acetate method for precipitating
　aluminum and iron, 298
Basic alumina in aluminum salts, determi-
　nation of, 13
" Basic hydrochloric acid " in bichloride
　of tin, 530
Basic carbonate of lead det., 278b
Basic nitrate, precip. of bismuth as, 74
Basicity of aluminum sulphate, 13
Baubigny's method, modified, for deter-
　mining halogens, 154
Baudisch's cupferron method for iron, 250
Baudouin's or Camoine's test for sesame
　oil, 1139, 1144b
Baughmann, W. F., 97
　and Skinner on iodine in water, 245
Bauxite, analysis of, determining soluble
　and total alumina, soluble and total
　iron, insoluble residue, silica, titanium
　oxide, 17f–17g
　arsenic determination in, 50
Bead test for titanium, 538
Beam test for matter susp. in gas, 1763
Bearing metal, determining bismuth in, 71
Beeswax, constants, 1150
Bechi's test for cottonseed oil, 1136, 1142
Beckstrom, on oil, 1158
Bekk's method for determination of the
　halogens, 155
Belasio on aluminum, 17
Bellier's test for oil, 1144a
Belt dressings, 1145
Beneker's method for carbon in steel, 130
Bennett's method for determining arsenic,
　45
Benzidine acetate test for gold, 229
　hydrochloric acid method for deter-
　　mining sulphates, 507, 1427

Benzoic acid standard for acidimetry, 1496
Berg, P. von, iodine titration of cadmium sulphide, 103
Berkeley's app. solubility dd., 1472, 1473
Berthelot's test for alcohol, 1743
Beryl, 69
Beryllium, 68–69b
  detection of, 68
  estimation, 68, 69a, 69b
  separations, 69
Betts, nitrometer method, 355
Bicarbonate, determination of, 1549
Bichloride of tin, Acker method for analysis, 530
Bichloride of tin—hot water precipitation of tin in, 530
  sulphide method for tin in, 532
Bichromate method for det. glycerol, 1758
Bidtel's method for valuation of fluor-spar, 225
Bishop, fuming sulphuric acid table, 673
Bishop and Allen, method for determining sulphur in ores, 498
Bismuth, detection of, general procedure, reducing agents, blowpipe test, 70
  estimation, general procedures:
    gravimetric, determination as basic chloride, 73
      as metal by cyanide reduction, 76
      as metal by electrolysis, 76
      as oxide, Bi_2O_3, 74
      as sulphide, Bi_2S_3, 75
    volumetric, bismuth iodide colorimetric method, 78
      cinchonine potassium iodide colorimetric method, 77
      permanganate titration of oxalate, 76
  estimation, special procedures:
    in alloys and metals, 1047
    in metallic copper, 200
    in metallic lead, 79, 286
    in ores, mattes, 80
    in pig lead, 286
  industrial application of methods, 70
  occurrence, 70
  preparation and solution of the sample, alloys, lead bullion, refined lead, ores, 70, 71
  properties, bismuth, basic nitrate, 74
    oxy-chloride, 73
    sulphide, 75
  separations, aluminum, chromium, iron, cobalt, manganese, nickel, zinc, magnesium, alkaline earths, alkalies, 72
    from arsenic, antimony, tin, molybdenum, selenium, tellurium, 72
    from cadmium and copper, 72
    from lead and mercury, 72
  solubility, metal and salts, 70, 73, 74, 75
  traces, determination of, 77, 78

Bismuthate method for determining manganese, 267, 303
  in bronze, 1097
  in steel, 267, 1360
  in water, 1426
Bisulphate fusion. See chapter " Decomposition of Sample," Vol. 2.
Bisulphite. See Metabisulphite.
Bitumen and pitch in rubber, 1570
Bituminous substances, asphalts, tars, pitches, 1289–1350
  Abraham's ductility test, 1304
  anthraquinone reaction, 1325
  bit. solvent examin., cements, paints, varnishes, 1346–1349
  carbenes, 1318
  characteristics of table, 1326–1327
  chem. tests, carbon free in tars, 1322
    oxygen in non-mineral matter, 1321
    solid paraffines, 1323
    sulphonation residue, 1323
    water, high and low distl., 1320
  composition of, 1289–1293
  crude, refined, blended, exam. of, 1294
  diazo reaction, 1324
  distillation test-flask and retort method, 1315–1316
  ductility, Dow test of, 1302
  emulsions, 1349
  examination of, 1289–1350
  fabrics, examination of, 1336
    physical tests of, 1337
      resist. dampness, elect. cur., heat, weather, 1338
      weight, pliability and strength, 1339
  fabrics separated, examin. of, 1344
  flash-point, Penski-Martins closed tester, 1314
  filler and pigment in, 1347
  fracture of, 1295
  hardness or consistency test by needle penetrometer, 1298
  heat tests, 1305–1309
    cube method, 1309
    ball and ring method, 1308
    Kramer-Sarnow method, 1305
  mineral aggregates, physical tests, compression and impact distortion under heat, 1328–1329
  mineral matter, examination of, 1333–1335
  physical characteristics, 1295
  saponifiable and unsaponifiable matter, 1323
  separation bitum. from mineral aggregate, 1330
    centrifugal method, 1332
    Forest's hot extraction, 1330
  sep. bitum. min. and fib. m., 1339

Bituminous substances—
　　fabrics—single layer, saturated or
　　　　coated roofings, laminated
　　　　fabrics, etc., 1339–1343
　　Smith's ductility machine, 1303
　　solubility tests by CS_2, 1317
　　　　test by petroleum naphtha, 1317
　　specific gravity by hydrometer, 1295
　　　　pycnometer, 1296
　　　　Westphal balance, 1295
　　streak on porcelain, 1295
　　susceptibility factor, 1302
　　table of, 1290–1292, 1294
　　viscosity, Engler and float tests, 1297
　　volatile matter, 1312
Black pigments, analysis of, 1177, 1199
Black powder, analysis of, 1372
Black oils, 1145
Blair, analysis of steel, 128, 301
Blanc fixe and barytes, analysis of, 67,
　　1188
Blangey's method for chloric acid, 152
Blast-furnace gas, analysis of, 1255
　　slag analysis of, 1610
Blasting caps, analysis of, 1396
Blattner and Brassuer, chlorine in chlo-
　　rates and perchlorates, 153
　　method for reduction of chlorates,
　　　　152
Blay and Burkhard, graduated weighing
　　burette (Fig. 83), 1500
Bleaching powder, evaluation of, 155
　　analysis of, in paper-making materials,
　　　　1779
Blister copper, electrolytic determination
　　of copper, 189
Blood, carbon monoxide determination by
　　means of, 1273
　　in carbon monoxide, 83
" Bloom " in oils, 1135
Blowpipe test for bismuth, 70
　　test for cadmium, 100
Blowpipe and flame tests, table of, 625
Blue lead, sublimed, analysis of, 1197
Blue pigments, analysis of, 1177, 1196
Blue vitriol, copper determination in,
　　206
Boiling, prolonged, effect on aluminum
　　hydroxide precipitate, 8
　　effect on glucinum separation from
　　　　aluminum, 227
　　point chart, sulphuric acid of varying
　　　　concentration, 1524
Bond, F. C., on silver, 458
Borax bead, boron test, 81
　　evaluation of, 86
　　table of tests, 627
Boric acid, Chapin's determination of,
　　87
　　evaluation of, 87
　　in foods, 83
　　in soap, 1604

Boron, detection of, borax bead test, prop-
　　erties, flame test, turmeric test, 81
　　Chapin's method, 87
　　estimation, general procedures:
　　　　gravimetric, lime fixation method, 84
　　　　method of Gooch and Jones (note),
　　　　　　85
　　　　volumetric determination, 86
　　estimation, special procedure:
　　　　determination as boric acid in butter,
　　　　　　83
　　　　in canned goods, 84
Boron, distillation app. for, 88
　　estimation, determination, in meat, 83
　　　　in milk, 83
　　　　in silicates, enamels, etc., 82
　　　　in mineral water, 82
　　industrial application of methods, 81
　　occurrence, ores, alloys, sundry prod-
　　　　ucts, 81
　　preparation and solution of the sample,
　　　　boric acid, boric oxide, boracite,
　　　　borocalcite, boronatrocalcite, cal-
　　　　cium borate, enamels, silicates,
　　　　etc., 82
　　　　carbonates, butter, meat and canned
　　　　　　goods, 83
　　　　mineral water, 82
　　solubility of boron, boric acid, borax, 82
　　traces, detection of, by Robin's test, 87
Bosworth and Gooch, method for silver
　　determination, 463
Bowman and Scott, ferrous sulphate
　　method for nitric acid, 1512
Bradbury and Owen, alkali carbonates
　　and hydrates present together, 1066
Brass and bronze,
　　determination of antimony in, 28b
　　determination of copper in, 211
　　determination of vanadium in, 598
　　method of National Brass and Cop-
　　　　per Tube Co., lead and copper,
　　　　207
Breyer, on analysis of zinc, 597
　　manganese determination in spiegel
　　　　iron, 306
　　separation of zinc as sulphide, 605
Briggs and Scott, modified Orsat appa-
　　ratus (Fig. 131), 1267
Brimstone, analysis of, determining mois-
　　ture, ash, arsenic, chlorine and avail-
　　able sulphur in, 519
Brines, preparation of, for alkali determi-
　　nation, 405
Brinton, H. M. P., chapter on Thorium,
　　522
　　zirconium, 618
Brinton and James det. of cerium, 135
British thermal unit (B.t.u.), calculation
　　of, 1627, 1639, 1659
　　determination of heat value of coal,
　　　　1622, 1634–1640

Brom-thymol blue, titrations with, 1457
Bromine, determination of, in illuminating gas, 1257
Bromate method for determining antimony, 26
Bromates, detection of, 92
  deter. of, by arsenous reduction, 96
Bromide paper for arsenic det., 47
Bromine, detection of, tests with carbon disulphide, carbon tetrachloride, barium chloride, magenta test, silver nitrate, 92
  estimation, general procedures:
    gravimetric, determination as silver bromide, 94
    volumetric, free bromine by potassium iodide method, 95
      chlorine method for soluble bromines, 95
      silver thiocyanate method of Volhard, 95
  estimation, special procedures:
    crude potassium bromide, analysis of, 96
  impurities in commercial bromine, chlorine in, 97
  in mineral waters, 97
  industrial application, 93
  occurrence, 93
  preparation and solution of the sample, organic matter, salts, etc., 93
  properties, 93
  separations from chlorine and iodine, 94
    heavy metals, cyanides, and silver, 93
  solubility of the element and its salts, 93
  traces, determination of, 95
Bromine-ammonia method for separating manganese from zinc, 600
  precipitating manganese dioxide with, 301
Bromine number in oil analysis, 1130
Bronze, analysis of, by A. S. T. M., 1047
  aluminum in, 16
Brown pigments, analysis of, 1176, 1190
Browne's heating tests for Chinese wood oil, 1170
Browning-Drushel, separation of magnesium from the alkalies, 407
Browning's test for fluorine, 213
  test for silica, 431
Brucine, 1734
Buckwheat coal, determination of B.t.u. in, example data, 1628
Budde's method for rubber analysis, 1568
Bulb, weighing acids, 1500
Bullion, assay of, 482, 484
Buovold's gravimetric method for nitrites, 358
Bunsen pump (Fig. 111), 1232
Bureau of Standards method for carbon in steel, 263

Bureau of Standards on manganese in steel, 266
  phosphorus in steel, 268
  silicon in steel, 270
  sulphur in steel, 269
  titanox pigment analysis, 1192
Burettes, standard, for acidimetry and alkalimetry, 1497
Burges' nitroso-beta-naphthol method for cobalt, 169
Burkhard and Blay, weighing burette, 1500
Burning oils. See Oils, 1109
Burrell, G. A., analysis industrial gas, 1288j
B. typhi, examination of, 1467
Butter, boric acid determination in, 83
  method of analysis. See Oils, 1143

Cadmium, detection of, general procedure, 99
  spectrum of cadmium, blowpipe test, 99
  estimation, general procedure:
    gravimetric, determination as cadmium sulphate, 102
      as cadmium sulphide, 101, 612
      as metallic cadmium by electrolysis, 102, 611, 1102
    volumetric, iodine titration of cadmium sulphide, 103
  estimation, special procedures:
    determination in alloys and metals:
      in metallic lead, 290
      in ores, det. of, 101
      in spelter, 612
  industrial application, 99
  occurrence, 99
  preparation and solution of the sample, alloys, carbonates, ores, sulphides, in presence of lead, 100
  separation from members of the ammonium sulphide group, alkaline earths and the alkalies, 100
    from arsenic, antimony and tin in presence and in absence of copper, 100
    from copper in alloys, 1089
    from bismuth and lead, 101
    from mercury, 101
    from silica, 100
Cadmium chloride and sulphate reagents for sulphur determination, 501
  sulphate, determination of, 102
  sulphide, gravimetric determination of cadmium as, 612
    volumetric determination of cadmium as, 103
Cæsium, detection of, 403
  separation from lithium and sodium, 408
Cahen-Little-Morgan, arsenic determination in organic matter, 36
Caillet, elaidin test for oils, 1126

Cain, J. R., and Cleaves, H. E., on carbon in steel, 118
Cain and Witmer, method for vanadium in steel, 591
Calcined ore, analysis of, 17j
Calcium, available, 108
Calcium, detection of, general procedure, 104
  flame test, spectrum, 104
  estimation, general procedures:
    gravimetric, oxalate method, 107
    other methods, 108d
    volumetric, permanganate titration of the oxalate, 17d, 108
    iodide method for, 108a
  estimation, special procedures:
    determination of, in composite white paints, 1190
    in green paint pigments, 1196
    in orange and yellow paint pigments, 1195
    in Portland cements as CaO (lime), 1216
    in sand, 448
    in water, 1424
    in water as calcium sulphate, 1125
  industrial application of methods, 104
  occurrence, ores, minerals, etc., 104
  precipitation from acetic acid solution, 108
  preparation and solution of the sample, cements, dolomites, limestone, magnesite, gypsum, plaster of Paris, silicates, sulphates, sulphides, pyrites, salts, decomposition of refractory ores, 105, 106
  rapid iodide method, 108a
  separation from aluminum, iron, copper, cobalt, nickel, manganese, zinc and members of the hydrogen sulphide group, 105
    from alkalies, barium, strontium, magnesium, P_2O_3, 106
    from silica, 105
  solubilities, 104
  traces, detection of, 104
Calcium acetate method for fluorine, 223
Calcium carbonate, rapid method for determining, in cement, 1220
  fluoride, decomposition of, 215
  method for fluorine, 216
Calcium oxide det. in presence of $CaCO_3$, 108a, 1804
Calcium phosphate, decomposition, 107
Calorie, definition of, 708
Calorific power of illuminating gas, 1257
  of fuel, 1622
  value of industrial gases, 1227
Calorimeter, Emerson bomb (Fig. 105), for coal, B.t.u. det., 1625
  Junker's for gas (Figs. 124, 125, 126), 1257, 1258

Calorimeter, Parr's for fuels, 1634–1640
  standardization, 1629
Camoin's test for sesame oil, 1139
Campbell, A., chapter on Soap Analysis, 1598
Candle-power, def. and method of det., 708
  of illuminating gas, 1256
Canned goods, arsenic determination in, 51
  tin determination in, 536
Caoutchouc in lubricating oil, 1121
Capometer, 1235
Capacity, unit table of, 702
Carbenes, 1318
Carbide of silicon, decomposition of, 435
Carbonic acid, free, det. of, 1549
  indicators, 1252
Carbonic acid, det. of, 1549, 1730
Carbon, detection of carbon dioxide in gas, 109
  carbonates, 109
  carbonic acid in water, 109
  carbon monoxide in blood, 109
  estimation, general procedures:
    gravimetric, dry combustion method, weighing CO_2, 111, 118
    wet oxidation process, weighing CO_2, 111, 120
    volumetric, barium hydroxide method, titration of carbonate formed, 127
    measurement of volume of CO_2 formed (ref.), 127
  estimation, special procedures:
    in alloy steels, 1359
    in black pigments, 1196
    in coal as "fixed carbon," 1622, 1646
    in coal tar pitch, 1358
    in iron and steel, 115–117, 128, 130, 263, 265, 1352, 1354, 1356
    colorimetric method, 128
    graphitic carbon, 115
    organic substances, 119, 120
    in rubber goods, 1580, 1592
  occurrence, 109
  preparation of sample, alloys, iron and steel, 110
  separation from iron and steel, cupric potassium chloride method, 110
  residue test of lubricating oils, Gray's method, 1122
Carbonate method for barium, 63b
Carbonate method for calcium, 108d
Carbonate, titration of, 1549
Carbonates in ores, 57, 101, 109, 110, 121, 223, 247, 350
  determination of, in presence of other combined acids, 514
  determination in soap, 1605
Carbon bisulphide. See Carbon Disulphide.

Carbon dioxide combined as carbonate:
estimation, general procedures for determination, 121
gravimetric determination in carbonates, 121
loss of weight method, 124
hydrometric method, 125
volumetric, measuring the gas evolved, 123
estimation, special procedures:
in alloys, 1102, 1106g, 1106i
in ammoniacal gas liquors, 344
in baking powder
available CO₂, 124
residual CO₂, 123
in barium ores, 67
in blanc fixe, 1189
in cement, 84
in composite white paint, 1190
in corroded white lead, 1181
in gypsum, 1188
in soap, 1605
in zinc, 1183
free in gaseous mixtures, 338, 1242, 1244, 1248, 1262
properties of, 1227b
Carbon disulphide, bromine detection with, 92
iodine determination with, 242
purification of (see Fig. 7), 75
monoxide in air, 1740
in blood, detection of, 109, 1741
in gaseous mixtures, determination of, 1085
in illuminating gas, determination of, 1248
properties of, 1227d
tetrachloride, bromine test with, 92
tubes, for colorimetric determination of carbon in steel (Fig. 25), 129
Carbonate in bicarbonate, 1553
Carbon steel, metallography of, 1713
Carborundum, silicon carbide, decomposition of, for silica det., 445
Carius method for halogens in organic matter, 145
Carney and Campbell on thorium, 423
Carnot's method, modified, for determining gold, 233
method for nickel, 336b
Carnotite, uranium in, 582
Case hardening, steel metallography, 1720
Castor oil, constants, 1147, 1148
Caustic, free in soap, 1601
standard solution, 1496
Caustic soda, sodium tartrate m. for distinguishing copper compds., 210
Causticized ash, analysis of, 1555, 1783
Cellulose in rubber, 1595
Cement, analysis and testing of, 1202
apparatus for testing, Fairbank's testing machine (Fig. 106), 1214

Cement, gang mold (Fig. 105), 1212
Gilmore needles (Fig. 103), 1211
Le Chatelier's specific gravity apparatus (Fig. 93), 1205
Riehlé automatic cement testing machine (Fig. 107), 1215
Vicat needle (Fig. 94), 1207
calcium in, 105
carbon dioxide in, 110
fineness, 1205
mixing, 1206
normal consistency, determination of, 1206
physical testing, 1202
Portland cement, analysis of, 1216
determination of alkalies, alumina, iron, insoluble residue, lime, loss on ignition, magnesia, silica, sulphur, 1216–1219
rapid method of analysis, 1220
sampling, 1204
setting time, 1210
specifications, 1202–1214
specific gravity, 1204
tension test, 1212
Cements in bituminous sub., 1346
Cement, rock, analysis of (limestone, lime, Rosendale cement, etc.), 1223
table of composition, 1225
Cerium, detection of, spectroscopic test, 133, 133b
estimation, gravimetric methods, 134, 136
volumetric method, 136
estimation of cerium, 136
in presence of rare earths, 136, 137
in thoria, thorium nitrate, etc., 138
industrial application, 133
occurrence and properties, 133
preparation of the sample, 133
fusion method, 136
separation of the rare earths from other elements, 134, 135
from rare earth metals, 135
from thoria, 134
table of compositions, 1215
technical methods of analysis, 138
Chamber burette (Fig. 79), 1497
Chancel's method for determining aluminium, 9
Chancel degree for specific volume of S, 519a
Chapin's method for boric acid det., 87
Chapman and Thornton on iron det., 258
Character of copper deposits by electrolysis, 191
Characteristics of some animal and vegetable oils, 1148, 1149
of some fatty acids from oils, 1147
of waxes, 1150
Charcoal in explosives, 1373, 1390, 1391
Chemical laws, 723

Chemical tests of water, 1412
Chesney on alkali analysis, 91, 1806
Chiddey on cyanide solution assay, 486
Chili saltpeter, 349
Chimney flue gases, 1252
China clay paint pigment, 1187
Chinese blue, analysis of, 1197
Chinese wood oil, analysis of, determining acid number, iodine number, saponification number, specific gravity, unsaponifiable matter, refractive index, heating and Jelly tests, 1169–1170
Chlorate, test for, 143
  determination of, 152
  in presence of perchlorates, 153
  method for chromium in steel, 165
  removal of, in sulphur det., 497
Chlorates in explosives, 1387
Chloric acid. See Chlorate.
Chloride and cyanide, det. of, 154
  chlorate, perchlorate exam. of, 1385 1397
  cyanide, thiocyanate det. of, 155
  detection of, 142
  in gases, 1505
  in soap, 1602
  method, for determining silver, 453
Chlorine, detection of free, 142
  combined chlorine, chloride by silver nitrate test, 142
  test in presence of bromide and iodide, 142
  test in presence of cyanate and cyanide, thiocyanate, 142
  test for free hydrochloric acid, 142
  test for chlorate, chlorite, hypochlorite, perchlorate, 143
  estimation of combined chlorine as chloride, general methods:
  gravimetric method as silver chloride, 148a
  volumetric methods, silver chromate method, in neutral solution, 150
  silver thiocyanate method in acid solution, 149
Chlorine, estimation of combined and free chlorine, special cases:
  determination combined chlorine in presence of bromine and iodine (combined), 154
  in presence of other acids, 154
  in bleaching powder, 155
  in brimstone, 519
  in bromine, 97
  in cement copper and copper ores, 206
  in gas, 147
  in nitric acid, 1511
  in organic compounds, 145–146
  in water, 1417, 1433
  in zinc oxide, 1183

Chlorine, determination of free chlorine, 151
  in hydrochloric acid, 1501
  in nitric acid, 1512
  industrial application of methods, 143
  occurrence, 143
  preparation and solution of the sample, ores, cinders, rocks, water soluble, and insoluble chlorides, silver chloride, 144
  organic matter, decomposition by Carius method, 145
  decomposition by lime method, 146
  decomposition by sodium peroxide method, 146
  separation from iodine, 148
  from cyanides, thiocyanates, 130
  together with bromine from iodine, 148
  halides from the heavy metals, 148
  halides from one another, 148
  halides from silver and from silver cyanide, 148, 155
  solubility of chlorine and its salts, 143
  traces, detection of, 142
Chlorine, free, liberation of bromine with, 95
  determination of, 151
  water, decomposition of hydrobromic acid, 342
Chloroform, det., 1728
Chloroplatinate method for determining potassium, 410
  Hicks' modification, 411
Chlorosulphonic acid, analysis of, 1540
Chromate, detection of barium with, 56
  method for determining barium as BaCrO₄, 63a
  volumetric method for determining barium, 65
  method for determining chlorine, 150
  method for determining lead, 275, 278
Chromate-ferrous-diphenylamine method for lead, 278b
Chrome green, 1198
Chromic acid, determination of, in presence of vanadic acid, 592
  removal of, from nitric acid, 342
  hydroxide, precipitation of, 159
Chromite, chromium in, 164
Chromium, detection of, tests with barium acetate, ether, lead acetate, mercurous nitrate, hydrogen peroxide, reducing agents, diphenyl carbazide, 156
  distinction between chromic and chromous salts, 156
  estimation, general procedures:
  gravimetric, determination as barium chromate, 160
  as the oxide, Cr₂O₃, 159
  det. by mercurous nitrate, 160

Chromium—volumetric, ferrous sulphate and permanganate method, 161, 1368f
 chlorate method, 165
 dichromate diphenylamine method, 164a
 iodine method, 161
estimation, special procedures:
 determination in chromate, 164
 in green paint pigments, 1196
 in nickel, 336e
 in orange and yellow paint pigments, 1195
 in presence of vanadium, 593
 in steel, elect. method, 1677, 1678
 in steel, rapid method, 164, 1368f
 traces by diphenylcarbazide, 163
industrial application of methods for, 156
occurrence, 156
preparation and solution of the sample, refractory materials, materials high in silica, chrome iron ores, 157
 iron and steel, 158
separations from alumina and iron, 158, 159
solubility of the metal, 157
traces, detection, 156
 estimation, 162–163
Chromium salts, comparison with vanadium salts, 583
Cinchonine method for det. tungsten, 560
Cinchonine potassium iodide method for determining bismuth, 77
 reagent for tungsten det., 560
Cinders, chlorine in, 144
Citric acid, analysis of, 1549
 reagent for calcium determination, 106
Clark on tin, 525–536
Clark's modification of Mohr's method for antimony, 27
 method for separation of antimony from tin, 22
Classen, deposition of gold, 231
 and Henz method for determining tin, 536
 and Reiss method for determining antimony, 24
Clay analysis, 1786–1788
 alkalies, 1787
 silica, state of, 1788
 titanium, 1787
Cleveland cup for fire test of lubricating oils, 1120
 open cup app., 1118d
Cloud and pour points, oil tests, 1118
Coal and fuel, methods of analysis, 1616–1660
 ash, determination of, 1618
 anthracite, 1641
 buckwheat coal, analysis of, 1628
 calculation of B.t.u., 1627, 1639, 1659

Coal, calorific value, determination of, 1622
 calorimeter, standardization of, 1629
 carbon total in, 1646
 coke, 1041
 composition of. See chapters on Fuel and Coal.
 conversion calculations, moisture, 1632
 correction factors, 1639
 definitions, 1651
 Emerson bomb calorimeter, 1625
 fixed carbon, determination of, 1622
 fusibility of coal ash, 1630
 gasoline, 1642, 1658
 Hoskins' electric furnace (Fig. 210), 1630
 moisture determination in coal, 1618
 Parr calorimeter, 1634
 petroleum oils, 1641, 1660
 preparation of the sample, 1618
 pyrophosphate method, 174
 quartering (Fig. 204), 1617
 radiation corrections, 1652
 references, 1632
 sampling coal, 1616
 thermometer Hythread, 1645
 turbidimetric sulphur table, 1620
 volatile combustible matter, determination of, 1618
 volatile sulphur, determination of, 1619 1623
  oxygen bomb method, 1651
Cobalt, detection of, general procedure, 166
 ammonium sulphocyanate test for, 166
 dicyandiamidine sulphate test for, 166
 potassium nitrite, potassium sulphocyanate tests, 166
estimation, general procedures:
 gravimetric, deposition of the metal by electrolysis, 170
 nitro-beta-naphthol method, 169
 potassium nitrite method, 169
 pyrophosphate method, 174
 volumetric method for, 175
estimation, special procedures:
 determination in cobalt oxide, 171
 in copper (metallic), 172
 in enamels, 173
 in ferro-cobalt, 172
 in lead (metallic), 172
 in metallic cobalt, 172
 in metallic nickel, 172
 in ores, 173
 in steel, 174
perborate method for, 175
preparation and solution of the sample, metallic cobalt, nickel, and cobalt alloys, cobalt oxides, ores containing cobalt, 167
separation of ammonium sulphide from the hydrogen sulphide group, 168

Cobalt, sep. ammonium sulphide group from alkaline earths and alkalies, 168

cobalt and nickel from manganese, 168

cobalt from nickel and from zinc, 168

Cocain, 1735

Cochineal indicator, 744

Codein, 1736

Cohen and Inouye app. for solubility det., 1476

Cold test for lubricating oils, 1119

Color in butter, detection of, 1144

Color comparitor or camera for det. carbon in steel (Fig. 26), 129

Color, organic, in red and brown pigments, 1191

Color test in turpentine, 1173

Color test of water, 1410

Colorimeter (Figs. 26a, 43, 69, 70), 165, 283, 546, 548

Colorimetric determination of aluminum, 14

of ammonia, 345

of bismuth, 78

of carbon, 128

of chromium, 162, 1368f

of copper, 197, 198, 199

of fluorine, 220

of gold, 233

of iron, 258, 259, 611

of lead, 282

of manganese, 305

of titanium, 545, 547, 550

Columbium, detection of, 575

estimation, procedure, 577

occurrence, 475

separation from antimony, silica, tin, tungsten, 577

isolation of columbium and tantalum oxides, 576

Coltman and Cunningham on manganese det., 303

Combination methods, silver determination, 447

Combinations of copper, det. of, 208

hypothetical in water, 1441c

Combined sulphuric acid in aluminum salts, 12

in soluble sulphates, 505

Combustion furnace for carbon determination, 112, 1352, 1356

hinged type (Fig. 32a), 206

for assaying, 460

heat of, 719

method for carbon determination, 112, 261, 1352, 1356

train. See C det. in steel.

Commercial aluminum ores, valuation of, 14

Commercial selenium, analysis of, 439

Conradson's method for carbon in oils, 1122

Constant temperature bath, 190

Constants of various oils, 1147–1149, 1172

of waxes, 1150

Container for gas sample (Fig. 112), 1233

Conversion factors, Baumé to specific gravity, 701

of compounds, alphabetical arrangement, 679

Engler, Redwood, and Saybolt times —comparison, 1151

temperature, Centigrade to Fahrenheit, 700

volume, weight and energy, 712–713

weights and measures customary and metric systems, 702

Converter efficiency NH_3–NO_2, 361c

Cooper-Hewitt mercury light (Fig. 44), 285

Copper anode slimes, platinum and palladium in, 386

antimony traces in, 32

Copper comb., distinction of, 208–210

Copper, detection of, general procedure, hydrogen sulphide test, flame test, reduction tests, 177

estimation, general procedures:

gravimetric, copper oxide method, 183

cuprous thiocyanate method, 181, 183

electrolytic methods, preliminary remarks, 185

rapid methods, 187

slow methods, 189

electrolysis, effect of impurities on, 191

precautions and notes on procedure, 191

removal of deposit, 191

hydrogen reduction method, 205

volumetric methods, potassium cyanide procedure, 194

colorimetric method Cu in steel, 1308d

potassium iodide method, 17b, 193–195

permanganate method, 195

Demorest's method for, 196

Gerigue's method for, 196

Volhard's method for, 196

estimation, special procedures:

determination of copper in alloys and metals, brass and bronze, 1049, 1053, 1058, 1067, 1071, 1076, 1098, 1099, 1106, 1106j

in alloys, 1049, 1053, 1058, 1067, 1071, 1076, 1098, 1099, 1106, 1106j

in babbit metal, 211

in blister copper, 189

in blue vitriol, 207

Copper, in brass, 211
    in gun metal, A. S. T. M., 1058
    in lead, metallic, 290
    in manganese bronze, 1047
    in molybdenite, 326
    in ores, 193a
    in refined copper, 205
    in selenium, commercial, 439
    in slag, 1613
    in steel, 181, 1368c
    in tungsten ores and concentrates, 568
    in water, 1437
    in wulfenite, 327
  impurities in blister and refined copper:
    antimony, arsenic, selenium, and tellurium, 202, 240c
    arsenic, 37, 202
    bismuth and iron, 200
    chlorine in cement copper and copper ores, 206
    cobalt, lead, nickel and zinc, 201
    oxygen and sulphur, 204
    phosphorus, 205
    selenium and tellurium, 440c
  industrial application of methods, 177
  occurrence, 177
  preparation and solution of the sample, alloys, cast iron, steel, matte, slag, iron ores, and iron ore briquettes and metals, sulphide ores, copper glance, copper pyrites, and iron pyrites, 178–181
  separations, deposition by a more positive metal, 182a, 184
    precipitation as copper thiocyanate, 181, 183
    removal of members of subsequent groups, 182a
    removal of arsenic, antimony, bismuth, lead, silver, tin, 182b
    removal of cadmium, 182b
    removal of Se and Te, 182a
  solubility of the metal, 178
  traces, colorimetric methods for determining, 197–199
    ammonia method, 198
    ferrocyanide method, 198
    hydrogen sulphide method, 199
    potassium ethyl xanthate method, 197
Copper bullion, assay of, 482
Copper pyrites, 179
  sulphate for determining hydrocyanic acid, 130
  standard solutions (see also "reagents"), 193, 194, 198
Copper slimes, Au, Ag, Pd, Pt in, 386
Copper sulphate treatment of water, 1452
Copper-zinc alloys, metallography of, 1710
Corn oil, constants, 1148

Corning Glass Works method for Se in glass, 440b
Correction factors in calorimetry, 1640, 1652
Corrosion, acid waters, calculation of, 1441b
  tests of oils, 1126
Cottonseed oil, test for (see Oils), 1136
Coulomb, definition of, 708
Coye, J. S., electrometric methods, 1667
Craig's method, modified, for basic alumina or free acid in aluminum salts, 12
Crank case oil, constants, 1145
Crawford-Lenher colorimetric method for titanium, 550
Crook's select methods of analysis (reference), 138
Crucible, Gooch, preparation of, 596d
Crushers and grinders, 1011
Culture media for water bacteria, 1456
Cunningham and Coltman on det. of manganese, 303
Cupel in fire assay, 468
Cupferron method for iron, 250
  reagent, 746
Cupric-potassium-chloride reagent, preparation of, 111
Cupro-vanadium, 596
Cuprous chloride, ammoniacal and acid, preparation for gas analysis, 1278
  -sulphocyanate method for determining copper, 181, 184
Cyanide method for copper, 194
  method for nickel, 336b
Cyanide process for tin ores, 526
Cyanide, silver determination as, 455
  separation chloride, thiocyanate, 154
  volumetric determination of silver, 456
Cyanide, Liebig's method for det., 131
  Volhard's method for det., 132
Cyanide and thiocyanate, det. of, 132
Cyanide solution, assay of, 486
Cyanogen, detection of, 131
Cylinder oil, constants, 1145

Davisson's scrubber-ammonia distill., 351
Decomposition of sample, chapter on, 1032–1035b
  reagents used, 1033
Definitions of special terms, 708, 1200
Dely weighing tube (Fig. 81), 1498
Demorest's method for det. copper, 196
Denigés and Chelle bromine test, 92
Denigés' cyanide method for determining silver, 462
Derby,
  chapter on gold, 228
  chapter on silver, 439
  and Scott, chapter on copper, 177
Deshey's method for manganese in steel, 266

Detonators, electric, analysis of, 1396
Devarda apparatus for determining nitrates (Fig. 51), 347
Devarda's method, modified determination of nitrates by, 346
Deville on iridium, 390
Diazo reaction, 1324
Dichromate of potassium method for iron, 253, 255
  titration in determining chromium, 162, 164a
Dicyandiamidine sulphate test for cobalt, 166
Diehl's method for PbO$_2$, 290d
Didymium in cerium salts, 138
Dietz and Margosches method for determining iodine, 241
Diluting mixtures, formulæ for, 1496, 1533
Dimethyl glyoxime method for nickel, 333
  test for nickel, 329, 1368c, 1368d
Dioxide of manganese, separation of, by means of bromine, 301
Diphenylamine in smokeless powder, 1405
Diphenylamine indicator in chromium det., 164a
  in iron det., 255, 257b
Diphenylamine test for nitrates, 338
Diphenyl carbazide test for chromium (chromate), 156
  determination of chromium, 163
  preparation of, 163
Diphenyl-endo-anilo-hydro-triazole (nitron) method for nitrates, 342, 345
Distillation of arsenous chloride, 38–39b
  method for separating selenium and tellurium, 432
  method for det. ethyl alcohol, 1743
  test for oils, 1111
Distinction of copper compounds, 208
Dittrich, small amounts of chromium, 162
Dividing pipette (Figs. 30 and 42), 190, 271
Dodge on the det. of red lead, 290d
Dolomites, 105, 110
Dole, field assay of water, 1441d
Donnan and White app. for solubility det., 1475
Dow's ductility test for bituminous sub., 1302
Dowsett's factory test for gold, 234
Drushel, W. A., Elston, C. M., on sulphur det., 520
Drying oils, list of, 1146
Drying test of oils, 1141
Duboscq colorimeter, 165
Dufty's sulphide pyrophosphate method for cobalt, 174
Du Pont's nitrometer, 354, 355
Dupre's method for iodine, modified, 243
Dust, determination of, in gas, 1763
Dynamite, analysis of, 1374
Dyne, definition of, 709

Earl of Berkeley solubility app., 1472
Ebonite in rubber, 1580
Edgar's method of reduction of vanadium with sulphur dioxide, 321
  volumetric determination of vanadium, arsenic or antimony, in presence of one another, 592
  of vanadium and molybdenum, in presence of one another, 591
  of vanadium and chromium acids, in presence of one another, 593
Edible fats (see Oils), 1143
  examination of, 1146
Eggertz's method for carbon in steel, 130
Elaidin test for oils, 1126
Electric Heating Apparatus Co., furnace, hinged design, 206
Electricity, units of, 708
Electrolyte, test for copper in, after electrolysis, 191
Electrolytic determination of antimony, 24
  bismuth, 76
  cadmium, 102
  cobalt, 170
  copper, 185
  gold, 122
  lead, 275b
  mercury, 310
  nickel, 335
  platinum, 381
  silver, 436
  tin, 536
  zinc, 599
Electro Metallurgical Co. Methods, 280–282, 322
Electrometric det., 1663–1682
  description of Kelley app., 1669, 1673–1674
  methods of analysis, 1677
  method for chromium in steel, 1677
    for manganese in steel, 1680
    for vanadium in steel, 1679
    for vanadium and chromium, 1681
  oxidation potential, 1671
Electromotive force, definition of, 708
  series of elements, table of, 659
Elliott apparatus for gas analysis (Fig. 121), 1244
Emerson's calorimeter, 1625
Emulsions, bituminous, 1349
Enamel, cobalt determination in, 173
Engine oil, constants, 1145
Engler flask and tests, 1112–1112d
Engler's method, dist. test of oil, 1111
  viscosimeter, 1114
Engler and Haase on flash test of oil, 1109
Eosin methylene blue agar, 1459
Erg, definition of, 708
Erbium, 133
Errors, causes of, in silica determination, 442
  in determining the alkaline earths, 57

Eschka's method for sulphur in coal, 495
Esters in alcohol, 1746
Etching test for fluorine (Fig. 33), 212
Ether-alcohol, 1400, 1405
Ether, chromium detection by, 156
Ether method for separating iron from sol., 248
Ethyl acetate test for alcohol, 1743
  alcohol analysis, 1743
Ethylene, properties of, 1227c
Evaluation of bauxite, 15
  of fluorspar, 225
Evaporation test of lubricating oils, 1117
Evolution apparatus for sulphur determination 500, 1367
  method for antimony, 28a
  method for sulphur, 500, 1368
Exit gases, sulphur dioxide in, 1266
Explosives, analysis of, 1372–1407
  ammonia dynamite, 1379
  ammonia picrate, 1393
  black powder, 1372
  blasting caps and detonators, 1396
  gelatine dynamite, 1380
  low freezing dynamite, 1381
  mercury fulminate, 1395
  nitrocellulose, 1399
  nitrochlorhydrin, 1383
  nitroglycerin-dynamite, 1374
  nitroglycerin smokeless powders, 1407
  nitropolyglycerin, 1383
  nitrostarch, 1389
  nitrosugars, 1383
  nitrotoluenes, 1381
  " permissible " explosives, 1384
  picric acid, 1392
  primers, 1398
  smokeless powder, 1404
  straight dynamite, 1374
  tetryl, 1394
  trinitrotoluene, 1391
Explosive ingredients in,
  ash in, 1378, 1389, 1392, 1394, 1395, 1401
  chlorates in, 1372, 1387
  chlorides in, 1396
  diphenylamine in, 1405
  gum arabic in, 1385, 1388
  insoluble matter, 1378, 1389, 1390, 1393, 1394, 1395
  nitrates in, 1373, 1377, 1387, 1390
  nitrogen in, 1373, 1377, 1380, 1387, 1390, 1393, 1402, 1406
  resins in, 1377
  solids in, separation of, 1385
  starch in, 1378
  sugar in, 1388
  sulphur in, 1373, 1377
Explosives, tests and sundries,
  extraction with acetone, 1395, 1401, 1405
  extraction with acid, 1378, 1388

Explosives, extraction with ether, 1375, 1376, 1387, 1389, 1400, 1405
  extraction with water, 1377, 1387, 1390
  melting point det., 1394
  moisture in, 1372, 1375, 1381, 1386, 1389, 1392, 1393, 1394, 1396, 1404, 1405
  pot. iodide-starch test for nitrocellulose, 1401
  sampling of, 1372, 1374, 1380, 1395, 1396, 1398, 1399
  solidification point det., 1391, 1392
  stability tests, 1401, 1403, 1405
  surveillance test, 1406
Extraction of aluminum ores—evaluation of, 14

Fabrics, separated, examination of, 1344
Factors, conversion, 685, 700. See also " Tables " in index.
Fairbanks cement testing machine, 1214
Fairbanks and Gooch method for molybdenum, 318
Fats (see under Oils), 1146
Fatty acids, table of, 1152
Fatty oils, test for, in lubricating oils, 1121
Fehling's solution, 1185, 1188
Ferguson's colorimetric method for bismuth, 77
  electrolytic method for copper, 189, 205
  tables of properties, see Part II, Vol. I
Ferric-alum method for det. phosphorus, 1105
Ferric chloride etching reagt., 1705
Ferric chloride oxidation of organic m., 341
  for tin, 535
  reagent for tin, 536
Ferric iron in aluminum salt, 12
  iron, determination with stannous chloride, 257
  oxide, determination of iron as, 249
  in sand, 448
  in zinc oxide, 1185
  salts, decomposition of iodides with, 241
  salt, titanium determination with, 543, 544
Ferricyanide, det. of, 132a, 1201
Ferro-carbon titanium, determination of titanium in, gravimetric method, 543
  determination of titanium in, volumetric method, 544
Ferrocyanide solution, standardization of, 600, 602, 604, 606b
  method for copper, 198
  for lead, 276
  for zinc, 600–608
Ferrocyanide, det. of, 132a, 1201
Ferromanganese, det. of Mn in, 303b
Ferrosilicons, 445

Ferrouranium, analysis of, 582a
Ferrous amm. sulphate, method for det. Mn, 1360
Ferrous iron in aluminum, 12
    reduction of chlorates, 152
        of chromates, 156
    test for palladium, 382
    test for platinum, 377
    salts for reduction, chromium determination, 161
    sulphate method for determining nitric acid, 1512
    preparation of reagents, 1514–1516
Ferrous sulphate method for nitric acid, 1512
    procedure for determining persulphates, 508
    test for nitrates, 338
Ferro-tungsten alloys, 558
    typical analysis of, 555
Ferro-vanadium, det. vanadium in, 594, 1681?
    method by American Vanadium Co., 594
Fertilizers, mixed, 404
    nitrogen in, 339
    organic compounds, 405
    phosphate in, 363
    potash salts in, 404
Fiber. See under Bituminous Sub.
Field assay of water, 1441d
Fillers and modifiers of rubber, 1571
    organic, in rubber goods, 1569
Filtration app., 1357
Fineness in cement testing, 1205
    sulphur det., 519a
Finn's method of basicity of white lead, 1182
Fire assay of gold and silver, 466–488
    assay slags, 475
    assay ton, 409
    borax, amount of, 475
    crucible assay, 471
    crucible charges, 477
    cupillation, 478
    cyanide solutions, 486
    copper bullion, 482
    definitions, 466
    furnaces and equipment, 468–469
    fusing the charge, 476
    general outline, 466
    gold and silver bullion, 482–484
    lead bullion, 482
    lead reduction with oxidized ores, 471
    lead reduction with sulphide ores, 472
    litharge, amount, 473
    parting, 480
    reagents for, 466–468
    sampling, 470
    scorification assay, 477
    sodium carbonate amount, 474
    weighing and mixing, 476

Fire test of lubricating oils, 1120
    for oils, 1110, 1118d, 1127–1128d
Fitzpatrick on antimony, 29
Fixed carbon in coal, 1622
Fixed oils, fats and waxes (see Oils, Fats, and Waxes), 1108
Fixed oils and resins in varnish, 1174
Flame, coloration of, by barium, 56
    boron, 93
    calcium, 104
    copper, 177
    potassium, sodium, cæsium, lithium, and rubidium, 401, 403
    strontium, 489
    temperature of, see table, 658
Flash test or point of burning oils, 1109
    of lubricating oils, 1119
    varnish, 1174
Fleming's gas absorption bulb, 114
Fleming's method for carbon in steel, 112
Flowers of sulphur in rubber, 1569, 1585, 1588
    see also brimstone, 519
Flue dust, Se and Te in, 440a, 440b
Flue gases, 1252
Fluid measure, table of, 703
Fluoride of potassium reagent, 12
Fluoride of sodium, evaluation of, determining sodium fluoride, sodium sulphate, sodium thiosulphate, sodium chloride, silica, volatile matter, water, 226
    det. of fluorine in, 224
Fluorides, effect on aluminum precipitation, 8
    silica determination in presence of, 444
Fluorine, detection of, etching, black filter and hanging drop tests, 212, 213
    estimation, gravimetric, calcium fluoride method, 216
    lead chlorofluoride method, 217
    volumetric methods, colorimetric method of Steiger, 220
    calcium acetate method for, 223
    silicon tetrafluoride method, Offerman's, 218
    occurrence of, 214
    preparation of the sample, calcium fluoride, hydrofluoric acid, organic substances, siliceous ores and slags, soluble fluorides, fluorspar, 214, 215
    separation, from boric, hydrochloric, phosphoric acids, 216
    from silica, 215
    solubility of salts, 216
    Steiger-Merwin colorimetric method, 220
    standard solutions, 220
    traces, determination of, 224
Fluorine in barium ores, 66b
    in alkali fluorides, 224, 226

Fluorspar, valuation of, determining calcium carbonate, calcium fluoride and silica, 225
Fluosilicic acid, precipitation of barium with, 56
Foaming and priming of water, 1441b
Foods, arsenic in, 51
Foot-candle, definition of, 709
Foot-pound, definition of, 709
Foots in linseed oil, 1165
Formaldehyde, detection and estimation of, 1754
Ford-Williams method for det. Mn, 306
Formic acid, analysis of, 1542
  in acetic acid, 1545
  test for iridium, 388
  test for palladium, 383
  test for platinum, 377
  test for rhodium, 393
Formulæ
  for determining areas, 703
  for diluting mixtures, 1533
  for gas velocities, 707
  fluorine determination, Merwin's, 222
  heat value of coal, 1627. See chapter on.
  of gas, 1259, 1281, table 3
  iodine value for SO_2, Reich test, 1266
  lime and soda value in water analysis, 1437
  reduction of volume of gas to standard volume, 1265
Forrest's extraction of bit. matter, 1330–1331
Free acid in aluminum salts, 12–13
  in presence of iron salts, 1541
  test in oils, 1140
Freezing and boiling pt. curves for H_2SO_4, 1524
French, D. K., chapter on water analysis, 1409
Fresenius, separation of magnesium and the alkalies (ref.), 407
  method for separating barium, calcium, and strontium, 61, 108d
  method for determining iodine, 242
  and Popp, boric acid in meat, 83
Friction test of lubricating oils, 1123
Friedrich's spiral gas washing bottle (Fig. 116), 1237
Fuel gases, 1255
  oils, analysis of, 1127
Fuels, analysis of, 1616, 1634
Fuming sulphuric acid, analysis of, 1529
  equivalent (table), 1539
Furfurol in acetic acid, 1543, 1545
  in alcohol, 1746
Furnace methods of assaying, 466
Fusel oil in ethyl alcohol, 1746
Fusibility of coal, 1630
Fusion, heat of, 721

Fusion method for arsenic ores, 35
  for potassium bisulphate, 4
  for silicon, 17a
  for sodium carbonate, 4
  for sulphur ores, 495
  for titanium ores, 540
  for tungsten minerals, 555
  of ores with sodium hydroxide, 20
  with sodium and potassium carbonate, 248

Gaillard on NH_3 to HNO_3, 361c
Gallon, grains per U. S., 1431
Gang mold for cement (Fig. 99), 1212
Gardner and Schaeffer, chapter on analysis of paints, 1161, 1199
Gas, analysis, 1231–1286
  apparatus, absorption bulbs, pipettes, tubes, 1237
  measurement of large quantities of gas:
    anemometer, capometer, orifice meter, Pitot tube, rotameter, Thomas electric meter, wet meter, 1233, 1236
  measurement of small quantities of gas:
    Hempel's gas burette, separatory funnel and graduate, 1236
  apparatus, analytical, Elliott's apparatus, 1244
    Hempel's, 1245
    Morehead, 1227a
    Orsat's, 1241
    Orsat modified by Briggs and Scott, SO_2 determination, 1267
  sampling tubes, pumps, containers, 1027, 1231–1233
  application and interpretation of results, 1252
  examination of gases, detection of, tables of, 1238–1240
    gases absorbed by silver nitrate, 1239
      by sulphuric acid, 1238
      by potassium hydroxide, 1239
    unabsorbed, 1240
  acetylene, det. oxygen, hydrogen, methane, nitrogen, sulphur-containing gases, phosphoric, 1271
  air, moisture, carbon dioxide, bacteria, carbon monoxide, ozone, 1273
    sulphur dioxide in, 1283
  chimney and flue gases, carbon dioxide, indicators, temperature determination of, 1252, 1253
  electrolytic gas, chlorine and other gases, 1271
  helium, analysis of, 1274g–1274i
  illuminating gas, 1247
    ammonia in, 1261
    calorific value of, 1257

Gas—candle-power of, 1256
  carbon dioxide in, 1228a, 1262
  illuminants, oxygen in, 1228c, 1248
  methane and hydrogen in, Hempel's and Hinman's methods, 1228a–1230, 1248, 1249
  naphthalene in, 1262
  nitrogen in, 1250
  specific gravity of, 1262
  sulphur and H₂S in, 1260, 1261
  tar in, 1264
  industrial gases, analysis of, 1227–1230
  mine gases, carbon dioxide in, 1270
  moisture in gases, 1275
  natural gases, 1274a–1274g
  nitrogen in gases, nitrometer method, 1276
  producer, fuel blast furnace gases, 1266
    dust determination in, 1256
  sulphuric acid gases, burner gases, 1264
    arsenic in, 1765
    chloride in, 1765
    dust in, 1763
    nitrogen oxide in, 1270
    solubility of, in liquids, 1487
    sulphuric acid mist in, 1765
    sulphur dioxide in exit gases, 1266
    in inlet gases, 1267
  Tyndall test of, 1763
  general procedure with special apparatus:
    Elliott, determination of carbon monoxide, carbon dioxide, oxygen, 1244, 1245
    Hempel, determination of oxygen by hydrogen combustion, 1247
      by phosphorus method, 1246
      by pyrogallate of potassium, 1246
    illuminating gas, 1246
    Junker's calorimeter, 1257
    Orsat, determination of carbon monoxide, carbon dioxide, hydrocarbons, oxygen, 1241, 1243
  tables, 1280, 1282
Gas velocity by Petot, formula for, 707
Gas volumes, conversion formulæ, 707
Gasoline, determination of calorific value of, 1642
  test for lubricating oils, 1222
  tests of, 1123, 1127
Gay-Lussac apparatus (Fig. 59), for silver determination, 457
  method for determining silver, 457
Geissler absorption bulb for carbon dioxide determination, 112
Gelatine dynamite, analysis of, 1380
Generator for det. traces of antimony, 29
Gerhardt absorption bulb for carbon dioxide determination, 112

Gerigue's method for copper, 196
Gibb's method for determining manganese, 300
Gilchrist on iridium, 390
Gill, chapter on fixed oils, fats and waxes, 1108, 1152
  chapter on analysis of gas, 1231–1282
  carbon monoxide in atmospheric air, 219, 1273
  on use of sodium pyrogallate (note 1), oxygen in gas, 1246
Gilmore's needles (Fig. 95), 1211
Glass analysis, 1789–1793
  density, 1789
  determination of Al₂O₃ Fe₂O₃, CaO, MgO, PbO, SiO₂, 1790–1791
  alkalies, 1791
  B₂O₃, 1791
  MnO₂, S, 1792
  BaO and Ca, separations, 1793
  factors, 1793
Glass making materials, analysis of, 1794–1798
  determination of:
    barium carbonate, separations, 1796
    calcium, lime, 1797–1798
    chlorides, moisture, potash, sulphates, 1796
    china clay, kaolin, feldspar, 1795
Glucinum, detection of, 68
  estimation, gravimetric method, 69a–b
  occurrence, 68, 69
  separation from aluminum, chromium, iron, manganese, zirconium, and yttrium, 69, 69b
Glucose in boron det., 91
Glue, in rubber, determination of, 1593
Glycerol, boric acid titration in, 86, 87
  determination of, 1755
  determination of, in soap, 1607
Gold, detection of, in alloys, 228
  benzidine acetate test, 229
  phenylhydrazine acetate test, 229
  test for, in minerals, 228
  estimation, general procedures:
    gravimetric, electrolytic method, 230
    wet assay of minerals, 230, 488
    volumetric methods:
      colorimetric method, 233
      procedures of Cassell, Moir, Prister, 233
      iodide method, 232
      Lenher's method, 231
      permanganate method, 231
    preparation of proof gold, 234
    solubility, 229
Gold bar, platinum and palladium in, 385, 387
Gold bullion, fire assay, of 484
Gold, fire assay of, 466–488

Goldenberg's method for det. tartaric acid, 1551
Gooch method for determining lithium, 414
for determining titanium, modified, 542
and Blake's method for determining bromates, 96
and Bosworth's method for determining silver, 463
and Ensiger, separation of bromine from iodine, 94
and Fairbanks' method for molybdenum, 318
and Gruener, method for det. nitrate, 352
and Jones, method for boron, 85
Gooch crucible, preparation of, 596d
Graphite, carbon determination in, 130
determination of, in crude mineral, 130
in iron and steel, determination of, 115
Graphitic silicon in aluminum, determination of, 17a
Gravimetric methods. See under element in question.
Gravity. See Specific Gravity.
Gray's method, carbon residue test in oil, 1122
distillation flask (Fig. 91), 1122
Green pigments, analysis of, 1177, 1198
Greenwood, H. D., selenium and tellurium, 430
Gregory, test for silver, 439
Grinders and crushers, 1011–1015
Gröger, decomposition of chromic oxide (note), 158
chromium determination (note), 161
Gum arabic in explosives, 1388
test for, 1385
Gun metal, analysis of, by A. S. T. M., 1058–1063
Gumming test in lubricating oils, 1121
Guttapercha and Balata, analy., 1584
Gutbier and Hüller, method for zirconium, 521
Gutzeit apparatus, arsenic determination (Fig. 6), 46
method for determining arsenic, modified, 52
Grain growth in steel, metallography of, 1719
Gruener, H. W., on nitrates, 352
Gryory's method for determining antimony, 25
Gypsum, 105
A. S. T. M. methods for, 108b

Hale, F. E., chapter on methods for analysis of coal, 1616
soap test for hardness in water, 1436
starch, preparation of, 1432
water analy., sanitary, 1442–1453
bacteriological, 1454–1468

Halogens, separation and determination in presence of one another, 155
Halphen's test for cottonseed oil, 1136, 1143
Handy's volumetric method for magnesium, 294
Hanging drop test for fluorine, 213
Hanus's method for iodine number of oils, 1128
method for oil, 1137
solution, 1167
Hardened oils (see Oils, Fats, Waxes), 1145
examination of, 1147
Hard lead, antimony, 25
decomposition of, 21, 25
Hardness, determination of, in water, 1438
Hawley, F. G., on silica det., 449, 450
Heat of fusion, table of, 720b
Heat definitions, 708
of fusion, table of, 720b
passing up chimney, calculation of, 1253
test for oils, 1123
treatment of steel, 1719
Heating value in gas, 1288k
Heath, permanent copper standard solution (ref.), 199
Heath's solenoid, rapid deposition of copper by, 187
Heavy hydrocarbons, 1227c
Hehner's test for formaldehyde, 1754
Helium in the atmosphere, 338
analysis of, 1274g–1274i
Hempel apparatus, 1245
apparatus, description (Figs. 122, 123), 1245, 1247
gas burette (Fig. 122), 1236
method for determining methane and hydrogen, 1249
Henrique's method in rubber analysis, 1582
Henz and Classen method for tin, 536
Herig automatic device for burette, 1497
Herschel's demulsibility test for oils, 1123
Herting, volumetric method for tungsten, 563
Hesse's method for carbon dioxide in atmospheric air (Fig. 132), 1272
Hexabromide test for linseed oil, 1137
Hibbard on halogens, ref., 154
Hickman, chapter on platinum and platinum group, 376
Hicks, chapter on potassium, sodium, and other alkalies, 401
chloroplatinate method for potassium, 411
Hillebrand, alkalies (ref.), 416
on silica determination (ref.), 436
uranium det., 583

Hinman's method for determining methane and hydrogen, 1248
and Jenkins, sulphur apparatus (Fig. 127), 1260
volumetric method for sulphur, 506
Hintz and Weber on sulphur precipitation, 497
Holde, caoutchouc in lubricating oils, 1121
Holladay, J. A., on molybdenum det., 313, 320, 322
on tungsten det., 554, 560
Holloway-Eschka process for determining mercury, 311
Holstein, L. S., on cadmium analy., 99
Hommel's process for separating molybdenum and tungsten, 558
Hooper's method for treatment of speisses, slags, mattes, etc., 20
Horse-power, definition of, 709
Hoskins' electric furnace (Fig. 107), 1630
Hot water precipitation of tin, 520
Howard-Harrison, fusion of sulphide ores, 20
Hübl's method for iodine number in oils, 1129
for oil, 1138
Hübner's method for estim. rubber, 1580
Humidity charts, air, 1288a, 1288b
Hydrazine sulphate, decomposition of nitrous acid, 342
reduction of chromic acid, 342
Hydrazine-hydrochloride-sulphur method for tellurium, 437
Hydriodic acid, removal of, from nitric acid, 342
Hydrobromic acid, removal of, from nitric acid, 342
Hydrocarbons in gas analysis, 1243
in illuminating gas, 1248
in natural gas, 1288h
in rubber, 1594
in soap, 1608
Hydrochloric acid, detection of free, 142
analysis of, 1501
estimation, gravimetric methods for, 148
free, det. of, 154
in acetic acid, 1547
in ammoniacal liquors, 344
in bichloride of tin, 530
in nitric acid, 1510
in presence of chloric and perchloric acids, 153
in sulphuric acid, 1528
volumetric methods, 149, 1501
impurities in, arsenic, 35, 50, 1502
barium chloride in, 1502
chlorine, free, in, 1501
nitric acid and nitrates in, 1501
silica and total solids in, 1502
sulphuric acid and sulphates in, 1502

Hydrochloric acid, preparation of arsenic-free acid (Fig. 5), 48
standard solution, 1495
table, sp. gr., 1504
test for iron, 246
test for lead, 271
test for mercury, 308
Hydrocyanic acid, volumetric det. 131, 1727
detection, 1726
Hydrofluoric acid, analysis of, 1507
gravimetric estimation, preparation of samples for, 215
decomposition of rare earth ores with, 136
method for alkalies, 417
hydrofluosilicic acid in, 1507
sulphuric acid in, 1507
sulphurous acid in, 1507
Hydrofluosilicic acid in hydrofluoric acid, 1507
Hydrogen chloride gas, generation of (note), 10
Hydrogen-ion concentration, det. of, 1430, 1663
Hydrogen combustion method for det. oxygen, 1247
determination in gas, 1248, 1249
generator, 1278
in the atmosphere, 338
properties of, 1227e
reduction method for copper, 205
reduction of rhodium salts, 395
reduction of tin ores, 527
Hydrogen peroxide, chromium detection by, 156
method for formaldehyde, 1754
method for iodine, 243
method for titanium, 545
method for detecting vanadium 583
-phosphoric acid method for decomposing iodides, 243
test for thorium, 522, 524
Hydrogen peroxide, det. of, 1761
Hydrogen sulphide, evolution method, 503
estimation of, 509
group, separation of, 168, 292, 405
in ammoniacal liquors, 345
in gas, 1261
in steel, 1368g
in water, 1435
method for det. iron, 611
method for ppt. Cu in steel, 1368c
precipitation of molybdenum, 317
reduction of chromates, 156
reduction of ferric solutions, 251
test for copper, 177
test for iridium, 388
test for lead, 271
test for mercury, 308
test for nickel, 329
test for palladium, 382
test for platinum, 376
test for rhodium, 393

Hydrogen sulphide, test for ruthenium, 390b
test for vanadium, 583
Hydrogen sulphide generator, 42
Hydrolysis of aluminum salt with ammonia, 7
method for tin, 528
with thiosulphate, 9
Hydrometer, Fig. 80a, 1502
Hydrometer for specific gravity of oils, 1111
Hydrometer method for CO_2 det., 125
sp. gr. of bituminous sub., 1295
Hydrosulphite of sodium, det. of, 516
Hydroxide of aluminum, precipitation, 7, 9
effect of boiling, 8
hydroxylamine hydrochloride, 1427
of bismuth, precipitation of, 74
of sodium and potassium, 1552–1556
table, 1558
Hydroxylamine, det. of, 352
Hypochlorite, test for, 143
in presence of Cl, 151
Hypochlorous acid, detection of, 143
determination of, 151
Hypophosphorous acid, test for, 362
Hypotheses and chemical laws, 723

Ignition loss in asbestine, china clay, silica, silex, 1187
in barytes and blanc fixe, 1188
in bauxite, 17h
in gypsum, plaster of Paris, 1188
Illuminants in gas analysis, 1248
properties of, 1227c
Illuminating gas, analysis of, 1227, 1247, 1256
Impurities suspended in gas, test for, 1763
Incrusting solids in water, 1421
Indicators, table of, 1491
Indigo sol. titration of hydrosulphite, 516
Indirect method for determining sodium and potassium, 413
Indium, detection and determination of, 139
Industrial gases, analysis of, 1227–1230
Inks, printing, analysis of, 1799–1803
determination of oil, 1799
separation from pigment, 1799
pigment analysis, 1800
black inks, 1800
blue inks, 1802
green inks, 1802
red inks, 1802
physical examination, 1804
Inlet gases, sulphur dioxide in, 1267
Insecticides, water-soluble arsenic in, 36
Insoluble matter in asbestine, china clay, silica, silex, 1187
in aluminum hydrate, 17i
in commercial selenium, 440

Insol.—in composite white paint, 1189
in orange and yellow pigments, 1195
in Portland cement, 1209
in sodium fluoride, 226
in sodium nitrate, 349
in zinc oxide, 1184
Interpretation of results in gas analysis, 1230, 1252
in analysis of oil, 1158
in mineral analysis of water, 1441
in sanitary analysis of water, 1419
Iodate, determination of, 244
and periodate in a mixture, 244
Iodate method for det. arsenic, 44
Iodate of potassium, decomposition of iodide with, 241
Iodide-chromate method for lead, 278
Iodide method for antimony, 28
for arsenic, 43
for chromium determination, 161
for copper determination, 193, 193b
for determining tin, 532
for gold determination, 232
for metabisulphites, sulphites, sulphurous acid, thiosulphates, 131
for peroxide determination, 1491
Iodide of potassium, reduction of ferric solutions with, 252
Iodide-phosphate method for Cu, 17b
Iodine, detection of free, combined, iodate, 236
estimation, general procedures:
gravimetric as palladous iodide, 239
as silver iodide, 239
volumetric determination of hydriodic acid and soluble iodides, 239
liberation of iodine with chlorine (Mohr-Dupré), 243
of ferric salts, 241
of hydrogen peroxide and phosphoric acid, 243
of iodate of potassium, 241
of nitrous acid, Fresenius method, 242
Volhard's method, 243
estimation, special procedures:
in nitric acid, determination of, 1511
occurrence, 236
preparation of the sample for estimation of iodine in iodides, iodates, commercial iodine, minerals, organic substances, phosphates, water, 237
reagent, 0.1 N, preparation of, 28, 731
separation from heavy metals, from bromine and chlorine, 238, 239
solubility of the element and its salts, 236
Iodine jelly test of paint vehicles, 1170
in mineral water and brines, 245
number (Hübl), in oil analysis, 1127, 1169

Iodine number, linseed oil, 1166
  number (Hubel), 1169
  standard solution, 28, 1167
  tung oil, 1170
Iodoform test for alcohol, 1746
Iodometric det. of nitrates, Gooch and
    Gruener, 352
Iridium, detection of, 388
  by alk., KCl, NH₄Cl, H₂S, Zn, Pb, acet.,
    Zn, K₂CO₃, formic a., etc., 382
  estimation, 389
    gravimetric methods, 390
      ammonium iridium chloride, 390
      ignition with ammonium salt, 390
      method of Deville and Stas modi-
        fied by Gilchrist, 390
      residue, obtained as, 390
      reduction by zinc, 390
    preparation and solution of sample, 389
    properties of, 389
    separations, from osmium, 389
      platinum, 389
Iron, detection of, tests with hydrochloric
    acid, ferrocyanide, salicylic acid,
    sodium peroxide, sulphocyanate, 246
  colorimetric method, 261
  distinction between ferrous and ferric
    salts, 246
  estimation, general procedures:
    gravimetric, determination as ferric
      oxide, Fe₂O₃, 249
    cupferron method, 17k, 250
    volumetric methods, oxidation pro-
      cedures, 251
    diphenylamine method, 255
    oxidation methods, 251
    preliminary reduction with hydro-
      gen sulphide, metal, potassium
      iodide, sulphurous acid, test
      lead, zinc, 251, 252
    potassium dichromate method, 253,
      255
    potassium permanganate method,
      17b, 256, 257b
    reduction procedure with stannous
      chloride, 260
    reduction with titanious salt, 258
  estimation, special procedures:
    determination in alloys and metals:
      in alloys, 1055, 1073, 1082, 1092,
        1097, 1106j
      in aluminum, 17a
      in aluminum hydrate, 17h
      in bauxite, 15
      in bronze, A. S. T. M., 1076
      in calcined ore, 17k
      in copper, 200
      in glass, 1790
      in ink pigments, 1800
      in lead, 290a
      in manganese phosphorus bronze,
        1047

Iron—in ores, 251
    in paper making materials, 1773
    in paint pigments (iron oxides),
      1185, 1189, 1193, 1196
    in phosphates, 372, 374
    in Portland cement, 1207
    in sand, 448
    in selenium, 432
    in slag, 1611
    in sodium nitrate, 322
    in spelter, H₂S and colorim. meth-
      ods, 611
    in sulphuric acid, 1526
    in spent oxide, 519
    in titaniferous ores, 552
    in water, as ferrous and ferric
      iron, 1423
  determination of, in presence of vana-
    dium, 589, 592
  industrial application of methods, 246
  occurrence, ores and minerals, carbon-
    ates, sulphides, 246, 247
  preparation and solution of the sample,
    iron and steel, 248
    ores, soluble salts, silicates, etc., 247,
      248
  separations, ether method, 248
    general procedure, 248
  separation from chromium, 158
  solubilities, general considerations, 247
  traces, colorimetric methods, salicylic
    acid method, 262
  sulphocyanate method, 261
Iron and steel analysis, decomposition of,
    for determining iron, 263, 1351
  A. S. T. M. methods, 1351–1368
  determination of aluminum in, 16
  arsenic in, 37
  carbon in alloy steels, 1359
  carbon in, combined, colorimetric
    determination, 128, 263, 1359
    graphitic, 265
    total, 95, 265, 1352, 1354
  chromium in, 158, 165, 1368f
  copper in, 181, 1368c
    by colorimetric method, 1368d
  cobalt in, 174
  hydrogen in, 1368g
  manganese in, bismuthate method
    for, 267, 301, 1360, 1362
    Deshey's method, 266, 306
    persulphate method, 266, 305
    Volhard's method, 302
  determination in alloy steels,
    1362
    Ford-William's method, 306
  method for cast iron, 1362
  molybdenum in, 314, 316
  nickel in, 331, 336a
  nitrogen in, 361a
  oxygen in, 1368i

Iron—phosphorus in, 268, 269, 368–370b
  in alloy steels, 1365
  reagents used in steel analysis,
    1351–1368
  silicon in, 270, 449
    procedure for iron and steel, 445
    rapid foundry method of deter-
      mination, 1368a, 1368b
  sulphur in, gravimetric, 269, 1366
    volumetric, 500–504, 1368
  sulphur in alloy steel, 1368a
  titanium in, 547
  tungsten in, 554, 556
  uranium in, 582a
  vanadium in, 584, 591, 595
  zirconium in, 232, 268
  specifications for elements in steel:
    carbon, 265, 1371
    manganese, 267, 1371
    phosphorus, 268, 1371
    silicon, 270, 1371
    sulphur, 269, 1371
Iron ores and iron ore briquettes, copper
    determination in, 180
  ore briquettes, reduction for sulphur
    determination, 502
  sulphide, available H₂S in, 503, 509
Iron salts, free acid det. in 1541
Iron, nickel, cobalt and zinc in As₂O₃, 54
Iron and alumina in barium ores, 67
Irrigating waters, 1441c
Ivanov on aluminum, 17

Jaeger, F., on platinum and palladium
    det., 385
Jackson's candle turbidimeter, 1620
Jamieson's arsenous method for peroxide
    det., 1761
Jannasch method for separation of the
    halogens, 238
  metallic test for palladium, 382
    for iodine (ref.) 147
    for platinum, 377
    for rhodium, 393
  precipitation of bismuth hydroxide 75,
Japanese wood oil. See Tung Oil.
Jenkin's apparatus for specific gravity of
    gas (Fig. 129), 1263
  and Hinman gas-sulphur apparatus
    (Fig. 127), 1260
Jones reductor apparatus (Fig. 40), 257
  method for iron determination, 257
  method for molybdenum determina-
    tion, 319
  method for phosphorus determina-
    tion, 369
Joule, definition of, 709
Junker's calorimeter (Figs. 124, 125, 126),
    1257, 1258

Kehrmann's separation of tungsten from
    arsenic and phosphorus, 558

Kelley, G. L., electrometric methods,
    1663–1682
  apparatus for electrom. methods, 1547
Kempf's oxalic acid method for determi-
    nation of persulphates, 508
Kerosene, analysis of, 1111–1112e
Kingzett's iodide method for det. perox-
    ides, 1761
Kjeldahl det. nitrogen in explosives, 1382
Kjeldahl digestion for nitrogen determi-
    nation, 340, 350
Kneeland, decomposition of ores and
    slags, 214
Knop's diphenylamine indicator for iron
    det., 225
Knorr arsenic distill. app., 39a, 365
Knorr's persulphate method for deter-
    mining manganese in water, 1426
  apparatus, modified, for carbon dioxide
    ide determination, 122
Kramer-Sarnow heat tests, bit. sub., 1305
Krypton in the atmosphere, 338

Lacmoid indicator, preparation of, 744,
    1152
  uses of, 1492
Ladd, R. M., on pyridine in amm. nitrate,
    360
Landolt-Boernstein on heats of fusion,
    720e
Landrum, cobalt in cobalt oxide, 171
  cobalt in enamels, 173
Lanthanum, 134, 135
Lard, cottonseed oil in, 1144
  water in, 1144
Latent heat, definition of, 708
  electrolitic det. of, A. S. T. M., 1092
Lawrence Smith (J.), method for alkalies
    in silicates, 416
Laws, chemical, 723
Leach's test for formaldehyde, 1754
Lead and copper in As₂O₃, 53
Lead, chromate-ferrous-diphenylamine
    method for, 278b
  detection of, tests with hydrochloric
    acid, hydrogen, sulphide, potassium
    dichromate and potassium chromate,
    271
  estimation, general procedures:
    gravimetric method, determining as
      chromate, PbCrO₄, 275
      as molybdate, PbMoO₄, 275a
      as peroxide, PbO₂, by electrolysis,
        275b
      as sulphate, PbSO₄, 274
    volumetric methods, ferrocyanide ti-
      tration, 276
      chromate-iodide method, 277c
      ferrocyanide method, 276
      molybdate method of Alexander,
        277b
      permanganate method of Low, 277

Lead, estimation, special procedures:
  determination in alloys and metals,
    1051, 1052, 1053, 1061, 1062,
    1067, 1070, 1071, 1080, 1081,
    1106, 1106a, 1106b
  in basic carbonate of lead, 278b
  in bronze, det. as PbSO₄, 1076
  in copper, 201
  in corroded white lead (volumetric
    and gravimetric), 1181
  in gun metal, A. S. T. M., 1058
  in nickel, 336d
  in paint pigments, chrome green
    and yellow, 1198
  in picric acid, 1393
  in red lead and orange mineral,
    290d, 290f, 1190
  in selenium, commercial, 439
  in slag, 1615
  in soft solders, 1080
  in spelter (electrolytic and lead
    acid methods), 609
  in sublimed blue lead, 1197
  in sublimed white lead, 1189
  in sulphuric acid, 1525
  in water, 1437
  in yellow basic lead chromate, 1195
  in zinc lead and leaded zinc, 1183
Lead, estimation, determination in small
  quantities (see Traces in Water), 1433
  impurities in metallic lead:
    antimony in hard lead, 25
    bismuth in lead bullion, 79
    complete analysis of pig, lead, deter-
      mining bismuth, silver, arsenic,
      antimony, tin, iron, cobalt, nick-
      el, manganese, zinc, 290–290e
  industrial application of methods, 271
  in minimum, 290d, 290q
  occurrence, minerals, ores, alloys, etc.,
    271
  preparation and solution of the samples
    —minerals, ores, alloys, etc., 272
  separations, isolation of lead as sul-
    phate, 273
    extraction of the impure sulphate by
      ammonium acetate, 273, 279
    separation from barium, 273
  solubilities of metallic lead and its salts,
    271
  traces, determination of:
    gravimetric, from large amounts of
      substances:
      a. acetate extraction, 279
      b. occlusion by precipitate of an-
        other metal, 280
      c. Seeker-Clayton method, modi-
        fied, 281
    volumetric, colorimetric method, 282
Lead acetate cotton, 30
Lead acetate method for precipitating
  vanadium, 588

Lead test for chromate, 156
  test paper, 49
Lead arsenate, arsenic determination in,
  36
Lead basic carbonate, det. of, 228b
Lead bullion, assay of, 482
  bismuth in, 79
  carbonate in sublimed blue lead, 1197
  zinc in, 617a
  chloro-fluoride method for fluorine
    determination, 217
  method for determining molybdenum,
    316
Lead oxide, electrolytic method, 1184
  method for manganese in steel, 266
  peroxide in red lead, 290f
  sulphate, decomposition of, for sulphur
    determination, 340
  in sublimed blue lead, 1197
  sulphite in sublimed blue lead, 1197
Lead oxide, method for det. manganese,
  263
Lead, pig, analysis of, 286–290e
Leaks, tests for, 1368h
Le Blanc and Eckhardt's ferrous sulphate
  method for persulphates, 508
Le Chatelier's specific gravity apparatus,
  1205
  reagent for etching, 1705
Ledoux and Co. methods, 280, 322, 560
  for tungsten det., 560
Length, unit table, 702
Lenher, V., chapter on selenium and
  tellurium, 430–440
Lenher's method for gold, 232
  -Crawford thymol method for titanium,
    550
  and Trogg, precautions on silica deter-
    mination, 447
Lennsen's iodide method for tin, Baker's
  modification, 532
Lewkowitsch on oil tests, 1135
Liebermann-Storch's test for rosin oil,
  1139, 1144b
Liebig's absorption bulb, 111
  method for determining hydrocyanic
    acid and cyanides, 131
Liddell on dust in gas, 1256
Lime, available, 108
  analysis of, 1784
Lime, effect on silica dehydration, 446
  and magnesia in barium ores, 67
  method for halogens in organic matter,
    146
  in sand, 448
  -value in water analysis, 1441
  in silicate of soda, 448
  in slag, 1610
Lime and limestone determination in
  cement and analysis, 1220
  water test for magnesium, 291

Limestone, lime, cement rock, analysis of, 1225

Lindo-Gladding's method for potassium, 412

Linseed oil, analysis of, 1165
 specifications, 1168

Liquid fuels, analysis of, 1125

Liquids, sampling of. See Sampling.

Litharge, 290
 charges in assaying. See chapter on.

Lithium, detection of, 403
 estimation, general procedures:
  as lithium chloride, 414
  as lithium sulphate, 414
  det. in water, 1428
  Gooch's method, 414
  Rammelsberg's method, 415
  spectroscopic method, 415
 sodium and potassium determination in presence of one another, 416

Lithopone, analysis of, 1186

Litmus indicator, uses of, 744, 1492

Little-Cahen-Morgan, det. arsenic in organic matter, 36

Logarithms, table of, 713

Loss of weight method for carbonates, 124
 on ignition aluminum hydrate, 17h
  bauxite, 17f
 on ignition in Portland cement, 1208

Low, A. H., electrolytic method for cobalt, 170
  method for decomp. antimony ores, 19
  method for lead, 277
  method for manganese, 307
  method for mercury, 312a

Low-freezing dynamite, analysis of, 1381

Lowenthal-Proctor on tannic acid, 1760

Lower oxides in nitric acid, 1511
 in oleum and mixed acids, 1530

Lubricating oils (see under Oils, Fats, Waxes), 1115, 1148

Lundell and Knowles, on molybdenum, 320

Lunge-Marchlewski on carbon (ref.), 127
 Ray pipette for weighing of liquids, 1498

Luteol indicator, 531

Lux, definition of, 708

McDaniel's app. for det. solubility of gases, 1488

MacMichael's viscosimeter, 1116d

Mackey's apparatus for spontaneous combustion-oils, 1140

Magenta test for bromine, 92, 96

Magnesia, effect on silica dehydration, 46
 in slags, 1613

Magnesium, detection of, 291
 estimation, methods for determining, general:
  gravimetric, as magnesium pyrophosphate, 17e, 293
  volumetric, titration of ammonium magnesium phosphate, 294
 estimation, special methods:
  determination in alloys, 1106c
  determination in gypsum, 1188
  in sand, 448
  in silicate of soda, 448
  in sodium nitrate, 350
  in water, 1425, 1436
 estimation, in composite white paint, 1190
  in green pigments, 1196
  in orange and yellow pigments, 1195
  in Portland cement, 1217
  with sodium and potassium in presence of one another, estimation of, 290
 occurrence, 291
 preparation and solution of the sample —ores, 291
 separation from the hydrogen sulphide group, Cu, Pb, Cd, As, etc., 292
  from iron, aluminum, manganese, and zinc, 292
  from the alkaline earths, 59, 292
 solubility, 291

Magnesia mixture, preparation of, 328, 733

Magnesium ammonium phosphate method for phosphorus, 367
 chloride in water, 1440
 metallic, test for platinum, 377
 pyroarsenate method for arsenic, 41
 pyrophosphate method for phosphorus, 367
 sulphate, arsenic in, 51

Maize oil, constants, 1148

Maletesta and De Nola, silver det., 440

Manganese-bronze, analysis of, A. S. T. M., 1047-1057

Manganese, detection of, general procedure and bead test, 295
 in soils, minerals, vegetables, etc., 295
 estimation, general methods:
  gravimetric, as manganese, pyrophosphate, 300
  Ford-Williams method, 306
  as manganese dioxide, 301
  volumetric, bismuthate method, 302a, 1360, 1362
   lead oxide method, 306
   persulphate method, 305
   sodium arsenate method, 17c
   Volhard's method, 302
 estimation, special procedures:
  determination in alloys, 1056, 1057, 1093, 1100, 1101, 1106d, 1107
  determination in iron and steel, 264, 266, 1360, 1362

Manganese in bronze, det. of A. S. T. M.,
    1047–1057
    in cast iron, 299
    in ferro-manganese, 303b
    in ferro-chrome, 299
    in ferro-silicon, 299
    in ferro-tungsten and tung. metal, 573
    in materials insoluble in acid, 299
    in metallic lead, 290
    in metallic manganese, 304
    in ores, 303, 307
    in slag, 1612
    in spiegel iron, 306
    in steel, 266, 267, 1360
    in steel, electrolytic method, 1680
    in tungsten alloys, 514
    ores, 508
    in tungsten ores and concentrates, 569
    preparation and solution of the sample,
        alloys, ferro-aluminum, ferro-chro-
        mium, ferro-titanium, manganese,
        bronze, molybdenum and tungsten
        alloys, silicon alloys; iron and
        steel; ores, iron ores, sulphides,
        slags, 296
    separation from H₂S group, alkaline
        earths and alkalies, nickel and co-
        balt, 298
    from iron and alumina by basic ace-
        tate, 298
    precipitation of manganese as dioxide,
        MnO₂, 301
    solubility of the metal and its oxides, 296
Manganese metal, Mn in, 304
Manganese oxide in paint pigments, 1185
Mannitol, boric acid titration in, 86, 87
Marsh, electrolysis of nickel, 335
Marsh gas, det. of, 1227e–1248
Marsh test for arsenic, 47
Martin, on absorption apparatus for CO₂,
    114
Martin, H. E., on bauxite analy., 15
Marvin, T., on vanadium, 596a
Masses, unit table of, 702
Matte, copper, solution of, 179
Mattes, decomposition of, 20
Maumené test for oils, 1126, 1135
McDonnell and Roark arsenic separation,
    37
McDowell, method for hydrocyanic acid,
    131
Meade, chapter on cements, 1202
Measuring apparatus vol., 1686
Meat, arsenic in, 51
    boron in, 83
Meiklejohn, R. M., properties of com-
    pounds, table XVII, 679–683
    conversion factors XVIII, 683–698
    volumetric apparatus, 1685
    weights standardization, 1695
Mellor, calcium oxalate, decomposition of,
    107

Mellor on precipitation of tungsten, 563
    traces of lead, 282
Melting temperature of elements, table of,
    658
Mene, ferric chloride method for tin, 535
Mennick, chloric and perchloric acids, 153
Mercuric bromide and chloride paper, 47
Mercuric cyanide test for palladium, 382
    oxide method for separating magnesia
        from the alkalies, 407
Mercurous nitrate method for chromium,
    160
    method for precipitating molybde-
        num, 316
    method for precipitating vanadium,
        587
    test for chromate, 156
Mercury chloride paper, for arsenic deter-
    mination, 47
Mercury, cleaning of, 1279
    detection of, 308
    estimation, methods of procedure:
        gravimetric, electrolytic method, 310
        Halloway-Eschka method, 311
        sulphide, precipitation, 310
        volumetric, by Seamon's process, 312
        thiocyanate method, 312a
    occurrence, 308
    preparation and solution of the sample.
        ores, 308, 309
    purification of the reagent, 1279
    separation from members of subsequent
        groups, 309
        from As, Sb, Sn, Pb, Bi, Cu, Cd, Se,
            Te, 309
        from organic substances, 309
    solubility, 308
Mercury, free, in fulminate, det. of, 1395,
    1397
Mercury in organic matter, 312b
Mercury in rubber, 1581
Mercury in zinc amalgam, 1107
    fulminate, analysis of, 1395
Merwin color screens, 402
    and Stiegers' method for fluorine, 220
Messinger's method for acetone det., 1759
Metabisulphite, gravimetric determina-
    tion, 511
    volumetric iodine method for, 512
    determination in presence of carbon-
        ates, chlorides, sulphates, sulphites,
        thiosulphates, 514
Metallic aluminum and its alloys, 5
    silicon and iron in, 17a
    cobalt, cobalt in, 167, 172
    copper, 178
        determination of gold, silver, lead,
            bismuth, arsenic, antimony, se-
            lenium, tellurium, iron, zinc,
            nickel, cobalt, oxygen, sulphur,
            phosphorus, chlorine in, 199–206
    gold, preparation of proof, 234

Metallic iron (and steel). See subject
 determinations of carbon, manganese,
 phosphorus, silicon, sulphur in, 263–
 270, 1351–1371d
 chromium, cobalt, nickel, titanium,
  tungsten, vanadium. See Iron
  and Steel Analysis.
 lead, determination of silver, bismuth,
  copper, cadmium, arsenic, antimony, tin, iron, cobalt, nickel, manganese, zinc in, 286–290c
 manganese, Mn in, 304
 nickel, aluminum in, 336d
  bismuth in, 336c
  cobalt in, 172
  lead in, 336d
 platinum, 380
 silver, preparation of pure, 448
 tellurium and selenium in, 440
 zinc in zinc dust, 607
  impurities, lead, iron, cadmium in
   spelter, 610
Metallography, 1701–1722
 carbon steel, microphotographs, 1713
 case hardening, 1720
 copper-zinc alloys, metallography of,
  1710
 equilibrium diagrams, 1706
 etching sample for micro examination,
  1705
  reagents for etching, 1705
   ammonia
   ferric chloride
   Le Chatelier No. 1
   nitric acid-alcohol
   nitric acid, concentrated, Sauveur
   picric acid-alcohol
   sodium picrate
   Yatsevitch's reagent
 heat treatment of steel, 1719
 influence of elements on iron and steel,
  1721
 influence of mechanical work, 1716
 iron-carbon alloys, 1711
 iron, pure, microphotograph of, 1707
 microscope, directions regarding, 1701
 photographic materials, 1703
 preparation of specimens, 1703
Metals. See Metallic.
Metaphosphoric acid, test for, 362
Meter, wet meter, rotameter, capometer,
 Thomas electric meter, orifice meter,
 anemometer, 1233–1236
Methane, determination of, 1248–1249
 properties of, 1227e
Methyl alcohol, detection and determination, 1753
Methyl borate, distillation of boron, 84
Methyl orange indicator, 26, 347, 744,
 1491
 red indicator, uses of, 1491

Methyl violet test paper, preparation of,
 1403
Metric and customary units, table XXI,
 702
Metzel and Vortman, method for anti-
 mony, 24
Meyer's apparatus for zinc determination
 (Figs. 72, 73, 74), 608
Microchemical examination of crystals for
 tantalic and columbic acids, 575
Microscope, 1701
 exam. of steel, 1701
Microscopical examination of water, 1442
 organisms in water, control of, 1451
  identification of, 1449
  illustrations of, plate,
  list of, 1443, 1448
Microscopical test of lubricating oils, 1123
Microcosmic salt-reactions, table of, 627
Milk, boron in, 83
Milliliter, def., 1694
Mine gases, carbon dioxide in, 1270
Miner, H. S., on det. of thorium, 523a
Mineral acids. See Acids.
 analysis of water, 1421
 matter in rubber, 1579
 oil. 1148
 residue in water, 1434
 salts in burning oils, 1113
Minerals, decomposition of, for determination of lead, 272
 detection of tungsten in, 554
 list of common, 717
 test for gold in, 228
  See list under dominating elements
   contained in Part I, also 717
Minium, lead det., 290f
Miscellaneous, 1743
Mispickel, preparation for arsenic determination, 37
Mitscherlich's app. for N det., 351
Mixed acid, analysis of, 1530
Mixtures, sodium and potassium carbonates and hydrates, 1556
Modified sodas, analysis of, 1555
Mohr's alkalimeter, 124
 method (modified) for antimony, 27
  for arsenic, 43
  for chlorine, 150
  for iodine, 243
Moir's method for gold, 233
Moisture in air, 338, 1272, 1275, 1494
 in arsenic, commercial, 53
 in bauxite, 15, 17f
 in brimstone, 519
 in butter and fats, 1143–1144
 in coal, 1618
 in explosives. See subject.
 in gases, 1275
 in nitrate of soda, 349
 in oils (burning), 1113, 1144

Moisture in paints and paint pigments,
  1163, 1186, 1187, 1188, 1190, 1193,
  1194,1195, 1196
  in phosphate rock, 362
  in silicate of soda, 448
  in silicates, 443
  in soap, 1600
  in sodium fluoride, 226
  in zinc pulp, 598
  See also under special subjects
    throughout text.
Molybdate method for lead, gravimetric,
  275a
  volumetric, 277b
Molybdate magnesia method for phosphorus in iron and steel, 1363
Molybdenite, comparison with graphite,
  313
Molybdenite, molybdenum in, 322
Molybdenum, detection, general procedure, 313
  tests with sodium thiosulphate, sul-
    phur dioxide, disodium phos-
    phate, sulphuric acid, 313
  estimation, general procedures:
    gravimetric, lead molybdate method,
      316
      mercurous nitrate, precipitation by,
        316
      molybdenum sulphide method, 317
    volumetric, iodometric r e d u c t i o n
      method, 318
    determination in presence of vana-
      dium, 321, 591
    zinc reduction with Jones' re-
      ductor, 319
  occurrence, 313
  preparation and solution of the sample
    ores, 314
    iron and steel, 314, 320a
  separation from iron, 314
    from alkalies, alkaline earths, bis-
      muth, cadmium, copper, lead, ar-
      senic, titanium, vanadium, tung-
      sten, phosphoric acid, 315
    ether extraction method, 315
  solubilities, 314
Molybdenum in molybdenum concentrates, 324
  in ores—wulfenite, molybdenite, 322
  ores, analy. of, det. As, Cu, P, 325
Monazite, decomposition of, 522a
Monel metal, analy. of, 1106i
Moody and Leyson sol. app., 1470
Morehead, J. M., gas analy., 1227
Morgan-Cahen-Little, arsenic det. in or-
  ganic matter, 36
Morphine, det., 1737
Morphine test for titanium, 538
Morphine sulphate test for formaldehyde,
  1754

Mortar, standard sand, water, percentage
  for (table), 1211
Moynahan, A. E., on silver, 458
Mulligan, J. J., on bismuth, 79
Muriatic acid, analysis of, 1501
Mustard oil, 1147, 1149
Myrtle wax, 1150

Narcotine, 1733
Naphtha solvent of rubber, 1573
Naphthalene in gas, 1262
Naphthylamine acetate reagent, 1414
National Brass and Copper Tube Co.
  method for brass analysis, 206
National Lead Co. method (modified)
  for metallic lead analysis, 286
Natural cement, U. S. Gov. specifications
  for fineness, 1198
Natural gas, analysis of, 1274a–
  1274g
Neat's foot oil, constants, 1147, 1149
Needle penetrometer, hardness test, 1214
Neon in the atmosphere, 338
Nephelometric method for silver, 463
Nessler jars for colorimetric titanium de-
  termination, 548
Nessler's method for ammonia, 1413
  test for ammonia, 337
New Jersey Zinc Co., on barium ores
  analy., 66
  analysis of barytes, 60
  zinc, 597
Neuman lines, metallography, 1718
Newhall, C. A., on sulphur, 493, 517, 519
Newton, method for titanium, 543
New York State Board of Health tester
  for oil, 1109
New York-Liverpool test for alkalies,
  1552–1554
Nickel, detection of, hydrogen sulphide
  test, 329
  aluminum in, 336d
  As, Sb, Cr, Si, Sn, W, Zn, etc., in,
    336e–336f
  bismuth in, 336c
  dimethylglyoxime and alpha benzyldi-
    oxime tests, 329
  estimation, general procedures:
    gravimetric, alpha benzyldioxime
      method, 332
      Carnot's method, 336b
    dimethylglyoxime method, 333
    electrolytic method, 335
    volumetric method of Parr and
      Lindgren, 336, 1368e
    potassium cyanide method, 336a,
      336b
  estimation, special procedures, nickel-
    plating solutions, 336
    determination in alloys, 336, 1083,
      1094, 1106b
    in copper, 199, 202

Nickel in iron and steel, 336b, 1368d, 1368e
  in metallic lead, 290c
  lead in, 336d
  preparation and solution of the sample,
      general procedure for ores, 330
  metallic nickel and its alloys, 330
  separation from alkalies, alkaline earths,
      and members of the hydrogen
      sulphide group, 331
    from aluminium, chromium, cobalt,
        iron, manganese, zinc, 331, 332
    solubilities, 330
Nickel-plating solution, determination of
    nickel in, 336
Nicotine, 1733
Niobium. See Columbium, 554
Nitrate, standard solution of, 1416
  of soda, analysis of, moisture, insoluble
      matter, sodium sulphate, iron and
      aluminum oxides, lime, magnesia,
      sodium cloride, carbon dioxide,
      349
Nitrates in black powder, 1373
  in explosives, 1373, 1377
  in nitrite salt, detection of, 359
Nitrates, removal of, in sulphur determi-
    nation, 497
Nitrates in water, 1416, 1433
Nitric acid, complete analysis of, 1509-
    1512
  conversion efficiency of NH₃ conversion
      to, 361c
  determination of acidity, chlorine, hy-
      drochloric acid, iodine, nitrous
      acid, sulphuric acid, 1509-1512
Nitric acid, det., arsenic in, 50
  by ferrous sulphate method, 1512
  free, determination of, ref., 357
  etching acid, 1705
  in arsenic acid, ferrous sulphate
      method, 1516
  in hydrochloric acid, 1501
  in commercial nitric acid, 1511
  in mixed acid, 341, 1531
  in oleum, nitrometer method, 357
  in phosphoric acid, ferrous sulphate
      method, 1516
  in sulphuric acid, ferrous sulphate
      method, 1514, 1528
  N/10 reagent for phosphate deter-
      mination, 368, 1364
  specific gravity table, 663, 1517
Nitric acid for etching, 1705
Nitrite (see also Nitrous Acid), 358
  detection of, 359
  estimation, 358
    gravimetric—Buovold's method, 358
    volumetric—permanganate method,
        358, 1530
    tables, 1517
Nitrite, in water, 1414

Nitrocellulose, analysis of, 1399
  in explosives, 1388
  in gelatine dynamite, 1380
Nitrochlorhydrin in explosives, 1383
Nitrocompounds, separat. from nitro-
    glycerin, 1382
Nitrosulphuric acid method for silicon in
    steel, 1368a
Nitrogen, detection of, combined as:
  ammonia, tests for, 337
Nitrogen, ammonia, Nessler's test, 337
  nitric acid, copper test for, 338
    diphenylamine test for, 338
    ferrous sulphate test for, 337
    phenolsulphonic acid test for, 338
  nitrous acid, acetic acid test for, 338
    permanganate test for, 338
  organic nitrogen, 337
  estimation, free, combined, and total
      nitrogen, 338
  combined nitrogen, methods for:
    ammonia, gravimetric determina-
        tion of, 342
    combined and free, volume-
        tric determination, 343, 1412,
        1560
    traces, 345, 1413, 1414
  ammoniacal liquor, analysis of, de-
      termining carbon dioxide, hy-
      drochloric acid, hydrogen sul-
      phide, sulphuric acid, am-
      monia, 344, 345
  nitrate of soda, 349
  nitrates, Devarda method modified,
      346
  as nitrate in water, 1415
  as nitric acid, gravimetric method
      as nitron nitrate, 345
    volumetric, 346
  as nitrite in water, 1414
  as organic nitrogen in water, 1413
  nitrogen in fertilizers, 339
    in green pigments, 1196
    in organic matter, nitrates being
        absent, 340
    in organic matter in presence of
        nitrates, 341
    in rubber, 1593
    in soil extracts, 350
    in steel, 361a
    Kjeldahl method, 339
  free nitrogen. See Gas Analysis, 1250
  per cent of, in air 338
  properties of, 1227f
  tetroxide in gas, 1270
  occurrence, 338
  preparation of the sample, ammonium
      salts and mixtures, 341
  nitrates in soils, nitric acids and
      mixed acids, 341
  organic substances in presence or
      absence of nitrates, 340, 341

separations, ammonia, isolation of, 341
  nitric acid, isolation of, 342
    removal of impurities, nitrous chromic, hydrobromic, hydriodic acids, 342
  solubilities, 339
  special methods, nitrometer method for nitrates and nitrites, 353
    nitrometer of du Pont, 354
      nitric acid in oleum, 357
Nitroglycerin, determination of, 1376
  dynamite, analysis of, 1374
  smokeless powders, 1407
Nitropolyglycerin in explosives, 1383
Nitrometer, 353, 354
  gas analysis, Fig. 160, 1276
Nitron nitrate method for nitric acid, 342, 345
Nitrosite method for rubber analy., 1568
Nitroso-beta-naphthol, precipitation of cobalt with, 169
Nitrous acid, decomposing of iodides with, 242
  and lower oxides in nitric acid, 1510
    in oleum and mixed acids, 1531
  gas, generation of, 94, 147
  permanganate method for, 358
  removal of, from nitric acid, 342
  oxide in gas, 1270
Nitrostarch in explosives, 1388, 1390
  test for, 1385
Nitrosugars in explosives, 1383
Nitrotoluenes in dynamite, 1381
Non-drying oils, list of, 1149
Normal consistency of cement, method of determination, 1206
Normal solutions. See Reagents.
Norton apparatus for carbon det., 117
Noye's app. for det. solubility, 1471

Occurrence. See under element in question.
Odor test of water, 1411
Offerman's method for fluorine, 218
Ohm, definition of, 709
Oils, fats, waxes, examination of unknown oil, 1108
  detection of oils in paint vehicles, 1164
  classified list, characteristics, and constants of oils (tables), 1152, 1154
  examination of:
    animal and vegetable oils, 1133
      general test for, 1133
        acetyl value, 1141
        antifluorescence, test for, 1141
        bromine number, 1139
        elaidin test, 1135
        iodine number, 1136
          Hanus's method, 1137
          Hübl's method, 1138
          in oxidized oils, 1139
        Maumené test, 1135
        refractive index, 1134

Oils—saponification value, 1140
  unsaponifiable oils, detection of, 1140b
  Valenta test for, 1134
  drying, semidrying and non-drying oils, 1149
  special tests for certain oils, 1141
    cottonseed oil, Becki's test for, 1142
    Halpen's test for, 1143
    drying on glass, 1144d
    free acid in, 1144c
    linseed oil, hexabromide test for, 1143
    peanut oil, Renard's test for, 1144a
    rapeseed oil, Bach's test for, 1144b
    rosin oil, Liebermann-Storch test for, 1144b
    sesamé oil, Baudoin's or Camoin's test, 1144b
    spontaneous combustion test, Mackey's apparatus, 1144c
    titer test, 1145
    Villa Vecchia test, 1144b
  fats, edible, 1146
    butter, 1146
    lard, 1147
  hardened oils, 1147
  interpretation of tests, 1158–1160
    crude oils, gasoline, kerosene, lubricants, waxes, heavy oils and asphalts, shale oils, 1158–1160
  miscellaneous oils and lubricants, 1148
  paint oils (see under Paints and Paint Pigments), 1164
    Chinese wood oil, tung oil (see subject under Paints), 1169, 1171
  paint, acid number, heating test, iodine jelly test, iodine number, refractive index, saponification number, unsaponifiable matter, specific gravity, standards of, 1169–1171
  petroleum products, 1109
    burning oils, 1109
      acidity, detection of, 1113
      color of, 1113
      distillation test, 1112e
      fire test, 1110
      flash test, 1109
      mineral salts in, 1113
      specific gravity, 1111
      sulphuric acid test, 1113
      sulphur determination in, 1112e
      water in, 1113
    lubricating oils, 1115
      carbon residue, test for in, 1122
      caoutchouc, test for in, 1121
      evaporation test of, 1116
      fatty oils, test for in, 1121
      fire test of, 1120
      flash test of, 1118d

Petroleum friction test of, 1123
    gasoline test of, 1123
    gumming test of, 1121
    microscopical test of, 1123
    soap, detection of in, 1121
    specific gravity of, hydrometer
        method, 1111
        Westphal balance method,
            1111
    viscosity, 1115
        Engler's viscosimeter, 1112–
            1112d
        Saybolt viscosimeter, 1116
        Universal viscosimeter, 1116
    turpentine (see subjects under Paints),
        1173, 1174
    color, distillation, polymerization,
        refractive index, specific
        gravity, standards of, 1173,
        1174
    U. S. Government specifications for
        petroleum products, 1150–1151
    fuel oils, greases, 1150a
    gasoline, burning oils, 1150
    lubricating oils, 1150b, 1151
    varnish (see subject), 1174, 1176
    waxes, 1148
Oil in black pigments, 1196
    in water, 1435, 1436
Oils, reagents used in, 1157a
    tables of characteristics and constants,
        fatty acids, 1150–1154
    mineral oils, properties of, 1148
    vegetable and animal oils, 1152–1154
    viscosity conversion tables, 1156
        Saybolt, Engler, and Redwood
            times, 1156
    waxes, 1148
Oil shale valuation, 1350
Oleum, complete analysis of, 1529
    acidity, lower oxides, nitric acid, sul-
        phuric anhydride in, 1530
    table of equivalents, 1539
Olsen, on analysis of alloys, 1071–1107
    test for fluorine, 213
Optical pyrometer (Fig. 107), 1228
Orange pigments, analysis of, 1198
Ores. See under Preparation of Samples
    of Various Elements.
Organic acids, analysis of, 1542
Organic matter, arsenic det. in, 36, 51
    decomposition of, for determination
        of antimony in, 21
    for determining barium, 57
        boron, 83
        bromide, 93
        chlorine and halogens, 145
            Carius method for halogens
                in, 145
            lime method for halogens in,
                146

Organic matter, sodium peroxide method
        for halogens in, 146
    fluorine, 214
    iodine, 237
    determination of carbon in organic
        matter, 119–121
    nitrogen, 339
    phosphorus in baking powder, 365
    potassium in soils, fertilizers,
        plants, 404
    organic matter in water, 1417, 1419
Organic matter, destroyed by persulphate, 36
Organisms in water, classification, 1443,
    1448
    identification of, 1449
Orifice meter, 1236
Osmium, detection of, 396
    by H_2S, KOH, NH_4OH, Zn, red.
        agts., KNO_2, Na_2SO_3, P, Hg,
        $SnCl_2$, etc., estimation of, 397
    gravimetric determination of, 398
    occurrence, 396, 397
    preparation and solution of sample, 397
    properties, 396
    separations, 397
Orsat apparatus (Fig. 120), modified
    (Fig. 131), 1241, 1267
Ottawa sand, standard, 1211
Oulman's method for tartaric acid, 1551
Ovens, drying, 1018–1020
Owen-Bradbury method for alkali car-
    bonates and hydrates in presence of
    each other, 1556
Oxalate method, separation of alkaline
    earths from the alkalies and mag-
    nesium, 59
    outline for separation of, 134
Oxalic acid, determination of, 1549
    method for manganese, 307
    method for persulphates, 508
Oxidation methods for det. iron, 251
    in platinum salts, 277
    test for methyl alcohol, 1753
    test for vanadium, 583
Oxide, determination of, aluminum, 7
    bismuth, 74
    cobalt, 167, 171
    cobalt, 169
    copper, 179, 192
    chromium, 159
    iron, 246, 247
    lead, 275b
    manganese, 301
    tantalum and columbium, 577
    thorium, 524
    tin, 531
    titanium, 542
    tungsten, 558
    uranium, 581a
    vanadium, 587
    zinc, 599
    zirconium, 618

Oxidized oils, iodine number of, 1130, 1139
Oxygen, determination of, see Gas,
Oxygen, properties of, 1227d
Oxygen consumed in water (organic matter in), 1417
Oxygen cylinders, illustrating method of connecting, 1224
  determination of, in air, absorption with phosphorus, 1246
    potassium pyrogallate, 1247
    sodium pyrogallate (note), 1246
  in copper, 204
  in gas, 338, 1244, 1246, 1247, 1248
  in steel, 1368i
  dissolved in water, 1436
  explosion with hydrogen, 1247
Paints and Paint Vehicles, analysis of (see Outline in Table of Contents), 1161
  pigments, classification of, 1176
    black pigments, analysis of, 1199
    blue pigments, analysis of, 1196
      Prussian blue, Chinese blue, Antwerp blue, 1197
      sublimed blue lead, 1197
      ultramarine blue, 1196
    green pigments, analysis of, 1198
      chrome green, 1198
    red and brown pigments, 1190
      iron oxides, 1196
      red lead, orange mineral, 290f, 1190
      vermillion, 1195
    yellow and orange pigments, chrome yellow, American vermillion, basic lead chromate, 1198
    white pigments, 1176
      barytes and blanc fixe, 1188
      composite white paint, 1189
      corroded white lead, 1181
      lithopone, 1186
      silica, silex, China clay, asbestine, 1187
      sublimed white lead, 1188
      titanox, analysis of, 1190, 1192
      whiting, Paris white, 1188
      zinc lead and leaded zinc, 1182
      zinc oxide, 1183
  vehicles, 1162
    liquid, percentage of, 1162
    oils, detection of, iodine number, 1164
      Chinese wood oil, or tung oil (see under Oils, Fats, Waxes), 1169, 1170
      constants for various oils, 615, 1171, 1172
      other materials, 1175
    separation of components, 1163
    resinates, detection of, 1164
    turpentine, examination of (see details under Turpentine), 1172
    varnish, examination of, 1173–1173
Paints in bituminous sub., 1346

Palladium—detection of, 382
  alk., NH4OH, SO2, CuCl, Hg(CN)2, KI, H2S, KNO2, FeSO4, NH4Cl, Sn, Cl2, red. agts., etc., estimation, 382–383
  estimation in gold bar, 385
    in refined gold, 385, 387
    in copper slimes, 386
    in silver, 386
  gravimetric methods, 384, 488
  preparation and solution of sample, 383
  properties of, 382
  separation from platinum and iridium, 383
  silver, gold, platinum, 383
Palladous chloride reagent, 1191
  iodide, method for determining iodine, 239
Palmer, L. A., on fire assay of gold and silver, 466
Palmer and Seibert, modified Gutzeit method for arsenic, 46
Paper making materials, analysis of, 1773–1785
  aluminum sulphate, analysis of, 1773
    determination, Al2O3, Fe2O3, Fe, SO3, H2SO4, KF, insol.
    sampling of, 1773
  bleaching powder, analysis of, 1779
    determination of avail. Cl, total Cl, ClO3, bases, CaO, sand, grit, SiO3, wood, etc.
    quality test, 1780
    sampling, 1779
  caustic soda, 1783
    alkalinity, sampling of, 1783
  lime, 1784
    determination of, causticizing power, impurities, lime, magnesia, moisture
    rapid methods for lime, free CaO, CaCO3, moisture, 1785
    sampling, 1784
  rosin, 1773
    determination of acid number, ester, ash, dirt and foreign matter, grade, saponification n., sizing, unsaponifiable matter, 1775
    sampling, 1775
  rosin size, 1776
    alkali, free and combined, insol., moisture, rosin, 1776–1777
    sampling, 1776
  rosin, rapid methods, rosin, size, etc., 1778
  soda ash, 1783
    alkalinity, moisture, sampling
  starch and starch products, 1781
    determination of acidity, alkalinity, alkali, moisture, viscosity, etc., 1781

Paper making, starches, converted, 1782
    acidity, alkalinity, added material, ash, moisture, etc., 1782
  sulphuric acid, 1783
    determination of acidity, iron, sediment, sp. gr., etc., 1783
Paraffin hydrocarbons in gas, 1288h
Paris white, paint pigment, 1188
Parr, S. W., analysis of fuels, 1634–1662
  and Lindgren's method for nickel, 236
  calorimeter, 1634
Parrodi-Mascazzini electrolytic method for antimony, modified, 24
Parsons and Barnes' method for glucinum, 69a
Patterson, det. of manganese, 301
Peanut oil (see under Oils, Fats, Waxes), 1138
Pechard's process for separating molybdenum from tungsten, 559
Pelouze, traces of lead, 281
Penfield's method for CO_2, 109
Penski-Martins closed flash point test, 1314
Perborate method for cobalt det., 175
Percarbonate, determin. of, 126
Perchlorate, detection of, 143
  determination of, 152
  method for determining potassium, 412
Perchlorates in explosives, 1388
Perchloric acid, determination of, 152
    in presence of hydrochloric acid and chloric acid, 153
Perchloric acid method for fluorine distill., 215
Periodates, determination of, 244
  and iodates, determination of, in a mixture, 244
Permanent standards for ammonia determination in water, 1415
Permanganate method for det. copper, 195
  for det. nitrites, 358
  for det. oxalic acid, 1549
  for det. peroxides, 1491
Permanganate N/10 reagent, 255, 1360
  test for nitrite, 138
  titration of, antimony, 28a
    barium, 65
    bismuth, 76
    calcium, 17d, 108, 1425
    chromium, 161
    formic acid, 1542
    gold, 231
    iron, 17, 18, 256, 257, 257b, 374, 610, 1207, 1423
    lead, 277
    manganese, 264, 302, 304, 1426
    molybdenum, 319, 320
    nitrous oxides, 1511, 1516, 1530
    peroxide, 1762
    phosphorus, 265, 369
    solution standard, 369, 1360
    tannic acid, 1760

Permanganate, titration of, titanium, 544, 544a
    uranium, 581
    vanadium, 589, 591, 595
    water for oxygen consumed, 1417
Permissible explosives, analy. of, 1384
  qualitative tests for, 1385
Peroxide bomb, 1637
  determination of, 1755
  method for chromium, 157
    formaldehyde, 1754
    lead as, 275b
    titanium, 545, 548
Persulphate alkali titration, 508
Persulphate of ammonium method for manganese, 266, 305
Persulphate method for manganese in bronze, 1196
Persulphates, ferrous sulphate method for determining, 508
  oxalic acid method for determining, 508
Petroleum naphtha solubility test, 1319
Petot formulæ for det. velocity of gases, 707, 1235
Petroleum products (see under Oils, Fats, Waxes), 1109
pH hydrogen ion concentration, 1430, 1457
Phenacetolin indicator, 745
Phenolphthalein indicator, 12, 745
  preparation of, 12, 1152
  uses of, 1491, 1492
Phenolsulphonic acid method for nitrates in water, 1433
  reagent, 1433
Phenyl, determn. of, 1549
Phenylhydrazine method for aluminum in presence of iron in titaniferous ores, 552
  acetate test for gold, 229
Phloroglucid method for furfurol in acetic acid, 1546
Phosphate baking powder, 365
  effect on alkaline earth determinations, 57
Phosphate rock, decomposition of, 364
  analysis of, 371
Phosphates in soap, 1606
Phosphates in water, 1424
  and phosphoric acid, arsenic in, 50
  typical analyses of, 363
Phosphomolybdate method for vanadium, 596b
Phosphoric acid and its salts, analysis of, 1521
  free, vol. det. of, 375
Phosphoric acid, effect on aluminum determination, 8
  in phosphate rock, 372
  removal of, from aluminum solutions, 6
    tables, 667, 1523

Phosphorus, detection of hydrophosphorous acid, 362
  metaphosphoric acid, 362
  orthophosphoric acid, 362
  phosphorus acid, 362
  pyrophosphoric acid, 362
  estimation, methods of procedure, general, 363
    gravimetric, direct precipitation of ammonium magnesium phosphate, 376
    as magnesium pyrophosphate, 367, 1363
    as phosphomolybdate, 366
    volumetric methods, alkali titration of phosphomolybdate, 368, 1364
    permanganate titration of reduced phosphate, 368b
  estimation, special methods, determination of, in iron and steel, 268, 364
    in alloys, 1059, 1063, 1078, 1084
    in alloy steel, 1365
    in cast iron, 370a
    in copper alloys, 368a
    in ferrosilicon, 370
    in ferrotitanium, 370
    in gun metal, 1060
    in steel, 258, 368a, 1363–1365
    in tungsten alloys, 570
    in tungsten ores, 564
    in vanadium steels, 370b, 1365
  occurrence, 363
  preparation of the sample, iron ores, phosphate rock, minerals, titanium-bearing ores, iron and steel, soluble phosphates, baking powder, 365
  separation of phosphorus as ammonium phosphomolybdate, 365
Phosphorus method for det. oxygen in gas, 1246
  pentoxide absorption bulb for moisture in gases (Fig. 134), 1275
Photometry, definitions, 708
Physical tests of water, 1410
Picric acid-alcohol for etching, 1705
Picric acid, examination of, 1392
Pig iron, arsenic in, 37
Pig lead, analysis of, 286
Pigments with titanic oxide. 553
Pigments of paint (see under Paint and Paint Pigments), 1176
Pipettes for gas analysis, 1237
  standard, 1690
Pisani's method for silver, 463
Pitch. See Bituminous Substances.
Pitch and bitumen in rubber, 1570
  carbon in coal tar, 1358
Pitman on du Pont nitrometer (ref.), 354
Pitot tube (Fig. 113), 1234
Plaster of Paris, 105
Platinum, care of, 723

Platinum, detection of, 376
  by KI, H_2S, NH_4Cl, KCl, $FeSO_4$, $SnCl_2$, NaOH, red. agts., etc., 376
  estimation of, 377
    gravimetric methods for—as met. Pt, 380, 488
    as ammonium salt, 381
    electrolytic method, 381
  occurrence, 377
  ores, assay of, 399
  preparation and solution of the sample, ores, 378
    platinum scrap, 378
    small amounts of platinum in presence of large amounts of iron, magnesia, etc., 378
  properties of, 376
  separation from gold, 379
    from iridium, 379
    from osmium, 380
    from palladium, 379
    from rhodium, 380
    from ruthenium, 380
    table of, 387b
  solubility of the element, 377
  reactions, table of, 400
  special methods, platinum ores, 381
    assay methods for platinum ores, 399
  substances examined for platinum, 377
Platinum metal group, 382
Platinum and palladium in gold bar (refined), 385, 387
  in copper anode slimes, 386
  in silver (refined), 386
  wire, turbidity det. in water, 1410
Poisons, detection and estimation, 1723–1742
  classification of, 1724
  general procedure, 1724
  preparation of sample, 1723
Poisons, alkaloids, glucosides, etc., 1731
  acetanilid, 1732
    bichromate-sulphuric a. phenylisocyanide tests, 1732
  atropine, 1735
    physiological, vitalis tests, 1735
  brucine, detection, 1734
  cocain, detection, 1735
  codein, 1736
    formaldehyde, Froehde, Marme's reagt., nitric a. tests, 1736
  morphine, 1737
    ferric chloride, Froehde, formaldehyde, iodic, Marme, nitric a. tests, 1737
  narcotine, 1736
    dil. sulphuric, Froehde, selenous-H_2SO_4, sod. carb. tests, 1736–1737
  nicotine, detection, 1733
  opium, detection, 1738

Poisons, strychnine, 1734
    bichromate, Bloxom's, sulphocyanate tests, 1734
    veronal, purification and detection, 1732
    carbolic acid, Millon's test, $FeCl_3$, bromine, hypochlorite, nitrite tests, 1730
    carbon monoxide in air, 1740
      in blood, 1741
    chloral hydrate, detect. decomp., 1730
    chloroform, 1728
      Nicoloux's t., phenylisocyanide, Schwarz's resorcinol tests, 1728
    ethyl alcohol, 1728
      chromic a., ethyl acetate, Lieben's iodoform, vitalis tests, 1728
    hydrocyanic acid, 1725
      estimation, 1727
      tests—prussian blue, Schonbein-Pagenstecher, silver nitrate and cyanide, sulphocyanate tests, 1726
    metallic poisons, 1739
      arsenic, 1740
    methyl alcohol (wood alcohol), 1728
    ptomaines, 1738
    reagents, Froehde's, 1741
      iodo-potassium iodide, 1741
      Marme's, 1741
      Mayer's, 1742
      Millon's, 1741
      selenious-sulphuric, 1741
Plumbago. See Graphite.
Polymerization in analysis of turpentine, 1173
Polymerized oils and resins, separation of, 1174
Portland cement, analysis of, 1216, 1219
    rapid method of analysis, 1220
    U. S. Gov. specifications for fineness, 1205
Potash, 1576, 1579
Potassium, detection of, 402
    estimation, general procedures:
      gravimetric, chlor-platinaté method, 410
        modified, 411
      indirect method, 413
      Lindo-Gladding method, 412
      perchlorate method, 412
      special methods, alkali determination in silicates, J. Lawrence Smith method, 416
      lithium, potassium and sodium in presence of one another, 416
      magnesium, potassium and sodium in presence of, 413
      preparation of the sample, fertilizers, soils, plant ash, saline residues, soluble salts, rocks and insoluble mineral products, 404, 405

Potassium, separation from hydrogen sulphide and ammonium sulphide groups, 405
    alkali metals from one another, 408
    from aluminum, chromium, iron, barium, calcium, strontium, phosphoric and sulphuric acids, etc., in one operation, 407
    from aluminum, chromium, iron, titanium, uranium, phosphoric acid, 406
    from barium, calcium, strontium, 406
    from boric acid, 407
    from magnesium, ammonium phosphate method, 408
      barium hydroxide method, 407
      mercuric oxide method, 407
    from sodium and lithium, 408
    from sulphates, 406
Potassium antimonyl tartrate standard solution, 29
    bromate solution N/10, 26
      method for antimony, 26
    bromide, crude, analysis of, 96
Potassium and sodium carbonates and hydrates, in presence of one another, determination of, 1556
    acid sulphate (bisulphate), fusion with, 248, 330
      fusion of monazite, 522
    carbonate, fusion with, 248
    chloride test for platinum, 376
      test for iridium, 377
    cyanide method for copper, 194
    cyanide method for nickel, 336a
    dichromate method for iron, 253
      0.1 N solution, 253, 734
    ethyl xanthate method for small amounts of copper, 197
    ferricyanide test for ferrous iron, 246
    ferrocyanide reagent, 600, 602, 604
      test for ferric iron, 246
    fluoride method for alumina in aluminum salts, 12
      reagent, 12
Potassium hydroxide, alcoholic ext. of rubber, 1578
    analysis of, 1553
    hydroxide test for iron, 246
      test for rhodium, 390
      test for ruthenium, 387
Potassium iodate det. of arsenic, 44
Potassium iodide starch test for nitrocellulose, 1401
    iodide method for antimony, 27
    iodide method for bismuth, 78
    iodide method for chromium, 161
    iodide method for copper, 193, 193b
    iodide method for lead, 278
      for selenium, 436
      test for palladium, 382
        for platinum, 376

Potassium nitrite method for cobalt, 169
　standard solution, 346
　test for cobalt, 166
　　for palladium, 385
　　for rhodium, 393
　permanganate. See Permanganate
　method for phosphorus, 369
　N/10 solution, 369, 737, 1360
　reagent oxygen consumed in water,
　　1417
　pyrogallate, det. oxygen with, 1247
　reagent for gas analysis, 1279
　sodium and magnesium, determination
　　of, in presence of one another,
　　413
　sulphate, estimation of potassium as,
　　410
　sulphocyanate test for cobalt, 166
　　for iron, 246
Powder—explosive. See Explosives.
Powell and Schoeller on cerium, indium,
　scandium, thallium, etc., 133, 139
Praseodymium, 133
Precipitation apparatus for sulphur de-
　termination (Figs. 61, 62), 497
Preliminary tests for alkaline earths,
　58
Preparation and solution of the sample.
　See chapter on element in question.
Preservatives in butter, 1144
Price and Olsen, chapter on alloys, 1036–
　1107
Primers, table of, 1398
Priming of water, 1441b
Pringsheim's method for halogens in
　organic matter, 146
Prister's method for gold, 233
Producer and fuel gases, 1230a, 1255
　composition of, 1230a
Proof gold, preparation of, 234
Properties of compounds, Part II table,
　683
　of elements and compounds. See chap-
　ter of element in question.
Protein in rubber, 1567
Prussian blue, 1197
Ptomaines, 1738
Pulp, zinc, moisture in, 598
Pumps, suction, 1232
Pycnometer, sp. gr. bitumin. sub., 1296
　sp. gr. det., 1493, 1494
Pyridine in ammonium nitrate, 360
Pyrite ores, 105, 178, 272, 296, 445
Pyrogallate of potassium, reagent, 1279
Pyrophosphate method for cobalt, 174
　for thorium, 523
Pyrophosphoric acid, test for, 362

Qualitative tests, tables of, 625–654
Quartering coal (Fig. 103), 1617

Radiation, correction for, 1652

Radium, detection, 420
　estimation, 420
　　alpha ray method, 421
　　emanation method, 421
　table, 428
Rammelsberg method for determining
　lithium, 415
Rapeseed oil, 1139
Rapid method for cement analysis, 1220
Rapid methods for copper (electrolytic
　determination), 187
Rare earths, detection of, 133
　estimation, gravimetric, 134, 137
　occurrence of, 133
　preparation of the sample, 134
　separation, 134
　　from iron, aluminum, thorium, 134
　　from other elements, 134, 135
Rarer elements of the allied platinum
　metals, 389
Raschig's method for det. hydroxylamine,
　352
　method for sulphur, 507
Reactions, tables of, 632, 653
Reagents: See also chapter on, Vol. 1,
　725–746
　acetaldehyde, 1745
　acetic acid, 726
　acetic anhydride, 1755
　acid mixture for silica determination in
　　aluminum, 16
　alcohol, 726
　alcohol for oil analysis, 1151
　aldehyde free, 1745
　alizarine S for aluminum det., 14,
　　726
　alkaline potassium permanganate for
　　det. of albuminoid ammonia, 1413
　tartrate solution, lead det., 282
　alpha-benzyldioxime, nickel det., 346
　amino-nitrosophenyl-hydroxylamine sol.
　　for det. iron, 250
　ammonium acetate, lead extraction, 280,
　　726
　ammonium carbonate, 726
　ammonium chloride solution for det. of
　　ammonia in water, 726, 1412
　citrate solution, lead det., 282
　molybdate solution, vol. det. of lead,
　　277, 726
　det. of phosphorus, 365, 726
　　of phosphorus in water, 1424
　oxalate solution, oxygen consumed
　　in water analysis, 1417
　persulphate for manganese det., 266
　phosphate, 727
　sulphide, 727
　sulphocyanate sol., colorimetric
　　method for iron, 258, 610
　antimonyl chloride solution, 25, 47
　antimony det. sols., 30, 727

Reagents, arsenite, N/10 solution, 28, 240, 727, 1360

arsenous acid solution, det. manganese, 306

azolitmin solution, 1458

barium chloride, 727

barium hydroxide, 1357

Baudisch's reagent for det. iron, 250

benzidine hydrochloride for det. sulphates, 507, 728, 1427

benzyldioxime, alpha, 728

benzoic acid standard, acidimetry and alkalimetry, 1008

bismuth standard solution for det. bismuth, 77, 78

bismuthate of sodium for det. manganese, 301

brilliant-green lactose-peptone bile, 1460

bromine-potassium-bromide sol. for oxidizing sulphides, 498

bromine, 1151

cadmium chloride sol. evolution method for sulphur, 345

calcium chloride sol., det. hardness in water, 1434

calcium hydroxide, 728

carbon dioxide, preparation, acidimetry and alkalimetry, 1008

chlorine water standard solution for det. bromine, 95

chromic acid for det. SO_2 in gas, 1267

citric acid, solution for calcium det., 106

cinchonine potassium iodide, colorimetric det. of bismuth, 77, 78

det. tungsten, 497, 509

reagt. for tungsten det., 560, 728

cochineal indicator, 744

color solution for det. traces of lead, 282

color solution permanent standard for det. nitrites in water, 545

for det. fluorine, 220

copper standard solution, copper analysis, 165, 166, 193, 197, 198

copper sulphate standard solution, det. hydrocyanic acid, 131, 729

cupferron reagent for det. iron, 250

cupric potassium chloride for separation of carbon from steel, 111

cuprous chloride, acid, for det. CO in gas, 1268

ammoniacal for det. CO in gas, 729, 1278

Devarda alloy for reduction of nitrates, 346, 730

dichromate of potassium N/10 and N/5 solutions for iron det., 252, 734–736

dimethylglyoxime reagents for nickel det., 333, 730

diphenylcarbazide for chromium det., 132, 730

reducing mixture for sulphates, evolution method, 502

Endow's medium, 1459

Reagents, etching steel for metallog. ex., 1705

Fehling's solution, 730, 1159

ferric ammonium sulphate, for titanium det., 544

ferric chloride solution for det. tin, 536, 730

chloride solution for det. tin, 586

indicator for det. chromates, 149

in Volhard's method for silver, 442

nitrate solution for zinc analysis, 602

ferricyanide of potassium indicator for iron titration, 253

ferrocyanide of potassium standard solution, zinc analysis, 600, 602, 604, 606b

ferrous ammonium sulphate for iron in water, 731, 1423

for decomposition of substances, 1033–1035

for glycerol det., 1758

for manganese in steel, 1360

for oil analysis, 1157a

ferrous sulphate for nitric acid test, 337, 731

N/10 sol., for det. barium, 65

reagent for manganese det., 301

for det. nitric acid, 15b

fluorine, standard solution for fluorine det., 220

fuchsin-sulphite, 1745

fuming sulphuric acid, 1278

gas analysis reagents, list of, 1278

glacial acetic acid. See Oils, Fats, Waxes. Reagents, 1151

glycerol, det. boric acid, 87

Hesse's agar, 1460

hydrochloric acid, preparation of arsenic, free, 49

hydrochloric acid, standard sol., 1495

0.1 N, 731 1357, 1495

for oil analysis N/2, 731, 1152

hydrogen, 730

hydrogen peroxide for titanium det., 546, 731

for gas analysis, 1278

for water analysis, 1426

hydrogen sulphide, 732

iodate N/10 solution for det. iodine, 242

iodide sol. for det. oxygen in water, 1432

iodine N/10 reagent, 28, 731

for oil analysis, 1152

solution for det. tin, 533

iodo-potassium iodide, 1741

iron standard solution for standardization of stannous chloride reagent, 257, 258, 730

for col. method of iron in spelter, 611

iron in water, 1423

lead acetate cotton, antimony det., 30

Reagents, lead acetate for molybdenum
    det., 316
  reagent for oil analysis, 1152
  acid solution, zinc analysis, 610
  standard solution for col. det. of
    lead, 282, 733
  subacetate, 1758
litmus indicator, 744
litmus-lactose agar, 1459
magnesia mixture for det. of phos-
    phorus, 328, 367, 733
manganous sulphate solution for det.
    dissolved oxygen in water, 1431
mannitol, boric acid det., 87
Marme's reagt., 1741
Mayer's reagt., 1742
mercuric chloride test paper for anti-
    mony det., 30, 733
  for arsenic det., 47
mercury for gas burettes, 1267, 1279
methyl orange indicator, 26, 347, 744
  red indicator, 347, 744
methyl violet test paper, 1403
Millon's reagt., 1741
naphthylamine acetate solution for det.
    nitrites in water, 1414
Nessler's solution, ammonia det. in
    water, 1412
nitrate standard solution, 734, 1416
nitric acid, N/10 solution, 368
nitric acid, pure, 149
nitrosulphonic acid for elaidin test of
    oils, 1152
nitrous acid solution for decomposing
    iodides, 242
nutrient agar, 1458
nutrient broth, 1457
nutrient gelatin, 1458
oils, fats, and waxes, list of reagents for
    examination of, 1157
oxalic acid, 734
palladous chloride, 734
paraffin, 734
permanganate solution for manganese
    det., 301, 307, 1360
  N/10 solution for det. of iron, 255,
    737
  solution for det. of oxygen consumed
    in water, 1417
peroxide solution for det. titanium, 548,
    734
phenolphthalein indicator, 12, 745, 1152
phenolsulphonic acid for det. of nitrates
    in water, 1415
phosphate standard solution for phos-
    phates in water, 1424
potassium antimonyl tartrate solution
    for det. antimony, 29
  bromate N/10 solution antimony det.,
    25
  chromate indicator, 1417
  cyanide solution for copper det., 194

Reagents, dichromate reagent for iron det.,
    253, 734–736
  ethyl xanthate for det. copper, 197
  ferricyanide indicator for iron det.,
    253, 736
  ferrocyanide for det. copper, 186
    for zinc det., 602, 736
  fluoride for free acid in aluminum
    salts, 12, 736
  hydroxide for carbon det., 737
  hydroxide for oil analysis, 1152
  iodide for det. bismuth, 78
  nitrate standard, 346, 737
  permanganate N/10 sol., 254, 369, 737
proof gold, preparation of, 234
pyrogallate of potassium for oxygen
    det. in gas, 739, 1279
reducing agents, 70, 152, 156, 177, 251,
    261, 420, 421
rosalic acid indicator, 744
Renard-Tolman test for oil, 1144a
Russell's media, 1460, 1468
salicylic acid reagent for traces of iron
    det., 259
salt solution for chlorine det. in water,
    739, 1417
Schiff's fuchsin bisulphite, 739
selenious—H_2SO_4, 1741
silver carbonate, 1758
silver nitrate, N/10 solution, 149, 150,
    740
  solution for det. chlorine in water,
    1417
silver nitrite, alkaline, 1745
  preparation of the pure metal, 448
  standard solution, 442
soap standard solution for det. hardness
    in water, 1434
sodium arsenite. See Arsenous Acid.
  bismuthate for det. manganese, 17c,
    301, 740
  carbonate standard solution for CO_2
    det. in water, 1429
  preparation of pure salt, 1493
  hydroxide N/10 solution, 368, 741,
    1357, 1364
  for Devarda method, 347
  or potassium hydroxide reagents,
    water analysis, 1416
  metabisulphite, method of produc-
    tion, 285
  nitrite solution, nitrite det. in water,
    1414
  hydroxide, det. nitrates in water, 1416
  sulphide, 741
  thiosulphate, 741
stains, standard (colored plate), 46
  antimony det., 31
  arsenic det., 47
  sulphur det., 520
stannous chloride solution for det.
  ferric iron, 253, 257, 743

eagents, starch solution, 241, 501, 743, 1152, 1279, 1432
steel analysis reagents. See chapter on.
subacetate of lead, 1758
sulphanilic acid solution for det. nitrites in water, 1414
sulphocyanate for colorimetric det. of iron, 258, 611
sulphuric acid standard solution, 1495
  for ammonia det., 346
tannin indicator, Alexander's molybdate method for lead, 277
tartrate, alkaline solution of, for det. traces of lead, 282, 743
test reagts. for linseed oil, 1167
thiocyanate of ammonium or potassium N/10 solution, 149
thiosulphate of sodium for det. of copper, 208
  N/100 solution, water analysis, 1432
  for pot. iodide method for copper, 193, 195
  N/10 solution, 240, 742, 1152, 1279
  reagent for lead det., 278a
thymol solution for titanium det., 551
tin, standard solution of, 533
titanium, standard solution of, for fluorine det., 220
  for titanium det., 546, 548
turmeric indicator, 745
Wagner's solution, calcium det., 106
Red lead, lead peroxide in, 290f
  determination of, 290d
  method for manganese, 266
Red pigments, 290d, 1176, 1190, 1196
Reduction of iron compounds, method for, 251
  method for nitrates, 341, 346
Reductor, Jones, 256, 319, 320
Redwood, viscosity of oils (note), 1115
References, list of, 747
Refineries, Se and Te det., 439
Refractive index, 1134
  animal and vegetable oils, 1125
  Chinese wood oil, 1169
  turpentine, 1173
Refractory materials, decomposition for chromium determination, 157, 257a, 1032
Refractometer, Abbé, 1125
Refractory ores, decomposition of, 257a
Reich method for SO₂ in gas, apparatus for (Fig. 130), 1265
Reichert-Meissl number, butter fat, 1143
Renard's test for peanut oil, 1144a
Residue, total solid, in water, 1419
Resinates in paint vehicles, 1163
Resins and polymerized oils, separation of, 1175
Resins in explosives, 1377
  in rubber, 1567, 1582
Reverberatory slag analysis, 1610

Rhodium—detection of, 393
  by H₂S, KOH, NH₄OH, KNO₂, Zn, red. agts.
  estimation, 393
  gravimetric methods, 395b
  preparation and sol. of sample, 394
  separation from iridium, 394
  palladium, platinum and ruthenium, 395
Richard's jet pump (Fig. 109), 1232
Riche and Bardy method for det. methyl alcohol, 1753
Rickett's overflow pipette, 444
Riehlé automatic cement-testing machine (Fig. 107), 1215
Riffle, sampling of copper, 190
Ring and ball method, fusing point, 1308
Roark and McDonnell, arsenic separation, 37
Robert's analysis for copper and lead, 207
Robert's L. D. Radium chapter, 419–429
Robin's test for boron, 87
Rock, phosphate, analysis of, 255
Roofings, exam. of, 1339
Rosalic acid, 745
Roscoe's lead acetate method for vanadium, 588
Rose's method for determining bismuth, 76
  mercurous nitrate method for vanadium, 587
Rosenbladt and Gooch, method for boron, 84
Rosenstein's method for sulphur in rubber, 1581
Rosin in rubber, 1564, 1567
  in paper making materials, 1773, 1776, 1778
  in soap, 1602
  oil (see subject under Oils, Fats, Waxes), 1139
Rotameter (Fig. 114), 1235
Rowell's method for antimony, 25
Rubber, analysis, 1563–1597
  acetone extraction of, 1576, 1585, 1587
  acidity in, 1570
  alcoholic KOH extraction of, 1578, 1585, 1588
  analysis of, 1563, 1587
    Alexander's method, 1568
    Budde's method, 1568
    Henrique's method, 1582
    Spence's method, 1567
  antimony and mercury in, 1572, 1581, 1591, 1592
  barium carbonate in, 1595
  barium sulphate in, 1591
  bitumen and pitch in, 1570
  calculations, 1596–1597
  carbon in, 1580, 1592
  cellulose in, 1595
  chloroform extract of, 1585, 1588

Rubber, commercial evaluation of, 1564
  compounding materials in, 1571
  constituent, essential of, 1563
  crude, analysis of, 1565
  estimation—Hubner's method, 1580
    of raw rubber, 1564
  fillers—organic in, 1569
  glue in, 1593
  gutta percha and balata, 1584
  hydrocarbons in, 1594
  mechanical goods, 1582
  mineral matter in, 1579
  nitrogen in, 1593
  outline table of analysis, 1577, 1583
  oxidation method, vulc. rub., 1578
  preparation of sample, 1586
  protein in, 1567
  reagents, 1586
  rosin in, 1564, 1567
  rubber det., 1585, 1594, 1597
  saponifiable matter in, 1569
  solutions, analy. of, 1580
  solvents, examination, 1573
  specific gravity of, 1574, 1587
  sulphur free and combined in, 1569,
    1585, 1588
  tackiness in, 1564
  unsaponifiable matter in, 1593
  vulcanized, examination of, 1575, 1576
  waste and reclaim, analy. of, 1570
  wet methods of analysis, 1597a
Rubber goods, antimony in, 21, 1581, 1591
Rubidium, detection of, 402
  separations, 408
Rudorff's apparatus for carbon dioxide in
  gas (Fig. 128), 1263
Ruthenium, detection of, 390b
  by KOH, H$_2$S, (NH$_4$)$_2$S, Zn, KCNS,
    AgNO$_3$, HgNO$_3$, ZnCl$_2$, KI.
  estimation, 390
    gravimetric methods, 392
    separations from iridium and plati-
      num, 391
    from rhodium, 392

Saint Sernin's method for calcium, 108d
Salas, L. E., on rubber analysis, 1563–1584
  tin, presence of, in silver det., 446
Salicylic acid method for small amounts
  of iron, 262
  test for iron, 246
Saline residues, preparation of, for alkali
  det., 405
Salt, standard solution, 1417
  analysis of table, 419
Sampling—general methods of, 1003–1031
  Introduction, 1003
  Gases—apparatus, 1027
    general considerations, 1028
    grab sample, taking of, 1029
  Liquids, apparatus, 1021
    in motion, sampling of, 1023

Sampling—special liquids, sampling of, 102
  solids—apparatus for reduction an
    preparation, 1012
    collection of gross sample, 1004
    cone and quartering of, 1010
    containers for shipment to lab.
      1018
    drying ovens for moisture det.,
      1018
    long pile and alternate shovel
      method, 1009
    mixing and dividing samples,
      1016
    reduction and preparation of,
      1008
    sieves standard, 1016
    unit of, 1003
    vacuum ovens, 1019
Sand, analysis of, 448
  silica in, 448
Sanger, method for traces of antimony,
  modified, 28
Sanitary analysis of water, 1410, 1442–
  1453
Saponifiable matter in rubber, 1569
Saponification number in analysis of oil,
  1131, 1169
  value in oils, 1140
Savell, chapter on cobalt, 166
  on nickel, 321
Saybolt viscosimeter, 1115–1116
Saybolt to Engler times conversion table,
  1151
  to Redwood times conversion table,
    1151
Scale in water, 1441b
Scandium detection and determination,
  140
Schaeffer and Gardner, chapter on analy-
  sis of paints, 1161
Scheelite, analysis of, 564
Scheibler and Dietrich, determination of
  carbon (reference), 125
Schmatolla, titration of aluminum salts
  (ref.), 11
Schmitz, W., method for antimony in
  rubber goods, 21
  for magnesium determination, 293
Schoeller and Powell, chapter on cerium
  and the other rare earths, 133–138
  chapter on indium, scandium and
    thallium, 139–141
Schroetter's alkalimeter, 124
Schum on aluminum, 17
Scott, apparatus, hydrogen sulphide generator, 42
  evolution, for sulphur determi-
    nation in steel, 543
  (and Briggs), modified Orsat for
    SO$_2$ gas determination, 1267
  arsenic and chlorine in gas, 1765
  beam test of gases for det. dust, 1763